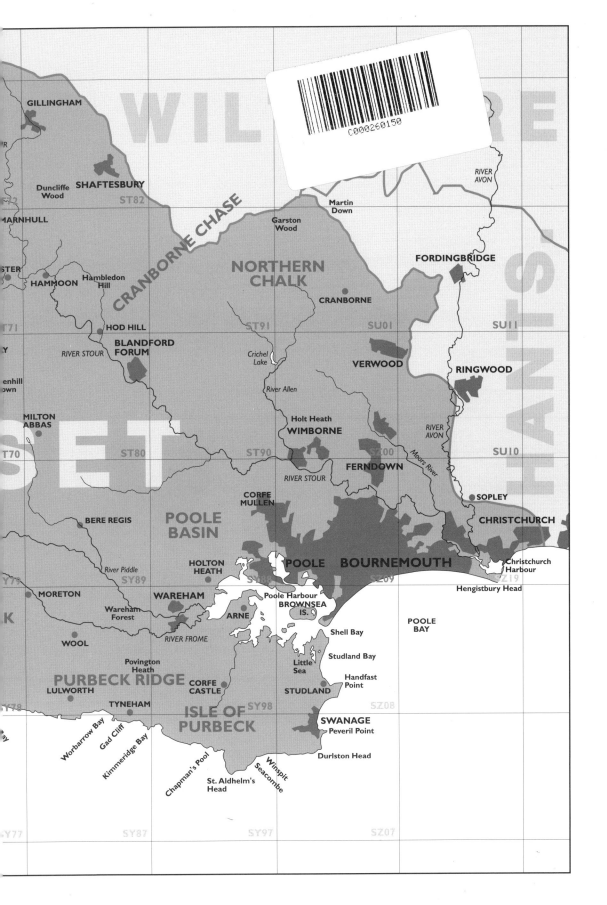

The Birds of
DORSET

Publication of this book
has been aided by financial assistance from

The Dorset Bird Club

The Birds of
DORSET

George Green

CHRISTOPHER HELM
LONDON

Published by Christopher Helm, an imprint of A & C Black Publishers Ltd., 37 Soho Square, London W1D 3QZ

ISBN 0-7136-6934-9

A CIP catalogue record for this book is available from the British Library

A & C Black uses paper produced with elemental chlorine-free pulp, harvested from managed sustainable forests.

Produced by Phoenix Offset/The Hanway Press Ltd
Printed in Hong Kong

Designed by Fluke Art, Cornwall

10 9 8 7 6 5 4 3 2 1

www.acblack.com

CONTENTS

This book is dedicated to the memory of

John Follett
and
Don Bowman

ACKNOWLEDGEMENTS

Since its inception back in 1992, this book has always been a Dorset Bird Club project. As such I would like to thank the Dorset Bird Club, its past and present chairmen and committee members, and the membership, for their support during the past 12 years.

The compilation of this book has been very much a team effort throughout its long and at times, tortuous history. During this period, I have been advised and guided by a small sub-committee, and two members in particular deserve special mention. I am very grateful to John Boys, who has a long-standing and exceptional knowledge of Dorset's birds. As author of a *Check List of the Birds of Dorset* (Boys 1972) and co-author of *The Birds of Dorset* (Prendergast & Boys 1983), John's involvement in this book has given it a sense of continuity. I am also equally grateful to Hugo Wood-Homer, who has been a constant member of the sub-committee offering valuable help and advice throughout. John and Hugo have been particularly supportive during the more difficult times and both have made significant contributions to the compilation of the text.

In the earlier stages of this book's compilation, a number of people volunteered to produce text for sections of the systematic list. Although they may no longer recognise their versions of the text, which have gone through at least four major 're-writes', their contributions have been vital to the final production of the book. I would like to thank the following for their help: Ian Alexander, Graham Armstrong, John Boys, Dave Chown, Paul Harris, Roger Peart, Phil Read, Tasie Russell, Steve Smith, Nigel Symes and Hugo Wood-Homer.

The book includes the results of the breeding bird Tetrad Survey (1987–1994), which was organised on behalf of the Dorset Bird Club by Hugo Wood-Homer. The 144 people who took part in the survey are acknowledged in the section on the Tetrad Survey.

I would also like to thank those who have helped me resolve a variety of queries, most of which related to records of rarities and sub-rarities including their current taxonomic status. I am particularly indebted to Grahame Walbridge, particularly in his capacity as a member of the *British Birds* Rarities Committee (BBRC), James Lidster, Dorset's current County Recorder who has responded so promptly to my requests for help, and Dave Smith as Christchurch Harbour Ornithological Group (CHOG) recorder. I have also received valuable help from Martin Cade, Dave Chown, Steve Groves, Paul Harris, Ian Lewis, Shaun Robson, Ian Southworth and Hugo Wood-Homer. Imogen Davenport, the current editor of the Dorset Bird Report, has been particularly helpful in providing early drafts of the recently published 2002 report.

No book on Dorset's birdlife would be complete without a set of colour photographs showing the character of the county's landscapes and habitats, and a representative selection of the birds that typify them. I am particularly grateful to Peter Coe for providing the majority of the photographs. I would also like to thank Graham Armstrong, Martin Cade, the late Frank Clafton, Dr David Godfrey, Carole and Peter Leigh and Enid Stanford for their valuable contributions of photographs for the book. Illustrations are another important element in enhancing the attractiveness of a book, and I am pleased that local bird illustrator Lawrence Chappell has provided a number of excellent pictures for this purpose. Special thanks also to Richard Allen, who has produced such fine artwork for the cover of the book.

Pete Fraser's help was crucial regarding the use of the COBRA software, which he developed, for storing and manipulating the data collected during the breeding bird Tetrad Survey (1987–1994). Pete also produced the tetrad distribution maps using the mapping programme DMAP written by Dr Alan Morton (Department of Pure and Applied Biology, Imperial College, Silwood Park, Ascot, Berks. SL5 7PY).

Early in the book's history, David Gumn of BAS Printers gave invaluable advice on the practicalities of publishing and printing a book such as this.

Finally, I would like to thank Jon Pontin for his help in preparing my computer for word-processing, and to my old friend Peter Hall who, despite having little or no interest in birds, has kindly proof-read important sections of the text.

With the agreement of the publishers, the Dorset Bird Club (DBC) has taken the opportunity to raise funds for conservation work in the county by raising sponsorship monies against each of the species in the systematic list. The club is very appreciative of work undertaken by Neil Gartshore, who devised and organised this scheme.

INTRODUCTION

The idea for this latest *The Birds of Dorset* book was conceived back in 1992, as a result of discussions on how best to publish the results of the Dorset Bird Club's breeding bird Tetrad Survey (1987–1994). At the time, there appeared to be two obvious choices, one of which was to follow the example of several other counties, including our near neighbours the Devon Bird Watching & Preservation Society, and produce a book limited to the breeding birds of the county. The alternative was to follow the Hampshire Ornithological Society's example and use the tetrad survey results to produce a book on the county's entire avifauna. Both options had obvious advantages and disadvantages, and after much debate it was decided to follow Hampshire's path and incorporate the tetrad survey results into a new book on Dorset's birds.

Whether this was the right decision is up to others to decide, but suffice it to say, the compilation of this book has taken over 12 years to complete. During this period, plans and deadlines for final production and publication have come and gone, ideas have changed, but at last we seem to be on the verge of finishing the task. It has been rather like 'painting the Forth Road Bridge', once one version of the text for the systematic list had been completed, one or two more annual Dorset Bird Reports had appeared! For reasons that seem both tidy and logical, it was decided that 1999 would be the final year for records to be incorporated into the main species accounts in the systematic list. Even so, this book will be well 'out of date' before publication, but this is inevitable given the time between receiving the 1999 records, completing the final text, and publication. An attempt has been made to include the more notable records for the period 2000–2002 in the main systematic list with the major highlights of 2003 listed separately.

With so many records to analyse and assimilate into a book of this nature, it is inevitable that mistakes and inaccuracies will have been made and possibly perpetuated from previous publications. A considerable amount of effort has been made to reduce such errors to a minimum, but undoubtedly some will have survived into the final text. If any errors are found by readers of this book, it would be very much appreciated if corrections were sent to the author for use in any further editions or revisions that might be published.

An attempt has been made to give a 'local feel' to the book by using, where possible, Dorset-based photographers and artists.

This book should be considered as one in a series of accounts of Dorset's birdlife dating back to *'A Catalogue of Birds Observed in Dorsetshire'*, which was written by Dr R. Pulteney in 1799, and subsequently followed by such landmark publications as *The Birds of Dorsetshire* (Mansel-Pleydell 1888), *Check List of the Birds of Dorset* (Boys 1972) and *The Birds of Dorset* (Prendergast & Boys 1983). As such, this latest book has attempted to build on what has gone before, rather than to replace them.

So, what are the main aims of the book. Hopefully, readers will find it an interesting, informative and reasonably accurate account of the county's avifauna. I would also like it to be regarded as a celebration of Dorset's birdlife, and a testament to those individuals and organisations, past and present, who have contributed to the study and conservation of birds within the county. Finally, looking to the future, it is hoped that the publication of this long-awaited book will serve to encourage membership of the Dorset Bird Club and so promote its primary objective, which is to record and survey the county's birds, and provide robust information of their status to the various conservation bodies within the county.

ABBREVIATIONS

The following abbreviations are used throughout the book:

Journals/Organisations/Committees

BBRC   British Birds Rarities Committee
BOU   British Ornithologists' Union
BOURC   British Ornithologists' Union Records Committee
BTO   British Trust for Ornithology
CHOG   Christchurch Harbour Ornithological Group
DBC   Dorset Bird Club
DNH&AS   Dorset Natural History and Archaeological Society
MoD   Ministry of Defence
NCC   Nature Conservancy Council
PBO   Portland Bird Observatory and Field Centre
RSPB   Royal Society for the Protection of Birds
SRG   Stour Ringing Group

Surveys

BoEE   Birds of Estuaries Enquiry
CBC   Common Birds Census
WeBS   Wetland Bird Survey
NWC   National Wildfowl Counts

Localities and Nature Reserves

PB   Portland Bill
DCP   Durlston Country Park
Xchurch   Christchurch

Others

ad./ads   adult/adults
approx.   approximately
Au.   Autumn
bds   bird-days – days in which one or more individuals of the species under discussion are present
br.   breeding
CBs   Cress-beds
cf   compare with
CP   Country Park
Dn   Down
excl.   excluding
FF   Fish Farm
GC   Golf Course
GP   Gravel Pit
Hbr   Harbour
Hd   Head
imm./imms immature/immatures
incl.   including
juv./juvs   juvenile/juveniles
km   kilometre
nc   no count
nr   near
max/mx   maximum/maxima
N   north, S – south, E – east, W – west
NR   Nature Reserve
NNR   National Nature Reserve
sev.   several
SF   Sewage Farm
Sp.   Spring
sp/spp   species (singular)/species (plural)
STW   Sewage Treatment Works
Vl/Vlly   Valley
yr/yrs   year/years

THE COUNTY OF DORSET

INTRODUCTION

There can be few other counties of Great Britain that offer the birdwatcher such a wide variety of birds in such an attractive and diverse landscape as Dorset. This is perhaps a biased assertion from one who has been birdwatching in the county as a visitor since 1962 and a resident since 1974. Nevertheless, the facts speak for themselves. Based on *The British List* as published by the British Ornithologists Union in September 2002, no less than 405 species have been recorded in Dorset up to the end of 2002, representing 72% of the British List. The Dorset List includes 124 species, which are regarded as 'official' rarities, i.e. species for which a description is required by the *British Birds* Rarities Committee (BBRC). These rarities include American Bittern (1804), Ruddy Shelduck (1776), Calandra Lark (1961), Lesser Short-toed Lark (1992), Brown Thrasher (1966), Desert Warbler (1970), Orphean Warbler (1955) and Savannah Sparrow (1982), which were all first recorded in Great Britain in Dorset. Indeed the records of two of these, Brown Thrasher and Lesser Short-toed Lark, remain the sole British occurrences of these species. Dorset can boast an impressive list of other rarities, some second British records, some the first British records of modern times, i.e. post-1950, and others that have gained 'fame' for giving many birdwatchers the first opportunity of seeing the species in Great Britain. A selection of such rarities would include the likes of Pallid Harrier, Little Bustard, White-tailed Plover, Laughing Gull, Yellow-billed Cuckoo, Egyptian Nightjar, Olive-backed Pipit, Alpine Accentor, Siberian Rubythroat, Red-flanked Bluetail, Pied Wheatear, American Robin, Sykes's Warbler, Iberian Chiffchaff and Wallcreeper.

Rarities, however, are only the 'icing on the cake'. A better reflection of Dorset's rich birdlife is the diversity of commoner birds that occur in the county. No less than 126 species are regular breeders, whilst a further 24 species breed sporadically. Where else in Great Britain can one find such diverse species as Little Egret, Hobby, Peregrine, Little Ringed Plover, Yellow-legged Gull, Kittiwake, Sandwich and Little Terns, Puffin, Turtle Dove, Woodlark, Dipper, Nightingale, Cetti's and Dartford Warblers, Bearded Tit, Raven and Corn Bunting breeding in one county? At least 61 species can be considered regular winter visitors including a wide range of waterfowl, waders and gulls, whilst 83 species regularly pass through Dorset on passage. No wonder Dorset is so popular with birdwatchers.

So why does Dorset support so many different kinds of birds?

LOCATION

Having a coastline is an obvious advantage. Prominent headlands such as Portland, St Aldhelm's Head, Durlston CP and Hengistbury, are ideally situated, not only to attract many small migrants as they arrive and leave our shores, but also as vantage points to observe the movements of seabirds passing through the English Channel. Estuaries and coastal wetlands such as Christchurch and Poole Harbours, Lodmoor and Radipole NRs, and the Fleet are favoured haunts for large numbers of passage and wintering waterfowl, waders and gulls amongst others.

Dorset lies closer to the European Continent than most of Great Britain and this means that we are usually the first to see our summer visitors arrive and the last to see them go. Situated about half-way along the south coast, the county is ideally positioned to attract not only a good number of rarities from the near Continent and southern Europe, but also when the correct weather conditions prevail, a reasonable selection of rare species from the east (Scandinavia, eastern Europe and Siberia) and the west (North America).

CLIMATE

Dorset's relatively benign climate of mild winters and warm summers is the most favourable in Great Britain for a variety of scarce and rare breeding birds. These include residents such as Little Egret, Cetti's and Dartford Warblers and summer visitors such as the Hobby. The county is also a transitional zone between the wetter west of Great Britain and the drier east. Several species such as the Turtle Dove, Nightingale and Corn Bunting, which are characteristic of the east, reach the western limit of their breeding ranges in Dorset. Furthermore, when much of northern and eastern Great Britain is caught in the grip of hard winter weather, many birds move south to seek the less severe conditions that usually exist in our county.

GEOLOGY AND LANDSCAPE

Another factor that has an obvious influence on our local birdlife is the diversity of habitat, which in turn is a reflection of the underlying geology. Reference to a geological map shows that the topography of east, south and central Dorset is dominated by the western extension of the Hampshire Basin, which is known as the Poole Basin.

The mainly Tertiary clays, sands and gravels within this basin have developed a variety of soil types, some of which support the most important vegetation type found in the county – lowland heath. The presence of extensive areas of forestry mixed with some deciduous woodland further enhances the diversity of habitat within the Poole Basin.

It is the chalk rim of the Hampshire Basin that dominates the landscape of north-east and central Dorset, extending south-westwards in a broad band from the Hampshire and Wiltshire borders across Cranborne Chase and the centre of the county to the west of Dorchester. In the south, the chalk rim forms a very narrow, but prominent ridge extending from west of Weymouth and south of Dorchester eastwards through Purbeck, and creating such notable landmarks as the Ridgeway, White Nothe, Corfe Castle, Ballard Down and Old Harry Rocks. Today, the downlands with their gently curving slopes and dry valleys present a predominantly agricultural scene. Areas of semi-natural grass-sward, chalk scrub and woodland are scarce.

To the north of the chalk rim, the low-lying landscape of north Dorset is dominated by the Blackmore Vale, which is formed largely on the Oxford Clay, interrupted in places by the gently rolling uplands of the North Dorset Limestone Ridges. Although much of the land is given over to dairy farming with small fields of pasture, there are some important habitats in the form of damp mixed woodlands, such as Deadmoor Common, and poorly-drained scrub-covered commons, such as Lydlinch Common.

The more complex geology to the west of the chalk rim creates a typical 'West Country' landscape. Here, clay vales comprising a patchwork of small fields are overlooked by steep-sided, well-wooded hills and drained by fast-flowing streams.

Dorset's rivers are varied in character and impose a major influence on the topography of the county. Whereas rivers such as the Avon, Frome and Piddle are generally regarded as 'chalk' rivers, sharing certain attributes and characteristics, the Stour offers contrasting features, which are typical of a lowland clay river. Further variety can be found in the shorter, faster-flowing 'riffle and pool' rivers such the Bride, Brit, Char and Axe in the far west of the county. The River Avon flows from north to south, whilst the Stour, Frome and Piddle flow initially from north to south, and then from west to south-east or east. As such, the valleys of these rivers divide much of central and east Dorset, and in particular the Poole Basin, into clearly defined segments, e.g. between the Avon and Stour, the Stour and Piddle, the Piddle and Frome, and finally between the Frome and the Purbeck coast.

Although there are a reasonable number of small ponds and lakes scattered throughout the county, medium and large inland stillwaters are scarce in Dorset. Apart from the southern tip of Sutton Bingham Reservoir, most of which lies within Somerset, there are no major reservoirs in the county, whilst medium-sized lakes are in short supply, the most notable being Sherborne Lake and Crichel Lake. Most gravel extraction in Dorset has taken place in the centre of the Poole Basin, and it is in this area where most of the county's relatively few flooded gravel pits can be found.

Dorset boasts a great diversity of coastal habits, reflecting both the complex geology of the county and the influence of its rivers. The major rivers flowing through Dorset's softer Tertiary rocks form Poole Harbour (Frome and Piddle) and the smaller Christchurch Harbour (Avon and Stour) to the east. Further west, in the general vicinity of Weymouth, the South Dorset Lowlands extend south from the chalk downs to the coast. This area of low ridges and broad valleys supports such notable wetland sites as Lodmoor NR, Radipole NR (which is the estuary of the River Wey), and the Fleet. The latter forms a long coastal lagoon sheltered from the open sea by the spectacular shingle bank of Chesil Beach and together these form a unique coastal feature within the British Isles. Travelling west along the Dorset coast, the last substantial areas of low-lying wetland are situated at West Bexington, Burton Mere and Cogden Beach, just before the high sandstone cliffs at Burton Bradstock.

Much of Dorset's coastline, however, consists of cliffs. The most spectacular of these are formed by the Jurassic limestone massifs of Portland and south-east Purbeck, and the Cretaceous chalk at White Nothe, Ballard Down and Old Harry Rocks. Elsewhere in west Dorset, along other parts of the Purbeck coast and at Hengistbury, the cliffs are formed of softer rocks mainly greensands, mudstones, clays and shales, which are prone to erosion and frequent landslips. Although they lack the high vertical cliffs of the limestone and chalk, they still provide a varied and attractive coastal landscape.

HABITATS

The heathlands

The counties of Hampshire and Dorset together hold over 90% of Great Britain's quota of this valuable habitat resource. Sadly the heathlands of Dorset have been severely depleted and fragmented as a result of reclamation for farming, afforestation and more recently, the increasing pressures of expanding urbanisation. In 1800 Dorset's heathlands covered 40,000ha of land extending from the Avon Valley in the east to Dorchester in the west. Today it is estimated that only c.6,500ha remain in fragmented areas. Nevertheless, Dorset's heaths remain one of the most valuable habitats to be found in the county. Combined with relatively warm summers and mild winters, the heathlands provide an environment suitable for a range of specialist plants and animals, many of which are at the northern limits of their range.

Due to their great importance to wildlife a considerable amount of effort has been put into protecting Dorset's heathlands by various conservation bodies, notably English Nature, the RSPB and the Dorset Wildlife Trust, together with the local authorities. As a result, the remaining heathland area has been more or less constant since 1980 and through active management, such as scrub clearance and grazing, it is hoped to reverse the decline and create an additional 500ha of heathland by 2010. The largest remaining areas of lowland heath are listed in Table 1.

Heath	Hectares
Povington and Grange Heaths	747
Studland and Godlingston Heaths	406
Holt Heath	356
Hurn Common	352
Canford Heath	272
Stoborough and Creech Heaths	271
Turnerspuddle Heath	271
Arne NR	267
Hartland Moor	188
Winfrith Heath	175
Upton Heath	173
Parley Common	168
Town Common	117
Morden Bog	102

Table 1. Most important areas of lowland heath remaining in Dorset

The Dartford Warbler is the true bird speciality of the open heath, which is also the haunt of such noteworthy breeding species as Nightjar, Woodlark, Tree Pipit and Stonechat, whilst heathland pools and bogs are favoured feeding areas for the Hobby in summer. Although the heaths appear rather desolate in winter, they remain the best areas in the county for seeing Hen Harrier and the occasional Great Grey Shrike.

The forests

In the first half of the 20th Century, large tracts of heathland were leased or bought by the Forestry Commission and planted with unbroken stands of conifers. At present, 10,660ha of Dorset are covered by forestry plantations representing 43% of the total wooded area. Wareham Forest is the most extensive tract of forestry in the county, other important areas being the Dorset part of Ringwood Forest, Hurn Forest, Rempstone and Newton Heaths, Puddletown Forest, and in the far west, Champernhayes Marsh.

In their early years, coniferous plantations produce good habitat for such breeding birds as Nightjar, Woodlark, Tree Pipit, Stonechat and Dartford Warbler, but as the forests mature they become unsuitable for these species, which are replaced by conifer specialities such as Siskin and Crossbill.

In recent years, as a result of a more enlightened management approach by Forest Enterprise, the successors to the Forestry Commission, significant areas of mature forestry, notably in Wareham, Rempstone and Hurn Forests, have been felled. Some of these felled areas have been replanted, but others have been left as open spaces for heathland restoration schemes using livestock grazing in the hope of increasing the extent of existing heaths. This has created a patchwork of habitats attractive to many breeding birds including those species that favour the open forest clearings and those that prefer mature conifers. Indeed, one of the more notable effects of this new management regime has been a dramatic increase in the Woodlark population. In addition, this mix of mature forestry, forest clearings and open heath, such as found in Wareham Forest, is particularly attractive to hunting and breeding raptors.

The woodlands

Dorset is a fairly well-wooded county with an estimated woodland area of 25,063ha (9.5% of the county) of which 14,402ha (57% of the total wooded area) is deciduous.

Coppice, mainly oak and Hazel, makes up 751ha (5%) of the county's deciduous woodlands. Traditionally this was managed by the regular cutting of Hazel to ground level every 8–10 years for making sheep hurdles, whilst the oak was felled for timber at much longer intervals of c.100 years. Woods were cut rotationally so that they contained areas at different stages of growth, providing a variety of habitats suitable for a wide range of wildlife. With the development of other forms of sheep fencing, much of the Hazel is now left unmanaged. As a consequence the ground flora is now shaded out. This is the most likely reason for the Nightingale abandoning most of its coppice woodland sites in recent years. Despite this, oak and Hazel woods still support a wide range of the commoner woodland birds.

On the chalk, particularly in the north-east of the county, Beech and Ash are more prevalent in the mixed woodlands. Beech tends to exclude the shrub layer and ground flora, but where it occurs mixed with other tree species it produces good bird habitat. The woods of Cranborne Chase are particularly important for some of the county's scarcer breeding birds. Most reports of Long-eared Owl come from this area, usually breeding in small forestry plantations or where small clumps of pines occur amongst mixed woodland. Where Beech is present, Wood Warbler is found, and perhaps also the elusive Hawfinch, whilst most of the county's breeding Turtle Dove population is closely associated with woods containing Ash.

Dorset's deciduous and mixed woodlands support a wide variety of commoner breeding birds. The greatest diversity of species, however, occurs mainly in the Poole Basin, particularly in the central area from Wareham Forest west to Puddletown Forest. Here, a heady mixture of heathland margin, forestry, and mixed and deciduous woodland support many of the county's scarcer breeding species. The Woodcock prefers a mixture of forestry and damp deciduous woodland, whilst mature stands of Silver Birch are favoured by Lesser Spotted Woodpecker and Lesser Redpoll amongst others. Mature mixed woodlands, where Beech is present, support a significant proportion of Dorset's tiny breeding populations of Redstart and Wood Warbler. Some of the scarcer species, notably Redstart and Wood Warbler, can also be found in some of the fine mixed woodlands in the extreme west of Dorset, notably Lambert's Castle and Champernhayes Marsh.

The chalk downlands

From the time Neolithic farmers arrived in 3500 BC, Man has had a profound influence on the subsequent development of the chalk downs. During the Medieval period the downlands were mostly given over to sheep rearing, which reached a peak just prior to the Industrial Revolution. The pressure of grazing by sheep, combined with that by the rabbit population, maintained the characteristic downland sward, which provides such an important habitat for plants and insects. As the wool industry became concentrated around the industrial towns, so the numbers of sheep on the chalk declined to be replaced by an increase in arable farming. The ploughing of the downs for cereal crops and grass ley accelerated dramatically during the Second World War. As a result, the original downland habitat only survived in areas unsuitable for agriculture such as steep hillsides, but even these have been threatened by the recent increase in afforestation.

Today it is remnant downland that is most important to birdlife. Where grazing by sheep and rabbits remains intense, the short downland sward survives. If the grazing pressures diminish, as they did when the rabbit population was decimated by myxomatosis during the 1950s, the short sward will revert to coarse grassland and eventually to chalk scrub. This consists of such shrubs as Hawthorn, Juniper, Yew and Gorse amongst others. The deciduous woodlands, which grace certain areas of the chalk downs, notably

Cranborne Chase in the north-east, typically comprise either oak with Hazel coppice or Beech. As mentioned earlier, forestry plantations have become an increasing feature of the contemporary downland scene. It is farmland, however, that dominates the present chalk downs. Modern farm practices, notably the removal of hedgerows, have tended to create an increasingly sterile environment for wildlife.

It is the surviving areas of remnant downland sward and scrub that support the greatest diversity of birds. Sadly both the Stone Curlew and Wheatear no longer breed on Dorset's chalk downlands. Indeed, several other species that were once considered to be typical, if not common, breeding birds of the chalk grasslands and scrub, are declining in the county. These include Grey Partridge, Lapwing, Linnet, Yellowhammer and Corn Bunting. For further information refer to the section on farmland. On a more positive note, the secretive Quail is more likely to be encountered (heard) on the chalk downs than anywhere else in the county.

In winter, the chalk downland fields attract wandering flocks of Golden Plover, Lapwing, Black-headed and Common Gulls along with the occasional Mediterranean Gull, and winter thrushes in search of suitable feeding areas. Fields of kale and stubble are sometimes favoured by mixed flocks of finches and buntings, which sometimes include Brambling.

The chalk downlands are also favoured by owls and raptors including resident Barn Owl, Hobby in summer, and very small numbers of Hen Harrier and Merlin in winter, when the occasional Short-eared Owl may also be encountered. Bird migration is not particularly prominent, but may involve a few Whinchat and Wheatear together with the occasional Ring Ouzel.

Farmland

The Ministry of Agriculture's Farm Census of June 1998 showed that 194,022ha (73%) of Dorset fell within agricultural holdings. Of this, 5,693ha comprised farm woodland, leaving a total of 188,329ha (71% of Dorset) actively managed for agriculture.

Farmland provides a wide range of habitats with the largest area occupied by arable land (99,193ha) comprising tillage, fallow and temporary grass. The broad belt of the chalk downlands, which extends from north-east to south-west across the centre of Dorset, is the heartland of the county's arable farming, and it is here that the problems for farmland birds are most severe. A selective survey carried out by the RSPB in 1999 showed a marked decline in the distribution of certain key farmland species, most notably Grey Partridge, Lapwing, Tree Sparrow (extinct) and Corn Bunting, since the Tetrad Survey (1987–1994). Although the intensity of the RSPB survey was less than that of the Tetrad Survey, these reported declines are both undoubtedly genuine and alarming. There was also some evidence that other farmland species such as the Linnet and Yellowhammer were also declining.

The reasons for these declines can be traced back to the Second World War when farmers were encouraged to clear and plough areas of scrub and permanent grass, including downland, in order to feed a hungry nation. After the war, successive governments gave a high priority to food production, which was backed by guaranteed prices and later grants to intensify production. At the same time advancing technology produced a range of fertilisers, herbicides and insecticides which contributed to an efficient and productive agriculture, but was detrimental to the environment and its birds. These policies were reinforced by a world grain shortage in the 1970s and were continued under the European Union.

In more recent years, a surplus of agricultural produce and an increasing awareness of the damaging impact of past policies, have resulted in a marked change of direction for arable agriculture. While production grants have been reduced, a number of agri-environmental schemes have been introduced to protect, restore and develop wildlife habitats. These include Organic Farming grants, Countryside Stewardship, the designation and protection of Environmentally Sensitive Areas, and several other less widely operated schemes. Countryside Stewardship in particular has been widely taken up in Dorset, and its provision for uncultivated field margins and hedgerow restoration amongst a range of other measures should produce beneficial effects for birdlife.

Another important innovation is the introduction of a 'set-aside' scheme to remove arable land from production and so reduce the grain surplus. In 1998 this included 4,782ha in Dorset. The greater part of this 'set-aside' is left over the winter as stubble, the grain and weed seeds from which have been shown to be a vital food source for farmland birds. This area is further increased by a recent trend from winter to spring sowing of barley where ploughing is often deferred until late winter or early spring.

In 1998 permanent grass and rough grazing together accounted for 80,018ha (30%) of the county. This is concentrated in the valleys of the Avon, Stour, Frome and Piddle, the Blackmore Vale in the north, and the vales of west Dorset. Intensive grazing and the post-war change from cutting grass swards of hay in mid-September to making silage in late spring has had a detrimental effect on bird populations. Fortunately, hedgerows have survived much better in Dorset than in most other counties, particularly in the vale districts in the north and west where they still hold good numbers of breeding birds.

Through a combination of environmentally friendly policies, increasing awareness amongst the farming community to the needs of wildlife, and the efforts of national and local conservation organisations, there is cause for limited optimism over the future of farmland birds.

The rivers

The Avon, Frome and Piddle are regarded as classic 'chalk' rivers with rich aquatic vegetation and good water quality. Indeed, the counties of Wiltshire, Hampshire and Dorset share, in the Avon, perhaps the finest river of its type in lowland Great Britain.

The flood plains of all three rivers have been used traditionally for dairy farming. Managed water-meadows, created during the 18th and 19th Centuries, formerly covered much of the middle and lower flood plains. These were irrigated mainly in winter and early spring, and used water retained by a series of well-placed sluices in the main river. This water flowed through channels at carefully prepared levels, typically forming parallel or 'herring-bone' patterns across the flood plain, and spilled over the grass in an even, shallow flow. It was then returned to the river and could be re-used at lower sluices. The water, being of recent spring origin, was relatively warm and helped to promote an early growth of grass, even during periods of frost. At the same time, it left an alluvial deposit, which acted as a natural fertiliser. The management of these water-meadow systems was labour-intensive, and with the advent of artificial fertilisers many were abandoned. Natural flooding may have also occurred to provide excellent habitat for wintering wildfowl and waders. In the spring, as the water levels receded and cattle grazing commenced, the meadows would have provided breeding habitat for waders and Yellow Wagtail.

In recent years, the increasing intensity of grazing and the use of fertilisers and herbicides, exacerbated by a decline in the water-meadow systems, droughts and low river levels, have resulted in a catastrophic decline in the breeding populations of such wetland birds as Lapwing, Snipe, Redshank and Yellow Wagtail. The Yellow Wagtail is long extinct as a breeding bird in Dorset, whilst even in the valley of the Lower Avon, once the stronghold of these breeding birds, both Snipe and Redshank face near extinction. Similarly there has been a decline in the numbers of wintering birds using the flood plain, notably Bewick's Swan in both the Avon and Frome, and White-fronted Goose in the Avon. It is hoped that recently proposed Water Level Management Plans and other conservation measures may reverse this situation. The value of the water-meadow systems is well demonstrated on the Devil's Brook, east of Puddletown, where 50ha continues to be actively managed and since 1980 has supported winter peaks of up to 3,000 Lapwing, over 1,000 Wigeon and 200 Teal together with large flocks of Snipe.

Despite these declines, the lower reaches of the Avon, Frome and Piddle still support good populations of the commoner riverine breeding birds such as Moorhen, Grey Wagtail, Sedge and Reed Warblers, and Reed Bunting. In the Lower Avon Valley and the lowest reaches of the Frome and Piddle these are joined by the Cetti's Warbler. Cress-beds are also a feature of 'chalk' rivers. In Dorset they are located mainly along the Frome and Piddle Valleys, and are favoured by passage and wintering Green Sandpiper and wintering Water Pipit. Recently, increasing numbers of Little Egret are frequenting the chalk river valleys, particularly in winter. The Lower Avon in particular is also good for migrants and regularly attracts rarer species.

The River Stour differs from Dorset's 'chalk' rivers with characteristics typical of a lowland clay river. As a result it tends to be more sluggish and slow-flowing in summer, but more prone to sudden, but often short-lived, flood events in winter. As a result the Stour with its high, often vertical banks, provides excellent habitat for Kingfisher and supports a good population of Grey Wagtail and other common riverine breeding birds. In winter, small numbers of Goosander, a scarce bird in Dorset, regularly frequent the Stour between Wimborne and Blandford.

The rivers of west Dorset, including the Wey, Bride, Brit, Char, Lim and Axe, are relatively short and fast-flowing with relatively little flood plain. They are most notable for supporting almost all of Dorset's small breeding population of Dipper.

Inland lakes and ponds

Most inland stillwaters in Dorset consist of small ponds and lakes scattered widely throughout the county. Together they form an important habitat resource supporting such notable breeding species as Little Grebe, Tufted Duck and at a few sites, Great Crested Grebe. Small flooded sand and gravel pits are favoured by the tiny breeding population of Little Ringed Plover. Moderate numbers of waterfowl, notably Gadwall, Pochard and Tufted Duck, frequent these small ponds and lakes in winter.

There are very few lakes of a substantial size. Just reaching into Dorset at its southernmost tip is Sutton Bingham Reservoir which supports breeding Great Crested Grebe, and a variety of waterfowl and gulls in winter. Passage birds include waterfowl, gulls, terns, and if water levels are low, waders also occur. Some of these birds, including the occasional rarity, obviously wander into Dorset from time to time.

The only other stillwater bodies of substance situated inland in Dorset are Sherborne and Crichel Lakes. Sherborne Lake hosts breeding Great Crested Grebe and sometimes a wintering flock of Goosander. Otherwise both lakes attract a variety of breeding, passage and wintering waterfowl, together with the occasional interesting migrant wader and tern.

Estuaries and coastal marshes

Poole Harbour is reputed to be the world's second largest natural harbour and covers c.3,700ha (as measured from the high-water mark at spring tides) with over 80% comprising the mudflats and saltmarshes of the inter-tidal zone. Even with the pressures of urban development along the north-east shore, its popularity for leisure activities, and the exploitation of underground oil reserves, the harbour with its islands and deeply indented shoreline remains an important haven for birds. With large areas of lowland heath and rough grazing marsh adjacent to much of the harbour's shoreline, plus the presence of a freshwater lake (Little Sea) and sand dunes on the Studland peninsula, Poole Harbour and its immediate environs are one of the most outstanding areas for wildlife in Great Britain. It is not surprising then, and indeed fortunate, that so much of the area enjoys protection as nature reserves. These include Brownsea Island, Studland and Godlingston Heaths, Hartland Moor, Arne, the Wareham Water-meadows, Holton Heath and Ham Common. Private estates with limited or no access lie between these nature reserves. Like the nature reserves, these private areas remain relatively undisturbed to the obvious benefit of the harbour's birdlife.

The harbour is a drowned valley with the higher land remaining as islands and promontories. It is almost entirely enclosed with only a narrow outlet to the sea between the Sandbanks and Studland peninsulas. There are also two smaller, almost enclosed inlets along the north shore of the harbour, these being Holes Bay and Lytchett Bay. Combined with the influence of the rivers Frome and Piddle, which both flow into the west of the harbour, the tidal regime, hydrology and salinity levels are very complex and variable. This increases the diversity of habitats found within Poole Harbour.

There have been important changes in the vegetation within the harbour. In the past, the mudflats supported extensive beds of *Zostera* (eel-grass), which attracted large numbers of wildfowl in winter. In the early 1930s, the *Zostera* beds began to disappear, and were gradually replaced by *Spartina townsendii*, which had first appeared in the early part of the 20th Century. The *Spartina* has little food value, but does consolidate soft sediments and raises the level of mud to form saltmarshes which are attractive as roosting and resting sites for birds at high-water. In recent years, the *Spartina* has begun to die off and the saltmarshes are retreating, providing larger areas of open mudflat and sand, and so increasing the potential feeding area for birds.

Poole Harbour supports the greatest diversity of scarce and rare breeding birds in the county. Brownsea hosts the majority of these including Little Egret, Sandwich and Common Terns, and Yellow-legged Gull, whilst both Avocet and Roseate Tern have bred here in the past. In addition, a few pairs of Mediterranean Gull nest amongst the massive colonies of Black-headed Gull out on the saltmarshes, and Cetti's Warbler and small numbers of Bearded Tit breed in the reedbeds fringing the lower reaches of the Frome and Piddle, and the western shore of the harbour.

The harbour, together with the sheltered waters of Shell and Studland Bays, supports an abundance of winter waterfowl, waders and gulls including internationally or nationally important numbers of Dark-bellied Brent Goose, Shelduck, Goldeneye, Red-breasted Merganser, Avocet and Black-tailed Godwit amongst others, along with small numbers of such notable species as Slavonian and Black-necked Grebes, Scaup, Sanderling and Purple Sandpiper. A few divers, seaduck, auks and the occasional Red-necked Grebe favour the eastern part of the harbour and the adjacent waters of Shell and Studland Bays. Winter raptors include a few Marsh and Hen Harriers, which both favour Middlebere and the neighbouring areas in the south-west and west of the harbour. Migrant waterfowl, waders, gulls and terns are also a feature of the area with both Spoonbill and Osprey reported annually.

Christchurch Harbour forms the combined estuary of the two largest rivers in the region, the Avon and Stour. The harbour itself is the focal point for a variety of habitats. To the north lies Stanpit Marsh, an area of low-lying grazing marsh intersected by deep muddy creeks with reedbeds, semi-permanent pools and scrub. Similar habitats are present along the southern shore of the harbour, notably at Wick Fields. The harbour itself consists mainly of open mudflats with a few isolated islands of grazing marsh and shingle. The southern side of the harbour is dominated by Hengistbury Head, which rises to a height of 36m.

Its geographical position and the diversity of habitats within a relatively compact area, make Christchurch Harbour one of the best localities in the region for observing bird migration. Hengistbury is the main site for landbird migrants and provides a vantage point for seawatching, whilst Stanpit Marsh and the harbour attract a wide selection of waterfowl, waders, gulls, terns and other waterbirds at times of passage. Certain scarce passage migrants including Garganey, Spotted Crake and some waders such as Little and Temminck's Stints, Curlew Sandpiper and Wood Sandpiper, occur more frequently here than elsewhere in Dorset. It is not surprising that Christchurch Harbour also boasts an impressive list of rarities. Although numbers are considerably lower than nearby Poole Harbour, a wide selection of waterfowl, waders and gulls frequents the harbour in winter. Cetti's Warbler is the most notable breeding bird of the area.

Lodmoor NR is situated between Weymouth to the west and the expanding village of Preston to the north and east. The southern side is bordered by the main A353 road, beyond which lie the sheltered waters of Weymouth Bay. Like its near neighbour Radipole, Lodmoor NR was once estuarine in character, but became an area of low-lying grazing marsh intersected by drainage ditches with several shallow lagoons and pools, some choked with rushes and sedges. Reedbeds flank the west and east of the main moor. As the result of recent work by the RSPB, who undertook to manage this area as a nature reserve in 1983, a bund has been constructed and the northern section of the main moor flooded to encourage the development of reedbeds. This has been a great success, and as a consequence, this new reedbed area almost links the two 'older' existing reedbed areas to the undoubted benefit of the local birdlife. The whole moor is susceptible to flooding and after prolonged spells of heavy rainfall, little or none of the remaining grazing marsh may be visible above the floodwaters.

Like nearby Radipole, Lodmoor NR is one of Dorset's best sites for wetland birdlife, there being considerable interchange of birds between the two reserves. Since the inception of the RSPB's management plan, Lodmoor's birdlife has shown some significant changes and improvements. This is most obvious amongst the waterfowl with a marked increase in numbers and diversity during the winter. The recently constructed reedbed has also boosted breeding waterfowl with several scarce species, notably Gadwall, Shoveler and Pochard, nesting successfully in recent years. It is also hoped that the Bearded Tit, which bred at Lodmoor up to at least 1998, may soon return, whilst a good population of Cetti's Warbler is still present. The reserve can boast another breeding success with the recent arrival of a small colony of Common Tern, which nests on artificial gravel islands on one of the coastal pools.

In its recent past, the existence of large refuse tips immediately adjacent to the main moor plus, for a short period only in the mid-1990s, the presence of factory fishing boats and trawlers in Weymouth Bay, attracted large numbers of gulls, particularly during the winter. These regularly included scarcer species such as Iceland and Glaucous. Smaller gulls also use the moor, particularly when flooded, as a pre-roost site, mainly during the winter when the Mediterranean Gull is also reported. Otherwise Lodmoor NR attracts a good selection of winter and passage birds including its fair share of rarities.

Situated in the heart of Weymouth and virtually surrounded by urban development, Radipole NR is the former estuary of the River Wey. The lake itself is no longer saline, the tidal influence having been eliminated by the construction of Westham Bridge at its southern end. The lower reaches of the lake consist of a shallow lagoon within which islands of reed have colonised many of the old estuarine mudbanks. Scrub-fringed footpaths run through the reedbeds and enclose the Buddleia Lagoon. To the north and west of the main lagoon lies the Island Sanctuary, a drier area where the reedbeds give way in places to grazing marsh and invasive scrub. Further west still, beside a small tributary stream flowing into the River Wey, there is a narrow stretch of reedbed, marshy vegetation and scrub known as Chafey's Lake. Part of

Radipole Lake was designated as an official bird sanctuary by Weymouth Borough Council as far back as 1928, but it was not until 1975 that the present reserve was established under the management of the RSPB.

In recent years, Radipole NR has become less attractive to birds than it was during its 'heyday' during the 1970s and 1980s. Although this is most apparent in the numbers of wintering waterfowl, the site still supports impressive numbers of Pochard and remains a favoured site for Scaup. In winter and early spring, large numbers of smaller gulls use Radipole NR as a pre-roost site *en route* to the main roost in Weymouth Bay. Mediterranean Gull is frequently seen amongst these pre-roost gatherings, which may occasionally include a Ring-billed Gull or perhaps something rarer. A wide range of migrants can be seen on passage and over the years, Radipole NR has acquired an impressive list of rarities with 'southern' herons and gulls particularly prominent. Breeding birds of interest still include Great Crested Grebe, Cetti's Warbler and Bearded Tit.

In winter the sheltered waters of Weymouth Bay and Portland Harbour are important for divers, grebes (including both Slavonian and Black-necked), seaduck and auks, whilst Weymouth Bay also hosts a huge roost of gulls, mainly Black-headed and Common. For a short period in the late 1980s, Common, and occasionally, Roseate Terns bred on the Portland Harbour Breakwaters.

Chesil Beach dominates the coastal scenery to the west of Portland extending for 16km from Chesil Cove to Abbotsbury and for 13km encloses the Fleet, a shallow estuarine lagoon. To the seaward, the shingle ridge of the Chesil Beach is exposed to the full force of the prevailing south-westerly gales. The Fleet itself varies in width from nearly 1km at Butterstreet Cove to less than 100m by the Bridging Camp. The tidal flow that enters through the narrow channel at Ferrybridge penetrates little further than the middle reaches of the lagoon, beyond which seepage through the Chesil Beach and freshwater flowing in from several small streams combine to produce a brackish environment in the West Fleet. Although most of the Fleet is normally very shallow with extensive mudflats exposed between Ferrybridge and the East Fleet at low tide, water levels vary considerably. These may be quite high during periods of persistent easterly winds, which cause a build up of water particularly in the West Fleet. The aquatic flora and fauna are very rich and include extensive beds of *Zostera* and Tasselweed. At the head of the Fleet lies Abbotsbury Swannery, an attractive mixture of reedbeds and damp woodland. A recently flooded meadow at this site has proved to be a major attraction for birds. Otherwise the landward shore of the Fleet is fringed mainly by farmland. The Fleet is one of the oldest wildlife sanctuaries in Great Britain and at present the entire Fleet and neighbouring Chesil Beach are maintained as a nature reserve by the Ilchester Estate.

The Fleet provides shelter and feeding for an abundance of wintering and migrant waterfowl including several thousand Dark-bellied Brent Goose, Wigeon and Coot, as well as important numbers of Gadwall, Pintail, Shoveler, Pochard, Tufted Duck, Goldeneye and Red-breasted Merganser. Small numbers of Scaup are usually present at Abbotsbury, whilst the Fleet is one of the more reliable sites in the county for Long-tailed Duck. Otherwise a good selection of waders and gulls frequent the Fleet in winter. During times of passage, the Chesil Beach and Fleet attract a good range of migrant waterfowl, waders, gulls and terns. Migrant Sanderling particularly favour Ferrybridge, the latter being the premier site in Great Britain for Kentish Plover, which occurs most years, mainly in spring. Osprey is an annual visitor to the Fleet. Again, a good selection of rarities have been recorded over the years, particularly from Ferrybridge, the Langton Herring area, and Abbotsbury. The world famous swannery at Abbotsbury has probably been in existence for about 900 years and is now an important tourist attraction. The Chesil Beach supports an important breeding colony of Little Tern, whilst in the past Common Tern also bred in large numbers, but most of these have deserted and now nest on artificial islands on the Fleet at Abbotsbury and Lodmoor NR. Abbotsbury was a traditional site for breeding Marsh Warbler during the first half of the 20th Century, but sadly no more. They have been replaced by Cetti's Warbler, and Bearded Tit has bred occasionally in the recent past.

West Bexington, Burton Mere and Cogden Beach are the last areas of low-lying coastal wetland before high cliffs dominate the Dorset coast westwards to the Devon border. These sites lie immediately behind the Chesil Beach. At West Bexington, there is a small seasonally flooded mere, which is flanked on the east side by a scrub-fringed reedbed. Recently, a small permanent pond has been constructed on the inland side of the reedbed. This area is now managed as a nature reserve by the Dorset Wildlife Trust. A little further to the west along the Chesil lies Burton Mere, a small reed-choked lagoon surrounded by rough ground and scrub. The entire stretch of coast is backed by open farmland.

The reedswamp scrub at West Bexington supports breeding Cetti's Warbler, and Bearded Tit has also bred in these coastal reedbeds in the past. In winter, there is a huge roost of Black-headed and Common Gulls, which regularly attracts a few Mediterranean, and very occasionally, Ring-billed Gulls. Otherwise the mere at West Bexington supports small numbers of waterfowl in winter and early spring. The entire area is good for migrants in spring and autumn, and several rarities have been recorded.

Headlands and coastal cliffs

The Isle of Portland dominates the middle section of the Dorset coast. This long triangular limestone massif juts out some 8km into the English Channel and is joined tenuously to the mainland by the Chesil Beach. The island rises sharply to a peak of 127m at its northern end before gently sloping and tapering away to the southernmost point at Portland Bill, which is only just above sea level. Much of the island is flanked by cliffs, although in many places these have become partially cloaked by a combination of natural landslips and quarry waste known as 'Weares'. Defence installations, housing developments and active or abandoned quarry workings cover large parts of Portland, only in the southern half does a mainly agricultural landscape of ancient field systems and common land survive. Vegetation is limited by strong winds and salt spray, but in the relative shelter of the east side, Verne Common and East Weare are covered by areas of dense scrub. A few hardy clumps of Sycamore grow in all the settlements.

Portland is one of the best-known birdwatching sites in Great Britain. The island's potential for studying bird migration was recognised by the Rev. F.L. Blathwayt as long ago as 1918. Its full potential, however, was not established until the early 1950s, when systematic coverage, undertaken by an enthusiastic group of observers based at Portland Bill, eventually led to the formation of the Portland Bird Observatory in 1955. Although the Bill area has received most attention, it has become increasingly apparent, particularly in recent years, that most of the island is good for migrant birds. The Bill provides an excellent vantage point from which to observe the offshore movements of seabirds, which usually feature Pomarine Skua in spring and Balearic Shearwater in late summer and autumn. Amongst the scarcer landbird migrants, spring Hoopoe and Serin, and autumn Melodious Warbler and Ortolan Bunting are more likely to be seen at Portland than anywhere else in mainland Great Britain. The island's list of rarities is truly impressive and includes Great Britain's first Orphean Warbler (1955), Calandra Lark (1961), Desert Warbler (1970), Savannah Sparrow (1982) and Lesser Short-toed Lark (1992). In addition, Portland supports important populations of breeding seabirds including Fulmar, Kittiwake, Guillemot, Razorbill and one or two pairs of Puffin. Both Peregrine and Raven also breed on the island. The Bill hosts one of the few flocks of wintering Purple Sandpiper in Dorset.

To the east of Portland lies the stunningly beautiful coast of Purbeck, now designated as a World Heritage Site. Extending from near Weymouth in the west to Durlston Head in the east and then north to Ballard Down, the coastal scenery is spectacular with such notable landmarks as White Nothe, Durdle Door, Lulworth Cove, Gad Cliff, Kimmeridge Bay, the high limestone cliffs extending from St Aldhelm's Head to Durlston Head, and the chalk cliffs of Ballard Down including the offshore stacks of Old Harry Rocks. Although the geology of the Purbeck coast is complex, it is dominated by the Cretaceous chalk of the Purbeck Ridge and the Jurassic limestone massif in the south-east corner.

With such an extent of high cliffs, it is not surprising that the Purbeck coast hosts some of the largest breeding seabird colonies along the English south coast. These include such species as Fulmar, Shag, Cormorant, Kittiwake, Guillemot, Razorbill and a few pairs of Puffin, the latter favouring the Dancing Ledge area. Like Portland, both Peregrine and Raven nest on the Purbeck cliffs.

In recent years, both Durlston CP and the St Aldhelm's Head/Chapman's Pool area have been shown to be important sites both for observing the offshore passage of seabirds and land-based migration. Indeed, most of the Purbeck coast and coastal valleys attract good numbers of landbird migrants, the most notable sites, other than those already mentioned, being Ballard Down, Winspit Valley, Tyneham Valley, Lulworth Cove, White Nothe and Osmington Mills. The potential of the Purbeck coast for bird migration is clearly demonstrated by the impressive list of rarities, which include Great Britain's first and only Brown Thrasher at Durlston CP in 1966, the long-staying Red-flanked Bluetail at Winspit in October and November 1993, and the short-staying Siberian Rubythroat at Osmington Mills in October 1997, not to mention the over-wintering Wallcreeper at Winspit from November 1969 to April 1970!

Hengistbury Head dominates the southern side of Christchurch Harbour and offers a range of habitats including saltmarsh, rough grassland and grazing marsh, bramble and gorse scrub, heathland, thickets of birch and sallow, and mature oak woodland. Hengistbury forms an integral part of Christchurch Harbour, being favoured by landbird migrants and also provides a vantage point for watching the movements of seabirds through Poole Bay during passage periods. In addition, divers, grebes, seaduck and auks winter offshore and a small flock of Purple Sandpiper frequents the rocky groynes. Like the rest of the harbour area, rarities regularly occur. Hengistbury also supports some interesting breeding birds include Little Egret, Grey Heron, Sand Martin and Dartford Warbler.

The West Dorset coast, particularly between Lyme Regis and Bridport, is dominated by high crumbling cliffs consisting mainly of fossil-rich Lias mudstones and clays capped in places by Cretaceous greensands (Golden Cap). Narrow beaches of shingle fringe the base of these cliffs and scrub covers much of the cliff-top areas, which overlook the long sweep of Lyme Bay from Devon in the west to Portland in the east. Sheltered spots are at a premium along this exposed coastline. Although these cliffs do not support the diversity of breeding birds found at Portland and Purbeck, Fulmar, Cormorant, Peregrine and Raven all nest along this coast. A few waders frequent the beaches, particularly the more extensive ones near Lyme Regis, at times of passage and during the winter, whilst coastal and cliff-top scrub attracts landbird migrants. The Cobb at Lyme Regis is a traditional haunt for wintering Purple Sandpiper.

A BRIEF HISTORY OF
DORSET ORNITHOLOGY

INTRODUCTION

A full account of Dorset's early ornithologists can be found in the opening chapter of *The Birds of Dorset* (Prendergast & Boys 1983). Entitled "Some Dorset Ornithologists", this chapter contains brief biographies of a number of people spanning some 1,300 years, but concentrates mainly on the period from c.1790 to 1980. For those wishing to learn more about the early history of Dorset's ornithology, Evelyn Prendergast's excellent account is essential reading. It is inappropriate to repeat his work fully in this article, but some reference is made to the more important of these early ornithologists, together with those who made vital contributions in more modern times.

PRE-1948

St Aldhelm of Malmesbury, who died in c.709, is said to be the father of Dorset ornithology and is credited in his writings with the first mentions in English literature of four out of the 16 species which had been named by 700, namely Woodpigeon, Swallow, Nightingale and Chaffinch. He was the first Bishop of Sherborne, and it is appropriate that one of Dorset's most notable birdwatching sites, St Aldhelm's Head, should be named after him.

The first recognisable coloured illustrations of birds by a Dorset artist appeared some 700 years later in c.1400, when John Siferwas of Sherborne, a Dominican friar and a member of a Dorset family who held the manor of Hooke, near Beaminster, illustrated *The Sherborne Missal*. This contains pictures of some 40 species of bird elegantly and accurately drawn and coloured.

The first account that can be considered to be a county avifauna is 'A Catalogue of Birds Observed in Dorsetshire', which was written by Dr R. Pulteney (1730–1801) in 1799, and included in the second revised edition of *Hutchin's History and Antiquities of the County of Dorset* (1813). When published, Pulteney had died and his list was amended by Thomas Rackett. Dr Pulteney, a physician who practised at Blandford, was also a distinguished botanist of sufficient eminence to have a genus of Australian flowering shrubs, *Pultenea*, named after him. His catalogue lists about 178 species of birds, but due to confusion in identification features at that time, some of this number are invalid.

The dominant figure during the 19th Century was J. C. Mansel-Pleydell (1817–1902), a country landowner and all-round naturalist who was elected president of the Dorset Natural History and Archaeological Field Club on its formation in 1875, a position he held until his death in 1902. In 1888, he published the first really authoritative book on the county's birds entitled *The Birds of Dorsetshire*. This was basically an up-dated and expanded version of his 'List of the Rarer Birds in the County' written in 1873 and published in the third revised edition of *Hutchin's History and Antiquities of the County of Dorset* (1861–1874). *The Birds of Dorsetshire* (1888) is also noteworthy for including engravings by the bird artist G. E. Lodge and one of the first bird photographs to appear in a book, which shows the swans and their swanherd at Abbotsbury.

Perhaps the most significant event associated with the formation of the Dorset Natural History and Archaeological Field Club was the production of annual bird reports in the *Proceedings*, which started to appear in 1889. Initially these were edited by N. M. Richardson from 1889 to 1913, and then by W. Parkinson Curtis up to 1917.

As Mansel-Pleydell had dominated the county's ornithology during the second half of the 19th Century, so the next editor of the annual bird reports dominated the first half of the 20th Century. The Rev. F. L. Blathwayt (1875–1953) was appointed Rector of Melbury Osmund in November 1916. Prior to his arrival in Dorset, Blathwayt had already published county lists of birds for Somerset and Lincolnshire. Although he only resided in Dorset from 1916 to 1929, he edited the annual bird reports from 1918 to 1948. Blathwayt pioneered a new attitude to ornithology in Dorset, away from the collection of rare birds and towards detailed field studies, recording the local distributions and numbers of birds, the changes in these and their causes. He wrote many papers during his tenure, the most important being 'A Revised List of the

Birds of Dorset', first published in the *Proceedings* in 1933, and revised and reprinted in both 1939 and 1945. It included 285 species or subspecies, with another six more doubtful.

There were a number of other notable ornithologists active in the county during the first half of the 20th Century. These include the Rev. F. C. R. Jourdain (1865–1940), one of the leading ornithologists of his generation who retired to live in Southbourne from 1925, and W. J. Ashford (1879–1970), born in Blandford and who lived in Bournemouth after the First World War. Both kept bird notes and were primarily interested in collecting and studying birds' eggs. The help they provided towards the production of 'A Revised List of the Birds of Dorset' and its revisions is acknowledged by the Rev. F. L. Blathwayt. Another leading naturalist of the time was W. R. G. Bond (1880–1952) of Tyneham, whose family had for generations protected the birds that nested on Gad Cliff. Apart from being a patient and careful observer, he actively campaigned for the creation of local nature reserves, especially a sanctuary at Weymouth – now the RSPB Reserve at Radipole.

THE PERIOD 1948–1986

The next era in Dorset's ornithological history began in 1948. A revival of interest in the county's birds after the restrictions of the Second World War was led by the notable trio of Dr Kenneth Rooke (1916–1987), Dr John Ash and Arthur Bull (1906–1962). Their drive and enthusiasm resulted in the formation, in 1948, of the Dorset Field Ornithology Group, and to the establishment of the Portland Bird Observatory on a permanent basis in 1955. In 1976 the Dorset Field Ornithology Group became the Dorset Bird Club, but remained under the patronage of the Dorset Natural History and Archaeological Society.

In 1948, the editorship of the annual bird report was handed over to Dr K. B. Rooke, who resigned in 1955 and was succeeded by A. J. Bull who continued in this role until his death in 1962. John Follett (1914–1991) took over the task of editor from 1962 to 1964 to be followed by the Rev. G. W. H. Moule (unknown dates) in 1965 and 1966, F. R. Clafton (1930–1995) from 1967 to 1973, John Boys from 1974 to 1979, and Dr George Green from 1980 to 1985.

By 1962 it was clear that Blathwayt's 1945 list was out of date, and the Rev. Moule undertook to produce a new list. This appeared in the *Proceedings* as 'A Revised List of the Birds of Dorset, up to 1962', and included 304 species and 11 subspecies. Prior to his tenure as editor of the annual bird reports, John Boys co-ordinated the work for the first *BTO Atlas Survey* in Dorset during 1968 to 1972. The desire to publish the results of this survey was no doubt responsible, in part at least, for the prompt appearance of the *Check List of the Birds of Dorset* (Boys 1972). This excellent publication, which at the time was the most comprehensive account of the county's birds, has been the foundation for succeeding books on Dorset's birdlife. The first of these appeared in 1983 with the publication of *The Birds of Dorset* (Prendergast & Boys). This represented the first comprehensive and authoritative account of the county's birdlife since Mansel-Pleydell's 1888 publication.

Since its formation in 1955, the work of the Portland Bird Observatory and Field Centre has contributed greatly to our knowledge of birds, particularly seabirds and migrants, not only locally in Dorset, but also nationally. Since it moved to its permanent home at the Old Lower Light in 1961, many birdwatchers have enjoyed the hospitality of the Observatory and the prospect of seeing one of the many rarities that Portland so regularly attracts. Miss Helen Brotherton C.B.E. has made an outstanding contribution to the success of the Portland Bird Observatory and Field Centre, along with the officers and committee members who have served during its existence, and the wardens – Peter Morgan from 1961 to 1962, Frank Clafton (1930–1995) from 1963 to 1975, Iain Robertson from 1975 to 1978, Mick Rogers (1944–2003) from 1979 to 1995 and finally Martin Cade from 1996 to the present. Portland Bird Observatory and Field Centre publish an annual report.

As a result of county boundary changes in 1974, the Bournemouth and Christchurch areas were transferred from Hampshire to Dorset. As a result, Dorset inherited Christchurch Harbour, undoubtedly a birdwatching site of national importance. The formation of the Christchurch Harbour Ornithological Group in 1956, owed much to the inspiration of Frank Clafton. CHOG, as it is known locally, has recorded and studied the birds systematically ever since. These studies include extensive ringing operations, particularly at Hengistbury and in the harbour's reedbeds. Although many have been involved in CHOG's activities, Dave Smith deserves special mention for the major contribution he has made to the recording of the harbour's birdlife and towards the production of the annual bird report.

Durlston Country Park was established by Dorset County Council in 1978. As a result of the efforts of the first warden, Hamish Murray, the birdlife of this south-east corner of Purbeck has been studied systematically ever since. Indeed we are fortunate to have three such major coastal watch-points as Portland, Christchurch Harbour and Durlston providing such a wealth of information and, in particular, increasing our understanding of bird migration in the county.

Ringing activities undertaken in Dorset have also made a vital contribution to our knowledge of birds and, in particular, bird migration in the county. Obviously much of this activity has been based at well established coastal watch-points such as Portland Bird Observatory and Christchurch Harbour. Amongst the other organised groups and dedicated individuals involved in ringing, special mention should be made of the Stour Ringing Group (SRG). This was formed in 1980 to facilitate the study of the Nightjar in Dorset and included Trevor Squire, Ian Alexander and Alan Martin amongst its founding members. With the expert guidance of Brain Cresswell, the SRG became one of the first amateur ringing groups to employ radio-telemetry as part of its Nightjar study. Other important subjects studied by the SRG include *Acrocephalus* migration, particularly the occurrence of Aquatic Warblers, at Keysworth, waders in Poole Harbour, and general passerine migration at Chapman's Pool, Lytchett Bay and Cranborne Common.

As a result of increasing public awareness of conservation issues and the efforts of the various national and local conservation organisations, notably English Nature, the RSPB and the Dorset Wildlife Trust, this period also saw the proliferation of many nature reserves in the county. Dorset can now boast a fine and varied selection of reserves including such important bird areas as Studland and Godlingston Heaths, Brownsea Island, Arne, Lodmoor, Radipole, the Fleet and Chesil Beach, Abbotsbury Swannery and West Bexington to mention but a few. The formation of the Dorset Naturalist's Trust (predecessor to the Dorset Wildlife Trust) in March 1961 was an important step in the process of securing our county's natural heritage. Over the years, the submission of records from these reserves on a systematic and annual basis has made a major contribution to improving our knowledge of the county's birdlife.

1987 ONWARDS

During the 1980s, a new generation of birdwatchers emerged. Many, but not all, regarded the Dorset Bird Club as the natural focus for their interest in the county's birds. The size of the club and the rapid expansion of activities in modern birding were making an increasing, but unfulfilled demand on the resources of the parent society. So in 1987, after a year of negotiations, the New Dorset Bird Club was formed as an independent body. This saw the end of an era, during which the Dorset Bird Club and its predecessors had enjoyed the patronage and financial support of the Dorset Natural History & Archaeological Society. Those involved in these negotiations, particularly the last chairman of the old club, remain extremely grateful for the co-operation received from the officers of the parent body throughout this period. It is a testament to all concerned, that the eventual formation of the New Dorset Bird Club went so smoothly. Once the new club had established itself, the word 'New' was dropped by mutual consent. The fact that the Dorset Bird Club has survived and prospered owes much to the hard work and dedication of its officers and committee over the past 16 years or so, along with the continuing support of its membership. In the early days, the club's long-term financial survival was largely secured by the efforts of Mark Constantine who raised considerable sums of money by organising sponsored 'bird-races'. Further details of the club, its aims and activities can be found on the cover of this book.

Almost immediately the new club embarked on an ambitious project to record the breeding distribution of birds throughout the county on a tetrad (2x2–km squares) basis. A more detailed account of the Tetrad Survey (1987–1994) is given later in this book, but the undoubted success of this survey is a tribute to its prime organiser, Hugo Wood-Homer. The Tetrad Survey led naturally to the next 'big' project to be undertaken by the Dorset Bird Club, the production of the present and latest book on the birds of Dorset.

The new club also took responsibility for producing and publishing the annual bird reports under the editorship of Martin Cade from 1986 to 1989 and again in 1993 and 1994, Richard Taylor from 1990 to 1992, Vaughan Ashby in 1995 and 1996, Steve Smith in 1997 and 1998, and finally Imogen Davenport from 1999 to the present. It should be added, that from 1995 at least, the bird report has been very much a team effort and has involved help from a number of people in collating records and writing text. In addition to the Bird Report editor, the county recorder has also played an important role in collating the mass of records submitted each year and assessing the validity of some of the more unusual occurrences. This role has been undertaken by Martin Cade from 1987 to 1995, Shaun Robson from 1996 to 1999, Neil Gartshore from 2000 to 2002 and now James Lidster. Since 1996, the county recorders have been ably assisted by a formal Dorset Bird Club Records Panel, whose expert assessment of those records of rare birds not required to be submitted to the *British Birds* Rarities Committee (BBRC), has added credibility to the scientific integrity of the Bird Report. It is also worth mentioning that Grahame Walbridge, resident of Portland and one of the county's best-known and well-respected field ornithologists, has served on the *British Birds* Rarities Committee since he was elected on 1st April 1992. Grahame's extensive knowledge of bird identification and his contribution to the assessment of rare birds, both locally and nationally, are widely acknowledged.

SOME FINAL THOUGHTS

In Evelyn Prendergast's account *The Birds of Dorset* (Prendergast & Boys 1983), he states "as it would be invidious to attempt to describe the qualities of some of the county's living ornithologists, and not others who may consider that they have a greater claim to fame, the task has not been attempted". In describing Dorset's recent ornithological history, it has been difficult to avoid naming those who have been associated with particular significant events. It is hoped that in doing so, no great offence has been committed or taken by those mentioned or omitted.

To attempt to acknowledge and name everyone, past and present, who in their own way have made, and are still making, a valuable contribution to our knowledge of the county's birds and their conservation is a mammoth task. Suffice it to say, their efforts and achievements are much appreciated.

THE TETRAD SURVEY OF BREEDING BIRDS 1987 to 1994

The Dorset Bird Club carried out a breeding survey of the county's birds between 1987 and 1994. It was co-ordinated by Hugo Wood-Homer and, where possible, organisers for one or more 10–km squares were appointed. Those filling these roles were Derek Beauchamp, Martin Cade, Rees Cox, George Green, Stephen Hales, Treleven Haysom, Richard Kershaw, Paul Martin, Hamish Murray, Jeremy Powne, Rosemary Rooke, Tasie Russell, Dave Smith, Kyle Turner, Grahame Walbridge and Bernard Watts. A total of 144 people took part in the survey, covering from one to over 250 tetrads each. A very large part of the work was carried out by a hardcore of about 20 surveyors. All those who helped with the survey are listed at the end of this section.

Those tetrads comprising nature reserves and/or 'local patches' received good and continuous coverage by the wardens/regular watchers throughout the survey period. Almost all other tetrads were surveyed in at least two, and sometimes three or four years during the same period. Usually at least two surveyors were used in each tetrad and all tetrads were visited at night to check for nocturnal breeding species. During the last two years of the survey, every effort was made to find any breeding species that were unaccountably missing from suitable habitat within the tetrads.

The purpose of the survey was to map the distribution of all the county's breeding birds by tetrads (2–km x 2–km squares), using three categories of evidence of breeding, possible, probable and confirmed. Where a tetrad fell only partly in Dorset, the whole of it was surveyed, including that part which extended into another county.

A total of 700 full tetrads and 63 part tetrads, which included coastal areas, were surveyed resulting in c.39,000 records. An average Dorset tetrad held just over 53 breeding species with a range of 24 to 90. The number of breeding species in the 700 full tetrads is shown in Table 2.

Range of breeding species	Number of tetrads
20–29	2
30–39	42
40–49	176
50–59	350
60–69	102
70–79	26
80–89	1
90–99	1

Table 2. Range of breeding species per full tetrad in Dorset 1987–1994

The tetrads with the higher diversities of breeding species were generally found in the Poole Basin, along the valleys of the Rivers Avon, Stour, Frome and Piddle, and in isolated areas of favourable habitat, particularly where there were lakes and ponds. Tetrads with the lowest diversities were located mainly in agricultural areas where there were few hedges and woods, particularly on the chalk downlands.

A total of 141 species were proved to have bred in at least one year during the survey period with a further ten species in the probable or possible categories.

On its completion in 1994, the tetrad survey was considered to have achieved excellent coverage throughout the county. Although there has been a considerable delay in publishing the results of the survey formally, an electronic copy of the database was given to the Dorset Environmenal Records Centre in 1997. As a result, valuable information on the distribution of Dorset's breeding birds has been readily available to everyone including conservation bodies and those engaged in serious research.

So, as the results of the Tetrad Survey (1987–1994) are about to be published in the systematic list of this book, perhaps it is time to consider repeating it in the near future. Certainly there is considerable evidence to suggest that the status of many of the county's breeding birds has changed in the past nine years. Yellow Wagtail, Grasshopper Warbler and Tree Sparrow have seemingly disappeared, Grey Partridge, Lapwing and Willow Tit, amongst others, have declined, whilst the Buzzard continues to expand its range, and Little Egret, Avocet and Yellow-legged Gull are new breeders in the county.

TETRAD SURVEYORS 1987 TO 1994

The Dorset Bird Club wishes to acknowledge and thank the following for their help with the Tetrad Survey 1987 to 1994.

Amies P
Andrews M
Armstrong G
Arnold D N
Baker P F
Baker R M
Bale Mrs J
Bandfield D
Barrett A
Beauchamp D
Benham P
Blackburn J H
Bowman D F
Bowman Mrs E
Boys J V
Branwhite R C
Brett E C
Butler R F
Butt Mrs J
Cade M
Chandler M R
Chown D J
Christie P
Cliff-Hodges Mr & Mrs
Cohen S
Constantine M
Cook K G
Corbett-Marshall G
Cornish E H
Cox J R
Cree Maj. G
Crocker R J
Cuff N J
Cuff P
Cundall G J
Dannreuther Capt. H H
Davis L R
Drake C R
Drake P R
Dutson G
Dykes P
Fair J
Flack P
Flatters E
Forrest P
Gardner I C
Gibbons M
Gillard N
Giovannini P

Goldsack J G
Graham Dr & Mrs G K
Graham W
Green Dr G P
Greenhill M
Groves S
Hales S
Hampshire Ornithological
  Society
Harding R J
Harris P M
Haysom W T
Hiscock T G
Hooker Mr & Mrs T
Hopkins G R
Howell J
Howell R
Hudson Dr M K G
Hughes Mrs A
Hull Mrs J
Hull N J
Humphrey W
Jessop G
Jones J M
Jones S
Kershaw R
Kitchin C
Knight Mr & Mrs
Lambert R
Lawrence C
Lewis I M
Lloyd E
Lockwood J
Marsh N A
Marshallsay F C
Martin J
Martin P
Mathews B J
May M
McLean I
Middleton P
Morrison S
Mould R C
Murray R J H
Newland Ms J
Newton R
Parker K
Parks R
Parsons A J

Pearce D
Pearman D
Peart R H
Phillips J
Pickess B
Powell Maj. J M N
Powne J D
Powrie K J
Prendergast Col E D V
Prowse S
Race Mrs C
Rashley D
Rashley Mrs A
Read P S
Reynolds C
Richards C E
Robertson Capt. M
Robson S
Rooke Mrs R
Rumbol Mrs P
Russell Mrs A
Seaward D R
Smith D N
Smith P
Spencer B
Stock A
Sturdy Miss P
Surry R
Taylor R J
Teagle B
Toogood Mrs F
Tooth Rev. N
Turner M G
Upton G
Vanstone F C
Vanstone Mrs N
Walbridge G
Watts B R H
Webb G
Whitby G
Whitby Mrs C A
Whitfield Dr P G
Whitfield Mrs A
Whitfield T
Widden B
Williams P
Wood-Homer H G

INTRODUCTION TO THE SYSTEMATIC LIST

The Systematic List provides a summary of published information, since scientific records began, about species that have occurred in Dorset and fall into the British Ornithologists' Union's (BOU) categories defined (in January 1998) as follows:

Category A: species which have been recorded in an apparently wild state in the British Isles at least once since 1st January 1950.

Category B: species which have been recorded in an apparently wild state in the British Isles at least once up to 31st December 1949 but have not been recorded subsequently.

Category C: species which, although originally introduced by Man, either deliberately or accidentally, have now established a regular feral breeding stock that apparently maintains itself without necessary recourse to further introduction.

> (C1) Naturalised Introductions: Species that have occurred only as a result of introduction.
> (C2) Naturalised Establishments: Species with established populations as a result of introduction by Man, but which also occur in an apparently natural state.
> (C3) Naturalised Re-establishment: Species with populations successfully re-established by Man in areas of former occurrence.
> (C4) Naturalised feral species: Domesticated species with populations established in the wild.
> (C5) Vagrant naturalised species: Species from established naturalised populations abroad.

Category D: species which would otherwise appear in categories A or B except that:

> (D1) there is a reasonable doubt that they have ever occurred in the wild state;
> (D2) they have certainly arrived with a combination of ship and human assistance, including provision of food and shelter;
> (D3) they have only ever been found dead on the tideline; or
> (D4) species that would otherwise appear in Category C except that their feral populations may or may not be self supporting.

Category E: species that have been recorded as introductions, transportees or escapes from captivity, and whose breeding populations (if any) are thought not to be self sustaining. Category E species form no part of the British List.

NOMENCLATURE AND SEQUENCE

The sequence follows the edition of the British Ornithologists' Union's (BOU) *The British List* published in 2002. The English names, however, that are most familiar have been retained and, where different, those used in *The British List* are given in parentheses. The accounts of species that have occurred in Dorset in the wild state (categories A to C) are given in the main Systematic List. Those that have occurred but are of uncertain status follow the main Systematic List in a section dealing with Category D and selected Category E species.

SUB-SPECIES

There are separate accounts for those subspecies that are either (i) likely to be 'split' as a full species in the near future, or (ii) particularly well-marked and regularly reported. Other subspecies, races and morphs are listed within main species text.

RECORDING BOUNDARIES

Only records and species that have occurred within the administrative boundary of Dorset are dealt with in the main Systematic List.

Coastal waters

The locations of seabird movements and offshore flocks are generally given by the viewing point, e.g.

Portland Bill. The locations of birds distributed over wider expanses of the sea are given by the name of the coastal water involved, e.g. Poole Bay. For further details – see Gazetteer.

Pre-1974 South-West Hampshire

On 1st April 1974, the government transferred a sizeable area of south-west Hampshire into the administration of Dorset. This area extends along the coast from the old county boundary at Westbourne to just east of Highcliffe, and then north to Ashley Heath incorporating a wide strip of land to the west of the River Avon and the entire valley of the River Avon south of Sopley. Bournemouth and Christchurch along with smaller communities including Hurn, St Leonards, St Ives, Winkton and Burton were now in Dorset along with such important bird areas as Christchurch Harbour and the Lower Avon Valley.

Bird records from Christchurch Harbour are well covered by the annual reports of the Christchurch Harbour Ornithological Group (CHOG), which was founded in 1956, whilst bird records from this whole area are included in the Hampshire Bird Reports up to 1973, the Dorset Bird Reports from 1975 onwards, and by both in 1974.

Unfortunately coverage in the county avifaunas (bird books) have suffered an interruption. This area is covered by *A Revised List of Hampshire and Isle of Wight Birds* (Cohen & Taverner 1972) up to the end of 1971, and by *The Birds of Dorset* (Prendergast & Boys 1983) from 1974 to 1980. The compilers of *Birds of Hampshire* (Clark & Eyre 1993) decided to omit the entire area and all its pre-1974 records. As a result, there is a distinct risk that records for 1972 and 1973 may be excluded from subsequent county avifaunas.

It was decided that to attempt to incorporate all historic records prior to 1974 from this area in the present book was both too complicated and largely unnecessary. As mentioned earlier, this area of Hampshire is well covered by *A Revised List of Hampshire and Isle of Wight Birds* (Cohen & Taverner 1972) and its predecessors *Birds of Hampshire and the Isle of Wight* (Cohen 1963) and *Birds of Hampshire and the Isle of Wight* (Kelsall & Munn 1905). Furthermore, more detailed records of birds from this area can be found in the Hampshire Bird Reports up to 1974 and the annual reports of the Christchurch Harbour Ornithological Group (CHOG) from 1956 to 1974. Consequently, only the more significant records prior to 1974, including those for 1972 and 1973, are summarised in a separate section at the end of the Systematic List.

Sutton Bingham Reservoir

Most of Sutton Bingham Reservoir lies within Somerset with only the southernmost tip extending into Dorset. Although a proportion of the commoner birds inhabiting the reservoir inevitably frequent the Dorset section, it is difficult to judge with any degree of consistency and certainty the species and numbers involved. Records of these commoner species are already covered by the annual Somerset Bird Reports and included in the county avifauna. Consequently for the purpose of this book, it was decided only to include records of national and county rarities that definitely occurred in the Dorset part of the reservoir. Unfortunately, there may be reports of some species that are rare visitors to inland Dorset that will be missing from this book. This will apply particularly to migrant waders and terns.

LOCALITIES

Historically, there has been some inconsistency in the naming of localities. For example, in the past many records referred to only Portland, when they almost certainly occurred at Portland Bill. In more recent years, records from Portland as a whole have referred increasingly to specific areas or sites on the island. For the purposes of this book an attempt has been made to rationalise these inconsistencies at some of the more systematically covered birdwatching sites.

Abbotsbury

Almost all records refer to Abbotsbury Swannery and its immediate environs, including the adjacent waters of the Fleet and the Fleet shore of the Chesil Beach opposite, rather than the nearby village. Records offshore in Lyme Bay are given by the viewing point at Abbotsbury Beach, which is also the coastal car park immediately to the west of Abbotsbury Swannery.

Bovington

Almost all records refer to the immediate environs of Bovington Camp (MoD) including the Tank Training area.

Chapman's Pool/St Aldhelm's Head

Chapman's Pool is situated immediately to the west of the base of St Aldhelm's Head. Over the years, records from Chapman's Pool have sometimes been included within the 'greater' area of St Aldhelm's Head. For the purposes of this book, all records from this 'greater' area are given under St Aldhelm's Head except for national and county rarities that definitely occurred at Chapman's Pool.

Chesil

The shingle bank of the Chesil is variously named 'the Chesil', the 'Chesil Beach' or the 'Chesil Bank'. In recent years, the Chesil has generally referred to the viewing points along the shingle bank between Ferrybridge and Chesil Cove, which are traditionally used by birdwatchers for seawatching. This convention has been retained in this book. The Chesil Beach is used for birds that have occurred and nest on the shingle bank.

Christchurch Harbour

Generally, most records of the commoner species simply refer to Christchurch Harbour, which includes Stanpit Marsh, Wick Fields and Hengistbury Head, as well as the main harbour itself. This convention has been largely retained for this book, with the exceptions of seabird movements and birds reported offshore, which are recorded under Hengistbury, and records of national and county rarities, which are given under the specific site names within the harbour area. Some rarities have wandered throughout the harbour area and consequently are recorded under Christchurch Harbour.

Portland

'Portland' refers to the island as a whole whereas 'Portland Bill' refers to birds that have occurred within, or have been observed offshore from, the Portland Bird Observatory and Field Centre recording area, which roughly lies south of a line along the southern edge of Southwell and the Admiralty Hedge. Records from the rest of Portland are given under the specific site name where known, e.g. Verne Common, Suckthumb Quarry, Reap Lane etc.

Puddletown

Almost all records refer to Bardolf Manor and its immediate environs including the water-meadows of the Devil's Brook, rather than the nearby town.

ASSESSMENT OF RECORDS

From 1958 onwards records of species (and subspecies) designated as 'nationally rare' have been assessed by the *British Birds* Rarities Committee (BBRC). The list of species requiring assessment by the BBRC has changed over the years with a number of 'commoner' rarities being removed from the list, e.g. Cory's Shearwater, White Stork, Ring-necked Duck, Pectoral Sandpiper, Ring-billed Gull, Bee-eater, Richard's and Tawny Pipits, Pallas's Warbler and Common Rosefinch. More exceptionally, some species have been re-instated after earlier removal, e.g. Ferruginous Duck and Savi's Warbler. As a general rule, for those periods that the various species (and subspecies) have been assessed by the BBRC, only accepted records have been published in this book. There are a few exceptions where there is overwhelming evidence that the record was genuine, but that for various reasons not submitted to the BBRC for assessment. These exceptions are clearly identified as such in the text and it is hoped that they will eventually be submitted to BBRC. No records rejected by the BBRC have been published in the book.

Pre-1958 records of national rarities have been included based on the judgement of previous authors and editors of the main accounts of Dorset's birds, notably *The Birds of Dorsetshire* (Mansel-Pleydell 1888), 'A Revised List of the Birds of Dorset' (Blathwayt 1945), *Check List of the Birds of Dorset* (Boys 1972) and *The Birds of Dorset* (Prendergast & Boys 1983). Many of these rarities would have appeared in pre-1958 issues of *British Birds*.

Records considered to be rare in Dorset but not requiring assessment by the BBRC have been published in the annual Dorset Bird Reports and various accounts of the county's birdlife at the discretion of the authors and editors, with the advice of the county recorders. There were short periods when such records were assessed more formally by *ad hoc* groups of local experts. In 1996, the Dorset Bird Club formed a Records Panel, which has systematically assessed all records of county rarities from 1995 onwards. Only records of county rarities accepted by the Dorset Bird Club Records Panel for the period of its existence have been included in this book.

SPECIES ACCOUNT LAYOUT AND PRESENTATION OF DATA

Status

The first line under the species heading is a brief statement on status in the county using the following definitions:

Abundant: occurs in large numbers in suitable habitat and season

Common: occurs regularly in fairly large numbers or is widely distributed in suitable habitat

Fairly common: occurs in moderate numbers in suitable habitat and season

Locally common: occurs in small numbers but restricted to specific habitats

Uncommon: occurs annually in very small numbers

Scarce: one to five records each year or restricted to specific habitats

Rare: occurs less than annually

Very rare: 6–25 records in past 50 years

Accidental: less than six records in past 50 years

Pre-1950

Where appropriate, a summary of the species' status in the county prior to 1950 is given at the beginning of the main text. This is largely based on *The Birds of Dorsetshire* (Mansel-Pleydell 1888), and 'A Revised List of the Birds of Dorset' (Blathwayt 1945).

1950–1999

Most of the main text describes in more detail the species' status during this 50 year period. The main sources of information for this period are *Check List of the Birds of Dorset* (Boys 1972), *The Birds of Dorset* (Prendergast & Boys 1983) and the annual Bird Reports.

For most breeding species, a comparison is made between the results of the first British Trust for Ornithology (BTO) *Breeding Bird Atlas Survey* (1968–1972) and the Dorset Bird Club's breeding bird Tetrad Survey (1987–1994). The comparison is based on evidence of breeding (confirmed, probable or possible) in the 10–km squares within the pre-1974 county boundary. Reference is also made to the abundance and more detailed distribution of the breeding species based on the results of the Tetrad Survey (1987–1994). In most instances, this is complemented by a map, the main exceptions being either where a species breeds in virtually all the tetrads in the county, e.g. Blackbird, or for security reasons, e.g. Hobby. Further details of the Tetrad Survey (1987–1994) are given in a separate section. For some species an attempt to show trends in breeding populations are shown where long-term data are available, most notably in the form of Common Bird Census (CBC) results. Population trends for the commonest of our breeding birds are shown by the Common Bird Census Index for the period 1981 to 1994, based on data kindly provided by the BTO.

For wintering birds, mainly wildfowl, waders and gulls, much of the information is based on the results of national surveys, most notably the Wetland Bird Survey (WeBS) and its predecessors the Birds of Estuaries Enquiry (BoEE) and National Wildfowl Counts (NWC). An attempt is made to show changes in abundance and distribution, as well as giving notably high and county record counts.

The status of most of our migrant birds, including seabirds, is largely dependent on the vast amount of data collected on a systematic basis from our three main coastal watch-points, Portland Bill, Durlston CP and Christchurch Harbour. Both Portland Bill (PBO) and Christchurch Harbour (CHOG) publish their own separate annual bird reports. Where possible, data from these sites are used to show changes in abundance and the pattern of migration within the county. Some interesting comparisons between these main coastal watch-points are also made.

The seasonal pattern and distribution of birds, particularly non-residents, is described with particular attention given to notably early, late and unseasonal records. For many summer visitors, changes in timing of the first arrivals in spring are shown.

For national and county rarities with less than 50 records, these are listed individually. Similarly, other important occurrences such as notable unseasonal and inland records, are also listed individually.

Ringing

Ringing statistics up to 1999 are summarised towards the end of the main text. For the most part, only the numbers of foreign recoveries and controls are given. Within this context, ringing records from the Channel Islands are included. For the purposes of this book, the term 'recovery' generally refers to a bird ringed in Dorset and recovered outside the county, whilst the term 'control' generally refers to a bird ringed outside Dorset and recovered inside the county.

World status

The final part of the main text summarises the species' world status including, where appropriate, a brief reference to its status within the British Isles. For national rarities assessed by the BBRC, the total number of occurrences in Great Britain is given up to 2002.

Post-1999 records

For national and county rarities with less than 50 records, occurrences during 2000–2002 are included in the main text of the species accounts. For other species, notable records during 2000–2002 are summarised in a postscript section at the end of the main text. The most interesting records for 2003, some of which have not yet been properly assessed by the relevant authorities, are given in a separate section entitled 'Bird Highlights of 2003'.

Accuracy and presentation of data

Throughout the main text, a great effort has been made to present data in a consistent manner. Unfortunately, this has not always been possible, particularly with regard to annual, seasonal and monthly totals. This is mainly because this data has been reported in different ways by the main sources of information used by this book. In addition, even for a single source of information, the way data has been reported has also changed over time. Inevitably, some assumptions have been made in an attempt to standardise the presentation of data. Despite the imperfections, it was considered better to present the data concerned to illustrate major trends and changes in status, rather than ignore it. It is hoped that most of the information given in this book is accurate.

Christchurch Harbour (*George Green*). One of Dorset's outstanding birdwatching haunts – the view from Hengistbury looking across the Common and Wick Hams towards Stanpit Marsh and Christchurch Priory.

Little Egret (*Pete Coe*). Now a familiar sight on estuaries and marshes throughout the county, the first report of breeding in Great Britain was from Dorset in 1996.

Little Stint (*Pete Coe*). One of several species of uncommon migrant wader that favour Christchurch Harbour during autumn passage.

Curlew Sandpiper (*Pete Coe*). Another of the uncommon migrant waders that regularly frequent Christchurch Harbour in the autumn.

Spotted Crake (*Graham Armstrong*). In recent autumns, Christchurch Harbour has been the most reliable site in Dorset to see this uncommon migrant.

Baird's Sandpiper (*Graham Armstrong*). Christchurch Harbour has hosted two of Dorset's three records of this rare American wader.

Hoopoe (*Pete Coe*). Small numbers of this exotic visitor are reported from Dorset's coastal watch-points every spring.

Subalpine Warbler (*Graham Armstrong*). Christchurch Harbour attracts its fair share of rarities from southern Europe.

Arne Nature Reserve (*Pete Coe*). A fine example of woodland and lowland heath meeting the saltmarshes and estuary of Poole Harbour to provide a wide diversity of habitats rich in birdlife.

Studland National Nature Reserve (*Pete Coe*). Dorset's only extensive system of sand dunes overlook the sheltered waters of Studland Bay, a regular haunt for fishing Sandwich Terns in summer, and divers, grebes and seaduck in winter.

Sandwich Tern (*Pete Coe*). Brownsea Lagoon has supported the only breeding colony in Dorset since colonisation took place in 1972.

Roseate Tern (*Pete Coe*). Although one or two individuals mingle with the nesting Sandwich and Common Terns on Brownsea Lagoon most summers, breeding has only been attempted once.

Avocet (*Pete Coe*). Poole Harbour supports internationally important numbers in winter with Brownsea Lagoon hosting the largest ever single flock recorded in Great Britain in December 2002.

Black-necked Grebe (*Pete Coe*). Small numbers of Black-necked and Slavonian Grebes can be found in Poole Harbour and Studland Bay in winter.

Red-breasted Merganser (*Pete Coe*). A 'classic' winter bird of Poole Harbour, which holds a population of national importance.

Spoonbill (*Pete Coe*). A frequent visitor to Poole Harbour with one or two birds regularly wintering in recent years.

Penduline Tit (*Graham Armstrong*). This fine male showed well in a reedbed at Lytchett Bay during late January and early February 1998.

Durlston Country Park (*Pete Coe*). The cliff ledges support breeding seabirds including large numbers of Guillemots.

Worbarrow Bay (*George Green*). The headlands and valleys of coastal Purbeck attract a wide variety of small migrants including the occasional national rarity.

Peregrine (*Pete Coe*). Since returning to nest on the Purbeck cliffs in the mid-1980s, the Peregrine has firmly re-established itself as a breeding bird in the county.

Puffin (*Pete Coe*). A few pairs still return each summer to the cliffs of Purbeck and Portland Bill.

Red-flanked Bluetail (*Carole Leigh*). This delightful 'Sibe' entertained hordes of birdwatchers during its 10 day stay in the Winspit Valley during late October and early November 1993.

Siberian Rubythroat (*Graham Armstrong*). The discovery of Great Britain's second ever Siberian Rubythroat at Osmington Mills in October 1997 further demonstrates the potential of the Purbeck coast for attracting 'top-class' national rarities.

Lodmoor Nature Reserve (*Pete Coe*). An important wetland site for birds throughout the year, where recent management has successfully converted a substantial area of the grazing marsh into reedbeds and freshwater pools.

Grasshopper Warbler (*Pete Coe*). Although virtually extinct as a breeding bird in the county, 'reeling' males are occasionally reported from Lodmoor Nature Reserve in the spring.

Sedge Warbler (*Pete Coe*). Lodmoor Nature Reserve supports a good breeding population of this lively songster.

Mediterranean Gull (*Pete Coe*). Radipole and Lodmoor Nature Reserves are renowned for attracting uncommon and rare species of gulls.

Glaucous Gull (*Pete Coe*). The large 'white-winged' gulls have become much scarcer in the Weymouth area since the closure of Lodmoor Tip.

Radipole Nature Reserve (*Pete Coe*). Most of the reserve consists of a shallow lagoon bordered by extensive reedbeds.

Bearded Tit (*Pete Coe*). Small numbers have regularly bred in Radipole's reedbeds since the mid-1960s.

Portland Bird Observatory (*Pete Coe*). An impressive list of national rarities have been found in the Observatory's garden.

Allen's Gallinule (*Pete Coe*). Found in a moribund state near Weston, Great Britain's second-ever Allen's Gallinule was taken to the Observatory but sadly failed to recover and subsequently died.

Scops Owl (*Martin Cade*). Dorset's only confirmed record was caught on a fishing boat one mile off Portland Bill and released later the same day at the Observatory.

Blyth's Pipit (*Martin Cade*). One of two birds which represented Great Britain's first multiple arrival of this rare 'eastern' pipit.

Pallas's Grasshopper Warbler (*Martin Cade*). Perhaps one of the more surprising discoveries to be found in the Observatory's nets.

Sykes's Warbler (*Martin Cade*). Although only present for one day, this was Great Britain's first 'twitchable' individual.

Razorbill (*Pete Coe*). A few pairs breed on Portland's West Cliffs.

Guillemot (*Pete Coe*). Large numbers nest on Portland's West Cliffs.

Kittiwake (*Pete Coe*). Portland's West Cliffs support one of Dorset's two surviving breeding colonies.

Avalanche Road 'Hump' (*Pete Coe*). Clumps of sycamores, which occur in the more sheltered parts of Portland, are particularly attractive to Pallas's and Yellow-browed Warblers in late autumn.

Tout Quarry (*Pete Coe*). Much of the centre and north of Portland consists of disused quarries, a favoured haunt of migrant Ring Ouzels.

Short-eared Owl (*Pete Coe*). Although mainly an autumn migrant, birds have overwintered on Portland in recent years.

Black Redstart (*Pete Coe*). Typically an early spring and late autumn migrant, a few birds remain to winter on Portland.

Wheatear (*Pete Coe*). A common migrant with one or two pairs breeding on Portland in most years.

Blackcap (*Pete Coe*). Another of Portland's common migrants.

Wryneck (*Pete Coe*). A few birds occur regularly on Portland during autumn passage.

Melodious Warbler (*Pete Coe*). Portland is the best site in mainland Great Britain for this scarce migrant.

Woodchat Shrike (*Pete Coe*). Virtually an annual visitor to Portland, particularly in late spring and early summer.

Ortolan Bunting (*Pete Coe*). Yet another scarce migrant which appears on Portland more often than at any other site in mainland Great Britain.

Buff-breasted Sandpiper (*Pete Coe*). Portland (excluding Ferrybridge) has hosted four species of American wader.

Desert Wheatear (*Pete Coe*). Two of Dorset's three Desert Wheatears have occurred on Portland.

Sardinian Warbler (*Pete Coe*). This first-summer male was present at Weston for two days in April 1995.

Northern Waterthrush (*Peter Leigh*). One of several American landbirds to have arrived on Portland.

Ferrybridge and the Chesil Beach (*Pete Coe*). Overlooked by the shingle bank of the Chesil Beach, Ferrybridge is an important site for birds at the eastern end of the Fleet.

Little Tern (*Pete Coe*). Dorset's only breeding colony is located on the Chesil Beach at Ferrybridge.

Brent Geese (*Pete Coe*). A few Pale-bellied Brent regularly mingle amongst the thousands of Dark-bellied Brent that winter of the Fleet.

Kentish Plover (*Pete Coe*). An annual visitor to Ferrybridge, which is one of the most reliable sites for this species in Great Britain.

Semipalmated Sandpiper (*Pete Coe*). The second example of this rare American wader to be found at Ferrybridge.

The Fleet at Rodden Hive (*Pete Coe*). The various bays along the landward shore of the Fleet are attractive haunts for wildfowl, waders and gulls.

Forster's Tern (*Pete Coe*). Although this bird wandered along the Dorset coast from Weymouth to West Bexington, it favoured the Fleet throughout much of its stay.

Lesser Yellowlegs (*Pete Coe*). One of several rare American waders that have been reported from the Fleet.

The Fleet at Abbotsbury (*Pete Coe*). The Chesil Beach encloses the Fleet along its 8 mile (13km) length from Ferrybridge in the east to Abbotsbury in the west.

Abbotsbury Swannery (*Pete Coe*). Feeding time in winter - the breeding colony of Mute Swans is unique within the British Isles and has existed since at least 1393.

West Bexington (*Pete Coe*). Together with nearby Cogden Beach, the most westerly coastal wetland of importance in the county.

Skua species (*Pete Coe*). This controversial bird, which was present from 27th January to 4th February 1996, may yet prove to be either a South Polar or Brown Skua.

Burton Cliffs (*Pete Coe*). A breeding site for Fulmars, whilst the offshore waters of Lyme Bay are favoured by Common Scoter in winter.

Fulmar (*Pete Coe*). Breeds at suitable locations along much of the Dorset coast.

Studland National Nature Reserve and Little Sea (*Pete Coe*). Heath, damp woodland and reedswamp surround Little Sea, a large freshwater lake formed during the 19th Century by the northwards development of sand dunes along Studland Bay.

Stonechat (*Pete Coe*). Breeds widely on the heaths of Poole Basin and in dry scrub along the coast.

Meadow Pipit (*Pete Coe*). A common breeding bird of the county's heaths.

Hartland Moor National Nature Reserve (*Pete Coe*). Many of Dorset's surviving heaths enjoy protection as nature reserves.

Dartford Warbler (*Pete Coe*). The 'classic' breeding bird of Dorset's heaths.

Wareham Forest (*Pete Coe*). A mixture of deciduous woodland, mature forestry, forest clearings and heath creates a rich mosaic of habitats supporting a wide range of breeding birds including Nightjar, Woodlark, Dartford Warbler and Crossbill.

Woodlark (*Pete Coe*). The dramatic increase the county's breeding population is largely due to improved management of the heaths and forestry areas.

Puddletown Forest (*Pete Coe*). Approximately 5% of the county is covered by deciduous woodland.

Chiffchaff (*Pete Coe*). The repetitive song is a familiar sound of Dorset's woodlands during the spring and summer.

Nuthatch (*Pete Coe*). A common breeding bird of Dorset's woodlands.

Hawfinch (*Pete Coe*). An elusive bird of the county's woodlands with very few reports of breeding.

Maiden Castle (*Pete Coe*). This ancient hill-fort is a prominent feature of the chalk downlands immediately to the south-west of Dorchester.

Red-legged Partridge (*Pete Coe*). A widespread bird of Dorset's chalk downlands, where it has largely replaced the native Grey Partridge.

Golden Plover (*Pete Coe*). Large flocks traditionally winter in fields close to Maiden Castle.

Fontmell Down Nature Reserve (*George Green*). The chalk downlands of Cranborne Chase dominate the landscape in the north-east of the county.

Skylark (*Pete Coe*). A typical breeding bird of the chalk downlands, which has benefited from changes in agricultural practices ('set-aside') in recent years.

Lydlinch Common (*George Green*). A fine example of the damp woodlands and scrubby commons that are characteristic of the Blackmore Vale.

Willow Tit (*Pete Coe*). Once a typical breeding bird of the Blackmore Vale and the adjoining chalk scarp, this species now seems to be on the verge of extinction in the county.

The western vales (*Pete Coe*). Viewed from Powerstock Common, the landscape of west Dorset is typically 'West Country' with rolling, well wooded hills interspersed by narrow valleys with fast flowing rivers.

Buzzard (*Pete Coe*). Although widely distributed throughout the county, the Buzzard is particularly common in west Dorset.

River Avon at Burton (*George Green*). In its lower reaches, the river passes through a wide floodplain mainly comprising meadows prone to winter flooding.

Grey Heron (*Pete Coe*). Frequently found stalking the margins of Dorset's rivers and lakes in search of prey.

Kingfisher (*Pete Coe*). A 'classic' breeding bird of Dorset's main rivers.

River Hooke (*Pete Coe*). The west Dorset rivers are typically shorter, faster-flowing and 'riffle and pool' in character compared to rivers in the centre and east of the county.

Dipper (*Carole Leigh*). The county's small breeding population is restricted to the rivers of west Dorset.

Lulworth Lake (*Pete Coe*). There are relatively few large lakes in the county.

Great Crested Grebe (*Pete Coe*). The county supports a relatively small breeding population, reflecting the relative paucity of lakes and ponds in Dorset.

Tufted Duck (*Pete Coe*). Found widely in winter on lakes, ponds and flooded gravel pits throughout the county.

Ruddy Duck (*Pete Coe*). Although still only an occasional breeder, there is evidence that this species may soon establish itself in the county.

Brown Thrasher (*the late Frank Clafton*). This famous Dorset rarity was present at Durlston Country Park from mid-November 1966 to early February 1967.

Wallcreeper (*Dr David Godfrey*). Dorset's second Wallcreeper frequented the cliffs and quarries at Winspit from mid-November 1969 to mid-April 1970.

Nutcracker (*Dr David Godfrey*). This confiding individual near Cerne Abbas was one of 7 birds seen in Dorset during the famous national influx of autumn 1968.

Ross's Gull (*Enid Stanford*). Considering the popularity of gull watching in recent years, it is perhaps surprising that there have been no further Dorset records since this bird at Christchurch Harbour during the summer of 1974.

Ivory Gull (*Graham Armstrong*). Chesil Cove hosted Dorset's only recent record of this high arctic gull during late January and early February 1980.

Mute Swan   *Cygnus olor*

A common resident and winter visitor

The Mute Swan is a familiar breeding resident of rivers and lakes throughout the county. The *BTO Atlas* (1968–1972) revealed evidence of breeding in 29 (78%) 10-km squares (confirmed in 28 and possible in one), the most notable absences being in the far north (ST72) and north-east (SU01). The Tetrad Survey (1987–1994) produced a similar result with evidence of breeding in 28 (76%) of the pre-1974 10-km squares (confirmed in 27 and probable in one), the most notable absences being in the west (ST40), centre (ST70) and north-east (ST91). The Tetrad Map shows that the Mute Swan breeds mainly in the south and east of the county with concentrations along the Lower Avon, the River Stour and its tributary the Allen, and the lower reaches of the Frome and Piddle. It is much scarcer in the west of Dorset where the rivers are less suitable for the species and breeding is generally confined to lakes and coastal lagoons.

The Swannery at Abbotsbury, which has existed since at least 1393, is by far the most important breeding site in the county. Although this colony is unique within the British Isles, as Mute Swans are normally aggressively territorial breeders, colonial breeding also occurs in Denmark. In the Middle Ages the young birds were kept in pens and fattened for the table. The tradition of rearing cygnets continues today, but they are now released and the colony is a tourist attraction. The Abbotsbury swans also have an unusual legal status as they belong to the local landowner, the Ilchester Estate, and not to the Crown. Unfortunately there is little historic information on the size of the swan flock, but it is known that there were 500 birds including 90 cygnets in

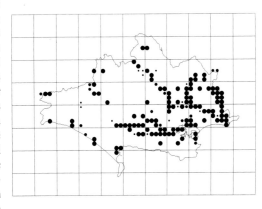

1591. During the years 1865 to 1881 numbers varied from 500 to over 1,400, with the flock reduced to half its previous strength when hard winters deprived the swans of their food supply as in 1864/65 and 1880/81. In the early 1900s there were 100–110 breeding pairs, whilst in the mid-1940s the average size of the flock was 800–900 birds. Although breeding numbers were relatively stable during the late 1970s and through the 1980s, there has been a marked increase during the 1990s reaching a peak of 158 pairs in 1999 – see Table 3. Radipole NR supports the only other substantial breeding population with numbers ranging between 8–24 pairs during 1976–1996, but it would appear that the population has 'crashed' at this site in recent years – see Table 3.

	1976	1977	1978	1979	1980	1981	1982	1983	1984	1985	1986	1987
Abbotsbury	52	47	51	64	101	nc	38	nc	48	55	68	58
Radipole NR	19	20	19	15	18	16	8	8	10	14	15	18

	1988	1989	1990	1991	1992	1993	1994	1995	1996	1997	1998	1999
Abbotsbury	nc	nc	103	133	103	114	112	77	97	106	141	158
Radipole NR	24	20	17	18	19	14	18	nc	12	1	1	nc

Table 3. Number of breeding pairs at Abbotsbury and Radipole NR 1976–1999

In 1961 a national survey revealed 153 pairs in Dorset, whilst another census in 1978 produced 157 pairs within the pre-1974 boundaries of the county and 174 pairs within 'new' Dorset. At this time, there was concern nationally about a decline in the Mute Swan population attributed to poisoning by ingesting the lead weights then widely used in angling. Dorset was an exception to this trend because the colonies at Abbotsbury and Radipole NR, which contributed so greatly to the county total, had not been affected by this problem.

Non-breeding birds form summer flocks at Christchurch Harbour and Radipole NR – see Table 4. These flocks build up to reach peak counts in July and August when the birds are flightless – see Table 5.

	1976	1977	1978	1979	1980	1981	1982	1983	1984	1985	1986	1987
Xchurch Hbr	306	307	143	322	346	380	437	356	389	370	392	341
Radipole NR	nc	108	52	84	108	84	85	65	94	100	87	111

	1988	1989	1990	1991	1992	1993	1994	1995	1996	1997	1998	1999
Xchurch Hbr	402	538	nc	352	401	340	359	373	350	419	302	400
Radipole NR	113	93	60	71	88	89	88	65	nc	nc	nc	nc

Table 4. Peak counts of non-breeding summer flocks at Christchurch Harbour and Radipole NR 1976–1999

Jan	Feb	Mar	Apr	May	Jun	Jul	Aug	Sep	Oct	Nov	Dec
36	31	36	44	147	256	351	339	212	100	65	47

Table 5. Average monthly maxima at Christchurch Harbour 1986–1999

During the autumn and winter the swan colony at Abbotsbury attracts birds from other areas of Dorset and adjoining counties. This makes the Fleet the most important wintering area for this species in the British Isles with peaks of over 1,000 birds in recent years – see Table 6. Radipole NR, the Lower Frome Valley, Poole Harbour and Christchurch Harbour are the other main areas attracting substantial numbers of Mute Swans during the autumn and winter – see Table 6.

	80/81	81/82	82/83	83/84	84/85	85/86	86/87	87/88	88/89	89/90
The Fleet	1238	1111	870	740	681	635	812	774	569	838
Radipole NR	83	67	49	30	67	77	88	83	91	74
Lower Frome	nc	nc	nc	nc	56	nc	36	32	31	76
Poole Harbour	61	44	61	63	58	37	53	40	54	51
Christchurch Hbr	nc	nc	nc	nc	nc	14	112	55	75	80

	90/91	91/92	92/93	93/94	94/95	95/96	96/97	97/98	98/99	99/00
The Fleet	1007	1163	1069	1245	1196	1124	1151	1381	1107	1168
Radipole NR	62	65	67	101	60	54	32	14	nc	68
Lower Frome	107	103	114	96	112	102	92	nc	70	nc
Poole Harbour	81	80	147	149	133	183	183	98	94	122
Christchurch Hbr	45	100	nc	45	365	323	175	217	180	180

Table 6. Autumn and winter maxima at the main sites 1980–1999

The Lower Avon Valley is the only other site where counts have exceeded 100 in recent years, the highest being 129 in November 1995. Otherwise counts of between 50–100 birds have been recorded from the Stour Valley between Corfe Mullen and Spetisbury, the highest being 82 at Shapwick on 16th January 1991, and occasionally from other sites, e.g. 90 at West Bexington on 2nd May 1977.

The British population is mainly non-migratory, but there are occasional sightings of birds passing coastal watch-points such as Portland Bill, Durlston CP and Hengistbury.

A total of 5,366 birds has been ringed in the county. Most recoveries/controls are local, but there have been eight recoveries from France, one from the Channel Islands and one from the Netherlands indicating a limited amount of cross-channel movement.

The original breeding range of the Mute Swan extended from Asia into eastern Europe, but it has been introduced widely in central and western Europe, also more locally in North America, South Africa and Australasia. In the British Isles the species has been domesticated since the Middle Ages.

Postscript 2000–2002

The breeding colony at Abbotsbury increased to 163 pairs (rearing 172 young) in 2001, which is the highest number since at least 1976 and possibly much earlier. The breeding population at Radipole NR recovered in 2000 with 14 pairs rearing 19 young. Autumn/winter maxima on the Fleet continued to exceed 1,000 birds during 2000–2002 making it by far the largest population in the British Isles.

Sponsored by Abbotsbury Swannery

Bewick's Swan (Tundra Swan) *Cygnus columbianus bewickii*

An uncommon winter visitor

Mansel-Pleydell (1888) described this species as a "rare visitant" and listed only three records involving one shot on the Fleet on 18th February 1855, another at Chickerell on 20th February 1871 and a third at Henbury near Wimborne in December 1879. Blathwayt (1945) considered it to be a scarce winter visitor that sometimes occurred in hard weather. There were no reports between 1947 and 1955.

Since 1956 Bewick's Swans have occurred annually except for 1959. Most of the records between 1956 and 1967 were from the Poole Harbour and Weymouth areas with notable influxes during severe winter weather in early 1956 (c.24 birds), 1961/62 (c.19 birds) and 1962/63 (89–106 birds, with a maximum of 67 at Abbotsbury in January). During the 1960s, the species was fairly regular at Little Sea with reports in most winters. This was perhaps the prelude to a regular wintering flock becoming established in the Lower Frome Valley from 1967/68 onwards. This wintering flock steadily increased with maxima occasionally exceeding 100 birds, usually but not exclusively during hard winters, the highest count being 127 on 12th January 1992 – see Table 7. The sudden collapse of this wintering population during the late 1990s, with no reports in 1999, is very disturbing. Birds favoured a number sites along the Lower Frome Valley between Poole Harbour and Dorchester, notably the Wareham Water-meadows, East Holme, East Stoke, Wool, Woodsford and Lewell.

Birds belonging to the winter population established in the Avon Valley during the mid-1960s regularly commuted between the Hampshire and the post-1974 Dorset parts of the valley, favouring the Avon Causeway and Sopley areas. Numbers peaked in the late 1980s with maxima of 167 in February 1989 and 163 in December 1989 – see Table 7. Like the Lower Frome Valley, virtually no birds visited the Dorset part of the Avon Valley during the late 1990s.

	70/71	71/72	72/73	73/74	74/75	75/76	76/77	77/78	78/79	79/80
Frome Valley	18	2	58	8	6	59	45	85	106	93
Lower Avon Valley	–	–	–	–	nc	nc	9	69	95	51

	80/81	81/82	82/83	83/84	84/85	85/86	86/87	87/88	88/89	89/90
Frome Valley	73	114	35	60	115	120	97	71	40	63
Lower Avon Valley	nc	35	58	139	80	153	100	51	167	163

	90/91	91/92	92/93	93/94	94/95	95/96	96/97	97/98	98/99	99/00
Frome Valley	50	127	81	40	47	46	68	8	8	4
Lower Avon Valley	95	40	50	48	24	13	34	3	0	5

Table 7. Winter maxima at the main sites 1970–1999

Elsewhere in Dorset, the number of records each year often reflects the strength of the main wintering populations, which typically increase during periods of severe winter weather. Such conditions may force birds to leave their traditional feeding areas both within and outside the county to seek respite, notably in coastal areas such as Christchurch Harbour, Poole Harbour and the Weymouth area including the Fleet. The Stour Valley, particularly at Throop and between Wimborne and Shapwick, is occasionally favoured by small flocks, which sometimes linger for several days or weeks. Although the species has occurred at a number of other wetland sites scattered throughout the county, there are relatively few sightings from the north and west. Most records involve 30 or fewer birds, but occasionally larger numbers occur, the most notable being 95 at Radipole NR on 13th–14th January 1987, 70 at Lower Common on an unspecified date in 1992 and 50N at Christchurch Harbour on 11th January 1986.

Although there are occasional sightings of birds passing Hengistbury, presumably moving to and from the Avon Valley, and Durlston CP where 22E on 17th October 1995 is notable, there are only two records from Portland Bill with 30 on 7th November 1975 and 1N on 1st November 1985. In addition, 2E at Winspit on 18th April 1969 is noteworthy.

The main arrivals are from mid-October, the earliest being 5th October 1981 with 12N at Abbotsbury, whilst most departures occur during late February and early March with late stragglers, probably injured birds, staying until April, the latest being 24th April 1991 at Avon Causeway.

Although no birds have been ringed in the county, there have been a number of interesting controls of collar-ringed birds. A total of seven 'blue-collared' birds, six originating from either the Lower Pechora Valley or nearby areas of northern Siberia, have been subsequently observed in the Lower Frome Valley as well as at other sites in the British Isles and Europe. A 'yellow-collared' bird ringed in the Netherlands has also been seen there. Observations of other colour-marked birds indicate more local movements between the main wintering areas in Dorset and nearby Hampshire, and the Somerset Levels and Slimbridge.

The Bewick's Swan breeds in the tundra areas of NE Europe and Siberia, whilst the nominate race *C. c. columbianus*, which is known as the Whistling Swan, breeds in the tundra areas of North America. The European and Siberian populations winter mainly in north-western Europe, notably the Netherlands and British Isles, and east Asia. In the British Isles, the main wintering area is the Ouse Washes.

Postscript 2000–2002
There has been no evidence of a recovery from the sudden collapse in Dorset's wintering population with only five records involving c.14 birds in 2000, five records involving c.19 birds in 2001, and four records involving c.11 birds in 2002.

Whooper Swan   *Cygnus cygnus*

A rare winter visitor and passage migrant
Mansel-Pleydell (1888) described this species as "not very uncommon, especially if the weather be very severe after Christmas" and mentioned that Colonel Hawker once killed eight at one shot in Poole Harbour. Blathwayt (1945) considered it to be a scarce winter visitor, which sometimes occurred in hard weather.

Since 1950 Whooper Swans have been recorded in all but ten winters – four in the 1950s, two in the 1980s and four the 1990s – see Fig 1. Many records are associated with periods of severe cold weather when birds are forced south and west from their normal wintering areas. The two most notable hard weather influxes occurred in early 1956 with 58 at Abbotsbury on 22nd February when there were possibly as many as 200 'wild swans' on the whole Fleet, and during the 'big freeze' in early 1963 with peaks of c.200 on the Fleet at Abbotsbury on 13th January and c.64 in Poole Harbour on 19th January.

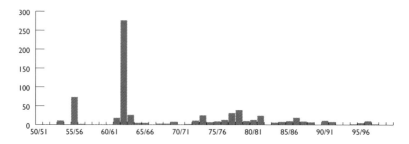

Figure 1. Annual totals 1950–1999

During 1950–1974 the majority of the birds were recorded from the Fleet (69%) and Poole Harbour (25%). Apart from the two large hard weather influxes, there were several reports of overwintering at Little Sea, namely in 1956/57, 1961/62, 1963/64, 1964/65, 1967/68 and 1971/72 (cf Bewick's Swan). A bird that frequented Poole Park intermittently between 9th March 1960 and 8th April 1961 was presumably injured.

Since 1974 records have been more evenly spread with Radipole NR (23%) and Christchurch Harbour (22%) the preferred sites, and relatively few sightings from the previously favoured areas of the Fleet (11%) and Poole Harbour (7%). Despite several hard winters, there have only been two recent reports of genuine overwintering, namely up to five on the Fleet during January–February 1979 with one remaining until early April, and two at Christchurch Harbour on 19th January 1985, which subsequently spent several weeks in the Hampshire part of the Avon Valley occasionally wandering into Dorset. Many of the mid-winter records, including those during periods of hard weather, have involved birds on short visits and often just flying over.

In recent years there is increasing evidence of autumn passage between mid-October and mid-December with a peak in late November – see Table 8. Several of these passage records come from Christchurch Harbour, whilst there are sightings from Durlston CP with 4E on 19th November 1985 and 1E on 12th November 1990, St Aldhelm's Head with 4E on 4th November 1995, and Portland Bill with 6 on 10th December 1987, 3S on 28th October 1988 and 2NE on 22nd October 1990.

Oct	Oct	Nov	Nov	Dec	Dec	Jan	Jan	Feb	Feb	Mar	Mar
1–15	16–31	1–15	16–30	1–15	16–31	1–15	16–31	1–15	16–28	1–15	16–31
0	13	21	27	22	14	18	10	0	2	0	0

Table 8. Half-monthly totals 1980–1999

The injured Poole Park bird apart, the earliest date is 19th October 1972 at Radipole NR, whilst there are few records after February the latest being 13th April 1996 at Lodmoor NR and later seen flying east at St Aldhelm's Head.

The Whooper Swan breeds in Iceland, Scandinavia, north-eastern Europe and northern Asia. The main wintering areas are north-western Europe, including the British Isles, the Black and Caspian Seas, and east Asia. The British wintering population, which is concentrated in northern parts of Ireland and Britain, consists mainly of Icelandic breeders.

Postscript 2000–2002

There was an exceptional influx during late autumn 2002 involving one at Abbotsbury from 23rd October to 2nd December, which was ringed on 31st October (first for Dorset), four at Coward's Marsh, Christchurch from 24th October to 11th December, seven at Lodmoor NR on 25th October and five of the same nearby at Friar Waddon from 12th November, one of which was found dead. A first-winter bird in the Lower Avon Valley on 25th November 2001 was the only other record.

Bean Goose   *Anser fabalis*

A very rare winter visitor

There are four 19th Century records involving one shot at Weymouth in February 1855, one at Lodmoor on 15th November 1871, five secured in Poole Harbour on 24th November 1876 (all eaten!), and two shot at Abbotsbury in winter 1890/91. During 1976–1999, there were c.11–14 records (c.14–17 birds) including two records in 1987/88 and c.3–5 records (c.5–7 birds) in 1995/96, which coincided with national influxes of the Tundra race in both winters. In December 2001, there were two further records including an exceptional flock of 26 birds, which far exceeded the previous county maximum of three! It seems likely that most, if not all, of the Dorset sightings refer to Tundra race *A. f. rossicus*.

1976   Poole Park: 11th December
1982   Swineham and East Holme: 31st December–27th February 1983
1985   Lower Avon Valley at Week Farm: 18th February
1987   Lower Frome Valley: one with Bewick's Swans 17th December–22nd February 1988; same
          flying north-west at Creekmoor 22nd February 1988 and later relocated at Ibsley in the
          Avon Valley (Hampshire) 23rd February–7th March
1988   Crichel Park: 31st January–28th February
1993   Abbotsbury: 6th December
1994   Keysworth and Little Sea: two 30th January
1995   Lodmoor NR and Littlemoor: three 5th–8th December, two remaining to 19th December
          Abbotsbury: 7th–12th and 20th December; possibly same at West Bexington 19th January
          1996 and at Abbotsbury again 19th January–18th February 1996
          Puddletown: 18th–29th December; presumably the same again 10th January–9th February
          1996
1997   Waddock Cross: 5th–6th January; possibly same at Wool 14th February
2001   Puddletown: two with White-fronted Geese 15th–19th December
          Lodmoor NR, Littlemoor and neighbouring areas: flock of 26 from 21st–29th December

Some authorities consider that the Bean Goose complex comprises three monotypic species including the Taiga Bean Goose *A. fabalis* and Tundra Bean Goose *A. serrirostris*, while others still regard these as subspecies. The Taiga Bean Goose breeds in the taiga zone from Scandinavia eastwards to eastern Asia, the main western wintering areas being the Low Countries and central Europe with two localised wintering populations in Norfolk and central Scotland. The Tundra Bean Goose breeds in the tundra zone from the Kanin peninsula eastwards across northern Asia to Anadyr, the main wintering areas in Europe being Sweden, Denmark and Germany, the Low Countries and France. Although formerly considered to be a winter vagrant to the British Isles, Tundra Bean Geese now occur annually with periodic influxes associated with severe weather on the Continent.

Pink-footed Goose   *Anser brachyrhynchus*

A rare winter visitor and passage migrant

There are only two 19th Century records with one shot at Moreton in 1855 and another in Tolpiddle Meadows on 3rd November 1881. Apparently there were no further reports until 1940 when one was shot from a flock near Sherborne on 1st February. Subsequently there were 12 records between 1950 and 1979, since when the species has occurred annually except for 1986, 1990, 1994, 1997 and 1999 – see Fig 2. The higher annual totals are mainly due to cold weather influxes. The most notable of these occurred during 1981/82 when a minimum of 86 and possibly as many as 161 birds were reported. This included up to 75+ in the Poole Harbour/Purbeck area in January and early February (with peak numbers at Arne NR on 17th January) and a flock of 24 on the Stour Meadows at Merley from 27th December–2nd January. Other noteworthy cold weather records/influxes involve 24 at Langton Matravers on 8th and 10th January 1963, c.27 birds in January 1987 including a flock of c.20 at Puddletown on 17th, 30E at Durlston CP on 10th February 1991, and a flock of 17 at Lodmoor NR on 28th January 1996, which was later seen at Abbotsbury on 7th–8th February.

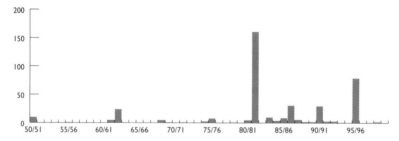

Figure 2. Annual totals 1950–1999

Most birds (70%) occurred during the mid-winter period (December–February) with a distinct peak in January (45%) – see Table 9. There is evidence of a small passage in spring with 16 birds (5%) recorded between 26th March and 28th May. Although autumn passage during October–November appears more substantial with 83 birds (25%), this is due mainly to an exceptional count of 60 at Durlston CP on 30th October 1995. Nearly all the passage birds have been recorded from Portland Bill, St Aldhelm's Head, Durlston CP and Christchurch Harbour.

Jan	Feb	Mar	Apr	May	Jun	Jul	Aug	Sep	Oct	Nov	Dec
150	41	2	5	9	0	0	0	0	69	14	44

Table 9. Monthly totals 1950–1999

The Pink-footed Goose breeds in Greenland, Iceland and Svalbard. The Greenland and Iceland populations winter mainly in Great Britain, whilst Svalbard breeders winter mainly in Denmark, Germany and the Low Countries.

Postscript 2000–2002

This species remains a rare bird in Dorset with only one record involving two at Middlebere from 31st January to 2nd February 2000.

White-fronted Goose
(Greater White-fronted Goose)   *Anser albifrons albifrons*

An uncommon winter visitor

Mansel-Pleydell (1888) described this species as "somewhat commoner than the Grey-lag in winter, but never plentiful". Blathwayt (1945) commented that it often occurs in severe weather and is the 'grey-goose' most frequently seen in Dorset, which is an accurate description of its subsequent status in the county.

The nearest regular wintering grounds were in the Avon Valley near Ringwood. This flock became established in about 1940 and during the severe weather of February 1947 was estimated at over 2,000 birds. Regular counts began in the 1950s with numbers peaking at 1,550 birds in the late 1960s. Subsequently the flock has steadily declined to less than 100 birds by the mid-1990s with a winter maximum of only 16 birds in 1997/98. Indeed, there were no records from the Dorset part of the Avon Valley in 1998! This general decline was relieved by cold weather influxes in early 1979 (maximum of 1,400), early 1982 (maximum of 1,500) and early 1986 (maximum of 790). Prior to 1979, the flock almost exclusively favoured areas in the Hampshire part of the valley to the north of Ringwood, notably around Blashford, and between Ibsley and Hucklesbrook. In recent years, however, birds have increasingly frequented the valley south of Ringwood including those areas within post-1974 Dorset, namely between Kingston North Common and Avon Causeway. Counts from the post-1974 Dorset parts of the valley follow the same pattern as for the whole Avon population – see Table 10. There was an exceptional flock of 1,217 near Sopley on 10th February 1979.

	75/76	76/77	77/78	78/79	79/80	80/81	81/82	82/83
Lower Avon Valley	nc	nc	nc	1217	nc	nc	nc	160
Christchurch Hbr	200	300	500	350	400	250	350	200

	83/84	84/85	85/86	86/87	87/88	88/89	89/90	90/91
Lower Avon Valley	385	220	450	295	300	245	65	110
Christchurch Hbr	75	160	nc	90	90	85	85	45

	91/92	92/93	93/94	94/95	95/96	96/97	97/98	98/99
Lower Avon Valley	110	105	135	89	100	62	150	12
Christchurch Hbr	80	60	nc	4	15	46	2	7

Table 10. Winter maxima from Lower Avon Valley and Christchurch Harbour 1975–1999

When the Avon Valley flock is disturbed, birds sometimes fly over and occasionally linger in neighbouring parts of Dorset, mainly Christchurch Harbour where substantial movements have been recorded – see Table 10. Similarly, periods of cold weather may force the Avon Valley flock and additional birds from further afield, including the Continent, to seek refuge in other areas of the county, particularly Poole Harbour and the Fleet. Some of these cold weather influxes have been substantial and have involved large flocks. In early 1962 there were 483 near Verwood on 11th February, whilst during the 'big freeze' in early 1963 peak counts were 400 at West Bexington on 22nd January and 300 in Poole Harbour on 12th February. In recent years, periods of severe cold have not always resulted in such numbers, the main exceptions being early 1979 with 200 in Poole Harbour, and early 1982 with 225 at Arne NR on 17th January. Although displaced flocks may linger for a few days and occasionally weeks in the Poole Harbour and Fleet areas, most records involve brief visits and overflying birds – a flock of 130 in the Stour Valley at Corfe Mullen from 2nd to 27th February 1982 being noteworthy. It is not certain whether a flock of between 600 and 900 over Canford School on 7th February 1970 was associated with cold weather.

There is a small passage of birds in spring (March–May) and autumn (October–November) involving reports from such coastal watch-points as Portland Bill, St Aldhelm's Head, Durlston CP and Christchurch Harbour.

Most birds occur between October and March. The earliest autumn records are 27th September 1981 with 45N over Hammoon and 29th September 1955 with 25 at Abbotsbury. Late spring migrants and presumed injured/feral birds are responsible for several reports in April and May, the latest being singles at Puddletown during 22nd April–4th June 1987, Lytchett Bay from February to 15th June 1997 (injured bird) and Arne NR on 29th June 1994. There was also a feral bird resident by the Stour at Throop during the early 1990s.

The European race of White-fronted Goose *A. a. albifrons* breeds in northern Siberia from the Kanin Peninsula to the Kolyma River. It winters in north-west, central and south-east Europe, the Middle East and extreme south-west Asia (mainly the Caspian Sea and Iraq). In Great Britain the main wintering grounds are in the south and east with the bulk of the population based at Slimbridge.

Postscript 2000–2002

Despite a count of 100 in the Lower Avon Valley on 22nd February 2000, the demise of the wintering population at this once traditional haunt continues with no records in 2001 and 2002. Elsewhere in the county, there was a notable influx during December 2001–January 2002 including 24 at Abbotsbury from 13th–25th December, 21–24 at Puddletown intermittently from 14th December to 5th January, 23 at Lodmoor NR on an unspecified date in December – the latter presumably involving either the Abbotsbury or Puddletown birds, 22 at Hengistbury on 7th January and 14 at Bestwall, Wareham on 31st January.

Greenland White-fronted Goose *Anser albifrons flavirostris*

Accidental: three records

There are only three records of the Greenland race of White-fronted Goose:

1992   Abbotsbury: 29th October
1998   Abbotsbury: three 1st November
2002   Lodmoor NR: ad. 27th October. Six White-fronted Geese had been seen to fly in here, but on closer searching only one bird could be found.

The Greenland race of White-fronted Goose *A. a. flavirostris* breeds in south-west Greenland and winters in Scotland (mainly on Islay) and Ireland (mainly on the Wexford Slobs) with a small flock in west Wales.

Greylag Goose *Anser anser*

A locally common feral resident, uncommon passage migrant and winter visitor

Both Mansel-Pleydell (1888) and Blathwayt (1945) considered this species to be a very rare winter visitor with one shot at Moreton in the winter of 1885 and one at Abbotsbury during April–May 1925. Although there were only nine records involving 13 birds between 1949 and 1969, it has occurred in all but one year since 1972 with a marked increase in sightings from the late 1970s onwards – see Fig 3.

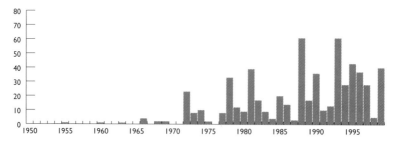

Fig 3. Annual totals excluding Lower Avon Valley/Christchurch Harbour 1950–1999

Substantial feral populations were already established as close as Kent and Norfolk by the time of the first *BTO Atlas* (1968–1972). In Hampshire feral breeding was first recorded in 1964 and the species had become established at Stratfield Saye and sites in the Test Valley by the late 1970s. Subsequently further feral populations were established at the Beaulieu Estuary and more significantly in the Avon Valley during the 1980s. In 1999 the Hampshire population was estimated at 700–800 birds with the Avon Valley, the Beaulieu Estuary and Stratfield Saye the three main sites.

The increase in Dorset records is partly due to the expansion of the feral population in neighbouring Hampshire, particularly in the Avon Valley where numbers in the post-1974 Dorset section reached a peak of 100 in January 1999 – see Table 11. In addition, one to two pairs have been confirmed breeding in the Lower Avon Valley in 1986, 1989, 1990 and 1991.

1978	1979	1980	1981	1982	1983	1984	1985	1986	1987	1988
10	2	3	4	10	1	4	7	8	11	9

1989	1990	1991	1992	1993	1994	1995	1996	1997	1998	1999
38	13	39	68	55	86	75	13	50	35	100

Table 11. Annual maxima from Lower Avon Valley and Christchurch Harbour 1984–1999

As these local feral populations have increased, so it has become more difficult to distinguish between wild and feral birds. It seems likely that most pre-1970 records refer to genuine migrants and winter visitors:

- 1949 Poole Harbour: two 2nd October
- 1955 Poole Harbour: 25th February
- 1960 Puddletown: 5th February
- 1963 Portland Bill: 1st–3rd January
- 1966 Arne NR: four 23rd October–7th November
- 1968 Studland NNR: 3rd March
  Radipole NR: 13th October
- 1969 Portland Bill: 21st February; same Langton Herring on 22nd February
  Hammoon: 25th February–3rd March

Since 1972 the best candidates as wild birds are those that appear during times of passage and periods of cold winter weather, particularly if they are associating with other wild geese or coincide with the influxes of other wildfowl. The most interesting sightings are:

- 1972 Portland Bill: 22 flying south on both 26th and 27th December (same flock)
- 1973 Portland Bill: seven flying east 5th October
- 1978 Christchurch Harbour: ten 20th February
  Bucknowle: 24 on 9th November
- 1981 Arne NR: 30+ on 30th October
- 1988 Lodmoor NR: 22 on 19th October and 19 flying south at Portland Bill on same day
- 1989 St Aldhelm's Head: 12 flying east 5th March
- 1993 Portland Bill: 12 on 2nd November
- 1995 Arne NR: 21 on 26th March

The Greylag Goose breeds in Iceland and across much of north-west, north-central and south-east Europe, and central Asia. The British native breeding population of wild birds is restricted to the Hebrides and the north-west Scottish mainland where they also winter, whilst there are feral populations elsewhere in the British Isles. Most of the Icelandic breeding population also winters in the British Isles. The species also winters at scattered sites throughout Europe, north-west Africa and the Middle East, and more widely in the Indian sub-continent and south-east Asia.

Postscript 2000–2002
The feral population in the Lower Avon Valley/Christchurch Harbour reached a new peak of 140 in January 2000. In addition, one pair raised three young at Poole Park in 2000. At Abbotsbury in 2002, one on 25th March and five on 5th December may have been 'wild' birds.

Canada Goose   *Branta canadensis*

A common feral resident, apparently still increasing

This species was introduced to the county many years ago, but apparently post-19th Century as there are no records in Mansel-Pleydell (1888). Although flocks were established at Weymouth, Crichel Park and Melbury Sampford prior to 1939, these apparently became virtually extinct after 1943. Apart from one shot at Sandbanks on 2nd October 1954, there were no further reports until the introduction of ten pairs to Poole Harbour in 1957 followed by more in 1959. In 1960, there were about 70 in Poole Harbour with additional records from Abbotsbury, Lodmoor NR and Sherborne Lake.

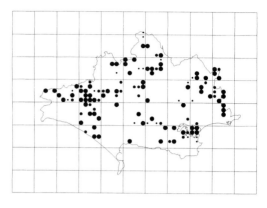

Subsequently the population has expanded rapidly, initially in the east of the county centred around Poole Harbour, but then spreading to the north, and eventually from the late 1980s to the Weymouth area and west Dorset. The extent of this expansion is reflected by the *BTO Atlas* (1968–1972), which confirmed breeding in only six (16%) 10-km squares (SY88, SY98, SY97, SZ08, SZ09 and ST90) all in the east of the county, whilst the Tetrad Survey (1987–1994) confirmed breeding in 24 (65%) of the pre-1974 10-km squares. The Tetrad Map shows breeding concentrated in the north-east and along the Avon Valley, in the Poole Harbour area, in the Blackmore Vale and notably in the north-west of the county. By far the largest numbers breed in Poole Harbour, mainly on Brownsea with a peak of 60 pairs in 1972, but generally ranging between 20–30 pairs subsequently – see Table 12. The only other area with a significant breeding population is the Lower Avon Valley with ten pairs in 1991 and 'many pairs' in 1995. Elsewhere most breeding records involve 1–3 pairs, although nine pairs bred at Sherborne Lake in 1989 (fewer since), and up to six pairs at Prior's Down in the mid-1980s.

1963	1964	1968	1972	1975	1983	1985	1986	1990	1991	1992	1993
4	5	40	60	30	25	10	27	33	24	26	30

Table 12. Selected counts of breeding pairs on Brownsea 1963–1993

During the 1960s and 1970s Poole Harbour was also the main site for the species outside the breeding season. Since 1970 annual maxima at this site have generally varied between 250–500 birds except for a county record of 622 in December 1978. Although peak counts have been recorded at any time between July and February, most occur during the autumn period August to October.

The continuing expansion of the population during the 1980s and 1990s is illustrated by the increase in the number of sites where annual maxima regularly exceed 100 birds – see Table 13. There has also been an increase in the frequency of counts over 100 at various other sites including Radipole NR with 208 on 15th September 1998 and 380 on 5th September 1999.

	1980	1981	1982	1983	1984	1985	1986	1987	1988	1989
Lower Avon Valley	nc	nc	nc	nc	185	10	25	52	nc	nc
Crichel Lake	nc	14	61	32	117	74	49	60	nc	nc
Sherborne Lake	nc	nc	70	105	150	90	200	118	165	221
Puddletown	nc	nc	nc	nc	nc	nc	91	118	131	133
Lodmoor NR	nc	13	nc	3	2	4	nc	nc	nc	nc
The Fleet	nc	18	40	nc	nc	nc	12	nc	nc	nc
West Bexington	1	12	nc	1	1	nc	25	nc	nc	48

	1990	1991	1992	1993	1994	1995	1996	1997	1998	1999
Lower Avon Valley	72	80	nc	190	285	349	nc	nc	nc	nc
Crichel Lake	100	115	106	54	nc	nc	nc	nc	nc	nc
Sherborne Lake	196	233	209	283	160	367	399	527	440	555
Puddletown	142	170	228	243	194	208	238	235	255	252
Lodmoor NR	nc	43	23	nc	nc	71	160	300	286	500
The Fleet	nc	91	270	300	260	260	200	600	300	253
West Bexington	52	nc	25	200	155	200	200	250	183	336

Table 13. Annual maxima at the other main sites 1980–1999

The species frequently feeds on cereals or stubble on farmland. For example, there are sometimes spectacular movements of birds flying between their roost in Poole Park and their feeding area on Ballard Down where an exceptional 500 were counted on 16th September 1988. More recently birds have been observed moving from Lodmoor NR to feed on winter cereals at Osmington. After breeding, there is a large moulting flock at Arne NR consisting largely of birds from Poole Harbour.

Small movements occur at the main coastal watch-points, usually involving less than ten birds per year at any one site, but there were 94W and 36E at Hengistbury during 15th September–19th October 1988.

A total of 768 birds has been ringed in the county.

The Canada Goose is a native of North America, which has been introduced to various parts of north-west Europe. In the British Isles it was introduced in the 17th Century and has expanded greatly in recent decades. Genuine vagrants occasionally occur in Ireland, Scotland and northern England.

Postscript 2000–2002

The breeding population on Brownsea reached a new peak of 66 pairs in 2001, the previous highest being 60 pairs in 1972. Generally numbers continued to increase across the county with record counts from several sites including 758 at Sherborne Lake in September 2001 (also a new county record), 630 at East Bexington on 12th September 2000 and 348 at Puddletown in January 2001.

Barnacle Goose   *Branta leucopsis*

An uncommon feral resident and wanderer, rare winter visitor and passage migrant

Mansel-Pleydell (1888) referred to a few records including some shot at Weymouth in 1857, and one or two shot on the coast in February 1879. Blathwayt (1945) described the Barnacle Goose as "a very rare winter visitor", but reported that some seen near Blandford in spring 1913 were thought to be escapes.

There are no other confirmed sightings until 1963 when one was present with White-fronted Geese at Portland Bill and Radipole NR on 12th January. This was followed by one at Langton Herring from 24th November to 8th December 1968, and two with five Pink-footed Geese at Lodmoor NR on 18th February 1969. These records, particularly those in 1963 and 1969, seem likely to refer to wild birds.

Subsequently, feral birds, presumably originating from expanding populations in southern England, have confused matters. In neighbouring Hampshire, a feral population has become established in the north-east of the county since the mid-1970s with regular breeding during the 1990s and a peak of 206 birds in November 1998. More recently feral birds have bred regularly at Baffins Pond in Portsmouth with a feral population of up to 43 birds in 1998. In Dorset, a small feral flock was regularly reported in Poole Harbour from 1978 to at least 1986 reaching a maximum of nine at Poole Park on 12th January 1985.

Some of Dorset's post-1970 records have occurred in conditions suggestive of wild origin, namely during times of passage and periods of cold winter weather. The best candidates as wild birds are:

1975 Puddletown: 2nd February
1980 Highcliffe: exhausted bird on 12th November
1981 Radipole NR: ten flying east 14th December
1982 Evidence of a small influx into the Weymouth area in December with two flying west at Lodmoor NR on 12th, three flying west at Radipole NR on 25th and one flying east with Dark-bellied Brent Geese over Weymouth Bay on 29th
1985 Christchurch Harbour: six flying north-east 19th November and one with Dark-bellied Brent Geese passing Durlston CP and Kimmeridge Bay on the same day
      Portland Bill: three with Pink-footed Geese 24th November
1986 Poole Harbour area associating with White-fronted Geese: two flying north at Studland Bay 6th January, three at Wytch 12th January, Middlebere 14th and 23rd January and Brownsea 20th January
1987 Lytchett Bay: three 23rd–24th February
1989 Durlston CP: six flying east 23rd April
1991 Durlston CP: one flying east with Pink-footed Geese 10th February
      Christchurch Harbour: 21 on 28th November
1992 Christchurch Harbour: 20 flying east 24th January

1993   West Bexington/Abbotsbury: up to nine 4th November–15th December
1996   The cold weather influx in late January and early February probably included wild birds from
        the Netherlands as well as feral birds from inland Great Britain:
    West Bexington/Abbotsbury: two 19th–29th January
    Abbotsbury: 16–17 from 21st–23rd February
    Radipole NR: 28th January
    Lodmoor NR: 7th–13th February
    Sherborne Lake: 27th January–4th February.
    Holes Bay: 18th February
    Lower Avon Valley: 12 on 20th January and 30 on 1st February
1998   Abbotsbury: two throughout January and early February
    Abbotsbury: 9th December
1999   Portland Bill: 13 arrived from the east 27th February, later seen at Weston
2002   Abbotsbury: three 12th February–7th March

There are three discrete populations of Barnacle Geese: one breeds in eastern Greenland and winters in western Scotland (mainly Islay) and Ireland, a second breeds on Svalbard and winters on the Solway Firth and a third breeds in western Siberia and winters mainly in the Netherlands. The latter is presumably the source of any genuinely wild birds occurring in Dorset. In addition, there are small feral populations throughout the British Isles.

Dark-bellied Brent Goose   *Branta bernicla bernicla*

A locally common winter visitor and passage migrant

Mansel-Pleydell (1888) regarded the Dark-bellied Brent or 'Black Goose' to be the most abundant of all the wild geese. Blathwayt (1945) considered it to be a frequent visitor to the coast and mentioned that large flocks arrived in Poole Harbour and Weymouth Bay during the cold spell in early 1929.

Nationally the numbers visiting Great Britain declined during the 1930s, following the widespread die-off through disease of the main food plant Eel-grass *Zostera marina*. Since the 1950s there has been a recovery in the wintering population, which is due to several factors including protection, better breeding success, and a change to a mixed diet of saltmarsh and agricultural grasses. In neighbouring Hampshire the recovery started during the 1950s and 1960s based around the eastern harbours of Chichester and Langstone, before spreading westwards to Southampton Water and the Solent from the late 1960s onwards. This recovery eventually reached Dorset during the 1970s with a dramatic increase during the 1980s and early 1990s – see Table 14. As a result both the Fleet and Poole Harbour are now sites of national importance.

	1950s	1960s	1970s	1980s	1990s
The Fleet	0.1	13	89	992	3408
Poole Harbour	10	16	245	800	1495
Christchurch Harbour	–	–	57	106	359

Table 14. Winter 10-year average peak counts at the main sites 1950–1999

Initially the main site for the Dark-bellied Brent Goose was Poole Harbour where the first substantial flock of 50–60 birds occurred in March 1968, which was followed by the first three-figure count of 100 during winter 1972/73. Subsequently there was a steady increase with winter maxima generally ranging between 500–1,000 birds during the 1980s, and between 1,300–1,700 birds during the 1990s with a peak of 1,711 on 9th February 1992. At low water the geese favour the south-central and south-east areas of the harbour, which in recent years have held 83% of the population. Birds also spend much of their time on the agricultural land along the western side of the harbour where the grass leys are the main attraction. Within the harbour, *Enteromorpha* and *Ulva* are the most important food sources.

Although substantial flocks were present on the Fleet during January–February 1970 (maximum of 95) and December 1973 (maximum of 110), regular wintering was not established until winter 1975/76 with numbers increasing rapidly during the mid-1980s to exceed those recorded in Poole Harbour. Since then the

Fleet has become the main site for the Dark-bellied Brent Goose in the county with winter maxima reaching a county record of 6,000 on 8th December 1991. Subsequently winter maxima have generally ranged between 3,000–5,000 birds with evidence of a decline in the late 1990s. Smaller numbers have wintered in Christchurch Harbour since the late 1970s with maxima ranging between 250–550 birds during the 1990s.

Since 1990 peak numbers have occurred mainly in November on the Fleet, but during the mid-winter period December–February in Poole Harbour – see Table 15. This suggests that the Fleet is a 'stop-over' site for birds destined to winter further west on the Exe Estuary in Devon. Coastal movements from Portland Bill and Durlston CP reflect this westwards passage during October and November with a smaller return passage in spring – see Table 16. The lower numbers observed from Portland Bill suggests that birds tend to cut across at Ferrybridge on their journey to and from wintering sites on the Fleet and Exe.

	Oct	Nov	Dec	Jan	Feb	Mar
The Fleet	1742	3141	1807	855	257	39
Poole Harbour	200	815	1104	1262	1153	778

Table 15. Average monthly maxima October–March from the Fleet and Poole Harbour 1990–1999

	Jan	Feb	Mar	Apr	May	Jun	Jul	Aug	Sep	Oct	Nov	Dec
Portland Bill	6	14	25	12	2	0	0	0.2	18	85	51	35
Durlston CP	67	77	58	31	4	0	0	0	26	230	179	93

Table 16. Average monthly bds for coastal movements at Portland Bill and Durlston CP 1986–1999

Elsewhere small numbers occur at various other coastal sites including West Bay, West Bexington, Portland Harbour, Radipole NR, Lodmoor NR, Weymouth Bay and the Purbeck coast. Well inland there are very few records as follows:

1970   Came Down nr Dorchester: 19 flying north-west 19th March
1977   Canford Bridge, Wimborne: nine 12th January
1981   River Stour at Corfe Mullen: 12th March
1982   Woolsbarrow: 21 flying south 31st December
1986   River Avon at Winkton: 2nd January
          Winterbourne Steepleton: 13th February
1991   Woolgarston: 30 flying east 13th October
1994   Winterborne Kingston: 300 flying east 25th October (an exceptional record)
1996   Sherborne Lake: 13th–14th October
1997   Sherborne Lake: 20th January

Although the Dark-bellied Brent Goose is mainly recorded between September and May, birds occasionally linger into the summer and presumed early migrants have occurred in August.

No birds have been ringed in the county, but colour-ringed birds have been recorded from the former USSR, Germany and the Netherlands, including one ringed on passage in Germany in April 1982 and subsequently observed in Christchurch Harbour in all but one winter between 1986/87 and at least 1995/96.

The Dark-bellied race of Brent Goose *B. b. bernicla* breeds in the Siberian tundra from Kolguev to the Taymyr Peninsula and winters in the Netherlands, France and southern England.

Postscript 2000–2002
In Poole Harbour, a count of 1,708 in December 2000 is the second highest ever from this site.

Pale-bellied Brent Goose   *Branta bernicla hrota*

An uncommon winter visitor and passage migrant

The Pale-bellied race of Brent Goose was poorly recorded in earlier years. Blathwayt (1945) commented that it occurs frequently and mixes with the dark-breasted race, but as careful records have not been kept, it is not possible to say which race is the more frequent in Dorset. There are only two published reports between 1950 and 1982 involving single birds at Ferrybridge on 8th April 1958 and 23rd November 1961.

Since 1982 this race has been identified more frequently with sightings in every year except 1983, 1991 and 1992 involving c.108 birds – see Table 17.

82	83	84	85	86	87	88	89	90	91	92	93	94	95	96	97	98	99
2	0	9	5	1	3	1	3	4	0	0	5	24	10	5	5	11	20

Table 17. Annual totals 1982–1999

The seasonal distribution of records shows a distinct peak during spring passage from mid-March to mid-April involving 42 birds (38% of the total) – see Table 18. This passage was particularly obvious in March 1994 with 2W at St Aldhelm's Head on 9th, five in Brand's Bay, Poole Harbour on 28th and 13 flying over Weymouth Bay on 30th. Otherwise there are reports scattered throughout the autumn and winter periods with evidence of a slight peak between mid-November and mid-December. The extreme dates involving single birds at Christchurch Harbour are from 30th April to 12th May 1984 and on 17th–18th September 1999.

Sep 16–30	Oct 1–15	Oct 16–31	Nov 1–15	Nov 16–30	Dec 1–15	Dec 16–31	Jan 1–15
1	4	6	6	7	10	2	6

Jan 16–31	Feb 1–15	Feb 16–28	Mar 1–15	Mar 16–31	Apr 1–15	Apr 16–30	May 1–15
2	7	4	2	34	8	1	2

Table 18. Half-monthly totals 1982–1999

The Fleet and Portland Harbour are by far the most favoured sites accounting for 69 birds (63%) with annual sightings in each winter since 1994/95 and overwintering confirmed in at least 1994/95 and 1998/99. Christchurch Harbour is the next most popular site with 14 birds (13%), but rather surprisingly there are only two records involving six birds from Poole Harbour. The remaining sightings are from Weymouth Bay (two records involving 18 birds), Lodmoor NR (a flock of six reported first at Ferrybridge), St Aldhelm's Head (one record of two birds) and West Bexington (one bird).

The Pale-bellied race of Brent Goose *B. b. hrota* breeds in arctic Canada east from Melville Island, northern Greenland, Svalbard and Franz Josef Land and winters in eastern North America, Ireland, northeast England and Denmark.

Postscript 2000–2002

In the Fleet/Portland Harbour area 1–2 birds were present during the winters of 1999/2000, 2000/01 and 2002/03 with up to six during October–December 2001. In 2002 there was an unprecedented spring passage at Portland Bill involving 90W (flocks of 55 and 35) on 20th April and seven on 27th April. Elsewhere there were single records in 2000 and 2001, the latter involving a late bird at Brownsea from 28th May to 16th June, and six records involving c.11 birds in 2002.

Black Brant   *Branta bernicla nigricans*

Accidental: four records.

Three of the four records are from the Fleet.

1991   The Fleet: ad. 23rd November–February 1992
1997   Ferrybridge/Portland Harbour: ad. 1st–17th January
1998   The Fleet: ad. 12th October–21st December
2002   Stanpit Marsh, Christchurch Harbour: 12th–14th October

The Black Brant *B. b. nigricans* breeds in the Siberian tundra east from the Taymyr Peninsula to northern Alaska, and Canada east to about the Perry River and west arctic islands, and winters in western North America. The Black Brant is a vagrant to Great Britain with 129 records up to 2002.

Red-breasted Goose   *Branta ruficollis*

Accidental: one record

    1983   Avon Valley: 27th December–14th January 1984

The single record involved an adult bird amongst a flock of White-fronted Geese in the Avon Valley and was seen several times over the Matchams and Week Farm area when the flock was disturbed.

    There are several other records involving escapes from wildfowl collections.

    This attractive goose breeds almost entirely on the Taymyr Peninsula in western Siberia and winters mainly on the Black and Caspian Sea coasts. A vagrant to Great Britain with 69 records up to 2002.

Egyptian Goose   *Alopochen aegyptiacus*

A rare wanderer from wildfowl collections and feral populations

Mansel-Pleydell (1888) mentioned that this species was frequently kept with other ornamental waterfowl in a semi-domesticated state and referred to a small flock formerly present at Morden Park. In addition, there are three records of birds being shot involving two at Dorchester in 1850, and singles at Crichel in February 1855 and Lodmoor in December 1856.

    The Egyptian Goose was admitted to Category C of the British List in 1971. Subsequently the first record involves an intriguing sighting of ten juveniles at Ferrybridge on 10th July 1978. There were further reports in two years during the 1980s followed by a marked increase in records during 1992–2002 perhaps associated with recent feral breeding in Berkshire and Hampshire.

    1982   Winterborne Monkton: January, perhaps the same as the next record.
            Poole Harbour and Purbeck: probably the same wandering bird at various sites between 16th April and 16th August
    1985   Avon Causeway: three 17th–20th February
    1992   Abbotsbury: two late March
            Spetisbury: 3rd–4th May
    1993   Winterborne Zelston: three, perhaps released birds 4th–20th March with the same at Stanpit Marsh, Christchurch Harbour 27th March, and subsequently two of the same at Abbotsbury 10th April, St Aldhelm's Head 27th April and Moors Valley CP 27th August
    1994   Throop: 3rd–9th January
    1996   Throop: two 10th–19th January
            Stanpit Marsh, Christchurch Harbour: three 25th July, one 13th August, two 21st September, one 12th October and two 27th November
            Poole Harbour: 5th September
    1997   Lower Stour at Tuckton: two 4th–12th January, one at Wick Lane 18th January and one at Throop 23rd March
            Durlston Bay: 23rd May
    1998   Abbotsbury: 2nd–10th August
    2001   Lodmoor NR: 24th November
    2002   Abbotsbury: 4th May
            Swineham: 16th December

    The Egyptian Goose breeds widely in sub-Saharan Africa. It was introduced to Great Britain in the 18th Century with a self-sustaining feral breeding population now established in East Anglia, mainly Norfolk.

Ruddy Shelduck   *Tadorna ferruginea*

An accidental and scarce wanderer from wildfowl collections and feral populations on the Continent

The earliest published record for the British Isles involves a bird shot at Bryanston near Blandford in the severe winter of 1776, whilst two shot at Lodmoor in 1892 formed part of a small national influx, which included flocks of up to 20. Although this and an earlier influx in 1886 were considered to involve genuine immigrants, the potential for the species to escape from ornamental waterfowl collections was recognised even in the late 19th Century.

Although most subsequent records are considered to involve escapes, there is recent evidence, particularly since the influx of birds into western Europe and the British Isles in 1994, that genuine vagrancy is still occurring. In Dorset the species may well have been under-recorded, but there are c.25 published records involving 43 birds between 1967 and 2000. These include 14 records involving 24 birds during July–October, which is the most likely time for genuine birds to arrive.

1967   Radipole NR: 5th–12th August
1986   Holes Bay: 2nd March
1987   presumably the same wandering bird at Langton Herring, Brownsea, Portland Bill and Radipole NR: various dates from 22nd July–17th August
1988   East Fleet: July
1990   Christchurch Harbour: 17th October
1991   Abbotsbury: 12th–16th August
1992   up to three wandering birds in Poole Harbour at Holes Bay and Little Sea, and at Radipole NR, Lodmoor NR, Langton Herring, Abbotsbury and Portland Bill: various dates from 31st August–12th November
1993   Christchurch Harbour: six 9th December
       Swineham: two 12th December
1994   Sandbanks: 11th August
1995   Brownsea: 9th June
       Abbotsbury: one 18th November and two on 19th November; presumed the same two later the same day at Brand's Bay, Poole Harbour and Coward's Marsh, Christchurch
1996   Lodmoor NR: four 18th August
       Sherborne Lake: 19th August
       Radipole NR: two 29th–30th December
1997   Poole Park: 6th June and from 16th June–15th July
       Portland Bill: three flying south 3rd October
       Sturminster Marshall GP: 6th November; same nearby on River Stour at Corfe Mullen 7th November
1998   Poole Park: female 12th–27th July
1999   West Bexington: two flying west 20th August
       Abbotsbury: three 'wary' individuals 23rd August and one 'tame' bird 10th November–20th December
       Wareham Water-meadows: 27th November; presumed same at Middlebere 27th December and Wool 31st December
2000   Wareham: 13th February; presumed same near Holme Bridge 16th February
       Swineham GP: female 6th August–31st December

The Ruddy Shelduck breeds in north-west Africa and from south-eastern Europe across central Asia to Mongolia and western China, also in Ethiopia. Most of the Asian population moves south to winter from Turkey east through Iran and the Indian sub-continent to south-east Asia.

Shelduck (Common Shelduck)   *Tadorna tadorna*

A locally common resident, winter visitor and passage migrant

Mansel-Pleydell (1888) considered this species to be not uncommon, and further commented that it bred regularly in rabbit burrows, from which habit it had acquired the provincial name of 'Burrow-duck'. Blathwayt (1945) recorded that many nest in the Poole Harbour district, which was their headquarters in Dorset, and further mentioned that a few pairs had nested near Abbotsbury from about 1922 and more recently near Weymouth.

There has been relatively little change in breeding distribution subsequently. The *BTO Atlas* (1968–1972) found evidence of breeding in the four 10-km squares around Poole Harbour (SY98, SY99, SZ08 and SZ09), the three 10-km squares covering the Fleet and Weymouth area (SY58, SY68 and SY67) and the 10-km square in the extreme west of the county (SY39). The Tetrad Survey (1987–1994) found that breeding was still centred around Poole Harbour (SY98, SY99, SZ08 and SZ09). In addition, there were smaller populations in the Fleet and Weymouth area (SY58 and SY68), and in post-1974 Dorset along the Lower Avon Valley from Christchurch Harbour northwards (SZ19, SU10 and SU11), whilst there was still the odd pair in west Dorset (SY49). There is evidence of a slight expansion in breeding range since the *BTO Atlas* (1968–1972), most notably at forest and heathland sites to the west of Wareham (SY89), and at Durlston CP (SZ07).

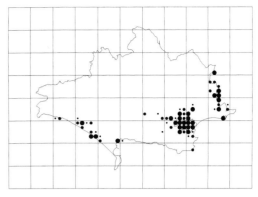

More recently, after annual reports of prospecting birds at Portland (SY67) since 1994, breeding was finally proved in 1999 involving a pair with six ducklings off Blacknor on 15th June.

Although many nesting sites are located immediately adjacent to the coast, some are situated further inland. In Poole Harbour, the most favoured breeding sites are at Arne NR and Brownsea, but away from the harbour birds can be found nesting in several heathland areas such as Wareham Forest, Upton Heath and Canford Heath. In the west of the county breeding has been recorded along the Bride Valley, which lies just inland from the Chesil and Lyme Bay, whilst along the Lower Avon Valley there are some outlying nesting sites in Ringwood Forest, notably in the vicinity of Moors Valley CP. There are also breeding reports from sites close to cliffs, notably at Portland and Durlston CP.

For a variety of reasons associated with the breeding biology of the Shelduck, it is difficult to assess the number of pairs nesting. In Poole Harbour, up to 30 pairs were estimated to be breeding between 1950 and 1970 increasing to 50–70 pairs in some years during the 1970s and 1980s. Systematic surveys of juveniles in the harbour produced counts of 197 in July 1992 and 169 in 20 groups on 10th July 1994, whilst at Arne NR there was a record creche of 110 ducklings with just one pair of adults in 1989. There is some evidence from Arne NR at least, to suggest a decline in the harbour breeding population during the 1990s. Breeding numbers from the Fleet have been relatively stable, generally ranging from 3–7 pairs during 1970–1999 – see Table 19. Counts from the Lower Avon Valley include nine pairs in 1982 and ten pairs in 1990, 1995 and 1996. Elsewhere most reports of breeding involve only 1–5 pairs. In late summer, birds from Dorset, in common with those from all over the British Isles, depart for their moulting areas on the German Waddenzee, leaving only the juvenile or first-winter birds and a few adults.

The main wintering site is Poole Harbour. Winter maxima were under 1,000 birds during the 1950s except for an exceptional cold weather count of 2,000–3,000 on 14th February 1954. Since 1961/62 maxima have exceeded 1,000 birds in every winter with numbers increasing to reach ten-year average peak counts of 1,964 for the 1970s and 2,143 for the 1980s followed by a marked increase to 3,005 for the 1990s, the highest individual count being 4,650 in January 1997 – see Table 20. Since the national wintering population over the past 30–40 years has been relatively stable, this suggests that the Poole Harbour population increased at the expense of other wintering sites. Birds wintering in Poole Harbour return fairly steadily through October to December with numbers in recent years usually exceeding 1,000 birds by November and reaching winter maxima typically during January–February. The number of birds required for Internationally important status has been increased to 3,000, as a result, this figure was exceeded in only four winters during the 1990s. Since the peak in winter 1996/1997, numbers have declined with a maxima of only 2,192 in winter 1999/2000.

	70	71	72	73	74	75	76	77	78	79	80	81	82	83	84
Arne NR	20	20	20	25	25	25	30	25	25	30	30	30	30	6	10
Elsewhere Poole H	3	nc	17	nc	nc	12	c23	nc	c21	c18	15	10	15	9	4
The Fleet	4	5	5	5	nc	7	6	4	6	nc	5	6	5	5	6

	85	86	87	88	89	90	91	92	93	94	95	96	97	98	99
Arne NR	25	25	25	25	25	20	20	20	15	15	15	nc	nc	nc	nc
Elsewhere Poole H	9	7	nc	c12	4	10	c10	nc	c15	nc	nc	8	14	5	nc
The Fleet	4	4	5	1	5	4	3	5	4	3	nc	5	1+	3	4

Table 19. Estimated number of breeding pairs from Poole Harbour and the Fleet 1970–1999

1950s	1960s	1970s	1980s	1990s
879	1529	1964	2143	3005

Table 20. Winter 10-year average peak counts from Poole Harbour 1950–1999

Much smaller numbers occur at the other favoured coastal sites, namely the Fleet, Radipole and Lodmoor NRs, and Christchurch Harbour – see Table 21. In Christchurch Harbour winter maxima are sometimes exceeded by peak counts of non-breeders in spring and early summer – see Table 22.

	80/81	81/82	82/83	83/84	84/85	85/86	86/87	87/88	88/89	89/90
The Fleet	108	164	173	87	147	68	176	56	59	32
Radipole NR	27	63	39	57	36	34	54	24	29	17
Lodmoor NR	40	54	13	39	37	22	29	22	35	15
Christchurch Hbr	nc	76	32	83	39	37	48	79	67	85

	90/91	91/92	92/93	93/94	94/95	95/96	96/97	97/98	98/99	99/00
The Fleet	150	94	71	113	76	102	131	91	68	61
Radipole NR	24	12	25	13	6	28	26	14	nc	23
Lodmoor NR	25	15	42	27	23	33	30	21	11	28
Christchurch Hbr	89	72	51	88	72	74	91	86	85	14

Table 21. Winter maxima at the other main sites 1980–1999

1974	1975	1976	1977	1978	1979	1980	1981	1982	1983	1984	1985	1986
112	183	nc	100	91	nc	70	78	76	84	84	64	70

1987	1988	1989	1990	1991	1992	1993	1994	1995	1996	1997	1998	1999
50	72	17	98	62	91	55	82	177	135	110	69	75

Table 22. Spring maxima at Christchurch Harbour 1980–1999

Elsewhere there are frequent reports from other coastal localities including West Bexington, Portland Bill, Portland Harbour and the Purbeck coast. Offshore movements occur throughout the year, but mainly in spring, late autumn and during periods of cold weather in winter – see Table 23. Spring movements are particularly prominent with April and May accounting for 40% of the total.

Jan	Feb	Mar	Apr	May	Jun	Jul	Aug	Sep	Oct	Nov	Dec
13%	7%	4%	23%	17%	5%	1%	1%	3%	6%	11%	9%

Table 23. Monthly coastal movements (%) at Portland Bill and Durlston CP 1986–1999

Away from the breeding sites, this species was apparently very rare inland prior to 1980 with only three published reports between 1955 and 1968. Subsequently there has been a marked increase in non-breeding inland records with most sightings from the Lower Frome Valley, where up to 196 were present during 2nd–5th March 1990, and the Stour Valley between Wimborne and Sturminster Marshall. There are records from as far inland as Sherborne Lake.

A total of 275 birds has been ringed in the county. There have been four recoveries from the Netherlands, and two each from France and Germany.

The Shelduck breeds mainly in northern Europe with a few isolated populations around the Mediterranean, also more widely from the Black Sea eastwards across central Asia to China. Most European birds undertake a major moult migration to the Waddenzee area in Germany. The main wintering areas are in north-western Europe with other winter populations in southern Europe and North Africa, the Middle East and parts of south-west and south-east Asia.

Postscript 2000–2002
The worrying decline in Poole Harbour's wintering population continued with maximum of only 1,754 in 2000/2001.

Sponsored by Matthew Andrews

Mandarin Duck   *Aix galericulata*

An uncommon feral resident

The only known records prior to 1978 involved a male shot at Sherborne Lake on 8th February 1924 and another at East Burton on 2nd October 1960, whilst known escapes were at Milton Abbas Lake in 1975. Subsequently there has been a steady increase in records with regular breeding established from 1996 onwards – see Table 24. This may be associated with the colonisation of the New Forest during the 1980s, whilst there are long-established feral populations in the north and east of Hampshire, and nearby in south Wiltshire.

78	79	80	81	82	83	84	85	86	87	88	89	90	91	92	93	94	95	96	97	98	99
2	4	1	7	8	3	5	3	5	7	7	10	13	9	16	12	6	13	17	20	9	12

Table 24. Annual totals 1978–1999 (excluding young, known releases and Merley Park birds from 1996)

The first suggestion of breeding in Dorset involved the presence of three males and one female at Brackett's Copse from 14th–29th April 1981 with four birds again reported at the same location on 3rd April 1982. A pair was also present at Creech Pond on 8th May 1982, this site providing the first confirmed breeding record for the county when a pair with six young were seen there on 27th May 1983. Although birds were recorded in suitable breeding habitat subsequently, the only evidence of breeding up to 1996 involves two juveniles at Coward's Marsh, Christchurch from 2nd–7th September 1990, and a pair present at Iwerne Steepleton from 16th February–20th March 1992 and seen entering a tree-hole on the latter date.

In 1996 confirmed breeding was again recorded in the county when a pair reared ten young in a nestbox at Merley Park. A thriving colony has since developed at this site, but breeding success is low, e.g. only 22 hatching from 96 eggs laid in 1997 and 167 eggs reported as being infertile in 1999 – see Table 25. Birds from this colony regularly visit nearby Broadstone GC during the autumn with peak counts of 15 on 29th September 1997, 20 in 1998 and 23 on 31st October 1999, whilst pairs were also present at this site in spring 1999. Nearby, breeding was suspected in the grounds of Deans Court, Wimborne in 1996 involving a pair, regularly present on the nearby river throughout 1995 and 1996. More recently, at least one pair was reported from various sites in the Wimborne area in January, May and December 1999.

	1996	1997	1998	1999
Nests/pairs	1	6	9	15
Eggs	nc	96	nc	302
Fledged young	10	16	52	32

Table 25. Breeding statistics of the colony at Merley Park 1996–1999

After reports of up to six birds in the Blandford area during 1989–1995, breeding was confirmed from the River Stour at Bryanston in 1996 with a female and four young on 20th and 23rd May. There were further reports of breeding from Bryanston in 1997 with a female and four young in late June, and again in 1999 with a female and 13 young on 13th May. Sightings from other sites in the general vicinity of

Blandford, namely Fontmell Magna in 1988, 1989 and 1990, Hod Hill in 1990, Iwerne Steepleton in 1992 and Durweston in 1999 may refer to the same birds. The only other breeding report in recent years involves a female with four juveniles at Lodmoor NR on 23rd August 1996.

Away from the regular breeding sites, the most favoured location for the species is Sherborne Lake where up to four males were regularly present during 1984–1996. Elsewhere there are several reports from Christchurch Harbour and the nearby River Stour at Tuckton and Iford, various locations in and around Poole, namely Poole Park, Hatch Pond, Creekmoor Ponds and Upton CP, and the Fleet and Weymouth area, notably Abbotsbury and Radipole and Lodmoor NRs. There are also isolated records from Little Sea, the Frome at Wareham, Wareham Forest, Oak Hill, Wool, Warmwell GP, West Stafford, Lower Bockhampton, Crichel Lake, Shapwick, Milton Abbas Lake, Winterborne Kingston, Puddletown and West Bexington.

The Mandarin Duck was introduced into Great Britain in the early 20th Century and has now established feral populations mainly in south-east England, but locally elsewhere. The native range of this species is the Asian Far East where it is in such severe decline that it is now less numerous than in Great Britain.

Postscript 2000–2002
Breeding continued at Merley Park with 18 pairs rearing only two young in 2000 due to predation by Magpies, and 20 pairs rearing 28 young in 2001. At Bryanston there were two females and four young in 2000, one brood in 2001 and birds present throughout the year in 2002. As usual the Merley Park birds dispersed to Broadstone GC in the autumn with up to 30 during September–November 2001.

Sponsored by Mandarin Productions

Wigeon (Eurasian Wigeon)   *Anas penelope*

A locally common winter visitor and passage migrant

Mansel-Pleydell (1888) described this species as "a winter visitor, sometimes arriving in very large flocks" and mentioned that it was well-known to wildfowl shooters on the coast. Blathwayt (1945) considered it to be a common winter visitor, sometimes abundant on the coast and inland waters, and further reported that breeding has been suspected in the Poole area.

The Fleet and Poole Harbour were the main sites for the Wigeon between 1950 and 1970. Except for a large influx of birds during the cold spell in early 1954, which included 4,000 at Abbotsbury on 7th February, counts in excess of 1,000 birds from these sites were infrequent before 1960. There has been a marked increase in wintering numbers subsequently – see Table 26. This is most evident on the Fleet where winter maxima have generally varied between 4,000–8,000 birds since 1960 with peak counts of 10,210 on 22nd November 1981, 10,399 in January 1987 and 15,000 on 30th December 1991. In Poole Harbour numbers did not increase significantly until the 1970s with subsequent winter maxima generally ranging between 500–2,000 birds, the highest count being 7,604 on 3rd January 1982. Some of the highest counts at both sites are clearly associated with cold weather influxes, notably in January 1982 and January 1987, the latter resulting in a county total of over 25,000 birds. If the more exceptional winter influxes in January 1982 (Poole Harbour) and January 1987 (the Fleet) are excluded, the ten-year average peak counts suggest that wintering populations at both sites have remained relatively stable after the initial increase in numbers – see Table 26.

	1950s	1960s	1970s	1980s	1990s
The Fleet	1187	5013	4531	5552 (5013)*	5204
Poole Harbour	533	648	1183	1727 (1074)*	1001

Table 26. Winter 10-year average peak counts from the Fleet and Poole Harbour 1950–1999; *excluding exceptional cold weather influxes in Jan 1982 (Poole Habour) and Jan 1987 (the Fleet)

In recent years peak numbers on the Fleet have generally occurred in the late autumn and early winter period October to December, with smaller numbers present during the rest of the winter, except when there are cold weather influxes such as in January 1987 and 1997 – see Table 27. This suggests that the Fleet is a 'stop-over' site for birds destined to winter elsewhere, either locally in Dorset or further west in

Great Britain (cf Dark-bellied Brent Goose). Although the species undoubtedly commutes between the Fleet and nearby Lodmoor NR, the latter site does not appear to be the main destination for these birds, since most peak counts here also occur during the late autumn and early winter period. The secondary peak on the Fleet in February suggests return passage. In Poole Harbour there is a steady increase in numbers throughout the winter to reach peak counts during December to February – see Table 27.

	Sep	Oct	Nov	Dec	Jan	Feb	Mar
The Fleet	796	2750	2882	3489	1944 (898)*	1387	617
Poole Harbour	114	281	472	588	837	469	267

Table 27. Average monthly maxima September–March from the Fleet and Poole Harbour 1986–1999; *excluding cold weather influxes in Jan 1987 and 1997

Since 1970 other sites such as the Lower Avon Valley, Christchurch Harbour, Puddletown and Lodmoor NR have become increasingly important – see Table 28. This may be due in part to the re-distribution of birds from the original main haunts. For example, the species regularly commutes between the Fleet and nearby Lodmoor and Radipole NRs, whilst a proportion of the Poole Harbour population is thought to have moved to Puddletown when shooting ceased at the latter site.

	80/81	81/82	82/83	83/84	84/85	85/86	86/87	87/88	88/89	89/90
Lower Avon valley	nc	450	nc	1055	500	nc	4130	1160	51	80
Christchurch Hbr	nc	300	120	100	200	51	2000	nc	120	45
Puddletown	nc	nc	300	320	214	600	2450	525	700	559
Lodmoor NR	nc	840	34	145	650	686	1124	1106	649	488

	90/91	91/92	92/93	93/94	94/95	95/96	96/97	97/98	98/99	99/00
Lower Avon valley	1250	1100	1000	5000	1000	500	nc	nc	nc	nc
Christchurch Hbr	160	80	1500	2200	800	350	1000	612	760	570
Puddletown	750	1157	865	1762	1621	866	1500	1236	993	1000
Lodmoor NR	978	250	1120	516	883	1500	3000	1200	285	400

Table 28. Winter maxima at the other main sites 1980–1999

Much smaller numbers occur at other localities widely scattered across the county, notably West Bexington, Radipole NR, various sites along the Frome and Stour Valleys, Crichel Lake and Sherborne Lake. Cold weather influxes may also be responsible for exceptionally high counts at these less important sites, e.g. 1,000 on floods near Pentridge on 31st January 1961, up to 1,500 in the Stour Valley between Corfe Mullen and Sturminster Marshall during January–February 1979, 2,000 at East Holme during 17th–19th January 1982 and 1,000 at Winterborne Came on 18th January 1987.

Birds normally arrive in September, sometimes in August, and depart during March and April. Some individuals, probably injured, linger through the summer, but there is no evidence of breeding in recent years. Small coastal movements occur at Portland Bill and off the Purbeck coast, but much higher counts from Christchurch Harbour, e.g. 3,000S on 30th January 1998, 2,500SW on 18th January 1986 and 2,000S on 2 dates in January 1996 probably refer to birds from the Avon Valley disturbed by shooting and seeking refuge on the sea off Hengistbury.

A total of 60 birds has been ringed in the county with one foreign recovery from Germany.

The Wigeon breeds in Iceland, northern Great Britain, Scandinavia and eastwards across north-east Europe and northern Asia. It winters mainly in western and southern Europe, North Africa, the Middle East, the northern Indian sub-continent and south-east Asia, also more locally to the northern tropics of Africa.

Sponsored by Hugo Wood-Homer

American Wigeon   *Anas americana*

A very rare winter visitor and passage migrant: 13 records involving c.11 individuals

This species was added to the Dorset list in 1984. Prior to 1997, all but one of the records had occurred at times of passage with three in spring (March–May) and three in autumn (September–November). More recently, one to two males have occurred on the Fleet in the four consecutive winters 1997/98 to 2000/2001.

1984   Avon Valley at Week Farm: male 5th–14th January
1987   Stanpit Marsh, Christchurch Harbour: male 2nd May; presumed same at Brownsea 2nd–5th May
        Lodmoor NR: male 24th–25th October; probably same 13th–21st November but aged as
           first-winter.
1992   Lodmoor NR and the Fleet: male 26th and 31st October and 15th–22nd November
1994   Stanpit Marsh, Christchurch Harbour: first-winter male 8th–12th March
1996   Sturminster Marshall: first-summer female 2nd–11th May
        Abbotsbury: female 26th September
1997   The Fleet: male 28th October to 25th March 1998
1998   Abbotsbury: male 5th–6th January – in addition to above
        The Fleet: male 26th September to 21st February 1999 – presumed to be different to the
           1997/98 individuals, second male present 7th November
1999   The Fleet: male 7th October to 14th November – presumed returning 1998/99 individual
2000   The Fleet at Butterstreet Cove: male 26th–28th November; presumed same at Abbotsbury 5th
           December – presumed returning 1998/99 individual

A bird on the Fleet in the late 1970s was considered to be an escape.

The American Wigeon breeds in northern North America and winters mainly along the coasts of the Pacific and Atlantic, in the southern USA and south through Central America into Colombia. A vagrant to Great Britain with 356 records up to 2001.

Gadwall   *Anas strepera*

An uncommon resident, locally common winter visitor and passage migrant

Mansel-Pleydell (1888) described the Gadwall or 'Grey Duck' as "a rare winter visitant" and listed only seven records involving nine birds between 1841 and 1885, all from the Poole and Weymouth areas. Blathwayt (1945) also considered it to be a rare winter visitor, which sometimes lingered into the spring, and referred to reports from Sherborne Lake including a pair on 3rd June 1920, but with no proof of breeding, Weymouth, and Poole Harbour including 16 on 16th August 1945.

Records have been annual since 1952 and more regular and widespread since the late 1960s. During the *BTO Atlas* (1968 -1972) breeding was confirmed in ST50 or ST51 (Sutton Bingham), but the evidence was 'sketchy', probable in ST90 (Crichel Lake) and possible in SY68 and ST91. The first definite proof of breeding was obtained in 1973 when a pair reared six young at Beer Farm Pond (SY89). This was followed by a pair, which bred at a site in central Dorset in 1978. Although display and mating was recorded on Brownsea in 1980, the next genuine breeding attempt occurred in 1981 at Radipole NR. Subsequently breeding has become regular, but numbers have increased rather slowly with a fairly stable population of 8–16 pairs during the 1990s –

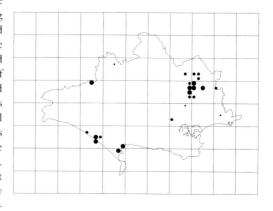

see Table 29. The Tetrad Survey (1987–1994) Map shows that breeding is largely confined to the Fleet and Weymouth area, and the Allen Valley including the nearby lakes at Crichel Park and Wimborne St Giles Park. Since 1994 most reports of confirmed breeding have been from the latter area including c.13 pairs in 1995 and 1997.

Initially Crichel Lake was the main site for wintering birds particularly during the 1950s with counts usually ranging between 1–5 birds, but 11 in February 1950 and 8 in early 1958. During the 1960s Sherborne Lake became an important site for the species, whilst a regular wintering population was established in Poole Harbour at Little Sea from 1968 onwards. By the end of the 1960s the Gadwall was also occurring regularly in the Weymouth and Fleet areas, notably at Radipole NR and Abbotsbury. Winter maxima at the favoured sites were still relatively small, the highest counts being 17 at Little Sea on 1st December 1968, 16 at Abbotsbury on 27th March 1969 and 16 at Crichel Lake on 17th December 1967. During the 1970s numbers increased dramatically throughout the county, and at the end of the decade the Fleet was the main site with winter maxima of 98 in 1977/78 and 84 in 1979/80. Although the wintering population continued to increase during the 1980s with a county record count of 187 on the Fleet on 9th December 1987, numbers have tended to stabilise during the 1990s. The Fleet has remained the main wintering site for the species throughout this period, but significant numbers have frequented other waters, notably Radipole and Lodmoor NRs, Poole Harbour and Crichel Lake – see Table 30. Since 1995, Wimborne St Giles Park has also become an important site with winter maxima of 52 in December 1996, 58 in February 1998 and 54 in October 1998.

	1980	1981	1982	1983	1984	1985	1986	1987	1988	1989
Abbotsbury	–	–	1	1	1	1	–	2	–	–
Radipole NR	–	1	2	1	3	–	1	2	3	3
Lodmoor NR	–	–	–	–	–	–	–	–	1	1
River Allen	–	–	–	–	–	–	–	–	–	7
other sites	–	–	–	–	–	–	2	1	–	–

	1990	1991	1992	1993	1994	1995	1996	1997	1998	1999
Abbotsbury	1	1	2	3	–	2	3	1	sev	2
Radipole NR	3	8	3	3	1	–	–	–	–	–
Lodmoor NR	–	–	–	–	1	–	1	1	–	–
River Allen	12	6	8	6	8	9	6	9	7	7
other sites	–	–	–	–	–	5	–	4	1	–

Table 29. Number of breeding pairs at the main sites 1980–1999

	80/81	81/82	82/83	83/84	84/85	85/86	86/87	87/88	88/89	89/90
The Fleet	142	176	30	44	175	125	54	187	70	14
Radipole NR	nc	23	14	22	32	30	60	22	37	43
Lodmoor NR	nc	35	8	26	70	62	87	31	79	18
Poole Harbour	59	119	55	52	9	58	15	50	35	40
Crichel Lake	10	48	18	50	60	50	100	63	53	26

	90/91	91/92	92/93	93/94	94/95	95/96	96/97	97/98	98/99	99/00
The Fleet	152	53	21	160	155	82	80	45	112	44
Radipole NR	43	25	19	40	11	24	22	12	15	16
Lodmoor NR	90	24	62	75	46	48	39	76	40	52
Poole Harbour	15	16	57	126	48	98	45	26	49	29
Crichel Lake	44	44	62	78	41	78	47	100	91	149

Table 30. Winter maxima at the main sites 1980–1999

Although Little Sea is the favoured haunt for the species in Poole Harbour, birds occur at several other sites including Brownsea, Arne NR, Holton Shore, Lytchett Bay, Hatch Pond, Brand's Bay and Newton Bay.

Since the early 1980s in particular, there have been records from other sites scattered widely throughout the county. Although most of these waters regularly support small numbers of birds with winter maxima of up to 40, some have recorded larger counts, namely Bridehead Lake (maximum of 117 in January 1987), Christchurch Harbour (maximum of 52 in January 1985), the Lower Avon Valley (maximum of 50 in February 1994) and West Bexington (maximum of 50 on 5th February 1977). On the debit side, numbers appear to have declined at Sherborne Lake since the mid-1970s.

Coastal movements are occasionally recorded mainly involving 1–5 birds, but 25 at Hengistbury on 6th December 1987 was noteworthy.

A total of ten birds has been ringed in the county and there has been one foreign recovery from France and one foreign control from Spain.

The Gadwall breeds across large areas of western Eurasia and western North America. The British breeding population is derived mainly from stock introduced between 1850 and 1970. The Eurasian population winters in western and southern Europe, North Africa and the Middle East, extreme south-west Asia, parts of the northern Indian sub-continent and southern Asia, also locally in East Africa. The British wintering population, which is greatly enhanced by birds the Continental, has increased in recent decades.

Postscript 2000–2002

There was a marked increase in breeding numbers in 2000 with c.25–26 pairs at four sites including 13 pairs at Lodmoor NR, but only three broods reported, and 8–9 pairs on the River Allen. More modest numbers in 2001 with c.7–8 pairs at four sites including three broods at Lodmoor NR, and again in 2002 with eight broods totalling 48 young at Lodmoor NR and four pairs at three other sites. Wintering numbers increased at some sites with record counts of 149 at Crichel Lake in January 2000, 80 nearby at Wimborne St Giles Park in October 2001, 70 at Puddletown in December 2002 and 61 at Hatch Pond, Poole in December 2002.

Teal (Eurasian Teal)   *Anas crecca*

A scarce resident, fairly common winter visitor and passage migrant

Mansel-Pleydell (1888) regarded this species to be the commonest wildfowl after Wigeon and Mallard, and mentions that it bred in suitable localities including Morden Park. Blathwayt (1945) considered it to be mainly a winter visitor, sometimes very numerous, which bred sparingly around Poole Harbour and increasingly on the east Dorset heaths.

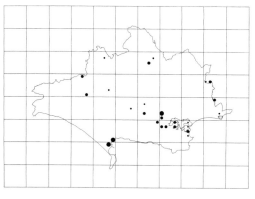

During the 1950s and early 1960s the only published reports of breeding were in 1953 at Clayes-moor Lake, and 1963 at Studland NNR and Brown-sea. Since the mid-1960s, breeding has occurred most years – see Table 31. The *BTO Atlas* (1968–1972) confirmed breeding in three 10-km squares around Poole Harbour (SY98, SY99 and SZ08), three 10-km squares in the Fleet and Weymouth area (SY58, SY67 and SY68) and one 10-km square in the west (SY49). There were no reports of probable breeding, whilst there was evidence of possible breeding in six 10-km squares. The Tetrad Survey (1987–1994) suggests little change in distribution with confirmed and probable breeding still largely confined to heathland and forest sites to the south and west of Poole Harbour (SY88, SY89, SY98, SY99 and SZ08). Breeding was also confirmed at both Radipole and Lodmoor NRs (SY67 and SY68), and recorded as probable along the Lower Avon Valley (SZ19, SU10) and in the north-west (ST50) and north (ST81) of the county. In the Poole Harbour area, the most favoured breeding sites are Studland NNR, Arne NR and Brownsea. Although breeding numbers are generally small, isolated good years such as 1978 (14 pairs) and 1995 (12 pairs) suggest that the population is perhaps higher than generally recorded.

66	67	68	69	70	71	72	73	74	75	76	77	78	79	80	81	82
8–9	6	5	2	4	4	9	nc	3	7	8–9	6	14	5	5	5	3

83	84	85	86	87	88	89	90	91	92	93	94	95	96	97	98	99
7	0	2	4+	4	2	2	1	2	2	1	4	12+	3	5	0	1

Table 31. Number of confirmed/probable breeding pairs 1966–1999

Post-breeding flocks of eclipse birds frequent the Fleet, Radipole NR, Lodmoor NR and Poole Harbour, the most notable count being 300 on the Fleet in August 1986.

Poole Harbour is the main wintering site for the species with maxima generally ranging between 700 and 1,800 birds. The ten-year average peak counts show that the wintering population was higher in the 1970s and 1990s than during other decades since 1950, the highest individual counts being 1,887 on

16th January 1977 and a county record of 2,297 in December 1996 – see Table 32. The most favoured feeding areas within the harbour are Holes Bay, Middlebere Lake, Arne Bay and Brownsea Lagoon. Several other coastal and some inland localities also support substantial numbers – see Table 33.

1950s	1960s	1970s	1980s	1990s
931	1025	1469	924	1342

Table 32. Winter 10-year average peak counts from Poole Harbour 1950–1999

	80/81	81/82	82/83	83/84	84/85	85/86	86/87	87/88	88/89	89/90
The Fleet	214	490	777	265	267	285	188	260	350	200
Radipole NR	380	580	380	148	550	395	360	197	215	250
Lodmoor NR	175	200	215	225	515	737	614	331	289	300
Sherborne Lake	nc	nc	nc	130	nc	200	nc	106	104	96
Puddletown	nc	nc	150	160	143	220	320	300	230	120
Christchurch Hbr	88	238	224	157	168	85	76	76	170	90
Lower Avon Vlly	nc	nc	nc	440	143	300	230	310	nc	nc

	90/91	91/92	92/93	93/94	94/95	95/96	96/97	97/98	98/99	99/00
The Fleet	560	350	540	377	191	260	300	120	780	450
Radipole NR	223	305	126	173	100	204	89	92	117	113
Lodmoor NR	433	317	235	430	300	300	600	255	394	246
Sherborne Lake	22	40	30	nc	nc	106	47	9	nc	nc
Puddletown	55	72	238	373	359	224	144	304	215	722
Christchurch Hbr	379	108	84	308	300	350	266	400	150	176
Lower Avon Vlly	283	132	nc	nc	nc	nc	nc	nc	nc	50

Table 33. Winter maxima at the other main sites 1980–1999

In recent years a few other sites have occasionally held numbers in excess of 100 birds, notably West Bexington (maximum of 150 on 31st January 1996), Morden Park Lake (maximum of 300 on 14th January 1982), Morden Bog (maximum of 100 on 14th February 1982), Stokeford Heath (maximum of 150 on 10th February 1999), the Lower Frome Valley (maximum of 150 at Wool on 4th February 1986), Hatch Pond, Poole (maximum of 101 in January 1999), the Stour Valley between Wimborne and Sturminster Marshall (maximum of 406 at Merley on 21st December 1982) and Marnhull (maximum of 300 on 26th December 1982). Elsewhere the species is widely recorded in lower numbers with peak counts of less than 100 birds.

High counts from earlier years include over 1,000 in one corner of Poole Harbour on 6th February 1954, c.2,000 at Abbotsbury on 7th February 1954, 1,000 on floods near Pentridge on 31st January 1961 and c.1,000 at Abbotsbury in January 1963.

Coastal movements are occasionally recorded mainly involving 1–10 birds, the most notable counts being from Christchurch Harbour with 112W on 19th September 1997, 104W on 20th November 1985, 70W on 4th February 1984 and 60W on 21st November 1988.

A total of 3,561 birds has been ringed in the county. There have been twelve recoveries from the former USSR, nine from Finland, at least eight from Denmark, four from France, two from Germany and one each from Estonia, Latvia, Sweden, Italy, Turkey and Eire, as well as four controls from the Netherlands, three from Poland and one each from Sweden, Denmark and France.

The Teal breeds widely across much of northern Eurasia and winters mainly in western and southern Europe, North Africa, the Middle East and southern Asia, also more locally in the northern tropics of Africa.

Postscript 2000–2002

Single pairs bred successfully at Brownsea in 2000 and 2001, whilst in 2002 breeding was reported from Ham Common and Lodmoor NR where two pairs fledged ten young. There were several notable winter counts including 2,086 in Poole Harbour in February 2001 – the second highest ever at this site, 1,051 on the Fleet in December 2001 – the highest at this site since at least 1980, 722 at Puddletown in January 2000 – the highest ever at this site, and 111 at Hatch Pond, Poole in March 2002 – the highest ever at this site.

Green-winged Teal   *Anas carolinensis*

A very rare winter visitor and passage migrant: c.14 individuals

All sightings refer to males with six records during 1978–1985 and five birds during 1999–2002:

1948 Radipole NR: 30th November
1969 Radipole NR: 4th and 7th April
1978 Radipole NR: 7th to 16th April; probably another 25th–26th May
1981 West Bexington: 13th–15th February; probably the same at Langton Herring on 6th–7th May
1983 Sutton Bingham: 15th January and 6th February
       Littlesea: 22nd and 29th January
1985 Wool: 28th–29th January; same bird at East Holme and sites around Poole Harbour–Holes
       Bay, Newton Bay and Brand's Bay up to 4th March; probably same at Brand's Bay 20th
       November
1989 Middlebere: 16th to 28th April
1999 Abbotsbury: 14th November–16th December
2000 Holes Bay: 12th February–5th March; same at Lytchett Bay 14th–17th April
       Hengistbury: 27th December
2001 Holes Bay: 2nd February–3rd March – presumed returning 2000 individual; presumed
       same on 23rd December and 1st January 2002, probably same at Brand's Bay 10th March
       2002
       Stanpit Marsh, Christchurch Harbour: 1st–17th April
       Abbotsbury: first-winter 5th November and 15th November–24th January 2002, occasionally
       visiting Rodden Hive

The Green-winged Teal breeds in northern North America and winters across much of the USA south into Central America and the West Indies. A vagrant to the British Isles with 441 records up to 1990.

Mallard   *Anas platyrhynchos*

An abundant resident, winter visitor and passage migrant

The Mallard or 'Wild Duck' has been a common and familiar species in the county since at least 1655, when reference is first made to a decoy at Abbotsbury.

The *BTO Atlas* (1968–1972) confirmed breeding in 33 (89%) 10-km squares, whilst the Tetrad Survey (1987–1994) produced an almost identical result with breeding confirmed in 34 (92%) of the pre-1974 10-km squares. The Tetrad Map shows that the species breeds wherever suitable habitat exists throughout the county. Systematic surveys from some sites suggest a decline in breeding numbers, but this may be due to local factors and not reflect the true situation in the county as a whole – see Tables 34 and 35.

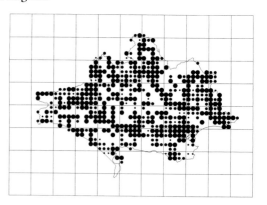

80	81	82	83	84	85	86	87	88	89	90	91	92	93	94	95	96	97
13	18	11	20	20	20	20	20	15	20	15	17	15	15	15	22	12	20

Table 34. Number of breeding pairs along River Stour between Corfe Mullen and Sturminster Marshall 1980–1997

Numbers are usually highest in the county during the autumn and early winter (August to November) and involve mainly post-breeding flocks. For many years Crichel Lake and Poole Harbour were the main

	80	81	82	83	84	85	86	87	88	89	90	91	92
Radipole NR	34	40	35	50	50	45	75	50	50	nc	50	20	22
Lodmoor NR	nc	nc	nc	34	25	24	21	23	18	12	nc	nc	nc
The Fleet	nc	nc	20	30	20	40	20	nc	nc	nc	20	30	30

Table 35. Number of breeding pairs at other selected sites 1980–1992

sites for the species outside the breeding season, but there has been a marked decline during the 1990s – see Table 36. Peak numbers at Crichel Lake usually occur during September–October, more occasionally earlier in August or later during November–December, the exceptions being 1,500 on 15th January 1966 and 1,000 on 14th January 1968, whilst the count of 2,500 at this site during September–October 1965 remains a record for the county. Poole Harbour supported particularly high numbers during 1976–1982 with a maximum of 1,755 in November 1978. Here post-breeding flocks result in a peak during the autumn, usually in September, which is followed by another usually larger peak during mid-winter (December–January), which presumably includes wintering birds from further afield.

	1950s	1960s	1970s	1980s	1990s
Crichel Lake	920	1143	785	836	302
Poole Harbour	532	539	1008	774	417

Table 36. Autumn/winter 10-year average peak counts from Crichel Lake and Poole Hbr 1950–1999

Several other sites also support substantial numbers outside the breeding season – see Table 37. At Radipole NR peak counts almost exclusively occur during August–September suggesting this a favoured site for post-breeding birds, which later disperse to other localities for the winter. These may include nearby Lodmoor NR, where winter maxima are usually recorded during October–December, and the Fleet, where the peak counts generally occur later during November–January.

	80/81	81/82	82/83	83/84	84/85	85/86	86/87	87/88	88/89	89/90
The Fleet	303	168	382	400	400	401	532	300	448	523
Radipole NR	338	333	450	363	483	539	471	474	584	587
Lodmoor NR	nc	nc	nc	139	144	214	290	248	152	128
Sherborne Lake	200	nc	280	400	200	250	156	495	430	513
Christchurch Hbr	nc	32	67	84	71	nc	nc	nc	nc	20

	90/91	91/92	92/93	93/94	94/95	95/96	96/97	97/98	98/99	99/00
The Fleet	406	526	503	284	569	329	492	632	650	650
Radipole NR	400	406	378	358	280	260	100	390	300	403
Lodmoor NR	187	139	226	212	200	258	180	175	180	116
Sherborne Lake	435	286	270	106	93	157	160	253	212	118
Christchurch Hbr	317	178	58	147	142	244	215	173	150	60

Table 37. Autumn/winter maxima at the other main sites 1980–1999

There is recent evidence to suggest that Wimborne St Giles Park (maxima of 480 in August 1998 and 400 in August 1999), and Puddletown (maximum of 392 in September 1995) should also be considered important sites for the species. Elsewhere the Mallard occurs widely in smaller numbers with counts rarely exceeding 200 birds.

Coastal movements are occasionally recorded, the most notable in recent years being 70W at Chickerell on 9th September 1990, 63W at Hengistbury on 20th September 1997 with 58W and 21E there on 19th November 1985. Other high counts include 60W at Portland Harbour on 1st August 1982, 30W and 28E on 13th November 1983 at Hengistbury with 34W at Portland Bill and 19E at Durlston CP on the same date.

A total of 1,935 birds has been ringed in the county. There have been six recoveries from France, two each from the Netherlands, Sweden and Finland and one each from Norway, Denmark, Poland and Estonia. In addition, there has been one control from Portugal.

The Mallard breeds throughout the northern temperate zone. In Europe the species is mainly sedentary in the west and south, but more migratory in northern, eastern and central areas. European birds winter mainly in western and southern Europe, North Africa and the Middle East.

Postscript 2000–2002

Lodmoor NR is an important breeding site with 138 young present on 12th May 2001. Counts of 520 at Wimborne St Giles Park in August 2000, 433 at Lodmoor NR in October 2001 and 360 at Christchurch Harbour in September 2002 are the highest ever recorded at these sites.

Pintail (Northern Pintail) *Anas acuta*

A locally common winter visitor and passage migrant – has bred

Mansel-Pleydell (1888) described this species as "a regular and not unfrequent visitor in winter, although never very numerous". Blathwayt (1945) considered it to be a regular winter visitor in small numbers.

During the 1950s numbers were generally rather low, particularly during the winters of 1957/58 and 1958/59, so counts of 200 at Abbotsbury in January 1950, and 200 in Poole Harbour and 104 at Abbotsbury during the cold spell of February 1954 were exceptional for the period. Since the early 1960s the Pintail has become more numerous with Poole Harbour and the Fleet the main wintering sites – see Table 38. In Poole Harbour numbers increased during the 1960s and 1970s, then declined in the 1980s, only to increase again during the 1990s with winter maxima reaching peaks of 525 on 17th January 1971, 456 in January 1973, 452 on 17th January 1982 (during a cold spell) and 451 in February 1998. By contrast, numbers on the Fleet remained fairly stable during the 1960s, 1970s and 1980s, but then increased in the 1990s with maxima reaching peaks of 452 in September 1995 and 411 in January 1997. Within Poole Harbour, the most favoured areas are concentrated in the south-east corner namely Little Sea, Brand's Bay, Newton Bay and Fitzworth.

	1950s	1960s	1970s	1980s	1990s
Poole Harbour	58	185	274	200	294
The Fleet	41	133	138	110	277

Table 38. Winter 10-year average peak counts from Poole Harbour and the Fleet 1950–1999

Elsewhere along the coast the Pintail is rather scarce and erratic with most records from West Bexington, Radipole NR, Lodmoor NR and Christchurch Harbour. From 1959 to the early 1970s small numbers regularly visited Radipole NR where peak counts usually occurred in the late autumn, which suggests the lake was used as a 'stop-over' site for birds destined to winter on the Fleet – see Table 39. More recently there is some evidence to suggest that Lodmoor NR and Christchurch Harbour are becoming sites of some importance to the species – see Table 40.

59/60	65/66	66/67	67/68	68/69	69/70	70/71	71/72	72/73	73/74
29	66	49	51	30	50	45	8	26	2
Oct	Nov	Nov	Feb	Oct-Dec	Oct	Sep-Oct		Oct	Dec

Table 39. Autumn/winter maxima at Radipole NR for available years 1959–1974

	90/91	91/92	92/93	93/94	94/95	95/96	96/97	97/98	98/99	99/00
Lodmoor NR	15	9	5	7	13	160	70	74	26	50
Christchurch Hbr	17	12	56	191	92	31	41	6	16	7

Table 40. Winter maxima at Christchurch Harbour and Lodmoor NR 1990–1999

This is an uncommon bird away from the coast, but high counts are occasionally reported from the Lower Avon Valley with a maximum of 400 in February 1994, and the Lower Frome Valley, reaching 60 at East Holme during 18th–21st January 1995. Otherwise there are records, often associated with periods of cold weather, from widely scattered inland sites, the most favoured being the Stour Valley between Wimborne and Sturminster Marshall (maximum of 15 on 31st December 1981), Crichel Lake (maximum of 17 on 15th December 1963), Puddletown and Sherborne Lake. Elsewhere inland, 50 at Marnhull (King's Mill) on 10th February 1985 is exceptional.

Coastal movements are recorded most years, usually at times of passage in spring (March–May) and autumn (September–November), but also occasionally in mid-winter. Most reports involve under ten birds, the most notable counts being 120W at Durlston CP during a day of remarkable wildfowl movements on 13th November 1983 with 60E there on 31st January 1992, and 60E at Radipole NR on 5th May 1976, whilst in spring 1992 a total of 283 were recorded at East Bexington during March–May including 121 in the latter month.

In 1983 a pair reared three young at a site in Poole Harbour, which is the only confirmed breeding record for the county. There are several instances of summering, notably during the 1980s, from Poole Harbour and Radipole and Lodmoor NRs. The only possible hint of breeding other than in 1983 occurred at Radipole and Lodmoor NRs where a summering male was joined by a female twice in 1986 and once in 1987.

A total of 357 birds has been ringed in the county and there have been two recoveries from the former USSR and one each from Denmark, France and Spain.

The Pintail breeds widely across much of northern Eurasia and northern North America, also more locally in central and western Europe including the British Isles. The Eurasian population winters mainly in western and southern Europe, North Africa and the Middle East, the northern tropics of Africa and the Indian sub-continent, and east and south-east Asia.

Postscript 2000–2002

A count of 750 on the Fleet at Rodden Hive on 15th December 2001 is exceptional and far exceeds the previous county record of 525 in Poole Harbour on 17th January 1971. Notable movements at Christchurch Harbour involving 200 on 27th December 2002, 195 on 30th November 2002, 147S on 10th January 2000 and 117SE on 17th January 2001 may involve birds moving to and from the Avon Valley. A male on a garden pond at Southwell, Portland from 23rd to 25th March 2000 is an unusual location.

Sponsored by Tony Conway

Garganey   *Anas querquedula*

An uncommon passage migrant – has bred

Mansel-Pleydell (1888) considered the Garganey or 'Summer Teal' to be a passage migrant, mainly in spring, but also suggested that breeding was annual in the vicinity of Poole Harbour. Blathwayt (1945) referred to the species as a summer resident in small numbers and an increasing passage migrant, and further mentioned that it had bred at Abbotsbury, probably in the Poole area, and more recently near Weymouth.

Since 1950 the Garganey has only bred successfully in 1966, 1982 and 1986 with some evidence of breeding in a few other years:

1960	Crichel Lake: male summered and behaved as one of a pair, but no female seen
1966	Abbotsbury: two with six young 11th June
1980	Abbotsbury: pair summered but apparently did not breed
1982	West Fleet: two males, a female and three juvs 15th June
	Radipole NR: pair reared four young
1986	Undisclosed site: female with eight young
1991	Keysworth: pair on several dates in June
1993	Lodmoor NR: one to three birds 7th–25th June
1996	Lodmoor NR: one pair displaying in May but no further evidence of breeding

As a passage migrant the Garganey has become more numerous since the early 1970s – see Figs 4 and 5. Although this is partly due to the addition of Christchurch Harbour after the boundary change in 1974, there is a genuine increase in numbers. This increase is perhaps more obvious in autumn with total counts sometimes exceeding those for spring, notably during 1983 – 1986 and 1994 – 1997. Generally annual totals for spring and autumn are very variable showing that the species is prone to good and bad years. Since 1980 the best springs were 1982 (50), 1988 (57), 1989 (39), 1990 (59), 1996 (80) and 1998 (52), whilst the best autumns were 1983 (46), 1984 (62), 1986 (71), 1995 (64) and 1996 (150). Most records involve fewer than ten birds, the highest counts being a flock of 15, which flew off the sea and alighted at Lodmoor NR on 28th March 1957, 10–14 birds at Radipole NR during 9th August–10th September 1984, 14E at Burton Cliff on 26th March 1989, 13 at Christchurch Harbour on 25th August 1984 with 12 there on 1st September 1983.

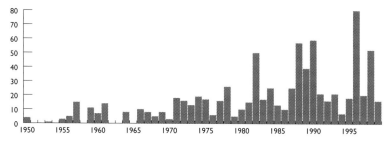

Fig 4. Spring annual totals 1950–1999

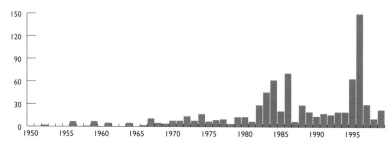

Fig 5. Autumn annual totals 1950–1999

Since 1974 the main sites have been Christchurch Harbour, Radipole and Lodmoor NRs, which together account for 78% of total passage birds, whilst Poole Harbour, the Fleet, West Bexington and Cogden Beach only account for 16% – see Table 41. During 1950–1973, Radipole NR was by far the most important site accounting for nearly half (47%) of the passage birds recorded in this period.

	1950–1973	1974–1999
Christchurch Harbour	n/a	36%
Poole Harbour	14%	2%
Lodmoor NR	16%	19%
Radipole NR	47%	23%
The Fleet	8%	12%
West Bexington/Cogden Beach	6%	2%
other	8%	7%

Table 41. Distribution (%) of passage birds at the main sites pre- and post-1974 Dorset

This species is uncommon inland. Since 1950 the most favoured sites have been the Lower Avon Valley with nine spring records involving 12 birds (maximum of three on 8th May 1989), and the Stour Valley between Wimborne and Sturminster Marshall with five spring records involving seven birds, one autumn record and one probable wintering bird. There are also reports from Wareham Forest (three records – six birds), East Stoke (two records – four birds), Woodsford (one), Charborough Park (one), Puddletown (singles twice), Milton Abbas Lake (pair once), Nether Cerne (three once), Crichel Lake (two records – three birds including 1960 summering bird), Cranborne CBs (pair once), Sturminster Newton (two records – six birds), Stalbridge (four once), Gillingham (two once) and Sherborne Lake (one).

Although coastal movements are rare, there were annual reports during 1988–1993. Most records are from the main coastal watch-points, namely Portland Bill (seven records involving 24 birds including 7E on 27th March 1989, 7E on 1st April 1990 and 5E on 24th April 1991), Durlston CP (three records involving five birds including two with Common Scoter on 31st July 1985), and Hengistbury (two records involving 7N on 30th August 1983 and 5W on 26th September 1992). Otherwise there are five further sightings involving coastal movements as follows:

1971   Kimmeridge Bay: flock of ten in mid-March
1972   Chapman's Pool: 22nd April
1989   Burton Cliff: 14 flying east 26th March
1992   Chesil Cove: 20th April
         East Bexington: one flying east 11th May

Spring passage extends from early March to mid-June, the earliest records being 3rd February 1974 on the River Stour at Corfe Mullen (probably wintering) and 26th February 1976 in the Weymouth area. The average date of the first arrivals became earlier from the 1950s to the 1970s, but then became later during the 1980s and 1990s – see Table 42. Autumn passage extends from mid-June to mid-October, the latest reports being 28th October 1992 at Lodmoor NR with perhaps the same bird at East Fleet the following day, and 30th October 1970 at Radipole NR. More recently there were exceptionally late birds at Abbotsbury on 16th December 1997 and 9th December 1998, which perhaps hints of wintering in the area.

	1950–1959	1960–1969	1970–1979	1980–1989	1990–1999
Range	16th Mar–	14th Mar–	26th Feb–	1st Mar–	4th Mar–
	22nd Apr	16th Apr	26th Mar	26th Mar	20th Apr
Average	3rd Apr	28th Mar	10th Mar	17th Mar	21st Mar

Table 42. Dates for first spring arrivals each decade 1950–1999

The Garganey breeds across most of temperate Eurasia and winters mainly in the northern tropics of Africa, the Indian sub-continent and south-east Asia. In the British Isles it is mainly a passage migrant, the breeding population being very small.

Blue-winged Teal   *Anas discors*

Accidental: five records

This species was added to the Dorset list in 1982. The four subsequent records are shared equally between Christchurch Harbour and Abbotsbury.

1982   Sutton Bingham: female briefly flew into Dorset 13th January
1989   Stanpit Marsh, Christchurch Harbour: female/first-winter 17th September
1991   Abbotsbury: female/first-winter 30th October–2nd November
1999   Abbotsbury: female paired with male Shoveler 27th April
2001   Stanpit Marsh, Christchurch Harbour: first-winter male 13th–15th September

The Blue-winged Teal breeds across much of North America and winters from the southern USA through Central America into South America. A vagrant Great Britain with 227 records up to 2002. Two British controls of birds ringed in New Brunswick and Newfoundland confirm transatlantic movement.

Shoveler (Northern Shoveler)   *Anas clypeata*

A locally common winter visitor and passage migrant – has occasionally bred

Mansel-Pleydell (1888) considered this species to be an uncommon winter visitor and lists only eight records involving ten birds up to 1885, whilst a report of breeding at Islington in 1857 was considered exceptional. Blathwayt (1945) recorded the improving fortunes of the Shoveler, both as a resident and winter visitor, towards the end of the 19th Century and during the early years of the 20th Century when a small breeding population became established in the county. Breeding regularly occurred near Weymouth from 1902 with up to six pairs at Lodmoor during the mid-1920s, in the Frome Valley near Wool by 1912, at Abbotsbury from 1918, and in the Poole area from 1926. Breeding was also suspected at Burton Mere in 1932 and almost certainly took place at Crichel Lake and on the River Allen during 1948–1951.

Regular breeding in the county apparently ceased by about 1952, although a pair and two juveniles were present in Poole Harbour on 26th June 1955. Apart from the *BTO Atlas* (1968–1972) claim of breeding at Crichel Lake in 1968, for which there was no supporting evidence, there were no further reports until a mini-revival during the 1980s and early 1990s:

1982   Brownsea: pair laid ten eggs, but then deserted
1983   Abbotsbury: pair reared seven young
1984   Abbotsbury: pair reared eight young
         Lodmoor NR: pair attempted to nest
1985   Abbotsbury: pair bred
1987   Arne NR: pair reared seven young
1990   Radipole NR: pair reared three young
1991   Abbotsbury: pair bred
1994   Lodmoor NR: pair reared six young

Post-breeding flocks were a fairly regular feature at Radipole NR and the Fleet in earlier years, but now occur less frequently. These occasionally resulted in high counts during the autumn period July–October, the most notable during the early part of the season being 130 at Radipole NR in August 1971 with 79 there in August 1987, and 100 on the Fleet in July 1989.

As a winter visitor, the species seems to have become more numerous since 1950. Despite this, numbers have varied considerably with a series of good winters interspersed with poor winters. The Fleet, Radipole NR and Poole Harbour have been the main sites for much of the last five decades – see Table 43. Numbers on the Fleet increased during the 1960s, but remained fairly stable during the 1970s and 1980s, before another increase during the 1990s with winter maxima reaching a peak of 380 in December 1992. By contrast, at nearby Radipole NR numbers declined during the 1960s, but then increased steadily during the 1970s and 1980s, before declining dramatically during the 1990s with winter maxima reaching peaks of 236 on 16th January 1983 and 230 on 29th November 1981, also 230 earlier on 31st December 1951. In Poole Harbour, the main increase in numbers occurred during the 1970s, followed by a small decline during the 1980s, before increasing again during the 1990s with winter maxima reaching a peak of 263 in January 1994 including 261 on Little Sea.

	1950s	1960s	1970s	1980s	1990s
The Fleet	82	119	116	110	164
Radipole NR	127	72	103	132	47
Poole Harbour	34	54	118	106	120

Table 43. Winter 10-year average peak counts at the main sites 1950–1999

Lodmoor NR and West Bexington have become sites of some importance since 1980 and 1990 respectively – see Table 44. There were also some high counts from Lodmoor NR during the 1950s with 250 on 5th March 1951, and again on 26th February and 20th March 1955. Elsewhere along the coast Christchurch Harbour sometimes supports good numbers in winter – see Table 44. Otherwise it is very scarce at other coastal sites, but at West Bay there were counts of ten on 10th January 1993 and 27 on 23rd February 1994.

Generally this is a rather scarce bird away from the coast, but high numbers are occasionally reported from the Lower Avon Valley (maxima of 150 on 1st March 1994 and 100 in February 1979), and the Lower Frome Valley (maximum of 50 at East Holme on 7th January 1982). From 1950 to the mid-1970s, the main inland sites were Crichel and Sherborne Lakes – see Table 45. In recent years Crichel Lake has continued to attract moderate numbers – see Table 44. Sadly Sherborne Lake no longer appears to be a regular site, but 12 were present on 26th November 1984, five on 28th January and 28th December 1996 and six on 1st August 1998. Otherwise there are records, sometimes associated with periods of cold weather, from other inland sites widely scattered across the county, the most favoured being Morden Park Lake (maximum of 30 on 29th January 1997), the Stour Valley between Wimborne and Sturminster

Marshall (maximum of 21 on 24th December 1982), Moors Valley CP (maximum of 13 on 27th August 1993), Wimborne St Giles Park (maxima of ten on 13th October and 17th November 1996), Hatch Pond, Poole (maximum of ten on 25th January 1997) and Puddletown (maximum of six during January–March 1991).

	80/81	81/82	82/83	83/84	84/85	85/86	86/87	87/88	88/89	89/90
West Bexington	135	nc	17	nc	nc	14	25	43	nc	15
Lodmoor NR	100	200	85	180	97	56	87	92	110	78
Christchurch Hbr	nc	54	5	nc	nc	12	25	13	14	4
Crichel Lake	4	nc	31	11	16	12	15	22	30	nc

	90/91	91/92	92/93	93/94	94/95	95/96	96/97	97/98	98/99	99/00
West Bexington	75	100	64	90	36	86	70	70	100	85
Lodmoor NR	90	28	81	171	100	70	51	38	nc	47
Christchurch Hbr	50	21	13	19	64	44	14	35	12	7
Crichel Lake	nc	14	14	14	32	46	44	24	32	24

Table 44. Autumn/winter maxima at the other important sites 1980–1999

	49/50	55/56	57/58	58/59	59/60	60/61	61/62	62/63
Sherborne Lake	20	nc	nc	24	nc	50	88	nc
Crichel Lake	50	25	23	nc	28	21	nc	30
	63/64	66/67	67/68	69/70	71/72	72/73	73/74	74/75
Sherborne Lake	50	10	nc	nc	40	40	50	40
Crichel Lake	nc	nc	5	9	nc	nc	nc	nc

Table 45. Winter maxima at Sherborne and Crichel Lakes 1949–1975

Coastal movements have been recorded annually in recent years, mainly in spring (March–May) and autumn (August–October), but occasionally in mid-winter. Most records involve under ten birds, but there have been some spectacular movements including 344E at Portland Bill on 31st March 1990, 76E at East Bexington on 21st April 1992 and 58E at Hengistbury on 10th January 1998.

A total of 46 birds has been ringed in the county.

The Shoveler breeds over much of northern Eurasia and western North America. The Eurasian population winters mainly in western and southern Europe, North Africa and the Middle East, the northern tropics of Africa and much of south and south-east Asia including the Indian sub-continent. The breeding population in the British Isles moves to the Continent, mainly France, Spain and Italy, for the winter, to be replaced by wintering birds from the east and north.

Postscript 2000–2002
In 2001 breeding occurred at Lodmoor NR with six young present on 25th July – the first report of breeding in the county since 1991. A count of 240 at Little Sea in January 2001 is the second highest ever for Poole Harbour. At Christchurch Harbour, 81SE on 17th January 2001 is a notably high coastal movement.

Red-crested Pochard   *Netta rufina*

An accidental visitor and scarce wanderer from wildfowl collections and feral populations on the Continent – has bred

The only old record concerns one shot on the River Stour at Bryanston early in the 19th Century.

There were no further sightings until 1950, which was followed by five further records up to 1974:

1950   Little Sea: male 24th–25th December and again 15th January 1951
1961   Sherborne Lake: male and two females 12th November–4th December
1963   Brownsea: male on several dates in April and 30th–31st May; possibly same at Little Sea 14th December

1968   Morden Decoy Pond: two juvs 13th October
1974   Radipole NR: female 13th–25th March with another 10th June

Since 1977 there has been a marked increase in reports with sightings in every year except 1980, 1991, 1992, 1994 and 1999 – see Table 46. Although some birds may be genuine vagrants from the Continent, the majority originate either from feral populations such as those at the Cotswold Water Park and London's St James' Park, or from nearby wildfowl collections such as that at Paultons Park near Romsey in Hampshire where 30 were counted in January 1995. More locally a small feral population was present at Nether Cerne from 1982 to at least 1984 with a maximum count of ten on 26th December 1982. These birds apparently attempted to nest every year with varying success. More recently there is a record of a female with four fledged young at Puddletown during 14th–21st August 1997.

77	78	79	80	81	82	83	84	85	86	87	88	89	90	91	92	93	94	95	96	97	98	99
2	9	3	0	1	5	2	3	2	5	5	6	3	1	0	0	12	0	1	3	16	12	0

Table 46. Annual totals excluding Nether Cerne population 1977–1999

The most favoured sites are the Fleet (mainly Abbotsbury), Christchurch Harbour, the Poole Harbour area, Sherborne Lake and Radipole NR – see Table 47. There are also reports from the Lower Avon Valley (one), Tuckton (one), Holt (one), the River Allen at Stanbridge Mill (two birds together), Crichel Lake (three singles), Sturminster Marshall GP (one and a flock of seven), Wool (one), Puddletown (one in addition to a report of a female and four young – see above), Lodmoor NR (three singles), Little Bredy (one), West Bexington (one) and Charmouth (one). Apart from the feral population at Nether Cerne, all records have involved 1–3 birds except for seven at Cloud's Hill on the Fleet on 15th–16th December 1978, and up to seven at Sturminster Marshall GP from 6th December 1997–27th March 1998.

	totals	%
The Fleet	24	28%
Radipole NR	6	7%
Poole Harbour	8	9%
Christchurch Harbour	13	15%
Sherborne Lake	7	8%
other sites	29	33%

Table 47. Distribution of birds at the main sites 1977–1999

Although there are records for every month of the year, there are distinct peaks in mid-winter (35 birds in December–January), autumn (24 birds in August–September) and spring (ten birds in April–May) – see Table 48. The peaks in autumn and spring suggest that some birds at least might be genuine migrants. In this context, a juvenile male at Ferrybridge on 7th September 1998, which later flew up the Fleet, is of particular interest.

Jan	Feb	Mar	Apr	May	Jun	Jul	Aug	Sep	Oct	Nov	Dec
11	3	2	6	4	1	2	14	10	1	6	24

Table 48. Monthly totals 1977–1999

The Red-crested Pochard breeds very locally in central and southern Europe and Turkey, and more widely in west-central Asia. It winters mainly in southern Europe, the Middle East, parts of west-central Asia and southern Asia (mainly the Indian sub-continent). Although small numbers of wild birds visit the British Isles in autumn and winter, mainly in the eastern counties, most records refer to wanderers from feral populations and escapes from wildfowl collections.

Postscript 2000–2002
Annual totals were seven birds in 2000 and a single bird in 2001.

Pochard (Common Pochard) *Aythya ferina*

A fairly common winter visitor and passage migrant – has occasionally bred

This species was known in the county during the late 18th Century with reports of birds shot at Bryanston in 1776 and 1796, and Spetisbury in 1795. Although Mansel-Pleydell (1888) considered the Pochard or 'Dunbird' to be mainly a winter visitor, breeding occurred annually in the neighbourhood of Poole Harbour for several years from 1876 and 30 young were hatched near Wareham in June 1877. Blathwayt (1945) described it as "a common visitor from autumn to spring" and records that the only evidence of recent breeding was a male at Morden Park Lake on 26th May 1921.

Subsequently one and sometimes two pairs bred at a confidential site in east Dorset in 1948 and during 1972–1977, whilst probable breeding was recorded during the *BTO Atlas* (1968–1972) at Sherborne Lake and confirmed there during 1973–1975. In addition, an adult with two juveniles at Little Sea in August 1955 suggests local breeding. Since 1980 most breeding records have come from Radipole NR, Sherborne Lake and the general vicinity of the River Allen in east Dorset:

1981   Radipole NR: pair attempted to breed, but the nest was flooded out
1982   Sherborne Lake: pair reported breeding
1983   Radipole NR: unsuccessful breeding attempt
1987   Sherborne Lake: pair reared three young.
       Wimborne St Giles Park: pair may have bred
1989   Sherborne Lake: pair hatched one young
1990   Sherborne Lake: two pairs reared two young
1991   River Allen near Stanbridge Mill: female with a young brood in July
       Wigbeth Ponds near Horton: pair summered; the species bred here at least once during 1987–1990
1992   River Allen near Brockington Farm: recently fledged young in July

The birds recorded on the River Allen in 1991 and 1992 may have originated from either Wimborne St Giles Park or Crichel Lake. In addition, the Tetrad Survey (1987–1994) recorded probable breeding at Crichel Lake, Milton Abbas Lake and a site near Woolland. Otherwise there are frequent reports of birds summering, but with no evidence of breeding.

The main wintering sites are Poole Harbour (mainly Little Sea), Radipole NR and the Fleet (mainly Abbotsbury) with a considerable interchange of birds between the two latter sites. Since the 1950s there has been a general increase in numbers at all the main sites – see Table 49. In Poole Harbour, this increase was particularly dramatic during the 1980s with population numbers maintained at this high level throughout much of the early and mid-1990s, the highest count being 2,000 at Little Sea in January 1993. On the Fleet, there was a marked increase in numbers during the 1990s, the highest count being 1,500 in November 1994. At Radipole NR, numbers have risen more steadily, the highest count being 1,108 in January 1986. In earlier years, the highest counts were the result of cold weather influxes, most notably during the winter of 1962/63 with 2,800 (a county record) in Poole Harbour on 17th February and 2,000 at Abbotsbury on 13th January.

	1950s	1960s	1970s	1980s	1990s
Poole Harbour	50	156	159	963	864
Radipole NR	53	287	552	607	658
The Fleet	62	274	471	541	808

Table 49. Winter 10-year average peak counts at the main sites 1950–1999

Both Crichel and Sherborne Lakes are also important sites for the species, but winter maxima only occasionally exceed 100 birds – see Table 50. Similar numbers were recorded at these sites pre 1980, the highest counts being an exceptional 240 at Sherborne Lake on 12th February 1967 with 150 there on 18th December 1960, and 115 at Crichel Lake in January 1978.

Elsewhere smaller numbers are recorded from widely scattered sites across the county with winter maxima generally ranging up to 50 birds, but there were 100 at Morden Park Lake on 5th January 1999, up to 70 at Milton Abbas Lake during January–February 1963 and 68 at Sturminster Marshall GP on 5th December 1993. Periods of severe cold may force birds to move to the rivers, e.g. 200 on the Lower Avon during January–February 1979, but counts on the Stour at Corfe Mullen of 150 during January–March 1970 and 90 on 16th January 1973 were apparently not associated with such conditions. Severe winter cold may also result in birds moving to the estuaries such as Christchurch Harbour (maximum of 144 in January–February 1979) and Poole Harbour, e.g. 764 in Parkstone Bay, 152 in Holes Bay and 100 at Arne NR on 12th February 1991. At Lodmoor NR there was an extraordinary influx from late January to early March 1984 reaching a maximum of 99 on 17th February.

	80/81	81/82	82/83	83/84	84/85	85/86	86/87	87/88	88/89	89/90
Crichel Lake	60	84	65	92	51	80	96	140	60	10
Sherborne Lake	60	nc	150	100	65	100	100	71	69	66

	90/91	91/92	92/93	93/94	94/95	95/96	96/97	97/97	98/99	99/00
Crichel Lake	nc	75	60	146	96	92	78	78	88	73
Sherborne Lake	35	50	14	39	nc	58	44	13	nc	11

Table 50. Winter maxima at Crichel Lake and Sherborne Lake 1980–1999

Coastal movements occur most years, mainly during autumn passage from mid-September to mid-December and as a result of cold weather in mid-winter. Records usually involve 1–10 birds and rarely exceed 25, but an exceptional 126E occurred at Durlston CP on 21st November 1985.

A total of 49 birds has been ringed in the county.

The Pochard breeds across much of Eurasia, except the Far East, mainly between 45°N and 60°N. It winters mainly in western and southern Europe, North Africa and the Middle East, the northern tropics of Africa, and south and south-east Asia including the Indian sub-continent.

Postscript 2000–2002
At Lodmoor NR, one pair reared four young in 2001 and two pairs reared 13 young in 2002 – these are the first reports of breeding in the county since 1992. A count of 428 at Lodmoor NR on 17th November 2001 is the highest ever for the reserve.

Ring-necked Duck   *Aythya collaris*

A very rare winter visitor and passage migrant: c.16 individuals

This species was added to the Dorset list in 1977. It is difficult to assess how many different individuals are involved since birds wander between various waters, most notably between Radipole NR and the Fleet at Abbotsbury, and between Little Sea and Poole Park. Together, these localities account for ten of the 16 birds. The male that commuted between Little Sea and Poole Park in 1989 and 1990 was widely considered to be the same individual that wintered at Timsbury GP in Hampshire from late 1987 to early 1995. Although there was no overlap in dates in 1989, in 1990 birds were present at both sites in late December – so presumably they were different individuals!

1977	Sutton Bingham: male 22nd April–21st May
1978	Radipole NR: female 26th–28th April
1980	River Avon at Sopley: male 10th January – also seen in Hampshire
	River Stour at Iford: male 9th–11th November
1985	Radipole NR: first-winter male 18th November–26th December
1986	Sutton Bingham: first-winter male 4th January with another first-winter male 16th April
1988	Radipole NR: male 5th September–23rd October; presumed same at Abbotsbury 6th November
1989	Little Sea: male 7th October; presumed same at Poole Park 20th November–13th December
1990	Poole Park: returning male 10th November–14th December and 18th–30th December; same at Little Sea 15th–17th December
1995	Poole Park: male intermittently 11th November into 1996; same at Little Sea 16th November, 6th–12th December, 17th, 18th and 22nd December and 13th January–11th February 1996
1996	Abbotsbury, imm. male intermittently 30th October–7th November
	Radipole NR: two imm. males 31st October–20th November – including Abbotsbury bird above

1997   Sturminster Marshall GP: female (possibly imm.) 25th September–4th October
1998   Abbotsbury, male 10th–27th April when joined by second male, one remaining to 28th April
2002   Radipole NR: female 25th April; same at Lodmoor NR 26th April–16th May

The Ring-necked Duck breeds across northern North America and winters mainly in the coastal and southern states of the USA south into Central America and the West Indies. A vagrant to the British Isles with 379 records up to 1993.

Ferruginous Duck   *Aythya nyroca*

A very rare winter visitor and passage migrant

There is only one old record from the 19th Century involving a bird shot at the mouth of the Wareham River on 3rd January 1879. There were no further sightings until 1945 when one was seen on the River Stour at Bryanston on 4th January, which was followed by one at Abbotsbury from 14th to 24th July 1949 and a male, probably first-winter, at Radipole NR from 4th to 13th December 1969.

An increase in records between 1976 and 1983 included a remarkable series of sightings from Radipole NR, which may have involved as many as ten different birds. Records from other sites, notably Sutton Bingham, during this period may have included the same birds. At Radipole NR the situation is further complicated by the fact that between 1980 and 1983 some observers considered at least one long-staying individual, sexed as male in 1980 and 1981, but as female in 1982 and 1983, to show features indicating a hybrid origin. Although there is no overlap in dates, it is possible that two hybrid birds were involved in these sightings, whilst some of the claims of pure Ferruginous Ducks during this period may also refer to these hybrids. Indeed all records prior to 1986 may include individuals that were not pure Ferruginous Ducks.

1976   Sutton Bingham: male 23rd–26th December
1977   Arne NR: female 24th August
         Sutton Bingham: male 26th September – possibly the same bird as 1976; probably the same at
             Radipole NR on various dates between 8th November and 18th February 1978; possibly
             the same male (in moult) at Radipole NR 21st–30th July 1978
1978   Radipole NR: in addition to the overwintering male, imm. female 28th January and 3rd–12th
             February; probably same two at Abbotsbury 12th -19th March and again 9th May
1979   Poole Park: female 8th January
         Abbotsbury: 29th January
         Radipole NR: female 15th November
1980   Radipole NR: hybrid-type bird 1st–10th February; presumed same, sexed as male, 7th
             December–21st January 1981 and again 1st November–31st December 1981
1981   Radipole NR moulting male 28th–29th July with second male 2nd December
         Christchurch Harbour: male 24th August
         West Bexington: male 29th November
1982   Radipole NR: hybrid-type bird, sexed as female, various dates between 3rd January and 8th
             February with another female 3rd April, one 11th–13th November, male paired with the
             hybrid-type female 19th–21st November with the male again 25th–31st December; same
             hybrid type female 1st–23rd January 1983

Subsequently the species reverted to being a rare visitor with only four further records up to 1993:

1986   Radipole NR: 26th and 30th March
1987   River Avon between Winkton and Sopley: male 28th December–6th February 1988 – also
             seen in Hampshire
1988   Christchurch Harbour: female 21st–22nd November
1993   Abbotsbury: female 13th–18th October

In recent years a single male has been recorded at various lakes in the Wareham Forest area, mainly Morden Park Lake and Lulworth Lake, during seven winters between 1993/94 and 2001/2002. It seems likely that the scarcity of records during the first four winters was due to lack of observer coverage at these sites.

1994   Morden Park Lake: male 13th February
1996   Morden Park Lake: male 13th February
1998   Morden Park Lake: male 23rd January, moved to Lulworth Lake 26th January; same at Morden
         Park Lake 19th December into 1999 visiting Lulworth Lake 28th December
1999   Morden Park Lake: from 1998 – 15th February visiting Lulworth Lake 10th January and
         Hyde Lakes 6th February; same at Morden Park Lake 20th December into 2000
2000   Morden Park Lake: from 1999 with latest sighting at Budden's Farm Lakes 24th February;
         presumed same at Lulworth Lake 27th and 28th September, and at Morden Park Lake
         23rd November into 2001 visiting Sturminster Marshall GP 18th December
2001   Morden Park Lake: from 2000 – 7th January; presumed same at Morden Park Lake 7th October
         into 2002
2002   Morden Park Lake: from 2001 – 9th March, and 1st December into 2003

Finally, the following record was the first new bird to be seen in the county since 1994:

2001   Abbotsbury: first-winter female 3rd–4th December

The Ferruginous Duck breeds locally in southern Europe, more widespread in eastern Europe and west-central Asia. It winters in southern Europe and North Africa, northern sub-Saharan Africa, Turkey and around the Black and Caspian Seas, in the Middle East and the north of the Indian sub-continent. A vagrant to the British Isles, but its true status is confused by escapes and hybrids.

Tufted Duck   *Aythya fuligula*

An uncommon resident, common winter visitor and passage migrant

Mansel-Pleydell (1888) considered the Tufted Duck or 'Blue-bill' to be a winter visitor and mentioned that breeding occurred, probably in the Poole district, in 1876. Blathwayt (1945) described the species as "a common visitor from autumn to spring" and recorded that it nested near Weymouth probably in 1926 and certainly in 1930.

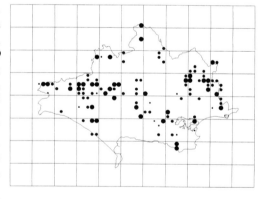

    There are no further reports of confirmed breeding until 1968 at Crichel Lake. Subsequently it has spread rapidly and widely to become an established, but uncommon breeding bird the county. The *BTO Atlas* (1968–1972) revealed evidence of breeding in 18 (49%) 10-km squares (confirmed in nine, probable in three and possible in six). The Tetrad Survey (1987–1994) clearly demonstrates a continuing expansion with evidence of breeding in 27 (73%) of the pre-1974 10-km squares (confirmed in 18 and probable in nine). The Tetrad Map shows that breeding is mainly concentrated in the east, centre and west of the county.

    Despite the spread in range, the size of the breeding population is small, variable and mobile with birds using some sites intermittently and others for a few years only before moving on to new localities – see Table 51. This may be related to the availability of food, since freshwater diving duck such as Pochard and Tufted Duck are known to suffer from competition

	1980	1981	1982	1983	1984	1985	1986	1987	1988	1989
Confirmed	15+	18	3	9	12	9	5	15	14	6
Probable/Possible	4	3	11	20+	15	8	nc	17	nc	nc

	1990	1991	1992	1993	1994	1995	1996	1997	1998	1999
Confirmed	5	8	8	5	7	17	8	12	2	6
Probable/Possible	nc.	22+	7+	6+	8	4+	6	8	nc	4

Table 51. Number of breeding pairs 1980–1999

at lakes with large populations of coarse fish. Most breeding sites support 1–3 pairs, occasionally more, the highest counts being ten pairs at Sherborne Lake in 1975, eight at Wigbeth Ponds in 1991, eight along the River Allen in 1989 with seven there in 1990 and 1991, seven at Nether Cerne in 1981 and 6–7 at Lulworth Lake in 1984 with 4–6 pairs there in 1997. It should be noted that not all of these counts relate to pairs actually proven to breed.

The main wintering sites are Poole Harbour (mainly Little Sea and Poole Park), Radipole NR and the Fleet (mainly Abbotsbury) with a considerable interchange of birds between the two latter sites. Numbers increased at all the main sites during the 1960s and 1970s – see Table 52. In Poole Harbour numbers continued to increase during the 1980s, the highest count being 700 in November 1981, but then declined dramatically during the 1990s. At Radipole NR numbers peaked in the 1970s, the highest count being 777 on 18th February 1979, but then declined gradually during the 1980s and more rapidly during the 1990s with winter maxima failing to reach treble figures towards the end of the decade. On the Fleet, numbers increased markedly during the 1980s and more gradually during the 1990s, the highest count being 739 on 17th January 1982. In earlier years, the highest counts were the result of cold weather influxes, most notably during the winter of 1962/63 with 3,200 in Poole Harbour on 17th February (a county record) and 2,000 at Abbotsbury on 13th January.

	1950s	1960s	1970s	1980s	1990s
Poole Harbour	73	140	367	471	188
Radipole NR	222	363	552	461	151
The Fleet	81	89	175	305	328

Table 52. Winter 10-year average peak counts at the main sites 1950–1999

Both Crichel and Sherborne Lakes are also important sites for the species – see Table 53. At Crichel Lake numbers were lower during the 1950s and 1960s when winter maxima rarely exceeded 50 birds, but increased during 1970s with maxima generally ranging between 50–100 birds. Counts only exceeded 100 twice during this period with 114 on 14th February 1960 and 113 on 18th January 1976. Similarly numbers have also increased at Sherborne Lake where winter maxima during the 1950s and 1960s never exceeded 30 birds.

	80/81	81/82	82/83	83/84	84/85	85/86	86/87	87/88	88/89	89/90
Crichel Lake	124	104	90	107	78	120	100	250	110	25
Sherborne Lake	80	nc	120	55	50	100+	45	78	87	85

	90/91	91/92	92/93	93/94	94/95	95/96	96/97	97/98	98/99	99/00
Crichel Lake	nc	62	126	152	100	129	111	114	128	92
Sherborne Lake	54	61	41	nc	nc	55	54	20	15	16

Table 53. Winter maxima at Crichel Lake and Sherborne Lake 1980–1999

Elsewhere smaller numbers are recorded from widely scattered sites with winter maxima generally ranging up to 50 birds, but there were 111 at Morden Park Lake on 27th December 1992 with 110 there on 28th January 1997, 100 at Up Cerne Lake on 16th November 1981, several counts of 50–75 from the Lower Avon during 1990–1995, 64 at Wimborne St Giles Park in January 1997, 60 at Milton Abbas Lake in January 1963 and 59 at Sturminster Marshall GP in November 1999. Periods of severe cold may force birds to move to the rivers, notably the Lower Avon and the lower and middle reaches of the Stour reaching a maximum of 82 between Corfe Mullen and Sturminster Marshall in January 1997. Similar conditions may also result in birds moving to estuaries and sheltered coastal waters such as Christchurch Harbour (maximum of 55 on 8th January 1985), Poole Harbour, e.g. 204 in Parkstone Bay on 12th February 1991 and 195 in Holes Bay on 22nd February 1991, and Portland Harbour (maximum of 120 in January 1997).

Coastal movements have occurred annually in recent years, mainly in spring (March–May) and autumn (October–November), but occasionally as a result of cold weather in mid-winter. Records usually involve 1–10 birds, the most notable movements being from Durlston CP with 40E on 31st January 1992, 30 on

31st December 1996 and 40 bird-days during 12th–17th January 1987, whilst at Hengistbury 77 moved in various directions during 19th–21st November 1985.

A total of 122 birds has been ringed in the county and there have been two recoveries each from the former USSR and Finland, and one from the Netherlands.

The Tufted Duck breeds widely across northern Eurasia and winters in Europe (except the north and east), North Africa and the Middle East, the north-eastern tropics of Africa, and southern and eastern Asia including the north of the Indian sub-continent.

Postscript 2000–2002

During the breeding season, there were c.14 pairs at nine sites in 2000, c.11 pairs at nine sites in 2001, and c.11 pairs at six sites in 2002.

Scaup (Greater Scaup) *Aythya marila*

An uncommon winter visitor and passage migrant

Mansel-Pleydell (1888) regarded the Scaup or 'Curre' to be one of the rarer ducks to visit the county in winter and reported that it had been occasionally killed at Poole, Weymouth and Abbotsbury. Blathwayt (1945) described the species as "a winter visitor to the coast, not common, but doubtless often occurs" and listed records from Abbotsbury in 1918, Weymouth in 1928 and Poole in 1929.

Since the mid-1940s there has been a marked increase in sightings and the Scaup has become a regular, if sometimes uncommon, winter visitor, the main sites being Poole Harbour, Radipole NR and the Fleet – see Table 54. Despite this overall increase, the numbers present in winter are highly variable with influxes in some years associated with periods of severe cold weather.

It is difficult to give maxima for the whole of Poole Harbour in some winters, since counts are only available for individual sites. The highest numbers in the harbour occurred during the severe winter of 1962/63 when c.356 birds (a county record) were present in mid-February including 300+ at Holton Shore. Other counts in excess of 100 birds include 186 on 15th February 1976 and 116 in January 1997. In addition, based on counts from individual sites, winter maxima for the entire harbour almost certainly reached totals of between 100 and 200 birds during 1969/70, 1972/73, 1973/74, 1985/86 and 1995/96. Within the harbour the most favoured haunts are Little Sea and the waters off Arne NR and Holton Shore. High counts from these and other sites within the harbour include 93 at Little Sea in mid-February 1996 with 89 there on 16th February 1997, 82 at Arne NR on 19th January 1997 with 81 there on 11th February 1970, 70 at Lytchett Bay in February 1970, 56 off Brownsea in mid-February 1963 with 54 there on 10th February 1986, and 20 in Poole Park in January 1974.

At Radipole NR, numbers increased during the 1970s and have stabilised subsequently, the highest count being 34 on 12th January 1985. Nearby on the Fleet, regular wintering has only occurred since the late 1970s with numbers steadily increasing during the 1980s and 1990s, the highest count being 43 during February–March 1991. Although Abbotsbury is the favoured area, the species occasionally occurs elsewhere along the Fleet as far as Ferrybridge and beyond into Portland Harbour. The latter site sometimes attracts reasonable numbers during periods of severe cold weather, notably during February–March 1991 (maximum of 43), during January–February 1997 (maximum of 31 on 31st January), during January–February 1985 (maximum of 27 on 25th January) and during January–February 1963 (maximum of 11), whilst 14 were present there on 31st December 1995.

	1950s	1960s	1970s	1980s	1990s
Poole Harbour	17	27	60	28	39
Radipole NR	4	7	11	13	12
The Fleet	5	5	11	19	25

Table 54. Winter 10-year average peak counts at the main sites 1950–1999

The Scaup is virtually an annual visitor to Christchurch Harbour with most records in cold winters, the highest counts being 15 on 8th January 1985, 13 in January 1997 and 11 in January 1987. Reports from other coastal sites of settled birds are very few with sightings from Burton Bradstock, West and East Bexington, Lodmoor NR, Weymouth Bay and the Purbeck coast where 12 at Chapman's Pool on 16th

January 1987 and up to seven in Kimmeridge Bay during 16th–21st January 1985 are particularly noteworthy.

Coastal movements are occasionally recorded, mainly from Portland Bill, Durlston CP and Hengistbury – see Table 55. The peak month is January with most sightings during periods of cold weather including 26E and 6W at Hengistbury during 1st–22nd January 1985, 19 at Durlston CP on 31st December 1996 and ten at Portland Bill on 3rd January 1997. There are also distinct peaks at times of passage in April (maximum of 8E at Hengistbury on 14th April 1988), and November (maximum of 11W at Hengistbury on 20th November 1985).

Jan	Feb	Mar	Apr	May	Jun	Jul	Aug	Sep	Oct	Nov	Dec
91	3	3	16	2	0	0	2	1	7	33	26

Table 55. Monthly totals for coastal movements 1950–1999

Inland the species is very uncommon with the majority of reports during periods of severe winter cold when birds may appear on the main rivers, notably the Lower Avon (maximum of four at Sopley on 24th February 1991), the lower/middle Stour including a male at Bryanston during 22nd–24th February 1956, and the lower/middle Frome (maximum of ten at Wool on 26th January 1985). Elsewhere inland there are sightings from Crichel Lake with seven records of 1–2 birds, Sherborne Lake with two records of single birds, Milton Abbas Lake with two during February–March 1963, Morden Decoy Pond with five on 29th October and 1–3 birds during 18th–20th November 1968, Creekmoor Ponds with one on 26th October 1998, Luckford Lake with four on 5th April 1970 and Puddletown with one on 6th March 1987.

Wintering birds usually arrive in October and November, occasionally earlier, and leave in March with a few individuals lingering into April and exceptionally May. In some years there is evidence of spring passage, mainly in March–April, and often involving small flocks which can remain for several weeks. For example, in 1992 monthly maxima for January to May at Radipole NR were 0, 1, 14, 17, 14, and at Arne NR there were six during 17th–28th April with seven on 1st May. There are also several early autumn records from Radipole NR with up to five in August 1981, three on 4th August 1982, three on 22nd July 1983, two on 27th–28th August 1984, one in August 1986 and one on 19th August 1993, whilst two singles have been recorded at Portland Bill in August including one on 9th August 1981. Mid-summer records are very scarce, but there were three males at Holton Shore on 10th July 1969, singles at Radipole NR during 3rd–10th June and on 6th July 1977, two males at Arne NR during 16th July–4th August 1978 and one at Christchurch Harbour on 2nd July 1992. The only instance of genuine oversummering occurred on the Fleet in 1988 when two birds were present from May to July with six there in August.

The Scaup breeds across the Holarctic and winters along the coasts of north-western Europe, the southern Baltic and Black Seas, eastern Asia and North America.

Postscript 2000–2002

A count of 36 at Radipole NR in January 2000 is the highest ever at this site. In 2002, 16 at Lodmoor NR on 17th February and 26 offshore at Hengistbury on 14th December are notable records. Inland sightings are uncommon, so singles at Sturminster Marshall GP during 9th–16th December 2001 and Morden Park Lake on 15th December 2001, and a pair on the River Stour at Corfe Mullen on 11th May 2002 are noteworthy.

Lesser Scaup   *Aythya affinis*

Accidental: two records

Both Dorset records are from the Poole Harbour area:

1992 Hatch Pond, Poole: first-winter male 28th November and 4th–5th December; same at Little Sea on 6th and 10th–11th December
2001 Swineham GPs: first-winter male 11th November–15th December; same at Little Sea 19th December–29th April 2002 and 14th December 2002 into 2003

The Lesser Scaup breeds across northern North America except the north-east and winters mainly in the coastal and southern states of the USA south through Central America to northern South America, also in the West Indies. A vagrant to Great Britain with 53 records up to 2002.

Sponsored by Shaun Robson

Eider (Common Eider)   *Somateria mollissima*

A locally common winter visitor and passage migrant

Mansel-Pleydell (1888) described this species as "a rare straggler to Dorsetshire" and listed four records involving one shot at Poole in 1868, one killed on the Fleet in December 1869 with nine present in the same place on 27th November 1871 (of which four were shot), and finally one 'obtained' at Poole on 26th November 1884. It remained a rare vagrant up to 1950 with Blathwayt (1945) only giving three further records, all from Studland with two on 25th December 1937, one on 12th June and two on 18th December 1939.

During the 1950s the Eider became a regular visitor, mainly in winter, to the Poole Bay/Poole Harbour and Portland Harbour/Weymouth Bay areas. Although winter maxima have fluctuated considerably, numbers increased steadily to peak during the 1980s, followed by a marked decline during the 1990s – see Table 56. Winter maxima at the main sites rarely exceed 50 birds, the highest counts being 150 (a county record) at Hengistbury and 135 in Poole Bay/Poole Harbour in February 1989 – presumably involving the same birds, 129 in Shell Bay in January 1976, 92 (mainly males) briefly in Poole Harbour on 13th March 1963, 80 in Portland Harbour/Weymouth Bay in November 1989 with 70 there in January 1989 (cf Hengistbury and in Poole Bay/Poole Harbour), and finally 74 at Hengistbury in early January 1974. There is obviously some interchange of birds between Poole Harbour and the favoured areas of Poole Bay, notably Shell/Studland Bays and Hengistbury, whilst birds from Portland Harbour and Weymouth Bay occasionally wander to the Fleet and along the nearest parts of the Purbeck coast, e.g. Osmington Mills. Although regularly recorded off Hengistbury, the species is a rare visitor inside Christchurch Harbour.

	1950s	1960s	1970s	1980s	1990s
Poole Bay at Hengistbury	–	–	29	35	8
Studland Bay/Poole Harbour	7	22	28	39	14
Portland Hbr/Weymouth Bay	2	12	11	33	11

Table 56. Winter 10-year average peak counts at the main sites 1950–1999

Otherwise settled birds are occasionally reported from Lyme Bay, Portland Bill and the Purbeck coast. Sometimes substantial flocks may be present for several weeks or throughout the winter, the most notable being at Portland Bill from October 1975 to January 1976 (maximum of 94 on 29th November) and during November–December 1996 (maximum of 29 on 14th December), the Chesil at Ferrybridge during November–early December 1981 (maximum of 40 on 24th November), Abbotsbury Beach with up to 30 during November–December 1993, Burton Bradstock with up to 20 during 8th–22nd January 1989, and Durlston CP with up to 20 in November 1988 and 20 during 20th April–3rd May 1987. Although there are no truly inland occurrences, birds have been recorded from Radipole NR with one during 8th–10th November 1980, one on 11th October 1988 and two on 23rd September 1997, Lodmoor NR with one on 21st January 1996 and Poole Park with one on 24th November 1993.

Coastal movements regularly occur at Portland Bill and Durlston CP, and to a lesser extent the Chesil, St Aldhelm's Head and Hengistbury. There are distinct peaks in spring (March–May) and from late autumn to mid-winter (November–January) – see Table 57. Movements in spring are predominantly easterly in direction, and those in the late autumn and early winter show a westerly bias. This is consistent with the idea that most of Dorset's Eiders originate from populations in the Netherlands and Baltic. Day-counts usually involve 1–20 birds, the highest being 77W at Durlston CP on 28th November 1988 with 56 there on 4th January 1989, 55W at Hengistbury on 21st November 1988 with 48 there on 7th May 1976, 52E at St Aldhelm's Head on 27th October 1984, and 48W at Portland Bill on 30th October 1983 with 47E there on 28th October 1969.

Jan	Feb	Mar	Apr	May	Jun	Jul	Aug	Sep	Oct	Nov	Dec
13%	3%	9%	15%	6%	1%	<1%	<1%	3%	6%	27%	17%

Table 57. Monthly coastal movements (%) at Portland Bill and Durlston CP 1987–1999

Although the species mainly occurs from September to May, there are frequent records for the mid-summer period. These include several instances of oversummering flocks, the largest being up to ten in Poole Harbour during June–September 1969, 20 in Studland Bay, eight at Hengistbury and four at Portland Bill during the summer of 1976, up to 16 at Hengistbury into June 1979 with up to 27 there during June–August 1989, and up to 19 in Studland Bay/Poole Harbour during June–August 1996. Coastal movements are also occasionally recorded in mid-summer, the most notable being 30 at Portland Bill on 14th June 1975 with 16 there on 10th July 1965.

One bird has been ringed in the county.

The Eider breeds across much of the Holarctic including the coasts of northern Europe, north-east Siberia, northern North America and Greenland. The main wintering areas in Europe are Iceland, Scandinavia and the Baltic. The British breeding stock is concentrated in Scotland and considered to be resident. The modest numbers reaching the English Channel in winter probably originate from populations wintering in the Netherlands and Baltic.

Long-tailed Duck *Clangula hyemalis*

An uncommon winter visitor and passage migrant

Mansel-Pleydell (1888) referred to six records between 1840 and 1887, including five shot out of several frequenting Poole Harbour in November 1887, and quoted Pulteney (1799) who stated "it visits the county of Dorset in hard winters, and has been shot at St Giles". Blathwayt (1945) described the species as "a scarce winter visitor" and listed five records between 1920 and 1933.

The Long-tailed Duck was not reported again until 1950 since when it has become a regular, if uncommon, winter visitor and passage migrant. The main wintering sites are Studland Bay/Poole Harbour and the Fleet/Portland Harbour areas – see Table 58. Numbers are generally small and highly variable with relatively good winters interspersed with poor ones when the species may be absent even from its favoured haunts, e.g. Poole Harbour in 1987/88 and 1989/90. In the Studland Bay/Poole Harbour area, overall numbers appear to have been relatively stable during 1960–1999 except for a marked increase in the 1980s. By contrast, in the Fleet/Portland Harbour area, numbers rose dramatically during the 1960s, declined slightly during the 1970s and 1980s, and then more sharply during the 1990s. Winter maxima usually range from 1–6 birds and rarely exceed ten, the highest counts being mainly from the Fleet at Abbotsbury with 27 on 17th January 1971 (a county record), 19 on 19th January 1968, 18 on 13th January 1963, 15 in March 1989 and 13 on 14th December 1991, whilst Poole Harbour's best count is 14 during January–March 1989.

	1950s	1960s	1970s	1980s	1990s
Studland Bay/Poole Harbour	3	3	4	6	4
The Fleet/Portland Harbour	4	8	7	6	4

Table 58. Winter 10-year average peak counts at the main sites 1950–1999

There are occasional records of settled birds from other coastal sites, the most favoured being Radipole NR and Christchurch Harbour. The species has overwintered at both these sites on a number of occasions, the highest counts being eight at Christchurch Harbour in December 1988, and four at Radipole NR on 14th March 1965 and during January–early February 1991. Otherwise there are a few reports from Burton Bradstock, West/East Bexington, Chesil Cove, Portland Bill, Weymouth Bay, Lodmoor NR and the Purbeck coast including Kimmeridge Bay, Chapman's Pool, Durlston Bay and Peveril Point. There was a notable influx during the winter of 1991/92 when exceptional numbers were present between Burton Bradstock and East Bexington with a peak of 23 at the latter site on 5th February, the second highest count for the county. Birds commuted between this stretch of coast and the nearby Fleet at Abbotsbury where movements included 14W during 3rd–7th November and 16E, 16W during 22nd–26th December.

Coastal movements are recorded annually and occur mainly in spring (March–May) and late autumn/ early winter (October–December) with distinct peaks in April and November (cf Eider) – see Table 59. Movements are predominantly easterly in spring (89%E), but more evenly balanced in the autumn and early winter (59%W). Most records are from Portland Bill, Durlston CP and Hengistbury, but there are reports from West Bexington, the Chesil, St Aldhelm's Head and Winspit. Day-counts are generally very small, mostly 1–2 birds and rarely more than five, the highest in recent years being 14W at Portland Bill on 13th November 1983, but there is an earlier record of 23E at this site on 15th April 1959, also 25E at Portland Bill during April 1980. In addition to the coastal movements, spring passage is further evident by occasional peak counts from other sites, e.g. nine at Abbotsbury during 9th–13th April 1958, nine in Poole Harbour on 23rd April 1983 and nine at East Fleet on 7th April 1985.

	Jan	Feb	Mar	Apr	May	Jun	Jul	Aug	Sep	Oct	Nov	Dec
Portland Bill	6	1	12	59	12	0	0	0	0	6	30	11
Durlston CP	8	1	5	21	6	0	0	0	0	3	18	8
Hengistbury	1	2	1	6	6	0	0	0	0	8	15	8

Table 59. Monthly totals for coastal movements at the main watch-points 1980–1996

Apart from near-coastal records of single birds from the River Frome at Wareham on 24th November 1977 and the River Avon at Christchurch in early 1979, there are only two recent records from well inland involving singles at Crichel Lake on 15th March 1981 and Sherborne Lake on 3rd–4th December 1988.

The species is mostly recorded between October and May. There are a few sightings for August and September, the earliest being 1st August 1968 at Chesil Cove, whilst there are only two records later than May involving a bird in Christchurch Harbour during 24th May–1st June 1981 and a pair in Shell Bay during 12th–16th June 1993.

The Long-tailed Duck breeds across the Holarctic and winters along the coasts of northern Europe, east Asia and northern North America.

Postscript 2000–2002
At Milton Abbas Lake in 2000, one on 2nd January, 29th April and from 22nd to 29th May – an extraordinary series of sightings both in terms of location (only the third inland record in recent years) and timing.

Common Scoter (Black Scoter) *Melanitta nigra*

A locally common non-breeding resident, winter visitor and passage migrant

Mansel-Pleydell (1888) described the Common Scoter or 'Black Duck' as "a common winter visitant" and noted that it favoured the rocky coast at Kimmeridge. Blathwayt (1945) commented that the species was frequently recorded from the waters outside Poole Harbour where flocks of up to 40 and more could be seen between November and mid-April.

Subsequently the status of the Common Scoter in Dorset has become increasingly complex. It has continued to occur as a winter visitor, although numbers have fluctuated considerably and winter flocks, when present, appear to be highly mobile both within and between their favoured wintering areas. This presumably accounts for some of the coastal movements recorded during the winter months. The occasional high counts of settled birds in March–April and October–November may refer to migrants rather than genuine wintering birds. Although summering was seemingly unknown prior to 1950, this has become an annual event with most records involving small numbers, but with larger flocks at the main wintering sites

on occasion. Again some of the coastal movements during the mid-summer period may involve these local flocks rather than long-distance migrants.

Poole Bay is the traditional wintering area for the species – see Table 60. During the 1950s and early 1960s rafts of a few hundred birds were usually present, counts of up to 1,000–1,500 in late March 1958 and 750–1,000 on 25th January 1960 being exceptional. There was a marked decline after the winter of 1966/67 with very low numbers recorded until December 1973 when there were 110 at Hengistbury. Subsequently there has been a partial recovery, but numbers are rather modest with winter maxima only occasionally exceeding 100 birds, the highest count being 235 in November 1988. Although birds frequent the entire length of Poole Bay, the largest flocks tend to occur at Southbourne and Hengistbury with smaller numbers in Shell/Studland Bays. Relatively few birds venture into Poole Harbour with most reports involving 1–10 birds, the highest count in recent years being 19 in December 1991. During the spring and summer large flocks are sometimes present, mainly at Southbourne and Hengistbury, the highest counts being 200 during April–July 1977, 150 on 27th April and 250 on 1st May 1978, up to 105 during April–July 1988 (peak in May), up to 156 during April–June 1994 (peak in May) and 99 in June 1996.

	1950s	1960s	1970s	1980s	1990s
Poole Bay incl Hengistbury	315	132	75	87	62
Portland Hbr/Weymouth Bay	nc	nc	nc	20	15
Lyme Bay incl Portland Bill	nc	48	35	119	139

Table 60. Winter 10-year average peak counts at the main sites 1950–1999

Records since the mid-1980s show that Lyme Bay is also an important wintering area for Common Scoters, but isolated counts during the 1960s and 1970s, notably 100+ at Abbotsbury Beach on 17th March 1966 and 70 at West Bexington in November 1974, suggest that this may have been the case in earlier years. Although birds may wander widely throughout Lyme Bay, the largest flocks in recent years have occurred mainly at Burton Bradstock with 320 in January 1989, 537 in December 1991 and 350 in November 1994. At Portland Bill the highest counts of settled birds are 250 in mid-November 1991 and 150 in early November 1988, which in both years preceded higher counts at Burton Bradstock. Summer flocks are frequently recorded in Lyme Bay, but unlike Poole Bay, the peak counts often occur later in the season. Exceptional numbers were present at Portland Bill during June–August 1992 reaching a peak of 400 in July (the largest summer flock recorded in Dorset). Otherwise counts are more modest, the highest being up to 120 in Lyme Bay during May–June 1994 (peak in May), 120 at Portland Bill in mid-May 1991 with up to 90 there during June–July 1994 (peak in June), and 90 at Burton Bradstock on 12th July 1986.

Apart from 200 in Weymouth Bay in the winter of 1952/53, much smaller numbers occur in the Portland Harbour/Weymouth Bay area with maxima rarely exceeding 30 birds. Peak counts sometimes occur in March–April and October suggesting these are migrants rather than wintering birds. The species is an infrequent visitor to the Fleet, reports from the Abbotsbury end being decidedly unusual. Settled birds are occasionally recorded off the Purbeck coast, usually in very small numbers, but 360 at Durlston CP during November–December 1988 is exceptional. In two recent winters flocks have occurred at Winspit with peaks of 25 in January 1998 and 50 during December 1998–January 1999. There are a few reports from near-coastal sites such as Burton Mere, Radipole NR, Lodmoor NR, Little Sea and Poole Park, but the only records from well inland involve one killed at Milborne St Andrew after a severe gale in the winter of 1863, one found with an injured wing below the BBC aerial at Rampisham on 1st July 1956 and released at Sutton Bingham the following day, and one on the River Stour at Merley on 7th April 1975.

The Common Scoter is perhaps better known as a passage migrant, particularly in spring when substantial and predominantly easterly movements can be expected. Autumn passage is mainly westerly and generally more modest in size. Precise figures for the strength of the movements in spring and autumn are difficult to assess, since wintering and summering birds obscure the start and finish of passage. Generally spring passage commences in March, peaks in April and sometimes extends into June, whilst autumn movements start in July and last through to October, more occasionally into November.

Since 1960 estimated totals for spring passage at Portland Bill have generally varied between 700–800 birds in poor years and 3,000–4,500 birds in good years, the highest being c.7,000+ in 1964 and nearly c.6,000+ in 1978 including 5,587E in April. The heaviest movements usually occur from late March to mid-April, and in good springs peak counts usually range from 500–1,000 birds, occasionally more, the highest being 6,653 during 16th–17th April 1964 with 4,193 on 16th and 2,460 on 17th, 4,020 on 16th April 1978, and 3,162 during 1st–2nd April 1990 including 2,050 on 1st. Passage is overwhelmingly easterly in direction accounting for 93% of overall movements. Autumn passage is generally lighter and more evenly spread through the season, although there tends to be a slight peak in July. Estimated totals vary from 500–1,000 birds in poor years to 1,500–2,500 birds in good years, the highest being 3,715 in 1979, 3,191 in 1985 and 3,058 in 1980. Unlike the spring, peak counts in autumn are rather modest, and rarely exceed 100 birds, the highest being 632 on 23rd September 1979 and 525 on 24th August 1981. The direction of passage is substantially biased to the west accounting for 79% of overall movements. Since the 1970s, spring passage has increased, whereas autumn movements have declined – see Table 61.

	1950s	1960s	1970s	1980s	1990s
Spring	718	2749	1916	2438	2861
Autumn	503	972	1964	1810	1064

Table 61. Coastal movements 10-year average annual totals at Portland Bill 1950–1999

Although spring and autumn coastal movements through Lyme Bay (West Bexington to Chesil Cove), along the Purbeck coast (mainly St Aldhelm's Head and Durlston CP), and at Hengistbury generally mirror those at Portland Bill, the volume of passage is smaller. Since 1987 estimated totals for spring movements at Durlston CP have generally varied between 1,000–2,000 birds with 3,329 in 1995 and 2,389 in 1994, the highest day-count being an exceptional 1,130 on 4th April 1987, whilst estimated autumn totals for the same period have ranged from 544 in 1993 to 1,766 in 1995. Spring passage at St Aldhelm's Head has been similar to nearby Durlston CP in recent years, the highest being 2,330 in 1994 with a peak day-count of 1,016 on 2nd April 1995. Elsewhere 3,061 were recorded at East Bexington between March and June 1992, whilst at Hengistbury the best movements are 494E during 2nd–3rd May 1980, 427W on 9th November 1992 and 302W on 21st September 1980.

The Common Scoter breeds across the Holarctic with the races *M. n. nigra* in north-west Europe and western Siberia and *M. n. americana* in eastern Siberia and North America. It winters mainly on the coasts of northern and western Europe, north-west Africa, east Asia and North America. In the British Isles there is a small breeding population in Scotland and the north of Ireland.

Postscript 2000–2002
A count of 125 in Lyme Bay in May 2001 is notably high for the locality and time of year. One at Sherborne Lake on 26th January 2002 is only the fourth inland record for Dorset.

Surf Scoter   *Melanitta perspicillata*

A very rare winter visitor and passage migrant: nine records

There are three 19th Century records from the Weymouth area in winter 1851, December 1853 and on 29th October 1880. More recently:

1961   Portland Bill: ad. male 30th September
1985   Portland Bill: ad. male flying east 9th April
1989   Burton Bradstock: first-winter male 8th–22nd January
1999   Portland Harbour: first-winter male 16th January–2nd February
2000   Portland Harbour: first-winter bird 6th December–27th January 2001; same at Littlesea on
           the Fleet 17th December
2001   Hengistbury: flying west 8th October

The Surf Scoter breeds in arctic North America, and winters along the west coast from Alaska south to northern Mexico and along the east coast from Newfoundland south to Florida. A vagrant to the British Isles with over 460 records up to 1990.

Velvet Scoter   *Melanitta fusca*

An uncommon winter visitor and passage migrant

Mansel-Pleydell (1888) described this species as "an accidental visitor to our coast in winter, mixing with the Common Scoter in the proportion of not more than one in twenty" and referred to a few records including single birds obtained in Poole Harbour on 5th January 1856 and at Portland on 2nd February 1869. Blathwayt (1945) considered it to be a rather scarce winter visitor and stated that definite records are not numerous, listing only singles off Poole Harbour on 22nd January and 7th August 1931, and three at Portland Bill on 10th December 1943.

Since 1950 the Velvet Scoter has become a scarce, but annual winter visitor and passage migrant often associating with flocks of Common Scoter. Not surprisingly the species is most frequently recorded in winter from the same sites favoured by the Common Scoter, namely Poole Bay including Shell/Studland Bays and Hengistbury, Poole Harbour, Portland Harbour/Weymouth Bay, and more recently Lyme Bay, mainly at Portland Bill and Burton Bradstock/West Bexington. Winter maxima are very small, usually ranging from 1–5 birds and rarely reach double figures. There was a notable influx into Lyme Bay during the winter of 1988/89 (cf Common Scoter) with a peak count of 31 at Portland Bill on 24th November followed by up to 20 at Burton Bradstock during 8th–19th January. Other high counts of settled birds at the main sites include 15–20 amongst large numbers of Common Scoter in Poole Bay on 25th March 1958, up to 18 at Hengistbury in January 1976 with up to 15 there during November–December 1986, up to 15 in Studland Bay on 29th–30th December 1990, and up to 13 at Burton Bradstock during 28th–31st December 1991. Elsewhere the species occasionally wanders to the Fleet, the most notable count being 8+ at Abbotsbury on 14th March 1956, whilst there are very few records of settled birds from the Purbeck coast in winter, up to 16 at Durlston CP during November–December 1988 (cf Lyme Bay influx) being exceptional. Although frequently present at Hengistbury, Velvet Scoters rarely occur inside Christchurch Harbour with singles on 6th October 1979 and 22nd January 1992 seemingly the only recent records. The species has occasionally visited such near-coastal sites as Burton Mere with two on 9th February 1996, Lodmoor NR with one on 26th February 1979, Little Sea with one on 1st February 1969 and two on 14th November 1971, and Poole Park with one on 24th December 1981 and two on 11th November 1987. The only recent inland record involves a pair on the River Frome at West Holme on 21st February 1970, but there is an old claim of a female shot on the Stour near Blandford prior to 1799.

Coastal movements in spring are predominantly easterly in direction, and occur within a fairly well defined period between late March and mid-May with April the peak month. Autumn passage is generally smaller and more extended with records from July through to a peak in November with the end of migration obscured by winter movements. Numbers involved in these coastal movements are small and fluctuate considerably from year to year. At Portland Bill spring totals have ranged up to 40 birds, except for an exceptional 104 during 8th–19th April 1979 with a record day-count of 75 on 14th, whilst autumn totals have only reached double figures in four years since 1950, the highest being 23 in 1973. Spring and autumn coastal movements also occur at various other sites including West/East Bexington, the Chesil, St Aldhelm's Head, Durlston CP and Hengistbury. Only a few birds are usually involved with seasonal totals generally ranging up to eight in spring and up to five in autumn. Spring passage has been occasionally prominent at Hengistbury, notably in 1979 (25), 1981 (19), 1985 (23) and 1986 (36). In spring 1992 movements through Lyme Bay at West/East Bexington were particularly noteworthy with a total of 81 birds, although there may have been some duplication between these two sites. There were also good numbers at West Bexington in spring 1976 with 17 birds, and St Aldhelm's Head in spring 1984 with 15 birds. The best autumn totals are from Durlston CP in 1991 (13) and 1988 (11), and West Bexington in 1988 (11). Winter movements are occasionally recorded. Some of these may involve genuine migrants, particularly in early December, but it seems likely that most sightings refer to local wintering birds.

Although autumn and winter birds usually first appear in October and November, there are a surprising number of records for the July to September period, the earliest being 6th July 1992 at East Bexington. Spring passage extends well into May and early June with the latest records from Hengistbury on 31st May 1985, 2nd June 1991 and 4th June 1986.

The Velvet Scoter breeds across the Holarctic except for north-east North America, Greenland and Iceland. It winters mainly on the coasts of north-western Europe, eastern Asia and North America.

Postscript 2000–2002
At Hengistbury, 21W and 2E on 14th December 2002 is a record count for the site.

Goldeneye (Common Goldeneye)   *Bucephala clangula*

A locally common winter visitor and passage migrant

Mansel-Pleydell (1888) described this species as "an annual visitor in winter, at which season it may be found generally distributed about our coasts in small flocks, occasionally coming inland". Blathwayt (1945) considered it to be a winter visitor in small numbers both to the coast and inland waters, but most frequent in Poole Harbour.

Subsequently the Goldeneye has become more numerous, the main wintering sites being Poole Harbour and the Fleet/Portland Harbour area – see Table 62. In Poole Harbour numbers have increased steadily since the 1960s to peak during the 1990s with winter maxima typically ranging between 100–300 birds, the highest being 405 in February 1998. High counts in earlier years were clearly associated with periods of severe cold, notably in early 1963 with a site record of 500 on 27th January. The species occurs throughout the harbour, but there are two interesting roost areas, namely Little Sea and the central harbour waters between Arne NR and Brownsea, the latter site shared with Red-breasted Mergansers. At Little Sea there have been some very high counts at the evening roost including 330 in February 1988, 291 on 24th December 1995 and 220 on 3rd December 1985, whilst 200 roosted in the centre of the harbour on 19th December 1985. In addition, birds often roost on Poole Park Lake during windy weather. Numbers recorded from the Fleet/Portland Harbour area increased markedly during the 1970s and 1980s, but stabilised during the 1990s, with winter maxima generally ranging between 100–300 birds, the highest being 520 (a county record) on 17th January 1987.

	1950s	1960s	1970s	1980s	1990s
Poole Harbour	79	74	114	166	230
The Fleet/Portland Harbour	13	44	118	220	214

Table 62. Winter 10-year average peak counts at the main sites 1950–1999

The Goldeneye also winters in Christchurch Harbour, albeit in modest numbers – see Table 63. The higher counts are associated with periods of severe cold weather with a record peak of 43 in February 1991.

80/81	81/82	82/83	83/84	84/85	85/86	86/87	87/88	88/89	89/90
19	33	10	14	30	25	28	10	12	7

90/91	91/92	92/93	93/94	94/95	95/96	96/97	97/98	98/99	99/00
43	21	15	23	20	24	32	14	13	12

Table 63. Winter maxima at Christchurch Harbour 1980–1999

Elsewhere along the coastal fringes, the species occurs with some regularity at West Bexington, Radipole NR and Lodmoor NR. Most records involve 1–4 birds, but there were seven at Radipole NR in December 1973 with five there in November 1967. There are very few sightings of settled birds from Lyme Bay, two at Lyme Regis on 25th–26th October 1983 being particularly noteworthy, and the Purbeck coast where most records are from Kimmeridge Bay.

Inland there are frequent reports, usually involving 1–3 birds, from the Lower Avon (maximum of 15 at Coward's Marsh on 16th January 1987) and the Stour between Wimborne and Shapwick (maximum of 13 at Corfe Mullen during January–February 1970). Other favoured sites are Sherborne Lake (maximum of four) and, particularly during the 1950s, Crichel Lake (maximum of three). Elsewhere there are records from other inland sites scattered across the county. Coastal movements are recorded most years, mainly from Portland Bill, Durlston CP and Hengistbury. Day-counts are usually small, the most notable being 20E at Portland Bill on 17th February 1985.

Although the species mainly occurs between October and April, there are a few records of early arrivals in August and September, and late/lingering birds in May. Mid-summer sightings are rare with one at Radipole NR during 5th–14th June 1976, one on the River Stour at Corfe Mullen on 22nd and 31st May and 31st July 1979, a pair at Puddletown on 29th May 1984, one in Christchurch Harbour throughout the summer of 1987 and one at Abbotsbury on 16th July 1990. In addition, a male of unknown origin took up residence at Radipole NR from 18th May 1987 through to at least 1994.

The Goldeneye breeds across the Holarctic except for Greenland and Iceland. The Eurasian population winters mainly in north-west, central and south-east Europe, Turkey and the Caspian Sea, very locally in parts of central Asia and more widely in eastern Asia, whilst the North American population winters mainly to the west and south of the breeding range south to the Gulf of Mexico. In Great Britain there has been a small breeding population in Scotland since 1970.

Smew   *Mergellus albellus*

A scarce winter visitor, subject to cold weather influxes

Mansel-Pleydell (1888) commented that "although never very numerous as a species, the Smew occurs every winter, generally in small flocks, which soon become scattered about our bays and estuaries, many individuals finding their way for some distance up the rivers". Blathwayt (1945) described it as "a regular winter visitor in small numbers".

This was very much the situation until the late 1960s, after which the wintering numbers declined rapidly – see Fig 6. Before 1970 numbers increased during periods of severe winter cold as the regular wintering population was augmented by influxes, but today this species tends to occur only during very cold spells. In the earlier years the most obvious cold weather influxes occurred during January–February 1950 (c.87) and February 1956 (c.83) with surprisingly low numbers during the severe winter of 1962/63 (c.26). In recent years there were impressive arrivals during cold spells in early 1985 (c.50), early 1986 (c.37), early 1987 (c.62) and during 1996/97 (c.66), but much smaller influxes were recorded during the hard weather of early 1979 (c.11), winter 1981/82 (c.12) and February 1991 (c.26).

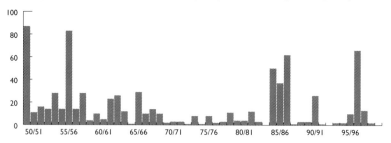

Fig 6. Annual totals 1949–1999

Poole Harbour and the Fleet are traditionally the main sites for the species – see Table 64. During the 1950s there was a regular wintering population based in the Wareham Channel area of Poole Harbour. Numbers were generally small with winter maxima only exceeding 20 birds during periods of very cold weather, notably in January 1950 when a county record of 60–80 birds were present on 28th, and February 1956 when c.50 were counted. Regular wintering in Poole Harbour ceased after 1962/63, but the Fleet at Abbotsbury remained an important site for Smew up to 1968/69, the most notable counts being 32 on 12th February 1956 (during cold weather), 27 on 13th February 1966, 22 on 16th March 1958 and 21 on 14th January 1962 and 17th March 1963. The high numbers in mid-March 1958 and 1963 may have involved migrants rather than wintering birds. Although regular wintering in the county had ceased by 1970, both Poole Harbour and the Fleet have continued to be favoured sites for the species, the highest counts being in January 1987 with 15 at Holton Shore on 22nd and up to 12 at Abbotsbury during 12th–24th.

	49/50	50/51	51/52	52/53	53/54	54/55	55/56	56/57	57/58	58/59
Poole Harbour	80	8	16	11	20	13	50	12	6	4
The Fleet	4	2	0	3	5	0	32	1	22	0

	59/60	60/61	61/62	62/63	63/64	64/65	65/66	66/67	67/68	68/69
Poole Harbour	10	5	1	5	2	0	1	0	1	0
The Fleet	0	0	21	21	10	0	27	10	10	10

Table 64. Winter maxima from Poole Harbour and the Fleet 1949–1969

Elsewhere the Smew is most frequently recorded from Portland Harbour (maximum of 13 on 25th January 1963), Radipole NR (maximum of 11 on 11th January 1997), Lodmoor NR (maximum of five in January 1985 and on 11th January 1987), Christchurch Harbour (maximum of ten on 9th January 1985), the Lower Avon (maximum of seven during January–February 1987) and the River Stour between Corfe Mullen and Sturminster Marshall (maximum of 12 on 28th February 1986). There are also reports from West Bexington, Weymouth Bay, Buddens GP, Hatch Pond, Moors Valley CP, Sturminster Marshall GP, Crichel Lake and Sherborne Lake (maximum of five in January 1985).

Coastal movements are very rare, the only records being from Portland Bill with 1W on 8th December 1980, 1W on 9th November 1982 and 1N on 3rd January 1997, Durlston CP with 1E on 11th December

1988, 1E on 16th November 1989 and 2E on 31st December 1996, Hengistbury with 2E on 7th February 1991 and 1E on 20th February 1996, and nearby Southbourne with 1E on 16th February 1975.

The vast majority of birds occur between November and mid-March. There are very few reports for October, the earliest being 3rd–4th October 1965 at Lodmoor NR, whilst the latest record is of a pair in Poole Harbour on 31st March 1955.

The Smew breeds in the forest zone from north-east Scandinavia eastwards across much of north-eastern Europe and northern Asia. It has a scattered winter range, mainly in parts of central and south-eastern Europe, and west-central and eastern Asia. The main wintering area in western Europe is the Netherlands. In the British Isles, the Smew mainly winters in south-east England and during periods of severe cold weather the normal population is enhanced by influxes from the Continent.

Postscript 2000–2002
Annual totals were a minimum of five birds in 2000, a single bird in 2001, and three singles in 2002.

Sponsored by Mrs Joy MacFadyen

Red-breasted Merganser   *Mergus serrator*

A locally common winter visitor and passage migrant

Mansel-Pleydell (1888) described this species as "a regular winter visitant" and referred to flocks of a hundred or more being seen together in the harbours. Blathwayt (1945) stated that it is frequent off Poole Harbour and on the Fleet in flocks of up to 30 and sometimes many more.

Since 1950 Poole Harbour and the Fleet/Portland Harbour area have remained the main wintering sites – see Table 65. Numbers at both sites increased substantially during the 1970s, and have continued to increase with winter maxima ranging between 300–550 birds since 1984/85, the highest being 550 (a county record) in Portland Harbour/East Fleet in March 1999 with 500 in Portland Harbour on 15th January 1997, and 535 in Poole Harbour on 16th December 1979 with 528 there on 15th December 1985.

	1950s	1960s	1970s	1980s	1990s
Poole Harbour	131	155	310	330	398
The Fleet/Portland Harbour	58	98	262	325	416

Table 65. Winter 10-year average peak counts at the main sites 1950–1999

In Poole Harbour, the dawn and dusk movements of birds flying in and out of the harbour mouth were first noted in December 1953 and continued well into the 1980s. It was traditionally assumed that birds were flying out to roost in Studland Bay and the sea beyond, but night fishing is another possibility. The fly-out at dusk was often relatively leisurely, whereas the fly-in at dawn was concentrated into about an hour with the birds in larger flocks. Counts for the period 1972 to 1982 show that numbers flying out peaked in November and declined during December and January, with a smaller secondary peak during February–April – see Table 66. A similar pattern was also noted in 1984/85, but the numbers roosting at sea, even in November, were much lower with birds preferring to roost in the centre of the harbour north of Fitzworth. The peaks in November and February–April suggest that Poole Harbour is used as a staging post for autumn and spring passage birds moving to and from wintering sites further west, including the Fleet/Portland Harbour area where peak counts are not usually reached until December. Since 1990 roosting at sea has seemingly become very sporadic, but 81 were counted at the Studland Bay roost on 2nd December 1995 with 34 there on 15th November 1997. In 1996 small numbers of Portland Harbour birds were noted roosting in Weymouth Bay with a peak of 21 on 3rd February, whilst there are counts from this site of 53 on 21st February 1985 and 25 on 27th November 1982.

	November	December	January	February	March–April
1972–1982	228	182	100	140	110
1984–1985	97	61	43	36	100

Table 66. Average dawn/dusk counts at Poole Harbour Entrance 1972–1982 and 1984–1985

Red-breasted Mergansers occur in Christchurch Harbour fairly regularly, but in very small numbers with winter maxima rarely exceeding ten, the highest counts being 28 in November 1992, 17 in December 1992, 14 in December 1993 and 12 in March 1998. There are frequent sightings from Radipole and Lodmoor NRs, mainly involving 1–2 birds, but there were five at Radipole NR on 19th January 1985. The species is occasionally recorded from West Bexington and Kimmeridge Bay, but generally there are very few reports of settled birds from the more exposed stretches of the coast.

Coastal movements occur at times of passage and during the winter with distinct peaks in April and November – see Table 67. These movements are predominantly easterly in spring, but more evenly balanced in the autumn and early winter. Most records come from Portland Bill, Durlston CP and Hengistbury, but there are reports from West Bexington, the Chesil and St Aldhelm's Head. At Portland Bill movements are mainly restricted to spring and autumn suggesting that these mainly involve long-distance migrants, whilst the greater volume of passage at Durlston CP is most apparent during the autumn and winter when many records may refer to local wintering birds. Day-counts are small and rarely exceed ten birds, the highest being 39W and 13E at Hengistbury on 9th November 1975 and 24 at Durlston CP on 9th November 1989.

Jan	Feb	Mar	Apr	May	Jun	Jul	Aug	Sep	Oct	Nov	Dec
11%	5%	9%	21%	4%	0%	<1%	<1%	<1%	13%	22%	13%

Table 67. Monthly coastal movements (%) at Portland Bill and Durlston CP 1987–1999

There are a surprising number of inland records:

1977   River Piddle at Wareham: 20th–24th February
1979   River Stour at Corfe Mullen: male with a female Goosander 1st March
1980   Milton Abbas Lake: 1st–8th December
1985   Milton Abbas Lake: two 21st February
1987   River Frome at East Stoke: 20th January
            Milton Abbas Lake: two 9th December
1995   River Stour between Corfe Mullen and Sturminster Marshall: 7th–8th February
1998   River Piddle: two pairs 15th–28th February

Although the bulk of the winter population arrives during October, there are a few early records for August and September. Most birds depart during April, but a few linger well into May. Very occasionally there are substantial counts in early May, e.g. 42 on the Fleet at Langton Herring on 5th May 1980. There are also records for the mid-summer period (June–July) in 1968, 1969, 1978–1981, 1985–1987, 1991, 1993, 1994 and 1996–1999.

The Red-breasted Merganser breeds across the Holarctic including the north-west British Isles, and winters mainly on the coasts of Europe south to the Mediterranean, east Asia, and North America south to the Gulf of Mexico.

Goosander   *Mergus merganser*

An uncommon winter visitor and passage migrant

Mansel-Pleydell (1888) considered the Goosander to be a not infrequent visitor to the estuaries and tidal harbours during the winter months, but a good deal less common than the Red-breasted Merganser, and referred to an early record of a pair shot at Bryanston in 1776. Blathwayt (1945) described it as "a not very rare winter visitor" to the coast and inland waters.

From the 1950s through to the late 1970s the Goosander was generally a very scarce winter visitor, which was prone to modest increases during periods of cold weather – see Fig 7. Subsequently both the size of these cold weather influxes and the numbers present in relatively mild winters have increased. In earlier years there was a notable cold weather influx in February 1956 (c.43), but like the Smew, numbers were surprisingly low (c.28) during the severe winter of 1962/63. More recently there were impressive cold weather arrivals during 1978/79 (c.102), early 1985 (c.98), early 1987 (c.121) and 1996/97 (c.102). It should be noted that not all recent cold spells have resulted in such influxes, for example in February 1991 only six birds were recorded.

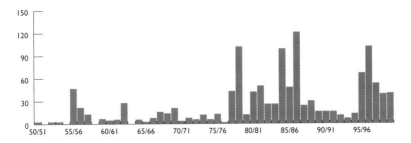

Fig 7. Annual totals 1950–1999

At Sherborne Lake a regular wintering flock became established from about 1978 to at least 1990 with sporadic records subsequently, the highest counts being 42 on 25th January 1985 and 34 in February 1987 – see Table 68. Annual reports since 1977/78 suggest that very small numbers may regularly winter along the River Stour between Wimborne and Blandford. Most sightings involve 1–3 birds, but an exceptional flock of 45 (a county record) was present at Corfe Mullen during a period of severe cold weather on 8th January 1979, the next highest count being 23 at Sturminster Marshall on 4th January 1997. There were occasional reports from earlier years including 23 at Corfe Mullen on 12th February 1956.

77/78	78/79	79/80	80/81	81/82	82/83	83/84	84/85	85/86	86/87	87/88
16	12	0	17	11	11	13	42	13	34	5

88/89	89/90	90/91	91/92	92/93	93/94	94/95	95/96	96/97	97/98	98/99
10	3	1	2	4	0	0	12	15	1	2

Table 68. Winter maxima at Sherborne Lake 1977–1999

Although wintering has not occurred regularly elsewhere in the county, the species is frequently recorded from Poole Harbour, the Weymouth area, and Christchurch Harbour and the Lower Avon. Poole Harbour is a traditional site with records in most winters since the early 1950s. Birds have occurred throughout the harbour area including Shell/Studland Bays, Little Sea, Brand's Bay, Arne NR, the Wareham Channel, Lytchett Bay, Holes Bay, Brownsea, Sandbanks, Poole Park and Hatch Pond, Poole. Numbers are generally small, the highest counts being up to c.20 at Arne NR and Hamworthy in February 1956, up to 20 at Arne NR during 17th–20th January 1987, 17 in Studland Bay on 5th April 1957 and 14 in the South Haven area on 15th and 16th November 1955. In the Weymouth area most reports are from Radipole NR and the Fleet, but there are sightings from Lodmoor NR, Weymouth Bay and Portland Harbour. Again numbers are usually small, the highest counts being 27 at Radipole NR on 6th January 1979 with 20W there on 30th December 1962, and up to 18 at East Fleet during 11th–18th January 1987. The species has been recorded from Christchurch Harbour and the Lower Avon in most winters since the mid-1970s, the best count being 17 at the former site during 1st–8th January 1997.

Crichel Lake was a favoured inland site between 1950 and 1980, but less so subsequently, with up to seven birds wintering in 1968/69 and again in 1969/70. There are also reports from various sites along the River Frome including East Stoke where up to ten were present in January 1987. Elsewhere there are records from other inland sites scattered across the county. A male on the River Char at Charmouth from 21st January to 8th April 1970 and two in Kimmeridge Bay on 15th January 1987 are noteworthy coastal sightings.

Coastal movements are occasionally recorded with peaks in January (associated with cold weather influxes), and at times of passage in spring (April–May) and autumn (October–November) – see Table 69. Counts are generally very small, the most notable being nine at Durlston CP on 24th October 1995, 9W at Hengistbury on 9th November 1997 with 7E and 1W there on 30th November 1980, and seven at Portland Bill on 10th October 1957.

Jan	Feb	Mar	Apr	May	Jun	Jul	Aug	Sep	Oct	Nov	Dec
46	3	5	20	13	2	0	0	0	17	36	8

Table 69. Monthly totals for coastal movements 1950–1999

The majority of birds occur between November and March. There are a few reports for October, the earliest being 6th October 1957 in Poole Harbour. Wintering birds occasionally linger into April, the latest being a long-staying individual that remained at Christchurch Harbour from January to 1st May 1984. There are rather more reports involving coastal passage in April and early May, the latest being at Hengistbury on 11th May 1987. There are only three later records involving one at Christchurch Harbour on 31st May 1997, 2W at Hengistbury on 11th June 1988 and one at Sturminster Marshall on 22nd June 1997.

The Goosander breeds across much of northern Eurasia including north-western Great Britain with isolated populations as far south as Switzerland and Tibet, also in northern North America. The Eurasian population winters mainly in north-west, central and south-east Europe, and central and eastern Asia.

Postscript 2000–2002

An intriguing set of records in 2000 involving eight flying out of Christchurch Harbour on 8th August, followed by four at Sturminster Marshall GP on 20th August, four nearby on the River Stour at Sturminster Marshall on 30th August with two there on 17th September, three at Lytchett Bay on 28th August with two there on 4th September, and two at Moors Valley CP on an unspecified date in September. These are the first August and September records for Dorset. The reports from Sturminster Marshall and Lytchett Bay at least included some juvenile birds, which is strongly suggestive of local breeding. Interestingly the species has bred nearby in Hampshire in recent years. There were further late summer/early autumn reports from Christchurch Harbour in 2002 with nine on 20th July, eight on 10th August and two on 23rd September. Singles at Hengistbury on 5th October 2000 and Blacknor, Portland on 14th May 2001 are unseasonal records.

Ruddy Duck   *Oxyura jamaicensis*

An uncommon feral winter visitor and passage migrant – has bred

The first records of this introduced American species were from Sutton Bingham during June–July and November–December 1969, followed by singles at Sherborne Lake on 8th–9th August 1975, and Radipole NR on 30th January 1977 and 5th–6th December 1978. In 1979 there was a marked cold weather influx during January–February. At Radipole NR numbers increased from three on 20th January to a peak of 12 on 16th February with two pairs remaining into April, one pair until 30th May and a female until 21st August. Elsewhere, there were up to six on the Fleet during January–February with one during 14th–21st March, four in Poole Park on 6th January with one on 10th March, and one at Christchurch Harbour on 1st January.

Since 1980 the Ruddy Duck has been recorded annually with further cold weather influxes in 1981/82 (c.100), early 1985 (c.34) and January 1997 (c.31) – see Table 70. The influx during December 1981–January 1982 was particularly impressive with peak counts in January of 29 at Radipole NR on 17th, 23 at Abbotsbury on 27th, 16 at Arne NR on 17th and ten at Christchurch Harbour during 10th–17th. In early 1985 the best counts were 14 at Abbotsbury on 13th January and ten at Radipole NR during 20th–24th February. Otherwise all counts have been in single figures.

79/80	80/81	81/82	82/83	83/84	84/85	85/86	86/87	87/88	88/89
7	3	c100	8	1	34	8	7	6	17

89/90	90/91	91/92	92/93	93/94	94/95	95/96	96/97	97/98	98/99
11	23	7	8	9	6	13	44	8	18

Table 70. Winter totals 1979–1999

Radipole NR is the main site for the species, whilst other favoured localities include the Fleet (mainly Abbotsbury), Poole Harbour (mainly Little Sea and Arne NR), Christchurch Harbour, Sherborne Lake and in recent years both Crichel Lake and nearby Wimborne St Giles Park. There are also reports from other coastal and inland sites scattered throughout the county.

At Radipole NR birds either summered or lingered into late spring in 1979, 1980 and during 1985–1988 followed by single pairs breeding in 1989 (raising five young), 1990 (raising two young) and 1991 (unsuccessful). Although birds were recorded during the summers of 1992 and 1995, there has been no further evidence of breeding at this site. At Wimborne St Giles Park up to four birds have been present during the summers of 1997–1999 with breeding confirmed in 1998 when two pairs reared five young. At nearby Crichel Lake birds were recorded in July 1995, and during May–July 1998 when up to three males and two females were present in May suggesting that breeding may have also been attempted at this site. Otherwise there are late spring and summer records from Sherborne Lake during 1987–1989, Abbotsbury in 1989 and 1993, and Moors Valley CP in 1992 and 1994.

The Ruddy Duck is native to North and South America. In Great Britain pinioned birds first bred at Slimbridge in 1949 and the young escaped to form a feral population based mainly in the West Midlands.

Postscript 2000–2002

At Lodmoor NR a pair produced seven young in 2001 and two pairs reared ten young in 2002 – these are the first reports of successful breeding in the county since 1998 and only the 4th and 5th ever. In 2000, 1–2 birds summered at Wimborne St Giles Park with seven in September, which may indicate local breeding. Elsewhere, there were exceptionally high counts of up to 25 birds at Abbotsbury during July–August 2002.

Black Grouse   *Tetrao tetrix*

A former uncommon resident, now long extinct

Mansel-Pleydell (1888) regarded this species as a very local resident of 'preserved' heaths such as those between Alderholt and Knighton where a few broods were reared annually. There were also occasional sightings from Chamberlayne's and Hyde Heaths, and reports of a nest on Bloxworth Heath in 1872 and one shot at Hamworthy in November 1876. Earlier in the 19th Century, when the species was more plentiful, Colonel Hawker relates how in one day the 'guns' at Uddens found eleven and shot eight brace.

The Black Grouse was virtually extinct in Dorset by 1900, the last records being near West Moors in November 1925 and at Trigon a little later. These may have involved birds from the New Forest where attempts at reintroduction were made without success.

The Black Grouse breeds across much of Scandinavia, eastern Europe and northern Asia with fragmented populations in central Europe and the Alps. In Great Britain, as elsewhere, there is a continuing decline in population, particularly in the southern part of its range.

Red-legged Partridge   *Alectoris rufa*

A common resident, augmented by releases

Although the first record of this species concerns a bird shot near Upwey prior to 1799, it does not seem to have gained a permanent foothold in the county before the beginning of the 20th Century. Since then the Red-legged Partridge has become well-established, though aided by frequent, widespread and often large-scale introductions. During the Second World War these introductions were halted, but viable populations remained on the central and northern chalk, and some heathlands.

The *BTO Atlas* (1968–1972) found evidence of breeding in 25 (68%) 10-km squares (confirmed in 18, probable in four and possible in three). The species showed a bias towards the east of the county, the most notable absences being in the extreme west (ST30, SY39, SY48 and SY49), parts of the Blackmore Vale (ST51, ST71 and ST72) and more surprisingly north of Dorchester in SY69 and ST60.

Since 1970 introductions of Chukar and Chukar X Red-legged Partridge hybrids have been widespread and since the two species hybridise in the wild, it is uncertain how many pure Red-legged Partridges remain. In view of the similarity of the two species and the presence of hybrids, no attempt was made to differentiate between them during the Tetrad Survey (1987–1994), which revealed evidence of breeding in 33 (89%) of the pre-1974 10-km squares (confirmed in 24 and probable in nine). This does not represent a natural expansion in range. Indeed breeding success in Dorset is low and easily affected adversely by wet or cold summers when many young birds die soon after hatching. Since 1992, the further introduction of Chukars has become illegal and this

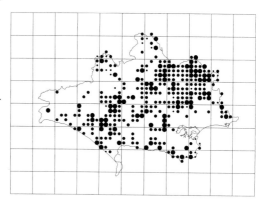

may result in a more hardy stock. Reports of breeding success can be misleading as introduced birds are often released at seven to eight weeks of age.

The Tetrad Map shows that breeding occurs widely throughout the county except for the extreme west, where it remains largely absent, parts of the Blackmore Vale, Portland and the Bournemouth and Poole conurbation. The greatest concentration of breeding occurs on the Central and Northern Chalk in particular on Cranborne Chase. Generally the species avoids the damper clay vales and shows a preference for the drier habitats found on the chalk, limestone (Purbeck and North Dorset), and some heathland areas.

There are occasional sightings away from the breeding areas including five records of 1–3 birds at Portland since 1980, two at Radipole NR on 10th May 1982 (first for the reserve) with one there from 17th–20th March 1985, and singles at Lodmoor NR on 16th November 1985, and Hengistbury on 2nd May 1984 and 24th April 1993. A Chukar X Red-legged Partridge pair bred at Stanpit Marsh, Christchurch Harbour in 1981 and 1982.

The highest counts in recent years are 100 at Ibberton Hill on 27th October 1989 and 66 at Winterborne Houghton on 14th October 1992.

Only one bird has been ringed in the county.

The Red-legged Partridge, which is a resident of western Europe (mainly France and Iberia), was introduced to Great Britain during the 18th Century. Aided by further frequent introductions, it is now well-established and widely distributed over much of southern and eastern England. In recent years the pure stock has been adulterated by introductions of Chukar and Chukar X Red-legged Partridge hybrids.

Grey Partridge   *Perdix perdix*

An uncommon and declining resident

Both Mansel-Pleydell (1888) and Blathwayt (1945) described this species as "resident and generally distributed", the former commenting that "its numbers obviously increased by the protection afforded it by game-preservers", whilst the latter mentions that it is "probably more numerous along the Wilts and Hants borders than in the west of the county". Between 1918 and 1939 Grey Partridges, often of Hungarian origin, were widely introduced to augment wild stocks. Scattered introductions continue to this day, but most shoots now prefer the Red-legged Partridge because it is less prone to straying.

The *BTO Atlas* (1968–1972) revealed evidence of breeding in 34 (92%) 10-km squares (confirmed in 33 and possible in one). By contrast the Tetrad Survey (1987–1994) found evidence of breeding in only 27 (73%) of the pre-1974 10-km squares (confirmed in 22 and probable in five), the main absences being in the west of the county (ST30, ST40, ST50, SY39 and SY48) and the extreme south-east (SZ08). The Tetrad Map shows that breeding is concentrated on the chalk downs with smaller populations on the

North Dorset Limestone Ridges around Sherborne and the Purbeck limestone plateau. Elsewhere the species is very sparsely distributed, being absent from the extreme west and much of the central and southern areas of the Poole Basin.

The decline in both range and population is clearly continuing and the Grey Partridge has now gone from some areas where it was found during the Tetrad Survey (1987–1994). For example, none were recorded from the St Aldhelm's Head area in 1995 and the Gillingham area in 1996. By the late 1990s, the chalk downlands in the north-east of the county were the last remaining stronghold for the species in Dorset.

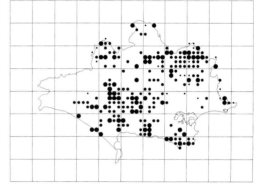

CBC data shows the decline of national breeding stocks between 1968–1972 and 1988–1991 as approximately 75% and the situation is probably similar in Dorset. The main cause of this dramatic decline is thought to be the widespread use of agricultural herbicides. These destroy the plants hosting the insects, particularly sawflies, on which the Grey Partridge feeds. Warm and dry weather around hatching time in mid-June is also very important to chick survival and temporary recoveries, as in 1960 and 1961, were probably attributable to this factor. The bag returns from a large shoot near Blandford during the 20th Century, which represents the 'shootable surplus' over a minimum breeding stock, clearly illustrates this decline. As on other shoots, efforts would have been made to increase the stock by predator control and habitat provision. Much work has been done by the Game Conservancy to determine the causes of decline and to find possible remedies. The traditional undersowing of cereal crops with grass seeds and the leaving of unsprayed headlands around field boundaries have been found to be very beneficial. The introduction of non-rotational 'set-aside' should also prove advantageous, but unless these practices are widely implemented the future for the Grey Partridge must be bleak.

Straying birds occasionally appear away from the breeding areas. Since 1980 there have been sightings from Radipole NR with two on 6th February 1981 and one on 8th April 1982, and Lodmoor NR in 1985 with eight on 9th January, one on 18th February and two on 15th March representing the first records for the site. One on 15th March 1985 was the first for Radipole School and one was present at Portland Bill intermittently from 11th November 1990–17th March 1991 with another on 24th September 1993. In addition, a flock of 23 at Lytchett Bay on 20th October 1999 is a notable report, particularly since it was the first for the area since the early 1980s.

Most high counts in recent years range between 10–20 birds, the highest being 34 at St Aldhelm's Head on 6th October 1984.

The Grey Partridge is resident across much of Europe from southern parts of Sweden and Finland south to the Pyrenees, Italy and Asia Minor and eastwards into west-central Asia. There is an introduced population in North America. It is a declining species in the British Isles.

Postscript 2000–2002

The status of the species in Dorset remains precarious with most reports from traditional sites on the chalk downs between Maiden Castle and Sixpenny Handley. At Hengistbury, one on 8th March 2001 is a notable record.

Quail (Common Quail) *Coturnix coturnix*

An uncommon summer visitor and passage migrant

The past status of the Quail in Dorset is rather vague. At the end of the 18th Century it was described as formerly very common, but now rare, whilst Mansel-Pleydell (1888) just referred to the species as being a summer migrant with a few remaining in winter. Blathwayt (1945) considered it to be a scarce summer resident, occasionally seen in winter.

    No mention is made of the widely fluctuating numbers reaching the British Isles annually, which is such a feature of recent times. This is clearly reflected in the annual totals for Dorset since 1950 – see Fig 8. The exceptional influx of 1989 produced at least 73 calling males at 37 sites with the majority of records (66 calling males) from the chalk areas. These included 6–9 males near Doles Hill Plantation, whilst 15 (presumably a family party) were reported from Little Bredy on 24th July. Good numbers were also recorded in 1964, 1967, 1970, 1982, 1987, 1988, 1992, 1994 and 1995. Some of these 'good Quail years' have resulted in notable concentrations of birds including eight or nine flushed from a field at Compton Valence in 1970 and six males at Southwell, Portland during May–early June of the same year, up to six males near Doles Hill Plantation in late July 1982, and up to ten males in the Bottlebush Down/Ackling Dyke area during 10th June–8th July 1995. The 1989 influx followed two good years, which suggests that birds bred in Dorset may show a tendency to return the following year. Other factors affecting influxes may include weather, with warm south-easterly winds considered favourable, the previous year's breeding success, and the degree of mortality on the wintering grounds and during passage.

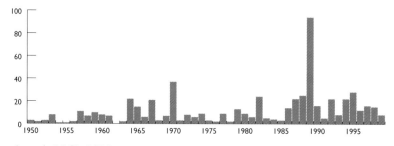

Fig 8. Annual totals 1950–1999

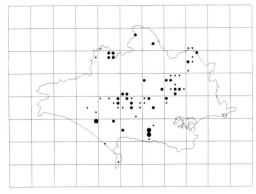

The majority of records are from the chalk and limestone uplands where the preferred habitat is cereal crops, notably barley, rather than grass. This is reflected by both the *BTO Atlas* (1968–1972) and Tetrad Survey (1987–1994) as shown by the Tetrad Map. Traditionally certain areas are particularly attractive to Quail. These include the chalk downs immediately to the west of Dorchester around Maiden Castle and Compton Valence, and those in the extreme north-east of Cranborne Chase around Pentridge and Bottlebush Down. It is also interesting that during two influx years, there were notable concentrations of calling males near Doles Hill Plantation. The species is largely absent from the Poole Basin, Blackmore Vale and far west of the county. Quail are secretive birds and breeding is extremely difficult to prove and must be much commoner than the records suggest.

Passage birds are occasionally recorded from coastal sites, mainly Portland, but there are reports from Radipole and Lodmoor NRs, St Aldhelm's Head, Durlston CP and Christchurch Harbour. The seasonal pattern of occurrences has changed markedly at Portland, being evenly spread between spring and autumn prior to 1976, but with spring reports predominating subsequently – see Table 71. The earliest spring arrivals are 1st April 1989 when one was found dead at Radipole NR, and 5th–6th April 1986 at Portland Bill, whilst the latest reports involve birds, possibly the same individual that subsequently overwintered, at Portland Bill on 25th October and 1st November 1979.

	Apr	May	Jun	Jul	Aug	Sept	Oct
1950–1975	1	11	4	2	8	9	1
1976–1996	9	22	10	2	1	0	3

Table 71. Monthly totals from Portland 1950–1975 and 1976–1999

There are six winter records as follows:

1957 Near Blandford: seven early March.
1958 Gussage St Michael: 6th December
1967 Netherbury: 9th January–28th March
1980 Portland Bill: 12th January; perhaps the bird recorded on 1st November 1979
1988 Puddletown: two 15th January with one still present 8th February
1993 Near Winterborne Stickland: 31st December

Only one bird has been ringed in the county.

The Quail breeds from north-west Africa through much of Europe north to Great Britain and southern Scandinavia, extending eastwards to the Middle East and central Asia east to China and south to the northern Indian sub-continent. It winters from the Mediterranean south to sub-Saharan Africa and throughout the Indian sub-continent. Another race breeds in tropical and southern Africa. The species occurs as a scarce summer visitor and passage migrant throughout the British Isles.

Postscript 2000–2002
There were only two records in 2000, the lowest annual total since 1978, followed by 12 records involving 13 birds in 2001, and 24 records in 2002 including 17 from Maiden Castle (maximum of five calling birds). One at Abbotsbury on 14th September 2002 was the first record for the site.

Pheasant (Common Pheasant)   *Phasianus colchicus*

An abundant resident

The Pheasant was certainly present in the British Isles at the time of the Norman Conquest and since then there have been many further introductions involving a variety of races. In Dorset the commonest of these

races are the nominate *P. c. colchicus*, the Mongolian Pheasant *P. c. mongolicus*, the Chinese Ring-necked Pheasant *P. c. torquatus* and the 'melanistic mutant' *'tenebrosus'*. Additionally, Japanese Green Pheasants *P. versicolor* were introduced at Nether Cerne in about 1968 where they hybridised freely with *P. colchicus*.

The *BTO Atlas* (1968–1972) revealed evidence of breeding in 35 (95%) 10-km squares (confirmed in 32, probable in one and possible in two), whilst the Tetrad Survey (1987–1994) produced virtually the same result with evidence of breeding in 34 (92%) of the pre-1974 10-km squares (confirmed in 30 and probable in four). The Tetrad Map shows that breeding is widespread throughout the county except for Portland and the Bournemouth and Poole conurbation.

The abundance of Pheasants is largely the result of massive and continuing introductions for shooting. Although one can only speculate as to how the species would have fared without these introductions, small and apparently viable populations exist well away from release areas. Furthermore, it survived in fair numbers during the Second World War when no introductions took place.

The Pheasant adapts well to a variety of habitats except for the larger towns and open heaths. Breeding success is far greater in warm and dry summers, and where predators such as foxes are controlled.

The nominate race is indigenous to Transcaucasia, northern Asia Minor, northern Iran and perhaps Bulgaria. There are 22–31 sub-species, which range from south-east Russia north to the Aral Sea, Mongolia and Manchuria, east to Korea, Japan and Taiwan, and south to Burma and China. It has been introduced to most of northern, central and parts of southern Europe as well as North America, New Zealand and elsewhere. The Pheasant is common and widespread over much of the British Isles except the far north and west of Scotland.

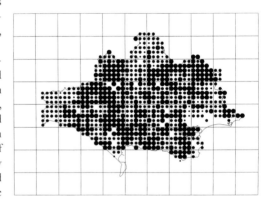

Golden Pheasant
Chrysolophus pictus

A scarce introduced resident of islands in Poole Harbour

The first introduction to Poole Harbour was on Green Island in the late 1950s and birds spread naturally from there to Furzey Island. In 1962 the species was introduced to Brownsea Island, where there is now a well-established and stable population thought to number about 30 pairs. Young birds are seen almost every year and the absence of foxes on the island is thought to contribute to breeding success. Rhododendrons are the most favoured habitat, but it is possible that the present policy of clearing large areas of this shrub may have a detrimental effect on the species.

The size of the population on Furzey Island is not known, but ten or more birds are sometimes seen together. There are no Golden Pheasants remaining on Green Island, which is surprising in view of the presence of apparently suitable habitat. Elsewhere the species is occasionally recorded as an escape.

The Golden Pheasant is native to the mountains of central China. There have been many introductions to Great Britain since the middle of the 19th Century, and feral populations have established themselves in a number of counties, particularly Norfolk.

Red-throated Diver

Gavia stellata

An uncommon winter visitor and passage migrant

One shot at Weymouth after a storm in 1795 would appear to be the first record for Dorset. Both Mansel-Pleydell (1888) and Blathwayt (1945) considered this species to be a common winter visitor to the coast, the former referring to it as the 'Sprat Loon' from its habit of accompanying or following shoals of Sprats in October.

Since 1950 the main wintering areas for settled birds have been Poole Bay/Poole Harbour, Portland Harbour/Weymouth Bay and more recently Lyme Bay – mainly between Abbotsbury Beach and Burton Bradstock. Numbers are generally small with winter maxima usually ranging from 1–8 birds, the highest counts for each of these areas being 34 in Poole Bay at Hengistbury on 25th December 1988, 22 in Lyme Bay between Abbotsbury Beach and West Bexington during 27th–30th December 1991 and ten in Weymouth Bay on 4th January 1986 – although there is a higher spring count of 16 in Portland Harbour on 28th March 1955. At Christchurch Harbour, most birds are seen off Hengistbury in Poole Bay with only occasional sightings, usually involving 1–2 individuals, from inside the harbour itself. Elsewhere there are scattered reports of settled birds from the Purbeck coast, usually in small numbers, but there are high counts of 29 feeding on sprats at Peveril Point on 30th December 1963 and 15 at Winspit on 7th December 1992. There are relatively few records from the Fleet.

A feature of the winter records is that high counts are invariably short-lived and even single birds often move on quickly. This suggests a highly mobile winter population, an impression supported by substantial mid-winter movements – see below. In Lyme Bay between Abbotsbury Beach and Burton Bradstock, higher counts, such as those in December 1994, usually coincide with offshore winds when inshore waters are relatively calm. It is possible that winter movements refer to birds moving to sheltered waters in response to changing wind conditions.

The Red-throated is by far the commonest of the divers passing the main coastal watch-points – see Table 72. The seasonal pattern indicates a negligible autumn passage overlapping with heavier winter movements, which are mainly westerly and vary considerably in strength between years, followed by a modest and predominantly easterly passage in spring – see Table 73. Winter movements account for the greatest proportion of overall passage at all three sites, being highest at Hengistbury (84%) and lowest at Portland Bill (60%). Heavy winter movements occurred on 7th January 1995 with 88 at Portland Bill and 60 at Durlston CP, also 46 at the former site the following day. Other high day-counts include 59 at Portland Bill on 8th January 1994, 38 at Durlston CP on 9th January 1988 and 21st December 1992 with 37 there on 17th January 1987, and 38 at Hengistbury on 1st December 1990.

	Red-throated Diver	Black-throated Diver	Great Northern Diver
Portland Bill	4494	1085	301
Durlston CP	3260	1600	1271
Hengistbury	902	234	243

Table 72. Totals for the three common divers spp at the main coastal watch-points 1980–1999

	Autumn: Aug–Oct	Winter: Nov–Feb	Spring: Mar–Jun
Portland Bill	1%	60%	39%
Durlston CP	3%	72%	25%
Hengistbury	1%	84%	15%

Table 73. Seasonal distribution of Red-throated Diver (%) at the main coastal watch-points 1980–1999

Spring movements extend from March to June with a peak in April, and at Portland Bill account for a greater proportion of overall passage than at the other two main sites – see Table 73. This may reflect the fact that long- distance spring migrants pass further from shore than birds making relatively local winter movements, and consequently are more likely to be observed from a promontory such as Portland Bill. The highest day-count during spring passage is 95E at Portland Bill on 4th April 1987. Elsewhere winter and spring movements are regularly recorded from various sites along the Chesil and the Purbeck coast, notably St Aldhelm's Head, the highest day-counts being 78W at St Aldhelm's Head on 2nd January 1964 and 27 at Winspit on 11th December 1998, whilst 15E in Weymouth Bay on 11th December 1990 is also a notable record.

The first birds in autumn typically appear in mid-September, occasionally in August, the earliest being 5th August 1978 at Hengistbury. The last spring migrants occur typically in late May and early June with the latest on 11th June 1986 in Weymouth Bay. There are very few records between these dates, namely at West Bexington for a week in mid-June 1975, Hengistbury on 23rd June 1980, Poole Harbour on 26th June 1961 and 6th July 1978, Shell Bay on 7th July 1988 and Portland Bill on 23rd July 1990.

The Red-throated is the most likely diver species to wander inland. Many records are from either near-coastal sites such as Radipole NR (c.15 including one over Radipole School), Lodmoor NR (five), Little Sea (c.15) and Poole Park (one) or the lower reaches of the main rivers, namely the Frome (five downstream from Wareham), Stour (two at Tuckton) and Lower Avon (three at Coward's Marsh). In addition, there are nine records from well inland:

1955	River Stour at Spetisbury: 13th February
1962	Sherborne: found dead 18th March
1970	Shillingstone: 23rd March
	Whitchurch Canonicorum: 5th November
1982	River Stour at Wimborne: 11th January
1983	Buddens GP: 21st February
1984	Sherborne Lake: 9th January–24th February
1985	Lower Avon at Sopley and Matchams: 20th February
1986	River Frome at Moreton: 2nd–4th March
	Woodbridge: 21st March

The Red-throated Diver breeds across northern Eurasia and northern North America south to between 55°N and 60°N and winters on the coasts of Europe, east Asia and North America. In the British Isles it breeds mainly in north-west Scotland and winters widely along the coasts.

Postscript 2000–2002
Records on unspecified dates in July 2000 at West Bexington and August 2001 at Ringstead are unseasonal. In 2002, there were two inland sightings involving singles at Sherborne Lake from 15th to 21st March when found dead, and Sturminster Marshall GP from 3rd to 8th December.

Black-throated Diver   *Gavia arctica*

An uncommon winter visitor and passage migrant

Mansel-Pleydell (1888) considered this species to be the least common of the divers, but noted that it appeared almost every winter at Weymouth and Poole. Blathwayt (1945) described it as "a rather scarce winter visitor to the coast".

Since 1950 the main wintering area for settled birds has been Portland Harbour/Weymouth Bay. Numbers are generally small with winter maxima usually ranging from 1–9 birds, the highest being from Portland Harbour with 16 on 31st January 1991 and 15 on 29th January 1986. During the 1950s and 1960s, this area appears to have been more important for birds on spring passage with the highest counts recorded between mid-March and mid-April, e.g. nine on 24th March 1957, up to six during 17th March–28th April 1961, six on 6th and 13th April 1962 and 11 on 25th March 1968. Since 1980 peak counts have occurred during the winter (December–February) period.

The Black-throated Diver is a rather scarce and sporadic visitor in winter to the Poole Bay/Poole Harbour area. The numbers of settled birds are very small with winter maxima typically ranging from 1–3 birds, the highest being five in Poole Bay in December 1988. Although the majority of records from Christchurch Harbour involve birds seen in Poole Bay off Hengistbury, the species occasionally wanders inside the harbour itself where most reports refer to singles, but four were recorded on 7th December 1992 and four in February 1997. Elsewhere there are occasional sightings of 1–2 settled birds from Lyme Bay – mainly between Abbotsbury Beach and Burton Bradstock, but it is a rarer visitor to the nearby Fleet, three at Langton Herring on 23rd November 1998 being most unusual. There are very few sightings of settled birds from the Purbeck coast.

Although the offshore movements of Black-throated Divers involve much smaller numbers than the previous species, the seasonal pattern is very similar, i.e. a negligible autumn passage overlapping with heavier winter movements, which are mainly westerly and vary considerably in strength between years, followed by a modest and predominantly easterly passage in spring – see Tables 72 and 74. Winter movements account for the greatest proportion of overall passage at all the three main coastal watch-points, being highest at Durlston CP (67%) and lowest at Portland Bill (51%). The highest winter day-counts are 27W at Portland Bill on 1st January 1978 with 23W there on 15th November 1992, 25 at Durlston CP on 7th January 1995 (cf previous species) and ten at Hengistbury on 1st January 1982. In earlier years, 14 flying west at Portland Bill in a 'loose pack' on 28th November 1961 was a notable record.

	Autumn: Aug–Oct	Winter: Nov–Feb	Spring: Mar–Jun
Portland Bill	2%	51%	47%
Durlston CP	4%	67%	29%
Hengistbury)	6%	52%	42%

Table 74. Seasonal distribution (%) at the main coastal watch-points 1980–1999

Spring movements extend from March to June and like the previous species, account for a greater proportion of overall passage at Portland Bill than at the other two main coastal watch-points – see Table 74. For an explanation of this – see Red-throated Diver. The highest day-count during spring passage is 35E at Portland Bill on 4th April 1987 (cf previous species). Elsewhere winter and spring movements are regularly recorded in small numbers from various sites along the Chesil and the Purbeck coast, notably St Aldhelm's Head.

The first birds in autumn usually appear in late September, the earliest being from Portland Bill on 16th August 1973 and 27th August 1978. The last spring migrants normally occur in late May, the latest being 13th June 1984 in Poole Bay and 14th June 1998 at Durlston CP. There are very few records between these dates, namely at Christchurch Harbour in July and early August 1977, Poole Harbour on 31st July and 1st August 1978, Osmington Mills on 26th July 1986 with perhaps the same bird at West Bexington on 3rd August, and two at Osmington Mills/Ringstead Bay on three dates between 27th June and 26th August 1994.

This species is very rare inland with only six records:

1969	Bindon Abbey: one caught on 23rd February and released at Studland
1979	Lodden Lakes near Gillingham: 23rd February
1985	Sherborne Lake: one in summer plumage 25th–26th January
1986	Coward's Marsh, Christchurch: 5th February
1989	Coward's Marsh, Christchurch: 15th and 17th December
1995	Hatch Pond, Poole: 21st–23rd January

In addition, there are reports from near-coastal sites such as Lodmoor NR on 1st February 1951 and Little Sea (at least once).

On 8th February 1962 a stranded adult bird was caught in Portland Harbour, ringed and released at Portland Bill.

The Black-throated Diver breeds across much of northern Eurasia and northern North America, but it is absent from Greenland, Iceland and Svalbard. In Asia breeding extends further south than the previous species, i.e. to between 45°N and 50°N. It winters along the coasts of Europe, east Asia and western North America. In Great Britain it breeds in north-west Scotland and winters widely along the coasts.

Postscript 2000–2002

Unseasonal sightings in 2000 involve a summering bird in Poole Bay, another in Weymouth Bay from 7th June to 5th July, and an early returning bird at Hengistbury on 16th August, whilst a single settled bird at Portland Bill on 27th July 2001 is the first mid-summer record for Portland. A winter maximum of seven in Poole Harbour in December 2000 is the highest count for Poole Bay/Poole Harbour since 1950.

Great Northern Diver   *Gavia immer*

An uncommon winter visitor and passage migrant

Both Mansel-Pleydell (1888) and Blathwayt (1945) considered this species to be a not uncommon winter visitor to the coast.

Since 1950 the main areas for settled birds have been Portland Harbour/Weymouth Bay and Poole Bay/Poole Harbour. Numbers are generally small with winter maxima usually ranging from 1–10 birds. Prior to 1998, the highest counts for each of these areas were 12–15 in Portland Harbour/Weymouth Bay on 27th December 1981, and 11 in Poole Bay between Bournemouth Pier and Southbourne on 7th March 1984. During the winter of 1998/99, however, exceptional numbers were reported with combined counts of 22 in Portland Harbour/Weymouth Bay on 29th January and 15 in Studland Bay/Poole Harbour on 2nd January. High numbers also occurred in late 1999 with 20 in Portland Harbour on 27th December, 11 in Weymouth Bay the following day, and up to 11 in Shell/Studland Bays during December. A spring peak of settled birds in the Weymouth Bay area has occurred during March–May in several recent years, and seems to involve at least some birds undertaking their pre-breeding moult and being rendered temporarily flightless. Counts rarely exceed seven birds, but there were nine at Osmington Mills on 18th March 1999 with eight there the following day. A similar phenomenon has also been noted occasionally in Poole Bay, the highest counts of settled birds being nine at Canford Cliffs on 11th April 1955, eight at Branksome Chine on 8th April 1985 and a maximum of eight in Poole Bay during April 1990. Like the previous two species, most reports from Christchurch Harbour involve birds seen in Poole Bay off Hengistbury with only a few sightings of mainly single birds from inside the harbour itself. Elsewhere along the coast there are occasional sightings of 1–3 settled birds from Lyme Bay – mainly between Abbotsbury Beach and Burton Bradstock, the Fleet and the Purbeck coast.

The Great Northern is the scarcest of the three species of diver passing the main coastal watch-points – see Table 72. The seasonal pattern at Durlston CP and Hengistbury is similar to the previous two species, i.e. a negligible autumn passage overlapping with heavier winter movements, which are followed by a more modest passage in spring – see Table 75. Winter day-counts are small and rarely reach double figures, the highest being 17 at Portland Bill on 3rd February 1966 with 15 there on 18th January 1964, and 15 at Durlston CP on 7th January 1995.

	Autumn: Aug–Oct	Winter: Nov–Feb	Spring: Mar–Jun
Portland Bill	5%	20%	75%
Durlston CP	4%	67%	28%
Hengistbury	1%	60%	39%

Table 75. Seasonal distribution (%) at the main coastal watch-points 1980–1999

At Portland Bill, however, movements are heaviest in spring and account for a much greater proportion of overall passage than at the other two main coastal watch-points – see Table 75. This tendency for a greater proportion of passage to occur in spring at Portland Bill is also shown by the previous two species of diver.

For an explanation of this – see Red-throated Diver. Unlike the previous two species, spring movements of Great Northern Divers are predominantly westerly in direction as would be expected given its north-western breeding distribution. There is some evidence to suggest that birds tend to move east earlier in the spring and west later in the season. Day-counts in spring are very small and rarely exceed five birds, the highest being six at Portland Bill on 16th April 1977. Elsewhere, winter and spring movements are recorded from various other sites along the Chesil and the Purbeck coast, notably St Aldhelm's Head.

The first birds in autumn usually appear during October, occasionally in September, the earliest being 24th August 1998 at Portland Bill. Spring passage often extends into early June, but there are very few sightings after mid-month. Apart from a remarkable bird which summered in Portland Harbour from 7th May to 7th August 1999, there are only three records between the extreme dates of 20th June and 24th August, namely singles at Hengistbury on an unspecified date in July 1976 and on 15th July 1982, and one in Weymouth Bay on 7th July 1990.

There are two inland records for the 19th Century involving one in spring 1862 at an undisclosed enclosed water owned by Lord Digby (presumably Sherborne Lake) and one obtained on Chettle Down (no date or year). Although there are no recent sightings from well inland, one flying from inland at Langton Herring on 30th March 1980, one flying over Godlingston Heath on 22nd December 1984 and one flying over Radipole NR on 7th May 1994 are unusual.

The Great Northern Diver breeds in northern North America, Greenland and Iceland, and winters along the coasts of north-west Europe and North America. Although it is mainly a winter visitor to the British Isles, the species has bred in Scotland.

Postscript 2000–2002

The high counts recorded from the main wintering areas during 1998/99 and 1999/2000 occurred again in 2000/01 with maxima of 20 in Portland Harbour in January 2001 and nine in Poole Harbour in December 2000. Nearby on the Fleet, a peak count of nine in February 2001 is very high for this site. Exceptional coastal passage was recorded from West Bexington in December 2000 involving 34 bird-days, maximum of 15E on 18th December–perhaps reflecting the high wintering numbers elsewhere in the county. Record counts also occurred during spring passage at Portland Bill in 2000 (31 birds), 2001 (30 birds) and 2002 (49 birds, maximum of 11 on 1st May). At Redcliffe Point, 12 settled birds on 20th April 2002 is the highest ever count for the spring gathering of moulting birds in Weymouth Bay. Finally there is an unseasonal report of one at Portland Bill on 29th June 2001.

Sponsored by W. G. Teagle

White-billed Diver (Yellow-billed Diver)   *Gavia adamsii*

Accidental: one record

1997   Portland Bill: 13th March

A winter-plumaged bird flew from east to west low past Portland Bird Observatory. A full account can be found in the Dorset Bird Report for 1997.

The White-billed Diver breeds in the Arctic Ocean from Siberia east to Alaska and northern Canada. Most winter in the North Pacific, but a minority travel west to winter off the coasts of Scandinavia. A vagrant to Great Britain with 233 records up to 2002.

Pied-billed Grebe   *Podilymbus podiceps*

Accidental: one record

1980   Radipole NR: 25th January to 4th February; same at Little Sea 10th February to at least 24th May

An adult in winter plumage was present at Radipole NR in January and early February. Subsequently it moved to Little Sea at Studland NNR where it remained well into the spring having attained full summer plumage. During its' stay on Little Sea, it established territory in a small well-vegetated inlet at the north end of the lake. In April and May the bird was frequently seen to display and its distinctive call could be heard from some distance away. A full account can be found in the Dorset Bird Report for 1980.

The Pied-billed Grebe breeds across much of North, Central and South America with northern populations moving south in winter. A vagrant to Great Britain with 37 records between the first in 1963 and 2002.

Little Grebe   *Tachybaptus ruficollis*

A locally common resident, winter visitor and passage migrant

Mansel-Pleydell (1888) commented that the 'Dabchick' or 'Didapper' "frequents our rivers and ponds, moving towards the sea as winter approaches". Blathwayt (1945) considered this species to be a common resident and reported that many move to the sea in winter.

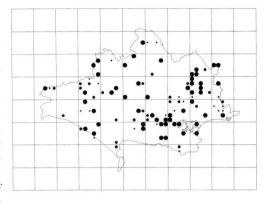

The *BTO Atlas* (1968–1972) revealed evidence of breeding in 28 (76%) 10-km squares (confirmed in 23, probable in three and possible in two), the most notable absences being in the south-west (SY39, SY49 and SY59) and the far north (ST72). The Tetrad Survey (1987–1994) produced a similar result with evidence of breeding in 29 (78%) of the pre-1974 10-km squares (confirmed in 22, probable in five and possible in two), the most notable absences being in the west (SY39 and ST40) and the north-east (ST91). The Tetrad Map shows that the Little Grebe breeds widely, if sparsely throughout the county. There are, however, notable concentrations along the River Allen, and in the west of Poole Basin where small heathland waters are particularly favoured. Breeding birds generally avoid larger rivers such as the Lower Avon and Stour, but its apparent absence from many of the county's smaller watercourses is curious and contrasts markedly with the situation in Hampshire. In Dorset the species seems to be much more dependent on well-vegetated stillwaters including farm ponds, small heathland waters and gravel pits, and on coastal lagoons and reedy meres such as West Bexington, Abbotsbury, and Radipole and Lodmoor NRs.

There is some evidence to suggest a decline in breeding numbers, notably along the River Allen – see Table 76. Poor weed growth associated with low river flows during the drought of the late 1980s and early 1990s is considered to be the most likely cause of this particular decline. Elsewhere, the limited information on population trends suggests a more stable situation with numbers ranging from 2–6 pairs at Radipole NR during 1978–1998 and 2–4 pairs at Brownsea during 1967–1998, except for an isolated peak of seven pairs in 1977. At Little Sea, the population varied between 5 and 8 pairs during 1967–1994, but increased to 11 pairs in 1997.

1989	1990	1991	1992	1993	1994	1995	1996	1997	1998	1999	2000
13	18	11	9	6	13	6	6	5	5	13	6

Table 76. Number of breeding pairs along River Allen 1989–2000

Little Grebes are more widely distributed after the breeding season and although some birds may remain on the breeding waters, others disperse to the larger rivers and sheltered estuaries. Winter maxima from the main sites usually range from 10–30 birds, the highest in recent years being 46 at Christchurch Harbour in early 1985, 45 at Radipole NR on 8th December 1985 and 42 on the Fleet in October 1993 – see Table 77. Elsewhere 31 at Lodmoor NR in December 1995 was a notable gathering. These counts are eclipsed, however, by an exceptional 217 on the Fleet near Abbotsbury on 16th December 1961, whilst winter maxima from the Fleet of 60 in 1970 and 50 in late December 1973 are notably high by recent standards.

The species is a rare visitor to non-estuarine coastal sites with reports of single birds from Portland Bill on 1st November 1974 and 14th October 1984, East Weare, Portland on 9th July 1968, the Nothe on 12th January 1983, Weymouth Bay on 3rd March 1986, 5th January, 28th February and 7th March 1991,

Kimmeridge Bay on 17th November 1980, and Durlston CP on 16th January 1987 (during cold weather) and 11th February 1999, also two at St Aldhelm's Head on 20th April 1986.

A total of nine birds has been ringed in the county.

	Range of Maxima
The Fleet	11–42
Radipole NR	7–45
Poole Harbour	13–33
Christchurch Harbour	8–46
Lower Avon Valley	13–38

Table 77. Range of winter maxima at the main sites 1980–1999

The Little Grebe breeds across much of central and southern Eurasia, North Africa and sub-Saharan Africa. It is largely resident except for populations in eastern Europe and the northern part of its Asiatic range. Wintering occurs mainly within the range of the resident population. The species is a widespread breeding resident in the British Isles.

Postscript 2000–2002
A count of 42 on the Fleet in November 2001 equals the highest winter maxima recorded from this site since 1980.

Great Crested Grebe   *Podiceps cristatus*

An uncommon resident, locally common winter visitor and passage migrant

Mansel-Pleydell (1888) regarded this species as a not uncommon winter visitor, which apparently moved southwards after Christmas when numbers declined and then returned in the spring. Perhaps more significantly, he also commented that "if allowed to remain unmolested in the spring, it is not unlikely that some would stay and breed with us". Blathwayt (1945) considered it to be mainly a regular visitor in small numbers to the coast and some inland waters, chiefly in spring and autumn, but also in winter.

The first definite breeding record did not occur until 1932 and it was not until the 1970s that the Great Crested Grebe began to establish itself in the county. Confirmed or probable breeding occurred at Crichel Lake regularly during 1932–1935 and again during 1964–1970, Abbotsbury in seven years during 1937–1978, Sherborne Lake in 1957 and 1958 and again in 1971 and 1972, and near Wareham in 1959. More recently breeding was first reported in the Lower Avon Valley in 1978 and at Radipole NR in 1980.

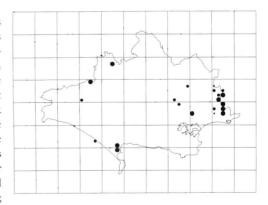

Subsequently the species has consolidated its position in the county with breeding numbers generally ranging from 9 to 15 pairs during 1983–1999 – see Table 78. During this period the main breeding sites have been Radipole NR, Sherborne Lake and the Lower Avon Valley. The population at Radipole NR appears to have declined since a peak of seven pairs in 1989, but at Sherborne Lake numbers have increased dramatically during the late 1990s to reach a peak of 12–14 pairs in 1999. It is difficult to assess population trends along the Lower Avon Valley as breeding birds are poorly recorded in some years. More recently, regular breeding involving 1–2 pairs has occurred or been attempted at Hatch Pond, Poole (since 1992), Sturminster Marshall GP (since 1993) and Moors Valley CP (1993, 1998 and 1999). Breeding has also been confirmed or suspected on a less frequent basis at a number of traditional and new sites, namely Crichel Lake (1983–1985, 1987 and 1995), the River Stour at Throop (regular summering with breeding confirmed in 1993), the Stour between Sturminster Marshall and Shapwick (1983–1985), Little Sea (1993, 1994 and 1997) and Abbotsbury (1990 and 1996). There are also occasional reports in summer from a number of other potential breeding sites in the county. The Tetrad Survey (1987–1994) generally reflects this situation, the Tetrad Map showing the concentration of breeding birds along the Lower Avon Valley.

	1980	1981	1982	1983	1984	1985	1986	1987	1988	1989
Radipole NR	1	2	2	4	2	4	5	3	4	7
Sherborne Lake	1	1	1	3	4	4	4	2	2	3
Lower Avon Valley	1	nc	1	nc	1	1	2	2	3	5
other sites	1	1	1	2	2	2	0	2	0	0
Total	4	3	4	9	9	11	11	9	9	15

	1990	1991	1992	1993	1994	1995	1996	1997	1998	1999
Radipole NR	5	3	5	5	3	2	2	1+	1+	1+
Sherborne Lake	5	1	nc	nc	nc	nc	2	4–5	6	12–14
Lower Avon Valley	9	7	sev	sev	2	8	nc	1	2	nc
other sites	2	0	1	5	4	3	3	3	4	4
Total	21	11	6+	10+	9	13	7	10+	13+	19+

Table 78. Number of breeding pairs at the main sites 1980–1999

Outside the breeding season the most important area is Poole Bay/Poole Harbour. It seems likely that the true wintering population may be higher than the figures suggest as winter maxima are typically reported separately for Poole Bay and Poole Harbour. Numbers were lower during the 1970s when winter maxima ranged from 10–30 birds, than in the late 1960s and during 1980–1999 when numbers generally ranged from 50–100 birds – see Table 79. The highest counts have been mainly from Poole Bay with an exceptional 261 in February 1992 (off Southbourne), also 145 in December 1995 (off Southbourne), 125 on 9th January 1986 and 117 in February 1987. Inside Poole Harbour, the highest count was 100+ at Arne NR on 19th January 1984. At Christchurch Harbour, the highest numbers usually occur at Hengistbury offshore in Poole Bay rather than inside the harbour itself.

	1950s	1960s	1970s	1980s	1990s
Poole Bay/Poole Harbour	23	49	20	77	91
Portland Hbr/Weymouth Bay	38	29	19	23	31

Table 79. Winter 10-year average peak counts at the main sites 1950–1999

Portland Harbour/Weymouth Bay is the other main area for Great Crested Grebes outside the breeding season – see Table 79. Again the true wintering population may be higher than the figures suggest as winter maxima are frequently reported separately for Portland Harbour and Weymouth Bay. Generally peak counts in winter range from 10–30 birds and rarely exceed 50, the highest being 71 in January 1997 and 65 on 22nd February 1954. Smaller numbers regularly occur on the Fleet (maximum of 26 in November 1989), at Radipole NR (maximum of 22 in September 1992) and well inland at Sherborne Lake (maxima of 33 in October 1998 and October 1999). It is a scarce visitor to Lyme Bay with most counts in single figures, 26 at West Bexington in February 1999 being exceptionally high. There are very few records of settled birds from the Purbeck coast.

There is a scattering of non-breeding records from inland waters, but apart from the Lower Avon and the lower reaches of the River Stour, birds are rarely reported from the main rivers. Consequently eight on floodwater east of Dorchester on 8th January 1967 and four on the River Frome at Dorchester on 11th and 12th January 1968 are notable sightings.

From the early 1970s to at least the mid-1990s, substantial gatherings in spring and early summer have been a regular feature in Poole Harbour with the waters off Arne NR being particularly favoured. This is reflected by peak counts in April and May of usually between 20–50 birds, but 65 in April 1991 and 93 on 10th May 1992. Smaller spring and summer gatherings have also occurred on the Fleet, particularly in recent years, with 20 in May 1990, April 1995 and June 1999, also 20 in late July–August 1982. Small numbers regularly remain throughout the summer at several of the non-breeding sites, notably Poole Harbour and the Fleet.

A few birds are seen passing the main coastal watch-points. Although records cover all months, most occur between October and April with a peak during December–January. Movements appear to be mostly westerly during the autumn to February and easterly from March to July.

The Great Crested Grebe breeds across much of central and southern Europe and central Asia as well as locally in Africa and Australasia. Populations in eastern Europe and much of central Asia winter to the south of the breeding range. In western Europe, wintering occurs largely within the breeding range and on nearby coasts. It is a widespread breeding resident throughout most of the British Isles except northern Scotland.

Postscript 2000–2002

In both 2000 and 2001 at least ten pairs were present at six potential breeding sites, Milton Abbas Lake in 2000 and Lodmoor NR in 2001 being new, whilst in 2002 there were 11 pairs at six sites. Counts from Poole Harbour of 171 in November 2001 and 151 in December 2000 are the second and third highest recorded in the county. Further west, a count of 29 in Lyme Bay at West Bexington in January 2000 is very high for this site, whilst 34 at Sherborne Lake in November 2002 is the highest winter count for this site. Higher than usual numbers were also summering on the Fleet with maxima of 35 in May 2001 and June–July 2002. One ringed in 2001 is the first in the county. This involved an injured bird found near the Oil Tanks at Portland Harbour on 11th July and later released successfully at Radipole NR.

Sponsored by Sheila Whitmore and Dee Williams

Red-necked Grebe   *Podiceps grisegena*

An uncommon winter visitor and passage migrant

Mansel-Pleydell (1888) considered this species to be a winter visitor, which was less numerous than the Great Crested Grebe, and quoted a Mr Pike who commented that "it is not unfrequently to be met in the neighbourhood of Poole". Blathwayt (1945) described it as "a rare winter visitor to the coast" and mentioned only three records, namely two at the mouth of Poole Harbour on 11th January 1925, one in Weymouth Bay on 1st February 1940 and one at the mouth of the River Frome on 8th August 1945.

The Red-necked Grebe remained a scarce visitor, mostly in winter, throughout the 1950s and much of the 1960s with an absence of confirmed sightings during the winters of 1950/51, 1953/54, 1963/64 and 1964/1965. From the late 1960s onwards, there has been a steady increase in records and it has now become a regular winter visitor and passage migrant, mainly in small numbers, but with occasional influxes.

Since 1950 the main wintering areas have been Poole Bay/Poole Harbour and Portland Harbour/Weymouth Bay – see Table 80. Numbers are generally small with winter maxima generally ranging from 1–6 and rarely exceeding 10 birds, the highest counts for each of these areas being 18 in Poole Bay in late December 1988 and on 15th April 1996 (off Branksome Chine), and 14 in Portland Harbour on 21st January 1999. High numbers tend to be reported in both areas during the same winters, but not invariably so. Peak counts in Weymouth Bay have occasionally coincided with autumn passage, notably in 1969 with nine on 27th October and again in 1986 with nine on 11th October and 4th November.

The species is rather scarce elsewhere with most sightings, nearly all involving 1–2 birds, from Lyme Bay – mainly between Abbotsbury Beach and Burton Bradstock, the Fleet, Portland Bill and Christchurch

Harbour. There are very few reports of settled birds from the Purbeck coast. Birds are occasionally observed passing the main coastal watch-points with peaks in mid-winter (January), spring (March–April) and autumn (September–November).

	1950s	1960s	1970s	1980s	1990s
Poole Bay/Poole Harbour	1	2	6	6	5
Portland Hbr/Weymouth Bay	1	3	3	5	7

Table 80. Winter 10-year average peak counts at the main sites 1950–1999

The first birds in autumn usually appear during September, more rarely in August, the earliest being 8th August 1945 near Wareham and in more recent years from 23rd to 27th August 1986 at Abbotsbury, and 23rd August 1998 at both Portland Bill and in Weymouth Bay. In spring, the last birds are usually reported in April, occasionally in May, the latest being 27th May 1996 at Ferrybridge. There is only one summer record involving a bird in Weymouth Bay on 21st July 1987.

The only sighting from well inland involves a bird at Milton Abbas Lake on 1st January 1973. Otherwise birds have wandered to Little Sea on at least seven occasions, whilst singles on the River Frome at Wareham on 12th January 1982 and in 1995 (no date), Lodmoor NR on 8th January 1982, Radipole NR on 18th February 1986 and Chafey's Lake, Radipole NR on 10th January 1998 are noteworthy.

The Red-necked Grebe breeds in eastern Europe, west-central and north-east Asia, and also in North America. It winters on the coasts of northern and eastern Europe, east Asia and North America. In Great Britain the species has attempted to breed in recent years, but it is mainly a winter visitor to the east and south coasts.

Slavonian Grebe   *Podiceps auritus*

An uncommon winter visitor and passage migrant

Mansel-Pleydell (1888) described this species as "a frequent winter visitant" and commented that after the Little Grebe it is the "commonest of the genus, especially in salt water". Blathwayt (1945) referred to the Slavonian Grebe as a not uncommon winter visitor to the coast, but contrary to Mansel-Pleydell observed that it was scarcer than the Black-necked Grebe.

Since 1950 the main wintering areas have been Studland Bay/Poole Harbour and Portland Harbour/ Weymouth Bay. The populations in both areas increased markedly during the 1970s. In the Studland Bay/ Poole Harbour area numbers remained relatively high until the late 1980s, but then declined to a lower and relatively stable level during the 1990s – see Fig 9. By contrast, numbers in the Portland Harbour/ Weymouth Bay area declined rapidly during the early 1980s and remained at a consistently low level until a recovery during the late 1990s – see Fig 10. From 1950 to 1967, winter maxima in both areas rarely exceeded ten birds, 23 at the mouth of Poole Harbour on 7th March 1954 being regarded as exceptional at the time. During the subsequent peak years, winter maxima generally ranged from 15–30 birds, the highest counts being 60 in Portland Harbour in February 1974 with 60 there on 21st December 1981 after a period of severe south-easterly gales, and 42 in Studland Bay on 15th February 1981. In more recent years, the best counts have been 30 in Portland Harbour on 30th December 1998 and 22 in Studland Bay in January 1997.

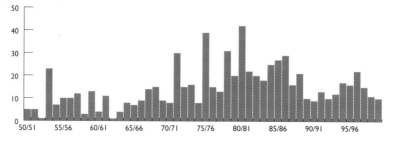

Fig. 9. Winter maxima in the Studland Bay/Poole Harbour area 1950–1999

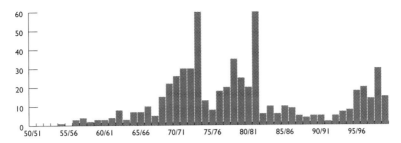

Fig 10. Winter maxima in the Portland Harbour/Weymouth Bay area 1950–1999

Kimmeridge Bay has been a fairly regular wintering site for the species. Numbers have been small with winter maxima of up to six birds from the mid-1950s to the early 1980s, but generally 1–3 birds recorded subsequently, except for isolated peaks of six on 17th January 1999 and five on 24th December 1996.

Elsewhere along the coast, settled birds occur less regularly with most sightings from Lyme Bay – mainly between Abbotsbury Beach and Burton Bradstock, the Fleet, Portland Bill and Christchurch Harbour. There are also sightings from various sites along the Purbeck coast (other than Kimmeridge Bay), but one at Lyme Regis on 10th December 1988 is the only confirmed report from the extreme west of the county. The species has wandered to near-coastal sites such as Radipole and Lodmoor NRs, Little Sea and Poole Park, but there is only one record from well inland, that of two at Crichel Lake on 14th January 1968. Most records involve singles and rarely more than three birds, the highest counts being eight at Ringstead Bay on 20th December 1965 and eight nearby at Osmington Mills on 21st and 22nd February 1998. Birds are occasionally observed passing the main coastal watch-points between August and May with a peak during mid-winter (December–February).

Although the first birds in autumn do not typically appear until October or even November, there are a few reports for September and three in August, namely 16th August 1998 in Brand's Bay, 21st August 1997 in Poole Harbour and 27th August 1997 at Portland Bill. In spring the last birds are usually reported in March, more occasionally in April, the latest records being 5th May 1988 at Christchurch Harbour, 7th May 1969 in Kimmeridge Bay, 9th May 1994 in Weymouth Bay and 15th May 1992 at East Bexington. There are two summer sightings involving single summer-plumaged birds in Portland Harbour on 17th June 1968 and Weymouth Bay throughout June and July 1982.

The Slavonian Grebe breeds across northern Eurasia, mainly between 50°N and 62°N, but further north in Scandinavia and including Iceland, also in northern North America except the north-east. It winters along the coasts of northern and eastern Europe, east Asia and North America. In the British Isles, it is a regular but rare breeder in Scotland and a scarce winter visitor along the coasts.

Postscript 2000–2002
The second and third inland records for the county occurred in 2002 with one at Sturminster Marshall GP on 10th March and four at Coward's Marsh, Christchurch on 17th December.

Black-necked Grebe   *Podiceps nigricollis*

An uncommon winter visitor and passage migrant
Mansel-Pleydell (1888) described this species as "a winter visitant, and the rarest of the genus on our coast". Blathwayt (1945), however, considered the Black-necked Grebe to be commoner than the previous species and refers to it as a regular winter visitor to the coast, usually in small numbers, but sometimes in flocks of 40.

Since 1950 the main wintering area has been Studland Bay/Poole Harbour where the fortunes of this and the previous species have differed. During the 1950s and 1960s, the Black-necked Grebe was the more numerous of the two species with winter maxima generally ranging from 20–40 birds, the highest counts being 51+ on 13th December 1959 and 50+ on 17th March 1956 – see Fig 11. A major oiling incident in the harbour in 1964 adversely affected the wintering Black-necked Grebe population, which was more than halved – see Table 81. Consequently winter maxima during the late 1960s and throughout

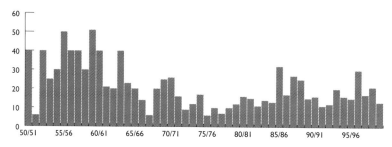

Fig 11. Winter maxima in the Studland Bay/Poole Harbour area 1950–1999

the 1970s only ranged from 6–26 birds. During the 1980s and 1990s, there has been a partial recovery in the winter population with maxima generally ranging from 11–20 birds, the highest counts being 32 on 12th December 1985 and 30 in Studland Bay on 8th February 1997. By contrast the wintering population of the Slavonian Grebe increased dramatically during the 1970s and 1980s to the extent that it became the more numerous of the two species. During the 1990s, the situation reversed again as a result of the decline in the numbers of Slavonian Grebe. These fluctuations are best illustrated by the 10-year averages of winter peak counts for both species – see Table 82.

1950/51–1963/64	1964/65–1979/80	1980/81–1989/1990	1990/91–1998/99
34	15	19	17

Table 81. Average winter maxima in the Studland Bay/Poole Harbour area 1950–1999

	1950s	1960s	1970s	1980s	1990s
Slavonian Grebe	9	8	20	23	14
Black-necked Grebe	35	23	13	19	17

Table 82. Winter 10-year average peak counts for Slavonian and Black-necked Grebes in the Studland Bay/Poole Harbour area 1950–1999

Although wintering Black-necked Grebes occurred fairly regularly in the Portland Harbour/Weymouth Bay area from the mid-1950s to the late 1970s, numbers were very small and usually involved only 1–2 birds with counts of 3–5 birds in only three winters. Since 1978/79 numbers have increased and the species has become well-established with winter maxima ranging from 5–9 birds during the 1980s and from 7–15 birds during the 1990s – see Fig 12. This increase has coincided with the marked decline in the counts of Slavonian Grebes in this area from the early 1980s through to the mid-1990s.

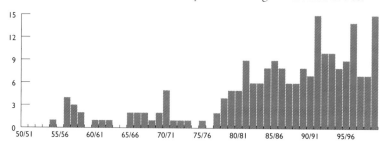

Fig 12. Winter maxima in the Portland Harbour/Weymouth Bay area 1950–1999

Elsewhere along the coast, the Black-necked Grebe is relatively scarce with most sightings from the Fleet and Christchurch Harbour. There are also a few records from Lyme Bay, mainly at West Bexington, Portland Bill and the Purbeck coast. Although the species has wandered to such near-coastal sites as Radipole and Lodmoor NRs, Little Sea and Poole Park, there are no sightings from well inland. Most records involve singles and rarely more than three birds, the highest count being ten at Chapman's Pool on 2nd

February 1963. There was, however, a remarkable gathering of 28 unidentified Slavonian or Black-necked Grebes at Hengistbury on 27th January 1987 – presumably birds wandering from Studland Bay/Poole Harbour. Birds are rarely observed passing the main coastal watch-points with scattered records during October–May, 4E at St Aldhelm's Head on 6th November 1990 being notable.

Wintering birds typically arrive during October and November, records earlier than this probably referring to passage birds. There are occasional sightings in September and a few for August (mostly since 1986), the earliest being 13th August 1990 in Weymouth Bay. Lingering winter birds and migrants are occasionally seen in April, but there are very few records after mid-month, the latest prior to 1992 being 13th May 1978 at Portland Bill. In the early 1990s, however, there was a number of late spring and early summer sightings from Poole Harbour with two in May 1992, one from May to 13th June 1993 and one or two in May and June 1994. The Fleet, between Langton Herring and Abbotsbury, hosted 1–3 birds from 13th May to 11th June 1994.

The Black-necked Grebe breeds locally over much of central, southern and eastern Europe extending east into central and south-west Asia, and also in central and western North America and very locally in eastern and southern Africa. It winters in western and southern Europe, south-west and east Asia, western North America and northern Central America, and eastern and southern Africa. In the British Isles it is a rare breeder with a small winter population mainly in south and west England.

Postscript 2000–2002
A winter maximum of 18 in Portland Harbour in January 2002 is the highest ever count from this site. One in Weymouth Bay from 22nd May to 4th June 2000 is an unseasonal record.

Black-browed Albatross   *Thalassarche melanophris*

Accidental: one record

1980   Durlston CP: 4th February

One, a probable adult, flew east at Durlston CP with Gannets. A full account can be found in the Dorset Bird Report for 1980.

The Black-browed Albatross is a very rare wanderer from the southern oceans. A vagrant to Great Britain with 19 records up to 2002.

Sponsored by Andrew Bellars and Mr & Mrs Michael Harry

Fulmar (Northern Fulmar)   *Fulmarus glacialis*

A locally common resident and passage migrant

During the 19th Century this species was a rare winter visitor to Dorset, the only records given in Mansel-Pleydell (1888) involving one shot between Bexington and Abbotsbury (date not given) and another procured in Poole Harbour on 5th September 1871. By the 1940s the Fulmar had begun to prospect the cliffs at Portland and Purbeck, Blathwayt (1945) commented "the species is now apparently about to spread to Dorset, and will perhaps breed in the county soon". Breeding was first proved at Portland Bill in 1952, but surprisingly not on the Purbeck cliffs until 1972 when a chick was discovered at Durlston CP.

On Purbeck, prospecting was first recorded in 1943 when three birds were present between Durlston CP and Anvil Point. The number of prospecting birds along this stretch of the Purbeck coast increased to six in 1947 and seven in 1950 when four birds were also present near Dancing Ledge. Subsequently the species spread to suitable nesting sites west along the Purbeck cliffs reaching Gad Cliff in 1960. By 1967 birds had become established further west at Bat's Head and to the north at Ballard Down. The number of Fulmars frequenting the Purbeck cliffs in summer has increased since the 1950s, and selected counts for the most systematically surveyed section between Durlston CP and St Aldhelm's Head are given in Table 83. The highest counts are 79 in June 1979 and 87 in May 1981. Elsewhere on Purbeck, there are counts of birds from Bat's Head with three in 1969, 11 in 1982, ten in 1984 and 40 in 1987, Gad Cliff with 18 in 1975 and 7–14 during 1981–1984, and Ballard Down with eight in 1983, four in 1984 and 1986, three pairs in 1990, 15 in 1996 and three in 1999.

Years	Number of birds (min and max)
1950–1962	6–12
1964–1969	21–32
1970–1972	3 –55
1975–1979	20–79
1980–1984	22–87
1985–1989	21–52
1990–1994	12–53
1996–1999	22–50

Table 83. Number of birds in summer between Durlston CP and St Aldhelm's Head 1950–1999

On Portland, prospecting first occurred in 1945 and by 1951 c.20 were prospecting the West Cliffs where breeding was proved in 1952. Numbers increased from 30–32 birds in 1953, 1958 and 1959 to around 50 birds by the mid-1960s, thereafter stabilising between 10–25 pairs – see Table 84. By the mid-1960s birds were prospecting along the East Cliffs, and by 1971 this activity had extended to cliffs at Blacknor, Grove Point and Verne Common. Subsequently the Fulmar has established new breeding colonies at other sites on Portland including Grove Point with nine pairs in 1984, five in 1987, 16 in 1990, ten in 1994 and 1997 and eight in 1999, Southwell with at least two pairs in 1991 and six in 1994, Blacknor to Chesil Cove with 16 pairs in 1997 and 25 birds in 1998, and Verne Common with three birds in 1997.

Years	Number of birds (min and max)
1950–1959	4–32
1963–1969	18–52
1970–1979	26–80
1980–1984	13–25 pairs
1985–1989	10–15 pairs
1990–1994	12–20 pairs
1995–1999	25–100

Table 84. Number of birds in summer on Portland West Cliffs 1950–1999

Since the first reports of prospecting in 1968, the species has rapidly became established along the west Dorset coast, notably between Burton Cliff and Eype's Mouth with a few birds further west at Lyme Regis. By the 1990s significant numbers of birds were present on the cliffs in summer – see Table 85.

Year	Number	Year	Number
1971	7	1988	13 pairs
1972	2	1991	10 pairs
1979	4+ pairs	1992	c.45 pairs
1980	3	1993	49 pairs
1981	16	1994	24–67 pairs
1984	1	1995	24 pairs
1985	14–15	1996	24 pairs
1986	31	1999	35 pairs

Table 85. Number of birds in summer on west Dorset cliffs (mainly Burton Cliff to Eype) 1971–1999

National surveys of Fulmar populations have reflected the spread of the species in Dorset with 89 birds recorded by the Operation Seafarer Survey during 1969–1970 increasing to 122 pairs recorded by the NCC/Seabird Group Survey during 1985–1987. There is slight evidence of a decline in numbers at the main colonies on Purbeck and Portland since the mid-1980s, but overall this is compensated by increases at the more recently established sites notably in west Dorset. The Tetrad Survey (1987–1994) Map reflects the recent breeding distribution in the county.

Offshore movements at the main coastal watch-points are complex and often contradictory with birds passing in opposite directions. In addition, feeding movements of local breeding birds further obscures true passage. There is a definite bias toward easterly movement at Portland Bill in spring (mid-February – early May), the most notable counts being 850E on 1st May 1983, 550E on 22nd April 1983 and 540E on 3rd May 1981, also 600 at the Chesil on 19th May 1996. Autumn movements are mainly westerly in direction and involve lower numbers with day-counts rarely exceeding 100 birds at Portland Bill, and 50 birds at Durlston CP and Hengistbury, but an exceptional 300W at Durlston CP on 6th

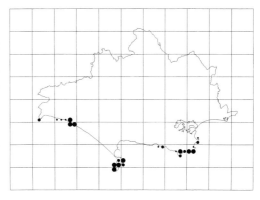

September 1992. Occasionally there are significant movements associated with winter storms, e.g. 175W at Durlston CP during 26th–31st December 1990, 131W at St Aldhelm's Head during 27th–29th December 1994 and 96W at Portland Bill during 28th–31st December 1994.

Birds are occasionally seen inside Poole and Christchurch Harbours and flying over sites close to the coast such as Radipole and Lodmoor NRs. More unusual sightings involve one flying westwards high over Stoborough near Wareham on 17th June 1978, one flying south-west over the Holdenhurst Road in Boscombe on 11th June 1983, one found grounded on a pavement in Wareham after a heavy hailstorm on 25th April 1991, and one resting on the Fleet on 9th September 1998. In addition, a bird seen a kilometre inland in the Winspit Valley on 23rd May 1970 flying up and down strip lynchets and twice alighting beside anthills is unusual behaviour for this species. There are only two records from well inland involving one flying along a hedgerow at Marnhull on 23rd June 1986 and one at Bovington on 25th September 1997.

Blue-phase birds have been recorded fairly regularly at Portland Bill since 1968. Most records involve singles, but two individuals were present in May and June 1975. There are also occasional sightings of this colour phase from Purbeck and west Dorset.

A total of eight birds has been ringed in the county. There are no recoveries or controls, but a colour-ringed bird known to be breeding at Eynhallow, Orkney in 1986 and 1987 was seen on cliffs near Winspit with a mate on 18th May 1989. This species normally stays faithful to its mate and nest-site over many years, to establish a new breeding area or even be prospecting so far from the original site is quite exceptional.

The Fulmar is one of the most numerous seabirds of the Northern Hemisphere and has undergone a spectacular expansion over the past two centuries with a major increase in range and numbers. The causes of this expansion are unclear, but may include increased availability of waste from trawling activities or the appearance of a genotype favouring range expansion. In the British Isles it breeds widely on all coasts, being most numerous in the west and north.

Postscript 2000–2002

Breeding reports from the Purbeck cliffs in 2000 include 14 pairs at Bat's Head, which is the first count from this site since 1987, and two pairs at Lulworth Cove, which is apparently a new site for the species.

Cory's Shearwater   *Calonectris diomedea*

A rare passage migrant and summer visitor

The first Dorset record involves three flying west at Portland Bill on 19th April 1965. There were no further sightings until 1970 but since then 69 birds have occurred in 17 years up to 1999. Many of these were reported during two periods of consecutive years, namely 1975–1978 with 18 birds and 1985–1991 with 44 birds – see Table 86.

Portland Bill is the main site for the species and accounts for all 23 birds recorded during 1965–1978 and 35 of the 49 birds recorded during 1983–1999. Most reports involved 1–3 birds, but six occurred on 28th June 1975 and a remarkable 17E on 19th August 1986. There were no sightings from elsewhere in the county until 21st June 1985 when a single bird was seen at Durlston CP, which was followed by further records at this site with 2E on 22nd May 1988 and 6E on 20th July 1990. The first reports from Hengistbury

occurred in 1987 with one on 3rd June and two on 5th June followed by 1E on 4th June 1988, whilst one seen in Poole Bay off Bournemouth during a boat trip to the Isle of Wight on 19th August 1994 is the only sighting away from the three main coastal watch-points.

70	71	72	73	74	75	76	77	78	79	80	81	82	83	84
1	1	0	0	0	11	3	2	2	0	0	0	0	1	0

85	86	87	88	89	90	91	92	93	94	95	96	97	98	99
1	20	4	4	3	11	1	0	1	1	0	0	0	0	2

Table 86. Annual totals 1970– 1999

There has been a distinct shift in the seasonal occurrence of records between the earlier (1965–1978) and later (1983–1999) years – see Table 87. In the first period 22 birds were recorded between 19th April–28th June with a peak of 15 birds in June, whilst the remaining single occurred on 20th July. In recent years only 11 birds were recorded between 8th April–21st June, but 38 birds occurred between 20th July–23rd September with a peak of 26 birds in August. The reason for this change in seasonal distribution is not obvious, but the more recent records reflect the national pattern of occurrence.

	Apr	May	Jun	Jul	Aug	Sep
1965–1978	3	4	15	1	0	0
1983–1999	1	4	6	10	26	2

Table 87. Monthly totals 1965–1978 and 1983–1999

The Cory's Shearwater breeds in the Mediterranean and eastern North Atlantic, and disperses widely across the Atlantic north to the latitude of south-west Ireland. In the British Isles, it occurs mainly in the waters off the south-west.

Postscript 2000–2002
One flying east at Portland Bill on 20th April 2002 is only the second record since 1994.

Great Shearwater   *Puffinus gravis*

Accidental: seven records

- 1868   Swanage Bay: summer
- 1877   Poole Harbour: 7th June
- 1885   Durlston Bay: 12th June, same bird in Swanage Bay 13th June
- 1963   Portland Bill: 21st June
- 1991   Portland Bill: flying west 15th September
- 1999   Portland Bill: flying west 23rd September
         Seatown, flying west 23rd September

Mansel-Pleydell (1888) described this species as "not an unfrequent visitant in autumn to the coasts of Devon and Dorset", but only listed three records for the county. There were no further sightings until 1963 and subsequently, there have been only three records including two different individuals on the same date in 1999.

The Great Shearwater breeds in the South Atlantic and disperses into the North Atlantic reaching the waters off the west of the British Isles and north-west Europe from August to October. It is a very rare visitor to the English Channel.

Sooty Shearwater   *Puffinus griseus*

An uncommon passage migrant, mainly in autumn

Mansel-Pleydell (1888) referred to one caught alive in Poole Harbour on 8th June 1877, which is the only old record. There were no further reports until the mid-1950s when singles flew east at Portland Bill on 11th September 1955 and 24th October 1956. Since 1959 the species has been recorded at this site in every autumn except for 1964, 1965 and 1967 – see Fig 13. Numbers are generally small with seasonal totals usually ranging from 5–25 bird-days, the highest being 125 in 1963, 104 in 1998 and 87 in 1985. The 1963 total included an exceptional 118 on 29th September, the next highest day-counts being 67 on 13th October 1998 and 26 on 17th September 1985.

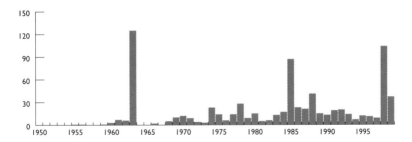

Fig 13. Autumn totals (bds) at Portland Bill 1950–1999

During the 1960s and 1970s there were a few autumn records from the Purbeck coast, namely Dancing Ledge with one on 22nd July 1969 and Winspit with one on 21st December 1969 and 9W on 3rd July 1972, whilst at Hengistbury one flew west on 17th October 1976. Since 1980 there has been a marked increase in autumn sightings away from Portland Bill with almost annual reports from Durlston CP and Hengistbury – see Tables 88 and 90. Elsewhere along the Purbeck coast there have been several records from St Aldhelm's Head, notably during the 1990s – see Table 89, and from Winspit with 1W on 15th August 1990, singles on 14th and 27th October 1998 and two on 16th September 1999.

80	81	82	83	84	85	86	87	88	89	90	91	92	93	94	95	96	97	98	99
0	2	7	6	3	17	19	11	16	11	14	16	18	10	9	11	13	12	30	13

Table 88. Autumn totals (bds) at Durlston CP 1980–1999

80	81	82	83	84	85	86	87	88	89	90	91	92	93	94	95	96	97	98	99
0	1	0	0	0	0	0	0	0	0	0	0	0	5	0	2	3	3	5	0

Table 89. Autumn totals (bds) at St Aldhelm's Head 1980–1999

80	81	82	83	84	85	86	87	88	89	90	91	92	93	94	95	96	97	98	99
1	1	1	2	3	5	1	4	5	1	0	1	1	2	0	1	1	3	1	1

Table 90. Autumn totals (bds) at Hengistbury 1980–1999

In the west of the county there are autumn reports from several coastal watch-points overlooking Lyme Bay with three at West Bexington and one off the Chesil at Chickerell on 19th August 1988, further singles at West Bexington on 24th July 1991 and 13th August 1997, one at Abbotsbury Beach on 11th August 1992, 1E at East Bexington on 6th September 1992, and singles in Chesil Cove on 2nd and 4th November 1996 and 28th October 1998.

Autumn passage extends from mid-July through to late December, but the overwhelming majority of birds (94%) occur during August–October with a distinct peak (51%) in September – see Table 91. Spring birds are very rare involving singles at Portland Bill on 9th March 1979 and 19th April 1965 with 2E there on 19th May 1972, 1W at Durlston CP on 15th April 1985, 1SW at Peveril Point on 26th May 1972 and one in Chesil Cove on 28th May 1995, whilst one 10 miles south of Lyme Regis on 30th June 1971 is the only record for this month. There is also one mid-winter sighting from Portland Bill on 11th January 1993.

Jul	Aug	Sept	Oct	Nov	Dec
3%	16%	51%	27%	2%	1%

Table 91. Monthly autumn distribution (%) 1970–1999

The Sooty Shearwater breeds on sub-Antarctic islands and winters in the North Atlantic and North Pacific. In the North Atlantic there appears to be a clockwise movement, the species frequenting the waters off the British Isles and other north-west European coasts mainly from July to October with a peak of abundance during August–September.

Postscript 2000–2002
A record number for the county occurred in autumn 2000 involving 196 bird-days including 156 at Portland Bill (also a record total for this site) during 26th August–25th November with a maximum of 49 (third highest day-count) on 27th September. Elsewhere there were 32 at Durlston CP during 18th September–11th November (maximum of 20 on 26th September), four at Chesil Cove during 5th September–30th October and four at West Bexington during 5th September–29th October. In autumn 2001 numbers were much lower with only 35 birds during 17th July–26th October. In 2002, there was a series of exceptional winter sightings from Portland Bill with one during 22nd–25th January, two on 24th January and one on 29th January, Durlston CP with one on 20th January and two on 20th February and West Bexington with one on 23rd January – there is only one previous January record for the county and none for February. Otherwise in autumn 2002 numbers were low again with only 24 birds during 9th August–11th November.

Manx Shearwater   *Puffinus puffinus*

A locally common non-breeding summer visitor and passage migrant

Both Mansel-Pleydell (1888) and Blathwayt (1945) considered the Manx Shearwater to be a spring and autumn visitor, the former commenting "the Portland fishermen call it the 'Mackerel Cock' and assert that it remains concealed inland during the day and feeds only at twilight and dawn".

Although Portland Bill is the main site for the species, good numbers also occur at coastal watch-points overlooking Lyme Bay and along the Purbeck coast, notably Durlston CP and St Aldhelm's Head. Much smaller numbers are recorded from Hengistbury and Poole Bay, whilst birds occasionally wander to the more sheltered waters of Portland Harbour and Weymouth Bay. Single birds have occurred inside

Poole Harbour on 7th September 1961, and Christchurch Harbour on 5th August 1978 and 1st August 1981. Inland birds have been rescued alive at Stour Provost on 20th September 1954 and Gillingham on 14th September 1980 (released at Portland Bill).

The first birds typically appear during March with numbers increasing rapidly thereafter, the period from April to July accounting for 98% of the total with a distinct peak (63%) in May and June – see Table 92. Numbers decline during August and only a few birds occur during September and October with stragglers into November. There are a few early reports for February, whilst mid-winter (December–January) records are rare and involve c.19 birds since 1970 including 3W at Hengistbury on 22nd December 1985 and three at Portland Bill on 1st January 1995.

Jan	Feb	Mar	Apr	May	Jun	Jul	Aug	Sep	Oct	Nov	Dec
<0.1%	<0.1%	0.3%	16%	30%	33%	18%	2%	0.3%	0.1%	<0.1%	<0.1%

Table 92. Monthly distribution (%) at the main coastal watch-points 1986–1998

Many movements, particularly during the peak month of June, are thought to involve birds commuting between distant breeding colonies off Dyfed (Skomer and Skokholm), south-west England (Lundy and Scillies), southern Ireland and northern France, and feeding areas in the western part of the English Channel. This accounts for the fact that there is little directional bias in the mid-summer movements, whilst in spring the direction is predominantly easterly and in autumn westerly. Upchannel passage is not pronounced east of Dorset, and the Isle of Wight appears to mark an easterly turn around point in the English Channel for the Manx Shearwater.

Although peak day-totals at Portland Bill rarely exceed 1,000 birds, there was an exceptional passage of c.10,000 on 10th April 1999, the next highest counts being 2,520 on 8th June 1987, 2,400 on 15th April 1998, 2,141E on 25th May 1975 and 2,000E on 1st May 1983. Since many of these birds pass through Lyme Bay, it is perhaps not surprising that there are several high counts from the Chesil including 2,200 on 2nd June 1999, 1,710 on 21st April 1999, 840 on 29th May 1988, 596 on 7th June 1975 and 500SW on 14th June 1980. On Purbeck, the highest count from Durlston CP is 400W on 3rd May 1980, whilst at Hengistbury there are four counts exceeding 100 birds, namely 90E, 62W on 29th May 1988, 64E, 69W on 13th June 1984, 120W on 20th June 1986 and 103W on 1st July 1990.

A total of 11 birds has been ringed in the county.

The Manx Shearwater breeds mainly in the west of the British Isles, which holds over 90% of the world's population, with other colonies scattered throughout the east temperate North Atlantic extending from Iceland and the Faroes south to the Canaries. The species disperses widely throughout the Atlantic outside the breeding season.

Postscript 2000–2002
One found in a garden in Sherborne and released at Sherborne Lake on an unspecified date in 2000 is only the third record from well inland.

111

Balearic Shearwater   *Puffinus mauretanicus*

An uncommon non-breeding summer visitor and autumn passage migrant

This species, which was regarded as a race of Manx Shearwater *P. puffinus*, until 1991, was first recognised as a regular visitor to the British Isles at Portland Bill in 1953. Subsequently the Balearic Shearwater has occurred annually at this site with annual totals varying considerably, ranging from a 'low' of ten in 1972 to an exceptional peak of 4,631 bird-days in 1978 – see Fig 14. There is a recurring pattern of periods of 'good' years interspersed with periods of 'poor' years. The most notable of these good years were 1953, 1958–1961, 1977–1979, 1993 and 1998. In the earlier of these 'good' years (1953, 1958–1961 and 1977) the highest numbers occurred relatively late in the autumn during September and October with peak counts of 160 on 13th September 1953, 134 on 16th October 1958, 131 on 11th October 1959, several counts in excess of 100 in 1960 including 208 on 18th September and 229 on 3rd October, and 268W on 28th September 1977. Subsequently peak numbers in 'good' years have been recorded earlier in the year with 4,187 bird-days in August 1978, 102 bird-days in June 1993 and 324 bird-days in July 1998 mainly involving offshore feeding flocks. There is some evidence to suggest that these mid-summer flocks consist of non-breeders in moult, which are augmented later in the autumn by fresh plumaged birds of the year. Since 1980, the seasonal pattern of occurrence at Portland Bill shows numbers increasing during June and July to peak in August, which is followed by a decline during September with a few stragglers into October – see Table 93.

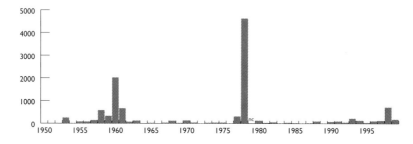

Fig 14. Annual totals at Portland Bill 1950–1999

Jan	Feb	Mar	Apr	May	Jun	Jul	Aug	Sep	Oct	Nov	Dec
0	<0.1%	0	0	0.6%	12%	25%	35%	24%	3%	<0.1%	0

Table 93. Monthly distribution (%) at Portland Bill 1980–1998

Elsewhere in Dorset records of Balearic Shearwaters follow the same annual and seasonal patterns as at Portland Bill, but on a smaller scale. Most reports come from coastal watch-points overlooking Lyme Bay, along the Purbeck coast, notably at Durlston CP and St Aldhelm's Head, and at Hengistbury. Numbers are generally small, but 150S at Peveril Point on 28th September 1977, coinciding with the county maximum day-count at Portland Bill, and 100 in Chesil Cove on 29th July 1978 are exceptional. Singles inside Poole Harbour on 2nd October 1977 and Portland Harbour on 21st July 1993 are unusual, whilst one was found in a ditch at Radipole NR on 24th August 1971 and subsequently released at Portland Bill.

The earliest records for the county are 20th March 1997 at St Aldhelm's Head, 11th April 1979 and 19th April 1970 – both at Portland Bill, and 22nd April 1998 at the Chesil, whilst the latest sightings are 12th November 1992 at Winspit and 14th November 1997 and 16th November 1958 – both at Portland Bill. Otherwise there are two exceptional mid-winter reports involving single birds at Portland Bill on 6th February 1998 and Hengistbury on 8th December 1999.

The Balearic Shearwater breeds in the western Mediterranean and disperses into the eastern North Atlantic north to the British Isles outside the breeding season.

Postscript 2000–2002

A county total of 843 bird-days in 2001 is the second highest since 1980, just ten less than the 853 bird-days recorded in 1998. In 2002, there was a series of exceptional winter sightings with singles at Portland

Bill during 21st–24th January, Chesil Cove on 26th January and Hengistbury on 2nd February – these include the first January sightings for the county; whilst two at Branksome Chine on 10th March represent the earliest spring record for the county.

Sponsored by John O'Sullivan

Little Shearwater   *Puffinus assimilis*

Accidental: one record

   1984   Hengistbury: 13th June

The single record involved a bird flying west amongst a flock of Manx Shearwaters attracted to a large shoal of fish.

     The race of Little Shearwater recorded in the British Isles is *P. a. baroli*, breeding in the Azores, Madeira, the Salvages and Canary Islands and dispersing locally outside the breeding season. A vagrant to Great Britain with 61 records up to 2002.

Storm Petrel (European Storm-petrel)   *Hydrobates pelagicus*

An uncommon non-breeding summer visitor and autumn passage migrant

Both Mansel-Pleydell (1888) and Blathwayt (1945) regarded this species as an occasional visitor to the coast and commented that birds may be driven inland by gales.

     From 1950 to 1979 Storm Petrels (including probables) occurred in every year except for 1950, 1953, 1955, 1966–1968 and 1973. Generally only small numbers were recorded with annual totals usually ranging from 1–4 birds, but there were seven in 1959, 1960 and 1976, six in 1978 and six at Portland Bill on 29th May 1979. During this period the vast majority of sightings, involving 65 out of a total of 70 birds, were from Portland Bill and the nearby Chesil, with further reports from Charmouth (one dead), Burton Bradstock (one dead), Peveril Point (two) and Poole Harbour (one). There was a spread of records from April to December with peaks in May (31%) and September–October (30%).

     Since 1980 numbers have increased, dramatically so during the 1990s when annual totals (as bird-days) reached peaks of 408 in 1991, 588 in 1993, c.635 in 1994, 696 in 1996 and 390 in 1998 – see Table 94. This increase has occurred mainly during the summer period (May–July), which accounts for 88% of the total with a distinct peak (41%) in June – see Table 95. Fewer birds were recorded during the autumn, the smaller peak (7%) in October reflecting storm-induced influxes such as those in 1987 and 1988 and 1997 and 1998. The increase in sightings during May–July and the results of tape-luring at Portland Bill suggests that Storm Petrels are regular in the English Channel during the summer, whilst in 1994 there was a hint of nesting amongst the screes along the West Cliffs at Portland.

	1980	1981	1982	1983	1984	1985	1986	1987	1988	1989
Portland Bill	3	0	3	4	23	20	53	47	38	47
the Chesil	0	0	0	1	0	0	0	0	1	0
St Aldhelm's Head	0	0	0	0	0	2	0	0	0	0
Durlston CP	0	0	0	3	5	0	2	4	4	3
Hengistbury	0	1	1	1	0	1	10	17	18	0

	1990	1991	1992	1993	1994	1995	1996	1997	1998	1999
Portland Bill	199	347	35	370	465	59	424	42	130	3
the Chesil	23	19	1	1	4	0	34	4	36	1
St Aldhelm's Head	9	0	0	42	4	0	16	nc	3	0
Durlston CP	52	14	15	26	65	18	81	55	46	22
Hengistbury	21	20	0	149	96	0	134	17	146	1

Table 94. Annual totals at the main coastal watch-points 1980–1999

Jan	Feb	Mar	Apr	May	Jun	Jul	Aug	Sep	Oct	Nov	Dec
1%	0	0	0	29%	41%	18%	2%	1%	7%	0.1%	0.1%

Table 95. Monthly distribution (%) at the main sites 1980–1999

The species is very scarce outside the period May to October and since 1950 at least, there are no county records for the months of February and March, and only one for April, namely two at Portland Bill on 26th April 1959. Although there are a few reports for November and December, two at Hengistbury on 26th January 1988 with one there on 4th January 1997 were the only sightings for this month prior to a remarkable influx of c.22 birds during 4th–9th January 1998, which included seven at Durlston CP and six at Portland Bill.

Although Portland Bill remains the main site for Storm Petrels, good numbers occur at other coastal watch-points – see Table 94. Day-counts rarely exceed 50 birds, the highest being from Hengistbury with 102 on 31st May 1993 and 70 on 6th June 1994, and Portland Bill with 100 on 19th and 22nd May 1996 and 78 on 31st May 1993 (cf Hengistbury). Elsewhere there is a scattering of records from various other sites overlooking Lyme Bay including 40 at West Bexington on 9th October 1988 and 12 at East Bexington during 15th–16th July 1992. There are also sightings from Weymouth Bay including five on 18th October 1987, Winspit, Peveril Point including three on 7th October 1995, Sandbanks and Branksome Chine including 7W on 23rd May 1996 and three in January 1998. Reports of one inside Christchurch Harbour from 3rd–5th September 1983 and another flying over rooftops at Chiswell, North Portland on 8th January 1998 are most unusual. The only recent inland record involves one at Charminster (near Dorchester) after the 'hurricane' on 17th October 1987.

A total of 353 birds has been ringed in the county, all but 18 during 1991–1998, mainly as a result of nocturnal tape-luring at Portland Bill. Local movements are indicated by five birds ringed at Portland Bill being later controlled at St Aldhelm's Head (including two subsequently recovered in Tyne & Wear) and one bird ringed at St Aldhelm's Head being controlled at Portland Bill, whilst five birds ringed at Portland Bill have been recaptured there in subsequent years. Movements outside the county are dominated by the regular interchange of birds within the western seaboard of the British Isles. There are single controls from France and Norway. In addition, a much travelled individual was ringed at Portland Bill on 26th June 1996, controlled at Pentire (Cornwall) less than a month later, then at the Calf of Man on 8th July 1997 and finally at Sanda Island (Strathclyde) on 29th July 1997.

The Storm Petrel breeds in colonies scattered throughout the north-east Atlantic and western Mediterranean with Atlantic breeders dispersing southwards to wintering grounds off Namibia and South Africa. Away from the breeding colonies, most in the British Isles occur after autumn gales and storms.

Postscript 2000–2002

In 2000, there was an unprecedented 'wreck' of birds on 30th October following south-westerly gales. A total of 217 birds were reported from the Portland, Fleet and Weymouth area, which undoubtedly involved some duplication, but an estimated 150 were present in Portland Harbour. As a result of this 'wreck', 100 flew west at Portland Bill during 31st October–3rd November. The 'wreck' was mirrored to a lesser extent at coastal watch-points in the east of the county including 16 at Branksome Chine during 30th October–2nd November, whilst one found dead at Stourpaine on 5th November is only the second record from well inland since 1950. In 2002, one at Durlston CP on 20th February is the first county record for that month, whilst singles at Portland Bill on 25th and 28th April are only the second and third Dorset sightings for that month.

Leach's Petrel (Leach's Storm-petrel) *Oceanodroma leucorhoa*

A scarce autumn and winter visitor, subject to large-scale 'wrecks' in adverse weather

Both Mansel-Pleydell (1888) and Blathwayt (1945) regarded this species as an occasional or irregular storm-driven visitor to the coast and gave instances of birds found well inland.

Leach's Petrels occurred in 12 years between 1948 and 1979. Apart from six in 1948 and the large 'wreck' of October 1952, the remaining sightings consist of 1–2 birds per year involving five singles 'wrecked' well inland, two singles on or near the coast, and six passing offshore including one at Portland Bill on 10th September 1970 – remarkably the only record from this site during 1950–1979.

Since 1982 there has been a marked increase with annual records including the post-hurricane 'wreck' of October 1987 and the 'wreck' of December 1989. Birds usually occur from August to January and, excluding 'wreck' years, there is a distinct peak during September–October – see Table 96.

Spring and summer records are exceptional with singles at Portland Bill on 1st May 1983 and Lyme Bay on 18th May 1983 – possibly involving the same bird, and one at Portland Bill on 27th June 1990. There is also a report for late winter involving a bird found long dead at Stanpit Marsh, Christchurch Harbour on 24th February 1990.

Aug	Sept	Oct	Nov	Dec	Jan
2%	27%	39%	12%	15%	4%

Table 96. Monthly autumn/winter distribution (%) 1950–1999 excluding 'wrecks'

The main sites are Portland Bill, Durlston CP and Hengistbury – see Table 97. Apart from the 'wrecks' of 1987 and 1989, which are described below, there are very few records from other coastal sites, namely singles at West Bexington, Ferrybridge, Portland Harbour, inside Poole Harbour, Holes Bay, Sandbanks and Branksome Chine, two inside Christchurch Harbour and four at Chesil Cove. Otherwise one was found well inland at Dorchester on 19th November 1982.

	1980	1981	1982	1983	1984	1985	1986	1987	1988	1989
Portland Bill	0	0	2	10	2	2	4	29	5	17
Durlston CP	0	0	0	0	0	1	6	19	4	69
Hengistbury	0	0	0	1	0	3	1	5	2	64

	1990	1991	1992	1993	1994	1995	1996	1997	1998	1999
Portland Bill	1	0	0	0	1	2	3	1	2	1
Durlston CP	4	1	2	0	1	0	1	2	1	0
Hengistbury	0	1	0	7	2	0	1	0	1	0

Table 97. Autumn/winter totals (bds) at the main coastal watch-points 1980–1999

Autumn and early winter storms can occasionally result in large numbers of petrels being forced inshore with some birds found stranded or dead well inland from the coast. Since 1950 there have been three of these 'wrecks', which are described in more detail below.

October 1952: as a result of severe Atlantic gales, a large influx occurred from 26th October with birds still being recorded up to 9th November. Only eight specimens were critically examined and identified as Leach's Petrels, but the majority of the rest were presumed to be this species. Estimated totals involved about ten dead or dying inland and c.440 on the coast including c.400 in Chesil Cove and c.20 in Portland Harbour/along East Fleet on 27th, c.seven in Poole Harbour on 31st and five at West Bay on 29th.

October 1987: as a result of the 'great hurricane', there was a notable influx of birds with 29 at Portland Bill during 17th–20th with a maximum of 25 on 18th, 19 at Durlston CP during 17th–21st, with a maximum of 14 on 18th, five at Hengistbury during 18th–19th, two in Weymouth Bay on 18th and well inland one at Warmwell on 17th. In addition there were a number of unidentified petrels including two 'wrecked' in Christchurch gardens on 17th.

December 1989: storm-force winds on 16th followed by gales on 24th produced the largest 'wreck' since 1952. Although some birds were reported earlier, the main influx occurred during 24th–25th with counts from the main sites summarised in Table 98. Otherwise there were sightings of singles from Charmouth (dead) on 25th, Langton Herring on 17th, Lodmoor NR on 24th and inside Christchurch Harbour on 23rd.

	Number and dates	Maximum and date
West Bexington	26–17th–26th	18 on 25th
Chesil Cove/Ferrybridge/Portland Hbr	29–17th–25th	8 on 21st
Portland Bill	15–18th–25th	3 on several dates
Weymouth Bay	14–21st–25th	12 on 24th
Durlston CP	69W–19th–27th	38W on 25th
Branksome/Bournemouth Pier	42–24th–25th	30 on 24th
Avon Beach/Hengistbury	64W–24th–25th	34W on 25th

Table 98. Summary of December 1989 'wreck' at the main sites

The Leach's Petrel breeds in colonies around the margins of the North Atlantic and North Pacific with birds migrating to winter in the equatorial waters of both oceans. British colonies are confined to islands off the north of Scotland. Away from the breeding colonies, most in the British Isles occur after autumn gales and storms.

Postscript 2000–2002
A county total of 19 birds in 2000 is the third highest since 1980 and includes 15 during 27th October–1st November coinciding with the large 'wreck' of the previous species. In 2002, there was an exceptional series of sightings in February involving two singles at Branksome Chine on 2nd with further singles at Hengistbury and Portland Bill on 2nd, West Bexington on 3rd and Portland Harbour on 9th – prior to this year there was only one Dorset record for this month.

Gannet (Northern Gannet)

Morus bassanus

A common non-breeding resident and passage migrant

Mansel-Pleydell (1888) considered this species to be an autumn and winter visitor noting that "it arrives about October and leaves again in April, being most plentiful during the Sprat season". Blathwayt (1945) described it as "a frequent visitor to the coast, usually in winter or spring, but may occur any time" and recorded the presence of 200 at Portland Bill on 28th January 1932.

Since 1950 the Gannet has been a common visitor throughout the year. Although most conspicuous at Portland Bill, it occurs along the entire coast of Dorset including the more sheltered waters of Lyme, Weymouth and Poole Bays. The species is most numerous in spring/early summer (April–June) and autumn (August–October) with slightly fewer birds in mid-summer (July) and a much smaller population offshore in winter (November–March) – see Table 99.

Jan	Feb	Mar	Apr	May	Jun	Jul	Aug	Sep	Oct	Nov	Dec
2%	4%	6%	11%	16%	14%	8%	13%	10%	10%	3%	2%

Table 99. Monthly distribution (%) at Portland Bill and Durlston CP 1986–1995

In the first half of the year, there is a net easterly upchannel movement, but increasing numbers move west as the year progresses. Although there are large breeding colonies as close as Alderney, Brittany (Sept Iles), Dyfed (Grassholm) and southern Ireland, Gannets seen in Dorset's waters do not necessarily derive from them, since juveniles and non-breeders range widely throughout the North Atlantic. Birds involved in feeding movements during the summer months, however, almost certainly come from the closest colonies on Alderney and Sept Iles as breeding adults are thought to have a foraging range of c.120km.

The strength of these offshore movements is often dependent on the prevailing weather, and the availability of favourable feeding conditions such as a run of Sprat or Mackerel. Prior to the mid-1980s, a large fishing flock became an established feature at Portland Bill during the summer months with peak counts often exceeding 500 birds and reaching 1,000 birds in July 1977 and July 1981. Subsequently there has been a steady decline in the size of this flock, so that by the mid-1990s it had virtually ceased to exist, the last maximum of consequence being 150 in June 1990. More recently, large fishing flocks have been recorded at other times of year, notably 500 on 19th October 1999 and 300 on 3rd and 4th January 1996. Other high counts at Portland Bill are 2,500W on 5th October 1988, c.1,500 on 5th November 1985 following a huge Sprat shoal, 1,500E during 1st–3rd October 1979 plus 1,000 present the following day, 1,350E on 4th February 1989 and 1,100E during 4th–5th May 1997. Large numbers sometimes occur in Lyme Bay including 1,000 at Chesil Cove on 8th October 1997. Elsewhere the highest counts are from Durlston CP with 510 on 27th June 1989 and 500 on 28th April 1995, Hengistbury with 300W on 29th August 1997 and coincidentally from nearby Branksome Chine with 300 on the same date.

The species is a scarce visitor to the Fleet and Portland, Poole and Christchurch Harbours, whilst there are a few sightings of birds flying over near-coastal sites including Radipole School and Radipole and Lodmoor NRs. Well inland, there are records of single birds from: North Chideock on 16th January 1949 (dead), Knowlton in late January 1951 (dead), Gussage All Saints on 13th September 1957 (released at Portland Bill), Cerne Abbas on 5th November 1959 (released on coast), Colehill on 29th August 1962 (flying over), Wynford Eagle in 1972 (dead), near Sturminster Marshall on 3rd January 1979 (flying low over fields), Church Knowle on 8th December 1983 (caught on a barbed-wire fence), Chedington on 28th March 1986 (dead), Long Bredy on 1st December 1989, Maiden Castle on 29th October 1998 (seen on ground before flying off) and Bardolf Manor, Puddletown on 31st May 1999 (flying over).

Five birds (all stranded) have been ringed in the county. There are also three controls involving two ringed as nestlings on Les Etacs (Alderney) and one ringed as a nestling at Bass Rock.

The Gannet breeds in the North Atlantic with 75% of the population being in north-west Europe and the British Isles supporting 185,000 pairs of the European population of 230,000 pairs. In the eastern North Atlantic, some birds, mainly adults, remain in the latitudes of the breeding colonies throughout the winter, whilst others migrate southwards to the sub-tropical and tropical waters off West Africa – this tendency being much stronger in juveniles.

Postscript 2000–2002

In 2000 at Hengistbury 500W on 25th October and 435E on 28th September were record counts for the site.
Sponsored by Mike Bramwell and Lt. Cdr A. T. Kennedy

Cormorant (Great Cormorant)   *Phalacrocorax carbo*

A fairly common resident, winter visitor and passage migrant

Since the 19th Century breeding has been largely confined to the Purbeck cliffs, the most important sites being at Ballard Down, Gad Cliff and Bat's Head/White Nothe. The number of occupied nests at these colonies are given in Table 100. Persecution by man has affected the strength of the breeding population during much of the 20th Century. In 1932 the *Proceedings* of DNH&AS stated that Cormorant sites were deserted because of the bounty paid by local river boards for heads, a practice which ceased in 1981. Blathwayt (1945) also recorded a decline in breeding numbers due to persecution and noted that nesting was almost confined to Gad Cliff. The colonies at Gad Cliff and Bat's Head/White Nothe remained under the protection of the Bonds of Tyneham and thus escaped decimation.

More recent counts show a marked increase in breeding numbers, notably at Ballard Down where the population was particularly low from the 1940s through to the 1970s. Between 1982 and 1990 the population at the three main colonies increased from 190 to 320 occupied nests, but there is some evidence to suggest a slight decline in breeding numbers subsequently. A nest being built on cliffs between Durlston CP and St Aldhelm's Head on 8th March 1992 was the only evidence of breeding along this section of the Purbeck cliffs for 35 years. Subsequently breeding was reported at St Aldhelm's Head in 1996, but no further details given, and again between Durlston CP and St Aldhelm's Head in 1998.

	32	37	40	48	66	69	70	73	74	75	76	77	78	81	82
Gad Cliff	200	77	45	180	108	100	80	100	86	99	100	80	83	78	84
Ballard Down	nc	nc	nc	2–3	3	nc	nc	nc	11	nc	15	nc	nc	nc	82
White Nothe*	nc	nc	nc	nc	nc	nc	nc	nc	nc	nc	nc	nc	24	nc	24

	83	84	85	86	87	88	89	90	91	92	94	96	98	99
Gad Cliff	90	90	83	88	106	110	111	108	94	89	89	80	nc	nc
Ballard Down	82	92	100	117	147	120	nc	172	122	127	nc	101	96	86
White Nothe*	nc	nc	nc	nc	15	15	18	40	38	53	nc	nc	nc	nc

Table 100. Number of occupied nests at the main Purbeck breeding colonies 1932–1999; * = between Bat's Head and White Nothe

Although there are claims of recent breeding along the west Dorset coast at West Bay in 1986 (one pair), 1991 (8–10 pairs) and 1993, there is evidence to suggest this is only a roost site. Boys (1972) and Prendergast & Boys (1983) mention that breeding formerly took place in west Dorset prior to 1948, but there is no reference to this in Blathwayt (1945). Breeding has only been proven once at Portland Bill in 1948, but probably occurred there in 1950, whilst the only evidence of inland breeding is given in Mansel-Pleydell (1888) who recorded "there is a tradition of the former existence of a Cormorant's nest in a tree on the Stour, near Langton, Blandford".

National surveys of Cormorant populations have reflected the increase in the Dorset breeding population with 122 pairs located by the Operation Seafarer Survey during 1969–1970 increasing to 197 pairs recorded by the NCC/Seabird Group Survey during 1985–1987. The later figure seems to be an under-estimate, since 272 pairs were present at the three main colonies in 1987 – see Table 100. The Tetrad Survey (1987–1994) Map reflects the recent breeding distribution in the county.

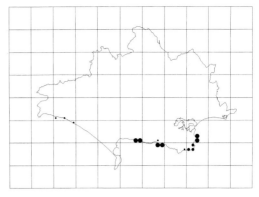

Away from the breeding cliffs Cormorants occur in a wide range of coastal and inland waters, particularly favouring the harbours and river valleys. Like the breeding population, there has been a marked increase in the size of the non-breeding population in the county. This is particularly evident in Poole Harbour, which is the main coastal water for the species outside the breeding season – see Table 101. Annual maxima at this site generally ranged from 350–450 birds during 1980–1999, the highest counts being 476 in September 1988 and 471 in August 1995. Christchurch Harbour is the only other coastal site where annual maxima have reached treble figures with some frequency in recent years, the highest count being 136 in September 1995. The Fleet, Portland Harbour and Radipole NR also attract substantial gatherings of Cormorants. Although annual maxima at these sites rarely exceed 50 birds, there are isolated peaks of 130 in Portland Harbour in December 1995 and 108 on the Fleet in March 1990. In earlier years, a count of 409 at Handfast Point, Ballard Down on 12th December 1968 was considered to be exceptional.

1963–1969	1970–1974	1975–1979	1980–1984	1985–1989	1990–1994	1995–1999
191	176	290	346	390	387	397

Table 101. Average annual maxima from Poole Harbour 1963–1999

At coastal sites, peak counts occur during the post-breeding and early winter period August to November – see Table 102. By contrast, the highest numbers at inland waters are usually present during the mid-winter period December to February – see Table 104. In Poole Harbour, the high autumn population is thought to comprise a combination of local breeders, which may remain throughout the winter, and migrants, possibly involving birds from colonies in south-west England, south-east Ireland and Wales. During the summer, breeding birds feeding in the harbour fly directly south over the Purbecks to the colony at Gad Cliff.

	Jan	Feb	Mar	Apr	May	Jun	Jul	Aug	Sep	Oct	Nov	Dec
Poole Hbr	148	133	154	81	85	64	161	239	345	327	274	211
Xchurch Hbr	39	59	44	47	60	69	84	94	91	85	71	74

Table 102. Average monthly maxima from Poole and Christchurch Harbours 1988–1999

Well inland, a night roost of Cormorants has been established on the Dorset/Hampshire border beside the River Avon at Avon Village since the mid-1950s. In recent years peak counts have regularly exceeded 100 birds with a maximum of 188 in February 1990. This roost attracts birds both from Christchurch Harbour to the south and from feeding areas further up the Avon Valley to the north. Elsewhere there is evidence of a recent increase in the numbers of Cormorants venturing inland in Dorset. At Sherborne Lake, a count of 45 in January 1991 was regarded as being exceptional at the time, but during 1996–1999 annual maxima have ranged between 35 and a peak of 61 birds in February 1998. By contrast, annual maxima at a well-watched roost on pylons over the River Stour at Corfe Mullen increased during the 1980s to a peak of 35 in February 1991, but subsequently declined to the levels of the early 1980s – see Table 103. Other inland waters usually hold smaller numbers of birds with peak counts rarely exceeding 15 birds, but up to 32 at Child Okeford fish ponds in 1999, 30 at Blandford on 7th January 1996 and 27 at Puddletown on 9th December 1996.

80	81	82	83	84	85	86	87	88	89	90	91	92	93	94	95	96	97	98	99
10	9	12	10	9	23	17	15	13	31	29	35	20	18	11	14	17	16	13	12

Table 103. Winter maxima at the Corfe Mullen roost 1980–1999

Jan	Feb	Mar	Apr	May	Jun	Jul	Aug	Sep	Oct	Nov	Dec
13	13	10	6	5	4	6	7	8	7	9	11

Table 104. Average monthly maxima at the Corfe Mullen roost 1980–1999

Although many offshore movements involve local birds, there is some evidence of passage. For example, there are distinct peaks in spring and autumn at Portland Bill where 65S on 2nd October 1983 and 73S during 28th–29th September 1999 are notable.

Prior to 1980, there were several reports, notably during the 1950s and 1960s, of the subspecies *P. c. sinensis*, but apparently only one was critically examined. Subsequently a few birds showing the characteristics of this subspecies at Abbotsbury in spring 1997 is the only recent published record.

The first bird ringed in Dorset was caught in a mist-net set after dark for waders in Poole Harbour in 1998. There are controls of colour-ringed birds from County Wexford and Wales.

The Cormorant is a cosmopolitan species with breeding sites on all continents except South America. The British Isles have about 28% of the breeding population of the nominate subspecies.

Postscript 2000–2002
A new county record of 504 at Brownsea on 1st October 2000 was superseded by 585 in Poole Harbour in October 2001 (WeBS). At Sherborne Lake 75 in January 2001 is a record count for the site. The presence of nests (no count) at West Bay in 2000 suggests that breeding does occur in west Dorset. There are several reports of the Continental race *P. c. sinensis* in both years. Finally a colour-ringed bird from the Netherlands was reported from Christchurch Harbour in 2001.

Shag (European Shag) *Phalacrocorax aristotelis*

A locally common resident, winter visitor and passage migrant

The Purbeck cliffs have been the breeding stronghold for this species since the 19th Century when Mansel-Pleydell (1888) stated "it is most abundant on the south coast of Purbeck from Gadcliff to Lulworth, and thence westward to Whitenore". Blathwayt (1945) considered that the Shag was rarer than formerly with some old breeding stations deserted, and further commented that it still bred sparingly in places from Whitenose to Anvil Point, e.g. about five pairs at Gad Cliff in 1940. The county breeding population during the 1940s was estimated at c.30 pairs.

Subsequently numbers increased to c.70 pairs in 1971 with the majority (56 pairs) located between Durlston CP and St Aldhelm's Head. Since then, this section of the Purbeck coast has remained the stronghold for the species in the county maintaining a fluctuating, but overall relatively stable, population – see Table 105. Elsewhere on Purbeck, there are intermittent counts from other breeding sites including Bat's Head, Gad Cliff and Ballard Down – see Table 106. Reasons for the annual variations in occupied nests are thought to include the availability of suitably weathered breeding ledges, which are liable to disappear with coastal erosion. It has also been observed that in Purbeck, Shags may takeover ledges formerly occupied by Guillemots, but in turn may be displaced by Herring Gulls.

64	69	71	72	75	76	77	78	79	80	81	82	83	84	85
23	35	56	56	40	48	37	36	49	27	33	47	39	37	40

86	87	88	89	90	91	92	93	94	95	96	97	98	99
53	37	47	48	46	48	66	nc	59	nc	41	51	44	61

Table 105. Number of occupied nests between Durlston CP and St Aldhelm's Head 1964–1999

Although the Shag is present at Portland Bill throughout the year, the only reports of confirmed breeding are for single pairs in 1950, and more recently in 1998 and 1999. The *BTO Atlas* (1968–1972),

	69	74	75	78	81	82	84	85	86	87	88	89	90	91	92	96
Bat's Head	6	nc	nc	4	nc	nc	nc	nc	nc	3	2	4	4	6	2	nc
Gad Cliff	nc	13	3	6	10	nc	nc	6	3	nc	nc	nc	3	5	2	2
Ballard Down	nc	nc	nc	nc	nc	6	3	3	nc	nc	nc	nc	nc	nc	nc	nc

Table 106. Number of occupied nests at other sites on Purbeck 1969–1996

however, also records that breeding was proven in SY66 (Portland Bill), but there is no reference to this in the Bird Reports of the time.

National surveys of Shag populations have suggested a slight increase in the Dorset breeding population with 51 pairs located by the Operation Seafarer Survey during 1969–1970 increasing to 79 pairs recorded by the NCC/Seabird Group Survey during 1985–1987. The Tetrad Survey (1987–1994) Map reflects the recent breeding distribution in the county.

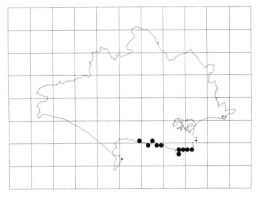

At Portland Bill, the non-breeding population has declined since the early 1980s – see Tables 107 and 108. This is likely to be related to available feeding locally. Annual maxima generally range from 35–65 birds, the highest counts being 100 on 4th September 1969 and 18th September 1973, 95 during late August–mid-September 1968, 91 on 3rd October 1982 and 90 after gales on 11th October 1997. The highest numbers usually occur during the post breeding and early winter period August to November – see Table 108.

1970–1974	1975–1979	1980–1984	1985–1989	1990–1994
60	56	58	43	34

Table 107. Average annual maxima at Portland Bill 1970–1994

	Jan	Feb	Mar	Apr	May	Jun	Jul	Aug	Sep	Oct	Nov	Dec
1983–1989	24	20	26	19	12	12	10	23	40	39	28	28
1990–1995	12	10	11	12	8	7	8	21	27	25	21	20

Table 108. Average monthly maxima at Portland Bill 1983 –1989 and 1990–1995

Away from the Purbeck cliffs and Portland Bill, the other main sites for the species are Poole Harbour, Portland Harbour/Weymouth Bay and Hengistbury. In Poole Harbour winter maxima usually vary between 50–100 birds, the highest counts being 131 in November 1976, 127 on 2nd December 1984 and 118 in November 1988. In Portland Harbour/Weymouth Bay winter maxima have been consistently in the range of 40–60 birds with occasional higher peaks such as 150 in November 1989 and 100+ during heavy storms in January–February 1974, on 2nd December 1978, and during both winter periods in 1980. Much smaller numbers occur at Hengistbury with annual maxima, mainly in winter, usually ranging from 20–30 birds, but 60 in August 1996.

Nocturnal roosts of this and the preceding species are not well recorded. There are evening flights of both species out of Poole and Portland Harbours with known roosts at Ballard Down and one or two sites on Portland. It is clear, however, that some Portland Harbour feeders leave towards a Purbeck roost and that one roost on Portland includes birds flying in from the west. This is curious since the Shag appears to be very scarce in the west of the county.

The species occasionally wanders to the Fleet and near-coastal sites such as Radipole NR with singles on 4th December 1974, 5th–6th January 1990 and 22nd April 1995, Lodmoor NR with singles on 18th November 1974 and in November 1997, and Hatch Pond, Poole with one on 21st January 1995. It is very rare inland with singles at Alton Pancras on 14th March 1962 (released at sea) and Cheselbourne on 21st November 1980 (released at Radipole NR) the only records.

A total of eight birds has been ringed in the county.

The Shag is a breeding resident along the coasts of north-western Europe, north-west Africa, the Mediterranean and the Black Sea.

Postscript 2000–2002

Recent (since 1998) confirmed breeding involving a single pair at Portland Bill continued in 2000 and 2001 with a pair present during the breeding season in 2002. At Abbotsbury two on 8th December 2000 is the first report from this site since 1966, whilst one at Lodmoor NR on 1st January 2001 is only the third recent record from this site.

Sponsored by Mitch and Dean

Bittern (Great Bittern) *Botaurus stellaris*

A scarce winter visitor and passage migrant

The Bittern bred in Dorset in the 19th Century, certainly in 1883, but the only evidence of breeding in more recent times involves at least one bird, which lingered into the early summer at an inland site in 1968. Otherwise this species was considered to be mainly a not uncommon and frequent winter visitor by Mansel-Pleydell (1888) and Blathwayt (1945), the latter referring to numerous records and further commenting that it had been reported in nearly every winter for the last sixteen years.

Since 1950 Bitterns have occurred in all but eight winters – see Fig 15. Although seasonal totals are typically very small, usually 1–5 birds, periods of severe winter weather often result in small influxes as birds, mainly from the near Continent, are forced to move south and west to find suitable feeding conditions. Such hard winters have produced between 6–18 birds, the most notable influxes being in 1962/63, 1981/82, 1984/85, 1986/87 and 1996/97.

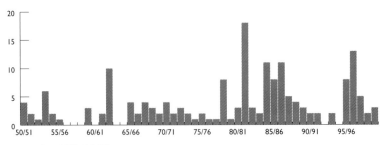

Fig 15. Winter totals 1950–1999

Wetlands, especially those with reedbeds, have yielded the vast majority of sightings – see Table 109. Radipole NR is by far the most regular site with records in every winter since 1965/66 except for a three-year period during 1992/93–1994/95, whilst nearby Lodmoor NR has attracted birds in 18 winters since 1970/71. These two sites account for 39% of the total of winter birds recorded since 1950/51. Other favoured winter haunts for the species include Abbotsbury, Wareham/Swineham, Studland NNR, Wimborne/Allen Valley, Christchurch Harbour and the Lower Avon Valley. At Sydling St Nicholas the same returning bird was present in four consecutive winters from 1986/87–1989/90. Otherwise there are winter sightings from sites widely scattered across the county including the coast, river valleys, cress-beds, lakes and small ponds. Perhaps the most unusual records involve one found in a built-up area of Parkstone during the 'big freeze' of January–February 1963, one at Portland Bill on 8th February 1986, 1N at Durlston CP on 29th December 1996 and one at the Grove, Portland on 14th January 1997. Most reports involve single birds, more than two being exceptional, the highest counts being from Radipole NR with up to four during January–February 1982, four on 5th January 1997, up to three during 13th January–10th March 1971 and three on 6th December 1986, also three at Abbotsbury on 9th February 1954.

	Total Winters	Total Birds
Abbotsbury	9	12
Radipole NR	34	48
Lodmoor NR	20	21
Wareham/Swineham	9	9
Studland NNR	9	9
Wimborne/R. Allen	7	8
Christchurch Harbour	11	13
Lower Avon Valley	5	6

Table 109. Total number of winters with records and total number of birds 1950–1999

Although records of presumably wintering birds extend from September to early April, the vast majority of birds are seen during the mid-winter period December–February. Some of the September–October and March sightings may involve passage birds. There are a number of other records, all involving single birds, that almost certainly refer to migrants with at least five in spring from: Abbotsbury on 28th May 1956, Lodmoor NR during 14th–20th April 1973, Christchurch Harbour on 21st April 1976, Portland Bill on 14th April 1994 and Brownsea on 26th May 1997, and at least eight in autumn from: Radipole NR during 4th–8th September 1975, 14th July–13th October 1976, 25th–28th August 1981 and on 22nd and 29th July 1999, Swineham on 21st September 1975, Lodmoor NR during 19th–30th September 1990, Hengistbury on 23rd September 1998 and Abbotsbury on 28th August 1999.

Two birds have been ringed in the county.

The Bittern breeds locally in Europe and more widely across central Asia, also very locally in southern Africa. It winters in western and southern Europe and southern Asia. In the British Isles it is a very rare breeder, and scarce passage migrant and winter visitor.

Postscript 2000–2002
At Radipole NR at least one bird wintered during 2000/01, up to three were present during November–December 2001 (maximum on 2nd December with one present from January to 4th March 2002), and one wintered during 2002/03. Elsewhere up to two birds wintered at Hatch Pond, Poole during 2002/03. Otherwise singles were reported from Swineham on 20th February 2000, Lodmoor NR on 28th January 2001, 11th January and 20th October 2002, Creekmoor Ponds on 29th December 2001, Hengistbury on 7th January 2002, Holes Bay on 4th November 2002 and Brownsea on 27th December 2002.

Sponsored by Purbeck Natural History Club

American Bittern   *Botaurus lentiginosus*

Accidental: two records

1804   Puddletown: autumn
1980   Tincleton: 12th November

The bird shot at Puddletown in 1804 was the first British record. The 1980 record involved a recently shot bird and it is an amazing coincidence that the two Dorset records should involve birds shot at locations a little over 3km apart. The latter specimen is preserved and resides at the Dorset County Museum. A full account of the 1980 bird can be found in the Dorset Bird Report for 1981.

The American Bittern breeds across much of North America, some moving south in winter. A vagrant to the British Isles, becoming increasingly rarer with 50 records before 1958, but only 11 between then and 2000.

Little Bittern   *Ixobrychus minutus*

A very rare passage migrant: c.19 records

There are about ten pre-20th Century records including singles near Swanage on 25th March 1886 and at Winfrith in spring 1891. The nine recent records have occurred since 1970 with eight in spring and only one in autumn. The most favoured sites are Radipole and Lodmoor NRs, which together account for seven of the nine recent sightings.

    1970   Lodmoor NR: male 13th–15th May
    1972   Radipole NR: male 23rd–25th April
            Radipole NR: female 1st to about 16th July
    1975   Lodmoor NR: male 18th May
    1977   Radipole NR: male 18th–20th May
    1981   Radipole NR: immature 25th August to 5th September
    1988   Portland Bill: female 16th April
    1990   River Allen at Hinton Parva: female 18th May
    1993   Radipole NR: male 7th May

The Little Bittern breeds across much of central and southern Europe eastwards into west-central Asia, also in the north of the Indian sub-continent, sub-Saharan Africa, and Australia. European breeders winter in sub-Saharan Africa. A vagrant to Great Britain with 342 records up to 2002.

Sponsored by Louise Collier

Night Heron (Black-crowned Night Heron)   *Nycticorax nycticorax*

A very rare passage migrant and winter visitor: 19 records

There are three 19th Century records with one shot at Radipole in May 1843, one 'procured' nearby in May 1883 and one at Poole in November 1891. Since 1949 there have been 16 records including 13 between 4th April and 24th June and three in November. Radipole NR is the most favoured site with six sightings, whilst four birds have occurred at Portland.

1949 Near Wareham: ad. 8th November
1960 Radipole NR: ad. found shot 18th April
1961 Radipole NR: ad. 25th November
1962 Radipole NR: ad. 14th April
1969 Charlton Marshall: imm. 23rd November
1970 Radipole NR: ad. 2nd June
1983 Radipole NR: probable second-summer 23rd June
1987 East Weare, Portland: ad. 17th April (part of national influx)
1988 River Avon at Winkton Weir: ad. 7th–17th April
1989 Stanpit Marsh, Christchurch Harbour: first-summer 22nd April
      West Stafford: probable second-summer 27th May
1990 Portland Bill: ad. 4th April (part of national influx)
1992 Radipole NR: ad. 22nd June
1995 Southwell, Portland: ad. 11th May
2000 Stanpit Village: first-summer 1st May
2001 Portland Bill: first-summer 24th June

The Night Heron breeds discontinuously across central and southern Europe as far north as the Netherlands (very local) and more widely in southern Asia, also in Africa, and North and South America. European breeders winter mainly in sub-Saharan Africa. A vagrant to Great Britain with 588 records up to 2001.

Squacco Heron   *Ardeola ralloides*

Accidental: c.10 records

There are about seven records between 1865 and 1905, when one was seen in Purbeck on 17th January after a south-easterly gale, and three recent occurrences:

1977 River Stour at Longham Bridge: 22nd May
1982 Radipole NR: adult 5th July to 8th August
1996 Hengistbury: 19th June

The Squacco Heron breeds locally in southern Europe and south-west Asia, also in sub-Saharan Africa where most European birds winters A vagrant to Great Britain with 145 records up to 2002.

Cattle Egret   *Bubulcus ibis*

A very rare passage migrant and winter visitor: eight records

The first county record concerns a bird which spent much of its time frequenting the Sutton Bingham and Lower Key areas of Somerset between 22nd December 1985 and 23rd February 1986, when it was discovered in a weakened state during a period of freezing weather and taken into care. During its stay it was seen on many occasions (probably nightly) flying into Dorset to roost in Clifton Wood.

Subsequently there have been seven further records, all during 1996–2001 including two in 1998 and three in 2001:

1996 Ower/Wytch Farm area: 26th August to 31st December; same at Christchurch Harbour 12th October
1998 Portland: briefly at the Bill 19th March before moving to Reap Lane; same in the Weymouth
      area at Tidmoor 19th March, Radipole NR, Redlands and flying east over Lodmoor NR
      20th March
      Abbotsbury: 11th December
2000 Lodmoor NR: 7th August; same at Abbotsbury 7th August
2001 Middlebere: 29th–30th July
      Radipole NR: 23rd–24th November and 7th–14th December; same in Portesham area 28th
      November to 14th December
      Morden Bog: 30th December

Single birds seen near Bradford Peverell on 23rd August 1974, and near Wynford Eagle and Compton Valence in mid-September 1975 were thought to be escapes from captivity and not submitted to the *British Birds* Rarities Committee. Since the species is now generally regarded as being a genuine vagrant to the British Isles, perhaps these records should be reconsidered if full details can be obtained.

The Cattle Egret now breeds as near as northern France, but otherwise in south-west Europe, also in parts of Africa, southern Asia, Australia, and North and South America. Some European breeders move south to North Africa. A vagrant to Great Britain, increasing in recent years as the species spreads north in France with only two records prior to 1958, but 118 between then and 2002.

Little Egret   *Egretta garzetta*

A very rare passage migrant prior to 1987, now a locally common resident

Originally a classic spring and summer 'overshooting' vagrant, the status of this species changed dramatically in the late 1980s with the start of an annual influx of birds into the county during the late summer and autumn. Many of these birds remained to overwinter and as the size of the annual influx steadily increased, so the colonisation of Dorset and Great Britain was widely anticipated. Successful breeding eventually occurred in 1996.

The first county records involve singles at Abbotsbury on 9th May 1940 and in Poole Harbour on 23rd February 1946. There were no further sightings for 15 years, but during 1961–1987 c.30 birds were recorded in 11 years including a remarkable influx of c.11 birds during spring 1970 – see Table 110. This influx involved the arrival of at least seven birds in the Weymouth area from 17th April, with a peak of six together at Lodmoor NR on 1st and 2nd May and the last bird on the Fleet at Langton Herring on 14th June. It also included a bird at Portland Bill from 17th–29th April, which was trapped and ringed. Further east, four birds appeared in Poole Harbour on 3rd May with three present at Arne NR until 18th May and at least one remaining on Brownsea from 22nd June until 26th September. It is possible that some of the Poole Harbour birds may have included birds dispersing from the Weymouth area. Otherwise the remaining 19 birds were recorded in other years from Radipole and Lodmoor NRs (seven), Poole Harbour (five), Christchurch Harbour (four) and the Fleet (one) with singles inland at Wool on 31st May 1979 and Charminster on 16th October 1987 – the latter moving to Puddletown on 18th October and finally overwintering in Poole Harbour from 4th November. Most birds (26) arrived during 17th April–17th June with three during 4th–16th July and isolated occurrences in February, September and October. The autumn records were both in 1987 and perhaps are best regarded as a precursor to the sudden increase in sightings from 1988 onwards.

1960	1961	1962	1963	1964	1965	1966	1967	1968	1969	1970	1971	1972	1973
0	1	0	0	0	0	0	2	0	0	11	0	0	0

1974	1975	1976	1977	1978	1979	1980	1981	1982	1983	1984	1985	1986	1987
0	0	3	3	2	1	0	1	1	0	2	0	0	3

Table 110. Annual totals 1960–1987

The first record of overwintering in Poole Harbour during 1987/88 was followed by a remarkable increase in records. Whereas previously most reports had been in spring, the pattern since 1988 has been quite different and involves a post-breeding influx of birds from mid-June onwards with numbers rising to peak during August–September. Although counts decline thereafter, substantial numbers remain to winter particularly in Poole Harbour. Generally fewest birds are present during the spring.

Poole Harbour attracts the largest numbers of Little Egrets, the highest counts usually occurring at the main roost at Little Sea. Both Brownsea and Arne NR are also used as roosting sites, whilst birds disperse widely throughout the harbour area to feed at low water. Christchurch Harbour, Radipole and Lodmoor NRs, and the Fleet are the other main sites for the species – see Table 111.

There were relatively few inland records up to 1993. Since early 1994, however, an increasing number of birds have dispersed inland along the river valleys, particularly during the winter months – see Table 112. The most favoured area is the middle Piddle catchment between Bere Regis and Puddletown where

	88	89	90	91	92	93	94	95	96	97	98	99
The Fleet	1	2	1	1	3	14	11	8	18	10	30	13
Radipole NR	1	1	1	1	7	6	4	6	10	16	15	23
Lodmoor NR	1	1	0	1	9	9	15	8	3	10	8	4
Poole Harbour	4	6	14	8	11	32	85	110	98	107	61	142
Christchurch Hbr	1	4	6	2	2	5	10	15	10	11	28	44

Table 111. Annual maxima at the main coastal sites 1988–1999

numbers reached notable peaks of 20 at Chamberlayne's Farm on 4th February 1999 and 17 at Bardolf Manor on 17th November 1999. Other popular areas along the river valleys include Coward's Marsh (Lower Avon), between Wimborne and Spetisbury (Stour), between Dorchester and Charminster (Frome), and between Nottington and Upwey (Wey). One attracted to a roadside puddle at Camp Down near Blandford on 14th February 1999 was unusual.

	1994	1995	1996	1997	1998	1999
Lower Avon	nc	7	5	5+	5	7
Stour	1	2	4	2+	3	2
Frome	3	2	2	2+	1	3
Piddle*	2	3	4	5+	10	20
Wey	0	0	4	5+	6	1

Table 112. Annual maxima along the main river valleys 1994 –1999; * = includes Bere Stream and Devil's Brook

As the numbers of birds in the county have risen, it is not surprising that Little Egrets are increasingly observed passing coastal watch-points including Portland Bill, Durlston CP, St Aldhelm's Head and Hengistbury.

Breeding first occurred in Great Britain in 1996 when two pairs raised three young on Brownsea. Subsequently the numbers of pairs nesting at this site have steadily increased to five pairs (12 young) in 1997, 9–11 pairs in 1998 and 23 pairs in 1999. In 1998 a second breeding site was established in the Nursery at Hengistbury where one pair raised two or three young, with at least two nests and nine juveniles present the following year. In 1999 there was also a hint of attempted breeding at a third site. Accounts of the first breeding of Little Egrets in Great Britain can be found in *British Birds* Vol. 91, Number 7, 1998, and the Dorset Bird Report for 1997.

The Little Egret breeds in western and southern Europe (as far north as northern France and southern England), also in southern Asia, Australia and Africa. Formerly a vagrant, mostly in spring, to the British Isles with 263 records up to 1980 and another 477 up to 1990. It is now an increasing breeding resident and post-breeding visitor mainly to south-west Great Britain.

Postscript 2000–2002

Breeding continued on Brownsea where numbers increased to 46 pairs in 2000, but declined to 45 pairs in 2001 and 42 pairs in 2002, and at Hengistbury with three nests in 2001 and 3–4 pairs in 2002. In addition, breeding occurred at Dudmoor Farm in 2000 (two pairs), but not in 2001, whilst there was a suggestion of breeding at Abbotsbury in 2001. Not surprisingly, the annual maxima at most of the main coastal sites increased during 2000–2002 with 197 in Poole Harbour in October 2001, 64 at Radipole NR in April 2002, 58 on the Fleet in March 2002 and 53 at Christchurch Harbour in August 2001. Similarly the annual maxima along most of the river valleys also increased with 27 along the Lower Avon in November 2002, 13 on the Stour at Langton Long during January–February 2001 and ten on the Frome at Wool in April 2001. At Merley Park, 21 on 28th December 2001 was a notable count.

Sponsored by John Elliot and Julian Francis

Great White Egret (Great Egret)   *Ardea alba*

A very rare passage migrant and winter visitor: seven records involving eight individuals

One at Ridge, Poole Harbour on 5th August 1951 was the first county record. Since then there have been six further sightings, one in 1974 and the remainder during 1993–2002:

1974   Lodmoor NR: 11th June; same flying over Brownsea 12th June and present at Stanpit Marsh, Christchurch Harbour 12th–13th June

1993   The Fleet, mainly at Langton Herring: 17th–22nd April

1995   The Fleet at Littlesea: 5th February

1998   Stanpit Marsh, Christchurch Harbour: flying south-westwards 2nd February; same at Arne NR later 2nd February and early morning 3rd February, and at Radipole NR afternoon on 3rd February

1999   Radipole NR: one colour-ringed bird 5th October – last seen flying west

2002   Radipole NR: two 27th–28th July

The Great White Egret breeds locally in south-eastern Europe and more recently in the Netherlands and France, also in central and southern Asia, sub-Saharan Africa, Australasia, and North and South America. Most European breeders winter in south-eastern Europe. A vagrant to Great Britain with 190 records up to 2002.

Grey Heron   *Ardea cinerea*

A common resident, winter visitor and passage migrant

According to Mansel-Pleydell (1888), the main heronries in the county were at Arne Heath, Bryanston Park, Crichel Park and Wimborne St Giles Park, the heronry on Branksea (Brownsea) Island having been 'broken up' some years previously. Mansel-Pleydell also reported other instances of nesting from Little Sea, Goatham (Goathorn) Wood, Duddle Farm at Fordington, and Whatcombe, and further described the species as being "exceedingly numerous in Poole Harbour, where as many as a hundred may sometimes be seen fishing".

The *British Birds* census of 1928 revealed existing colonies at Arne Heath (c.70 pairs), Crichel Park (19 pairs), Knighton Heath Wood (15 pairs) and Sherborne Park (6 pairs). The Knighton and Crichel heronries were destroyed in 1931 and 1962 respectively, whilst the large heronry at Arne Heath had disappeared by 1948. Blathwayt (1945) also commented that heronries had existed formerly at Branksea (Brownsea) Island, Dewlish, Admiston Hall, Upton near Wimborne, Duddle Heath, Moreton Plantation, Bryanston Park, Wimborne St Giles Park and Goathorn Wood.

The largest heronry for many years was established on Brownsea in the 1930s with 50 or so nests present during the late 1930s/early 1940s, increasing to a peak of 131 nests in 1971 – see Fig 16. These may have involved birds relocating from the declining colony at Arne Heath. In addition, a small heronry near Marnhull flourished during 1957–1963 before moving to nearby Tan-Hill Wood at Hammoon.

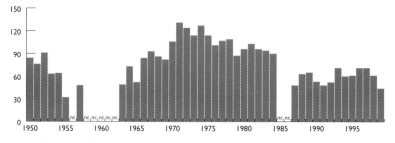

Fig 16. Number of occupied nests at the Brownsea heronry 1950–1999

The *BTO Atlas* (1968–1972) proved breeding in five 10-km squares including established heronries at Brownsea (SZ08), Sherborne Park (ST61) and Hammoon (ST71). During the 1970s and 1980s there was an increase in breeding reports including several newly established colonies – see Table 113. This is reflected by the Tetrad Survey (1987–1994), which revealed confirmed breeding in 20 tetrads distributed within 14 10-km squares. It seems likely that this proliferation of smaller colonies is due in part to the dispersal of the Brownsea heronry, where numbers diminished from the peak of 131 pairs in 1971 to 90 pairs in 1984, followed by a sharper decline with the population ranging between 44–71 pairs during 1987–1999 – see Fig 16. It should be noted that the Sherborne Park heronry ceased to exist in 1990, whilst there are no reports from Moigne Combe since the Tetrad Survey (1987–1994). In addition to the main heronries, there have been occasional reports of isolated breeding, usually involving 1–2 pairs.

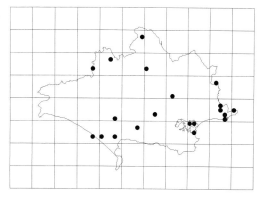

	Established/ First Recorded	Most Recent Count	Peak Count
Sherborne Park	1928	1 in 1989	15 in 1972
Marnhull/Hammoon	1957	28 in 1999	as 1999
Sopley/Dudmoor Fm	1970	16 in 1999	25 in 1991
Moigne Combe	1973	12 in 1981	as 1981
Abbotsbury	1978	7 in 1999	15 in 1992
Nottington	1983	20 in 1999	as 1999
Clifton Wood	1984	11 in 1999	as 1999
Hengistbury Head	1990	5 in 1999	9 in 1993

Table 113. Details (where available) of the other main heronries occupied during 1970–1999

Away from the breeding sites, the highest numbers of Grey Herons occur in the autumn at such favoured coastal sites as Poole Harbour (maxima of 63 in August 1992 and 62 in October 1993), Christchurch Harbour (maximum of 39 in August 1995), Radipole NR (maximum of 35 in September 1990), the Fleet (maximum of 34 in July 1987) and Lodmoor NR (maximum of 30 in July 1980). High counts from the Stour Valley between Corfe Mullen and Sturminster Marshall, where annual winter maxima ranged from 23–42 during 1980–1987, diminished after the closure of the nearby fish farm. Elsewhere counts of up to 34 roosting at Warmwell Quarries in June–July 1997, 30 at Woodsford on 10th January 1999 and 27 at Sydling St Nicholas in October 1981 are noteworthy. Otherwise the species is widely reported from other coastal and inland sites throughout the year.

Coastal movements have been observed from a number of sites, most notably Portland Bill and Durlston CP – see Table 114. The period June to October accounts for 88% of the Portland Bill and 85% of the Durlston CP records, which reflects post-breeding dispersal followed by autumn passage, whilst the slight increase during April–May may represent spring passage. At Hengistbury, 32E on 21st August 1999 is exceptional as a coastal movement.

	Jan	Feb	Mar	Apr	May	Jun	Jul	Aug	Sep	Oct	Nov	Dec
Portland Bill	6	4	12	15	30	86	90	148	153	62	7	3
Durlston CP	6	8	7	16	15	54	91	123	89	36	7	8

Table 114. Monthly totals (bds) for coastal movements at Portland Bill and Durlston CP 1987–1999

A total of 6 birds has been ringed in the county.

The Grey Heron breeds throughout Europe, but locally in the north and south, and across much of central and southern Asia, also in sub-Saharan Africa. Many European breeders move south and south-west in autumn, but the population in the British Isles is mostly non-migratory.

Postscript 2000–2002

In 2000, a total of 136 nests were counted at nine sites. There were only 29 nests at Brownsea, which is the lowest number since at least 1950 and almost certainly since the foundation of the heronry in the 1930s. In compensation, 19 nests at Hengistbury is the highest since the heronry was established at this site in 1990, whilst six nests were found at a new site at Warre Wood. The presence of 12 nests at Arne NR in 2001 is particularly significant. This site supported a large heronry from the 19th Century into the first half of the 20th Century, but it had apparently disappeared by 1948 with birds presumably relocating to nearby Brownsea. Also in 2001, a count of 35 nests at Brownsea represents a slight recovery, whilst three nests at Canford may herald the start of another new heronry. In 2002, a total of 88 nests were counted at seven sites including 33 at Brownsea. Counts of 52 at Christchurch Harbour in July 2001, 46 on the Fleet in June 2000 and 44 at Radipole NR in March 2001 are all the highest on record for these sites.

Purple Heron   *Ardea purpurea*

A rare passage migrant

There are three 19th Century records with one shot at Hyde in an unspecified year, one 'procured' in the neighbourhood of Dorchester in 1848 and one shot at Fiddleford in 1891. Since 1968 there have been 43 sightings of which the vast majority (34) have occurred in spring and early summer with one in March, six in April and 27 between 10th May and 26th June. The remaining nine sightings have been in July (three), August (three), September (one) and October (two). There have been near-annual records since 1980, the best years for the species being 1994 (seven), 1987 (five) and 1998 (four). Christchurch Harbour (15), Lodmoor NR (11*) and Radipole NR (seven*) are the most favoured sites. (Footnote* totals include two birds which occurred at both sites).

1968	Lodmoor NR: ad. 27th–30th April
	River Stour at Hampreston: ad. 11th–12th June
1970	Lodmoor NR: ad. 11th–14th May
1971	Lodmoor NR: first-year 15th–16th May
1976	Lodmoor NR: second-year 12th–29th April; also visited Radipole NR
	Christchurch Harbour: 2nd June
1980	Radipole NR: ad. 16th May, 18th–19th May and 5th June
1981	Lodmoor NR: first-year 26th–31st May
1983	Christchurch Harbour: ad. 22nd May
	Lodmoor NR: imm. 4th June
1984	St Aldhelm's Head: first-year flying out to sea 1st October
1986	Christchurch Harbour: flying north 2nd June
	Radipole NR: 22nd June
1987	Lodmoor NR: 16th May; also visited Radipole NR
	Christchurch Harbour: 12th June
	Durlston CP: 19th June
	Radipole NR: 19th–20th June and 25th June to 2nd July
	Hengistbury: 17th October
1990	Christchurch Harbour: ad. flying north 26th April
	Christchurch Harbour: imm. 28th July
1991	Christchurch Harbour: ad. flying north 28th May
1992	Lytchett Bay: second-year 8th–12th April
1993	Christchurch Harbour: ad. flying east 18th May
1994	Radipole NR: 31st March
	Christchurch Harbour: 10th, 21st and 30th May and 15th June (four different birds)
	Lodmoor NR: 13th and 16th June
	Lytchett Bay: ad. 23rd July
1995	Radipole NR: 28th May
	Cogden Beach: flying north-west 23rd June
1996	Fleet at Butterstreet Cove: 26th June

1998   West Bexington/Cogden Beach: 8th–10th April; moved to Abbotsbury where it remained
      until 13th April
    Lodmoor NR: 21st April to 12th May, possibly same as above
    Abbotsbury: juv. 7th August
    West Bexington: imm. flying east 19th August
1999   Hatch Pond, Poole: juv. 28th August to 29th September
2000   Christchurch Harbour: ad.17th May
    Lodmoor NR: 3rd June
    West Bexington: 10th September
2001   Hengistbury: flying north 10th May
    Lodmoor NR: 19th July

The Purple Heron breeds from north-west Africa, across southern and central Europe, locally north to northern France and the Netherlands, and eastwards into west-central Asia, also in south and south-east Asia and sub-Saharan Africa. European breeders winter mainly in sub-Saharan Africa. A rare visitor to the British Isles (mainly in spring) with 425 records up to 1982.

Black Stork   *Ciconia nigra*

Accidental: seven records

1839   Poole Harbour: 22nd November (shot)
1849   Poole Harbour: autumn (shot)
1977   Middlebere: 28th May; same over Purbecks 29th May
    Lodmoor NR: flying west 13th September
1988   Arne NR: 16th July
1990   Radipole NR: juv. 14th–15th September.
1991   Ringstead Bay, flying north 8th August

The Black Stork breeds in Iberia, central and eastern Europe and central Asia, also in southern Africa. European breeders winter mainly in sub-Saharan Africa, though Iberian birds may be partially resident. A vagrant to Great Britain with 151 records up to 2002.

White Stork   *Ciconia ciconia*

A very rare passage migrant

There is one 19th Century record involving two birds seen in Poole Harbour in April 1884 and subsequently shot at Christchurch. Since 1972 there have been 18 sightings (19 birds) with 11 in spring involving five (six birds) between 22nd April and 4th May and six between 13th May and 1st June. The other sightings are for mid-summer (two), August (two) and September (three) with the September 1976 bird staying for the winter. It is interesting to note that eight birds (relating to seven records) have occurred in the Frome Valley at some time during their stay, and that three of these (1979, 1988 and 1996) have also been seen on the Purbecks at either Swanage or nearby Durlston CP.

1972   Weymouth: flying over on 22nd August; same at Portland Bill 30 minutes later from where it
      flew back northwards
1976   Steeple/Kimmeridge: 22nd to 27th April
    Moreton: 20th to 27th September (at least); presumed same at Boys Hill, Longburton from
      early December to late January 1977, at Moreton from 22nd January to 3rd March 1977,
      and flying over Winfrith on 21st March 1977
1977   Compton Valence: 24th to 26th May
    Radipole NR: 23rd August
1979   Swanage: 4th May; same near Dorchester on 4th and 5th May
1984   Arne NR: flying north-west on 28th April; presumed same at East Holme and then flying
      north-west at East Stoke on 30th April.
1986   Stalbridge: 27th May; presumed same at Lodmoor NR on 29th May

Charminster: two on 1st and 2nd June; presumed to include the Stalbridge and Lodmoor NR bird
East Stoke and Bindon Abbey: 1st July
1988   Dorchester: 24th April; presumed same at Durlston CP on 30th April
Weymouth Bay: 25th May
1993   Godlingston Heath: two flying north-east on 1st May.
1996   Moreton: flying east on 13th May; same at Durlston CP also on 13th May
1999   Hazelbury Bryan: 17th May
Forston: 13th September
2001   Bestwall near Wareham: 21st June
2002   Lower Avon Valley at Coward's Marsh and Sopley: 2nd–7th September; same flying over
Hengistbury on 5th and 7th September.

In addition birds, which were either considered or known to be escapes, were seen as follows: one wandering the county during 1963/64, two at Chickerell and then at Radipole NR on 22nd August 1990, possibly the same two at Christchurch on 7th and 8th September 1990, one at Radipole NR from 6th–14th November 1990 and one at Christchurch Harbour from 18th–21st April 1991 – also seen in the Lower Avon Valley on the first date.

The White Stork breeds in north-west Africa, Iberia, central and eastern Europe, also in parts of southern Asia. It winters in sub-Saharan Africa, the Indian sub-continent and eastern Asia. A rare visitor to the British Isles (mainly in spring) with 298 records up to 1982.

Glossy Ibis   *Plegadis falcinellus*

Accidental: c.12 records

There are about eight records involving 18 birds from the 19th Century. These include six records (16 birds) from the Poole Harbour area with seven birds obtained in late September 1859 and a further four in October 1877. More recently there have been four sightings:

1956   Stratton: 3rd December
1977   Nyland: 27th–30th August; same at Lodmoor and Radipole NRs 9th–18th September
1986   Lodmoor NR: 19th–20th September
1987   Radipole NR: 11th–14th June

The Glossy Ibis breeds discontinuously from the Balkans to southern Asia, also in Australia, sub-Saharan Africa, eastern North America and the Caribbean. Markedly dispersive after breeding and many European breeders are trans-Saharan migrants. A vagrant to Great Britain with 86 records between 1958 and 2002, less rare in the 19th Century.

Spoonbill (Eurasian Spoonbill)   *Platalea leucorodia*

An uncommon passage migrant and winter visitor

Although this species was not infrequently to be seen in the neighbourhood of Poole during the 18th Century, it became much scarcer during the 19th Century. Mansel-Pleydell (1888) only listed five records between 1841 and 1881, three from Poole Harbour and one each from Weymouth and the Fleet, but further reported that a Mr Pike saw Spoonbills several times in autumn and occasionally in spring about Poole Harbour and the Corfe division of the estuary. Blathwayt (1945) described it as "a rare vagrant" and referred to 11 records involving 22 birds during 1906–1946, all from the Poole Harbour, Weymouth and Abbotsbury areas.

Since 1950 the Spoonbill has been recorded annually except for 1950, 1955, 1959–1961, 1963, 1966, 1973 and 1986 – see Fig 17. From 1951 to 1977 annual totals varied between 1–4 birds, but seven were present in 1952. In recent years there has been a marked increase in sightings with annual totals typically ranging from 4–15 birds, but an exceptional 20 birds were recorded in 1996.

The vast majority of reports are from Poole Harbour (c.82 birds), Christchurch Harbour (c.51 birds since 1974), the Fleet (c.49 birds), Lodmoor NR (c.21 birds) and Radipole NR (c.18 birds). The most favoured sites within Poole Harbour are Brownsea and Arne NR. There is some overlap in records,

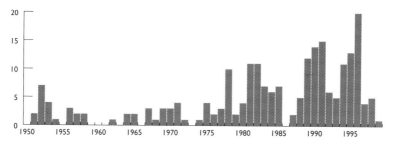

Fig 17. Annual totals 1950–1999

particularly in the Weymouth area where birds frequently commute between the Fleet and Radipole and Lodmoor NRs. The only two inland sightings involve the same wintering bird at Christchurch Harbour, which wandered up the Lower Avon Valley to Avon Causeway on 17th December 1983 and Coward's Marsh on 22nd April 1984. Records usually involve 1–2 birds, occasionally three, the highest count together being four moving east at Christchurch Harbour on 9th January 1985 – an unusual cold weather movement!

Coastal movements account for the remaining records with sightings from Portland Bill (nine records – 10 birds), Easton, Portland with three heading north-westwards on 13th June 1996, North Portland (two records – three birds), St Aldhelm's Head (three singles) and Durlston CP (one bird). Some of the Portland reports involve birds either arriving or departing from the Fleet and Radipole and Lodmoor NRs, whilst a few of the Christchurch Harbour records include birds moving over the harbour or past Hengistbury.

Although birds have occurred in all months, most (87%) have appeared from April to October with distinct peaks during April–June (45%) and September–October (28%). Wintering has occurred in Poole Harbour in 1970/71, 1971/72, 1981/82, 1983/84 and annually since 1989/90, usually involving single birds, but two were present in 1989/90, 1994/95 and 1996/97, and three in 1990/91 and 1995/96. An immature bird also wintered in Christchurch Harbour in 1983/84.

No birds have been ringed in the county, but there have been three controls of colour-ringed birds from the Netherlands: two from Christchurch Harbour including the wintering bird of 1983/84, and one from Langton Herring. These controls clearly indicate the source of many of our birds.

The Spoonbill breeds locally in the Netherlands, southern Spain and south-east Europe, also in central and southern Asia and East Africa. European breeders winter around Mediterranean with some in sub-Saharan Africa. It is a scarce passage migrant (mainly to the east coast) and winter visitor to the British Isles.

Postscript 2000–2002

At Christchurch Harbour, 12W on 1st November 2001 is an exceptional record and far exceeds the previous highest count for the county. Otherwise regular wintering continued in Poole Harbour involving a single bird in 1999/2000 and 2000/01, and two birds in 2001/02 and 2002/03. Excluding the above, there were c.11 birds in 2000 including 4E at East Fleet on 16th October, c.15 birds in 2001, and c.31 birds in 2002 including flocks of eight at Lodmoor NR on 19th October and six at Stanpit Marsh, Christchurch on 11th and 12th September. It is interesting to note that the three largest flocks ever recorded in Dorset have occurred during 2001–2002.

Honey Buzzard (European Honey-buzzard)   *Pernis apivorus*

An uncommon passage migrant – has bred

This species was occasionally recorded during the 19th Century including one trapped at Chetter Wood in autumn 1861, one at Kimmeridge in autumn 1868, one feeding on an ant-hill at Hurn Common in 1875 and a female shot near Wimborne in early June 1887.

Apart from one shot in the east of the county in autumn 1924 and another seen near Swanage on 5th August 1926, there are no other reports until 9th June 1967 when one flew over Arne NR. Subsequently presumed migrant Honey Buzzards have occurred in every year except 1970 and during 1972–1974 – see Table 115. A total of 191 have been recorded during 1967–1999 involving 75 in spring/summer and 116 in autumn with distinct peaks in May (50) and September (66) – see Table 116. Except for 1981, annual totals ranged consistently from 4–6 birds during 1980–1991, but then increased to 5–20 birds during

133

1992–1999. The relatively high numbers in 1969, 1976, 1981, 1993 and 1997 were associated with autumn influxes. The most notable of these occurred in 1976 when ten birds were recorded from Portland during 3rd September–3rd October, including four on the last date when further singles were also seen at Radipole NR and Studland, and in 1993 when 15 birds were reported from various coastal sites between 31st August and 11th October including ten during 14th–24th September.

68	69	70	71	72	73	74	75	76	77	78	79	80	81	82	83
1	6	0	1	0	0	0	1	14	5	2	2	5	11	4	5

84	85	86	87	88	89	90	91	92	93	94	95	96	97	98	99
4	5	5	4	6	6	5	4	10	18	11	9	12	20	5	9

Table 115. Annual totals of presumed migrants 1968–1999

Apr	May	Jun	Jul	Aug	Sept	Oct
9	50	13	3	29	66	21

Table 116. Monthly totals of presumed migrants 1967–1999

The majority of records are from the main coastal watch-points with Portland, Durlston CP and Christchurch Harbour accounting for 63% of the total, whilst the Weymouth area, notably Radipole NR, and the Fleet account for a further 14% – see Table 117. Away from the coast 26 migrants have been reported from inland sites scattered throughout the county.

	Spring	Autumn	% of total
The Fleet	4	1	3%
Portland	24	46	37%
Radipole NR	7	6	7%
elsewhere in Weymouth	3	4	4%
Durlston CP	8	19	14%
elsewhere on Purbeck	1	9	5%
Poole Harbour area	7	5	6%
Christchurch Harbour	9	13	12%
elsewhere in Dorset	12	13	13%

Table 117. Distribution of presumed migrants 1967–1999

The earliest arrival dates are 6th April 1977 at Radipole NR, and 15th April at Lodmoor NR in 1981 and Maiden Newton in 1985, whilst the latest dates are 18th October 1997 at Bere Regis and 20th October 1988 at Portland Bill.

There is some evidence of breeding in recent years with very irregular sightings from five areas during the summer. These include two individuals from different locations found dying in late May and on 22nd June 1986, both of which were presumed poisoned, and one seen excavating a bees' nest on 17th July 1980. Breeding was proved in 1992 and in subsequent years.

The Honey Buzzard breeds across much of Europe eastwards into western Asia. It is strongly migratory and winters mainly in the western and central tropics of Africa. In Great Britain there is a small and fragmented breeding population. Otherwise it is a scarce passage migrant mainly to the south and east.

Postscript 2000–2002

Along with other parts of eastern and southern Great Britain, Dorset experienced an exceptional influx during autumn 2000 with c.144–160 sightings involving a minimum of 77 birds during 23rd September–10th October. Peak movements occurred on 30th September with c.75–90 sightings including a minimum of 35 and possibly as many as 50 from Portland, and 23 from Christchurch Harbour. Portland, Durlston CP and Christchurch Harbour together provided c.127–143 (88–89%) of the sightings during the period. Otherwise passage was average with six migrants in May and two in early September 2000, four during May–June and three during September–October 2001, and one in May and six during August–September 2002.

Black Kite   *Milvus migrans*

A very rare passage migrant: 19 records involving 20 individuals

All records of this classic spring 'overshoot' have occurred between 26th March and 16th June with a distinct peak of 11 birds in May. The majority of sightings are from coastal sites including eight (nine birds) at Portland and three at Christchurch Harbour.

1980	Lodmoor NR: 2nd May
1981	Portland: 11th April; presumed same at Corfe Castle 12th–14th April
	Stanpit Marsh, Christchurch Harbour: 21st May
1986	Stratton: 30th–31st May
1987	Hengistbury: 4th May
1988	Bat's Head near Lulworth: 14th May; also later the same day at Stanpit Marsh, Christchurch Harbour
1990	Yetminster: 26th March; probably same at Winfrith Newburgh 28th March
1991	The Grove, Portland: 23rd May
	Near Cranborne: 23rd May
1992	Portland: 15th May; presumed same at East Knighton 16th May
	Durlston CP: 5th–6th June; presumed same at Creech Heath near Wareham 6th June
1994	Weston, Portland: 4th May
	Abbotsbury: 10th May
	Edmondsham: 16th June
1996	Verne Common, Portland: 26th April
1997	Verne Common, Portland: 22nd April
	Blacknor Point, Portland: two together 24th April
1999	Portesham/Abbotsbury Hill: 1st June
2002	Easton, Portland: 31st May

The Black Kite is regarded as one of the world's most numerous birds of prey with a worldwide distribution except for the Americas. It breeds locally but quite commonly in central France and over much of Europe except the north-west. The European and north Asian populations are migratory and winter mainly in sub-Saharan Africa and southern and eastern Asia. The gradual extension of its breeding range towards Great Britain accounts for the recent increase in sightings with 313 records up to 2002.

Red Kite   *Milvus milvus*

An uncommon passage migrant and winter visitor

Mansel-Pleydell (1888) stated that this species was very common at the beginning of the 19th Century, but subsequent extinction was rapid and breeding apparently ceased in Dorset about 1850. There are seemingly only three reports during the next hundred years involving one shot near Puncknowle in April 1881, a pair near Dorchester in early summer 1888, one of which was poisoned, and one near Wareham on 25th September 1922. Blathwayt (1945) noted that in the accounts of the Melbury Osmund Churchwarden for money paid for 'vermin', one penny was entered as paid for a Kite in 1690 and the same sum in 1693!

The first modern records involve singles at Portland Bill on 29th April 1956 and Arne NR on 6th September 1966. Since 1972 there have been sightings in every year except six with an increase during the 1990s, most notably during 1996–1999 – see Table 118. It should be noted that some duplication in records is likely since individual birds may wander widely throughout the county. There are reports for every month except July with a marked peak in spring (March–May), which accounts for 43% of the total – see Table 119. Since 1992 the situation has become obscured by the increasing appearance of birds, several wearing wing-tags, from re-introduction schemes. Nevertheless, the strength of the spring peak suggests that some of the birds recorded at this season may include genuine immigrants from the Continent. Sightings during the autumn and winter are more likely to involve birds dispersing from Wales and the re-introduction schemes. For example, a roost of up to seven birds was discovered in January 1998 and remained largely intact until April, with one bird lingering until 4th June. The roost attracted birds from Wales (two adults), from the re-introduction schemes in southern England and the Midlands (one adult and three immatures), as well as birds that were neither ringed nor tagged and so of unknown origin. Although two birds returned to this roost in late October 1998, one was found dead and the other disappeared. In May 1999, one of two tagged birds at Chapman's Pool was from a release site in the east Midlands.

1972	1973	1974	1975	1976	1977	1978	1979	1980	1981	1982	1983	1984	1985
2	0	0	2	2	0	1	2	1	0	0	3	1	3

1986	1987	1988	1989	1990	1991	1992	1993	1994	1995	1996	1997	1998	1999
0	2	4	1	4	4	2	9	5	1	11	11	10	18

Table 118. Annual totals 1972–1999

Jan	Feb	Mar	Apr	May	June	July	Aug	Sep	Oct	Nov	Dec
16	5	18	14	11	9	0	4	1	7	8	8

Table 119. Monthly totals 1956–1999

There are records from sites throughout the county. Prior to 1997 the vast majority (69%) of birds occurred in the west and south of Dorset including the Weymouth area, Portland and Purbeck. During 1997–1999 there has been an increase in reports from the north and east of the county. Birds are occasionally recorded from the main coastal watch-points, notably Portland with singles on 29th April 1956, 7th–8th January 1972, 9th April 1975, 8th April 1979, 13th October 1985, 21st March 1996 and 1st February 1998.

The world breeding range of the Red Kite is confined mainly to central and southern Europe. The northern populations are partially migratory and winter mostly in southern Europe, notably Iberia. Within Great Britain the resident Welsh population has now recovered from near-extinction and together with the two areas of successful re-introduction now support increasing numbers of breeding birds.

Postscript 2000–2002
The recent increase in records has been maintained with c.21 birds in 2000, c.14 birds in 2001 and c.45 birds in 2002.

White-tailed Eagle *Haliaeetus albicilla*

Formerly a very rare winter visitor, no recent records – the last in 1941
Mansel-Pleydell (1888) described the White-tailed Eagle as "now only a rare straggler" and commented that it was more frequently seen at the beginning of the 19th Century. A number of records are listed, most of which involved birds trapped or killed, although one that remained at Kimmeridge for several weeks in the winter of 1880 left without suffering the usual fate of rare birds! The species continued to be recorded into the early years of the 20th Century, the most recent being one shot in east Dorset in 1935 and one, probably this species, at Eggardon on 14th November 1941.

Some of the surviving specimens were labelled as Golden Eagles, but re-examination shows that they refer to this species.

The White-tailed Eagle breeds from Scandinavia and eastern Europe eastwards across much of northern Asia to the Pacific, also in south-west Greenland and Iceland. Most of the eastern populations are migratory, the more western and southern European populations less so with adults largely resident. Wintering birds occur locally over central and eastern Europe, Asia Minor, the Middle East and parts of south-west, south-east and eastern Asia. Re-introductions on the west coast of Scotland have been successful with new areas being gradually colonised. Otherwise it is a vagrant to the rest of the British Isles with 25 records between 1958 and 1998.

Marsh Harrier (Eurasian Marsh Harrier) *Circus aeruginosus*

An uncommon passage migrant and winter visitor – formerly bred

This species was frequently seen on the wet moors of the county during the 18th and 19th Centuries when it probably bred. Mansel-Pleydell (1888) commented that drainage had very much limited its favourite haunts, although it still frequented the saltmarshes between Wareham and Arne. Subsequently the Marsh Harrier was rarely observed up to the mid-1940s with Blathwayt (1945) describing it as "a scarce vagrant" and listing only three records involving two at Chardstock in November 1902, one at Weymouth on 10th September 1932, and one in east Dorset on 16th June 1935.

From 1943 onwards birds were increasingly reported from around Poole Harbour and breeding certainly occurred in 1950, perhaps earlier. Subsequently the population built up to a peak of at least five pairs in 1954, but then decreased with the last pair breeding in 1962. At least 49 young were reared during this period. Singles and the odd pair were reported occasionally in summer up to 1969. Since then the only evidence of genuine summering in the Poole Harbour area is limited to 1976, 1991 and 1996.

The only published records away from Poole Harbour during the 1950s and 1960s involve singles at Portland Bill on 19th September 1960 and 25th April 1965, one near Cranborne on 30th May 1965, two at Lodmoor NR on 30th August 1965, and one at Abbotsbury on 3rd and 31st July 1969 with one nearby on 30th December 1969. Since 1970 there has been a steady increase in reports, the vast majority of which involve migrants – see Table 120. Passage mainly occurs during April–May and August–September with distinct peaks in May and September – see Table 121. Most sightings are from the coast, the main sites being Poole Harbour and Radipole and Lodmoor NRs, which together account for 53% of the total migrants recorded during 1970–1996 – see Table 122. There are very few reports from the coast to the west of Abbotsbury, one at Lyme Regis on 16th August 1994 being particularly noteworthy. It should be noted that some duplication in records is likely since individual birds may wander widely, particularly within the Poole Harbour and Weymouth/Portland/Fleet areas. Most of the relatively few inland sightings (only 14 during 1970–1996), are from sites along the lower and middle reaches of the Avon, Frome and Piddle Valleys. It is much rarer well inland, the most notable reports being at Gussage All Saints on 29th May 1981, Iwerne Steepleton on 28th April 1982, Gussage Hill on 24th May 1983, Milton on Stour on 2nd April 1995 and Martin Down on 20th August 1997.

70	71	72	73	74	75	76	77	78	79	80	81	82	83	84
5	0	2	1	6	6	8	6	2	7	8	17	15	6	8

85	86	87	88	89	90	91	92	93	94	95	96	97	98	99
9	7	15	21	15	21	16	18	18	23	32	23	35	28	13

Table 120. Annual totals of presumed migrants 1970–1999

Mar	Apr	May	Jun	Jul	Aug	Sept	Oct	Nov
7	53	87	14	7	40	71	21	4

Table 121. Monthly totals of presumed migrants 1970–1996

There are only two winter records during 1970–1987 involving a pair at Abbotsbury from 16th December 1971 to 1st January 1972, and one in Poole Harbour on 27th December 1973. Since 1987/88, the species has wintered annually in Poole Harbour involving 1–2 birds up to 1996/97, but three during 1997/98–

	% of total
west Dorset	2%
The Fleet	13%
Portland	13%
Radipole & Lodmoor NRs	25%
Poole Harbour	28%
Purbeck	6%
Christchurch Harbour	10%

Table 122. Distribution (%) of presumed migrants at the main coastal sites 1970–1996

1999/2000. Probably the same birds are responsible for occasional winter sightings elsewhere in the county, most notably from Christchurch Harbour, the Lower Avon Valley and the Weymouth area.

Most records involve singles, the highest counts being up to four at Radipole NR on 2nd and 3rd October 1976, and four at Portland Bill on 19th September 1995.

During the period when breeding occurred 23 nestlings were ringed with a few recoveries within Dorset and from adjoining counties. In addition, there is one foreign control from Belgium.

The Marsh Harrier breeds across much of Europe and central Asia east to northern Mongolia, also in north-west Africa and the Middle East. It winters from western and southern Europe south over much of sub-Saharan Africa and eastwards to Asia Minor and the Middle East, also in southern Asia. In Great Britain it is a rare but increasing breeding species, mainly in eastern England.

Sponsored by John and Jackie Day

Hen Harrier   *Circus cyaneus*

An uncommon winter visitor and passage migrant

This species bred in the county during the early part of the 19th Century, but had become rare by 1865. Subsequently a pair with nest and young were taken from just over the Hampshire border on 30th June 1874 and Mansel-Pleydell (1888) recorded breeding near Poole prior to 1888. A pair possibly bred in the Poole area as recently as 1922, but confusion with the Montagu's Harrier cannot be ruled out.

Although the Hen Harrier was considered to be a scarce visitor during the 1930s and 1940s, mainly to the Poole Basin area, there was evidence of regular wintering around the southern shores of Poole Harbour. During the 1950s and 1960s fluctuating, but generally small numbers were recorded with regular wintering established in the Poole Harbour and Cranborne areas. The numbers of wintering birds increased from the late 1960s to peak during the mid-1980s with evidence of a decline subsequently – see Table 123. Several of the higher counts coincide with cold winters, notably 1978/79, 1981/82, 1984/85, 1985/86 and 1986/87. For example, in 1978/79 severe conditions across much of Europe resulted in an unprecedented influx into Great Britain during January, which was reflected by a sharp increase in Dorset with 73 sightings from January to March as compared to 24 during the October–December period.

Since 1984/85 monthly counts have been made at winter roost sites as part of a national survey. These provide a more realistic assessment of the winter population in the county – see Table 124. During the period of the survey there has been a shift from a predominance of 'ringtails' during the mid-1980s to mainly males in the mid-1990s. Lowland heathland is of major importance as a roosting habitat in Dorset. Reedbeds were used in the past and these are occasionally still used as roost sites.

68/69	69/70	70/71	71/72	72/73	73/74	74/75	75/76	76/77	77/78	78/79	79/80	80/81
72	71	71	55	78	59	46	64	37	55	97	58	65

81/82	82/83	83/84	84/85	85/86	86/87	87/88	88/89	89/90	90/91	91/92	92/93	93/94
105	113	104	113	113	149	95	80	85	81	108	76	65

Table 123. Winter totals 1968–1994

	1984/85	1985/86	1986/87	1987/88	1988/89	1989/90	1990/91	1991/92
males	6	5	8	4	8	4	5	5
ringtails	7	7	8	3	7	4	5	3
Total	13	12	16	7	15	8	10	8

	1992/93	1993/94	1994/95	1995/96	1996/97	1997/98	1998/99	1999/00
males	10	7	11	12	7	6	10	8
ringtails	3	2	5	5	2	2	1	2
Total	13	9	16	17	9	8	11	10

Table 124. Peak counts from winter roosts 1984–1999

Although birds have been recorded from all parts of the county, the majority of sightings since the late 1960s are from the Poole Basin, the coastal margins and unimproved areas of chalk downland. Poole Basin alone accounts for 75% of the reports since 1968.

In most years a few birds occur on passage at coastal watch-points, notably Portland Bill, Durlston CP and Christchurch Harbour, with a distinct peak from late September to mid-November. The earliest of several August records is 8th August 1995 at Weston, Portland, whilst the latest spring date is 28th May 1991 at Southwell, Portland. There are two exceptional summer sightings from Portland Bill involving singles flying south on 14th June 1988 and 15th July 1998.

At least 11 wing-tagged birds have been seen in the county during 1981–1996, but it has proved impossible to precisely determine the origins of these individuals on every occasion. At least seven of these birds were marked in mainland Scotland, one in Orkney and one in either North Wales or Scotland.

The Hen Harrier breeds locally across western and central Europe south to northern Spain and more extensively from eastern Europe and east Scandinavia across much of northern Asia, also in northern North America and western and southern South America. It is migratory in northern and eastern Europe and northern Asia, partially so or locally resident elsewhere, and winters mainly in Europe, except for the east and most of Scandinavia, Asia Minor, the Middle East and in a narrow band across south-central Asia. It breeds locally across the north and west of the British Isles.

Sponsored by Tasie Russell

Pallid Harrier   *Circus macrourus*

Accidental: one record

1938   Whatcombe near Blanford: ad. male shot 11th April

This individual was the second British record of Pallid Harrier and the specimen is now in the County Museum.

The Pallid Harrier breeds from Romania eastwards across west-central Asia and winters mainly in sub-Saharan Africa and the Indian sub-continent. It is a vagrant over much of Europe with occasional breeding in the more eastern countries. A vagrant to Great Britain with 14 records up to 2002 including 11 during 1993–2002.

Montagu's Harrier   *Circus pygargus*

An uncommon passage migrant – occasionally breeds

Information relating to the past status of this species is sparse, possibly due to confusion with the Hen Harrier. Mansel-Pleydell (1888) considered it to be an occasional visitor and referred to one instance of breeding involving a nest found in a clover field at Winterborne Kingston in June 1887. Blathwayt (1945) mentioned that one or two pairs still attempted to breed annually on heathland in the east of the county and commented "this species at one time was a feature of the Dorset heaths and its present scarcity is much to be regretted".

Subsequently the Montagu's Harrier has bred or attempted to do so in all but five years between 1946 and 1964 and annually during 1976–1993 – see Table 125. At least 65 young were fledged with a minimum of 29 during 1946–1964 and 36 during 1976–1993. Apart from 1971, there was no evidence of breeding between 1965 and 1975. Although birds were present in the traditional breeding area in 1994 and 1999 with isolated records in 1995 and 1996, breeding has not been attempted since 1993 and this formerly regular site now seems to have been abandoned. In earlier years breeding sites were associated with heathland, but more recently nesting has taken place in arable crops.

	1946	1948	1950	1951	1952	1954	1955	1956	1958	1959	1960	1961
Pairs present	1	1	1	3	1	1	1	2–3	2	1–2	1	1
Pairs bred	1	1	1	1–2	1	1	1	1–2	2	?	1	1
Pairs successful	1	?	1	1	1	?	1	1	0	?	1	1
No of young	?	?	3	1	2	?	2	5	0	–	4	5

	1962	1964	1971	1976	1977	1978	1979	1980	1981	1982	1983	1984
Pairs present	3	2	1	1	1	1	1	1	1	1	2	1
Pairs bred	1–2	2	–	1	1	1	1	1	2n	1	2	1
Pairs successful	1	2	–	1	0	0	1	1	0	1	0	0
No of young	2	5–6	–	4	0	0	4	4	0	4	0	0

	1985	1986	1987	1988	1989	1990	1991	1992	1993	1994	1999
Pairs present	1	1–2	1	1–2	2	2	2	1	1	1	1
Pairs bred	1	1	1–2	1	1(2f)	2	2	1	1	–	–
Pairs successful	–	1	1–2	1	1	1	1	0	0	–	–
No of young	–	2	4	4	3+1	2	4	0	0	–	–

Table 125. Number of breeding pairs and young 1946–1999. 2n = 2 nests; (2f) = 2 females

Since 1950 sightings other than those associated with breeding have been fairly consistent with annual totals generally ranging from 2–8 birds – see Fig 18. Most of these non-breeding records involve migrants. Passage mainly occurs during April–May and August–September with distinct peaks in May and August – see Table 126. The earliest arrival is 8th April 1985 at Stanpit Marsh, Christchurch Harbour, whilst the latest date is 2nd November 1975 at Langton Herring apart from an exceptionally late bird in Poole Harbour on 28th December 1959.

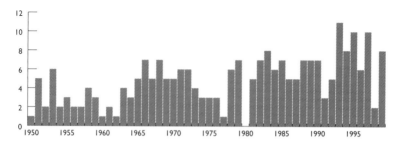

Fig 18. Annual totals of presumed migrants 1950–1999

Apr	May	Jun	Jul	Aug	Sept	Oct	Nov
28	87	16	15	45	32	5	1

Table 126. Monthly totals of presumed migrants 1950–1999

Migrant birds are mainly recorded from the coastal fringes, notably Portland, Purbeck and Poole Harbour, which together account for 52% of the total – see Table 127. Inland, 71 birds have been reported during 1950–1999 mainly in the east of the county. Most records involve single birds, the highest counts being 3–4 'ringtails' at Abbotsbury on 18th–19th July 1984 and three at Christchurch Harbour on 24th August 1993.

	% of total
The Fleet	6%
Portland	17%
Durlston CP	13%
elsewhere on Purbeck	6%
Poole Harbour	16%
Christchurch Harbour	8%
other coastal sites	4%
inland sites	31%

Table 127. Distribution (%) of presumed migrants 1970–1999

There are two recoveries from France of nestlings ringed at breeding sites in Poole Basin North.

The Montagu's Harrier breeds locally across much of central and southern Europe and more extensively from eastern Europe east into west-central Asia, also in north-west Africa and Asia Minor. It winters in sub-Saharan Africa and the Indian sub-continent. The breeding population in Great Britain is very small and largely confined to central-southern counties and East Anglia.

Postscript 2000–2002

It is pleasing to report that a pair held territory in the traditional area in 2002, but the outcome was thought to be unsuccessful. This is the first evidence of attempted breeding since 1993.

Sponsored by John Vickerman and Catherine Whitby

Goshawk (Northern Goshawk)   *Accipiter gentilis*

A rare passage migrant and winter visitor – has bred

Although the species was described as being "not very uncommon" at the end of the 18th Century, it subsequently suffered considerably from persecution by gamekeepers and loss of habitat. The Goshawk's status in the county during the 19th Century and the first half of the 20th Century is vague with one shot at Canford about 2nd November 1913 the only definite report.

The first modern records involve single birds by the Fleet on 2nd September 1956 and at Cranborne on 21st May 1957, with no further sightings until one at Winspit on 7th October 1968. From 1971 to 1989 presumed non-breeding birds were recorded annually except for 1973, but more recently there are reports for only five years during 1990–1999 – see Table 128. As individual birds may wander widely, some duplication in records is likely and this may be partly responsible for the peak counts in 1981, 1982 and 1988. Most sightings are for the period August to April with slight peaks in April and September – see Table 129. Although an uncertain proportion of records are thought to refer to escapes as importation is still taking place and captive breeding is increasing, the peaks in April and September suggest there is some genuine passage in spring and autumn. This presumably involves mainly dispersing young birds since adults are sedentary. Further evidence that some migration occurs is shown by the bias of records from the coastal fringes – see Table 130. The most favoured sites are the Poole Harbour area, Christchurch Harbour and the nearby Lower Avon Valley, which together account for 49% of all records of presumed non-breeding birds. Virtually all sightings involve single birds.

70	71	72	73	74	75	76	77	78	79	80	81	82	83	84
0	1	1	0	1	2	4	4	4	6	3	15	22	5	9

85	86	87	88	89	90	91	92	93	94	95	96	97	98	99
8	9	3	15	5	0	0	1	0	6	0	3	7	0	2

Table 128. Annual totals of presumed non-breeding birds 1970–1999

Jan	Feb	Mar	Apr	May	Jun	Jul	Aug	Sep	Oct	Nov	Dec
12	15	14	23	5	1	2	11	19	11	11	7

Table 129. Monthly totals of presumed non-breeding birds 1970–1999

	Number
Lower Avon Valley	15
Christchurch Harbour	23
Poole Harbour	28
Purbeck	12
Radipole & Lodmoor NRs	10
Portland	9
The Fleet	5
other sites	34

Table 130. Distribution of presumed non-breeding birds 1970–1999

The first evidence of attempted breeding in recent times involves an unmated female that appeared near Milton Abbas in April 1975, built a nest in May, and remained in the area until January 1976. More recently breeding has been proved twice during 1990–1996.

The Goshawk breeds across much of Europe, northern Asia and northern North America; also in north-west Africa and Asia Minor with an isolated population in central south-east Asia. Northern populations are partially migratory. Although one of the most persecuted raptors in Europe, populations in many countries are thought to be stable or even increasing. The present British stock, which is expanding, is believed to have descended, in part, from falconers' escapes and releases.

Postscript 2000–2002
This species remains elusive within Dorset with only three records in 2000, two in 2001 and none in 2002.

Sparrowhawk (Eurasian Sparrowhawk) *Accipiter nisus*

A common resident, winter visitor and passage migrant

This species was seemingly a common and widespread resident until the late 1950s and early 1960s when the population declined due to the increased use of organochlorine pesticides. Due to concern over this decline, special surveys were undertaken in 1962 and 1963, which revealed that the Sparrowhawk was widely but thinly dispersed throughout the county.

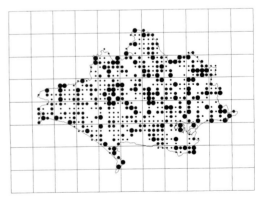

A further survey in 1967 showed a substantial recovery in the fortunes of this species as indicated by the number of sightings with 57 in 1962, 117 in 1963 and 291 in 1967. The BTO Atlas (1968–1972) further confirmed this recovery with evidence of breeding in all but two (95%) 10-km squares (confirmed in 26, probable in five and possible in four). There is some evidence to suggest that this recovery continued up to the Tetrad Survey (1987–1994) when evidence of breeding was found in all but one (97%) of the pre-1974 10-km squares (confirmed in 33, probable in one and possible in two). The Tetrad Map shows that breeding occurs widely throughout the county including many urban locations such as the centre of Bournemouth.

Besides the availability of prey, population levels within Dorset may be linked to the presence of woodland and scrub for nesting. The species has benefited from afforestation and shows a particular preference for coniferous woodland. The population is now thought to be relatively stable after its post-decline recovery.

The decline and recovery of the Sparrowhawk is well illustrated by the number of reports from Portland

Bill during 1959–1998 – see Table 131. Although many of the records are migrants, an increasing proportion of sightings in recent years refer to birds that are semi-resident and breed elsewhere on Portland. Spring passage occurs between late March and early May with a peak in April, whilst autumn passage extends from mid-August to early November with a peak in early October – see Table 132. This passage is also evident, but to a lesser extent, at other coastal watch-points.

1960s	1970s	1980s	1990s
15.2	43.8	305.1	232.7

Table 131. 10-year average annual totals at Portland Bill 1950–1999

Jan	Feb	Mar	Apr	May	Jun	Jul	Aug	Sep	Oct	Nov	Dec
206	209	415	586	299	152	281	669	995	1106	572	306

Table 132. Monthly totals (bds) at Portland Bill 1959–1998

A total of 292 birds has been ringed in the county and there have been single foreign recoveries from France and Norway.

The Sparrowhawk breeds across most of Europe and northern Asia, also in north-west Africa and Asia Minor with a separate population in the Himalayas.

Sponsored by Morrish Builders

Buzzard (Common Buzzard)   *Buteo buteo*

A common resident

Mansel-Pleydell (1888) described this species as "the most frequently seen of the larger hawks; generally birds of the year from the Continent on migration". Although Blathwayt (1945) referred to occasional nesting and mentioned that it bred near Wimborne in the early 1870s and attempted to do so in east Dorset in 1932, the Buzzard remained only a frequent visitor up to 1935.

During the late 1930s colonisation started in west Dorset from east Devon, and in east Dorset from the New Forest, so that by 1945 it had become a widely scattered breeding species in many parts of the county. By 1954 breeding covered much of Dorset, except for the urban areas and Portland, with the highest numbers in the west. In most areas the breeding density was not as high as in Devon, i.e. less than two pairs per square mile. The Buzzard has continued to spread and increase despite setbacks during the mid-1950s, when myxomatosis destroyed the rabbit population, and again during the early 1960s, which was caused by agricultural poisons. The *BTO Atlas* (1968–1972) found evidence of breeding in 31 (84%) 10-km squares (confirmed in 24, probable in six and possible in one), the most notable absences being in the south-east (SZ08 and SZ09). The Tetrad Survey (1987–1994) produced a similar result with evidence of breeding in 32 (86%) of the pre-1974 10-km squares (confirmed in 31 and probable in one).

The Tetrad Map shows that breeding occurs widely throughout the county except for urban areas, notably the Bournemouth and Poole conurbation, and some coastal areas including Portland and the extreme south-east tip of Purbeck. The densest population occurs in west Dorset. This is very similar to the distribution described in 1954 and shown by the *BTO Atlas* (1968–1972). The main change between the *BTO Atlas* and the Tetrad Survey is the colonisation of squares SZ08 and SZ09. The spread into the south-east corner of the county has been particularly obvious since the mid-1980s, and appears to be continuing

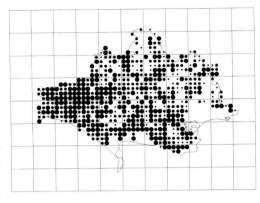

through the 1990s with evidence of breeding in several new areas since the Tetrad Survey. This includes an increasing number of sightings from the margins of Bournemouth and Poole. A good illustration of this spread comes from the Stour Valley between Corfe Mullen and Sturminster Marshall where the Buzzard was a rare visitor in the early 1980s, but by the mid-1990s had established at least three and possibly four territories.

Since 1990 a study undertaken by Kenward *et al.* (2000) using radio-telemetry and ringing has found a maximum nest density of one pair per four square kilometres, which compares with estimates of one pair per 2–4 square kilometres in parts of Wales and Devon. Breeding birds comprise only about 28% of the total population and non-breeding numbers are increasing with saturation level not yet reached. The breeding population has been estimated to be in excess of 500 pairs with larger non-breeding numbers. This is at least 5% of the total British population, which is given as 20,000 pairs and increasing. The diet of the Buzzard in Dorset was found to contain a wide variety of vertebrate prey including a snake and toad. Young rabbits were widely taken and breeding success probably depends on the abundance of these, but one Buzzard brought several adult Woodpigeons to its young. Studies of the winter diet of the radio-tagged birds have found that much time was spent in low-lying pastures where the main food taken was worms.

Large gatherings are increasingly reported, the highest counts in recent years being 37 in one seed field at Beaminster on 4th September 1993 and 30 in one field north of Dorchester on 22nd November 1999.

The species occurs as a scarce passage migrant at various coastal sites including Portland Bill, Radipole and Lodmoor NRs, Durlston CP and Christchurch Harbour. Records from Portland Bill since 1980 suggest that the species is becoming more frequent on migration with passage almost restricted to April–May in spring and peaking in September during the autumn – see Tables 133 and 134. Most sightings at Portland Bill involve single birds, but five flew north on 5th May 1987, whilst there was a movement of 15N on Portland as a whole during 16th March–14th April 1998.

80	81	82	83	84	85	86	87	88	89	90	91	92	93	94	95	96	97	98	99
0	4	0	1	0	1	5	12	3	3	5	2	1	6	1	4	7	5	6	5

Table 133. Annual totals at Portland Bill 1980–1999

Jan	Feb	Mar	Apr	May	Jun	Jul	Aug	Sep	Oct	Nov	Dec
0	1	4	8	14	1	1	6	17	9	2	1

Table 134. Monthly totals at Portland Bill 1980–1995 and 1997–1999

Several hundred birds have been ringed in the county. During the radio-telemetry studies birds have been routinely located as far as Newbury, Bristol and near Salisbury with single records from Yeovil, Warminster, Ringwood and Beaulieu.

The Buzzard breeds across much of Europe, except northern Scandinavia, and temperate Asia, also in parts of Asia Minor. Although the western populations are largely resident or short distant migrants, the eastern populations are migratory mainly wintering in Asia Minor, eastern and southern Africa and southern Asia.

Postscript 2000–2002

Along with the Honey Buzzard, there was an exceptional autumn passage in late September 2000 including peak counts of 25 at Portland on 30th, 11 at Lytchett Bay on 28th and eight at Christchurch Harbour on 30th. Portland reported its highest ever annual total in 2002 with 138 bird-days with a maximum of 12 together on 28th March. A flock of 28–30 feeding on the ground at Winterbourne Abbas on 18th November 2001 is a high count.

Sponsored by Robert E. Kenward, Sean S. Walls and Biotrack Limited

Rough-legged Buzzard   *Buteo lagopus*

A very rare winter visitor and passage migrant

Mansel-Pleydell (1888) listed eight records involving nine birds all but one either shot or 'obtained', whilst Blathwayt (1945) referred to at least four subsequent reports including one killed near Dorchester on 20th April 1918 and one seen just west of Lyme Regis on 23rd December 1938.

   More recently there were c.10–12 records during 1961–1982 followed by single reports in 1993, 1997 and 2002. The sightings in 1967 and 1974 coincided with national influxes of the species.

1961	Blandford: late October–4th November
1967	Boveridge near Cranborne: 19th February
	Worgret near Wareham: 11th and 13th May
1968	West Holme: 10th and 12th January; possibly same at East Stoke 12th–13th April
1969	Little Bredy: 26th January
1974	Portland Bill: one flying north on 22nd October
1978	Sandford: immature picked up 4th December was fed and then released 9th December near Arne NR where it was seen 11th and 13th December; same at Studland NNR 17th December, Durlston CP 19th–20th December and finally at Moreton on 28th December
1979	Corfe Castle: 12th and 14th February
1982	Arne NR: 25th April
	Winspit: 10th October; possibly same there 1st November
1993	Ibberton: 22nd March
1997	Barnsfield Heath: 22nd April
2002	Christchurch Harbour: one flying south, then heading north-east 25th March

The Rough-legged Buzzard breeds across the Holarctic, except for Greenland and Iceland, and winters in central and eastern Europe, central Asia and central North America. It is a very scarce winter visitor to the east coast of Great Britain.

Osprey   *Pandion haliaetus*

An uncommon passage migrant

Although Mansel-Pleydell (1888) described this species as "not an unfrequent visitor to the estuaries of Poole and Weymouth, where several have been seen and killed", it had become a rare visitor by the early 20th Century. Blathwayt (1945) only listed six records with singles at Poole Harbour on 10th May 1918, Broadstone on 25th November 1927, Abbotsbury in September 1930, September 1935 and on 14th August 1937, and Radipole NR on 24th September 1943.

   Since the recolonisation of Scotland in the early 1950s, migrant Ospreys have occurred more frequently in Dorset with annual sightings from 1960 onwards As the fortunes of the species have improved nationally so the number of records have steadily increased, particularly during the 1980s and 1990s – see Fig 19. It should be noted that in recent years some duplication in records is very likely since individual birds wander widely, notably in the Poole Harbour, Weymouth/Portland/Fleet, and Christchurch Harbour/Lower Avon Valley areas. Passage is heavier in autumn than in spring with most sightings during April–May (29%)

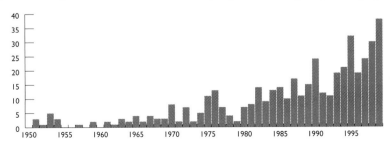

Fig 19. Annual totals 1950–1999

and August–September (50%) – see Table 135. There are nine records for March, all since 1991, the earliest being 10th March 1999 flying north at Winfrith. The latest reports are from 8th September to 15th November 1982 at Brockington Farm, 18th November 1994 at Portland Bill and 23rd November 1997 at Stourpaine. There is also an old record for 25th November 1927.

Mar	Apr	May	Jun	Jul	Aug	Sep	Oct	Nov
9	64	64	29	20	86	132	28	4

Table 135. Monthly totals 1950–1999

The main sites are Christchurch Harbour, Poole Harbour and the Fleet, which together account for 53% of the total records since 1950 – see Table 136. Smaller numbers have been reported from Portland, Radipole and Lodmoor NRs and the Purbeck coast, notably Durlston CP. A substantial proportion of sightings are from inland sites, mainly the larger lakes and river valleys, notably the Lower Avon.

	% of total
Christchurch Harbour	18%
Poole Harbour	18%
Purbeck	7%
Radipole and Lodmoor NRs	11%
Portland	11%
The Fleet	17%
other coastal sites	2%
inland sites	16%

Table 136. Distribution (%) of migrants 1950–1999

Most records involve single birds recorded on single dates. This is particularly so in spring when birds rarely linger and move on quickly. During the autumn birds are prone to remain longer, sometimes for several weeks, mainly in such favoured haunts as Poole Harbour, the Fleet and to a lesser extent Christchurch Harbour and the nearby Lower Avon Valley. There are a few reports of two birds, mainly in the autumn, whilst prior to 1997 the only record involving three birds was from Christchurch Harbour on 17th September 1993. More recently counts of three birds have been reported annually in Poole Harbour, namely at Arne NR on 21st and 30th September 1997, Arne NR and Studland NNR on 5th October 1998, and Lytchett Bay and Rockley Point on 29th–30th August 1999.

The Osprey has a patchy worldwide distribution, breeding in Scotland, Scandinavia, eastern Europe, northern and south-east Asia, Australasia and North America. It is largely migratory and appears in all continents, the main wintering areas being sub-Saharan Africa, the Indian sub-continent, south-east Asia and Central and northern South America. The Scottish population is increasing with breeding recently confirmed in England.

Postscript 2000–2002

There were 92 sightings in 2000 including up to three in Poole Harbour during 27th July–2nd November, whilst on 30th September there were four at Portland and three at Christchurch Harbour coinciding with the exceptional passage of Honey Buzzards and Buzzards. A more modest total of 44 sightings in 2001 included a long-staying bird at Holes Bay, Poole Harbour from 1st October to 30th November – the latest ever sighting for the county. There was a record number of 135 sightings in 2002 including up to four birds in Poole Harbour during 26th August–6th October.

Sponsored by Christchurch Harbour Ornithological Group and A. A. Hill Electrical Contractors Ltd

Kestrel (Common Kestrel) *Falco tinnunculus*

A common resident, winter visitor and passage migrant

Both Mansel-Pleydell (1888) and Blathwayt (1945) considered this species to be a common and well distributed breeding resident, favouring, in the 19th Century at least, areas near to the sea where it found suitable and safe nesting places among the cliffs.

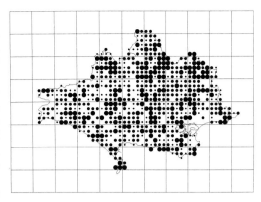

There has been little change in status subsequently. The *BTO Atlas* (1968–1972) found evidence of breeding in all 10-km squares (confirmed in 33 and probable in four), whilst the Tetrad Survey (1987–1994) produced a similar result with evidence of breeding in all but one (97%) of the pre-1974 10-km squares (confirmed in 34 and probable in two). The Tetrad Map shows that breeding occurs widely throughout the county except for parts of the Bournemouth and Poole conurbation. It is found on farmland, downland and heathland, as well as along the cliffs and in urban areas with open spaces.

It is not possible to assess whether the Kestrel is the most numerous raptor in Dorset without studies comparable to those currently being undertaken on the Buzzard. In 1964 the species was selected for a special survey as numbers were considered to have declined, but the results suggested otherwise. Several observers commented on a decline in numbers during 1986, but this was contradicted by an increase in records two years later. More recently there is evidence of a long-term decline locally at Portland Bill, which is thought to be due to the lack of prey resulting from current agricultural practices – see Table 137. It seems likely there are differing levels of population in the county associated with the abundance of prey species.

1970s	1980s	1990s
636	619	291

Table 137. 5 to 10-year average annual totals at Portland Bill 1975–1999

The Kestrel also occurs as a migrant. At Portland Bill passage is slight in spring, mainly in April and May, but more obvious in the autumn during August–November with a peak in October – see Table 138. This pattern is reflected at other coastal watch-points. Autumn passage was responsible for some notable concentrations of birds at Portland Bill in 1951 with up to 20 hunting over grass and stubble during 21st–25th September and 15 on 21st October, whilst 17 were present at St Aldhelm's Head on 10th October. Other high counts include 22 at Chapman's Pool on 22nd October 1983 and 20 at Portland Bill on 13th October 1985.

Jan	Feb	Mar	Apr	May	Jun	Jul	Aug	Sep	Oct	Nov	Dec
343	388	667	897	784	639	721	1328	2108	2643	1124	642

Table 138. Monthly totals (bds) at Portland Bill 1975–1999

A total of 104 birds has been ringed in the county and there has been one foreign recovery from France.

The Kestrel breeds throughout Europe, North and sub-Saharan Africa, Asia Minor, parts of the Middle East and much of Asia except the south.

Red-footed Falcon   *Falco vespertinus*

A rare passage migrant: 29 records

There are two old records involving one shot at Parley in 1854 and one shot near Wareham on 19th May 1904. Since 1958 there have been 27 sightings with reports in every month between April and October, the earliest being on 16th April 1979 and the latest from 21st to 23rd October 1982. Spring is the peak time and accounts for 20 records, including 14 in May, with 18 arriving between 3rd May and 10th June. The most favoured sites are Christchurch Harbour and the Lower Avon Valley (six birds) and the Poole Harbour heaths (five birds).

	Apr	May	Jun	Jul	Aug	Sept	Oct
	2	14	4	2	1	2	2

Table 139. Monthly totals 1958–1997

All records are given below:

1958   Near Wareham: first-summer female 21st–24th May
1959   Burton Bradstock: first-summer male 16th–17th May
1960   Hammoon: first-summer female 16th–24th May
1963   Near Wareham: male 27th July
1969   Portland Bill: first-summer male 11th–14th May
1972   Cranborne Common: male 9th–11th July
1974   Hengistbury: second-year male 18th September
1975   Portland Bill: female 3rd May
1976   Lodmoor NR: first-summer male 8th May,
   female 8th–11th May, and male 24th May
1977   Clifton Wood: female 12th–14th May
1978   Near Arne NR: male 6th August
1979   Lodmoor NR: female 16th April
1982   Portland Bill: juv. 21st–23rd October
1984   Stanpit Marsh, Christchurch Harbour: female
   7th June
1985   Durlston CP: female 18th May
1986   Coward's Marsh, Christchurch: male 24th May
1987   Town Common near Christchurch: first-
   summer male 24th April
  Godlingston Heath: male 13th–24th May
1989   Hartland Moor: first-summer female 10th–
   11th June
1990   East Stoke: male 7th–8th May
1991   Hengistbury: male 28th May
  Yetminster: male 16th October
1992   Hengistbury: first-summer male 3rd–4th June
1995   Ballard Down: female 3rd–4th June; same at Durlston CP 4th–10th June
1997   Durlston CP: female 26th September

The Red-footed Falcon breeds in eastern Europe and west-central Asia and winters in southern Africa. A vagrant to Great Britain with 738 records up to 2002.

Merlin   *Falco columbarius*

An uncommon winter visitor and passage migrant

Mansel-Pleydell (1888) regarded this species to be a winter visitor but only refers to c.12 birds, the last being a pair at Warmwell in December 1886. Blathwayt (1945) considered it to be an autumn and winter visitor, which was frequently observed from the end of October to early March, chiefly near the coast, and also stated "said to breed occasionally on the heath south of Poole Harbour, but proof lacking".

Since 1950 the Merlin has occurred annually as a passage migrant and winter visitor. There is considerable annual fluctuation in sightings with high numbers recorded at Portland Bill in autumn 1954, and more widely throughout the county in 1968, 1975 and during 1977–1979. There was a notable influx in autumn and winter 1977/78 with 114 sightings during August–December and 120 sightings during January–April. This fluctuating pattern has continued during the 1980s and 1990s – see Table 140.

The first migrants usually arrive during the latter part of August with records increasing during September, peaking prominently in October and declining through November. Return passage peaks in March and early April with much fewer birds recorded during the rest of April and May. Migrant birds

1985	1986	1987	1988	1989	1990	1991	1992	1993	1994	1995	1996	1997	1998
242	265	341	383	209	240	165	136	232	172	88	228	166	c.230

Table 140. Annual sightings/records 1985–1998

account for c.77% of the total sightings during 1985–1998, passage being smaller in spring (15%) than in autumn (62%) – see Table 141. Records from Portland Bill during 1980–1999 mirror this pattern – see Table 142. The earliest arrival is 1st August 1999 at Lodmoor NR, whilst the latest record is 28th May 1989 at Portland Bill.

Jan	Feb	Mar	Apr	May	Jun	Jul	Aug	Sep	Oct	Nov	Dec
8%	6%	8%	6%	1%	0%	0%	2%	12%	31%	17%	10%

Table 141. Monthly distribution (%) 1985–1997

Jan	Feb	Mar	Apr	May	Jun	Jul	Aug	Sep	Oct	Nov	Dec
4%	3%	8%	6%	1%	0%	0%	2%	12%	33%	19%	11%

Table 142. Monthly distribution (%) at Portland Bill 1980–1999

It is hard to assess wintering numbers, but two roosts in January 1986 each held four birds and an estimate of the normal winter population would be fewer than 20 birds.

Although the species may occur anywhere in the county, most are recorded from the coastal areas and heathlands of the Poole Basin. Portland Bill alone accounts for 33% of reports during 1985–1994, whilst the combined totals for Portland Bill, Durlston CP and Christchurch Harbour account for 57% of sightings during same period – see Table 143.

Portland Bill	Durlston CP	Christchurch Hbr	the rest
33%	19%	5%	43%

Table 143. Distribution (%) of sightings from various sites 1985–1994

Apart from winter roosts, most records involve single birds, the highest numbers recorded on passage being 8N at Christchurch Harbour on 14th October of an unspecified year, 6S at Portland Bill on 16th October 1985 and 4–6 birds thermalling in the Lower Avon Valley on 2nd March 1987.

There is one report of attempted breeding during the past ten years involving a pair with a female on a nest, the outcome of which was unknown. Otherwise the only summer records since 1950 involve a female on a Poole Basin heath on 27th June 1961, and singles at Seatown on 2nd June and 31st July 1964.

Two birds have been ringed in the county.

The Merlin breeds across most of northern Eurasia and northern North America. The Eurasian population winters throughout Europe mainly to the south and west of the breeding range, also in north-west Africa, Asia Minor, the Middle East and parts of south-west and south-east Asia. It breeds sparingly on the moors and mountains of the British Isles where numbers have declined nationally throughout the 20th Century, until recently when there has been a slight recovery.

Sponsored by Pen Harwood & Gez Thompson

Hobby (Eurasian Hobby) *Falco subbuteo*

A locally common summer visitor and passage migrant

The Hobby has been traditionally associated with the heathland areas of the county, as evidenced by egg-collectors' records, since the 19th Century. Although there are a few early reports from other habitats such as downland, it is not certain whether the species was either overlooked in these areas or was genuinely restricted to heathland. The continuing fragmentation and degradation of many heaths during the 20th Century has reduced this type of breeding habitat. As a result pairs have relocated to neighbouring habitats, but heathland areas continue to be used for hunting. This is reflected by the Tetrad Survey (1987–1994),

which found the breeding population concentrated in the Poole Basin and adjacent areas of the chalk downs with smaller numbers in the Blackmore Vale, but very few in the west of the county.

Data collected from various sources over the past four decades suggest a minimum breeding population of 100 pairs. There are 29 confirmed breeding records west of a line through Dorchester giving a density of 3.2 pairs per 100km², whilst in the eastern part of the county 73 confirmed breeding records gives a density of 4.3 per 100km². These figures, combined with 33 probable records, suggest a minimum of 130 territories, which may include some yearling birds, the majority of which do not attempt to breed until the following year. Old Carrion Crow nests in Scots Pine are favoured breeding sites, but in areas where these trees are absent, oak, Beech, Sycamore and elms (formerly) may be used. This species is particularly susceptible to cold and wet weather conditions when low insect numbers can affect feeding activity, whereby a smaller number of young fledge successfully. During warm summers a maximum of three young are often raised. For much of the season the Hobby is both elusive and vulnerable to disturbance. This species was undoubtedly under-recorded in the past, and it would now appear to be stable with Dorset continuing to support an important part of the British population.

In spring birds generally appear from mid-April onwards, the earliest dates being 22nd March 1991 at St Aldhelm's Head, 27th March 1994 at Godlingston Heath and 30th March 1989 at Dancing Ledge. Since the 1950s, the average date of the first arrivals has gradually become earlier, particularly so during the 1980s and 1990s – see Table 144. Passage increases during the second half of April to reach a peak during the first week of May, and continues at a relatively high level throughout the remainder of the month before diminishing rapidly during the first half of June. During the autumn, there is some evidence to suggest a double peak in passage. The first and smaller peak in late August represents non-breeding birds and failed breeders, whilst the main peak during the second half of September involves successful breeders. By October there are few records, the latest dates being from Portland Bill on 28th–29th October 1975 and 30th October 1976, whilst there is a report from an unknown site on an unspecified date in November 1998. Since the mid-1980s, there has been a marked increase in the annual totals of migrants at Portland Bill, which is also reflected at the other main coastal watch-points – see Fig 20.

	1950–1959	1960–1969	1970–1979	1980–1989	1990–1999
Range	5th–28th April	8th–30th April	9th–25th April	30th March–18th April	22nd March–19th April
Average	21st April	19th April	18th April	11th April	7th April

Table 144. Dates for first spring arrivals each decade 1950–1999

Hobbies regularly gather to feed on insects, particularly during May and June. These flocks may involve birds on passage and non-breeding first-years as well as the local pairs. The highest counts are 12 feeding over an area of unimproved grassland in Purbeck on 8th June 1989 and 11 hawking for insects near Christchurch on 28th April 1988.

Nine birds have been ringed in the county.

The Hobby breeds over much of Europe, except the far north, and northern and central Asia, also in north-west Africa and Asia Minor. It winters mainly in the southern third of Africa, the northern Indian sub-continent and parts of south-east Asia. In Great Britain there is evidence of an increase in range with breeding extending north, east and west of former limits.

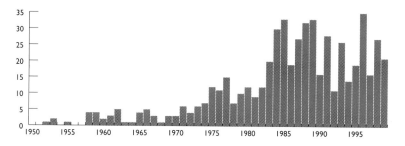

Fig 20. Annual totals (bds) at Portland Bill 1959–1999

Postscript 2000–2002

Very early migrants were recorded from Durlston CP with two on 27th March 2000 and one on 31st March 2001. A total of 42 birds at Portland Bill during May 2001 is exceptionally high.

Sponsored by Tasie Russell, Graham Whitby and the Travelling Naturalist

Gyr Falcon   *Falco rusticolus*

Accidental: two or three records

Mansel-Pleydell (1888) referred to a bird of the 'Iceland race' found dead in the early part of the 19th Century on Cranborne Chase and preserved in Viscount Portman's collection at Bryanston. Subsequent authorities cast doubt on the validity of this record since it was not critically examined.

There are two records of the 'Greenland race' with one identified at Lyme Regis on 11th June 1882 and one seen at Ballard Down, Swanage after a blizzard on 5th February 1912.

The Gyr Falcon breeds across the Holarctic. The high latitude populations are migratory and winter immediately to the south of the breeding range. A vagrant to Great Britain with 124 records between 1958 and 2002.

Peregrine Falcon   *Falco peregrinus*

An locally common resident, winter visitor and passage migrant

Mansel-Pleydell (1888) described this species as "the commonest of our larger birds of prey, and at present is well established in the county, owing to the protection extended to it by many of the landed proprietors". This is perhaps a surprising situation considering the fate of many birds of prey during the 19th Century! Mansel-Pleydell also referred to Purbeck as its headquarters, where precipitous cliffs afforded an additional protection.

The Peregrine has suffered mixed fortunes during the 20th Century. From 1920 to 1939 15 territories were regularly occupied and a further three used irregularly or occasionally. During this period nests were relentlessly robbed and yet remarkably the species managed to maintain a population averaging 12 pairs per year until 1939. In the Second World War the Air Ministry persecuted the Peregrine in order to protect carrier pigeons and the population was severely depleted. In 1946 at least one pair bred and numbers recovered to eight occupied territories in 1951 with eight pairs in ten territories by 1953. Although seven pairs bred in these ten territories in 1956, there followed a rapid and complete decline caused by prey contaminated by agricultural pesticides and also by persecution. In 1957 only six territories were occupied and at least two pairs failed to lay, whilst in 1958 numbers were down to five pairs with breeding proved for only two of these. Only one pair was left by 1960, and from 1961 only single birds were reported.

Immediately after the cessation of breeding, the Peregrine rapidly became a very scarce, mainly winter visitor to the county. Numbers remained at a low ebb for much of the 1960s and early 1970s, but then gradually increased from 1975 onwards – see Table 145.

During the early 1980s this increase accelerated culminating in the re-establishment of breeding in 1985. Prior to this, birds were present in a previously known territory for two years. Subsequently the breeding population has rapidly increased to reach 20 pairs by the late 1990s – see Table 146. Most of the

60	61	62	63	64	65	66	67	68	69	70	71	72	73	74	75	76	77	78	79
nc	14	nc	7	12	3	nc	16	22	16	10	8	12	3	12	nc	17	29	18	nc

Table 145. Annual totals 1960–1979

breeding territories are located along the coastal cliffs from Lyme Regis to Purbeck. The species has also nested successfully on the now demolished Poole Power Station, and since 1995 breeding has spread inland with at least five sites occupied by the late 1990s. This recolonisation still gives cause for concern with several known nest failures, some due to natural causes and others suspected or known to be due to human interference.

	85	86	87	88	89	90	91	92	93	94	95	96	97	98	99
Coastal pairs	1	2	3	4	6	7	8	10	12	13	12	12	12	15	15
Inland pairs	0	0	0	0	0	0	0	0	0	0	1	2	2	5	5
Total pairs	1	2	3	4	6	7	8	10	12	13	13	14	14	20	20
Young	2	4	5	4	4	13	24	13	22	c.15	19	27	32	18	c.24

Table 146. Number of breeding pairs 1986–1999

There has been a general increase in sightings in all months of the year throughout the 1980s and 1990s reflecting the improving status of the breeding population. Although many records are from the coastal fringes and the Poole Basin, there has been a marked increase away from these areas and the Peregrine is becoming a familiar sight at inland locations throughout the county. Sites with concentrations of wildfowl, waders or flocks of passerines, notably in winter, are particularly favoured. There is some evidence of passage at coastal sites. This is most obvious at Portland Bill where records for the period 1980–1987 peaked during March–April and September–October – see Table 147.

Jan	Feb	Mar	Apr	May	Jun	Jul	Aug	Sep	Oct	Nov	Dec
14	13	35	32	23	7	2	33	61	50	21	7

Table 147. Monthly totals (bds) at Portland Bill 1980–1987

Four birds have been ringed in the county.

The Peregrine has a worldwide breeding distribution occurring on all continents. In Europe there have been marked declines in many countries due to contamination from pesticides, nests robbed for falconry, and shooting. With the banning of toxic chemicals, the population in the British Isles has increased in recent years.

Postscript 2000–2002

The breeding population continues to thrive and increase with 22 pairs (16 coastal and six inland) rearing 28 young in 2000, 23 pairs (18 coastal and five inland) rearing 22 young in 2001, and 18 pairs (15 coastal and three inland) rearing 27 young in 2002. In 2001, one of the coastal pairs attempted to raise Herring Gull chicks!

Sponsored by Edmund Harwood and Jonathan Taylor

Water Rail   *Rallus aquaticus*

A locally common resident, winter visitor and passage migrant

Mansel-Pleydell (1888) described the Water Rail as "resident, and not unfrequent in suitable places". Blathwayt (1945) also considered it to be a resident, which bred around Poole Harbour and probably near Weymouth. Both suggested that due to its shy and skulking habits, the species was under-recorded.

Little has changed in recent times and it seems likely that the Water Rail continues to be overlooked particularly during the breeding season. Despite this, the *BTO Atlas* (1968–1972) found evidence of breeding in no less than 21 (57%) 10-km squares (confirmed in seven, probable in six and possible in eight). Although confirmed or probable breeding was recorded from such traditional areas as Poole Harbour (SY98, SY99 and SZ08) and Weymouth (SY67 and SY68), there were also reports from several inland squares (SU01, ST90, ST80, ST70, ST60, SY59, ST50 and ST51). By contrast the Tetrad Survey (1987–1994) revealed evidence of breeding in only 14 (38%) of the pre-1974 10-km squares (confirmed in three, probable in three and possible in eight). Surprisingly the Tetrad Survey (1987–1994) overlooked breeding at Radipole NR, which was confirmed in 1992 and 1994. Further additional reports during the Tetrad Survey (1987–1994) include up-grading breeding from probable to confirmed at both Lodmoor NR (in 1987 and 1988) and Winkton (in 1988), and possible breeding at West Bexington in 1989. If these additions are taken into account, breeding during the Tetrad Survey

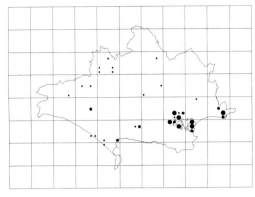

(1987–1994) was confirmed in four and probable in two of the pre-1974 10-km squares. The decline between the *BTO Atlas* (1968–1972) and the Tetrad Survey (1987–1994) is reflected by the national trend, which showed a 34% reduction over the same period. The most likely cause of the retraction in Dorset is loss of habitat due to agricultural improvement.

The Tetrad Map shows that breeding is mainly concentrated around Poole Harbour and Christchurch Harbour. The most favoured sites in the Poole Harbour area are Brownsea, Studland NNR, Arne NR, Keysworth, Holton Shore and Lytchett Bay. Evidence of confirmed breeding and population estimates for the main sites are not consistently recorded, but the best available data since 1980 are summarised in Table 148. Although most breeding takes place in reedbeds, at least three nests were found in low *Spartina* grass in the vicinity of Keysworth and Holton Shore in 1972.

	Population Estimate	Year Breeding Confirmed
Brownsea	1–3prs 1980–1989, 3–6prs early 1990s	1983, 1988, 1989, 1990, 1991, 1992
Studland NNR	5–6prs 1980–1983, 10–15prs 1987, many 1993, 20prs 1995, 8–15prs 1997	1987
Arne NR	1–2prs 1980–1994 at least	1988, 1990, 1991, 1992
Lytchett Bay	4prs 1984, 2–3prs 1985, 6prs 1995	1986, 1987, 1994, 1995 (16y), 1996 (28y), 1998
Christchurch Hbr	2prs 1987, several 1990	1982, 1983, 1984, 1987, 1990
Radipole NR	1–2prs 1981–1996 except 3prs 1984	1981, 1982, 1983, 1992, 1994, 1996
Lodmoor NR	6–8prs 1980–1985 but 14prs 1983, 3–4prs 1986–1988	1980, 1982, 1987, 1988, 1996

Table 148. Breeding data from the main sites 1980–1999

Numbers increase greatly in winter and birds can be found in almost any wet area where there is cover including reedbeds, willow and alder thickets, overgrown riverbanks and sometimes wet hedgerows. During the late 1970s high numbers were recorded from Radipole NR with 150 in mid-January 1978 and 100–200 during January–February 1979. Subsequently winter numbers at both Radipole and Lodmoor NRs have been more modest with estimates of 40–100 in several years up to 1988. Other notable counts during this period included up to 50 at Little Sea in winter 1987, at least 30 at Lytchett Bay in autumn 1984 and up to 30 at Abbotsbury in winter 1983. Autumn and winter numbers have declined during the 1990s, the only counts exceeding 15 birds being 30 at Christchurch Harbour on 19th October 1990 with 20 there on 26th September 1992, and 16 in Poole Harbour in November 1999.

Water Rails can suffer high mortality in cold weather and it has been suggested that severe winters in the early and mid-1980s have reduced the population. Periods of severe cold often force birds into the open and some may appear in unexpected places including gardens.

A few birds are recorded on passage most years from such coastal watch-points as Portland Bill, St Aldhelm's Head and Durlston CP. Since 1980 there have been c.52 records from Portland Bill excluding birds that have overwintered regularly since 1993. The majority of birds have occurred in October and November (25) with a smaller peak in March (six), whilst cold weather is responsible for most of the sightings in January and February – see Table 149. Elsewhere on Portland, birds have overwintered at East Weare and Verne Common where at least 20 were recorded from January to 2nd May 1984. In earlier years breeding was even suspected at East Weare in 1968 and 1975, whilst a bird seen on the rocks at Portland Bill on 13th December 1974 was an unusual sighting.

Jan	Feb	Mar	Apr	May	Jun	Jul	Aug	Sep	Oct	Nov	Dec
7	5	6	0	0	0	0	2	1	14	11	6

Table 149. Monthly totals at Portland Bill 1980–1999 (excluding overwintering birds)

A total of 238 birds has been ringed in the county. There has been one foreign recovery from Denmark and one foreign control from former Czechoslovakia.

The Water Rail breeds over much of Europe, including Iceland but excluding all but southern Scandinavia, as well as extensive areas of central Asia, also locally in North Africa and Asia Minor. Although the western and some southern populations are resident, it is migratory or partially migratory elsewhere with birds wintering mainly in western Europe, north-west Africa, the Middle East and south-east Asia.

Postscript 2000–2002
There were notable counts by recent standards of 24 in Poole Harbour in November 2002 and at least 23 at various sites around North Portland during the second winter period in 2001.

Spotted Crake   *Porzana porzana*

An uncommon passage migrant, mainly in autumn, and very rare winter visitor – has bred

Mansel-Pleydell (1888) considered this species to be a rare visitor in spring and autumn. Blathwayt (1945) referred to it as a scarce summer resident, which was also recorded on passage, and further mentioned that "the call note has recently been heard in summer from east Dorset where a pair or two probably breed". The only evidence of confirmed breeding, however, involved a nest found near Wareham in 1868 and young seen at Ferndown in 1932.

Since 1950 the only evidence of breeding has involved birds calling with a remarkable series of records during 1968–1974. The most notable were two birds, considered to be a pair, heard regularly at Radipole NR from 27th April to 3rd June 1968 with one again heard on 28th June, at least one heard regularly at Lodmoor NR from 22nd May to 14th June 1969, and 1–2 birds heard intermittently at Brownsea from

25th September 1969 to 5th January 1970 and during November–December 1970. There are also records of birds calling at Little Sea on 26th May 1971, Brownsea again on 5th March 1972 (two birds) and 27th August 1974, and remarkably, four at Radipole NR on 21st September 1972. More recently single birds have been heard calling at Christchurch Harbour on 21st May 1988 and 24th–25th April 1993, and Radipole NR intermittently during 19th–24th May 1998.

The Spotted Crake was a rare visitor during the 1950s with one at South Haven, Poole Harbour on 3rd January 1954 and two at a site elsewhere in Poole Harbour on 22nd July 1957 the only reports. Since 1961 the species has occurred annually, except for 1966, with a marked increase during the 1970s – see Table 150. Subsequently numbers have fluctuated through the 1980s with peak years in 1981 and 1986 followed by a decline during the 1990s. The majority of birds occur in the autumn with August and September accounting for 67% of the total – see Tables 151 and 152. It is interesting to note that all the winter and most of the spring records occurred prior to 1983.

60	61	62	63	64	65	66	67	68	69	70	71	72	73	74	75	76	77	78	79
0	1	1	1	1+	4	0	3	4	3+	3+	5	11	1	1	10	11	11	11	6

80	81	82	83	84	85	86	87	88	89	90	91	92	93	94	95	96	97	98	99
7	15	9	9	6	1	10	5	7	2+	3	6	2	9	5	6	4	4	3	4

Table 150. Annual totals 1960–1999

Jan	Feb	Mar	Apr	May	Jun	Jul	Aug	Sep	Oct	Nov	Dec
7	4	2	7	4	0	4	50	27	7	6	5

Table 151. Monthly totals 1950–1982

Jan	Feb	Mar	Apr	May	Jun	Jul	Aug	Sep	Oct	Nov	Dec
0	0	2	2	3	0	4	43	21	9	2	0

Table 152. Monthly totals 1983–1999

Radipole NR and Christchurch Harbour are by far the most favoured sites, accounting for 48% and 30% respectively of the total records – see Table 153. Most of the remaining sightings are from various sites around Poole Harbour, notably Brownsea and Keysworth, Lodmoor NR and Abbotsbury. Away from these areas there are only six reports with singles at Sherborne (dead) on 10th October 1962, Winterborne Stickland on 21st January 1963, Clayesmore from 22nd to 24th November 1965, Sutton Bingham on at least 17th August 1976, Christchurch Meadows on 26th August 1978 and St Aldhelm's Head on 25th October 1987.

	Total
Abbotsbury	4
Radipole NR	100
Lodmoor NR	15
Poole Harbour	22
Christchurch Harbour	62
elsewhere	6

Table 153. Distribution of migrants 1950–1999

Due to the species' secretive behaviour, it is often difficult to assess numbers accurately. Most reports concern one or two birds, but occasionally more have been present, the highest counts being from Radipole NR with up to nine during 28th August–2nd September 1977 (maximum on 2nd), five on 4th September 1979 and 25th August 1981 and four on 30th August 1976 and 21st September 1972, whilst there were up to four in Christchurch Harbour during August 1981.

A total of 20 birds has been ringed in the county.

The Spotted Crake breeds over most of Europe, except for northern Scandinavia, and west-central

Asia, but it is very local over much of central and western Europe. It winters mainly in sub-Saharan Africa and the Indian sub-continent. Locally fairly common in the British Isles before the mid-19th Century, the species has since declined dramatically due to land drainage and the subsequent loss of habitat. It is now a very scarce and sporadic breeder with few regular sites.

Postscript 2000–2002
Most records were from Christchurch Harbour with a minimum of four birds in autumn 2000, c.4–8 birds in autumn 2001 and c.5–6 birds in autumn 2002. Elsewhere there was a single bird at Radipole NR in autumn 2000 and two singles at Abbotsbury in autumn 2001.

Little Crake   *Porzana parva*

Accidental: three records involving four individuals

There is an old record involving two shot at Alderholt prior to 1888. More recently:

    1975   Lodmoor NR: 8th and 10th November, and again 8th December
    1994   Stanpit Marsh, Christchurch Harbour: juvenile male moulting to first-winter 17th August

The Little Crake breeds mainly in eastern Europe and a few scattered areas in west-central Asia with much smaller numbers in central, western and southern Europe. The wintering range is imperfectly known, but it is thought to be in the north-eastern tropics of Africa. A vagrant to Great Britain with 99 records up to 2002.

Baillon's Crake   *Porzana pusilla*

Accidental: one record

    1893   Swanage: 1st June

There are no recent records.

The Baillon's Crake breeds mainly in south-eastern Europe and central Asia, also very locally in central, western and southern Europe. There are also populations in southern Africa and Australasia. European breeding birds are thought to winter mostly in sub-Saharan Africa. Although there are two or three breeding records for the 19th Century, it is essentially a vagrant to Great Britain with only 15 records between 1958 and 2001.

Corncrake (Corn Crake)   *Crex crex*

A rare passage migrant – formerly bred

Mansel-Pleydell (1888) described this species as "a common summer visitant". Blathwayt (1945) commented that it became much rarer as a breeding bird about the end of the 19th Century, but of recent years a little more frequent. Both mention that the Swanage area was favoured during autumn passage with up to 30 shot in one day in early October prior to 1888, many seen during 1st–15th October 1927, and 23 shot and many others spared on 2nd September 1929.

By 1950 the Corncrake had virtually disappeared as a breeding species. A few reports of calling birds since then may have indicated breeding, the most recent being a pair seen and heard at Loscombe between mid-April and late May 1978, and singles heard at Woolland on 7th May 1978, Stourpaine from 19th May to 2nd August 1981 and Bulbarrow in 1988.

The number of records, most of which refer to passage birds, has declined since 1950 reflecting the species parlous fortunes as a breeding bird elsewhere in the British Isles – see Fig 21. Even so, there were occasional 'good years' notably in 1953, 1956, 1959, 1960 and most recently 1967, whilst at Portland it occurred almost annually on passage during 1953–1977 – see Fig 22. Since 1980 it has become very scarce in the county with 16 records in the 12 years up to 1991, but only six records in the eight subsequent years 1992–1999! The peak passage months are April–May and September–October – see Table 154. The earliest arrival is 20th March 1969 at Portland Bill, whilst the latest departures are 27th November 1997 at Portland Bill and 30th November 1969 at Turnworth.

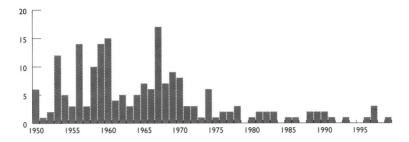

Fig 21. Annual totals 1950–1999

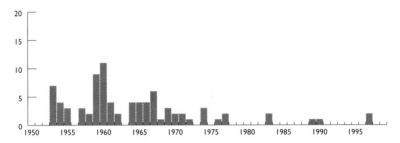

Fig 22. Annual totals at Portland 1950–1999

Jan	Feb	Mar	Apr	May	Jun	Jul	Aug	Sep	Oct	Nov	Dec
0	0	1	13	11	0	0	6	41	16	1	0

Table 154. Monthly totals at Portland 1950–1999

Most records involve single birds, the most notable counts being at least seven at Portland Bill on 9th September 1956 with four there on 4th September 1959, and four at Swanage (a traditional passage site) on 15th August 1950.

The reason for the disastrous decline of the Corncrake is almost certainly agricultural intensification with the widespread use of fertilisers stimulating early grass growth. This has resulted in higher stocking rates and earlier and more frequent cutting of grass swards so that the hay meadows of former years, which formed the species' main breeding habitat, are no longer available.

The Corncrake's breeding range covers most of Europe north of the Mediterranean, except northern Scandinavia, and extends eastwards across west-central Asia. It winters in south-eastern Africa. There has been a marked and continuing decline in central and western Europe and this is nowhere more marked than in the British Isles where it is thought to have started as long as 150 years ago. The British breeding population is now almost entirely confined to the Scottish Islands and adjacent areas of west and north Scotland.

Postscript 2000–2002
This species remains a rare migrant with one picked up dead at Weymouth on 29th September 2000, one at Tout Quarry, Portland on 17th October 2001 and one in private gardens at Southwell, Portland on 24th–25th October 2002 the only records. The 2002 bird was trapped, ringed and released at Portland Bill.

Moorhen (Common Moorhen) *Gallinula chloropus*

An abundant resident, winter visitor and passage migrant
Both Mansel-Pleydell (1888) and Blathwayt (1945) considered the Moorhen to be a common and widely distributed breeding resident in suitable habitat throughout the county.

The same is true of the species today as demonstrated by the *BTO Atlas* (1968–1972), which confirmed breeding in 34 (92%) 10-km squares, and the Tetrad Survey (1987–1994), which found evidence of breeding in all but two (95%) of the pre-1974 10-km squares (confirmed in 33 and probable in two). The Tetrad

157

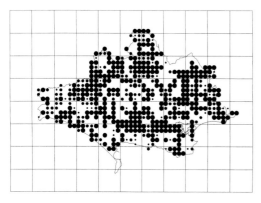

Map shows that breeding occurs at any site where freshwater and suitable vegetation exists. Rivers, streams, lakes, ponds, gravel pits and marshes all find favour, whilst small ponds far removed from other water are often occupied. The proliferation of farm ponds during the 1970s and 1980s has provided the Moorhen with further valuable breeding sites and many of these have been rapidly colonised.

Population estimates are available for a number of sites – see Tables 155–157. The dramatic decline at Radipole NR reflects local influences, the fluctuating but generally stable populations along the River Stour between Corfe Mullen and Sturminster Marshall and along the River Allen being more typical of the county as a whole. As long ago as 1970, 70 pairs were located on the River Allen between Clapgate and the Horton Inn. There are also counts of up to 25–30 pairs from several other sites around the county, but a large proportion of the Dorset population must reside in the many small and unrecorded sites. One adverse factor has been the increase in feral mink in Dorset, which has resulted in the virtual disappearance of local populations in some places, although these quickly re-establish if the mink are controlled.

76	77	78	79	80	81	82	83	84	85	86	87	88	89	90	91
25	25	25	35	30	30	28	25	30	30	14	8	7	nc	nc	4

Table 155. Number of breeding territories at Radipole NR 1976–1991

1978	1979	1980	1981	1982	1983	1984	1985	1986	1987
18	9	14	15	21	21	27	20	21	18

1988	1989	1990	1991	1992	1993	1994	1995	1996	1997
12	20	13	14	15	15	13	18	20	17

Table 156. Number of breeding territories along River Stour between Corfe Mullen and Sturminster Marshall 1978–1997

1989	1990	1991	1992	1993	1994	1995	1996	1997	1998	1999
38	74	77	71	63	71	74	52	39	44	71

Table 157. Number of breeding territories along River Allen 1989–1999

Prior to 1980 winter counts were generally below 100, the highest being 243 at Radipole NR on 17th October 1971 and 121 at Milton Abbas Lake in March 1962. Subsequently winter maxima at Lodmoor NR regularly exceeded 100 during the 1980s with a peak of 201 on 16th February 1985 – see Table 158. Nearby at Radipole NR, there was a substantial reduction in wintering numbers during the early 1990s – see Table 158. This reflects a similar decline in the breeding population at this site.

	80/81	81/82	82/83	83/84	84/85	85/86	86/87	87/88
Lodmoor NR	130	102	145	135	201	165	127	86
Radipole NR	83	89	50	70	68	54	81	85

	88/89	89/90	90/91	91/92	92/93	93/94	94/95	95/96
Lodmoor NR	167	48	100	83	88	143	93	nc
Radipole NR	101	62	50	27	22	18	29	nc

Table 158. Winter maxima at Lodmoor and Radipole NRs 1980–1995

The species is occasionally recorded from Portland and the Purbeck coast, for example, ten birds occurred at Portland Bill during 1980–1999.

A total of 457 birds has been ringed in the county. There have been four recoveries from Germany and three from the Netherlands, and one foreign control from Germany.

The Moorhen breeds over most of Europe except northern Scandinavia, as well as large areas of Asia, Africa and North and South America. In the British Isles it is common and widely distributed except for some areas of western and northern Scotland.

Postscript 2000–2002

At Lodmoor NR 257 in November 2001 is exceptional and appears to be a record count for the county, the previous highest being 243 at Radipole NR on 17th October 1971.

Allen's Gallinule   *Porphyrula alleni*

Accidental: one record

   2002   West Cliffs, Portland: 10th February

This record involved a juvenile found in a moribund state close to the West Cliffs at Weston, Portland, which was taken to Portland Bird Observatory but failed to recover and subsequently died. A full account can be found in *Birding World*, Vol. 15, No 2: February 2002.

Allen's Gallinule breeds widely throughout sub-Saharan Africa. It is a rare vagrant to the Western Palearctic with most occurrences in mid-winter. There is only one previous British record involving a juvenile caught alive on a fishing boat off Hopton, Norfolk on 1st January 1902.

Coot (Common Coot)   *Fulica atra*

A common resident and winter visitor

Mansel-Pleydell (1888) considered this species to be more local in distribution than the Moorhen. Blathwayt (1945) described it as "a common resident" and referred to a large increase in numbers during the winter months with thousands on the Fleet at Abbotsbury.

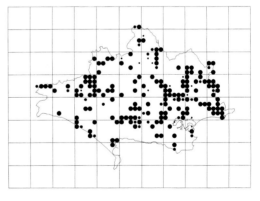

Subsequently there appears to have been little change in status. The *BTO Atlas* (1968–1972) found evidence of breeding in 31 (84%) 10-km squares (confirmed in 27, probable in one and possible in three), the most notable absences being in the west (ST40), the far north (ST72) and south Purbeck (SY97). The Tetrad Survey (1987–1994) produced a similar result with breeding confirmed in 31 (84%) of the pre-1974 10-km squares, the main differences from the *BTO Atlas* (1968–1972) being that breeding occurred in ST40, ST72 and SY97, but not in the far west (SY39). The Tetrad Map shows that breeding is more localised and less widespread than the Moorhen. This is because the Coot prefers more substantial waters, including slower-flowing rivers and streams, where there is suitable vegetation to which nests can be anchored. It avoids very small ponds, streams and ditches. Many of the new farm ponds have been colonised during the last two decades, but the species is fiercely territorial in the breeding season and the smaller sites can usually only support two or three pairs.

Population estimates are available for a number of sites – see Tables 159–161. At Radipole NR the dramatic and steady decline from the high numbers present during the late 1970s and early 1980s is due to local influences. The same may be true at Sherborne Lake where a population of 40–50 pairs in the early 1970s declined to 10–13 pairs in the early 1990s. Along the River Stour between Corfe Mullen and Sturminster Marshall, the population trend is characterised by periods of relative stability interspersed by sudden increases or decreases, whilst breeding numbers along the River Allen fluctuate widely from year to year. It is difficult to assess how typical these latter two trends are of the county population as a whole. Like the Moorhen, Coots are predated by feral mink, but appear to be less vulnerable than the former species.

76	77	78	79	80	81	82	83	84	85	86	87	88	89	90	91	92
40	60	58	60	65	65	60	55	50	50	40	35	25	nc	nc	20	14

Table 159. Number of breeding territories at Radipole NR 1976–1992

1978	1979	1980	1981	1982	1983	1984	1985	1986	1987
10	8	8	9	20	16	20	18	19	11

1988	1989	1990	1991	1992	1993	1994	1995	1996	1997
11	12	12	12	16	11	3	3	9	15

Table 160. Number of breeding territories along River Stour between Corfe Mullen and Sturminster Marshall 1978–1997

1989	1990	1991	1992	1993	1994	1995	1996	1997	1998	1999
18	25	8	14	4	19	16	10	9	13	5

Table 161. Number of breeding territories along River Allen 1989–1999

By far the largest winter counts are from the Fleet. Since the 1960s winter maxima have ranged from 1,000 to peaks of 5,000 on 16th January 1966, 31st December 1968 and during November–December 1981 with counts of 1,500–3,000 birds being more typical. The ten-year average peak counts show that the wintering population on the Fleet declined between the 1960s and 1970s, but then remained relatively stable subsequently – see Table 162. A similar pattern is revealed for Christchurch Harbour where winter numbers have declined since the mid-1970s, when c.1,300 were present in early 1974, but subsequently remained relatively stable during the 1980s and 1990s – see Table 162. Elsewhere there were unusually high counts of 850 at Lodmoor NR in January 1982 and 650+ in Poole Harbour during the cold spell in February 1963. Otherwise winter maxima of 100–500 birds have been recorded from Radipole NR, Milton Abbas Lake, Crichel Lake, Sherborne Lake, Lake Gate floods at Corfe Mullen, Poole Park, Little Sea, the Lower Stour at Tuckton (cold weather) and Iford, and the Lower Avon at Christchurch (cold weather).

	1960s	1970s	1980s	1990s
The Fleet	3464	2157	2463	2253
Christchurch Harbour	–	744	437	431

Table 162. Winter 10-year average peak counts from the Fleet and Christchurch Hbr 1950–1999

In recent years peak numbers on the Fleet have generally occurred during November–December – see Table 163. This suggests that the Fleet is a 'stop-over' site for birds destined to winter elsewhere either locally in Dorset or further west in Great Britain (cf Brent Goose and Wigeon).

Sept	Oct	Nov	Dec	Jan	Feb	Mar
792	1223	1770	1903	1540	1038	609

Table 163. Average monthly maxima from the Fleet 1986–1999

This species is rarely recorded on passage at Portland Bill where there are only six records, the last on 1st April 1981, whilst at Durlston CP there are four reports involving seven birds during 1984–1989.

A total of 647 birds has been ringed in the county. There have been four recoveries from France, two each from Germany and the Netherlands, and one control from Denmark.

The Coot breeds over all but extreme northern Europe, also in central Asia and the Indian sub-continent, Australasia and locally in North Africa, Asia Minor, the Middle East and Indonesia. The northern and eastern populations are migratory with birds mainly wintering in central, western and southern Europe, Asia Minor, the Middle East, the Indian sub-continent and south-east Asia.

Postscript 2000–2002
One at Chesil Cove on 4th January 2002 is the first record for Portland since April 1981!

Crane (Common Crane)　　　　　　　　　　　　*Grus grus*

A very rare passage migrant and winter visitor

There are three 19th Century records with one shot at Poole on 12th November 1839, another shot there in 1849, and one shot on the banks of the Wareham River in May 1869. There were no further sightings until one at Weymouth on 15th June 1930. On 31st October 1963 at least 26 were seen in Dorset with 14 at West Bexington, seven at Portland and five at Charmouth. These formed part of an invasion into southern England, which was thought to involve about 500 birds. Since 1972 a total of 55 birds have been recorded including 27 in October, ten in December and nine in February:

1972	Portland Bill: 14th October; presumed same flying east at Seacombe 15th October
1975	Lytchett Bay: 16th August
1978	Brand's Bay: six 2nd December
	St Catherine's Hill, Christchurch: three immatures 20th December
1979	Winspit: two flying east 25th February – later seen in Hampshire
1983	Abbotsbury: 14th June
1984	Monkton Up Wimborne: 26th April
1985	Lytchett Matravers: ad. 28th April
1986	Bere Regis: 1st–4th August
1987	Hengistbury: 14 flying south-west 22nd October
1988	Christchurch Harbour: seven flying north 22nd February
1994	Throop: first-winter 2nd January–2nd February; presumed same at Christchurch Harbour 17th January
	Hengistbury, Crossways and West Fleet: 11 flying west or south-west on 17th October – later seen in Devon
	Winspit and Durlston CP: 23rd October
1995	Portland Bill: ad. flying north 12th April
1999	Lytchett Bay: ad. 19th and 22nd September and 3rd and 10th October; presumed same at West Bexington 19th October
2000	Southwell and Portland Bill: ad. 24th March
	Avon Causeway: flying north 26th December

The Crane breeds from Scandinavia and Germany east across north-eastern Europe and much of northern Asia; also locally in Asia Minor. It winters in France, Iberia, north-west Africa, Sudan, Ethiopia, Asia Minor, the Middle East, the northern Indian sub-continent and south-east Asia. The population breeding in Scandinavia and the south Baltic migrates south-west to winter in Iberia and birds straying from this route must account for the great majority of British records.

Little Bustard　　　　　　　　　　　　　　　*Tetrax tetrax*

Accidental: four records, but only one recent

There are three old records with single birds shot at Winfrith on 26th December 1853, at Warmwell in the 19th Century (date unknown), and at an unknown locality on 21st January 1902. More recently:

1987	Coward's Marsh, Christchurch: 30th December

This bird was first found at Coward's Marsh, Christchurch and relocated nearby the following day, before moving to fields near Burton. Subsequently the bird proved to be very mobile and often elusive moving widely over an area of the Lower Avon Valley between Christchurch and Sopley in Hampshire.

The Little Bustard breeds in western, central and southern France, but its European stronghold is in Iberia. There are small scattered populations elsewhere in southern Europe and in north-west Africa, and a well separated population in extreme south-eastern Europe and west-central Asia. It has disappeared from much of its former range and is declining almost everywhere. Many birds disperse in winter from their breeding grounds, which accounts for most of the British records being in that season. A vagrant to the Great Britain with 111 records, but only 19 between 1958 and 2000.

161

Great Bustard $\qquad$ *Otis tarda*

A former resident now long extinct

In Dorset, breeding on Cranborne Chase had probably ceased by 1810, but single stragglers were recorded in the area as recently as 1880 (shot at Handley on 1st January) and 1888 (seen near Shaftesbury on 17th May and in September). In addition a pair reputed to have been shot in Dorset in 1865 resides in the Russell-Coates Museum, Bournemouth. There are no recent records for the county.

The Great Bustard breeds in Iberia, eastern Europe and parts of central Asia. The species has disappeared from most of western and central Europe and last bred in Great Britain in 1832. A vagrant to the British Isles with only 20 records between 1958 and 2000.

Sponsored by David Waters and Estlin Waters

Oystercatcher (Eurasian Oystercatcher) $\qquad$ *Haematopus ostralegus*

An uncommon resident, and locally common winter visitor and passage migrant

Mansel-Pleydell (1888) suggested that this species was most frequently seen along the coast in the autumn and mentioned that a few pairs bred on the sandy portions of Poole Harbour, Studland, Worbarrow and Weymouth. Blathwayt (1945) described it as "a common resident" that bred somewhat sparingly in the Poole Harbour area and possibly on the Purbeck coast, but not from Weymouth westwards.

Poole Harbour has continued to be the main breeding area. Although the bulk of the population nest on Brownsea, numbers have fluctuated considerably from year to year – see Table 164. For example, only four pairs were present in 1980, but in 1978 c.40 pairs raised c.50 young. Breeding has also occurred annually on Green Island from 1991 to at least 1996 with numbers increasing from one pair in 1991 to 6–7 pairs in 1996. Elsewhere within the harbour breeding has been occasionally recorded in recent years from Arne NR (1981 and 1982), Furzey Island (1985 and 1994), Goathorn (1985), Fitzworth (1987), Holes Bay (1991 and 1996) Long Island (1994) and Round Island (1994) – all involving 1–2 pairs except for seven pairs on Furzey Island in both 1985 and 1994.

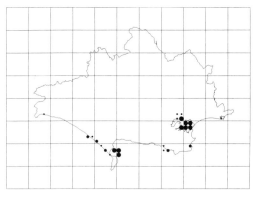

Breeding occurred fairly regularly on the Chesil Beach during 1965–1987 and nearby on the Portland Harbour Breakwaters during 1977–1990. Numbers at both sites were small, usually 1–3 pairs and never more than five pairs. The only records of breeding in this area since 1990 have been from the Chesil Beach/Fleet in 1995, 1997 and 1998. Although one pair bred regularly on the Purbeck coast up to 1951, the only confirmed reports subsequently involve two juveniles at St Aldhelm's Head in 1987 and a pair, which attempted to nest there in 1989. During the Tetrad Survey (1987–1994) probable breeding was also recorded along the Purbeck coast from the vicinity of Peveril Point and Rope Lake Head. In Christchurch Harbour single pairs bred unsuccessfully during 1975–1977 and in 1985 with two pairs present in 1999.

	63	64	65	66	67	68	69	70	71	72	73	74	75	76	77	78	79	80	81
Brownsea	11	nc	10	12	16	19	nc	nc	16	25	nc	22	21	nc	7	40	nc	4	11
other sites	0	0	2	0	1	1	2	3	1	1	2	1	3	6	5	0	0	3	5

	82	83	84	85	86	87	88	89	90	91	92	93	94	95	96	97	98	99	00
Brownsea	9	5	18	30	13	10	10	5	15	12	20	nc	20	20	2	15	15	15	28
other sites	2	2	4	11	5	8	3	7	2	2	3	3	13	4	8	1	2	2	0

Table 164. Numbers of confirmed breeding pairs 1963–2000

Poole Harbour is the most important site for passage and wintering birds. During the 1950s and 1960s, peak counts occurred mainly in the autumn and usually ranged between 300–600 birds, but there were at least 1,000 on Brownsea in September 1965. The wintering population has increased subsequently with maxima regularly exceeding 1,000 since the mid-1980s, the highest counts being 1,726 in January 1992, 1,771 in January 1994 and a county record of 2,034 in December 1999 – see Table 165. The seasonal pattern of occurrence for 1986–1999 shows the population increasing rapidly during the autumn (July–September) and then more slowly during October–November to peak in mid-winter (December–January) – see Table 166. Numbers then decline during the spring to a small summer population consisting of breeding adults and non-breeding immatures. Wintering Oystercatchers in the British Isles originate from several different breeding areas. Those that winter mainly in the west are from the Scottish/Faeroes populations and those wintering in the east are mainly from Norway's eastern North Sea population. The results of ringing show that Oystercatchers wintering in the harbour originate from both these breeding areas. Studies undertaken in the mid-1980s show that the main roosting sites were Brownsea, Shipstal Point/Long Island, Arne Spit, Furzey Island and Baiter, whilst the most favoured feeding areas were Holton Shore, Round Island and Arne Bay.

1950s	1960s	1970s	1980s	1990s
300–500	480	903	1148	1552

Table 165. Winter 10-year average peak counts from Poole Harbour 1950–1999

Jan	Feb	Mar	Apr	May	Jun	Jul	Aug	Sep	Oct	Nov	Dec
1228	1060	716	308	186	173	319	738	1058	1128	1164	1252

Table 166. Average monthly maxima from Poole Harbour 1986–1999

Christchurch Harbour is the only other site to support substantial numbers of Oystercatchers with a distinct autumn peak when counts frequently exceed 100 birds, the highest being 190 in September 1988 and 180 in August 1998 – see Table 167. The species regularly occurs in the The Fleet/Portland Harbour area, but peak counts rarely exceed 50 birds. High numbers, however, were present on the Fleet during August–October 1997 with monthly maxima of 175, 150 and 157, the next highest count from this area being 67 in March 1996. At Lodmoor NR numbers appear to have declined during the late 1990s, but in earlier years the highest counts were recorded typically during spring passage in March with a maximum of 84 on 5th March 1989. Nearby a few birds are recorded with some frequency from Weymouth Bay, the Nothe and Radipole NR, a count of 120 from Weymouth Bay on 22nd February 1997 being exceptional for the site. Small numbers are also recorded from Portland Bill and the Purbeck coast, most notably at Kimmeridge Bay where counts have reached 50 or more birds in winter. Although generally scarce at coastal sites in the west of the county, there is evidence of a small wintering population of 10–12 birds in the Charmouth/Lyme Regis area.

Jan	Feb	Mar	Apr	May	Jun	Jul	Aug	Sep	Oct	Nov	Dec
46	51	44	52	53	48	58	118	110	78	55	46

Figs 167. Average monthly maxima from Christchurch Harbour 1986–1999

Coastal movements, which show no directional bias, are recorded mainly from Portland Bill, the Purbeck coast and Hengistbury with distinct peaks in spring and autumn.

Up to 1995 at least, there was a regular wintering flock in the Lower Avon Valley where peak counts often exceeded 50 birds with maxima of 125 in November 1987, 88 in January 1993 and 75 in January 1988. The Oystercatcher is rare elsewhere inland with c.20 records since 1968. Most of these sightings involve 1–2 birds including a pair at Merley during May–July 1992, but there were 4SE over Radipole School on 21st September 1985 and five at Fontmell Magna on 16th July 1992.

A total of 1,506 birds has been ringed in the county. There have been foreign recoveries from Greenland (where it is a rare vagrant), Iceland, Faeroes (four), Norway (three), Denmark (two), the Netherlands (three), Germany (one) and France (c.6), and one foreign control each from Poland, Iceland and the

Netherlands. A remarkable double recovery involves a first-year bird ringed at Brownsea in April 1967, controlled at Fitzworth in September 1989 and again at Hengistbury in September 1990.

The Oystercatcher breeds widely in north-western Europe including Iceland, eastern Europe and west-central Asia and east Asia, also more locally in southern Europe and Asia Minor. The north-west European population winters mainly in western Europe with small numbers south to West Africa.

Postscript 2000–2002

A welcome return of breeding reports from the Weymouth area in 2002 involved three pairs on the Portland Harbour Breakwaters, one pair at the Nothe and one pair at Lodmoor NR. Otherwise, there were notably high counts from the Fleet in 2001 with 123 in October, and 80 in February and December.

Black-winged Stilt   *Himantopus himantopus*

A very rare passage migrant: nine records involving ten individuals

There is a 19th Century report of a bird shot at Lodmoor in 1837. The eight more recent records have occurred during two relatively short periods of years, namely 1956–1960 (three) and 1985–1990 (five).

1956	Abbotsbury: 26th July
1959	Lodmoor NR: 14th–15th May
1960	Wareham SF: immature 3rd August–6th September
1985	Radipole and Lodmoor NRs: 27th April–1st May
1987	Stanpit Marsh, Christchurch Harbour: two 2nd May
	Radipole NR: first-summer 17th–19th June; same at Lodmoor NR 19th June
1990	Cogden Beach: 31st March–3rd April
	Stanpit Marsh, Christchurch Harbour: first-summer 12th–13th May

The Black-winged Stilt is a summer visitor that breeds locally in north-west Africa, Iberia, France and eastwards across southern Europe to Asia Minor, the Middle East and west-central Asia. The European population winters mainly in the northern tropics of Africa with smaller numbers in North Africa, the Middle East and southern Spain. It is a cosmopolitan species with largely resident breeding populations in sub-Saharan Africa, southern Asia, including the Indian sub-continent, Australia, New Zealand and the Americas. A vagrant to Great Britain with 300 records up to 2002.

Avocet (Pied Avocet)   *Recurvirostra avosetta*

A locally common winter visitor and uncommon passage migrant – has bred

Both Mansel-Pleydell (1888) and Blathwayt (1945) considered this species to be a scarce vagrant, the former noting its earlier decline from breeding sites in Lincolnshire and Norfolk due to drainage of the marshes, and persecution by gunners and egg-collectors. Records were very infrequent during the 19th Century, and subsequently the only reports prior to 1952 were in 1921, 1935, 1940 and 1943. The

Avocet recolonised East Anglia during the 1940s, and since the early 1950s records in Dorset have reflected the increasing British breeding population.

The most obvious result of the species' improving fortunes has been the establishment of a wintering flock in Poole Harbour – see Fig 23. The first evidence of wintering occurred during the late 1950s with 1–3 birds recorded throughout the 1960s and into the early 1970s. There was a modest increase during the late 1970s and early 1980s with peaks of 21 in February 1978 and 46 in February 1984. The British wintering population increased sharply during the early 1980s, but this was not evident in Poole Harbour until the late 1980s. Subsequently numbers have increased dramatically during the 1990s to reach a county record of 870 in December 1998. Poole Harbour is now the second most important British wintering site for Avocets, being surpassed only by the Alde Estuary in Suffolk. Furthermore numbers have exceeded the threshold for international importance in the three successive winters since 1997/98.

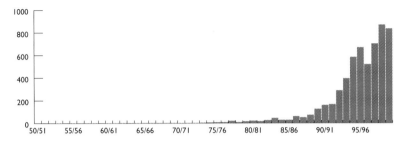

Fig 23. Winter maxima from Poole Harbour 1950–1999

The lagoon on Brownsea is the primary site for wintering Avocets in Poole Harbour, almost exclusively so during the earlier years. During the 1980s the flock started to visit the Arne/Middlebere/Wytch area, which is now the other main site for the species in the harbour. As the size of the population has grown during the 1990s, so birds have been increasingly recorded from other areas of the harbour including Poole Park Lake where unusually 36 were present on 4th February 1996. The main flock will also disperse to other areas of the harbour if the Brownsea Lagoon becomes frozen during periods of hard weather. For example, during the cold spell in early 1997 sizeable concentrations were present in Holes Bay with 420 on 8th January and 450 on 1st February, whilst a report of three at nearby Hatch Pond, Poole during snow on 11th January is most unusual.

As the winter population has increased so birds have appeared as early as July, but the main arrival occurs during September–October with peak counts being recorded between November and February. Numbers decline rapidly during March with a few birds lingering well into the spring. In 1999 birds remained throughout the summer on Brownsea with two pairs rearing young, which were probably predated. This constitutes the first breeding record for the county.

There has also been an increase in sightings from other coastal sites, notably Christchurch Harbour and in the Weymouth/Fleet area – see Table 168. Despite this, the Avocet remains a scarce bird away from Poole Harbour with the majority of records referring to passage migrants – see Tables 169 and 170. In the Weymouth/Fleet area, the peaks in November and March presumably involve birds moving to and from their wintering haunts on the Exe Estuary in Devon, whilst the May peak may refer to migrants from the Continent. Numbers are generally small, usually 1–5 birds, the most notable counts prior to November 1999 being 23W at Christchurch Harbour on 19th September 1997 with 19 there in September 1999 and 17 circling overhead on 2nd December 1984, and 18 at Lodmoor NR and Abbotsbury on 14th November 1992. These counts are eclipsed, however, by an incredible 230 on the Fleet at Herbury/Rodden Hive on 3rd November 1999.

	1950s	1960s	1970s	1980s	1990s
Christchurch Harbour	–	–	3	7	25
Weymouth/Fleet area	1	2	2	5	10

Table 168. 10-year average annual totals from Christchurch Harbour and the Weymouth/Fleet area 1950–1999

Jan	Feb	Mar	Apr	May	Jun	Jul	Aug	Sep	Oct	Nov	Dec
4	11	33	32	18	9	0	24	68	36	37	19

Table 169. Monthly totals from Christchurch Harbour 1974–1995, 1997–1999

Jan	Feb	Mar	Apr	May	Jun	Jul	Aug	Sep	Oct	Nov	Dec
10	5	37	9	30	7	3	12	6	10	271	21

Table 170. Monthly totals from the Weymouth/Fleet area 1952–1999

There are eight records from Portland Bill including 20E on 2nd April 1960, 20S on 27th September 1992 and 17E on 6th November 1993. Coastal movements have also been recorded from East Bexington with 1E on 16th April 1992, Chesil Cove with four on 28th April 1987 and 15 on 10th October 1994, St Aldhelm's Head with 1E on 15th May 1985 and 2E on 1st April 1998, Durlston CP with six records including 22 on 26th May 1994, and Hengistbury/Christchurch Harbour.

The only sightings from the extreme west of the county involve one at West Bay on 2nd December 1952 and two at West Bexington on 27th March 1975. The species in very rare inland, the only report involving one at Charminster Water-meadows on 20th January 1999.

Only three birds have been ringed in the county. A bird colour-ringed at Holme, Norfolk in August 1991 was subsequently seen at Farlington Marshes (Hampshire) in April 1992 and Christchurch Harbour in May 1992.

The Avocet breeds locally throughout Eurasia mainly between 35°N to 58° N, with other populations in eastern and southern Africa. The northern populations are migratory, becoming more dispersive in the south. It winters in western and southern Europe, Africa, Asia Minor, the Middle East, Arabia and parts of the Indian sub-continent and south-east Asia.

Postscript 2000–2002
The wintering population in Poole Harbour continues to increase with a county record count of 1,862 in February 2002. On Brownsea, 1,155 on 5th December 2002 is not only the highest count for the site, but also the highest count ever for a single flock anywhere in the UK! Only the second inland record for the county, two flying south-west over Canford Heath on 9th April 2000, was followed by a remarkable flock of 19 at Charminster Water-meadows on 20th November 2002. There is also an interesting report of a traffic-dodging individual at Portland Bill on 20th March 2001, which went on to spend several hours feeding on worms in the Hut Fields.

Sponsored by Jennifer Thompson

Stone Curlew (Stone-curlew)   *Burhinus oedicnemus*

Scarce passage migrant – formerly bred.

Mansel-Pleydell (1888) described this species as "a summer visitant, usually frequenting the chalk uplands of the county", and also referred to a report of one shot on the Sandbanks in Poole Harbour on 10th December 1873. Blathwayt (1945) considered it to be a summer resident, which bred sparingly on the uplands of the chalk throughout the county, being not uncommon in the Cranborne/Blandford district, but only occasionally as far west as Beaminster and Charmouth. Increasingly intensive agriculture during and after the Second World War resulted in a rapid decline in the population.

Since 1950 breeding has been virtually restricted to the chalk downs in the north-east of the county. Away from this area, the only breeding season reports were from former haunts in west Dorset in 1950 and 1953, and the central chalk downs in 1954 and 1976. During the 1950s the breeding population was estimated to be 4–8 pairs, whilst special surveys in 1960 and 1961 revealed 8–10 pairs including up to eight pairs in the Cranborne area (SU01). Subsequently breeding numbers declined further with only 1–3 pairs reported during 1963–1990 with the exception of 4–5 records of probable breeding in 1966, one confirmed and three possible breeding pairs during a special survey in 1976, and four pairs breeding, threesuccessfully in 1985. Since 1990 the only report of confirmed breeding occurred in 1998 when two pairs successfully fledged two young, but there were isolated breeding season reports from the traditional area in 1991 and 1994–1996.

The decline in the breeding population is also reflected by the size of the post-breeding gatherings. Blathwayt (1945) referred to autumn flocks of up to 70 birds, especially in the Pentridge area. Since 1950, however, counts have rarely reached double figures, the highest being from the Pentridge and Cranborne area with 11 in early August 1951, 8–10 during September–October 1962 and 11 as recently as 24th August 1985. There have been no reports of autumn gatherings in subsequent years.

Since 1950 the Stone Curlew has occurred as an occasional migrant, mainly on or near the coast, with more reports in spring (47 birds) than autumn (26 birds) – see Table 171. Spring records extend from mid-March to late May with a distinct peak during the first half of April. Autumn migrants have been reported from early July through to late October with a late peak during the second half of October.

Mar 1–15	Mar 16–31	Apr 1–15	Apr 16–30	May 1–15	May 16–31	Jun 1–15	Jun 16–30
0	8	17	9	9	3	0	0

Jul 1–15	Jul 16–31	Aug 1–15	Aug 16–31	Sep 1–15	Sep 16–30	Oct 1–15	Oct 16–31
3	4	3	4	1	2	2	7

Table 171. Half-monthly totals of migrants 1980–1999

Portland Bill and Christchurch Harbour are the main sites for migrants accounting for 34% and 21% respectively of the total – see Table 172. It is interesting to note that at Portland Bill the greatest proportion of migrants occur in spring (80%), whilst at Christchurch Harbour the reverse is true with autumn migrants predominating (67%). Away from the main coastal watch-points, there are three records each from Lodmoor NR and Studland NNR, and singles from Langton Herring, Charleston, St Aldhelm's Head, Peveril Point, Ower, Brownsea, Arne NR, and inland records from Whitcombe, Owermoigne, Hambledon Hill, Avon Forest Park, Dudmoor/Avon Causeway and Woolgarston.

	Spring		Autumn		Total	
Portland Bill	20	43%	5	19%	25	34%
elsewhere Portland	6	13%	2	8%	8	11%
Durlston CP	6	13%	0	0	6	8%
Christchurch Harbour	5	11%	10	38%	15	21%
elsewhere coastal or near coastal	8	17%	5	19%	13	18%
inland	2	4%	4	15%	6	8%

Table 172. Distribution of migrants 1950–1999

Although there is at least one winter record from the 19th Century, and Blathwayt (1945) states that it occurred exceptionally in winter, the only recent report of possible overwintering involves two at Cranborne on 19th February 1957. Otherwise the earliest spring records are 16th March 1953 at Cranborne and 16th March 1987 with two at Portland Bill, whilst the latest sightings are 27th October 1954 with seven at All Hallows Water-meadows, 29th October 1997 with two at Greenland Farm, Studland, and 31st October 1948 at Newton Heath.

The Stone Curlew breeds across North Africa, southern and central Europe north to south-east England, eastwards to Asia Minor, the Middle East and south-west and southern Asia including the Indian sub-continent. It is very local throughout much of its European range. The more northern populations are migratory with birds mainly wintering in Iberia and extreme south-east Europe, North Africa and the northern tropics of Africa, the Middle East, Arabia, and southern Asia including the Indian sub-continent.

Postscript 2000–2002
The only reports involve migrants with four (five birds) in 2000, one in 2001 and three in 2002.

Cream-coloured Courser   *Cursorius cursor*

Accidental: one old record

    1853   Batcombe Down: no date

Lord Digby, whilst following the hounds, observed one on Batcombe Down. Next day the Earl of Ilchester sent his keeper Walton who found and shot it. There are no recent records.

The Cream-coloured Courser breeds around the northern and southern fringes of the Sahara, eastwards across north-east Africa, the Middle East and Arabia to the north-west of the Indian sub-continent, also in the Cape Verde and Canary Islands. All but the northern populations winter within the breeding range. A vagrant to the British Isles with 33 records up to 2000, the last being in 1984.

Collared Pratincole   *Glareola pratincola*

Accidental: seven records

There are three old records prior to 1856 involving one shot on the banks of the River Stour near Bryanston, one seen in the east of the county, and one seen flying over the Weymouth Backwater in November 1855. With modern knowledge of pratincole identification and the proven occurrences of Oriental Pratincole *G. maldivarum* in Great Britain, it would probably be advisable not to assign the early records to any particular species.

More recently there have been the following records:

    1974   Lodmoor NR: 7th June
    1977   Holes Bay: 24th May
    1990   Abbotsbury: 3rd May
    1992   Portland Bill: 31st M\ay

In addition, two pratincoles at Portland Bill on 9th October 1971 were not specifically identified.

The Collared Pratincole breeds locally across southern Europe from Iberia eastwards to west-central and south-west Asia, also in North and sub-Saharan Africa. It winters in sub-Saharan Africa. A vagrant to the Great Britain with 85 records up to 2002.

Little Ringed Plover (Little Plover)   *Charadrius dubius*

An uncommon passage migrant and scarce summer visitor

The first Dorset record involves a pair at Radipole NR on 3rd May 1950 behaving as though they might have bred if left undisturbed. There were no further sightings until 1959 when singles were noted in Poole Harbour on 2nd April and at Ferrybridge on 8th September. Subsequently reports, which have been annual since 1967, have steadily increased particularly from the mid-1970s onwards – see Tables 173 and 174.

60	61	62	63	64	65	66	67	68	69	70	71	72	73	74	75	76	77	78	79
0	0	1	0	0	0	0	0	0	1	3	4	0	3	1	5	8	8	8	3

80	81	82	83	84	85	86	87	88	89	90	91	92	93	94	95	96	97	98	99
24	24	24	15	42	21	35	21	38	22	22	20	8	23	35	33	29	28	20	22

Table 173. Spring totals 1960–1999

60	61	62	63	64	65	66	67	68	69	70	71	72	73	74	75	76	77	78	79
0	0	0	0	6	2	0	3	4	5	4	5	8	2	7	16	14	11	13	21

80	81	82	83	84	85	86	87	88	89	90	91	92	93	94	95	96	97	98	99
38	58	63	81	60	14	36	46	8	36	11	59	48	18	79	77	29	27	25	17

Table 174. Autumn totals 1960–1999

Despite this increase, breeding did not occur until 1976 when a pair successfully nested on a shingle bank in the River Avon on the border with Hampshire. Single pairs bred at Chard Junction GP in 1984 and Sturminster Marshall GP in 1987, whilst more recently confirmed breeding has occurred annually during the 1990s except for 1992 and 1998 – see Table 175.

Breeding Status	1990	1991	1992	1993	1994	1995	1996	1997	1998	1999
Confirmed	1	1	0	2	1	1	3	5	0	2
Probable/possible	0	1	1–2	0	0	1	3	1	3	1

Table 175. Number of breeding pairs 1990–1999

Passage birds typically occur on or near the coast, the principal sites being Christchurch Harbour, Radipole and Lodmoor NRs, and the Fleet – mainly at Ferrybridge and Langton Herring. The species is surprisingly scarce in the Poole Harbour area with recent sightings mostly from Lytchett Bay and Brownsea. There are several reports from West Bexington and single records from Portland Harbour and Weymouth Beach. Coastal movements are occasionally noted at Portland Bill and more rarely from elsewhere on Portland, West and East Bexington, the Chesil, Durlston CP and Hengistbury. Inland passage is most frequently recorded from the Lower Avon Valley. Elsewhere inland migrants are rare with records from Hatch Pond, Poole (one), River Stour at Corfe Mullen (two once), River Stour at Sturminster Marshall (one), Sturminster Marshall GP (two once, singles twice), Wimborne St Giles (one), Bere Regis CBs (one), Sherborne Lake (singles twice), Bride Valley Fish Farm (one) and Chard Junction GP (two once, singles twice). Most sightings involve 1–2 birds with very few counts in excess of five, the highest being eight at Christchurch Harbour on 1st August 1981 and Lodmoor NR on 11th April 1988.

The earliest spring records are on the exceptional date of 21st February 1969 at Ferrybridge and 6th March 1994 at Christchurch Harbour. Since the 1970s the average date of the first arrivals has gradually become earlier – see Table 176. Spring passage mainly occurs between early April and late May with the odd late straggler in early June. The first returning birds sometimes appear in late June, but the main passage takes place from early July through to early September with a distinct peak in July. Relatively few birds occur after mid-September and in some years there are no reports for that month. The latest records are 5th October 1997 at Christchurch Harbour, 7th October 1975 at Radipole NR and exceptionally 11th November 1968 at Shell Bay.

	1970–1979	1980–1989	1990–1999
Range	27th March–8th May	13th March–4th April	6th March–8th April
Average	11th April	26th March	21st March

Table 176. Dates for first spring arrivals each decade 1970–1999

A total of 10 birds has been ringed in the county.

The Little Ringed Plover breeds widely across much of Eurasia, also in north-west Africa and locally in the Middle East. It winters mainly in the northern tropics of Africa and southern Asia with smaller numbers in the Mediterranean Basin and Arabia.

Postscript 2000–2002

In 2000 there were breeding reports from five sites with two pairs successfully rearing young. In 2001, there were three pairs at one site, but only one pair successfully reared young, the remaining two pairs deserting. In 2002, one pair successfully reared young.

Ringed Plover

Charadrius hiaticula

A scarce resident, and locally common winter visitor and passage migrant

Mansel-Pleydell (1888) described this species as "resident and generally distributed along the coast" and further mentions that it breeds in numbers on the Chesil Bank, as well as on the sandbanks of Poole and Studland. There was little change in status during the first half of the 20th Century with Blathwayt (1945) commenting that the Ringed Plover breeds numerously on the shores and islands of Poole Harbour and along the Chesil Beach up to Bridport Harbour.

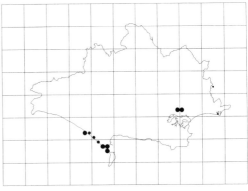

Subsequently there has been a marked decline in the breeding population caused mainly by human disturbance of the pebble beaches favoured by this species. In 1967 a full census of the Chesil Beach revealed around 100 pairs, but this declined to 75 pairs in 1973 and 28 pairs in 1980, after which numbers have fluctuated between ten and 46 pairs – see Table 177. Up to 1978 at least, birds were reported nesting along the Chesil Beach as far west as West Bexington, and more recently one pair bred successfully there in 1998. In the Poole Harbour area, the decline was evident by 1950 when comments in the Bird Report refer to "changes starting prior to 1939 have driven them from most haunts there". Subsequently a few pairs bred most years up to 1981, initially at Studland Bay where 1–3 pairs nested up to 1974, but at other sites in 1972, 1976 and during 1978–1981 including 4–5 pairs at two locations in 1980. In recent years, the only reports of breeding in Poole Harbour involve single pairs at Holes Bay in 1986, 1988, 1991 and 1992. At Christchurch Harbour breeding was regularly recorded during 1975–1979 with a peak of seven pairs in 1976, whilst at Portland Bill a pair with three young were present on 5th June 1977, but had disappeared by the 10th June suggesting predation.

80	81	82	83	84	85	86	87	88	89	90	91	92	93	94	95	96	97	98	99
28	46	35	24	29	nc	15	10	39	nc	20	20	13	20	nc	30	2*	1*	22	2*

Table 177. Number of breeding pairs on the Chesil Beach 1980–1999; *full census not undertaken

The most important sites for passage and wintering birds are Christchurch Harbour, Poole Harbour and the Fleet. There is a distinct peak in numbers during the autumn, notably August and September, which is most evident at Christchurch Harbour and on the Fleet – see Table 178. At these sites the autumn peak counts are usually higher than winter maxima. This is not the case in Poole Harbour, where peak counts in winter are generally higher than those recorded during autumn passage. There is evidence of a small spring passage at all three sites.

	Jan	Feb	Mar	Apr	May	Jun	Jul	Aug	Sep	Oct	Nov	Dec
Xchurch Hbr	74	64	27	20	24	7	16	124	107	78	83	92
Poole Hbr	93	47	12	8	14	-	9	78	84	66	90	121
The Fleet	37	42	27	49	30	16	40	178	171	110	87	55

Table 178. Average monthly maxima at the main sites 1986–1999

Although the wintering population in Poole Harbour has seemingly increased since the 1970s, winter maxima are highly variable – see Table 179. For example, a county record count of 500 at Hamworthy on 26th December 1987 contrasts with winter peaks of only 42 in 1983/84 and 45 in 1995/96. Low numbers during the late 1990s are attributed to lack of suitable feeding areas and roosting sites, since Sandbanks and Shell/Studland Bays suffer from considerable disturbance. Studies undertaken in the mid-1980s show that the main roosting sites were Shell/Studland Bays and Holes Bay, whilst the main feeding areas were

Parkstone Bay and Sandbanks Bay. In earlier years Baiter had been an important roosting area. More recently the most favoured sites have been located along the eastern side of the harbour, notably Baiter, Parkstone Bay, the Blue Lagoon, Sandbanks, Brownsea, Shell/Studland Bays and Brand's Bay.

By comparison, the wintering population on the Fleet has apparently declined since the 1970s, but again winter maxima are highly variable – see Table 179. For example, a site peak count of 330 at Ferrybridge on 4th December 1974 contrasts with winter peaks of only 20 in 1990/91 and 37 in 1991/92. The numbers wintering in Christchurch Harbour have been relatively stable since 1970 with winter maxima varying the least at the three main sites, ranging between 50 and 150 birds in all but four winters since 1975/76, the highest count being 300 in November 1995.

	1970s	1980s	1990s
Christchurch Harbour	124	103	126
Poole Harbour	99	153	158
The Fleet	141	109	86

Table 179. Winter 10-year average peak counts at the main sites 1970–1999

There is evidence to show that autumn maxima have increased at the three main sites since the 1970s – see Table 180. Occasional influxes are a feature of autumn passage, the most notable being in August 1974 with 324 in Poole Harbour, August 1981 with 400 at East Fleet and 315 in Christchurch Harbour, 1993 with 401 in Christchurch Harbour in August and 304 in Poole Harbour in September, October 1996 with 410 on the Fleet, and August 1997 with 350 on the Fleet. Studies undertaken in Poole Harbour in the mid-1980s show that the main autumn sites for Ringed Plovers were Brownsea and the north shore of Arne NR.

	1970s	1980s	1990s
Christchurch Harbour	132	148	166
Poole Harbour	90	99	112
The Fleet	164	177	233

Table 180. Autumn 10-year average peak counts at the main sites 1970–1999

Elsewhere the species is recorded with some frequency from Radipole and Lodmoor NRs, West Bexington and the Charmouth/Lyme Regis area. Although peak numbers are usually small and rarely exceed 50 birds, there are several high counts from Lodmoor NR notably 100 on 19th May 1996, 90 on 22nd November 1981, 75 on 17th May 1984 and 70 in December 1979. In earlier years, high numbers occurred at Radipole NR including 100 on 29th August 1950 and frequent counts of 40–50 birds during the 1960s, but more recently maxima have rarely reached double-figures. There would appear to be a small wintering population of 20–30 birds in the Charmouth/Lyme Regis area. Otherwise it is a scarce visitor to the Purbeck coast with most records from Kimmeridge Bay including an exceptional count of 80 in August 1973.

Coastal movements are recorded mainly from Portland Bill, the Purbeck coast and Hengistbury. Passage is much heavier in autumn than spring with a distinct peak in August – see Table 181. Overall numbers are modest. For example, at Portland Bill during 1980–1999 autumn totals ranged from 49–218 bird-days with spring totals rarely reaching double-figures. Although day-totals are generally small, there have been a few notable movements including 200+ at Portland Bill on 5th–6th September 1962 and 130E at Hengistbury on 2nd May 1980. Movements are predominantly easterly in spring and westerly in autumn.

Jan	Feb	Mar	Apr	May	Jun	Jul	Aug	Sep	Oct	Nov	Dec
4	3	9	27	66	4	72	910	355	101	2	2

Table 181. Monthly totals for coastal movements at Portland Bill 1980–1994

There are surprisingly few inland records:

1975   Sherborne Lake: two August
1983   Lake Gate floods, Corfe Mullen: six 17th April and two 18th April

1984   Coward's Marsh, Christchurch: three 20th March
1987   Sturminster Marshall GP: two 14th August and one 25th August
1988   Coward's Marsh, Christchurch: 25th July
1997   Sturminster Marshall GP: 11th September and two 12th September

A total of 233 birds has been ringed in the county with two foreign recoveries from northern France and two foreign controls from Germany. An interesting double recovery involves a bird ringed in Poole Harbour in January 1979, found there in November 1982 and in Essex in July 1983.

The Ringed Plover breeds in north-east Canada, Greenland, Iceland, northern Europe including the British Isles and Russia north of 65°N. It winters mainly in western Europe, the Mediterranean Basin, Arabia, and north-west and much of sub-Saharan Africa.

Postscript 2000–2002
Although no full census of the Chesil Beach was undertaken, breeding was reported in all three years. In addition, an adult sitting on a nest at Poole Yacht Club on 27th June 2000 is the first evidence of breeding from Poole Harbour since 1992.

Sponsored by K. D. and E. V. F. Coe

Kentish Plover   *Charadrius alexandrinus*

A scarce passage migrant
The only 19th Century record involves one obtained near Weymouth in 1870, whilst during the first half of the 20th Century singles were recorded at Studland on 24th April 1925 and 27th April 1934, and Weymouth on 25th September 1931.

There were further reports in 1950 (two), 1953, 1959, 1960 (two) and 1961 (two). Since 1965 there has been a marked increase in records, which have been annual during 1975–1999 – see Table 182. Yearly totals are small and rarely exceed seven birds, the highest being 10 in 1980 and an exceptional 22 in 1993.

64	65	66	67	68	69	70	71	72	73	74	75	76	77	78	79	80	81
0	1	1	3	3	3	2	4	2	0	0	3	3	3	7	4	10	9

82	83	84	85	86	87	88	89	90	91	92	93	94	95	96	97	98	99
4	6	4	3	3	5	8	2	5	7	7	22	9	1	5	3	1	1

Table 182. Annual totals 1964–1999

This species is very site-specific with Ferrybridge and Christchurch Harbour accounting for 42% and 44% respectively of the post-1950 total. Elsewhere on the Fleet there have been six sightings from the Herbury Gore/Langton Herring area – all in spring. The few remaining records are from Radipole NR on 29th August 1950, 23rd July 1978 and 9th September 1983, Lodmoor NR on 20th June 1978 and 4th May 1980, the Weymouth area on 5th–6th August 1979 (1–2 birds), Shell Bay on 24th October 1950 and 9th April 1953, Brownsea during 22nd–25th August 1977 (1–2 birds), Arne NR on 14th May 1983 and 20th April 1988, and rather surprisingly Portland Bill on 23rd March 1959, 23rd March 1969 (found dead on 12th April) and 22nd April 1976 (moved to Ferrybridge the same day).

Passage is most obvious in spring, which accounts for 62% of the total. Spring records extend from mid-March to early June with a distinct peak from mid-April to mid-May, whilst autumn migrants have occurred from mid-July through to mid-November with a distinct peak from mid-August to mid-September – see Table 183. There are four mid-summer records (five birds) in late June and early July. In spring the earliest report is from 19th–22nd March 1993 at Christchurch Harbour, and in autumn there are three late sightings from Ferrybridge on 3rd November 1981, 13th November 1993 and 22nd November 1998.

Mar 1–15	Mar 16–31	Apr 1–15	Apr 16–30	May 1–15	May 16–31	Jun 1–15	Jun 16–30	Jul 1–15	Jul 16–31
0	5	13	26	39	13	1	4	1	3

Aug	Aug	Sep	Sep	Oct	Oct	Nov	Nov	Dec	Dec
1–15	16–31	1–15	16–30	1–15	16–31	1–15	16–30	1–15	16–31
8	12	16	7	3	3	2	1	1	1

Table 183. Half-monthly totals 1950–1999

Most records involve single birds, the highest counts being three at Christchurch Harbour on 23rd September 1992 and 15th May 1993, and a remarkable flock of eight at Ferrybridge on 13th September 1993.

Overwintering is exceptional, but occurred in 1991/92 and 1992/93 involving at least two individuals as follows:

1991   Shell Bay: first-winter 1st to 15th December; same at Ferrybridge 26th December–1st March 1992
1992   Ferrybridge: one from 18th October with two from 30th December to 23rd January 1993, one to 7th February and two again from 6th to 8th March

The Kentish Plover has a widespread world breeding distribution mainly within the northern temperate zones between 20°N and 50°N, but also along the Pacific coast of South America. The Eurasian populations are migratory north of 40°N and winter south to the northern tropics of Africa and Asia.

Postscript 2000–2002
At Ferrybridge, there were three records in 2000 involving singles on 24th–25th April, 16th and 24th July, two records in 2001 involving singles on 3rd April and 1st July, and one record in 2002 with one on 29th April. Elsewhere there were singles at Cogden Beach on 11th May 2002 and Stanpit Marsh, Christchurch Harbour on 26th August 2002.

Dotterel (Eurasian Dotterel)   *Charadrius morinellus*

A rare passage migrant
Mansel-Pleydell (1888) considered this species to be a rare visitor and referred to singles near Pimperne and on Pimperne Down prior to 1799, three at Waterson Ridge in the early spring of 1843, one at Milborne St Andrew in June 1853, two near Lulworth on 3rd September 1876 and three at Bradford Abbas in 1884 – all these records involve birds that were shot! Apparently there were no reports between 1893 and 1953.

Subsequently there have been 64 records involving 102 birds during 1953–1999 – see Fig 24. The majority of birds (60%) occurred in autumn between mid-August and late October with a distinct peak during late August and early September – see Table 184. There was a notable influx of 11–12 birds in September 1993. Spring migrants were recorded from early April to late May with no obvious peak – see Table 184. The number of spring sightings has increased in recent years with 13 of the 20 records occurring during 1985–1999 including mini-influxes in 1985 (three records involving 12 birds) and 1990 (four records involving 11 birds). The earliest spring report is 6th April 1990 at Portland Bill, whilst the latest record is from 15th–23rd October 1992 at Black Hill.

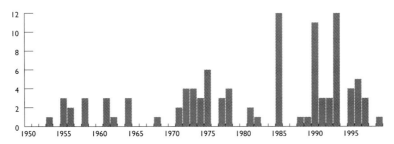

Fig 24. Annual totals 1950–1999

Portland is the main site for the species with ten spring and 32 autumn records involving 22 and 38 birds respectively, which together accounts for 59% of the total. Single birds are mainly recorded, but there are several reports of 2–3 birds, the highest counts being at the Bill in May 1985 with seven on 11th and

Apr 1–15	Apr 16–30	May 1–15	May 16–31	Aug 1–15	Aug 16–31	Sep 1–15	Sep 16–30	Oct 1–15	Oct 16–31
3	12	14	11	1	20	19	13	5	3

Table 184. Half-monthly totals 1953–1999 (excluding winter record)

four on 21st. Nearby at Ferrybridge there are reports of single birds during 12th–17th September 1956, and on 25th August 1973, 7th May 1988, 30th April 1991 and 16th April 1996, the first two having been recorded first at Portland Bill. Lodmoor NR has three records with two on 27th August 1955, and singles on 5th October 1975 and 23rd September 1993. The Purbeck coast has attracted several small flocks in recent years with two at St Aldhelm's Head during 7th–10th September 1993 followed by up to seven at White Nothe during 20th–26th September of the same year, up to three at St Aldhelm's Head during 17th–28th August 1995 and three at White Nothe on 29th August 1996. In earlier years there were singles at Winspit on 20th May 1968 and White Horse Hill on 5th September 1982. Elsewhere along the coast there are records from Christchurch Harbour with two at Hengistbury on 21st May 1975, 6N on 30th April 1990, one at Stanpit on 14th August 1992 and a pair on the golf course at Stanpit on 10th May 1997. The only passage bird from Poole Harbour involves one at Shell Bay on 28th May 1953. A male seen in the inner harbour at Poole on 12th February 1961 was more likely to be an overwintering bird than an early migrant.

Records from well inland are rare with only four sightings as follows:

1956 Corfe Mullen: 16th September
1972 Corfe Mullen: 10th April
1977 Maiden Newton: pair 23rd May
1992 Black Hill: 15th–23rd October

Four birds have been ringed in the county.

The Dotterel breeds across the arctic tundra and alpine zones of Scandinavia and Siberia as well as in northern Scotland and mountain ranges in central Asia. There are also small isolated populations in some mountainous regions of central and southern Europe, and it has bred on the polders of the Netherlands. It winters mainly in the semi-arid belt of North Africa and the Middle East extending from Morocco eastwards to Iran with a few birds wintering in Spain.

Postscript 2000–2002

There were six records, one in 2000 involving a single bird flying north at Portland Bill on 23rd September, three in 2001 involving one at Southwell, Portland on 2nd May, three at Tout Quarry, Portland on 11th May, and six at St Aldhelm's Head during 25th–27th August, and two in 2002 involving singles at White Horse Hill from 2nd to 8th September and flying west over Winspit on 1st October.

American Golden Plover   *Pluvialis dominica*

Accidental: three records

All three Dorset birds have occurred in May:

1992 Ferrybridge and the Fleet: first-summer 20th–22nd May
        Stanpit Marsh, Christchurch Harbour: ad. 22nd–24th May
1998 Stanpit Marsh, Christchurch Harbour: moulting ad. 6th May

The American Golden Plover breeds in arctic North America from Alaska east to Baffin Island, also in extreme north-east Siberia, and winters in central South America south to Argentina. A vagrant to Great Britain with 231 records up to 2002.

Pacific Golden Plover   *Pluvialis fulva*

Accidental: three records

1990 Stanpit Marsh, Christchurch Harbour: ad. 25th–27th July

1996   Lodmoor NR: 11th–12th March
        Lodmoor NR: first-winter 29th November–21st December

The Pacific Golden Plover breeds in northern Siberia and western Alaska, and winters from north-east Africa through south and south-east Asia to Australasia and Polynesia. A vagrant to Great Britain with 52 records up to 2002.

Golden Plover (European Golden Plover)   *Pluvialis apricaria*

A locally common winter visitor and passage migrant

Although it was claimed that the species bred regularly on Charlton Down prior to 1799, there is no subsequent evidence of breeding. Both Mansel-Pleydell (1888) and Blathwayt (1945) considered the Golden Plover to be a winter visitor mainly to the downland areas of the county.

From 1950 to the mid-1980s, the two most favoured wintering sites were the Maiden Castle area to the south-west of Dorchester, and the Allen Valley, notably in the vicinity of Witchampton and the Horton Inn – see Figs 25 and 26.

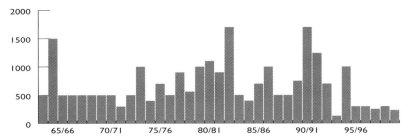

Fig 25. Winter maxima at Maiden Castle 1963–1999

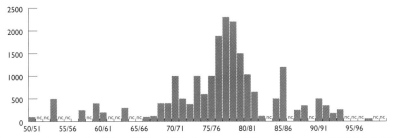

Fig 26. Winter maxima in the Allen Valley (Witchampton/Horton Inn area) 1950–1999

Numbers at Maiden Castle were consistently high up to the mid-1990s, winter maxima generally ranging between 500–1,000 birds with notable peaks of 1,700 in December 1982 and December 1990. It seems likely that smaller flocks recorded particularly during the 1970s and early 1980s from Compton Valence, and more recently from Warmwell belong to the same wintering population. Since the winter of 1992/93 large numbers have used Lodmoor NR as a resting/roosting site with peak counts of 1,060 in January 1995, and 1,000 on 31st January 1994 and in November 1995 – see Table 185. These are considered to be birds feeding on the downlands south of Dorchester from Maiden Castle in the west to Warmwell in the east, and perhaps further afield. The wintering population in this area has seemingly declined during the late 1990s with maxima generally ranging between 300–500 birds at Lodmoor NR, and 200–300 birds at Maiden Castle. Lodmoor NR was also a regular wintering site for Golden Plovers from at least 1950 through to the mid-1960s with maxima usually ranging between 200–600 birds. Good numbers were also occasionally recorded from nearby Radipole NR during the 1950s reaching a maximum of 500 on 18th December 1953.

1992/93	1993/94	1994/95	1995/96	1996/97	1997/98	1998/99	1999/00
506	1000	1060	1000	340	520	500	550

Table 185. Winter maxima at Lodmoor NR 1992–1999

The wintering population in the Allen Valley peaked during the late 1970s with counts of 1,884 on 19th December 1976, a county record of 2,300 on 11th December 1977, and 2,200 on 24th December 1978 – see Fig 26. Numbers have declined subsequently, particularly since the mid-1980s. Birds from this population appear to be highly mobile and may account for flocks recorded from the Cranborne/Pentridge area, the Tarrant Valley and the general vicinity of Blandford, particularly during the 1950s–1970s. The Lower Avon Valley and the Burton area is another traditional wintering site, and since Dorset inherited this area from neighbouring Hampshire in the mid-1970s, winter maxima have generally ranged from 120–500 birds.

Since the mid-1980s the winter distribution has changed with an increase in the number of sites attracting good numbers of Golden Plovers on a fairly regular basis – see Table 186. This seems to be due to the fragmentation and partial relocation of larger flocks from the traditional wintering sites at Maiden Castle and the Allen Valley, where numbers have apparently declined, particularly during the 1990s. For example, there is a suggestion that in recent years flocks from Lodmoor NR and Warmwell may commute as far east as the Wareham area. The most notable count from these relatively new sites was 2,000 in the Woodsford/Tincleton/Hurst area of the Frome Valley in November 1992.

	First recent high count	Peak count and winter
Morden/Almer area	1985/86–124	750–1990/91
Stalbridge	1987/88–250	300–1988/89
Toller Down	1989/90–114	160–1990/91
Puddletown/Briantspuddle	1989/90–425	478–1992/93
Bere Regis	1989/90–150	153–1995/96
Woodsford/Tincleton/Hurst	1989/90–200	2000–1992/93
Abbotsbury/The Fleet	1990/91–100	700–1995/96
Blandford/Sutton Waldron	1991/92–500	500–1995/96
Wareham	1997/98–280	300–1999/00

Table 186. Regular wintering sites since the mid-1980s

The species is prone to cold weather influxes involving records of settled birds and overhead movements. The majority of such reports come from river valleys and the coast, including Portland Bill and the Purbecks. These cold weather influxes can be impressive, the most notable being on 27th December 1962 with 2,000S at Pentridge, during 30th–31st December 1978 with c.1,000 at Lodmoor NR, 350 at Hengistbury, 200 on the Chesil Beach and 100 at Radipole NR, on 12th December 1981 with 708W at Radipole NR, and on 10th February 1985 with 1,400 along the Fleet including 1,000 at Abbotsbury, 560S + 70 at Christchurch Harbour, and counts of 100–360 birds at six other sites. The highest cold weather count from Portland Bill is 310 on 16th February 1978. Otherwise there are a number of apparently isolated high counts, the best being 1,000 at Fiddleford/Manston on 8th December 1992 (possibly the Blandford/Sutton Waldron flock), 750 at Sturminster Marshall on 9th January 1986, 700 at Maiden Newton on 5th December 1991 and 600 at the Brit Estuary on 4th January 1955. Elsewhere smaller flocks are recorded widely throughout the county.

A small coastal passage is well exemplified by records from Portland Bill, Durlston CP and Christchurch Harbour, which show obvious peaks in March and September–October – see Table 187. There is a scattering of migrants from other coastal and inland sites.

	Mar	Apr	May	Jun	Jul	Aug	Sep	Oct	Nov
Portland Bill	121	67	6	6	3	18	139	165	67
Durlston CP	14	10	9	1	7	14	40	106	57
Christchurch Hbr	25	12	17	2	3	19	58	48	69

Table 187. Monthly totals for coastal movements at the main watch-points 1986–1999

Only two birds have been ringed in the county.

The Golden Plover breeds in northern Europe, including Iceland and the upland areas of the British Isles, eastwards across arctic Russia to 100°E. It winters in western and southern Europe, North Africa, Asia Minor and the Middle East.

Postscript 2000–2002

A count of 1,000 at Maiden Castle in February 2001 represents a welcome increase in the wintering population at this traditional site, the last count of 1,000 being on 4th January 1995. In 2002, counts of 500 near Wincanton on 17th December and 340 at Bestwall, Wareham on 19th November were notably high.

Grey Plover   *Pluvialis squatarola*

A locally common winter visitor and passage migrant

Mansel-Pleydell (1888) considered the Grey Plover to be a spring and autumn visitor, being commoner in the latter season, and further mentioned that "a few are met with on the coast sometimes in winter". Blathwayt (1945) described it as "a winter visitor not uncommon on the coast", but further added "perhaps better known as a passage migrant mid-March to mid-May and September to mid-October".

The wintering population remained relatively small until the early 1970s after which numbers increased dramatically – see Table 188. At Poole Harbour, which is the main site for the species, winter maxima typically ranged between 20–80 birds from 1950 to the early 1970s, before increasing to range between 100–400 birds up to the mid-1990s, and 400–600 birds during the late 1990s with county record peaks of 599 in February 1999 and 560 in February 1995. Although small numbers are recorded on passage, peak counts usually occur during December to February – see Table 189. Studies undertaken in the mid-1980s show that the main roosting sites were Shell/Studland Bays, Brand's Bay, Fitzworth East and Brownsea, whilst the most favoured feeding areas were along the southern and western shores of the harbour. A later study undertaken in the 1990s also concludes that at low water most birds (71% of the population) were found at four sites along the southern and western shores of the harbour, namely Brand's Bay, Fitzworth, Gigger's Island and Holton Shore.

	1950s	1960s	1970s	1980s	1990s
Poole Harbour	30	60	130	296	427
The Fleet	6	17	79	132	90
Christchurch Harbour	-	-	14	31	56

Table 188. Winter 10-year average peak counts at the main sites 1950–1999

	Jan	Feb	Mar	Apr	May	Jun	Jul	Aug	Sep	Oct	Nov	Dec
Poole Hbr	301	321	126	29	10	7	2	8	17	50	171	260
The Fleet	90	75	31	5	16	1	1	3	4	6	28	44
Xchurch Hbr	36	26	26	16	21	5	2	3	17	26	32	39

Table 189. Average monthly maxima at the main sites 1986–1999

The Fleet is also an important wintering site for Grey Plovers. During the 1950s and 1960s very few birds were present with counts usually in single figures up to 1968. Subsequently winter maxima increased to between 50–150 birds from the mid-1970s onwards with peaks of 240 in January 1985 and 260 in January 1987. There is evidence of some passage, notably in May, but peak numbers are usually present in January and February – see Table 189. Unlike the other main sites, wintering numbers appear to have declined during the 1990s – see Table 188.

Christchurch Harbour is the only other site where the species occurs regularly. Although winter numbers have increased since the mid-1970s, maxima rarely exceed 60 birds, the highest being 72 in January 1997 – see Table 188. Numbers are generally highest during December to February, but the best site counts have occurred at times of passage with 92 in October 1991 and 76 in September 1993 – see Table 189.

Elsewhere along the coast it is an occasional visitor to West Bexington, Portland Bill, Newton's Cove, Radipole and Lodmoor NRs, and the Purbeck coast, mainly Kimmeridge Bay. Numbers are very small with counts rarely reaching double figures, the highest being 19 at Radipole NR on 16th May 1984 and 15 at Kimmeridge Bay in January 1985. At Lodmoor NR most sightings occur in spring. It is very rare in the extreme west of the county with one at Lyme Regis on 8th January 1993 seemingly the only published record since two there in January 1951!

Coastal movements occur mainly during times of passage with peaks during April–May and September– October – see Tables 190 and 191. The numbers passing Portland Bill in spring are lower than at watch-points along the Purbeck coast and at Hengistbury – see Tables 190 to 192. Although day-totals are generally very small, some notable movements have been recorded including 125E at Durlston CP on 23rd April 1984, 105E at St Aldhelm's Head on 7th May 1981 with 68E there on 1st May 1997, 72E at Hengistbury on 3rd May 1980 with 62E there on 26th October 1991, and 62E at Portland Bill on 13th September 1993. Passage is predominantly easterly in spring, less so in autumn.

Jan	Feb	Mar	Apr	May	Jun	Jul	Aug	Sep	Oct	Nov	Dec
13	10	29	23	70	0	2	11	98	34	5	1

Table 190. Monthly totals for coastal movements at Portland Bill 1980–1996

Jan	Feb	Mar	Apr–May	Jun	Jul	Aug	Sep	Oct	Nov	Dec
1	23	3	573	0	13	4	77	60	27	0

Table 191. Monthly totals for coastal movements at Durlston CP 1982–1996

1987	1988	1989	1990	1991	1992	1993	1994
36	41	39	103	34	13	115	82

Table 192. Spring totals for coastal movements at St Aldhelm's Head 1987–1994

Inland it is a very rare visitor with only six records since 1950 including a remarkable three in 1997:

1962 Holwell CBs: 27th March
1987 Nether Cerne: 20th November
1988 Maiden Castle: two 17th September
1997 Empool CBs: 4th January
     Maiden Castle: two 6th August
     East Holme: 21st November

A total of 46 birds has been ringed in the county and there has been one foreign recovery from Germany.

The Grey Plover breeds across the Holarctic except for Greenland, Iceland, northern Scandinavia and extreme north-west Russia. It is a long-distance migrant with birds wintering from the coasts of western and southern Europe as far south as South Africa, southern Asia, Australia and South America.

Postscript 2000–2002
In Poole Harbour, 646 in February 2001 is a record count for the site and county, exceeding the previous high of 599 in February 1999. By contrast, wintering numbers on the Fleet were very low in 1999/2000, 2000/01 and 2001/02.

Sociable Plover (Sociable Lapwing) *Vanellus gregarius*

Accidental: three records

1961 Clapgate near Wimborne: ad. 6th–24th April
1975 Langton Herring: ad. 28th September–10th October
1995 Radipole NR, Lodmoor NR and Poxwell: first-winter 15th October; same at Wareham Water-
     meadows 16th October and Brand's Bay, Poole Harbour 18th October

The Sociable Plover breeds in the steppes of south-western Russia from the Volga River eastwards through Kazakhstan, and winters in north-east Africa, Iraq and the north-western Indian sub-continent. A vagrant to Great Britain with 41 records up to 2002.

White-tailed Plover (White-tailed Lapwing)   *Vanellus leucurus*

Accidental: one record

   1979   The Fleet at Abbotsbury: 3rd July

The only Dorset record involved a bird beside the Fleet at Abbotsbury which was only identified after the event from film taken by the observers.

   The White-tailed Plover breeds mainly in Iraq and the desert regions of west-central Asia, and winters in north-east Africa and the northern Indian sub-continent. A vagrant to Great Britain with only four records up to 2000, the last two being in 1984.

Lapwing (Northern Lapwing)   *Vanellus vanellus*

A locally common resident, and common winter visitor and passage migrant

Both Mansel-Pleydell (1888) and Blathwayt (1945) considered this species to be a common resident, the latter also mentioned that it is a winter visitor sometimes in very large flocks.

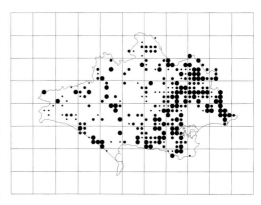

   The *BTO Atlas* (1968–1972) revealed evidence of breeding in all but two (95%) 10-km squares (confirmed in 29, probable in two and possible in four). The subsequent decline is reflected by the Tetrad Survey (1987–1994) with evidence of breeding in 32 (86%) of the pre-1974 10-km squares (confirmed in 22, probable in seven and possible in three), the most notable absence being in the east (SZ08). Although the Tetrad Map shows that breeding still occurs widely, the population is clearly concentrated in the east of the county favouring the Lower Avon Valley, the Poole Basin heathlands and the immediately adjacent downlands. There is strong evidence that the breeding population has continued to decline during the late 1990s.

   The numbers of Lapwing breeding in southern Great Britain declined significantly during the 1960s and this trend has continued to the present day. A major reason for this decline is almost certainly the change in agricultural practices, particularly the switch from spring to autumn sown cereals as the species prefers to nest on bare land rather than in tall crops. Although Dorset has not escaped this trend, it is difficult to quantify the extent of the decline. In 1950 an incomplete survey in the Cranborne area revealed 103 pairs, whilst subsequent surveys in the same general area of the county produced 64 pairs in 1980 and 98 pairs in 60km^2 in 1985. This suggests that breeding Lapwings may have fared better in this area than other parts of Dorset. More recently the populations breeding in the river valleys have shown a disturbing decline. The species is now an intermittent breeder in the Stour Valley between Corfe Mullen and Sturminster Marshall where up to 7–8 pairs regularly bred during 1978–1986 – see Table 193. Nearby along the Allen Valley, only a few pairs bred during the 1990s in meadows at Wimborne St Giles where 24 pairs were located in 1984. There is also concern over the population in the Lower Avon Valley where breeding numbers have seemingly declined severely during the late 1990s – see Table 194. In 1997 the RSPB's 'Review of Breeding Waders in South West England' estimated Dorset's breeding population to be between 100 and 150 pairs.

78	79	80	81	82	83	84	85	86	87	88	89	90	91	92	93	94	95	96	97	98	99
4	5	3	4	2	3	7	8	1	0	0	0	1	2	2	2	2	0	0	0	0	0

Table 193. Number of breeding pairs in Stour Valley between Corfe Mullen and Sturminster Marshall 1978–1999

   Post-breeding movements take place from June onwards with over 1,000 birds recorded on occasions at Christchurch Harbour.

1979	1982	1983	1984	1989	1991	1995	1997	1998
60	57	38	65	25	50	40	10	15

Table 194. Number of breeding territories in Lower Avon Valley 1979–1998

The Lapwing is much more widely distributed at times of passage and during the winter when large flocks may be found in suitable habitat throughout the county. Flocks of 1,000–2,000 birds are regularly recorded and at certain favoured sites winter maxima may sometimes reach c.6,000 birds, the highest count in recent years being 10,454 in Poole Harbour on 9th January 1994 – see Table 195. The highest count from earlier years was c.10,000 at the Wareham Water-meadows on 27th December 1955.

	90/91	91/92	92/93	93/94	94/95	95/96	96/97	97/98	98/99	99/00
Poole Harbour	4037	2158	6005	10454	4418	5097	4666	4912	3096	1000
Xchurch Hbr	2000	2600	3250	nc	2000	6000	2000	3000	2270	2100
Lodmoor NR	1200	1000	3200	nc	4000	2000	4000	2500	1000	700

Table 195. Winter maxima at some favoured sites 1990–1999

Lapwings are very susceptible to cold weather, particularly snow cover, and huge immigrations can arrive in the county if there is severe weather elsewhere. The most spectacular of such movements are c.10,000S at Cranborne during 24th–27th December 1962, c.15,000 at Portland Bill on 28th December 1962, c.10,000S at Wimborne on 8th January 1967 and 26th December 1970, c.30,000 county-wide on 30th–31st January 1972 including 10,000S at Langton Herring, and 13,173SW at Radipole NR on 12th December 1981.

A total of 594 birds has been ringed in the county and there have been eight foreign recoveries from France, four from Spain and one from the former USSR, and single foreign controls from Germany, the Netherlands and Belgium.

The Lapwing breeds over much of Europe except the extreme south, also in Asia Minor and central Asia. It winters mainly in western and southern Europe, North Africa, Asia Minor, the Middle East and parts of southern Asia.

Postscript 2000–2002
In 2000, the RSPB study of Lapwings breeding on arable land recorded 141 pairs. Generally there is concern regarding the apparent continuing decline in both the breeding and wintering populations.

Sponsored by English Nature

Knot (Red Knot)   *Calidris canutus*

An uncommon winter visitor and passage migrant

Both Mansel-Pleydell (1888) and Blathwayt (1945) considered this species to be a passage migrant and occasional winter visitor.

Subsequently the Knot has continued to be most widely reported as a passage migrant, particularly during the autumn. Since the 1950s, however, a regular wintering population has become established in Poole Harbour, which along with the Fleet and Christchurch Harbour, are the principal sites for the species in the county.

Although the winter population in Poole Harbour is generally small, usually from 10–70 birds, numbers fluctuate considerably. Relatively high counts were recorded during 1966/67–1970/71 (with a maximum of 150 at Arne NR on 11th January 1970), during 1982/83–1985/86 (maximum of 220 in Brand's Bay on 26th December 1984), and again during 1994/95–1996/97 (maximum of 112 in February 1997). Some of these high counts seem to be associated with severe cold weather. By contrast, the species has been very scarce in some winters with maxima of only six during 1986/87 and four during 1989/90. Studies undertaken in the mid-1980s show that the main roosting sites were Shell/Studland Bays, Brand's Bay, Fitzworth East and Brownsea, whilst the most favoured feeding areas were along the southern shores of the harbour. From earlier years, there is an exceptional count of 800 at Arne NR in January 1949, which is by far the highest count for the county.

Otherwise the Knot is a scarce and sporadic winter visitor to the Fleet and Christchurch Harbour with maxima rarely reaching double figures. On the Fleet the highest counts are clearly associated with very cold winters, notably 20 on 25th February 1979, 30 in January 1982, 40 on 23rd February 1985 and 20 in February 1991, whilst at Christchurch Harbour the only double figure counts occurred during the winter of 1987/88 with 12 in December and 14 in March.

Spring passage is most evident at Christchurch Harbour and the Fleet, and extends from April to mid-June with the peak in May – see Table 196. Numbers are generally small with maxima often in single figures and rarely exceeding 20 birds, the highest counts being an exceptional 107 on the Fleet in May 1987, 60 in Poole Harbour on 1st April 1956, 57 on Brownsea in April 1983 and 40 on the Fleet in May 1990, which coincided with heavy coastal movements at the Chesil.

	Jan	Feb	Mar	Apr	May	Jun	Jul	Aug	Sep	Oct	Nov	Dec
Poole Hbr	25	30	13	7	3	<1	1	7	25	24	18	21
The Fleet	2	3	3	1	14	1	1	11	16	5	2	1
Xchurch Hbr	1	1	2	4	9	2	3	13	17	4	2	2

Table 196. Average monthly maxima at the main sites 1980–1999

Autumn passage at all the main sites is heavier and extends from July through to October with the peak during September – see Table 196. Like the winter, numbers fluctuate considerably, but maxima generally range from 10–50 birds. The highest counts coincide with marked influxes during autumn 1978 including 300 at Lytchett Bay on 6th October, 88 at Langton Herring on 12th September and 75 at Christchurch Harbour on 28th August, and again in 1979 including 105 at Brownsea and 70 on the Fleet at Butterstreet Cove in September. Other high counts from Poole Harbour include 96 at Brownsea in September 1982 with 80 there in September 1984, and 84 in the entire harbour in October 1970, whilst up to 65 on the Fleet at Langton Herring during August–September 1982 and 60 at Christchurch Harbour in August 1994 are notable counts.

Radipole and Lodmoor NRs are the only other sites where the species occurs with any frequency, mainly on passage in spring and autumn. Most records involve 1–2 birds with counts rarely reaching double figures, the highest being 33 at Radipole NR on 4th September 1993 with 30 there on 9th March 1954 and 5th September 1975, and 12 at Lodmoor NR on 11th February 1965. Elsewhere reports of settled birds are very scarce with a few sightings from West Bexington, Portland Bill, Portland Harbour, Weymouth Bay and the Purbeck coast, mainly Kimmeridge Bay. At Portland Bill there was an exceptional influx during the cold weather of January 1987 with a peak of 73 on 17th. It is very rare in the extreme west of the county with up to ten in the Charmouth/Lyme Regis area during 31st January to 7th February 1954 and one at Lyme Regis on 7th September 1997 seemingly the only published records since 1950.

Coastal movements occur mainly at times of passage with peaks during April–May and August–September – see Tables 197 and 198. Although day-totals are generally small, some spectacular movements have been recorded, most notably 709 from the Chesil in early May 1990 including 401E on 4th and 110 on 2nd, also 215E there on 4th May 1995 when 200 also flew inland from the Fleet at Littlesea, c.425 at Portland Bill on 6th–7th September 1962 and 160E at St Aldhelm's Head on 3rd May 1994. There are several more modest, but nevertheless noteworthy day-counts from Portland Bill with 80 on 13th August 1986, 70–80 on 14th August 1985 and 60E on 20th April 1983. Passage is predominantly easterly in spring.

Jan	Feb	Mar	Apr	May	Jun	Jul	Aug	Sep	Oct	Nov	Dec
74	5	1	63	173	1	0	171	58	11	0	0

Table 197. Monthly totals for coastal movements at Portland Bill 1980–1999

Jan	Feb	Mar	Apr	May	Jun	Jul	Aug	Sep	Oct	Nov	Dec
20	6	0	42	36	2	0	24	28	0	0	0

Table 198. Monthly totals for coastal movements at Durlston CP 1982–1999

There is only one recent inland record involving one at Coward's Marsh, Christchurch on 7th February 1991. In addition, there is an old report of 13 at Verwood on 10th November 1844.

A total of 225 birds has been ringed in the county and there have been single foreign recoveries from Germany and Poland.

The Knot breeds in the high Arctic, mainly Canada and Greenland with smaller populations in Siberia and northern Alaska. Birds from the Canadian high arctic islands and Greenland winter in western Europe, whilst those from north-central Siberia winter in West Africa with some travelling as far as South Africa. Small numbers of this population pass through western Europe on passage. Birds from north-east Siberia and northern Alaska winter mainly in Australia and New Zealand, whilst those from the rest of Canada winter in South America.

Postscript 2000–2002

In Poole Harbour counts of 146 in December 2001, 100 in January 2001 and 70 in September 2000 are notably high. At Sturminster Marshall GP, one on 21st September 2001 is only the second recent inland record for the county.

Sponsored by E. M. Raynor

Sanderling   *Calidris alba*

An uncommon passage migrant and scarce winter visitor

Both Mansel-Pleydell (1888) and Blathwayt (1945) considered this species to be a passage migrant and occasional winter visitor, the former commenting that "it is usually very common in autumn on the Poole sandbanks and in the neighbourhood of Weymouth".

There has been little change in status since and the Sanderling has continued to occur mainly as a passage migrant, most notably in spring. In recent years Christchurch Harbour has been the principal site, the other main localities being the Fleet and the Poole Harbour area.

Spring passage is generally much stronger than during the autumn and sometimes involves high counts of settled flocks, which may coincide with heavy coastal movements. Passage extends from March through to mid-June and there is evidence, particularly from earlier years, of a double peak in movements, the first during late April–early May and the second during late May–early June. Numbers fluctuate widely, but peak counts generally range from 10–80 birds at Christchurch Harbour and 10–50 birds on the Fleet. Christchurch Harbour is the only locality where spring maxima frequently exceed 50 birds, the highest counts being 135 in May 1994 and 111 in May 1993. On the Fleet, there was a series of high spring counts during 1968–1973 culminating in a peak of 100 on 13th May 1973, but subsequent maxima have only exceeded 50 birds once with 80 in May 1996. In the Poole Harbour area there has been a decline in numbers – see Table 199. The highest counts were recorded prior to the mid-1970s with c.150 at Studland Bay on 11th May 1964, 112 at Shell/Studland Bays on 7th May 1953, a total of 107 at three sites on 19th May 1974 and 100+ on 7th May 1962. Since 1980 spring maxima have not exceeded 40 with very low numbers during the 1990s when peak counts failed to reach double figures in six years.

	1950s	1960s	1970s	1980s	1990s
Spring	49	48	34	20	10
Autumn	15	15	6	5	5

Table 199. Spring and autumn 10-year average peak counts from Poole Harbour 1950–1999

	Jan	Feb	Mar	Apr	May	Jun	Jul	Aug	Sep	Oct	Nov	Dec
Xchurch Hbr	1	<1	1	6	50	10	9	15	12	4	3	1
Poole Hbr	5	5	4	2	11	<1	2	2	3	1	1	5
The Fleet	<1	<1	1	5	28	2	7	8	8	<1	<1	<1

Table 200. Average monthly maxima at the main sites 1986–1999

Numbers recorded during autumn passage are much more modest – see Table 200. Even at Christchurch Harbour, the principal site for the species, maxima rarely exceed 30 birds, the highest being an isolated peak of 80 on 28th July 1975. On the Fleet, autumn maxima only occasionally reach double figures, the highest counts being 40 in August 1997 and September 1998. Like the spring, numbers in the Poole

Harbour area have declined since the mid-1970s with most subsequent autumn maxima in single figures except for 20 at Baiter on 9th October 1982, 12 in August 1997 and 11 in July 1990 – see Table 199. Increased disturbance on the beaches of the Shell/Studland Bays and Sandbanks may explain the decline in passage birds recorded in the Poole Harbour area.

Since the late 1960s small numbers have wintered most years in the Poole Harbour area where they favour the sandy beaches of Shell/Studland Bays and Sandbanks – see Table 201. Winter maxima are generally very low and only occasionally reach double figures, the highest counts in recent years being 17 in February 1987 and 15 in January 1998, whilst the best counts from earlier years were 36 on 7th February 1954 and 30 in November 1974. The species is only an occasional winter visitor to Christchurch Harbour and the Fleet. Numbers at these sites are generally very small, but there are a few isolated high counts including 31 at Rodden Hive on the Fleet on 29th December 1976 and 26 in Christchurch Harbour in November 1992.

1970s	1980s	1990s
6	5	8

Table 201. Winter 10-year average peak counts from Poole Harbour 1970–1999

Away from the main sites, most reports of settled birds come from Radipole and Lodmoor NRs, particularly in spring and autumn. Although numbers are generally small, high counts are occasionally recorded most notably at Lodmoor NR with 70 in May 1996, 67 bird-days in May 1987 and 102 bird-days during April–May 1984 (maximum of 45 on 22nd May). In earlier years exceptional numbers were present at Radipole NR during the winter of 1952/53 peaking at 150 on 2nd January, whilst 40 were present there on 10th August 1953 and 30 on 11th January 1950. Otherwise there is a scattering of records, mainly at times of passage, from Lyme Regis (maximum of 14 on 4th February 1954), Charmouth, West Bexington (maxima of 41 in May 1998 and 39 on 8th May 1979), Portland Bill, Portland Harbour, Weymouth Beach with isolated high counts in spring of 100 on 15th May 1970, 35 on 17th May 1987 and 27 on 4th May 1997, and the Purbeck coast.

Coastal movements mainly occur in spring with a pronounced peak in May, whilst autumn passage is much smaller and peaks in August – see Table 202. Although both overall passage and day-totals in spring are usually fairly modest, some heavy movements have been recorded notably from Hengistbury with 316E on 23rd May 1984, a total of 312E on 28th and 29th May 1983 including 200E on the latter date, and in 1980 150E on 25th April and 115E on 3rd May. At Portland Bill the highest day-total is 250E on 2nd May 1994, which far exceeds the previous best of 56 on 21st May 1989 and 50W on 6th May 1979. Elsewhere the highest counts are 97 at St Aldhelm's Head and 60 at Durlston CP on 10th May 1987, 82 at the Chesil on 28th April 1987 and 61W at East Bexington on 12th May 1992. Autumn day-totals are usually in single figures. Passage is predominantly easterly in spring.

Jan	Feb	Mar	Apr	May	Jun	Jul	Aug	Sep	Oct	Nov	Dec
<1%	0	0	6%	79%	1%	3%	6%	1%	2%	1%	0

Table 202. Monthly coastal movements (%) at Portland Bill 1980–1999

There is only one inland record involving a bird in the Lower Avon Valley on 10th September 1993. A total of 14 birds has been ringed in the county.

The Sanderling breeds in the high Arctic, mainly Canada, Greenland and north-central Siberia. It is a long-distance migrant with birds wintering mostly on the coasts of western Europe, Africa, southern Asia, Australia and both Americas.

Postscript 2000–2002
At Studland Bay/Poole Harbour, 21 in January 2001 and again in January 2002 were the highest winter counts since November 1974, whilst 20 in July 2000 was the highest autumn count since 1982.

Sponsored by David Holman and Tony Long

Semipalmated Sandpiper   *Calidris pusilla*

Accidental: three records

> 1982   Sutton Bingham: juv. 2nd–7th October
> 1989   Ferrybridge/East Fleet: juv. 20th–25th August
> 2002   Ferrybridge, moulting ad. 13th–14th September

In addition a bird at Sutton Bingham from 18th to 20th October 1973 was accepted as either this species or the very similar Western Sandpiper.

The Semipalmated Sandpiper breeds in arctic Alaska and Canada, and winters from Central America and the West Indies south to Ecuador and Brazil. A vagrant to Great Britain with 71 records up to 2002.

Little Stint   *Calidris minuta*

An uncommon passage migrant, mainly in autumn, and rare winter visitor

Mansel-Pleydell (1888) referred to this species as a spring and autumn migrant, which was "not uncommon in the neighbourhood of Weymouth and in the Poole Estuary". Blathwayt (1945) considered it to be a fairly regular passage migrant, chiefly in autumn.

There has been little change in status subsequently, except for an increase in spring and winter records. Christchurch Harbour and the Fleet are the main sites, the other favoured localities being Poole Harbour – mainly Brownsea, and Radipole and Lodmoor NRs.

The strength of autumn passage fluctuates considerably from year to year with periodic influxes such as those in 1993, 1996 and 1998 – see Table 203. Generally numbers are small with many records only involving 1–2 birds. Any counts in double figures are noteworthy, the highest being a county record 68 at Christchurch Harbour on 8th September 1993 with 36 there on 22nd September 1998 and 30 on 28th September 1996. Other high counts include 37 at Langton Herring on 23rd September 1973, 31 at East Fleet on 3rd September 1951 with 30 there on 15th September 1996, 30 at Abbotsbury on 20th and 22nd September 1996, and 30 at Lodmoor NR during 15th–18th September 1998. Although birds may appear in July, the main passage period extends from early August to mid-October with a distinct peak in September. A few migrants occasionally linger through late October and rarely into November.

	70	71	72	73	74	75	76	77	78	79	80	81	82	83	84
Christchurch Hbr	–	–	–	–	5	3	20	4	7	5	5	9	6	2	5
Brownsea	4	1	10	0	0	4	4	1	2	6	3	6	1	4	4
Lodmoor NR	1	0	0	0	0	0	4	2	6	4	2	2	1	3	3
Radipole NR	2	1	2	3	3	4	2	1	9	1	1	1	2	2	1
The Fleet	10	1	17	37	5	12	14	2	5	4	3	4	2	10	10

	85	86	87	88	89	90	91	92	93	94	95	96	97	98	99
Christchurch Hbr	6	nc	4	14	1	7	3	2	68	2	4	30	1	36	4
Brownsea	6	nc	nc	nc	nc	17	1	0	1	2	6	0	3	10	6
Lodmoor NR	1	nc	0	5	5	2	3	1	12	3	6	22	2	30	2
Radipole NR	1	nc	nc	5	5	2	4	0	6	1	0	12	6	3	0
The Fleet	5	nc	nc	10	7	21	5	1	18	0	8	30	1	20	4

Table 203. Autumn maxima at the main sites 1970–1999

In spring there are occasional reports between 1959 and 1969 after which the species has occurred annually, except for 1983, with a marked increase during the 1990s – see Table 204. Although migrants have been recorded from early April through to late June, peak passage occurs during May. Numbers are generally very small with seasonal totals rarely exceeding seven birds and the vast majority of records involving 1–2 birds. In some recent springs, however, passage has been exceptional, particularly at Christchurch Harbour with 25 bird-days during 13th May–1st June 1992 (with a maximum of 11 on 13th May), and 12 bird-days during 7th–26th May 1994 (maximum of nine on 15th). Other notable spring counts are ten at Holton Shore on 24th May 1963 and four at Lodmoor NR on 11th June 1994.

58	59	60	61	62	63	64	65	66	67	68	69	70	71	72	73	74	75	76	77	78
0	1	0	2	0	12	1	0	0	1	0	0	1	2	1	1	7	4	7	9	5

79	80	81	82	83	84	85	86	87	88	89	90	91	92	93	94	95	96	97	98	99
2	5	1	4	0	3	2	3	4	6	1	6	13	32	6	21	3	7	10	1	2

Table 204. Spring totals 1958–1999

Away from the main sites, migrants have been recorded at Portland Bill in at least 18 autumns (mainly September) since 1960. Otherwise there a few reports from Lyme Regis, Charmouth, West Bexington, Chesil Cove and Portland Harbour, whilst singles at Kimmeridge Bay on 18th November 1973 and Durlston CP on 20th August 1999 would appear to be the only sightings from the Purbeck coast.

Although the Little Stint is rare in winter, there have been near-annual records since the mid-1970s – see Table 205. Christchurch Harbour accounts for 76% of the winter total including four on 17th and 20th January 1987 and remarkable numbers in early 1994 with ten on 26th February and eight on 19th March. Elsewhere wintering birds have been recorded from Baiter and Keysworth in Poole Harbour, Radipole and Lodmoor NRs, the Nothe, and the Fleet at Ferrybridge and Butterstreet Cove. These include two which wintered at Lodmoor NR during 1985/86. In earlier years, one at Brownsea from 1st–6th January 1963 was regarded as exceptional at the time, whilst one in Poole Harbour on 31st March 1964 may also have been a wintering bird.

	75/76	76/77	77/78	78/79	79/80	80/81	81/82	82/83
Christchurch Hbr	1	1	1	0	0	1	1	1
other sites	0	0	0	0	0	0	0	0

	83/84	84/85	85/86	86/87	87/88	88/89	89/90	90/91
Christchurch Hbr	2	1	0	4	1	0	1	0
other sites	1	2	3	0	0	0	0	1

	91/92	92/93	93/94	94/95	95/96	96/97	97/98	98/99
Christchurch Hbr	1	0	10	0	0	0	2	1
other sites	0	0	0	0	0	1	1	0

Table 205. Winter totals 1975–1999

Inland the species is very unusual with five records as follows:

1959 Holwell CBs: 5th April
1975 Sherborne Lake: up to five in September
1993 Lower Avon Valley: 1–2 from 7th–11th September
1996 Chard Junction GP: four 20th September
1998 Warmwell GP: six 21st September

A total of 25 birds has been ringed in the county.

The Little Stint breeds on the arctic tundra from northern Scandinavia eastwards across northern Siberia to c.140°E. It winters mainly in sub-Saharan Africa and on the coasts of Arabia eastwards to the Indian sub-continent with smaller numbers around the Mediterranean Basin.

Postscript 2000–2002
Two at Abbotsbury on 28th March 2002 were either exceptionally early migrants or wintering birds.

Temminck's Stint   *Calidris temminckii*

A rare passage migrant
There are two 19th Century records both from near Weymouth on 24th October 1870 and 2nd September 1872.

The first recent sighting involves one at Radipole NR on 10th September 1967. Subsequently occurrences have increased and the species has been recorded annually since 1981 except for 1991, 1994 and 1998 – see Table 206. A total of 55 birds have occurred during this period with a slight bias towards autumn (29 birds) rather than spring (25 birds). Spring migrants are virtually restricted to May with a peak during the second half of the month, whilst autumn sightings extend from mid-June through to early October with a peak in early September – see Table 207. The earliest and latest reports are 20th April 1982 at Christchurch Harbour and 4th October 1983 at Lodmoor NR. There is one winter record from Lodmoor NR on 25th December 1969.

66	67	68	69	70	71	72	73	74	75	76	77	78	79	80	81	82
0	1	0	2	3	1	0	0	0	1	2	1	0	0	0	1	5

83	84	85	86	87	88	89	90	91	92	93	94	95	96	97	98	99
4	2	1	1	4	2	1	1	0	4	5	0	4	5	3	0	1

Table 206. Annual totals 1967–1999

Apr	May	May	Jun	Jun	Jul	Jul	Aug	Aug	Sep	Sep	Oct
16–30	1–15	16–31	1–15	16–30	1–15	16–31	1–15	16–31	1–15	16–30	1–15
1	7	17	0	2	2	2	5	5	8	4	1

Table 207. Half-monthly totals 1967–1999 (excluding winter record)

The main site is Christchurch Harbour, which accounts for 26 birds (47%) with 12 in spring and 14 in autumn. Since 1982 Temminck's Stints have been recorded at this site in every year except 1984, 1991, 1994 and 1998. The next most popular localities are Lodmoor NR with 15 birds (seven in spring, seven in autumn and one in winter) and Radipole NR with seven birds (six in spring and one in autumn) – two of the spring birds being first reported from Lodmoor NR. Nearby on the Fleet there are records from Langton Herring with two on 28th May 1970 and one during 6th–8th September 1984, and Abbotsbury with singles on 24th June 1993 and 2nd August 1996 – the latter was also seen at West Bexington, whilst one at Charmouth Beach on 23rd–24th September 1995 is a particularly noteworthy sighting. Rather surprisingly one at Brownsea on 14th September 1995 was the first from the Poole Harbour area. The only inland reports come from Sutton Bingham with singles during 29th–31st July 1982 and 6th–10th September 1984.

All records refer to single birds except for two at Langton Herring on 28th May 1970, two at Radipole NR on 31st May 1976 and three at Christchurch Harbour on 19th May 1992.

The Temminck's Stint breeds in northern Scandinavia and arctic Siberia with a very small population in northern Scotland. It winters mainly in the northern tropics of Africa and southern Asia including the Indian sub-continent, also smaller numbers around the eastern Mediterranean, and in the Middle East and Arabia.

Postscript 2000–2002

The only record during this period involved one at Christchurch Harbour on 10th August 2002.

White-rumped Sandpiper *Calidris fuscicollis*

Accidental: four records

The four Dorset records are shared equally between Ferrybridge and Lodmoor NR.

- 1974　Ferrybridge: 4th–9th September
- 1982　Lodmoor NR: juv. 27th September
- 1999　Ferrybridge: ad. 26th July
- 2000　Lodmoor NR: juv./first-winter 14th–15th October

The White-rumped Sandpiper breeds in arctic North America and winters in southern South America. A vagrant to Great Britain with 365 records up to 2002.

Sponsored by Geoff Barlow and Sheila Barlow

Baird's Sandpiper

Calidris bairdii

Accidental: three records

    1967   Portland Bill: 18th–19th November
    1988   Christchurch Harbour: juv. 6th–19th October
    1998   Christchurch Harbour: juv. 24th August–2nd September

The Baird's Sandpiper breeds from north-east Siberia eastwards across arctic North America to north-west Greenland and winters from Ecuador to southern South America. A vagrant to Great Britain with 168 records up to 2002.

Pectoral Sandpiper

Calidris melanotos

A rare autumn passage migrant

The first Dorset bird was reported from the Wareham side of Poole Harbour on 22nd September 1935. There were no further sightings until 1964 when one was present at Lodmoor NR during 10th–13th September. Subsequently a total of 50 birds have been recorded during 1967–1999 with annual occurrences since 1976 except for 1989, 1991, 1994, 1997 and 1999 – see Table 208.

64	65	66	67	68	69	70	71	72	73	74	75	76	77	78	79	80	81
1	0	0	1	0	0	1	0	1	0	0	0	2	2	1	3	1	3

82	83	84	85	86	87	88	89	90	91	92	93	94	95	96	97	98	99
6	4	1	2	3	1	3	0	1	0	4	2	0	4	2	0	2	0

Table 208. Annual totals 1964–1999

Although there are records for the period mid-July to early November, the earliest being from 14th–16th July 1977 at Lodmoor NR and the latest being on 4th November 1984 at Radipole NR, the peak time for the species is September, which accounts for 33 birds (63%) – see Table 209. There is a mini-peak in late July, presumably involving adults, which predominate earlier in the autumn whereas most birds seen from mid-August onwards are juveniles.

Jul 1–15	Jul 16–31	Aug 1–15	Aug 16–31	Sep 1–15	Sep 16–30	Oct 1–15	Oct 16–31	Nov 1–15	Nov 16–30
1	3	2	3	15	18	7	2	1	0

Table 209. Half-monthly totals 1935–1999

Christchurch Harbour is the most favoured site with 23 birds (44%) followed by Lodmoor NR with 12 birds (23%). At Radipole NR single birds were present during 18th–22nd September 1978 and on 10th August 1982, 10th September 1983 and 4th November 1984 – the birds in 1978 and 1983 being first reported from Lodmoor NR. Nearby on the Fleet, there are records from Langton Herring with singles during 24th August–5th September 1972 and on 17th September 1986, Ferrybridge with one on 19th July 1982, and Abbotsbury with singles during 18th–26th October 1995 and 4th–16th October 1996. The species is scarce in the Poole Harbour area, the only additional reports to the first county record being one at Wareham SF on 24th September 1967, one at Lytchett Bay on 11th September 1992 and 1–2 birds on the Wareham Water-meadows during 20th–22nd September 1992. Rather surprisingly single birds have been recorded at Portland Bill on 21st September 1982, 28th October 1986 and 16th September 1988. There are only three inland sightings involving singles at Sutton Bingham during 4th–12th September 1970 and 14th–21st September 1976, and more notably at Sturminster Marshall GP during 15th–20th September 1987.

    Although records mostly refer to singles, there are several reports of two birds, but only two records of three birds from Christchurch Harbour on 5th October 1979 and Lodmoor NR on 5th–6th October 1995.

    One bird has been ringed in the county.

The Pectoral Sandpiper breeds across the arctic tundra from eastern Siberia eastwards to Alaska and north-west Canada. It winters mainly in South America with smaller numbers across the Pacific to New Zealand and Australia. The species is a rare migrant to the British Isles, annual in small numbers in autumn, but occasional in spring.

Postscript 2000–2002
There were four records involving one at Lodmoor NR on 14th October 2000, one inland at Sutton Bingham during 3rd–8th September 2001, a very late bird at Stanpit Marsh, Christchurch Harbour from 11th November 2001 to 2nd January 2002, and one at Hengistbury on 30th September 2002.

Sharp-tailed Sandpiper   *Calidris acuminata*

Accidental: one record

   1978   The Fleet at Langton Herring: ad. 2nd April

This individual at Langton Herring, remains the only spring record for the British Isles.

   The Sharp-tailed Sandpiper breeds in north-east Siberia and winters in Australasia and Polynesia. A vagrant to Great Britain with only 25 records up to 2002.

Curlew Sandpiper   *Calidris ferruginea*

An uncommon passage migrant, mainly in autumn, and very rare winter visitor

Mansel-Pleydell (1888) described this species as "not an infrequent visitor in spring and autumn". Blathwayt (1945) considered it to be a fairly regular passage migrant in small numbers, being less common in spring than autumn.

   Since 1950 the Curlew Sandpiper has occurred mainly as an autumn migrant, but there has been a marked increase in spring sightings in recent years. It was seemingly rather scarce at times during the 1950s and 1960s, for example there were no confirmed reports in 1958 and 1965. The main sites are Christchurch Harbour, Poole Harbour – mainly Brownsea, Radipole and Lodmoor NRs, and the Fleet.

   The strength of the autumn passage varies enormously from year to year – see Table 210. There have been several influx years resulting in particularly high numbers, the best counts being a county record of 75 at Brownsea on 31st August 1969 with 60 there on 4th September 1986, and 66 at Christchurch Harbour on 14th August 1985. Elsewhere in Poole Harbour, there are noteworthy counts from Baiter with up to 47 during 12th–15th September 1993 and Middlebere with 44 on 13th September 1996. These autumn influxes often coincide with good years for Little Stints, presumably reflecting favourable breeding conditions. There are occasional reports of early returning migrants in late June and early July, but passage usually extends from mid-July to mid-October and peaks from mid-August through to mid-September. In some autumns a few birds may remain through to late October, but much more rarely through to mid-November.

	68	69	70	71	72	73	74	75	76	77	78	79	80	81	82	83
Christchurch Hbr	–	–	–	–	–	–	2	50	5	7	9	15	9	12	14	4
Brownsea	1	75	3	2	8	3	0	47	1	9	41	16	5	8	9	8
Lodmoor NR	0	10	0	0	2	0	0	1	0	2	16	0	1	1	6	3
Radipole NR	0	21	3	1	14	3	1	14	1	0	9	1	4	2	1	4
The Fleet	0	14	14	4	16	4	0	10	6	1	10	10	1	3	6	1

	84	85	86	87	88	89	90	91	92	93	94	95	96	97	98	99
Christchurch Hbr	11	66	20	3	47	1	31	21	4	18	14	14	38	4	15	19
Brownsea	3	3	60	nc	19	2	12	32	5	20	0	1	9	4	6	35
Lodmoor NR	2	3	1	1	6	1	8	6	1	15	3	10	16	3	11	4
Radipole NR	1	4	1	0	6	nc	4	7	0	3	1	0	11	1	3	2
The Fleet	3	14	nc	nc	12	1	3	6	1	5	2	5	27	5	10	5

Table 210. Autumn maxima at the main sites 1968–1999

Although the species was only recorded in three springs between 1950 and 1966, it has occurred nearly annually since with a marked increase during the 1990s (cf Little Stint) – see Table 211. Spring passage extends from mid-April to mid-June with a distinct peak in May. Numbers are generally very small with seasonal totals rarely exceeding ten birds and the vast majority of records involving 1–2 birds. In some recent springs, however, passage has been exceptional, particularly at Christchurch Harbour with 29 bird-days during May 1990 (maximum of eight on 9th), 24 bird-days during 28th April–early June 1992 (maximum of six on 19th May), ten bird-days in May 1995 and 12 bird-days during 14th April–20th May 1996.

56	57	58	59	60	61	62	63	64	65	66	67	68	69	70	71	72	73	74	75	76	77
1	0	0	0	1	5	0	0	0	0	0	1	1	1	1	4	2	0	4	1	2	0

78	79	80	81	82	83	84	85	86	87	88	89	90	91	92	93	94	95	96	97	98	99
7	3	2	8	3	5	7	0	3	15	9	0	31	3	40	4	4	10	12	2	4	1

Table 211. Spring totals 1956–1999

There are occasional reports of coastal movements. Those in spring have been exclusively recorded from the Chesil with seven on 28th April 1987, 1E on 5th May 1990 and 15 on 20th April 1992. In autumn there are c.13 records from Portland Bill since 1959, whilst movements have also been observed from West Bexington (once), East Bexington (twice in September 1992), Durlston CP (five records), and Christchurch Harbour including 30W during 21st–29th August 1999 (maximum of 19W on 29th). Otherwise there are autumn reports from West Bexington with four on 30th September 1990 and singles on 19th September 1993 and 16th September 1999, Chesil Cove with one on 8th September 1973, and Kimmeridge Bay with one on 1st–2nd September 1973.

The Curlew Sandpiper is rare in winter with most records from the Poole Harbour area:

1961   Poole Park: two 5th January; also one found dead as a result of oil pollution in Poole Harbour during January
1979   Christchurch Harbour: 21st–22nd December
1983   Poole Park: 15th February
1985   Poole Park: 16th February
          Brownsea: 15th December; possibly same at Shore Road, Sandbanks 11th March 1986
1987   East Fleet: 17th March – presumed winterer rather than early migrant
1996   Lytchett Bay: 15th–19th March; possibly same bird as recorded on 11th November 1995
          Holes Bay: 22nd December; presumed same at Parkstone Bay 26th December and Poole Park 2nd January 1997

The only inland record involves one at Bere Regis CBs on 31st July 1974.

A total of 119 birds has been ringed in the county. There has been one foreign recovery from Tunisia and one foreign control from the former USSR.

The Curlew Sandpiper breeds in arctic Siberia. It winters mainly in sub-Saharan Africa and on the coasts of Arabia and most of southern Asia south to Australia and New Zealand.

Purple Sandpiper   *Calidris maritima*

Uncommon winter visitor and passage migrant.

Both Mansel-Pleydell (1888) and Blathwayt (1945) considered this species to be a regular winter visitor to the rocky parts of the coast, the latter also referred to it being a passage migrant.

There has been little subsequent change in status. Portland Bill is the principal site for the Purple Sandpiper in Dorset. Since the 1950s numbers have increased at this site, particularly during the late 1970s, to reach a peak in the early 1980s – see Table 212. Prior to 1975/76 maxima ranged between 5–25 birds, but exceeded 30 birds during 1976/77–1986/87 with a county record count of 57 on 18th March 1981. Since 1986/87 there has been a decline in numbers, which has become particularly pronounced since 1992/93 with maxima generally ranging between 14–18 birds except for an isolated peak of 32 on 11th January 1997. Seasonally, there is evidence of a slight peak in spring (March–April) reflecting passage with numbers rapidly declining during May – see Table 213. A single on 3rd June 1976 is the latest spring bird and seemingly the only county record for June. The first returning birds appear from early July through to early September, but numbers are small and records often erratic until October, after which the wintering flock becomes established again with counts increasing during November and December.

1950s	1960s	1970s	1980s	1990s
9	16	26	36	20

Table 212. Winter/spring 10-year mean peak counts from Portland Bill 1950–1999

Jan	Feb	Mar	Apr	May	Jun	Jul	Aug	Sep	Oct	Nov	Dec
21	19	23	23	20	0	<1	1	3	7	14	16

Table 213. Average monthly maxima at Portland Bill 1980–1999

There are a number of other sites where the species has regularly occurred in small numbers. The Cobb at Lyme Regis is a traditional locality with records as far back as the 1920s including 17 on 12th December 1926 and 24 wintering there in 1927. Subsequently reports were regular during 1950–1957, infrequent up to 1977, fairly regular up to 1996, but very scarce during 1997–1999. During these periods maxima typically have been in single figures and only exceeded 15 birds once with 24 in April 1992.

Various localities in the Portland Harbour area, notably the north shore and the breakwaters together with Balaclava Bay on Portland and the Nothe, were reliable wintering sites from about 1970 to 1980. Usually only 1–4 birds were involved, but up to eight were present during January–April 1974 and six during November–December of the same year. Although subsequent reports, including 21 on the breakwaters on 3rd January 1985 and 14 in Portland Harbour on 4th January 1996, have been rather intermittent, there was evidence of regular wintering on the breakwaters again during 1986/87 and 1987/88 with a maximum of five in January 1987. Otherwise there are a few sightings from other sites on Portland.

In the east of the county the main haunts for the species are Poole Harbour Entrance and Hengistbury with some evidence that birds may commute along the length of Poole Bay between these two sites, resulting in occasional sightings from Branksome and Alum Chines, Bournemouth, Boscombe and Southbourne. At Poole Harbour Entrance birds favour the rocks by North Haven and Pilot's Point. Numbers are generally small, with only 1–2 birds during 1953–1976, increasing to 3–5 birds up to 1981/82 and 6–8 birds during 1982/83–1985/86, before declining to 2–5 birds in most subsequent winters. At Hengistbury numbers have steadily declined since the 1970s – see Table 214. Although maxima generally ranged between 10–16 birds during the 1970s, they have rarely reached double figures since then. Very low numbers were recorded in the mid-1990s, but there has been an encouraging increase during the late 1990s.

74/75	75/76	76/77	77/78	78/79	79/80	80/81	81/82	82/83	83/84	84/85	85/86	86/87
13	10	12	16	12	8	9	9	7	10	8	9	7

87/88	88/89	89/90	90/91	91/92	92/93	93/94	94/95	95/96	96/97	97/98	98/99	99/00
8	10	7	12	6	15	2	2	2	2	4	12	10

Table 214. Winter/spring maxima at Hengistbury 1974–1999

There are occasional records of settled birds from the Purbeck coast, notably Durlston CP and Kimmeridge Bay where up to seven birds wintered fairly regularly during the mid-1970s.

The species has been recorded from a number of unexpected localities. For example, on the Fleet there are sightings from several sites including Ferrybridge and Abbotsbury. There are also reports from well inside Poole Harbour including one at Arne NR during 23rd–27th August 1966, seven at Poole Quay on 8th January 1983, one at Poole Park on 18th January 1987 and three at Hamworthy Beach on 17th March 1996, whilst birds have occurred inside Christchurch Harbour. Perhaps the most unusual reports involve one in a flooded field at West Bexington on 16th November 1970 and one at Lodmoor NR during 28th August–11th September 1983.

There are occasional reports of coastal movements in spring and autumn, mainly from Hengistbury and Durlston CP.

Only three birds have been ringed in the county.

The Purple Sandpiper breeds across part of the Holarctic from north-east Canada eastwards to north-central Siberia including Greenland, Iceland, and Scandinavia with a few pairs in northern Scotland since 1978. It winters further north than any other wader on the ice-free coasts of western Europe south to 40°N, and eastern North America south to 30°N.

Postscript 2000–2002
At Hengistbury, 20 in November 2002 was the highest count at this site since at least 1974 and continues the recent recovery in numbers since the low population levels of the mid-1990s, whilst 22 at Portland Bill in February 2002 was a high count by recent standards.

Dunlin   *Calidris alpina*

Common winter visitor and passage migrant

Mansel-Pleydell (1888) referred to this species as a very common spring and autumn visitor, but curiously made no mention of its winter status. Blathwayt (1945) considered it to be a winter visitor and passage migrant, and the commonest wader on the coast, a situation which has not changed subsequently.

Poole Harbour is the principal site for the Dunlin, particularly in winter. Although there were a few high counts during the 1950s and 1960s including c.3,000 at Brownsea on 5th December 1967, 2,500 in the Sandbanks area on 20th January 1954 with c.2,000 there on 16th January 1950, the true size of the wintering population was not revealed until the start of systematic counts in 1969/70. Since then, winter maxima have generally ranged between 2,500–7,000 birds with evidence of an increase, particularly during the 1990s resulting in a county record count of 8,300 at the Studland roost on 24th November 1991 – see Table 215. Generally winter numbers are at their highest during December to February – see Table 216. Studies undertaken in the mid-1980s show that at high water the roosting population was divided into two, with a southern group based at Brand's Bay and Fitzworth East, and a northern group centred in Holes Bay. As the tide dropped, the southern group mostly moved westwards, feeding as the mud was exposed and moving as far as the Wareham Channel, before making the return journey. The northern group began to feed in Holes Bay as soon as the mud was exposed, but soon small groups drifted off to nearby Lytchett Bay, and by low water very few birds remained. At Lytchett Bay, peak counts occurred after low water. Shell/Studland Bays were also an important roosting site at high water, when the main feeding areas were Baiter and Wareham Water-meadows, but these sites were only used if standing water was present. Evidence of passage is obscured by the high winter population, but there have been occasional peak counts during spring and autumn, notably 2,501 in September 1996 and 2,000 in August 1986.

	1960s	1970s	1980s	1990s
Poole Harbour	–	3692	4080	6403
Christchurch Harbour	–	1517	649	1275
The Fleet	483	455	339	379

Table 215. Winter 10-year average peak counts at the main sites 1950–1999

	Jan	Feb	Mar	Apr	May	Jun	Jul	Aug	Sep	Oct	Nov	Dec
Poole Hbr	4752	4723	1424	213	134	21	59	455	467	661	3052	4338
Xchurch Hbr	761	797	622	159	482	101	153	380	221	289	481	630
The Fleet	318	223	163	63	278	26	141	335	198	44	142	189

Table 216. Average monthly maxima at the main sites 1986–1999

Christchurch Harbour and the Fleet are the other main sites for the species. By contrast to Poole Harbour, passage is more obvious with distinct peaks in May and August – see Table 216. At Christchurch Harbour winter maxima have generally ranged between 500–2,000 birds, but the population was seemingly higher during the 1970s and 1990s than in the 1980s with site record counts of 3,000 during January–February 1976 and in February 1996 – see Table 215. Peak numbers on passage, notably in spring, sometimes reach or exceed winter maxima, the best counts being 2,000 in August 1986 and 1,000 in April 1974 and May 1988. Wintering numbers on the Fleet have been more stable with maxima generally ranging between 200–700 birds with isolated peak counts of 1,000 in December 1973 and 913 in January 1985 – see Table 215. Passage is particularly prominent with counts frequently exceeding winter maxima, the highest being 2,000 during September–October 1981, 1,200 on 18th April 1970 and 1,000 at Abbotsbury on 13th September 1970, Langton Herring on 6th May 1972 and again there on 27th April 1973.

In earlier years up to 250 birds were frequently present at Lodmoor NR during the winter months. Since 1982, however, most records have been at times of passage, which is heaviest in spring with a distinct peak in May – see Table 217. Although monthly maxima rarely exceed 100 birds, there is an exceptional recent count of 400 in May 1996. At nearby Radipole NR there are several winter counts of 100–270 birds during 1950–1972, but subsequently the species has been mainly recorded on passage, most notably during the autumn – see Table 217. Again monthly maxima rarely reach treble figures, the highest recent counts being 175 in May 1984 and 150 in August 1988. Numbers have declined at Radipole NR during the 1990s.

	Jan	Feb	Mar	Apr	May	Jun	Jul	Aug	Sep	Oct	Nov	Dec
Lodmoor NR	16	30	32	28	67	6	23	38	22	9	13	12
Radipole NR	3	4	2	6	22	8	27	37	30	9	8	8

Table 217. Average monthly maxima at Lodmoor and Radipole NRs 1982–1996

Elsewhere along the coast, small numbers of settled birds are occasionally reported from the Charmouth/Lyme Regis area, West Bay, West Bexington, Portland Bill and the Purbeck coast.

Inland, the Dunlin occurs fairly regularly in the valleys of the Lower Avon and Lower Frome, usually when standing water is present as a result of winter flooding. These records are likely to involve birds from Christchurch and Poole Harbours respectively, which are taking advantage of high-water feeding opportunities. In the Lower Avon Valley counts of up to 300 are not unusual, the highest being 700 at Sopley in February 1979, whilst in the Lower Frome Valley there are several counts of between 250–600 birds. In earlier years, birds were recorded with some frequency from the Stour Valley between Wimborne and Sturminster Marshall, notably in the vicinity of Corfe Mullen where the highest count was 150 on 6th February 1972. The last substantial count was 25 in January 1982, after which there has been a rapid decline in reports as the incidence of flooding in this section of the Stour Valley diminished. There are occasional records from the upper catchment of the Stour including 75 at Marnhull on 28th February 1975 and 60 at Fiddleford/Manston on 9th December 1992. Otherwise there are a few records from other inland sites scattered throughout the county.

Coastal movements occur mainly at times of passage with distinct peaks in May and August – see Table 218. Numbers passing Portland Bill, notably in spring, are lower than at watch-points along the Purbeck coast and at Hengistbury – see Table 219. Consequently day-totals at Portland Bill are generally very small, but there have been some large movements most notably 235E on 2nd May 1994, a day of unprecedented wader passage, and 106E on 7th November 1982. Large day-totals are recorded more often at the other main watch-points, the best counts being from the Chesil with 300E on 22nd April 1994 and 226E on 28th April 1987, St Aldhelm's Head with 284E on 2nd May 1997 and 247E on 2nd May 1994, Durlston CP with 250E on 2nd May 1994, and Hengistbury with 480E on 8th and 400E on 9th May 1995, 275N on 29th April 1992, 250W on 25th November 1995 and 220W on 3rd January 1992. In 1956 night passage was recorded at Portland Bill involving c.250+ during 4th/5th May and 250SE between 19.45 and 23.30 hrs on 10th August.

Jan	Feb	Mar	Apr	May	Jun	Jul	Aug	Sep	Oct	Nov	Dec
7	5	13	252	554	2	137	572	255	218	227	7

Table 218. Monthly totals for coastal movements at Portland Bill 1982–1999

	1986	1987	1988	1989	1990	1991	1992
Portland Bill	29	21	9	52	11	42	8
Durlston CP	88	42	103	140	69	94	31
St Aldhelms Hd	112	148	104	270	243	89	34

	1993	1994	1995	1996	1997	1998	1999
Portland Bill	13	237	93	39	99	59	127
Durlston CP	nc	408	209	168	182	147	92
St Aldhelms Hd	343	365	nc	228	513	nc	nc

Table 219. Spring totals (bds) for coastal movements at the main watch-points 1986–1999

A total of 10,289 birds has been ringed in the county. There have been numerous foreign recoveries and controls from Sweden, Poland, Germany and the Netherlands, several from Finland, Norway, Denmark and France, and one or two from the former USSR, Belgium, Spain and Morocco. One ring was recovered in Dorset in 1975 from a Hen Harrier pellet, whilst in Norfolk a ring from a Dorset bird was recovered from a Short-eared Owl pellet in 1992.

The Dunlin breeds mainly across the Holarctic, but in Europe sparingly as far south as the British Isles, Denmark and countries bordering the Baltic. The Eurasian population mainly winters on the coasts of western Europe, the Mediterranean, West, north-west and north-east Africa, Arabia, and southern Asia.

Broad-billed Sandpiper   *Limicola falcinellus*

Accidental: four records involving five individuals

1973   Sutton Bingham: 5th–6th September
1975   The Fleet at Herbury Gore: 18th May
1986   Ferrybridge: 8th May
1986   Stanpit Marsh, Christchurch Harbour: two 16th–17th May

The Broad-billed Sandpiper breeds in Scandinavia and northern Siberia and winters mainly in southern Asia and Australia. A vagrant to Great Britain with 202 records up to 2002.

Buff-breasted Sandpiper   *Tryngites subruficollis*

A very rare autumn passage migrant: nine records involving ten individuals

The Fleet is the favoured area for the species hosting the first four of the nine county records.

1955   Ferrybridge: trapped and ringed 28th September–11th October
1965   West Fleet: 16th August
1974   Ferrybridge: 9th–11th September with two 12th (also an unconfirmed report of seven on 12th)
1975   Ferrybridge: 1st September
1984   Sutton Bingham: 15th September
1993   White Nothe: one with Dotterel flock 20th–26th September
1994   Lodmoor NR: 29th August–31st August
1996   Stanpit Marsh, Christchurch Harbour: juvenile 17th September
2000   Portland Bill and Weston: juvenile 18th September; same at Blacknor, Portland 19th–
            21st September

The Buff-breasted Sandpiper breeds in arctic Alaska, north-west Canada and extreme north-east Siberia, and winters in Argentina, Uruguay and Paraguay. A rare visitor to the British Isles, mainly in autumn, with over 400 records up to 1982.

Ruff   *Philomachus pugnax*

An uncommon passage migrant and winter visitor

Both Mansel-Pleydell (1888) and Blathwayt (1945) considered this species to be a mainly a spring and autumn visitor.

Numbers were very small up to 1952, but have increased since with regular wintering established briefly during the 1960s and 1970s. The main sites for passage birds are Christchurch Harbour and Lodmoor NR, other favoured localities being Poole Harbour – mainly Brownsea, Arne NR and Lytchett Bay, Radipole NR, the Fleet – mainly Langton Herring and Abbotsbury, West Bexington, and inland along the Lower Avon Valley.

Spring passage is somewhat obscured by wintering birds, but genuine migrants occur from early March through to early June with a peak between mid-April and mid-May. Although relatively small, passage can vary considerably in strength with spring totals ranging from 1–65 birds, but more typically between 10–40 birds since the mid-1970s. Autumn migrants may appear as early as late June, but the main passage usually occurs between mid-July and late October with August and September the peak months. Some November records may refer to late migrants rather than wintering birds. Although generally more numerous than in spring, autumn passage also varies considerably ranging from 2–12 birds in poor years to 30–80 birds in good years, the highest seasonal totals being c.195 in 1988 and c.110 in 1994. Counts of passage birds are low, usually from 1–5 and rarely exceeding ten birds, the highest being 65 at Radipole/Lodmoor NRs during 3rd–9th April 1965 and 36 at Christchurch Harbour in September 1976. Away from the Lower Avon Valley, inland passage birds are very scarce with a few scattered records of 1–2 birds from East Holme, East Stoke, Wool, Tadnoll, Woodsford, Warmwell, Dorchester, Bucknowle, Morden Bog, Winterborne Anderson, Stanbridge Mill (twice), Nether Cerne, Marnhull and Sherborne Lake (twice).

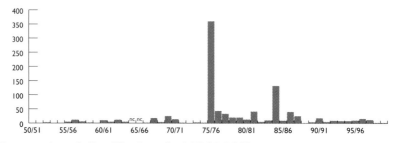

Fig 27. Winter totals excluding Wareham flock 1950–1999

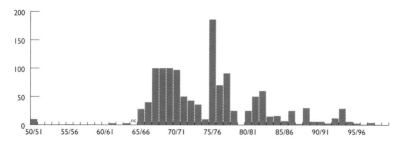

Fig 28. Winter maxima for Wareham flock 1950–1999

Coastal movements are rarely observed in spring with only four records from Portland Bill and three from Durlston CP, so 15E at Hengistbury on 3rd May 1980 is unusual. By contrast, autumn birds frequently occur at Portland Bill with reports in all but nine years since 1971 including 8N on 24th August 1979, 7N on 4th September 1997 and 6W on 11th September 1992. Surprisingly few observations elsewhere, 4W at Durlston CP on 4th November 1988 being the only autumn record from this site.

The first evidence of wintering occurred in the mid-1950s followed by an increase in records from 1961 onwards – see Fig 27. By the mid-1960s a regular wintering flock had become established in the Wareham area where maxima rapidly increased from 28 in February 1966 to a peak of 100 in four consecutive winters from 1967/68 to 1970/71 – see Fig 28. The size of the flock diminished during the early 1970s until the exceptional influx of early 1976, which resulted in a peak count of 186 on 24th February. Numbers remained fairly high during the following two winters, but then declined rapidly, and since 1980 the species has become a rather erratic visitor to this area with sporadic influxes often associated with periods of severe cold. There are occasional sightings, presumably involving birds from this wintering population, from the Lower Frome Valley upstream to Wool and exceptionally to Woodsford and West Stafford, but reports from other sites in the Poole Harbour area are rather infrequent.

Elsewhere in Dorset, the numbers of wintering Ruff have generally followed the same pattern – see Fig 27. The influx in early 1976 was reported throughout the county, notably in the Weymouth area where numbers at the large Weymouth Beach/Radipole NR evening roost reached peaks of 220 on 27th February and a county record of 232 on 1st March with 150 still present on 10th March, also 150 at Lodmoor NR on 6th March. Other noteworthy counts during early 1976 included 61 in the Lower Avon Valley at Burton on 4th March, 28 at West Bexington on 10th February, 16 on the Fleet during February–March and six at Portland Bill on 31st January. Since 1980 most winter influxes have been associated with periods of severe cold, notably in early 1982, 1985 and 1987.

Regular wintering has never become established at other sites within the county. Nevertheless, there are frequent records from Christchurch Harbour and nearby along the Lower Avon Valley. In early 1985 there were particularly good numbers at Christchurch Harbour including 34 on 7th January and 48 on 22nd February. It is an occasional winter visitor to other coastal sites including the Fleet, and Radipole and Lodmoor NRs, whilst cold weather influxes have been detected at Portland Bill in 1982, 1985, 1987 and 1991. The species is more widely reported inland during the winter than at times of passage. Away from the Lower Avon and Lower Frome Valleys, there are c.15 records from the Stour Valley between Wimborne and Sturminster Marshall including up to ten at Corfe Mullen during December 1969–January 1970 with six there on 22nd February 1985. Elsewhere there are sightings from Puddletown including up to seven during January–March 1987, Martinstown/Winterborne Monkton including up to six in January 1985, Marnhull including five during February–March 1976, Sherborne Lake with three in March 1976, Cranborne, Stanbridge Mill (twice), Tarrant Hinton, Hammoon, West Morden and Maiden Castle.

A total of 13 birds have been ringed in the county and there has been one foreign recovery from Morocco.

The Ruff breeds in Europe between 50°N and 70°N discontinuously from eastern Great Britain eastwards through the Netherlands to Poland and more widely from northern Scandinavia eastwards to eastern Siberia. It winters mainly in sub-Saharan Africa and the Indian sub-continent with much smaller populations in western and southern Europe, North Africa, Asia Minor, the Middle East and Arabia.

Jack Snipe   *Lymnocryptes minimus*

An uncommon winter visitor and passage migrant

Both Mansel-Pleydell (1888) and Blathwayt (1945) considered this species to be a regular winter visitor and passage migrant in small numbers. There has been little change in status subsequently.

Since 1950 the Jack Snipe has been recorded from sites both along the coast and well inland where favoured habitats include heathland bogs, cress-beds and small sewage works. In recent years Christchurch Harbour and Lodmoor NR have been the main sites for both wintering and passage birds – see Figs 29 and 30. Numbers were highest during the late 1970s and early 1980s, notably at Christchurch Harbour with winter maxima of 26 in December 1975 and a county record of 29+ during the cold weather in January 1982. A marked decline from the mid-1980s onwards resulted in very low winter maxima at both sites, which at Lodmoor NR coincided with the formation of the reserve and the consequent lack of public access to the areas preferred by the species.

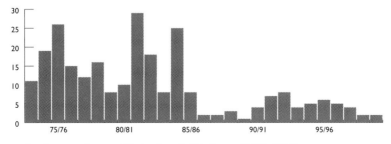

Fig 29. Winter/spring maxima at Christchurch Harbour 1974–1999

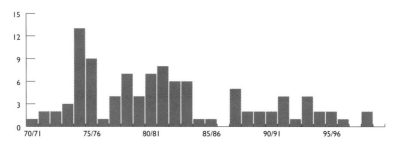

Fig 30. Winter/spring maxima at Lodmoor NR 1970–1999

	1970s	1980s	1990s
Christchurch Harbour	15	11	5
Lodmoor NR	5	4	2

Table 220. Winter/spring 10-year average peak counts at the main sites 1950–1999

There are several other favoured sites where records suggest that wintering has occurred fairly regularly over a number of years since 1950 – see Table 221. Otherwise there are occasional sightings from sites widely scattered throughout the county.

	Years Recorded	Winter Maxima
Cranborne CBs	1959–1965	11 on 15th January 1960, and in December 1962 and January 1963
Radipole NR	Most years 1969–1998	5 on 13th October 1981
West Bexington & Cogden Beach	1976–1984, 1991–1994 and 1997–1999	5 on 3rd February 1978
Lytchett Bay	1981, 1983–1985, 1996, 1997 and 1999	4 on 1st February 1996
Upton Heath	1982–1984, 1987–1988 and 1994	8 on 23rd January 1983
Wareham Water-meadows & Swineham	1983–1985, 1990 and 1997–1999	5 on 11th December 1984 and 4th November 1990
Compton Valence	1983–1986	1–2 birds
Charminster Water-meadows	1987, 1989–1993, 1995 and 1999	1–2 birds
Puddletown	1990–1996	1–2 birds
Abbotsbury	1991–1999	3 on 28th January and 26th February 1996
Winterborne Steepleton & Winterborne Abbas	1991–1998	6 on 31st December 1996

Table 221. Winter maxima at other favoured sites 1950–1999

Many birds have been recorded during periods of severe cold with notable influxes in December 1981 (c.28), January 1982 (c.48), December 1984 (c.21), February 1991 (c.22) and January 1997 (c.20+). During such conditions Jack Snipe often appear in more unusual localities such as Poole Park with singles on 12th January and 9th–10th February 1991, and Portland Bill including 2–4 birds during 11th–17th January 1982 and 1–3 birds in February 1986.

Passage in spring (March–April) and autumn (September–November) is indicated by peak counts at the main sites, notably 25 at Christchurch Harbour in March 1985 with 18 there in March 1983, and 13 at Lodmoor NR in October 1974, as well as reports from coastal watch-points such as Portland – see Table 222.

Mar	Apr	Sep	Oct	Nov
3	7	1	14	5

Table 222. Monthly totals of migrants at Portland 1950–1999

The majority of birds occur between September and April. There are a few records for August, the earliest being 2nd August 1968 with two at Wareham SF, whilst five at Bere Regis CBs on 17th August 1972 is noteworthy. The latest report is 14th May 1977 at Lodmoor NR – the only record for that month.

In earlier years, there were notable high counts of c.20 flushed by beaters during a snipe shoot near Cranborne on 23rd January 1958 and 20 near Wareham on 13th September 1959.

A total of 40 birds has been ringed in the county.

The Jack Snipe breeds locally in south Sweden and more widely from northern Scandinavia eastwards across Siberia to about 160°E. It winters in western and southern Europe, North Africa and the northern tropics of Africa, Asia Minor, the Middle East, the Indian sub-continent and parts of south-east Asia.

Sponsored by John Reeve

Snipe (Common Snipe)   *Gallinago gallinago*

A scarce resident, and fairly common winter visitor and passage migrant

Mansel-Pleydell (1888) described this species as "a winter visitant, many remaining on our moors and heaths to breed". Blathwayt (1945) referred to it as a numerous resident, but better known as a winter visitor and passage migrant.

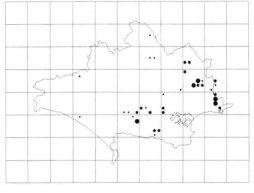

By 1951 the Snipe was considered to be a scarce and very local breeder in the county, being absent from large areas with no records from the Yeo/Wriggle Valleys during 1943–1951 and south-west Dorset during 1947–1951. Subsequently there has been a continuing decline in the breeding population, which has accelerated in recent years. The *BTO Atlas* (1968–1972) found evidence of breeding in 24 (65%) 10-km squares (confirmed in five, probable in nine and possible in ten). Although there were reports from widely scattered sites, most records of confirmed and probable breeding were confined to areas in or around the Poole Basin. By the time of the Tetrad Survey (1987–1994) evidence of breeding was recorded in only 12 (32%) of the pre-1974 10-km squares (confirmed in two, probable in five and possible in five). Additional reports during the Tetrad Survey involve a pair at Powerstock during the breeding season of 1992, and drumming males at Arne NR in 1987 and Godlingston Heath in 1988. If these additions are taken into account, breeding during the Tetrad Survey was recorded in 15 (41%) of the pre-1974 10-km squares (confirmed in two, probable in eight and possible in five). The Tetrad Map reflects the species' preference for breeding in wet flood meadows in river valleys, e.g. the Lower Avon Valley and upper River Allen, and extensive heathland bogs, e.g. Holt Heath NNR and various sites scattered in the centre and south of the Poole Basin.

The breeding population has seemingly continued its catastrophic decline throughout the late 1990s. The number of territories in the Lower Avon Valley between Sopley and Christchurch remained fairly stable during the 1980s, but declined during the 1990s almost to the point of extinction – see Table 223. The RSPB Survey in 1979 revealed that 81% of territories occurred in wet flood meadows. Although less well documented, a similar decline has taken place in the Allen Valley. In 1973 several pairs were present at Witchampton with one pair reported there in 1982, when a total of seven pairs were located in the valley as a whole. Regular surveys during 1989–1999 revealed an absence from the Witchampton area with a small population of 1–4 pairs surviving at 1–2 sites in the upper valley until at least 1997, but with no reports in 1998 and 1999. There is evidence of a decline elsewhere in the county. Drumming males were frequently reported from sites along the southern margins of Poole Harbour such as Studland NNR, Arne

NR and Ridge Moors up to 1988, but the only subsequent records involve about six pairs on Ridge Moors in 1995 and two drumming birds at Arne NR/Hartland Moor in 1999. Reports of drumming birds at Canford Heath and Bovington in 1999 suggest that a few birds may still survive at traditional breeding sites elsewhere in the Poole Basin. During the 1980s a pair breeding at Lodmoor NR in 1982 and a drumming male in the Bourne Valley near central Bournemouth in spring 1983 were noteworthy records. The effects of drainage schemes and the improvement of meadows in river valleys, exacerbated by the drought of the late 1980s and early 1990s, have clearly contributed to the species' decline as a breeding bird in Dorset as elsewhere in lowland Great Britain.

79	80	81	82	83	84	85	86	87	88	89	90	91	92	93	94	95	96	97	98	99
15	nc	nc	12	11	19	nc	10	nc	8	10	15	10	nc	2	5	5	nc	nc	3	1

Table 223. Number of breeding territories in Lower Avon Valley 1979–1999

Outside the breeding season, the Snipe occurs widely in suitable habitats both on the coast and inland. Like the breeding population, there has been a marked decline in wintering numbers in recent years – see Table 224. At Christchurch Harbour, which was once the main site for the species in winter, numbers declined dramatically during 1986/87–1991/92 followed by a partial recovery during 1992/93–1997/98 – see Table 225. There was an exceptional count of 1,000 birds at this site during the severe cold of January 1982.

	1960s	1970s	1980s	1990s
Christchurch Harbour	–	475	313	159
Lodmoor NR	98	112	329	81
Radipole NR	67	111	104	80

Table 224. Winter 10-year average peak counts at the main sites 1950–1999

1974/75–1985/86	1986/87–1991/92	1992/93–1997/98
480	53	230

Table 225. Winter average peak counts at Christchurch Harbour 1974–1998

In the Poole Harbour area most wintering birds frequent the wet fields and damp pastures adjacent to the harbour itself. During the 1980s winter maxima at such favoured sites as the Wareham Water-meadows and Lytchett Bay usually ranged between 100–200 birds, but 500 at the former locality during cold weather in January 1982 with 600 there in similar conditions on 2nd January 1984. Since 1991 numbers have declined with winter maxima only in double figures.

The main winter haunts in the Weymouth/Fleet area are Lodmoor NR, Radipole NR and Abbotsbury. At Lodmoor NR numbers were generally highest during the 1980s with winter maxima ranging between 70–350 birds, except for a cold weather peak of 1,000 in February 1982 and 600 on 12th March 1981. Nearby at Radipole NR winter maxima during 1970–1999 were usually lower and more variable, generally ranging between 40–200 birds except for a peak count of 285 on 1st January 1987. The wintering population at both sites has declined during the 1990s – see Table 224. During the 1980s there were several winter counts of 100–200 birds at Abbotsbury with 600+ there during the cold weather in December 1982, but seemingly smaller numbers have been recorded subsequently.

Inland, there has been a marked decline in the wintering population of Snipe in the Blackmore Vale area of the Stour Valley. During the 1970s large numbers occurred in the vicinity of Marnhull where winter maxima included 600 in December 1974, 1,000 in December 1976, 1,600 in December 1977, 2,000 in February 1980 and 500 in January and December 1981. In 1982 only 40+ were recorded and the comment made that numbers were much lower than in previous years due to drainage operations at the regular roost sites. Subsequently no large counts have been reported from Marnhull until 394 on 11th January 1995, which was the first count in excess of 100 from anywhere in the Blackmore Vale since 1982, with the exception of 140 at Motcombe on 25th December 1988. Elsewhere in the Stour Valley, the Wimborne area regularly attracted large numbers up to the early 1980s with several counts of up to 400 birds with a maximum of 406 at Merley on 23rd February 1978, but since then numbers have been much lower. Good numbers have been reported from other river valleys, notably the Lower Avon Valley (maximum of 350 at

Sopley on 4th March 1984), the Frome Valley (maximum of 251 at Wool on 15th January 1986), the Piddle Valley (maximum of 700+ at Puddletown on 29th January 1987), and the Allen Valley (maximum of 187 at Clapgate in January 1962). Lakes, cress-beds and heathland bogs can also support substantial numbers during the winter, for example 130 at Sherborne Lake on 19th November 1950, 110 at Cranborne CBs in January 1963, and between 100–200 birds at Upton Heath during the early 1980s.

Many of the high counts at the more regular winter sites result from influxes during periods of severe cold weather, when ice-free habitats along the coast and at inland locations such as cress-beds and small sewage works are frequently favoured. During these cold spells birds may also appear at more unusual sites along the coast, e.g. up to 70 at Portland Bill in January 1982, and elsewhere including gardens and town parks, e.g. three near the town centre of Bournemouth on 8th February 1991.

Small numbers are reported from the main coastal watch-points. For example, during 1976–1999 the average number of bird-days at Portland Bill was 3.4 (range 0–10) and 35.9 (range 17–65) for spring and autumn respectively with passage extending from March–May and July–December.

A total of 1,118 birds has been ringed in the county. There have been 14 recoveries from France, two each from the Netherlands, Denmark, Norway, Finland and the former USSR, one from Portugal, and one foreign control from Sweden.

The Snipe breeds widely across northern Eurasia and North America. The Eurasian population winters mainly in western and southern Europe, Asia Minor, North and the northern tropics of Africa, the Middle East, the Indian sub-continent and south-east Asia. There are also separate and partly resident populations in East and southern Africa and South America.

Postscript 2000–2002

The status of this species in the county remains precarious with only two reports of breeding in 2000 and one in 2001, and no passage or winter counts in excess of 100 birds in either year. There was some evidence of a slight improvement in 2002 with breeding reported from three sites including four pairs at Hartland Moor and a winter count of 200 at Christchurch Harbour in December.

Sponsored by Nick and Jackie Hull

Great Snipe   *Gallinago media*

A rare winter visitor and passage migrant prior to 20th Century, no recent records

Pulteney (1799) referred to one shot on the Dorset side of the River Avon in the winter of 1793, whilst a manuscript entry in Mr Dale's copy of Pulteney's List states "I have seen two or three Great or Solitary Snipes in Islington Wood". Mansel-Pleydell (1888) referred to records of one shot at Buckland Newton on an unspecified date, one near Binegar Hall, Wareham on 11th October 1880, one at Worgret Farm on an unspecified date, and one near Wool on 12th October 1885. In addition, singles were shot near Dorchester on 29th November 1866 and 20th September 1871. The species was last reported in the county on 10th October 1896 at Wareham.

The Great Snipe breeds from Scandinavia across eastern Europe to north-west Asia and winters throughout much of sub-Saharan Africa. A vagrant to Great Britain with 296 records up to 2002.

Long-billed Dowitcher   *Limnodromus scolopaceus*

Accidental: six records possibly only involving four individuals

Remarkably five of the six records occurred in 1976 and 1977, but those in the latter year may have only involved two birds.

1976	Arne NR: 3rd August
1977	Lodmoor NR: 28th September; same at Radipole NR 28th–30th September
	Radipole NR: probably a different individual from above 17th–18th October
	Sutton Bingham: first-winter 8th–22nd October
	The Fleet at Herbury Gore and Langton Herring: 10th December to at least 23rd February 1978
2000	Middlebere: juvenile/first-winter 7th–11th November

The Long-billed Dowitcher breeds in north-eastern Siberia and along the coasts of western and northern Alaska extending to extreme north-west Canada, and winters from western and southern USA south through Central America to Guatemala. A vagrant to Great Britain with 167 records up to 2002.

Woodcock (Eurasian Woodcock)　　　　　*Scolopax rusticola*

A locally common resident, winter visitor and passage migrant

The Woodcock was apparently not widely-known as a breeding bird in the 19th Century and earlier part of the 20th Century. Mansel-Pleydell (1888) described this species as "a regular winter visitant, a few pairs annually remaining to breed in favourable localities" and referred to a nest found in Clenston Wood in May 1869. Blathwayt (1945) considered it to be a regular winter visitor with a few pairs remaining to breed, but nesting was not noticed every year, and gives records of confirmed breeding from east Dorset in 1912, Lyme Regis in 1921 and Verwood in 1925.

By the time of the *BTO Atlas* (1967–1972), the Woodcock was widely distributed in suitable woodlands throughout much of Dorset, except the south, with evidence of breeding in 27 (73%) 10-km squares (confirmed in four, probable in nine and possible in 14). The Tetrad Survey (1987–1994) shows a decline with breeding recorded in 22 (59%) of the pre-1974 10-km squares (confirmed in five, probable in ten and possible in seven). This decline is associated with a marked change in distribution. The species has virtually disappeared from the extreme west and some of its northern haunts, while there is evidence of an increase in and around the Poole Basin in the east of the county.

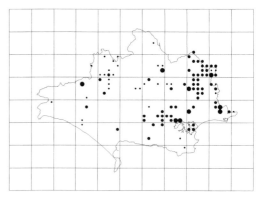

The Tetrad Map shows that the breeding population is concentrated in the Wareham Forest area and the east of Poole Basin, and extends to the chalk in the extreme north-east of Cranborne Chase. The Woodcock is scarce or absent on the remainder of the chalk downs, and from much of the Blackmore Vale except in the western part where there is a small population based in ST60 and ST61. It is also very scarce in south and west Dorset and, with the exception of possible breeding in one tetrad, the species is absent west of a line between Beaminster and Bridport. This distribution reflects the habitat preferences of this species, which favours broad-leaved and mixed woodlands with damp areas for feeding. They can also be found in conifer plantations up to the thicket stage, but tend to avoid monocultures of mature coniferous forests. The apparent scarcity in woodlands over much of the chalk is associated with the lack of suitable feeding areas. Since the Tetrad Survey (1987–1994) most breeding reports have been from the traditional areas in the east of the county, the most interesting exception being from Chickerell in 1997.

In winter, the Woodcock is more generally distributed throughout the county, being found in a wider variety of habitats including damp woodlands not occupied during the breeding season. Studland NNR and Arne NR are classic examples of such winter sites. Numbers are generally small, usually ranging from 1–8 birds, and rarely reaching double figures except during periods of severe cold when large scale immigrations may take place. In such conditions this inconspicuous species is often forced to seek refuge in more open habitats, particularly along the coast. In winter 1890/91 160 birds were shot in one week at Abbotsbury. Other large influxes occurred during 1947/48, 1962/63, 1978/79, January 1982, January 1985, February–March 1986, January–March 1987, February 1991 and January 1997, the highest counts being 65 at Portland Bill on 19th January 1985, 50 on the whole of Portland on 10th February 1991, up to 40 along the Fleet during 8th–20th February 1991, 32 at Radipole NR on 11th January 1982 and 22 at Portland Bill on 12th January 1982. During the severest of these cold spells, birds are sometimes found in more unusual sites such as suburban gardens. Up to 25 birds in Milton Woods during November–December 1980 would appear to be the highest count recorded during normal winter conditions.

The species is a rare coastal migrant in spring, mainly during March and April, with about nine records from Portland Bill and four from Durlston CP since 1980. More frequently reported during the autumn with peak passage occurring between mid-October and the end of November. Numbers are small with autumn totals ranging between 0–10 birds (average 2.8) at Portland Bill since 1980, and between 0–11 birds (average 4.5) at Durlston CP since 1983.

A total of 26 birds has been ringed in the county. There has been one foreign recovery from the former USSR and single controls from Denmark and the former USSR.

The Woodcock breeds over most of Europe north of 40°N and across central Asia to Japan with isolated populations in the Caucasus and Himalayas. It winters mainly in western and southern Europe, North Africa, Asia Minor and parts of southern Asia – most widely in the south-east.

Postscript 2000–2002
A count of 16 from the Sherborne Estate on 30th December 2000 is noteworthy.

Black-tailed Godwit   *Limosa limosa*

A locally common winter visitor and passage migrant

This species was a rare visitor in the 19th Century, Mansel-Pleydell (1888) listed only seven records involving ten birds up to 1882. Regular passage developed after about 1930, and Blathwayt (1945) referred to counts from Poole Harbour of 70–100 on 24th August 1935 and 400 on 13th March 1942.

By 1950 the Black-tailed Godwit had become a locally numerous passage migrant and winter visitor, principally to Poole Harbour. The highest counts typically occur during the spring reflecting passage, which can be particularly heavy in some years, whilst there are smaller peaks in late autumn and winter – see Table 226. Although numbers were relatively stable from 1950 to the mid-1980s, there has been a marked increase in both the passage and winter populations subsequently, resulting in a county record count of 2,046 in March 1995 with a winter peak of 1,895 in February 1998 and an autumn peak of 1,371 in October 1996 – see Table 227. Smaller numbers remain through the summer with counts in June rarely exceeding 100, the highest being 200 in 1991. Studies undertaken in the mid-1980s show that the main feeding areas changed seasonally, birds favouring Newton Bay, Fitzworth East and Wareham Water-meadows (when flooded) during the winter, but Wytch Lake, Middlebere, Fitzworth North, Round Island and Holes Bay in spring. The main roosting sites were Arne Spit, Cleavel Field, Ower, Green Island, Brownsea and Brand's Bay. A 1990s study concluded that at low water the key feeding areas in the harbour were Newton Bay, Arne Bay, Swineham, Gigger's Island and Holes Bay. In addition, Lytchett Bay has also become an important site for the species during the 1990s, particularly in spring. Currently Poole Harbour is Great Britain's fourth most important wintering site for the Black-tailed Godwit and holds c.7% of the British wintering population.

Jan	Feb	Mar	Apr	May	Jun	Jul	Aug	Sep	Oct	Nov	Dec
771	998	1243	976	112	56	136	457	644	788	691	915

Table 226. Average monthly maxima from Poole Harbour 1986–1999

	1950s	1960s	1970s	1980s	1990s
Spring (Mar–May)	633	402	488	683	1470
Autumn (Jul–Oct)	nc	160	388	512	928
Winter (Nov–Feb)	393	280	370	592	1419

Table 227. Spring, autumn and winter 10-yr average peak counts from Poole Harbour 1950–1999

The species is much less numerous elsewhere along the coast. At Christchurch Harbour it was a scarce visitor prior to 1990, being most frequently recorded in spring and autumn, but sporadically in winter. During the 1990s, however, the Black-tailed Godwit has become more regular, particularly in winter. Numbers are generally low with monthly maxima rarely exceeding 25 birds. There have been, however, several three-figure counts since 1990, but these are mainly isolated and, in the case of the 700 in January 1996, associated with cold weather. The exception to this was a series of high counts during 1993 with monthly maxima of 484, 107, 108, 178 and 150 for January, February, March, October and December respectively.

In the Weymouth area, it is a scarce but increasing visitor to Radipole and Lodmoor NRs and the Fleet with the majority of records occurring during passage. Numbers are generally low with monthly maxima rarely exceeding 25 birds. At Lodmoor NR 320 on 15th November 1986 was described as a freak occurrence, whilst at Radipole NR 120W on 10th February 1978 was an exceptional record, the highest count of settled birds at this site being 81 in October 1992. At West Bexington it is very rare with only about nine records during 1974–1999.

Inland, Black-tailed Godwits frequently wander to the wet fields and areas of temporary floodwater along the Lower Frome Valley as far upstream as Wool. Occasionally this can involve most if not all of the Poole Harbour population. For example, at East Holme there were 300–400 birds during February–March 1990 with peaks of 1,330 and 1,331 on 20th and 24th February, whilst other high counts include 450 on 21st November 1997, and 400 on 30th January and 330 on 11th December 1986. Although formerly only an occasional visitor to the Lower Avon Valley, records have increased since 1993 with several high counts including up to 300 during January–March 1993, 137 in February 1994 and 500 during 9th–11th March 1995. Good numbers were also present in April 1979 (maximum of 390 at Sopley on 10th). A record of 130W at Ramsdown Plantation near Hurn on 13th August 1985 is a curious report.

The species is rare elsewhere inland. There are only nine reports from the Stour Valley between Wimborne and Sturminster Marshall including 130 at Corfe Mullen on 10th February 1957 with 30 there on 11th January 1969. Otherwise there are a few records as follows:

1972 Bere Regis CBs: one in January
1976 Buckhorn Weston: one in March
1986 Puddletown: one on an unspecified date
1989 Sherborne Lake: one on 13th May

Coastal movements are rarely observed. At Portland Bill there are c.31 records, seven in spring and 24 in autumn, during 1959–1999. Day-totals are generally small, the highest counts being 36 on 17th August 1964, 24E on 19th August 1970, 23 on 6th September 1991 and 20N on 16th April 1978, also 43 passed on three dates from 23rd August to 5th September 1961. There are very few sightings from the Purbeck coast with 12 records from Durlston CP since 1984 and six records from St Aldhelm's Head since 1978, the best counts being from the former site with 21S on 7th June 1995 and 10 on 29th April 1996. In some years coastal movements are detected from Hengistbury, e.g. 80 on 29th August 1999, 35E on 13th May 1998, 22E on 18th March 1991, 67 bird-days during 26th May–25th August 1988, and 15 bird-days in April and 14 bird-days in August 1987.

A of total 75 birds has been ringed in the county. There is one foreign control from Iceland.

The Black-tailed Godwit breeds mainly in Iceland, the Netherlands, eastern Europe, and west-central and eastern Asia, also locally in other parts of western and central Europe including Great Britain. It winters in western and southern Europe, North Africa and the northern tropics of Africa, the Middle East, parts of the Indian sub-continent and south-east Asia, and Australia.

Postscript 2000–2002
In Poole Harbour, 2,501 in January 2000 is a record count for the site and county, exceeding the previous high of 2,046 in March 1995, whilst 2,115 in February 2002 is the second highest winter count from this site. One at Hatch Pond, Poole on 28th January 2000 is a notable inland record.

Bar-tailed Godwit   *Limosa lapponica*

A locally common winter visitor and passage migrant

Both Mansel-Pleydell (1888) and Blathwayt (1945) considered this species to be a regular passage migrant, but only an occasional visitor in winter.

By 1950 Poole Harbour had become a regular site and subsequently became the principal wintering haunt for the Bar-tailed Godwit in the county. During the 1950s and 1960s the winter population was typically between 30–100 birds, but since 1970 numbers have increased with winter maxima generally ranging between 100–250 birds – see Table 228. Higher counts have been recorded on several occasions, often during periods of cold weather, the most notable being 386 in January 1987 and 340 during January–February 1963. Although Sandbanks is the favoured area for both feeding and roosting birds within the harbour, this site has suffered from considerable disturbance in recent years. Brownsea is also an important roosting site, whilst more recently Arne NR has attracted good numbers in winter. Studies undertaken in the mid-1980s show that a small flock regularly inhabited the southern shore between Brand's Bay and Ower.

1950s	1960s	1970s	1980s	1990s
71	116	148	166	193

Table 228. Winter 10-year average peak counts from Poole Harbour 1950–1999

It is a scarce and erratic winter visitor to Christchurch Harbour and the Fleet. Numbers are low with most counts in single figures, rarely exceeding 20 birds, the highest being 80 at Christchurch Harbour in January 1993, which coincided with a high count in Poole Harbour, and 50 on the Fleet during the severe cold of January 1987. It is very rare elsewhere in winter.

Although variable in strength from year to year, spring migration is typically heavier than in autumn and sometimes results in spectacular coastal movements, which are predominantly easterly in direction – see Tables 229 and 230.

70	71	72	73	74	75	76	77	78	79	80	81	82	83	84
nc	39	15	nc	373	2562	1130	377	588	53	162	45	62	329	681

85	86	87	88	89	90	91	92	93	94	95	96	97	98	99
634	90	872	68	296	386	519	81	478	221	375	732	473	55	370

Table 229. Spring totals for coastal movements at Portland Bill 1970–1999

Spring passage generally extends from early April to early June, but peaks during a relatively short period in late April and early May, and in some years it can be concentrated in 2–3 days, e.g. 26th–27th April 1975, 2nd–3rd May 1980, 1st–2nd May 1986 and 2nd–4th May 1990. Movements were particularly

	1980	1981	1982	1983	1984	1985	1986	1987	1988	1989
Durlston CP	60	25	26	33	2344	180	728	747	1007	332
St Aldhelm's Hd	nc	155	nc	nc	4188	152	1024	329	829	828

	1990	1991	1992	1993	1994	1995	1996	1997	1998	1999
Durlston CP	1149	434	333	nc	193	2436	501	547	646	436
St Aldhelm's Hd	1893	176	73	1725	255	nc	669	2072	nc	nc

Table 230. Spring totals for coastal movements at Durlston CP and St Aldhelm's Head 1980–1999

heavy in the springs of 1975 and 1984. On 26th April 1975 easterly movements involving 1,820 at Hengistbury, 1,500 at Portland Bill, 300 at West Bexington and 150 at Portland Harbour were recorded, and on the following day passage involved 1,016 at Hengistbury and 1,015 at Portland Bill. In April 1984 there were easterly movements involving 1,266 including a single flock of 250 birds at St Aldhelm's Head on 27th with 2,424 including a single flock of 160 birds there on 29th, whilst nearby at Durlston CP there were 640 including an incredible single flock of 420 birds on 27th with 720 there on 30th. Heavy movements were also recorded from Portland Bill in 1962 with 1,732E during 25th–29th April, and in 1976 with 1,110E during 19th April–5th May including 705 on 21st April. Heavy spring passage also occurred at the Chesil in 1994 and 1995 with 626 (reaching a maximum of 300E on 22nd April) and 868 during 1st–5th May (maximum of 393E on 4th) respectively. Although a heavy movement of 1,859E occurred at St Aldhelm's Head on 21st April 1997, smaller numbers were reported elsewhere that spring.

Coastal movements are complex in the Weymouth area as birds sometimes overfly the Chesil rather than pass Portland Bill. For example, seasonal totals in spring 1988 involved 301 at the Chesil, but only 68 at Portland Bill, whilst in spring 1999 the seasonal total of 370 at Portland Bill was exceeded by a single day-total of 426E at the Chesil on 30th April. There are also occasional heavy movements reported from Radipole NR including 799E on 29th April 1984 and 302E on 27th April 1982, and Lodmoor NR including 253E on 27th April 1985 and 155E on 26th April 1994. This passage of birds over the Chesil may also explain the discrepancy in some years between numbers passing Portland Bill and those moving along the Purbeck coast further east – see Tables 229 and 230.

Christchurch Harbour, Poole Harbour and the Fleet are the main sites for settled migrants – see Tables 231 to 233. Spring maxima are normally in double figures, but occasionally exceed 100 birds. These isolated high counts are often, but not invariably, associated with heavy visual movements, e.g. 650 on the Fleet on 28th April 1984 with 600 there next day, a monthly maxima of 302 at Christchurch Harbour also in April 1984, and 200 at Brownsea on 26th April 1975. High counts of settled birds from earlier years includes 465 along the whole Fleet on 3rd May 1971. Elsewhere the species is regularly recorded from Radipole and Lodmoor NRs in spring with maxima generally in single figures and counts rarely exceeding 20 birds, but 87 were at Lodmoor NR on 25th April 1980. There are also a few spring reports from West Bexington. Studies undertaken in the mid-1980s show that within Poole Harbour the main areas for feeding and roosting in spring were different to those used in winter, Arne NR and Wytch Lake being the favoured sites.

70	71	72	73	74	75	76	77	78	79	80	81	82	83	84
–	–	–	–	nc	nc	186	nc	54	67	86	52	28	12	302

85	86	87	88	89	90	91	92	93	94	95	96	97	98	99
81	27	30	123	87	50	246	52	67	62	42	8	40	38	20

Table 231. Spring maxima of settled birds from Christchurch Harbour 1974–1999

70	71	72	73	74	75	76	77	78	79	80	81	82	83	84
nc	43	34	30	26	200	53	33	nc	50	22	20	47	26	75

85	86	87	88	89	90	91	92	93	94	95	96	97	98	99
60	69	15	49	117	30	18	126	14	21	24	24	85	12	28

Table 232. Spring maxima of settled birds from Poole Harbour 1970–1999

70	71	72	73	74	75	76	77	78	79	80	81	82	83	84
20	465	63	34	170	nc	130	nc	90	nc	28	24	43	2	650

85	86	87	88	89	90	91	92	93	94	95	96	97	98	99
20	20	90	50	70	300	82	5	132	110	190	40	60	46	1

Table 233. Spring maxima of settled birds from the Fleet 1970–1999

The strength of migration is smaller in autumn and mainly involves reports of settled birds. In Poole Harbour passage is reflected by a small peak in September. Numbers are low and rarely exceed 50 birds, but occasionally there are isolated high counts such as 180 at Holton Shore on 17th September 1980, 162 at Brownsea in September 1976, and monthly maxima for the harbour of 150 in September 1991 and 119 in October 1988. At Christchurch Harbour, autumn maxima are generally less than 30 birds with occasional higher counts including 115 in September 1988, which coincided with high autumn numbers in Poole Harbour and along the Fleet. The bird is a regular but rather scarce autumn visitor to the Weymouth area with counts rarely exceeding ten birds, the highest being 40 on the Fleet in September 1988.

Coastal movements are virtually non-existent in autumn. At Portland Bill, bird-day totals have reached double figures in only six years since 1973, so 110W on 18th August 1973 and 100+ on 4th September 1963 are exceptional records. The species is rarely observed from the Purbeck coast in autumn, although 32 bird-days were recorded at Durlston CP in 1988. A report of 32E at West Bexington on 3rd September 1993 is noteworthy.

Apart from West Bexington in spring, there are very few records from the west of the county, the most notable being 20 at Lyme Regis on 4th February 1954.

The species is very rare inland with only seven records, all but two within a few miles of the coast:

1962   Clapgate near Wimborne: 40 flying south 15th August
1978   Sopley Wood: 30 flying south 12th March
1980   River Stour at Corfe Mullen: one with Whimbrel 1st May
1981   Puncknowle: one flying east 21st July
1983   Nottington: two flying north-west 9th May
1987   Coward's Marsh, Christchurch: 15th January
1993   Burton near Christchurch: small flock flying south 4th May

A total of 231 birds has been ringed in the county and there has been one foreign recovery from France.

The Bar-tailed Godwit breeds across the northernmost mainland tundra from Scandinavia eastwards through Asia to Alaska. It winters on the coasts of western Europe, the Mediterranean, Africa (mainly the Atlantic coast), the Red Sea and the Persian Gulf, the western Indian Ocean (including islands), south-east Asia, Australasia and western Polynesia.

Postscript 2000–2002

At Christchurch Harbour, a movement of 60S on 8th December 2000 was unusual for the time of year.

Whimbrel   *Numenius phaeopus*

A locally common passage migrant and rare winter visitor

Both Mansel-Pleydell (1888) and Blathwayt (1945) considered this species to be a regular passage migrant, the former referring to its local name 'Chickerel' and recording the presence of up to 200 on the sandy shores of Little Sea in spring.

There has been little change in status since and the Whimbrel has continued to be a regular passage migrant, typically far more numerous in spring than autumn.

In spring the first migrants occasionally appear during the first half of March, the earliest being 7th March 1994 at East Fleet, 8th and 10th March 1983 at Portland Bill and 9th March 1991 at Abbotsbury. Since the 1950s the average date of the first arrivals has gradually become earlier – see Table 234. The main passage period extends from late March or early April to late May with stragglers into early June. The heaviest movements, however, generally occur in late April and early May (cf Bar-tailed Godwit).

	1950–1959	1960–1969	1970–1979	1980–1989	1990–1999
Range	11th–19th April	22nd March–22nd April	3rd–18th April	8th March–9th April	7th–31st March
Average	16th April	10th April	9th April	28th March	18th March

Table 234. Dates for first spring arrivals each decade 1950–1999

During the 1950s and early 1960s spring passage was modest with peak counts rarely exceeding 30 birds. Since 1967 numbers have increased markedly, notably in Poole Harbour where evening easterly movements were a major feature at Arne NR from 1968 to at least 1987. In some springs these movements were particularly heavy, the best counts being in 1973 with 2,493E (maximum of 356 on 6th May), and 1977 with 3,360E (maximum of 397 on 1st May) – see Table 235. There are occasional reports of similar movements from elsewhere in the harbour, notably 200E at Brownsea on 27th April 1984. In more recent years the highest counts in Poole Harbour have been recorded from Fitzworth with 250 on 25th April 1990 and 200 on 10th May 1988, 6th May 1989 and in April 1991, Lytchett Bay with 157 on 27th April 1996 and 145 in April 1983, and Holes Bay with 120SW on 29th April 1998.

	1968	1969	1970	1971	1972	1973	1974	1975	1976	1977
Bds	nc	nc	700	1331	2070	2493	1146	500	2032	3360
Max	290	250	195	175	–	356	–	–	177	397

	1978	1979	1980	1981	1982	1983	1984	1985	1986	1987
Bds	1046	nc	1193	870	749	940	1726	nc	nc	600
Max	–	–	50	270	–	–	200	150	131	150

Table 235. Spring easterly evening movements at Arne NR 1968–1987

Christchurch Harbour is also a good site for spring Whimbrel with peak counts often in excess of 50 birds, but rarely over 100, the best being in 1994 with maxima of 417 in April and 471 in May, also 127 in April 1992 and 120 in late April 1980 – see Table 236.

1980	1981	1982	1983	1984	1985	1986	1987	1988	1989
120	42	72	65	28	28	nc	28	27	33

1990	1991	1992	1993	1994	1995	1996	1997	1998	1999
46	65	127	72	471	38	nc	65	39	nc

Table 236. Spring maxima at Christchurch Harbour 1980–1999

Since the late 1970s, inland feeding flocks have become a feature of the spring in the east of the county. Birds seem to favour the main river valleys and poorer quality pastures around the margins of heathland. Although the Stour Valley between Corfe Mullen and Sturminster Marshall was a regular site during 1978–1987, records have been more erratic in recent years. Numbers were generally small, but peak counts of 80 on 4th May 1985 and 110 on 27th April 1986 – see Table 237.

	1978	1979	1980	1981	1982	1983	1984	1985	1986	1987	1988
Bds	19	48	30	58	43	89	54	342	455	44	1
Max	10	13	13	40	31	45	17	80	110	27	1

	1989	1990	1991	1992	1993	1994	1995	1996	1997	1998	1999
Bds	1	74	61	1	45	31	23	63	15	0	0
Max	1	17	58	1	31	20	7	30	15	0	0

Table 237. Spring feeding flocks in Stour Valley between Corfe Mullen and Sturminster Marshall 1978–1999

Other favoured sites for inland feeding include the Sherford Bridge/Organford area (maxima of 95 on 5th May 1991 and 90 during 29th April–3rd May 1980), Holt Heath NNR (maximum of 100 during 28th April–2nd May 1990), Lower Common/Moors Valley CP (maximum of 150 on 7th May 1991) and the Lower Avon Valley. There is evidence to show that these inland birds move to roost in Poole Harbour at night, e.g. 170 birds flew south over Canford Heath during the hour prior to dusk on 3rd May 1983. Similarly small flocks are sometimes seen flying south at dusk over Holt Heath NNR and Colehill. These roosting movements of inland feeders may have accounted for the evening passage of birds at Arne NR.

In the Weymouth area, Lodmoor NR and the Fleet are the main sites for settled birds in spring. Numbers are typically lower than in the east of the county with peak counts generally less than 50 birds, sometimes in single figures, the best counts being 100 at Lodmoor NR in May 1994 with 68 there in April 1983, 65 at Radipole NR on 9th May 1984 and 60 at Abbotsbury on 5th May 1960.

Like the previous species, easterly coastal movements can be prominent in spring – see Table 238. Peak day-totals are usually below 50 and rarely exceed 100 birds, the highest being recorded from Christchurch Harbour with 291 on 13th May 1985, the Chesil with 250 on 22nd April 1994, 150 on 8th May 1987 and 123 on 21st April 1996, St Aldhelm's Head with 200 on 25th April 1972 and 26th April 1976, 146 and 162 on 20th and 21st April 1996 and 139 on 7th May 1993, and Portland Bill with 120 on 22nd April 1987. The best day-total at Durlston CP is 82 on 21st April 1996, whilst 140 at West Bexington on an unspecified date in April 1998 and 102E at Lodmoor NR on 27th April 1985 are also noteworthy. Again movements in the Weymouth area are complicated by the fact that birds sometimes overfly the Chesil rather than pass Portland Bill. This may explain the discrepancy in some years between numbers passing Portland Bill and elsewhere along the Dorset coast. For example, in 1992 East Bexington recorded 608 bird-days with a peak of 105 on 24th April, but Portland Bill only recorded 247 bird-days with a peak of 33 on 23rd April.

	1980	1981	1982	1983	1984	1985	1986	1987	1988	1989
Portland Bill	108	94	184	132	275	204	194	457	179	175
St Aldhelm's Hd	nc	79	16	12	143	140	120	448	201	258
Durlston CP	nc	28	18	26	136	125	95	323	177	178

	1990	1991	1992	1993	1994	1995	1996	1997	1998	1999
Portland Bill	160	315	247	579	230	173	364	182	169	229
St Aldhelm's Hd	222	270	91	482	378	nc	582	418	nc	nc
Durlston CP	247	154	144	156	206	327	385	208	260	225

Table 238. Spring totals for coastal movements at the main watch-points 1980–1999

A few birds occur mainly at coastal sites throughout June including both late spring and early autumn migrants. Autumn passage quickly builds up to peak during July–August and then gradually declines during September–October with occasional stragglers through to November. Numbers are generally much lower than in spring with autumn maxima in Poole Harbour usually ranging between 20–35 birds, the highest counts being 120 at Brownsea on 21st August 1967, 72 in August 1992 and 65 in July 1994. Elsewhere on the coast counts of settled birds rarely exceed 12 birds. Inland autumn feeding flocks were regularly present in the Stour Valley between Corfe Mullen and Sturminster Marshall during 1977–1987 but not subsequently – see Table 239. There is no evidence of inland feeding elsewhere in the east of the county during the autumn.

	1977	1978	1979	1980	1981	1982	1983	1984	1985	1986	1987
Bds	–	94	110	71	58	28	50	1	292	36	26
Max	40	65	31	15	18	6	25	1	55	15	14

Table 239. Autumn feeding flocks in Stour Valley between Corfe Mullen and Sturminster Marshall 1977–1987

Coastal movements, which are generally westerly, are much smaller in autumn than in spring with seasonal totals generally ranging between 20–80 bird-days at Portland Bill and Durlston CP. High counts of 100 at Portland Bill during the night of 4th/5th September 1961 and 42 there on 28th July 1988 are particularly notable.

Otherwise small parties of settled and moving birds are recorded both in spring and autumn from other coastal and inland sites throughout the county, the familiar call being often heard at night.

Although wintering birds are rare, there are records from Poole Harbour in 1960 and all but eight winters since 1970/71. Most reports refer to single birds, but six at Fitzworth on 27th February 1996, up to four at Upton CP on 23rd–24th January 1989 and three possible wintering birds at Parkstone on 14th March 1972. At Christchurch Harbour singles were recorded in December 1982, January 1985, December 1987 and January 1992. Elsewhere three flew south at the Chesil as part of a cold weather movement on 26th December 1961 and there was one inland in the Stour Valley at Corfe Mullen on 6th and 28th January 1988.

A total of 153 birds has been ringed in the county and there have been two recoveries and one control from France.

The Whimbrel has a patchy Holarctic breeding distribution mainly between 55°N and 70°N, which includes Iceland, Scandinavia and the Northern Isles of Scotland. It winters along the coasts of all five continents between 40°N and 60°S and occurs widely as a passage migrant.

Postscript 2000–2002
Coastal movements of 160NE at Peveril Point on 9th May 2001 and 120 at Winspit on 2nd May 2000 are noteworthy.

Curlew (Eurasian Curlew)   *Numenius arquata*

A scarce resident, and locally common winter visitor and passage migrant

This species apparently first bred during the 1870s in the neighbourhood of Poole Harbour. There was a marked expansion during the first half the 20th Century with breeding spreading to the heaths near Dorchester and Verwood by 1920, other eastern heaths and the Marshwood Vale from 1935, and the Blackmore Vale from 1944. This formed part of a national expansion of the population from the traditional upland areas to river valleys and low heather moors.

As a result of this continued expansion through-out the 1950s and 1960s, the *BTO Atlas* (1968–1972) recorded breeding in 21 (57%) 10-km squares (confirmed in 12, probable in three and possible in six). The population was concentrated in two main areas, the Blackmore Vale and the heaths of Poole Basin. Subsequently there has been a marked decline, the Tetrad Survey (1987–1994) finding evidence of breeding in only nine (24%) of the pre-1974 10-km squares (confirmed in 2, probable in three and possible in four).

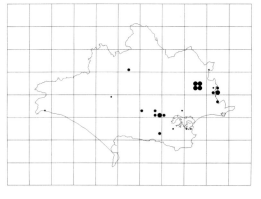

This decline is most evident in the Blackmore Vale where the Curlew was apparently well-established during the 1970s, but had ceased breeding by the late 1980s. In the Poole Basin the species has also disappeared from a number of traditional heathland sites, being largely confined to the Wareham Forest area and Holt Heath NNR during the Tetrad Survey (1987–1994). In 1990 territorial behaviour was noted in the Avon Valley for the first time since 1954, but seemingly there have been no further reports. The reasons for the collapse in the breeding population are not clear. In the Blackmore Vale it is likely to have been associated with loss of habitat through land drainage, perhaps exacerbated by the drought conditions in the late 1980s. On the heaths, loss of habitat and increasing disturbance may be contributory factors. The population has continued to decline since the Tetrad Survey (1987–1994) with Holt Heath NNR seemingly the last regular breeding site in the county, although there are still occasional reports from the Wareham Forest area and other heaths in the west of the Poole Basin.

There is little consistent information on the size of the breeding population, the most notable records being eight pairs in the Folke/Holnest area south of Sherborne in 1950, where only one pair was present in 1944, four pairs at Lydlinch in 1967 and 1969, four pairs at Cranborne Common in 1955 and 1966, declining to two in 1978 and 1979 and one in 1985 and 1986, and finally 2–3 pairs at Holt Heath NNR from 1960 to at least 1999.

Poole Harbour is the main site for passage and wintering birds, the latter population being of national importance. Studies undertaken in the mid-1980s concluded that wintering numbers had not changed significantly since the winters of 1950/51 and 1951/52, when the population level was reported to be in the region of 700–1,400 birds. Since the mid-1980s, there has been an increase in the winter population with maxima generally ranging from 1,200–1,800 birds, the highest count being a county record 1,912 in January 1993 – see Table 240. Spring passage is difficult to detect as numbers decline rapidly from March to their lowest levels in May. Autumn passage is more prominent, the first birds appearing from mid-June with numbers rapidly increasing during August–October. In some autumns peak counts can be substantial and similar to those recorded in mid-winter. Like the winter population, autumn numbers have also increased during the 1990s with maxima generally ranging between 1,200–1,450 birds compared to 500–1,200 during 1950–1989, the highest being 1,899 on 11th October 1953 and 1,784 in September 1996– see Table 240.

	1960s	1970s	1980s	1990s
Winter	528	913	1269	1681
Autumn	718	688	826	1354

Table 240. Winter and autumn 10-year average peak counts from Poole Harbour 1950–1999

Studies undertaken in the mid-1980s show that the most favoured feeding areas at low tide were mainly located along the southern and western shores of the harbour including Brand's Bay, South Lake, Fitzworth, Round Island, Swineham, Holton Shore and Holes Bay. At high tide feeding occurred in fields close to the harbour shores, the main sites being Brand's Bay, Cleavel, Ower, Fitzworth, Wareham Water-meadows and Keysworth. The other important high tide roosts were located at Brownsea, Arne Bay and Holton Shore. A later study undertaken in the 1990s concludes that the most important feeding areas were situated on the western side of the harbour, notably the extensive mudflats immediately adjacent to the confluence of the Frome and Piddle, and the Wytch Channel. These key areas may also be important to Curlew as they are adjacent to, or only a short distance from agricultural land in and around the river valleys, where birds can find roosting and feeding sites at high water.

Much smaller numbers occur at other coastal sites. Birds are recorded from Christchurch Harbour in all months, but maxima are low and rarely exceed 40 birds during the late summer and autumn, and 30 birds in mid-winter. Like in Poole Harbour, both the autumn and winter populations have increased during the 1990s with peak counts of 72 in June 1991 and 76 in December 1995 – see Table 241. The previous highest count for the harbour was 60 in April 1974.

	1980s	1990s
Winter	15	28
Autumn	22	39

Table 241. Winter and autumn 10-year average peak counts from Christchurch Harbour 1980–1999

In the Weymouth area, the species is regularly recorded from the Fleet with fewer reports from Lodmoor NR and only occasional sightings from Radipole NR. On the Fleet numbers are generally highest in winter, but counts rarely exceed 20 birds, the main exceptions being in winter 1988/89 when between 31–51 birds were present during November–March (peak in March), and 50 in January 1997. At Lodmoor NR the peak time for the Curlew is March when counts may sometimes reach double figures, e.g. 25 in 1988, 12 in 1990 and 11 in 1987. Otherwise records usually involve only 1–3 birds and rarely exceed five.

Although only an occasional visitor to West Bexington, there does appear to be a regular flock in autumn and winter further west in the Charmouth/Lyme Regis area. Reports of six on 29th–30th December 1982, 12 on 21st October 1983 and 32 on 23rd November 1983 were followed by regular sightings from

January 1992 to January 1994 with up to 45 during September–December 1992 and 28 in October 1993. On Purbeck, records suggest that the species wintered regularly at Kimmeridge Bay between 1975/76 and 1980/81 with annual maxima of 23, 40, nc, 30, 19, 16.

Inland, small numbers have regularly wintered in the Lower Avon Valley up to 1995 at least, the highest counts being 17 in February 1984 and November 1995. Regular wintering also occurred in the Stour Valley between Corfe Mullen and Sturminster Marshall up to 1982 reaching peaks of 43 in 1979 and 32 in 1970. Subsequently the species has become a scarce and erratic visitor to this part of the Stour Valley. Otherwise there are scattered reports from other inland areas. Numbers are generally small, so counts of 75 at Deadmoor Common in February 1975, 60 roosting at Holt Heath NNR on 28th July 1991, 41 near Corfe Castle on 19th January 1982 and 40SE at Buckland Newton on 26th June 1981 are noteworthy.

Although coastal movements occur throughout the year, most records are for spring and autumn. Numbers are generally small with monthly totals at the main coastal watch-points often in single figures and rarely exceeding 20 bird-days. At Portland Bill 63 bird-days in April 1988 and 54 bird-days in April 1976 and March 1987 are high for this site, while at Durlston CP 100+ on 5th March 1984 is an exceptional count. High daily totals have been occasionally recorded from Hengistbury, notably 77W on 19th April 1982, 66W on 28th June 1991 and 60W on 15th September 1974.

A total of 677 birds has been ringed in the county. There have been five foreign recoveries from Germany, three from Finland and one each from Sweden, Denmark, the Netherlands, France and Portugal, as well as two foreign controls from Germany. The Swedish recovery in July 1974 followed ringing at Brownsea in January 1967 and control there in November 1971.

The Curlew breeds across much of Europe, except Iceland and the Mediterranean countries, and across central Asia to about 120°E. It winters mainly on the coasts of western Europe, the Mediterranean Basin, most of Africa and south and east Asia.

Postscript 2000–2002

Although breeding was not confirmed, there were reports from six potential nesting sites in 2000 , but none in 2001 and only one in 2002.

Upland Sandpiper   *Bartramia longicauda*

Accidental: one record

1976   Portland Bill: 15th September

The Upland Sandpiper breeds from Alaska through west-central Canada to the north-central and north-east USA, and winters mainly in southern South America. A vagrant to Great Britain with 44 records up to 2002.

Sponsored by John Blackburn

Spotted Redshank   *Tringa erythropus*

An uncommon passage migrant and winter visitor

The Spotted Redshank was a rare visitor until 50 years ago. Mansel-Pleydell (1888) referred to only three records with one shot at Weymouth on 7th September 1853, one at Lodmoor on 1st September 1856 and one shot in Poole Harbour on 8th September 1877, whilst Blathwayt (1945) listed a further seven sightings between 1929 and 1943.

During the 1950s reports became more frequent with a marked increase from 1961 onwards. Numbers reached their peak from the late 1960s to the mid-1980s before a subsequent decline. The species is mainly a passage migrant, being most numerous during the autumn, with smaller numbers in winter. Spring passage mainly takes place between mid-April and mid-May, whilst peak autumn counts usually occur in August and September.

Poole Harbour is the main site for both passage and wintering birds. Numbers were at their highest during 1968–1983 when autumn maxima generally ranged between 90–175 birds, the best being a county record count of 228 at Brownsea on 26th September 1977 with 220 at the same site on 7th October 1968. During this period, spring maxima generally ranged between 20–45 birds, the highest being 46 at Arne

NR in late April 1971, whilst winter peaks varied between 8–19 birds. Since the mid-1980s there has been a rapid decline in numbers, most notably during autumn passage – see Table 242. By the late 1990s, peak counts at times of passage did not exceed 15 birds.

Although there are records from sites scattered throughout the harbour, three localities have been particularly favoured during the last 30 years. In the late 1960s and during the 1970s Arne NR and Brownsea were the main haunts, the species showing a marked preference for the former during the spring. The importance of these sites diminished as numbers declined from the mid-1980s onwards. During the early 1980s Lytchett Bay became the favoured locality for spring migrants, and by the mid-1990s this site had become the main haunt for birds in spring and autumn, but wintering individuals tended to frequent nearby Holes Bay.

	1950s	1960s	1970s	1980s	1990s
Spring	<1	9	28	27	13
Autumn	4	62	123	90	26
Winter	2	9	15	7	5

Table 242. Spring, autumn and winter 10-year average peak counts from Poole Harbour 1950–1999

At Christchurch Harbour the species is regularly recorded during the autumn, but less frequently in spring and winter. Monthly maxima are usually between 1–5 and rarely exceed ten birds, the highest counts being 20 in August 1989, 16 in May 1987, 15 in August 1981 and 14 in April 1985.

Although perhaps commoner during the late 1960s and early 1970s, the Spotted Redshank is now a scarce, but annual visitor to the Weymouth/Fleet area. Most reports are from Radipole and Lodmoor NRs, the latter being the favoured site in more recent years. It occurs mainly in autumn, being infrequent in spring and rare in winter. Most records involve 1–3 birds with no counts exceeding seven, except for 12 on the Fleet on 2nd May 1990 and ten at Lodmoor NR on 31st August 1965. Further west at West Bexington, there were eight spring records during 1972–1984 with five sightings in 1984 including three on 28th April, whilst singles on 8th March 1998 and 19th August 1999 are the only subsequent reports from this site.

Inland there are c.20 records during 1966–1994 with seven sightings from the Lower Avon Valley including a few at Winkton on 17th February 1979, three at Avon Causeway on 3rd May 1980 and up to three at Coward's Marsh, Christchurch from 17th November to 2nd December 1994. There are also three reports from the Stour Valley between Wimborne and Corfe Mullen including two at Lake Gate floods on 17th November 1982, and two reports from the Lower Frome Valley. The remaining eight inland records are as follows:

1966   Clayesmore School: 4th March
1968   Came Park: 9th April
1973   Sherborne: 23rd September
1974   Morden Bog: two 26th August
1980   Warmwell: 20th August
1985   Avon Forest Park: 24th April
1987   Radipole School: 17th August
1989   Nether Cerne: two 2nd May

Although coastal movements occur infrequently, there are c.54 records from Portland since 1956 with 52 in autumn, including 50 during August–September, and two in spring involving singles on 17th May 1984 and 2nd May 1994. Typically there are 1–4 sightings each year, the exception being ten birds during 20th August–24th September 1974. There are only eight reports from the Purbeck coast with five at Durlston CP, two at St Aldhelm's Head and one at White Nothe. Elsewhere there are several records from Christchurch Harbour including 5N on 1st May 1984, 5E on 18th September 1988 and 5W on 4th September 1999, and single sightings from East Bexington, the Chesil and Portland Harbour.

A total of ten birds has been ringed in the county.

The Spotted Redshank breeds across the tundra zone from northern Scandinavia eastwards across Siberia. It mainly winters in western and southern Europe, North Africa and the northern tropics of Africa, Asia Minor, the Middle East, the Indian sub-continent and south-east Asia.

Postscript 2000–2002
Numbers in the county continue at a low level with seasonal peaks of 12 in autumn and seven in spring at Lytchett Bay, the main site for the species, and seven in winter at nearby Holes Bay.

Sponsored by Phyl England

Redshank (Common Redshank) *Tringa totanus*

An uncommon resident, and fairly common winter visitor and passage migrant

Mansel-Pleydell (1888) described this species as "one of our commonest wading birds". It seemingly first bred in about 1880 and rapidly became established over a wide area around Poole Harbour and in east Dorset, subsequently spreading westwards up the Frome Valley to Dorchester, also to the Weymouth area, and sparingly to Abbotsbury by 1921 and possibly further west by 1932.

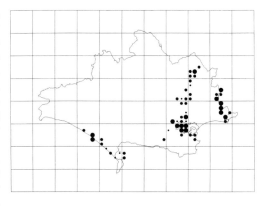

The population then remained stable until 1963 when the severe winter caused drastic reductions, which was followed by a steady recovery so that by the time of the *BTO Atlas* (1968–1972) there was evidence of breeding in 15 (41%) 10-km squares (confirmed in eight, probable in six and possible in one). Most of these 10-km squares were in the south and east of the county. Like elsewhere in lowland Great Britain, there has been a decline in the breeding population. This is reflected by the Tetrad Survey (1987–1994) when breeding was recorded in 11 (30%) of the pre-1974 10-km squares (confirmed in four and probable in seven). The Tetrad Map shows that breeding is concentrated along the eastern river valleys, around Poole Harbour and along the Fleet.

Poole Harbour is the stronghold for the coastal population. Although breeding has been reported from sites scattered throughout the harbour, the majority breed on the saltmarshes along the western shoreline between Arne NR and Lytchett Bay. At Arne NR there has been an increase in breeding numbers from 6–8 pairs during 1966–1971 to 10–12 pairs during 1972–1977, 15 pairs during 1978–1992 and 25 pairs in 1995, whilst 20 pairs at Swineham and Keysworth in 1992 with 12–15 pairs there in 1982 are the only other counts in double figures. In 1985 the breeding population of the entire harbour was estimated at 50–100 pairs, whilst further surveys in the 1990s revealed at least 103 territories in 1994 and at least 85 pairs in 1997.

The Fleet and Chesil Beach supported a good breeding population from at least 1967 to 1984 with numbers increasing during the late 1970s and early 1980s as a result of wardening – see Table 243. Since then, the only published reports involve single pairs in 1987, 1990, 1991, 1994 and 1996 with two pairs in 1998 and probable breeding recorded in 1999. Nearby breeding occurred at the unusual site of the Portland Harbour Breakwaters in 1986 and 1988.

67	68	69	70	71	72	73	74	75	76	77	78	79	80	81	82	83	84
15	15	nc	15	12	10	12	nc	5	15	15	nc	nc	15	24	22	27	12

Table 243. Number of breeding pairs along the Fleet and Chesil Beach 1967–1984

The species bred fairly regularly at Lodmoor NR and West Bexington from at least the late 1960s (probably earlier) to the early 1980s, but not subsequently except for probable breeding at the latter site during the Tetrad Survey (1987–1994). Display has also been noted at Radipole NR without any proof of breeding. At Christchurch Harbour up to eight pairs bred during the 1970s, but subsequently the only reports of breeding appear to be in 1984 and during the Tetrad Survey (1987–1994).

The recent decline in the breeding population is most obvious inland. Numbers in the Lower Avon Valley fell between 1979 and 1987, but after a period of relative stability during 1987–1993 increased temporarily in 1995, before declining dramatically during 1997–1999 – see Table 244. It should be noted, however, that the figures for 1997–1999 were described as under-estimates. The RSPB Survey in 1979 revealed that 85% of territories occurred in wet flood meadows.

1979	1980	1981	1982	1983	1984	1985	1986	1987	1988	1989
57	nc	nc	42	23	38	nc	25+	10	10	11–16

1990	1991	1992	1993	1994	1995	1996	1997	1998	1999	2000
10	15–20	nc	5–10	nc	40	nc	5	6	1	nc

Table 244. Number of breeding territories in Lower Avon Valley 1979–1999

The Allen Valley supported a healthy breeding population during the 1970s including about eight pairs at Witchampton in 1973 and the same at Bowerswain in 1977. Although there was evidence of a decline during the 1980s, e.g. only one pair at Witchampton in 1983 and none there in 1989, 13 pairs were still present in the valley as a whole in 1990. Subsequently the decline accelerated and by 1996 the Redshank had disappeared as a breeding species – see Table 245. Nearby breeding continued to occur by the headwaters of the River Crane near Cranborne up to the beginning of the Tetrad Survey (1987–1994) at the very least.

1989	1990	1991	1992	1993	1994	1995	1996	1997	1998	1999
11	13	8	7	2–3	1	2	0	0	0	0

Table 245. Number of breeding pairs in Allen Valley 1989–1999

In the Stour Valley between Wimborne and Shapwick, a small breeding population of up to four, but mainly 1–2 pairs survived up to at least 1999. Breeding also used to occur along the Frome Valley as far upstream as Moreton and Woodsford where the species was last reported in 1985. A few pairs also nest on heathland bogs, mainly in the close vicinity of Poole Harbour, but again the species has deserted a number of these sites since the early 1980s. In 1998 one pair was reported from Chard Junction GP. The recent decline in breeding numbers, particularly in the river valleys, is due to the loss of wet meadows through drainage schemes and agricultural improvements, exacerbated by the drought of the late 1980s and early 1990s.

Poole Harbour is also the main site for the species outside the breeding season and supports wintering numbers of national importance. During the winters of 1949/50 to 1951/52, the population level was reported to be in the region of 400–600 birds. Subsequently wintering numbers increased and have remained relatively stable during 1970–1999 with maxima generally ranging from 900–1,500 birds, the highest count being a county record of 1,997 in February 1989 – see Table 246. Lower winter maxima during 1986/87 (730) and 1987/88 (662) may have reflected increased mortality due to the cold winters. Although passage in spring is obscured by the presence of breeding birds, it is more obvious in autumn with birds returning to the harbour from mid-June and numbers rapidly rising to peak during August–October. In some years, autumn numbers can be similar to the winter population with maxima generally ranging from 600–1,300 birds, the highest being 1,629 in September 1992. Autumn numbers appear to have been lower during the 1980s, than the other decades during 1960–1999 – see Table 246.

	1960s	1970s	1980s	1990s
Winter	–	1261	1144	1187
Autumn	870	932	664	1097

Table 246. Winter and autumn 10-year average peak counts from Poole Harbour 1960–1999

Studies undertaken in the mid-1980s show that the most important feeding areas were situated in the north-west of the harbour, notably Holes Bay, Lytchett Bay and Holton Shore. The other main feeding sites, namely Middlebere, Wytch Lake, Brand's Bay, Newton Bay, Arne Bay and Fitzworth, being located along the southern shore. The main roost sites were Arne Bay, Holton Heath Island, Holes Bay, Middlebere Point, Lytchett Bay, Brand's Bay, Green Island, Brownsea and Keysworth Point. A 1990s study concluded that the most important feeding area was Holes Bay where, on average, over 44% of the harbour's population could be found at low water. The reason why Redshank favour this site may be due to the discharge of enriched and warmer water into the head of the bay from Poole SF, which increases the densities of certain principle prey items, notably the annelid worm *Nereis diversicolor*.

The species is much less abundant at other coastal sites. At Christchurch Harbour, the highest numbers are usually recorded during passage in spring (March–May) and autumn (June–October), the best counts being 282 in April 1983 and 231 in October 1993 – see Table 247. In some autumns there is an early peak in June followed by a later one in September–October. The winter numbers tend to be lower with maxima ranging from 50–150 birds and rarely exceeding 200, the highest being 260 in November 1990 – see Table 248.

	1980	1981	1982	1983	1984	1985	1986	1987	1988	1989
Spring	75	123	100	282	130	105	50	100	57	8
Autumn	104	153	104	74	156	136	60	70	105	24

	1990	1991	1992	1993	1994	1995	1996	1997	1998	1999
Spring	150	137	158	220	50	55	51	138	162	86
Autumn	165	95	180	231	82	117	130	125	125	128

Table 247. Spring and autumn maxima from Christchurch Harbour 1980–1999

80/81	81/82	82/83	83/84	84/85	85/86	86/87	87/88	88/89	89/90
75	50	146	100	80	115	80	80	80	45

90/91	91/92	92/93	93/94	94/95	95/96	96/97	97/98	98/99	99/00
260	225	66	134	80	115	117	205	108	84

Table 248. Winter maxima from Christchurch Harbour 1980–1999

The main site for Redshank in the Weymouth area is the Fleet where peak numbers usually occur during the winter. From the mid-1980s to the early 1990s winter maxima generally ranged between 40–100 birds, but declined subsequently to between 10–50 birds – see Table 249. Occasionally there is evidence of a secondary peak during spring passage, e.g. 70 at Langton Herring on 1st and 4th April 1970 with 60 there on 8th April 1979. Isolated counts of 187 in September 1988, 140 on 13th January 1985 and 107 in December 1998 are particularly high for the Fleet. It is a frequent, but by no means regular visitor to Radipole and Lodmoor NRs with most counts in single figures and rarely exceeding 20 birds, a count of 57 at the former site in February 1992 being noteworthy. Otherwise up to ten or so birds are occasionally reported from the Charmouth/Lyme Regis area, West Bexington and the Purbeck coast.

1984/85	1985/86	1986/87	1987/88	1988/89	1989/90	1990/91	1991/92
140	45	80	53	66	70	92	76

1992/93	1993/94	1994/95	1995/96	1996/97	1997/98	1998/99	1999/00
83	34	11	33	13	12	107	46

Table 249. Winter maxima from the Fleet 1984–1999

During the winter wet fields and areas of temporary floodwater in the Lower Avon Valley, the Stour Valley between Wimborne and Sturminster Marshall, and the Frome Valley as far upstream as Wool often attract flocks of up to 200 birds. In 1982 exceptional numbers were reported from the Stour Valley at Lake Gate floods with 290 on 1st January and 340 on 26th November. There are occasional reports, mainly in autumn and winter, from other inland sites including cress-beds, and the margins of lakes and gravel pits. Like the breeding population, the incidence and size of inland flocks have diminished since the mid-1980s.

At Portland Bill spring passage is negligible and rarely exceeds five birds, so 23 in May 1976 is exceptional. Autumn passage is more pronounced, but still involves small numbers with seasonal totals usually ranging between 10–40 birds, the highest being 73 in 1973 and 64 in 1978. Coastal movements along the Purbeck coast are also small and obscured by wintering birds.

A total of 761 birds has been ringed in the county.

The Redshank breeds mainly in Iceland, the British Isles, the Netherlands, Scandinavia and from eastern Europe across central Asia, also in Asia Minor and very locally in other parts of western Europe. It winters mainly on the coasts of western and southern Europe, North and West Africa, Asia Minor, the Middle East and much of southern Asia.

Postscript 2000–2002
Breeding numbers continued to decline with apparently no records from the Lower Avon Valley during 2000–2002.

Marsh Sandpiper   *Tringa stagnatilis*

Accidental: one record

2000   Stanpit Marsh, Christchurch Harbour: 10th–15th April

The above record involved an adult in breeding plumage; a full account can be found in the Dorset Bird Report for 2000.

The Marsh Sandpiper is a summer visitor to Europe breeding from Belarus and the Ukraine eastwards into central Asia to about 120°E. It winters in sub-Saharan Africa, the Middle East, southern Asia including the Indian sub-continent, and Australia. A vagrant to Great Britain with only 119 records up to 2002.

Greenshank (Common Greenshank)   *Tringa nebularia*

A locally common passage migrant and uncommon winter visitor

Both Mansel-Pleydell (1888) and Blathwayt (1945) considered this species to be a regular passage migrant in small numbers with counts rarely exceeding six birds, so 23 in Poole Harbour on 11th September 1949 was thought to be exceptional at the time.

Since 1950 numbers have increased with regular wintering becoming established from 1957/58 onwards. Spring passage mainly takes place between mid-April and mid-May, whilst peak autumn counts usually occur in August and September.

Poole Harbour is the main site for the Greenshank during migration and winter. Passage numbers were at their highest during 1976–1986 with autumn maxima generally ranging between 40–60 birds, the best being a county record count of 90 in October 1978. During the same period spring maxima frequently reached double figures, the highest being 17 at Lytchett Bay in April 1985. Subsequently passage numbers have declined with autumn maxima generally ranging between 20–50 birds with a peak of 62 in September 1991, and spring maxima only reaching single figures except for two double-figure counts (a maximum of 15 in May 1990) – see Table 250. Since 1973/74 the wintering population has usually ranged from 4–10 birds and has never exceeded 16 except for a remarkable count of 37 in January 1976. Although birds may be encountered throughout the harbour, the most favoured sites are Arne NR, Brownsea and Lytchett Bay. Although passage numbers have declined since the mid-1980s, the wintering population has remained relatively stable – see Table 250.

	1950s	1960s	1970s	1980s	1990s
Spring	<1	1	4	11	6
Autumn	15	23	37	45	31
Winter	<1	2	8	8	9

Table 250. Spring, autumn and winter 10-year average peak counts from Poole Harbour 1950–1999

At Christchurch Harbour, the species is mainly a passage migrant, being rare in winter. Spring maxima are low and rarely exceed six birds, the highest being an exceptional 31 in May 1990 and 13 on 11th April 1996. Autumn numbers are higher with maxima frequently reaching double figures, but never exceeding 25 birds except for a site record count of 42 in September 1991 – see Table 251.

1974	1975	1976	1977	1978	1979	1980	1981	1982	1983	1984	1985	1986
9	8	23	5	7	14	22	25	7	11	25	21	8

1987	1988	1989	1990	1991	1992	1993	1994	1995	1996	1997	1998	1999
15	12	12	18	42	15	20	9	7	12	15	9	10

Table 251. Autumn maxima at Christchurch Harbour 1974–1999

	1970s	1980s	1990s
Christchurch Hbr	11	16	16
Lodmoor NR	9	8	8
Radipole NR	13	18	5
The Fleet	12	10	7

Table 252. Autumn 10-year average peak counts at various sites 1970–1999

In the Weymouth area, Greenshanks regularly winter on the Fleet and in most years at Radipole NR, but they are only occasional visitors to Lodmoor NR during this season. Wintering numbers are small, usually varying between 1–7 birds, but higher counts were recorded from the Fleet during 1969–1977 including 15 in December 1969 and 12 in December 1977. Spring passage is small at all three sites with maxima rarely exceeding six birds, the highest being 13 on the Fleet on 1st May 1997 and occasional counts of 10–12 birds at Radipole and Lodmoor NRs during 1968–1980. Radipole NR was the favoured site for autumn migrants from the late 1970s to the late 1980s when maxima regularly reached double-figures and occasionally exceeded 20 birds, the highest being 26 in September 1978, but numbers at this site have declined markedly during the 1990s – see Tables 252 and 253. Autumn maxima from the Fleet and Lodmoor NR generally range from 4–15 birds, the best counts being 28 on the Fleet and 25 at Lodmoor NR in September 1993, and 27 at Abbotsbury on 27th August and 18th September 1955 – see Table 253. Since the 1970s, autumn numbers have declined on the Fleet, but remained stable at Lodmoor NR – see Tables 252 and 253. There are several sightings from West Bexington, particularly during the late 1970s, whilst in the extreme west there are about three records from the coast between West Bay and Lyme Regis.

	70	71	72	73	74	75	76	77	78	79	80	81	82	83	84
Radipole NR	10	7	7	15	p	6	20	14	26	12	22	22	21	19	23
Lodmoor NR	7	nc	14	2	9	2	15	11	p	p	10	14	13	15	4
The Fleet	9	4	13	15	15	10	20	8	p	p	9	12	10	6	11

	85	86	87	88	89	90	91	92	93	94	95	96	97	98	99
Radipole NR	18	15	17	10	11	6	8	4	10	3	4	5	3	3	2
Lodmoor NR	10	4	4	5	2	p	4	2	25	8	9	5	5	8	12
The Fleet	10	13	15	9	4	1	4	3	28	4	6	4	6	12	2

Table 253. Autumn maxima at Radipole NR, Lodmoor NR and the Fleet 1970–1999

Coastal movements are regularly recorded, but mostly in autumn. In some years there are no spring records and generally totals are very small, usually 1–5 bird-days, but at Portland Bill heavy passage at night on 30th March/1st April 1984 and ten bird-days there during 29th April–8th May 1990. Autumn numbers are moderate with totals at Portland Bill and Durlston CP often in double figures, but rarely exceeding 20 birds, the best being 36 at the former site in 1981 – see Table 254. Not surprisingly day-totals are usually in single figures, so reports from Durlston CP of 18W on 28th August 1990 and 15 on 2nd September 1983 are noteworthy, whilst at Portland Bill 'tens' of birds were heard at night on 18th September 1982. Elsewhere movements are occasionally reported from various other coastal sites including St Aldhelm's Head and Hengistbury.

Inland, the species has occurred almost annually since the mid-1960s with a distinct peak during the 1980s – see Table 255. Although there are records for all seasons, most are for the autumn. The Lower Avon Valley, the Stour Valley upstream to Spetisbury, the Frome Valley upstream to Dorchester, the Piddle

	80	81	82	83	84	85	86	87	88	89	90	91	92	93	94	95	96	97	98	99
Portland Bill	18	36	31	31	25	9	14	15	17	12	15	19	6	17	3	9	4	9	14	11
Durlston CP	–	7	1	15	7	15	9	11	10	12	22	7	13	7	8	16	17	11	17	14

Table 254. Annual totals for coastal movements at Portland Bill and Durlston CP 1980–1999

Valley upstream to Puddletown and the immediate hinterland of Poole Harbour are the most favoured areas. There are also reports from other sites widely scattered throughout the county. Most sightings concern 1–3 birds, occasionally more, the highest counts being 11 at East Holme on 1st January 1986 with seven there during 1st–5th January 1982 and 20th–27th February 1990, and six well inland at Nyland on 27th August 1977.

66	67	68	69	70	71	72	73	74	75	76	77	78	79	80	81	82
1	1	0	2	1	3	0	7	4	11	3	9	0	4	8	4	10

83	84	85	86	87	88	89	90	91	92	93	94	95	96	97	98	99
6	13	4	23	21	10	9	17	1	4	3	2	9	1	8	0	1

Table 255. Inland totals 1966–1999

A total of 53 birds has been ringed in the county and there has been one foreign control from the Netherlands.

The Greenshank breeds across the taiga and boreal regions of northern Eurasia including northern Scotland. Most winter in sub-Saharan Africa, Arabia, southern Asia and Australia with small numbers on the coasts of western Europe and the Mediterranean.

Postscript 2000–2002

In Poole Harbour, 50 in September 2000 is the second highest autumn count since 1983, whilst 30 at Christchurch Harbour in August 2001 is the second highest autumn count at this site since 1974. At Warmwell GP, nine on 22nd May 2001 is the highest count from a site well inland in the county.

Lesser Yellowlegs   *Tringa flavipes*

A very rare passage migrant and winter visitor: eight records

Typically most birds have occurred in the autumn (four), but there are also two reports for winter and two for spring. There are six records from the Weymouth area and two from the Christchurch area.

1963	Lodmoor NR: 26th September–10th October; same at Radipole NR 10th October
1976	Stanpit Marsh, Christchurch Harbour: 16th–31st October
1977	Radipole and Lodmoor NRs: 3rd–9th September
1981	Lodmoor NR: 30th–31st January and 11th February–14th March; same at Radipole NR 21st February
1983	Ferrybridge: 27th March; same at West Bexington 27th March–9th April
1993	Radipole and Lodmoor NRs: 11th–24th September
1994	Coward's Marsh, Christchurch: 30th November–4th December; same at Stanpit Marsh and Wick Fields, Christchurch Harbour 4th–12th December
2000	The Fleet at Butterstreet Cove: first-winter 7th–19th May

The Lesser Yellowlegs breeds in eastern Alaska and across much of Canada east to James Bay and winters in the southern USA, and Central and South America. A vagrant to Great Britain with 236 records up to 2002.

Green Sandpiper   *Tringa ochropus*

A locally common passage migrant and winter visitor

Both Mansel-Pleydell (1888) and Blathwayt (1945) considered this species to be a passage migrant, but only the latter mentioned that it sometimes wintered in the county.

Subsequently there has been little change in status except perhaps for an increase in the wintering population. The Green Sandpiper frequents both coastal and freshwater habitats scattered throughout the county. Inland, it shows a marked affinity for cress-beds, particularly those located in the Frome and Piddle Catchments at Tincleton, Waddock Cross and Bere Regis. River meadows and marshes, notably water-meadow systems such as those at Puddletown, the margins of lakes and gravel pits, and small sewage works are also favoured. The main coastal localities are Christchurch Harbour and Radipole and Lodmoor NRs. These sites are characterised by the presence of brackish and freshwater pools. Similar habitats are also preferred in the Poole Harbour area where the species is most often reported from Arne NR, Brownsea and Lytchett Bay. It is rather an infrequent visitor to the Fleet with most sightings from Langton Herring and more recently Abbotsbury, whilst there are a several records from further west at West Bexington.

The species occurs in all months, but it is most numerous during the autumn and winter. Spring passage is small and in some years hardly detected, e.g. only two birds in 1986 and 1995. Records extend from mid-March to mid-May with the peak in April. Numbers at individual sites are very low with most reports involving 1–3 birds, the highest counts being seven at Arne NR in April 1992, and six at Warmwell in May 1979 and Lodmoor NR on 21st March 1981.

Although returning birds have been reported in early June, the first autumn migrants normally appear during the second half of that month. Passage extends through to October with the peak usually in August. Like spring, the majority of sightings involve 1–3 birds with peak counts rarely exceeding ten, the highest being a county record 22 at Bere Regis CBs on 17th August 1972 with 18 there on 31st July 1974, 19SW at Christchurch Harbour on 26th August 1985 with 17 there in August 1997, and 18 at Radipole NR in July 1994.

Most coastal movement occurs during the autumn. At Portland Bill spring passage is negligible with only c.12 birds recorded during 1952–1999. In autumn there are reports for most years since the mid-1960s, but numbers are small with seasonal totals rarely exceeding ten birds – see Table 256. Elsewhere birds are occasionally recorded from the Purbeck coast at Durlston CP and St Aldhelm's Head.

80	81	82	83	84	85	86	87	88	89	90	91	92	93	94	95	96	97	98	99
4	4	9	5	6	7	13	11	5	4	5	1	1	0	3	3	3	5	2	1

Table 256. Autumn totals at Portland Bill 1980–1999

In winter the majority of reports come from inland sites with most sightings involving only 1–2 birds. The best gatherings are usually found at the favoured cress-bed sites where counts of 4–5 birds are not unusual, the highest being ten at Tincleton on 4th January 1986 and nine at Waddock Cross on 7th January 1997. Other winter counts of note include six on floating vegetation in the River Avon at Avon Castle on 7th November 1985, and six between Dorchester and Tincleton on 26th January 1991.

A total of 15 birds has been ringed in the county. At Merley a colour-ringed bird appeared for four successive winters between 1976/77 and 1979/80. According to the BTO, this bird was not part of any UK ringing scheme.

The Green Sandpiper breeds mainly in the boreal regions of northern Eurasia from Scandinavia eastwards. It winters in western and southern Europe, North and sub-Saharan Africa, Asia Minor, the Middle East, Arabia and much of southern Asia.

Postscript 2000–2002
At Wareham Water-meadows, 11 on 5th May 2000 is a record count for spring, the previous highest being seven at Arne NR in April 1992.

Wood Sandpiper   *Tringa glareola*

An uncommon passage migrant, mainly in autumn

Mansel-Pleydell (1888) considered this species to be a spring and autumn visitor, but much less common than the Green Sandpiper. Blathwayt (1945) referred to it as being mainly a rare autumn migrant and listed eight records involving 17 birds from the Weymouth area between 1928 and 1943, including a party of up to eight during 3rd–19th August 1931, as well as singles at Verwood on 6th June 1921 and Wareham on 16th July 1937.

Since 1953 the Wood Sandpiper has been a regular autumn migrant with records increasing from the mid-1970s onwards – see Table 257. It remained a rare and infrequent visitor in spring up to the 1970s, but subsequently records increased and since 1980 there have been reports in every year except 1983, 1997 and 1998 – see Table 258. Prior to 1970, singles at Ferrybridge on 3rd June 1961, Radipole NR on 6th May 1962 and Wareham on 7th May 1966 were the only spring sightings since 1921.

1950s	1960s	1970s	1980s	1990s
4	8	15	23	25

Table 257. Autumn 10-year average totals 1950–1999

70	71	72	73	74	75	76	77	78	79	80	81	82	83	84
8	0	0	0	2	3	1	6	0	0	5	2	4	0	1

85	86	87	88	89	90	91	92	93	94	95	96	97	98	99
4	2	5	3	6	6	4	1	2	3	1	1	0	0	1

Table 258. Spring totals 1970–1999

Spring passage extends from late April, the earliest report being 20th April 1970 at Langton Herring, through to early June with no obvious peak. Numbers are small with the vast majority of records involving only single birds, so up to six at Langton Herring during 20th–23rd April 1970 and four at Christchurch Harbour on 20th May 1989 are exceptional. The main site for spring migrants in recent years is Christchurch Harbour, which accounts for 55% of the total since 1980, whilst the other favoured locality, Lodmoor NR, accounts for 22% of sightings since 1961. Spring birds have also been reported from West Bexington (one), Langton Herring (seven), Ferrybridge (one), Portland Bill (three) Radipole NR (six), Durlston CP (two) Wareham (two) and Lytchett Bay (two). Rather surprisingly there have also been reports from several inland sites with singles at Stanbridge Mill in May 1977, the River Frome at Dorchester on 21st April 1980, Boscombe on 4th June 1981, Coward's Marsh, Christchurch during 12th–17th May 1986, Sugar Hill, Wareham Forest on 17th May 1987 and Monkton Up Wimborne on 15th May 1988.

Although there are a few records of early autumn migrants from mid-June to mid-July, the main passage occurs between mid-July and mid-September with a trickle of birds through to mid-October, the latest being in 1982 at Lodmoor NR from 9th October to 5th November and Christchurch Harbour on 15th November (possibly the same bird). Seasonal totals are fairly small and during 1970–1999 usually ranged between 10–30 birds, but reached c.56 in 1991 and c.40 in 1988 and 1995. Maxima at individual sites rarely exceed six birds, so counts of 11 at Lodmoor NR on 17th August 1977 and 15th August 1982 are notably high. The main sites in autumn are Christchurch Harbour and Radipole and Lodmoor NRs, which together account for 72% of the total since 1974. There are also records from Poole Harbour – mainly Brownsea and during the 1960s Wareham SF, the Fleet – mainly Langton Herring and Abbotsbury, and West Bexington. Coastal movements regularly occur at Portland and to a lesser extent at Durlston CP with 1–4 birds recorded in most years, but six at Portland in 1982. Elsewhere 10S at Hengistbury during 5th–6th September 1988, and singles at Chesil Cove on 18th September 1976 and Kimmeridge Bay during 28th–30th August 1968 are noteworthy.

Inland there have been c.28 autumn records involving c.37 birds during 1955–1999 with near-annual sightings from 1968 to 1983. Cress-beds are favoured haunts, particularly in the Frome and Piddle Catchments where notable reports include three singles at both Bere Regis in 1974 and Tincleton in 1978 with four at the latter site on 21st September 1980. There is also a remarkable series of records from the Stour Valley at Corfe Mullen with two in 1955 and singles in 1958, 1962, 1964 and 1968, whilst well inland there are sightings from Sherborne Lake on 4th August 1975, Cranborne on 16th August 1975, Nyland in 1977, Lodden Lakes with two on 30th July 1982, Puddletown with two on 9th August 1983, and Warmwell GP from 5th August to 4th September 1999.

Instances of wintering are exceptional with only two records:

1983   Wareham Water-meadows: 10th January–20th February
1984   Waddock Cross CBs: 15th January–29th February

A total of eight birds have been ringed in the county.

The Wood Sandpiper breeds across northern Eurasia from Scandinavia eastwards with a very small isolated population in northern Scotland. It winters throughout sub-Saharan Africa, much of southern Asia and Australia with smaller numbers in north-west Africa, Iraq and Arabia.

Terek Sandpiper   *Xenus cinereus*

Accidental: four records

1974	Radipole NR: 6th–7th May; presumed same at Brownsea 8th–9th May
	Sutton Bingham: 18th August
1988	Stanpit Marsh, Christchurch Harbour: 15th–24th July; presumed same at Ferrybridge 25th July
1998	Stanpit Marsh, Christchurch Harbour: 13th–16th May

The Terek Sandpiper breeds from the Baltic States and western Russia eastwards across Siberia with a tiny population in Finland. It winters from the Gulf of Guinea eastwards around the coasts of Africa to Arabia, the Persian Gulf, the Indian sub-continent, south-east Asia through Indonesia to Australia. A vagrant to Great Britain with 62 records up to 2002.

Common Sandpiper   *Actitis hypoleucos*

A fairly common passage migrant and scarce winter visitor

Mansel-Pleydell (1888) considered the Common Sandpiper or 'Summer Snipe' to be a summer visitor, but commented that "direct evidence of its nesting in Dorsetshire is wanting". Blathwayt (1945) regarded it to be a common passage migrant and casts doubt on reports of breeding on islands in Poole Harbour and elsewhere.

There has been little subsequent change in status except for the increasing frequency of wintering from the late 1950s onwards, whilst the only hints of breeding in recent years concern a pair regularly present on the River Brit at Netherbury during the summer of 1967 and one displaying at Maiden Newton on 10th May 1991.

Passage birds occur widely along the coast where they frequent both muddy and rocky shores, and inland where they favour the margins of rivers, lakes and gravel pits. Although the start of spring passage is obscured by wintering birds, genuine migrants have been reported during the first half of March, the earliest being 5th March 1956 at Wimborne and 8th March 1992 at Christchurch Harbour. Since the 1960s the average date of the first arrivals has gradually become earlier – see Table 259. The main passage commences from the second week of April and peaks in late April and early May, numbers then diminish with odd stragglers occurring as late as early June. Returning migrants appear from mid-June with peak passage in July and August. Numbers decline through September with a few late birds recorded through October and occasionally into early November.

	1950–1959	1960–1969	1970–1979	1980–1989	1990–1999
Range	5th March– 20th April	7th–23rd April	16th March– 18th April	22nd March– 7th April	8th March– 8th April
Average	9th April	12th April	7th April	1st April	23rd March

Table 259. Dates for first spring arrivals each decade 1950–1999

Spring maxima at both coastal and inland sites rarely exceed 12 birds, so counts of 37 at Christchurch Harbour in May 1984 with 20 there in May 1995, 23 at West Bexington in May 1999, 21 at Merley on 5th May 1976, and 20 at Sherborne Lake on 20th April 1989 with 19 there in April 1990 are noteworthy. Autumn passage is much stronger, particularly on the coast. Although numbers at Christchurch Harbour have declined since the 1970s, this remains the main coastal locality for autumn migrants with maxima usually exceeding 15 birds, the highest being site record counts of 41 in July 1980 and 40 in August 1979 – see Tables 260 and 261. Elsewhere autumn maxima rarely exceed 25 birds, the highest being a county record count of 55 at Portland Harbour on 20th August 1983 with 30 there on 18th July 1986, and 36 at Poole Harbour on 16th July 1950 with 33 there on 20th July 1968. In addition, a flock of 34 on the East Cliffs at Portland Bill on 30th August 1974 is exceptional for the site.

1974	1975	1976	1977	1978	1979	1980	1981	1982	1983	1984	1985	1986
36	36	20	30	21	40	41	33	37	32	24	24	17

1987	1988	1989	1990	1991	1992	1993	1994	1995	1996	1997	1998	1999
31	27	18	38	16	19	37	14	15	17	27	15	17

Table 260. Autumn maxima at Christchurch Harbour 1974–1999

1970s	1980s	1990s
31	28	22

Table 261. Autumn 10-year average peak counts at Christchurch Harbour 1970–1999

Wintering has occurred annually since 1957/58 except for 1964/65 and 1998/99. Numbers are small with seasonal totals ranging between 1–9 birds. Most records involve 1–2 birds, but there have been counts of three at Hamworthy on 5th February 1963, the Nothe/Newton's Cove during November–December 1973, Cleavel Point on 13th January 1980 and Holes Bay on 26th February 1986. Birds often return to some sites for several successive winters. For example, in the Nothe/Newton's Cove/Portland Harbour area, the species was recorded in all but two winters between 1968/69 and 1990/91. Other favoured winter sites include Christchurch Harbour, Holes Bay and Chapman's Pool. It is a very rare bird inland in winter with only seven records since 1958:

1961 Holwell CBs: 26th November–10th December
1975 Hyde near Wareham: November–December
    Bere Regis: November–December
1982 River Stour at Sturminster Marshall: 15th January
1987 River Stour at Shillingstone: 30th January
1992 Druce near Puddletown: 6th January
1996 Bere Regis: 24th February

A total of 235 birds has been ringed in the county and there are single foreign recoveries from France and Morocco.

The Common Sandpiper breeds across much of Eurasia south to 35°N, but locally over much of western, central and southern Europe. Most winter in sub-Saharan Africa, Arabia, southern Asia and Australia with small numbers on the coasts of western Europe and the Mediterranean.

Postscript 2000–2002
A maximum of 27 at Sherborne Lake in April 2002 is the second highest ever spring count for Dorset, whilst a wintering bird at this site from November 2000 to February 2001 is unusual for an inland locality.

Sponsored by Bill Stevens

Spotted Sandpiper   *Actitis macularius*

Accidental: three records

1973 The Nothe, Weymouth: 8th November–24th March 1974
1976 Christchurch Harbour: 7th–14th May
1984 Stanpit Marsh, Christchurch Harbour: juv. 14th September

The Spotted Sandpiper breeds across much of North America except the southern USA, and winters from the southern USA and Caribbean south through Central and South America to northern Argentina. A vagrant Great Britain with 124 records up to 2002.

Turnstone (Ruddy Turnstone)   *Arenaria interpres*

A locally common winter visitor and passage migrant

Both Mansel-Pleydell (1888) and Blathwayt (1945) considered this species to be a regular passage migrant, but a rare visitor in winter, the former referring to its local name 'Variegated or Chicken Plover'.

Although the Turnstone has continued to be a passage migrant, regular wintering has also occurred since at least 1950.

The Fleet/Portland Harbour (including Balaclava Bay) is the most favoured area with winter maxima usually ranging between 30–60 birds during 1980–1999, the highest being 65 in January 1990. High counts may also occur on passage, particularly in spring when maxima of 60 or more have been occasionally recorded including a count of 68 in April 1984. Autumn numbers are generally more modest, but include peaks of 59 in September 1999, 54 in October 1984 and 50 in September 1988. The species is also regularly recorded from various sites along Weymouth Bay including the Nothe/Newton's Cove, Weymouth Beach, Preston Beach and nearby Lodmoor NR. Winter maxima generally range between 15–30 birds, but there was an increase in wintering numbers during the mid-1990s with a peak of 58 at Lodmoor NR on 14th January 1996. It is only an occasional visitor to nearby Radipole NR.

The main haunts for Turnstones in the east of the county are the Poole Harbour area and Christchurch Harbour. Shell/Studland Bays and Baiter are the favoured sites in the Poole Harbour area where winter maxima generally vary between 10–40 birds, the highest being 95 on 31st December 1970 (a county record), 60 in January 1970, and 58 in January 1976 and November 1986. Wintering numbers in the Poole Harbour area have declined since the 1970s, perhaps reflecting increasing levels of disturbance at the main sites – see Table 262. Christchurch Harbour normally supports a winter population of between 10–30 birds with a maximum of 43 in January 1982. Passage is sometimes reflected by occasional high counts, the most notable being 49 in March 1989 and 38 in October 1988 from the Poole Harbour area, and 30 in April 1978 and 32 in October 1984 from Christchurch Harbour. Elsewhere the species is occasionally reported from the Charmouth/Lyme Regis area, West Bexington and the Purbeck coast.

	1970s	1980s	1990s
The Fleet/Portland Hbr	18	45	34
Poole Harbour area	37	26	16
Christchurch Harbour	20	24	17

Table 262. Winter 10-year average peak counts at the main sites 1970–1999

A small, but pronounced passage in spring and autumn is detected at Portland Bill – see Table 263. Spring movements are predominantly easterly in direction and peak between mid-April and mid-May, whilst autumn passage extends from July through to November. Elsewhere coastal movements are mainly recorded in spring, 95E at St Aldhelm's Head during 27th April–13th May 1993 being a particularly high total. Birds also occasionally occur at Portland Bill during the winter.

	1980	1981	1982	1983	1984	1985	1986	1987	1988	1989
Spring	27	7	33	16	37	71	9	26	21	29
Autumn	49	25	47	26	125	112	57	156	119	91

	1990	1991	1992	1993	1994	1995	1996	1997	1998	1999
Spring	23	33	nc	17	24	7	21	31	nc	23
Autumn	29	46	nc	17	16	17	8	37	nc	18

Table 263. Spring and autumn totals for coastal movements at Portland Bill 1980–1999

A total of 44 birds has been ringed in the county. There is one foreign control from Sweden, whilst a colour-ringed bird on the Fleet at Pirates Cove on 10th February 1998 was thought to originate from the Netherlands.

The Turnstone breeds across the Holarctic except for Iceland. It is a long-distance migrant with birds wintering mainly on the coasts of western Europe, Africa, southern Asia, Australasia and both Americas.

Sponsored in memory of Ron Slater

Wilson's Phalarope   *Phalaropus tricolor*

Accidental: four records

    1984   Radipole and Lodmoor NRs: ad. female 2nd July–5th August; same on the Fleet at Langton
                Herring 22nd July
    1987   Radipole NR: 6th–17th September
    1988   Holes Bay: ad. female 20th June
                Sutton Bingham: juv. 28th–30th September

The Wilson's Phalarope breeds mainly on the prairie wetlands of south-west Canada and the north-western USA, and winters in the southern half of South America. It is a vagrant to Great Britain with 210 records up to 2002.

Red-necked Phalarope   *Phalaropus lobatus*

A very rare passage migrant, mainly in autumn

There are three old records from the Weymouth area with two killed at Lodmoor in the autumn of 1847, one on 23rd September 1930, and one at the Weymouth Backwater for several days from 6th October 1945.

Since 1960 the species has been reported on 20 occasions, seven during spring and summer between 25th April and 26th June, and 13 in autumn between 15th August and 18th October. The most favoured site is Christchurch Harbour with seven birds followed by Lodmoor NR with four. All records, presumably involving juveniles unless otherwise stated, are listed below:

    1960   Portland Bill: one with a Grey Phalarope flock 5th October
    1962   Shipstal Point, Arne NR: ad. in summer plumage on an unspecified date in May
    1963   The Chesil: offshore 4th October
    1970   Lodmoor NR: presumed ad. 26th June
    1971   Lodmoor NR: 15th August
    1972   Ferrybridge: ad. in summer plumage 23rd May
    1974   Lower Rowe near Holt: ad. in summer plumage 22nd May
    1977   Lodmoor NR: 24th–26th August
    1980   Portland Bill: 10th October
    1983   Stanpit Marsh, Christchurch Harbour: moulting ad. 25th April–3rd May
    1984   Stanpit Marsh, Christchurch Harbour: 21st–28th September; moved to Hengistbury where it
                remained until 30th September
            Hengistbury: moulting ad. 3rd–5th October
    1986   Radipole NR: 22nd–25th August
    1987   Hengistbury: 16th and 18th October
    1988   Hengistbury: 1st September
    1989   Brownsea: 17th–19th August
    1991   Stanpit Marsh, Christchurch Harbour: ad. male in summer plumage 19th–22nd June
    1993   Stanpit Marsh, Christchurch Harbour and Christchurch Waterworks: 8th–17th September
    1999   Lodmoor NR: 1st–2nd September
    2002   Ferrybridge: first-winter 26th April

The Red-necked Phalarope breeds across the Holarctic mainly north of 60°N but further south in Canada and Alaska. It is a rare breeding bird in Scotland. The species is a long-distance migrant and winters at sea with the main concentrations off western South America (mainly Peru), in the Arabian Sea and amongst the East Indies.

Grey Phalarope   *Phalaropus fulicarius*

An uncommon autumn passage migrant and rare winter visitor, subject to large-scale 'wrecks' in adverse weather

The first Grey Phalarope for Dorset was recorded in 1774 when one was shot on the River Stour near

Blandford only eleven years after it had been first described as a British bird. Apparently well-known in the 19th Century, Mansel-Pleydell (1888) described the species as "an occasional winter visitor", but noted that it was sometimes very common during the autumn with large influxes in 1847, 1849 and 1866. The 1847 influx included a flock of several hundred birds at Lodmoor, whilst at least 100 were 'obtained' seemingly from the Weymouth area during the 1866 influx, which also produced inland records from Piddletrenthide Manor House on 20th September, Whatcombe (shot), Herringston Manor (two shot) and Dorchester. One in summer plumage shot at the Weymouth Breakwater in spring 1849 and another killed inland at Glanville's Wootton in an unspecified year are also noteworthy. There was another invasion in September 1886 involving hundreds of birds.

Although regarded an irregular passage migrant by Blathwayt (1945), the Grey Phalarope has been recorded almost annually since 1950. The vast majority of birds appear during or after gales and periods of unsettled weather in the autumn and early part of the winter. Generally annual totals rarely exceed ten birds, but occasionally larger numbers are reported as a result of particularly severe storms – see Fig 31. There was a major 'wreck' during September–October 1960 including 715 bird-days at Portland Bill between 15th September and 4th December (maximum of 54 on 5th October), also 125–150 at West Bay on 7th October and c.60 at Lodmoor NR from 14th–16th October, whilst c.500–1,000 birds were estimated to be present in the county on 9th October. Rather surprisingly the 'hurricane' of October 1987 only produced c.43 birds including 26 at Hengistbury during 16th–21st (maximum of 14 on 19th). Smaller influxes also occurred in 1958, 1959, 1981, 1983, 1984, 1985 and 1996, the most notable counts being 26 at the Nothe on 9th October 1981 with 28 there the following day, 14 including six picked up dead at Abbotsbury on 20th September 1958 and 14 (phalarope spp but presumably this species) at Portland Bill on 5th October 1958. Otherwise most reports involve 1–2 birds with counts rarely exceeding five.

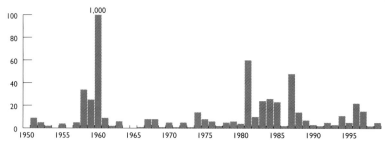

Fig 31. Annual totals 1950–1999

Records extend from 31st July, involving a moulting adult at Stanpit Marsh, Christchurch Harbour in 1988, to 31st January, involving single birds at Portland Bill in 1962 and Ferrybridge/Portland Harbour in 1970, but the vast majority occur during September and October. All 17 August sightings have been since 1985 when a particularly early influx of nine birds occurred from the 9th, whilst only nine birds have been recorded in January. A dead bird found well inland at Piddletrenthide on 12th February 1958 is the only report for that month. Otherwise, there are two exceptionally unseasonal sightings involving singles at Stanpit Marsh, Christchurch Harbour on 6th May 1976 and Charmouth on 7th–8th June 1977.

Although the species has occurred at sites along the entire coastline from Lyme Regis to Christchurch, records are concentrated in the Fleet/Chesil Cove/Portland Harbour, Portland Bill and Christchurch Harbour areas with fewer reports from Weymouth Bay, Radipole and Lodmoor NRs, the Purbeck coast and Poole Harbour.

Inland sightings are very rare with only eight records (incl. unidentified phalarope spp) since 1958 including six during 1958–1961:

1958   Piddletrenthide: found dead 12th February
1959   Shillingstone: feeding on a garden lawn 20th October
       Dorchester SF: 1st December
1960   Everley near Blandford: found dead on or about 7th October
       Corfe Mullen: 30th October, also a phalarope spp on 9th October
1961   Corfe Mullen: 5th November

1971   River Stour near Fiddleford Mill: one, presumably this species 12th December

1974   Holwell: one, presumably this species on a farm pond 11th September

A total of 13 birds has been ringed in the county.

The Grey Phalarope breeds across the Holarctic except for Scandinavia and north-west Russia. It is a long-distance migrant and winters at sea with the main concentrations around plankton-rich upwellings off West and south-west Africa and the west coast of southern South America.

Postscript 2000–2002

There were four records involving five birds during September–December 2000, c.15 records involving c.26 birds from late September–late October 2001 (maximum of eight at Chesil Cove on 9th October), and seven records of single birds during October–December 2002.

Sponsored by Peter Christian

Pomarine Skua   *Stercorarius pomarinus*

An uncommon passage migrant and rare winter visitor

Mansel-Pleydell (1888) described this species as "an occasional spring and autumn visitant" and referred to one killed on the Weymouth Backwater on 23rd September 1868, one obtained in Weymouth Roads on 14th October 1870, one shot from a flock in Poole Harbour on 16th October 1879, and one shot near Weymouth in an unspecified year. Blathwayt (1945) considered it to be a rare visitor in spring and autumn and listed two records involving one in Poole Harbour on 25th October 1909 and four harrying terns at Abbotsbury on 26th July 1918.

There were no further reports until 1958 when a dying first-winter bird was found at Portland Bill on 16th January followed by an adult flying east there on 4th May. Since 1960 the number of sightings have increased due to systematic seawatching, initially at Portland Bill, but later at various other coastal watch-points from the early 1970s onwards.

Although records at Portland Bill during 1967–1971 hinted at the up-channel passage of birds in spring, this was not fully detected until 1972. Subsequently this has become a regular feature with county totals generally ranging from 30–66 birds during 1972–1982, but increasing to 80–168 birds during 1983–1999 with a peak of 200 birds in 1986 – see Table 264. Due to the species' habit of moving in loose flocks, day-totals are higher than might be expected considering the overall numbers involved. Peak counts often reach double figures but rarely exceed 25 birds, the best day-totals being 40E at St Aldhelm's Head on 2nd May 1997, 34 at Portland Bill on 6th May 1972 with 31 there on 11th May 1979 and 8th May 1986, whilst the largest flocks reported are 22 at Blacknor Point, Portland on 11th May 1979, 21 'probably this species' at West Bexington on 14th May 1981 and 16 at St Aldhelm's Head on 2nd May 1997.

	1960s	1970s	1980s	1990s
Spring	4	32	104	122
Autumn	7	9	59	33

Table 264. Spring and autumn 10-year average totals 1960–1999

Unlike the other skuas, spring passage is usually far heavier than in the autumn – see Table 264. Between 1960 and 1981 autumn totals were very modest and rarely exceeded 12 birds, the highest being 28 in 1963 including 25 at Portland Bill. Since 1982 numbers have increased with seasonal totals ranging from 13–77 birds except for an isolated peak of 244 in 1985. The higher totals result from heavy movements associated with inclement weather. The most notable of these movements occurred during November 1985 when a total of 165 bird-days were recorded at Portland Bill with peaks of 30 on 4th and 55 on 5th, the best count elsewhere being 19W,4E at Hengistbury on 4th. Otherwise day-totals in autumn rarely exceed ten birds, the highest being 19 at Durlston CP and 13 at Portland Bill on 27th October 1986, 17 at Portland Bill on 8th November 1999 and 16 at Durlston CP on 6th September 1992.

There is an exceptionally early record of one at Portland Bill on 31st March 1999. Otherwise, the first birds of the spring usually occur during the latter half of April, records prior to the 16th of the month being rare. Generally peak movements take place during the first half of May, but in some years they may start a little earlier, at the end of April, and in others they may be delayed until late May. Passage often extends into early June, but otherwise the species is rarely reported in mid-summer. Autumn passage is more prolonged extending from August through to November and occasionally into December, with September and October the peak months. The species is rare in mid-winter with only c.16 records on various dates between early January and 3rd March including three during January–February 1986 (after the autumn influx of November 1985), four during January–March 1992 and seven during January 1998 (cf Great Skua). This seasonal pattern is well illustrated by records from the main coastal watch-points, which show April–May accounting for 67% of the total (55% in May) and August–November accounting for 27% of the total (19% in September–October) – see Table 265.

Jan	Feb	Mar	Apr	May	Jun	Jul	Aug	Sep	Oct	Nov	Dec
5	1	1	186	843	49	12	82	148	145	45	11

Table 265. Monthly totals at the main coastal watch-points 1986–1996

The majority of birds are recorded from the main coastal watch-points with Portland Bill accounting for 49% of the total since 1980, and the Chesil, St Aldhelm's Head, Durlston CP and Hengistbury together accounting for a further 46% – see Table 266. Birds are frequently observed in Lyme Bay from West/East Bexington and Abbotsbury Beach, the most notable movements being 28 at West Bexington during May 1981 and 19W at East Bexington on 12th May 1992. Although there are a few records from other coastal sites, it is a very rare visitor to the Fleet with singles at Langton Herring on 15th May 1976 and 13th September 1984, Lodmoor NR with singles on 25th June 1974 and 7th January 1986, inside Poole Harbour with one at Arne NR on 2nd October 1983, and inside Christchurch Harbour. There are no inland records.

Portland Bill	the Chesil	St Aldhelm's	Durlston CP	Hengistbury	elsewhere
1582	250	231	759	263	153

Table 266. Totals at the main sites 1980–1999

The Pomarine Skua breeds across the Holarctic except for eastern Greenland, Iceland, Scandinavia and extreme north-west Russia. Outside the breeding season the species is pelagic and occurs widely, the main wintering areas in the Atlantic being from the Caribbean to the Sargasso Sea and north to North Carolina, and off West Africa.

Sponsored by Hugo Wood-Homer

Arctic Skua   *Stercorarius parasiticus*

A locally common passage migrant and rare winter visitor

Mansel-Pleydell (1888) considered this species, then known as Richardson's Skua, to be an occasional visitor on migration and referred to one killed on the Chesil Bank in February 1855, one at Chickerell in the same year, one at Wareham in 1868, and one at Weymouth in September 1870. Blathwayt (1945) described it as "an uncommon passage migrant on the coast, but regular out in the channel" and listed ten records involving at least 15 birds between 1913 and 1939.

Subsequently there has been a marked increase in records mainly due to systematic seawatching, which started at Portland Bill during the mid-1950s and later commenced at various other coastal watch-points from the early 1970s onwards – see Table 267. Since 1980 spring passage has been relatively stable with county totals generally ranging between 100–350 birds, but autumn passage during the same period has been much more variable with totals ranging between 100–800 birds. Day-totals in spring are modest and peak counts rarely exceed 20 birds, the best being 29 at the Chesil on 22nd April 1994 and 26 at Portland Bill on 22nd April 1983. High totals in autumn are the result of heavy movements induced by adverse weather, the most notable being 180W at Portland Bill, 136 at Durlston CP and 82W at Hengistbury on 6th September 1992, 130 at Portland Bill on 23rd September 1988, 120 at Portland Bill on 9th September 1993, and 114W at Durlston CP, 84W at Hengistbury and 82 at Portland Bill on 19th August 1990.

	1950s	1960s	1970s	1980s	1990s
Spring	9	40	99	222	252
Autumn	37	73	75	356	347

Table 267. Spring and autumn 10-year average totals 1950–1999

Spring migrants are occasionally recorded in March, the earliest sightings being 4th March 1977 at Sandbanks and 4th March 1998 in Poole Bay. Otherwise most passage takes place in April and May with smaller numbers into June. There are usually a few sightings in mid-summer followed by the main autumn passage, which extends from August to October with a distinct peak in September. Late birds are frequently reported in November and exceptionally into early December. The species is rare in mid-winter with only c.13 records involving c.15 birds since 1980, on various dates between 31st December and 15th February, including five during January–February 1995. This seasonal pattern is well illustrated by records from the main coastal watch-points, which show April–May accounting for 30% of the total and August–October accounting for 62% of the total (34% in September) – see Table 268.

Jan	Feb	Mar	Apr	May	Jun	Jul	Aug	Sep	Oct	Nov	Dec
5	1	19	1137	980	298	141	1208	2389	710	99	6

Table 268. Monthly totals at the main coastal watch-points 1986–1999

The majority of birds are reported from the main coastal watch-points with Portland Bill accounting for 54% of the total since 1980, and the Chesil, St Aldhelm's Head, Durlston CP and Hengistbury together accounting for a further 41% – see Table 269. In some years good numbers have been observed in Lyme Bay from West/East Bexington and Abbotsbury Beach, notably 46 at East Bexington on 6th September 1992 and 34 at West Bexington in September 1988. There are occasional records from other coastal and near-coastal sites including the Fleet, Radipole and Lodmoor NRs and Poole Harbour. The species is very rare inland, the only reports being singles at Chewton Common on 28th July 1984, Sutton Bingham on 26th May 1990 and Woolgarston on 17th September 1993.

Portland Bill	the Chesil	St Aldhelm's	Durlston CP	Hengistbury	elsewhere
6365	722	739	2291	1046	605

Table 269. Totals at the main sites 1980–1999

The Arctic Skua breeds across the Holarctic including Iceland, Scandinavia and northern Scotland. Outside the breeding season the species is pelagic and occurs widely, European birds mainly wintering in the South Atlantic.

Postscript 2000–2002
Heavy passage involving c.396 bird-days in spring 2002 resulted in the highest ever count for this season in Dorset with 42 at the Chesil on 9th June.

Long-tailed Skua   *Stercorarius longicaudus*

A scarce passage migrant

The first Dorset record involves two museum specimens, which had been shot in Weymouth Bay in 1890 and originally misidentified as Arctic Skuas. Two more were shot in Poole Harbour in October 1891, but sightings near Poole in 1905 and 1907 are perhaps open to doubt.

Although three probables were reported at Portland Bill on 23rd September 1955 with three more there in October 1956, the latter subsequently rejected by the editors of *British Birds*, there were no further accepted records until 1961 when single adults were seen at Ferrybridge on 26th August and Portland Bill on 4th October. Subsequently two adults flew east at Portland Bill on 4th June 1972. Since 1981, the species has occurred annually except for 1996 with a total of 76 birds, 16 in spring, three in summer and 57 in autumn – see Table 270.

Spring/sum	81	82	83	84	85	86	87	88	89	90	91	92	93	94	95	96	97	98	99
Portland Bill	1	0	0	5	1	2	2	1	1	0	0	0	0	1	0	0	0	0	0
Durlston CP	0	0	0	0	0	0	0	0	0	1	0	0	0	0	0	0	0	0	0
elsewhere	0	0	0	1	0	0	1	0	0	0	0	0	0	0	0	0	0	1	1

Autumn	81	82	83	84	85	86	87	88	89	90	91	92	93	94	95	96	97	98	99
Portland Bill	0	10	1	0	4	0	1	0	0	0	4	4	0	1	0	0	2	1	3
Durlston CP	0	1	0	1	1	2	0	1	0	0	0	0	0	0	0	0	0	0	1
Hengistbury	0	0	0	0	1	1	1	1	0	1	2	1	0	0	2	0	0	0	1
elsewhere	0	1	0	0	0	0	1	2	0	0	2	0	1	0	0	0	0	1	0

Table 270. Annual totals for spring/summer and autumn 1981–1999

All but three of the spring records are from Portland Bill on dates ranging from 1st May to 12th June, with 11 of the 13 birds occurring during 10th–22nd May including a flock of 5E on 15th May 1984. The remaining reports involve an adult flying north-east over Radipole School on 5th May 1984, and single adults at Durlston CP on 10th May 1990 and Chesil Cove on 8th June 1998. There are three mid-summer sightings involving singles at Chesil Cove on 29th June 1999, Portland Bill on 6th July 1981 and Weymouth Bay on 19th July 1987.

Although there are five reports for August, most of the autumn records have occurred in September and October with 27 and 24 birds respectively, whilst there is a late report of an adult in Chesil Cove on 13th November 1991. There was a notable influx during 12th–26th October 1982 involving ten birds including nine at Portland Bill (maximum of 3E and 1W on 17th). During autumn 1991 a nationwide influx of birds was reflected locally by eight records including 3W at Portland Bill on 7th October. Other notable day-totals from Portland Bill are 3W on 9th September 1985 and 6th September 1992.

Most of the autumn sightings are from Portland Bill (31 birds), Hengistbury (11 birds) and Durlston CP (seven birds). Otherwise the eight remaining birds have been recorded as follows:

1982 Canford Cliffs: flying west 24th September
1987 Southbourne: 7th October
1988 West Bexington: two imms 7th October
1991 Ferrybridge: imm. 14th September
    Chesil Cove: ad. 13th November
1993 Abbotsbury: imm. flying inland 9th September
1998 Hartland Moor: imm. flew into Poole Harbour on a south-easterly gale, passed up Middlebere
    Lake before heading west overland (cf previous record)

The Long-tailed Skua breeds across the Holarctic except for Iceland. Outside the breeding season the species is pelagic and occurs widely, the wintering areas being generally poorly known, but in the Atlantic are thought to be mainly off south-western Africa (Benguela Current off Namibia).

Postscript 2000–2002
There were four records involving an adult at Portland Bill on 13th August 2000, one at Hengistbury on 18th September 2000, an adult at St Aldhelm's Head on 9th June 2001 and an immature at Hengistbury on 22nd October 2002.

Great Skua   *Catharacta skua*

An uncommon passage migrant and winter visitor

Mansel-Pleydell (1888) described this species as "an occasional spring and autumn visitant" and referred to several that had been shot near Weymouth in unspecified years, one at Abbotsbury in autumn 1881, and one shot in Poole Harbour on 19th November 1887 "amongst a lot of Wigeon, one of which it had just struck down". Blathwayt (1945) considered it to be a very rare winter visitor, the most recent report being from Abbotsbury on 22nd December 1921.

The Great Skua remained a rare visitor until the late 1950s when systematic seawatching from Portland Bill revealed it be a regular offshore passage migrant, mainly in autumn. Subsequently records have increased, notably during the 1970s and 1980s, reflecting increased seawatching activity at the main coastal watch-points – see Table 271. Since 1980, totals for spring passage have typically ranged between 30–90 birds except for peaks in 1985 (297) and 1986 (128), and again during 1997–1999 (150, 136, 162). During the same period autumn passage has been considerably more variable with totals ranging from 30 birds in 1981 to 518 birds in 1987. In earlier years there were notable totals in spring 1979 (149) and 1972 (87), and autumn 1974 (125). Day-totals in spring are small and rarely exceed ten birds, so 110E at Portland Bill on 13th April 1985 is truly exceptional, the next highest count being 34 at the same site on 23rd April 1979. Like the other skuas, high autumn totals usually reflect heavy movements caused by severe weather, the most notable being an astonishing 240W at Portland Bill on 18th October 1987 (after the 'hurricane'), 108 at Durlston CP and 80W at Portland Bill on 6th September 1992, and 83 including 78W at Portland Bill on 27th September 1974.

	1950s	1960s	1970s	1980s	1990s
Spring	1	5	46	80	94
Autumn	6	14	48	199	176

Table 271. Spring and autumn 10-year average totals 1950–1999

Although spring migrants occur from March through to June, the main passage takes place during April–May with a distinct peak in the former month. A few birds are regularly recorded in mid-summer. Autumn passage extends from late July through to November, but mainly occurs during August–October with a protracted peak during September–October. This seasonal pattern is well illustrated by records from the main coastal watch-points with April–May accounting for 22% of the total (15% in April), and August–October accounting for 66% of the total (49% during September–October) – see Table 272.

Jan	Feb	Mar	Apr	May	Jun	Jul	Aug	Sep	Oct	Nov	Dec
124	27	62	583	252	75	83	455	944	923	185	77

Table 272. Monthly totals at the main coastal watch-points 1986–1999

This species is the most frequently recorded of the skuas in winter with sightings in all but two years since 1966. Although generally small, numbers have increased in recent winters with notable influxes during 1987/88 (22 bird-days), 1989/90 (34 bird-days), 1992/93 (25 bird-days), 1994/95 (46 bird-days) and 1998/99 (23 bird-days). These totals were totally eclipsed during 1997/98 when 170 bird-days were recorded during December–January including 140 bird-days in the latter month. Most sightings were from Portland Bill and the Chesil with 98 bird-days, the highest count being 38 at Chesil Cove on 4th January. Apart from 1997/98, most records involve 1–2 birds, but five were recorded at West Bexington on 10th–11th February 1990. Unfortunately several reports relate to dead birds, mainly from the Chesil Beach including four at Chesil Cove during 16th–24th January 1993. In earlier years there was an influx of c.23 birds during January–February 1974 including c.20 from Portland Bill peaking at eight on 5th January.

The majority of birds are recorded from the main coastal watch-points with Portland Bill accounting for 61% of the total since 1980, and the Chesil, St Aldhelm's Head, Durlston CP and Hengistbury together accounting for a further 34% – see Table 273. Elsewhere there have been regular sightings in Lyme Bay from West/East Bexington and Abbotsbury Beach, notably 15 at East Bexington on 6th September 1992 and 11 at West Bexington on 1st May 1979. There are occasional reports from other coastal sites, but the species is a rare visitor to the Fleet, Radipole and Lodmoor NRs, and inside Poole and Christchurch Harbours. Although there are no inland records, singles birds have reported flying overland at Abbotsbury on 19th April 1998 and 18th April 1999.

Portland Bill	the Chesil	St Aldhelm's	Durlston CP	Hengistbury	elsewhere
3635	358	169	1164	311	269

Table 273. Totals at the main sites 1980–1999

Although no birds have been ringed in the county, there have been three controls: two from Shetland and one from Orkney.

The Great Skua breeds mainly in Iceland, the Faeroes and northern Scotland. Outside the breeding season the species is pelagic and winters mainly in the North Atlantic.

Postscript 2000–2002

One flying south over Upton Heath on 30th October 2000 is the first inland record for the county. One found dead at West Bexington on 10th January 2001 was ringed on Foula, Shetland on 14th July 1998.

Mediterranean Gull   *Larus melanocephalus*

A locally common winter visitor and passage migrant, scarce resident

The first two county records were in 1958 when an adult in summer plumage was seen following the plough at Puddletown on 1st April, and a near-adult in winter plumage was observed fishing at Portland Bill for several hours on 19th October. Subsequently the species occurred in nine of the next 12 years involving a total of about 18 birds with four during March–April, two in July, 11 during August–October and one in November. Most birds were recorded from the Portland and Weymouth areas including 12 at Portland Bill and four at Radipole NR, the only reports from elsewhere being singles at Peveril Point on 16th October 1964 and 1st October 1968.

During the 1970s there was a marked increase in records reflecting a change in status from its previous rarity to a regular passage migrant and winter visitor. By the end of the decade estimated annual totals for Dorset were generally in the region of 40–60 birds, and in 1979 there were c.200 records just from the Weymouth area, mostly at Radipole NR, involving at least 40 individuals with a peak of eight first-summer birds on 15th June. The expanding presence of Mediterranean Gulls across the county has continued through the 1980s and 1990s. This was reflected by increasing numbers at Radipole NR culminating in 321 bird-days in 1992 – see Tables 274 and 275.

1980	1981	1982	1983	1984	1985
65	155	94	135	145	110

Table 274. Annual totals of records at Radipole NR 1980–1985

1986	1987	1988	1989	1990	1991	1992
139	82	222	209	161	227	321

Table 275. Annual totals (bds) at Radipole NR 1986–1992

Ever since the early 1970s, the environs of Weymouth has been the main area for the species in Dorset. Traditionally birds have been most commonly recorded at Radipole NR, but Lodmoor NR has become an important site in recent years. Both localities are mainly used as pre-roosting areas where birds loaf and wash before moving to the main gull roost in Weymouth Bay. There are regular sightings from other sites in the Weymouth/Fleet area, notably Portland Harbour, Ferrybridge and Abbotsbury. Further west there is another regular winter roost at West Bexington and, during the mid-1980s at least, this site attracted birds from as far inland as Sutton Bingham. Although recorded in all months, Mediterranean Gulls are most numerous during the winter period. Peak counts rarely exceed ten birds, the highest being 15 at West Bexington on 16th November 1984 and 14 at Radipole NR in November 1993, in November 1995 and on 10th December 1997. The wintering population in the Weymouth area has been estimated on several occasions, notably eight in February 1974, 18 during January–April 1977, 20 during January–February 1983 and 10–15 during November–December of the same year, whilst at least 15 birds were present in the Ferrybridge/East Fleet area during December 1997.

By comparison the species is scarcer in the east of the county. It is most frequently recorded from Christchurch Harbour where numbers have increased from annual totals of 5–12 bird-days during 1974–1979 and 8–18 bird-days during 1980–1990 to 36 bird-days in 1991 and 41 bird-days in 1992 – see Table 276. There were surprisingly few reports from Poole Harbour with no sightings until 1976. Subsequently annual totals have gradually increased, but still rarely exceeded ten birds until the late 1990s – see Table 276.

	1970s	1980s	1990s
Christchurch Harbour	8	12	26
Poole Harbour	1	6	12

Table 276. Annual 10-year average totals from Christchurch Harbour and Poole Harbour 1970–1999

There are scattered reports from other coastal sites including some movement off Portland Bill and the Purbeck coast – see Table 277. Despite this, it remains a rare visitor to the extreme west of the county with apparently only four records involving two at Charmouth on 9th May 1987, and singles at West Bay on 2nd January 1993, Charmouth on 2nd February 1994 and Lyme Regis on 6th April 1994.

	1980	1981	1982	1983	1984	1985	1986	1987	1988	1989
Portland Bill	10	2	2	15	8	12	5	6	15	26
Durlston CP	0	0	0	0	0	4	1	4	14	4

	1990	1991	1992	1993	1994	1995	1996	1997	1998	1999
Portland Bill	7	5	8	4	9	19	15	14	nc	nc
Durlston CP	11	9	20	6	22	nc	nc	18	13	12

Table 277. Annual totals for coastal movements at Portland Bill and Durlston CP 1980–1999

Breeding was first attempted, but unsuccessfully, on Brownsea in 1977 and 1978, whilst further attempts were made there in 1980 and 1981. The possibility of Mediterranean Gulls breeding in Poole Harbour was again suspected in 1985 when birds were observed amongst the Black-headed Gull colonies. There were no further sightings that year, but nesting pairs are notoriously difficult to locate amongst thousands of Black-headed Gulls. The next evidence of breeding came in 1990 when six pairs were located amongst two colonies of Black-headed Gulls. Breeding success was uncertain, but a juvenile was recorded nearby at Hatch Pond, Poole on 18th July. Since then breeding attempts have continued with success generally unrecorded except for a juvenile at Redhorn Bay in mid-summer 1996 – see Table 278. Surveillance by wardens is undertaken to protect against illegal egg-collecting. In addition, flood tides pose another threat, for example in 1991 three nests with eggs on the point of hatching were flooded out on 12th/13th June.

1990	1991	1992	1993	1994	1995	1996	1997	1998	1999
6	3	2	5	2–3	2–3	6	8	3	2–3

Table 278. Number of pairs attempting to breed in Poole Harbour 1990–1999

Although the county's first record was at Puddletown, the only other inland records prior to 1983 were in 1979 with one following the plough at Long Bredy on 12th March, and two first-summer birds in the Stour Valley at Sturminster Marshall on 2nd–3rd June, which appeared amongst an influx of gulls after unseasonable flooding. Subsequently there has been an increase in sightings from inland localities, the highest totals being 33 birds in 1999 and 23 birds in 1993 – see Table 279. Research on inland gulls, which was undertaken between August 1992 and March 1993, suggested that inland records of this species tend to occur at times of passage in early autumn and early spring with most birds being found amongst flocks of Common Gulls. There is also evidence to indicate that inland Mediterranean Gulls favour the upper catchments of the Frome and Piddle and surrounding hills including the Ridgeway south of Dorchester. Most records involve 1–2 birds, rarely more, the highest count being five at Durweston on 16th February 1996.

80	81	82	83	84	85	86	87	88	89	90	91	92	93	94	95	96	97	98	99
0	0	0	11	6	4	3	0	3	8	6	7	10	23	9	8	12	15	8	33

Table 279. Inland totals 1980–1999

Although no birds have been ringed in the county, ten Dutch and four Belgian colour-ringed birds have been observed in Dorset including ten at Radipole NR and three at Lodmoor NR. Some of these birds have been well travelled. For example, a bird ringed in the Netherlands in June 1994 was subsequently observed in Devon, the Netherlands, Poole Harbour and at Radipole NR during 1995, whilst another bird ringed in Belgium in June 1997 was subsequently seen in France and at Radipole NR during August–December 1997, in Poole Harbour in 1998, and in France and Hampshire during 1999, and finally a bird ringed in the Netherlands in June 1996 travelled to two sites in Devon in 1998, and to Kent, East Sussex and Radipole NR in 1999. In addition, a bird colour-ringed in the Ukraine in July 1994 was seen at Radipole NR in August and September of the same year.

The Mediterranean Gull breeds almost entirely within Europe where the Ukraine has over 90% of population. Since the 1950s the breeding range has expanded, albeit in small numbers, north-westwards as far as the Netherlands and Great Britain. It winters chiefly in the Mediterranean, but also in the Black Sea and more recently along the Atlantic and North Sea coasts of Europe.

Postscript 2000–2002
In Poole Harbour, five pairs bred in 2000, but no breeding reports were submitted in 2001 and 2002. Otherwise there were notable counts of 11 at Lytchett Bay on 7th July 2001 (the highest count for Poole Harbour) and seven at Wimborne Meadows on 4th April 2001 (the highest count from an inland site).

Laughing Gull *Larus atricilla*

Accidental: five records

No less than four of the five records involve birds seen at Radipole NR.

- 1969 Radipole NR: first-winter/first-summer 17th February–6th October; also visited Lodmoor NR on four occasions, Ferrybridge twice in May, Langton Herring twice in June and Wyke Regis playing fields once in July
- 1980 Lodmoor and Radipole NRs: second-summer 13th April
- 1983 Radipole NR: ad. 20th October
- 1990 Ferrybridge: ad. 18th March
- 1998 Radipole NR: ad. 15th July; also later the same day at Abbotsbury and then West Bexington

The Laughing Gull breeds in North America from Nova Scotia along the eastern seaboard south to Florida and along the Gulf of Mexico as far as Venezuela and French Guiana, also in the West Indies. It winters along the Atlantic coast from the southern USA to northern South America, and along the Pacific coast from southern Mexico to Peru. A vagrant to Great Britain with 96 records up to 2002.

Franklin's Gull *Larus pipixcan*

Accidental: three records

- 1982 Radipole NR: first-winter/first-summer 29th April–10th May; same at Weymouth Beach 30th April. This bird was seen earlier in the year at Plymouth.
- 1990 Sutton Bingham: ad. 9th–10th July
- 2000 Radipole NR and Weymouth Bay: second-winter 13th–19th February and intermittently 26th February–2nd March; same at Maiden Castle and Maiden Newton 25th February

The Franklin's Gull breeds on the prairie wetlands of North America, and winters mainly on the Pacific coasts of Central and South America from Guatemala to Chile. A vagrant to Great Britain with 41 records up to 2002.

Little Gull *Larus minutus*

A locally common passage migrant and winter visitor

Mansel-Pleydell (1888) described this species as "a rare winter visitant" and mentioned five records involving seven birds between 1818 and 1872, including one shot at Bryanston on 21st September 1818. Blathwayt (1945) considered it to be a passage migrant and winter visitor in small numbers, but only referred to five reports of single birds between 1920 and 1937.

During the 1950s there was a marked increase in sightings and by 1959 the annual total had reached c.40 birds with c.20 including a flock of 14 at the Chesil on 8th December – see Table 280. Subsequently the Little Gull has become a regular passage migrant and winter visitor with reports in all months. This increase is mirrored nationally and may be related to the expansion of the Finnish breeding population by at least 50%.

1950	1951	1952	1953	1954	1955	1956	1957	1958	1959
0	1	5	1	25	10	11	12	18	40

Table 280. Annual totals 1950–1959

This species is characterised by erratic appearances, which are frequently associated with inclement weather. These influxes may occur at times of passage or in winter, and occasionally involve several hundred birds – see Table 281. Otherwise peak counts are often in single figures and rarely exceed 20 birds, the most notable being 42 at Portland Bill on 27th September 1963, 32 at Chiswell Lane, Portland on 17th October 1982, a flock of 30W at Lodmoor NR on 12th November 1994 and 30 at Chesil Cove on 1st November 1991, whilst 19 at Lyme Regis on 12th February 1974 is an unusual record for the place and time.

1960: Heavy autumn passage at Portland Bill with 261 birds between 12th September and 13th November (maximum of 42 on 22nd October).

1961: Heavy autumn passage at Portland Bill with 387 birds between 24th August and 30th October (maxima of 69 on 14th October and 78 on 20th October).

1974: Remarkable passage on 3rd May with 113E at Portland Bill and 80E + c.75 grounded at Ferrybridge.

1986: Notable westerly passage on 27th–28th October with 66 at Durlston CP and 25 at Portland Bill.

1987: Modest passage after the 'hurricane' of 15th/16th October (maximum of 28 at Hengistbury on 16th).

1990: Notable influx associated with westerly gales during February resulting in monthly bird-day totals of 109 at Christchurch Harbour, 81 along the Fleet, 24 at Chesil Cove and 18 at Lodmoor NR with a maximum of 28 at Christchurch Harbour on 20th. Heavy easterly passage on 1st May with 88 at St Aldhelm's Head and 58 at the Chesil.

1991: Notable passage of 93E at Portland Bill on 10th April.

1996: Large influx in January with maxima of 100 at Burton Bradstock on 15th and 31 at Chesil Cove on 12th.

Table 281. Largest influxes/movements 1960–1996

The strongest hint of breeding in the county concerns an adult associating with the Kittiwake colony on the West Cliffs at Portland Bill from 22nd April to 25th June 1959. The bird was often heard calling loudly, whilst on the 6th June it was observed carrying nesting material. An immature was also seen in the Kittiwake colony at Portland Bill on 18th June 1967. Finally a bird summered with the Portland Harbour tern colony in 1986. Otherwise there are occasional records in mid-summer, often involving immature birds which rarely linger, so singles at Arne NR during 28th May–10th July 1989 and Radipole NR during 3rd July–7th September 1993 are notable 'long-stayers'.

The environs of Weymouth is the main area for Little Gulls in the county. Although Radipole NR is the most favoured site, there are regular records from Lodmoor NR, Weymouth Bay, Portland Harbour and the Fleet. In the east, the species is mainly recorded from Christchurch Harbour with fewer sightings in the Poole Harbour area. Otherwise there are scattered reports from elsewhere along the coast as far west as Lyme Regis including Portland Bill and Purbeck.

Coastal movements at Portland Bill and Durlston CP reflect the seasonal pattern for the county as a whole with distinct peaks in spring and autumn, notably in April–May when passage is predominantly easterly, and again in October often associated with stormy weather – see Table 282. Considering the sporadic nature of the species' occurrences in Dorset, it is not surprising to find that the strength of these coastal movements is highly variable, particularly in spring – see Table 283.

Jan	Feb	Mar	Apr	May	Jun	Jul	Aug	Sep	Oct	Nov	Dec
14	11	34	216	145	3	3	14	47	185	48	14

Table 282. Monthly totals at Portland Bill and Durlston CP 1986–1995

	80	81	82	83	84	85	86	87	88	89	90	91	92	93	94	95	96	97
Spring	60	0	1	2	28	6	4	16	9	20	68	113	1	4	30	32	15	14
Autumn	26	26	54	14	17	17	38	31	23	24	6	11	16	21	27	7	19	1

Table 283. Spring and autumn totals at Portland Bill 1980–1997

79	80	81	82	83	84	85	86	87	88	89	90	91	92	93	94	95	96	97	98	99
3	0	0	3	0	0	0	0	2	10	0	6	2	0	2	1+	7	2	0	1	3

Table 284. Inland totals 1979–1999

Inland records were very rare prior to 1979, but subsequently there has been an increase, particularly since 1987 – see Table 284. The majority of reports are from the Lower Avon Valley, mainly Coward's Marsh, Christchurch including about eight birds during 18th April–26th May 1988 (maximum of four in May), four on 25th February 1990, and five on 21st -22nd January 1995. There are a few sightings from elsewhere inland:

1972   River Stour, Corfe Mullen: 17th April
1979   River Stour, Sturminster Marshall: three 2nd–3rd June–appeared amongst an influx of gulls
        after unseasonable flooding
1982   Modbury FF: two 30th September and three 1st October
1987   Corfe Castle: 8th March
1988   Herrison: 10th September
        Nether Cerne: 1st–2nd October
1990   Dorchester: 15th, 21st and 22nd February with a second bird on 22nd February
1996   Sherborne Lake: singles 20th–21st January and 10th September
1998   Lower Bockhampton: 20th December
1999   Sturminster Marshall GP: singles 16th and 27th March
        Sherborne Lake: 6th November

Only one bird has been ringed in the county.

The Little Gull breeds mainly from the Baltic eastwards across Russia to eastern Asia and sporadically to the west and south of the main range. It has recently colonised North America. Knowledge of winter distribution is incomplete, but the species occurs offshore from the North Sea and Irish Sea southwards along the Atlantic seaboard of Europe to north-west Africa, also in the Mediterranean, Black and Caspian Seas.

Postscript 2000–2002

There were notable autumn movements in each year including c.125 at Chesil Cove during November–December 2000 (maximum of 40 on 22nd November), 61 at Portland Bill and 46W at Peveril Point on 26th October 2001, and in 2002–50E at Portland Bill on 20th October with 67W there on 10th November, and 42W at Hengistbury on 12th October with 34W there on 29th October. In addition, there were unusually high numbers of inland sightings with eight records involving ten birds in 2000, two records of single birds in 2001 and one bird in 2002.

Sabine's Gull   *Larus sabini*

A scarce passage migrant

There are five old records involving one at Wareham in 1867, one in Poole Harbour in October 1891, and the rest from Weymouth with one in early November 1893, two (one shot) in autumn 1896 and one in autumn 1916.

There were no further reports until 1951 when an immature flew south at Portland Bill on 24th September. Subsequently sightings have increased and since 1980 this delightful gull has occurred annually.

The vast majority of records (94%) are for the autumn with seasonal totals normally between 1–5 birds and rarely reaching double figures except for 15 in 1988, 13 in 1960 and 10 in 1992 – see Fig 32. These counts 'pale into insignificance', however, when compared with the remarkable influx resulting from the 'hurricane' of October 1987. A total of 123 birds were recorded during 16th–26th October including an amazing 88 bird-days at Hengistbury, but only 15 bird-days at Portland Bill and seven bird-days at Durlston CP. At Hengistbury the peak counts were 14W on 18th and 58W on 19th including flocks of 22 and nine, whilst at Portland Bill the maximum was seven on 17th. Otherwise most autumn sightings involve 1–2 birds, the only other count exceeding three being 7W at Hengistbury on 7th September 1992.

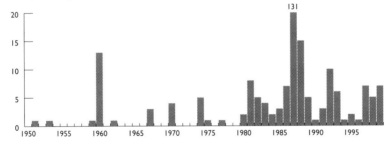

Fig 32. Autumn totals 1951–1999

Although autumn reports extend from 23rd August to 26th November, most occur in September and October which account for 48% and 41% respectively of the total (excluding records for 1987) – see Table 285.

	August	September	October	November
Excluding 1987	6 (5%)	60 (48%)	51 (41%)	8 (6%)
Including 1987	6 (2%)	65 (25%)	174 (68%)	11 (4%)

Table 285. Autumn monthly totals 1950–1999

In autumn most sightings are from Portland Bill, the Chesil Cove/Ferrybridge/East Fleet/Portland Harbour area, Durlston CP and Christchurch Harbour – see Table 286. Elsewhere birds have been recorded from West Bexington (ten), the Nothe/Weymouth Bay (five), Lodmoor NR (four), Peveril Point (four), Lyme Regis (two), Radipole NR (two), Fitzworth (two) and singles from: Abbotsbury Beach, Kimmeridge Bay, St Aldhelm's Head, Dancing Ledge, Poole Harbour Entrance, Little Sea, Brownsea and Branksome. The 1987 influx also produced the only inland record for the county at Warmwell on 23rd–24th October.

	Excluding 1987 influx	Including 1987 influx
Portland Bill	46 (37%)	62 (24%)
Chesil Cove/Fleet area	19 (15%)	22 (9%)
Durlston CP	9 (7%)	16 (6%)
Christchurch Harbour	27 (21%)	119 (46%)
elsewhere	25 (20%)	38 (15%)

Table 286. Autumn totals at the main sites 1951–1999

The species is rarely reported outside the autumn period. There is some evidence of spring passage involving ten birds between late April and mid-June as listed below:

1958   Portland Bill: near-ad. 10th May
1961   Peveril Point: imm. 13th–17th June; same at Brownsea 18th June
1968   Peveril Point: 13th May
1975   Chesil Cove: 2nd May
1976   Hengistbury: imm. 25th April
1987   Portland Bill: ad. 30th May
1988   Portland Bill: two first-summer birds 24th April
1994   Durlston CP and Peveril Point: ad. 4th June
1996   St Aldhelm's Head: first-summer 20th May

There are three mid-summer records as follows:

1993   Hengistbury: 30th June
1998   Chesil Cove: single first-summer birds on 12th and 23rd July

There are only two winter records as follows:

1968   Peveril Point: 6th February
1994   Hengistbury: ad. 29th December

The Sabine's Gull breeds from the subarctic to the high Arctic with the Canadian and Greenland populations migrating across the North Atlantic, south through the Bay of Biscay and along the west African coast to winter off Namibia and South Africa.

Postscript 2000–2002
At Portland Bill, one on 10th December 2000 constitutes only the second county record for that month. In addition, there were four singles at four sites during 26th August–11th October 2000. In 2001 10 birds were reported from five sites during 22nd September–26th October including the first record from Abbotsbury on the latter date. There were no sightings in 2002.

Bonaparte's Gull   *Larus philadelphia*

Accidental: four records

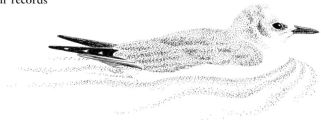

1970   Durlston CP: ad. 14th March
1975   Christchurch Harbour: ad. 9th–12th April
1981   Weymouth Bay, Radipole and Lodmoor NRs: first-summer 2nd–16th April; same at Hengistbury 20th April; returned to Radipole and Lodmoor NRs 22nd May–30th June and 13th July–2nd August
1990   The Grove, Portland: first-winter 2nd March

Bonaparte's Gull breeds in the taiga regions of North America from Alaska across Canada to James Bay. It winters from the Great Lakes and along the coasts of the USA south to northern Mexico and the West Indies. A vagrant to Great Britain with 115 records up to 2002.

Black-headed Gull   *Larus ridibundus*

An abundant resident, winter visitor and passage migrant

Both Mansel-Pleydell (1888) and Blathwayt (1945) considered this species to be a numerous resident. In the Poole Harbour area breeding was first recorded at Little Sea in about 1877 and spread to nearby Rempstone Heath where the colony was estimated to be c.1,000 pairs in c.1900. The Little Sea colony was deserted between 1888 and 1913, but breeding was re-established with numbers rising to 60 pairs in 1919, before declining and finally disappearing by 1938. Nearby at Rempstone Heath a major heath fire in 1916 drove the colony to Arne. By 1919 the gullery was mostly at Arne, but then spread to Morden Heath, which held 800 pairs by 1921. These colonies subsequently dwindled and moved to saltmarshes along the western side of the harbour at Holton Shore where there were 1,320 pairs in 1938 and c.2,000 pairs during the early 1940s, before the bulk of the colony shifted to Brownsea with c.1,000 pairs present in 1948. By 1955 all breeding sites in the Poole Harbour area had disappeared.

Recolonisation took place at Brownsea during the early 1960s with 100–250 pairs present during 1961–1964 – see Table 287. Although numbers declined to very low levels during the late 1960s, the colony maintained its tenuous foothold and increased during the 1970s to 200 pairs in 1980 and 150 pairs in 1981. Since then the size of the colony has varied considerably, but c.209 pairs (418 birds) were present on 29th June 1996 and 175 pairs in 1999. By 1970 colonies were well established at two other sites in Poole Harbour, at Fitzworth and Holton Shore where c.144 and c.68 birds respectively were counted in May 1971. There is only one further report of breeding from Fitzworth, but the colony at Holton Shore survived up to 1980 at least with counts of 263 nests in 1972, c.1000 birds in 1975 and 400 pairs in 1976, whilst breeding was recorded at Holes Bay in 1977 (20 pairs) and 1978 (40 pairs). There are no references to colonies other than Brownsea until 1984 when many pairs were present on Round/Long Island. Subsequently the main colonies were based at Holton Shore and Round/Long Island during 1985–1992, but then only at the former site for the rest of the 1990s, except for 650 pairs at Fitzworth in 1994. Numbers at these main colonies increased dramatically with 2,000–4,000 pairs during 1985–1990, 5,500 pairs in 1991, 4,740 pairs in 1992 and 5,000–6,000 pairs during 1993–1998 – see Table 288. In addition, seven pairs bred at Furzey Island in 1994 with 30 pairs there in 1998 and 35 pairs in 1999, whilst three pairs bred at Green Island in 1996. At 5,000+ pairs the harbour holds a population of national importance, representing 3.4% of the British breeding population.

1961	1962	1963	1964	1965	1966	1967	1968	1969	1970	1971	1972	1973
150	100	150	250	few	40	1	9	nc	22	20	30	63

1974	1975	1976	1977	1978	1979	1980	1981	1982	1983	1984	1985	1986
40	20	13	49	85	nc	200	150	90	150	19	28	70

1987	1988	1989	1990	1991	1992	1993	1994	1995	1996	1997	1998	1999
nc	66	91	70	42	120	100	120	120	209	220	150	175

Table 287. Number of breeding pairs on Brownsea 1961–1999

1991	1992	1993	1994	1995	1996	1997	1998	1999
5500	4740	5000	5750	5000	6000	5000	5000	1466

Table 288. Number of breeding pairs at the main colonies in Poole Harbour excluding Brownsea 1991–1999

There was a colony of 20 pairs near Wimborne at Uddens Heath in the 1930s, but the area was burnt in 1938. Otherwise there are very few reports of breeding from elsewhere within the county. Odd pairs occasionally nest with terns on the Chesil Beach, whilst there is a curious reference to breeding at Portland Bill in 1976 with the first juvenile seen on 2nd July. Finally a pair nested at Stanpit Marsh, Christchurch Harbour in 1990.

Outside the breeding season Black-headed Gulls are found commonly throughout the county, spreading from their more favoured sites to forage along the entire coast and well inland where they utilise a wide range of habitats including pasture, ploughed fields, refuse tips, urban parks and even gardens. The species is very much an opportunistic feeder exploiting chances as they arise, for example 15,000 feeding on dead fish washed up on Overcombe and Preston Beach on 28th January 1984, 10,000 on flooded meadows at Wimborne on 16th October 1976 with 5,000 on flooded meadows between Corfe Mullen and Sturminster Marshall on 15th–16th July 1982, 5,000 on plough on the Ridgeway between Weymouth and Dorchester 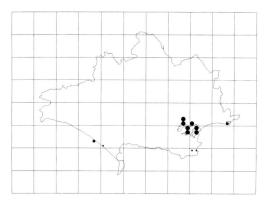 during winter 1992/93, 4,000 at Canford Heath Tip during both winter periods in 1985, and 1,500 hawking midges at Radipole NR in late August 1984.

The population, which includes immigrants, is at its highest in winter when huge roosts develop. In January 1993, the ten-yearly BTO Gull Roost Survey collected data from important sites on the weekend of 23rd/24th producing a county total of over 44,000 birds. Peak counts at most of the individual roost sites have been exceeded on other occasions, notably c.30,000 in the Wareham Channel on 29th December 1991, 28,000 at Christchurch Harbour on 20th January 1999 and 20,000 in Weymouth Bay on 7th January 1989 – see Table 289. Although there are no specific counts, the Dorset Bird Reports for 1998–1999 assert that 20,000–25,000 birds roost in the Wareham Channel in winter. In addition, the WeBS counts for the whole of Poole Harbour in recent years have produced counts of 25,157 on 13th August 1995, 23,462 in January 1992 and 19,183 in February 1996. Before the Weymouth Bay roost develops, there are pre-roost gatherings at Radipole and Lodmoor NRs where counts number in the thousands and sometimes reach 10,000 or more, the highest being 18,000 at Radipole NR in December 1985, and c.10,000 at Lodmoor NR on 4th February 1985 and during November–December 1986. In November 1986 the pre-roost gatherings of 15,000 at Radipole NR and 10,000 at Lodmoor NR suggest that the peak count for the Weymouth Bay roost may have exceeded the site maximum of c.20,000.

Flocks of Black-headed Gulls commuting between their roosting sites on the coast and inland feeding areas are a familiar sight during the non-breeding season. Regular flight lines develop, usually along river valleys, the highest count being 8,000 commuting to floodwater in the Lower Avon Valley during January 1995.

Coastal movements are mainly easterly in spring and westerly in autumn with peak day-totals rarely exceeding 1,000, the highest in recent years being 2,700W at Durlston CP on 10th September 1982, 1,659E at St Aldhelm's Head during 3rd–4th March 1994 and 1,500W at Hengistbury on 14th October 1998. In addition, c.2000 fed offshore at Portland Bill during 21st–23rd September 1988. Coastal movements may also occur during periods of cold weather, for example at Durlston CP 2,800E during 3rd–18th January 1985 and 2,340E in January 1982.

A total of 2,989 birds has been ringed in the county. Recoveries show that after the breeding season Dorset ringed birds generally disperse westwards mainly to Devon, Cornwall and south Wales. Further afield there have been foreign recoveries from the Netherlands (5), Sweden (4), Belgium (2), Finland (2),

238

and Germany, Denmark, Poland, Estonia, Spain and remarkably Algeria (all 1 each). The proportion of Black-headed Gulls controlled in the Britain Isles with foreign rings is small, which suggests that most of the native population remains in the country during the non-breeding season. Those Dorset birds that remain to winter in the county are supplemented by many others from the east and north east of Great Britain and particularly the southern North Sea coasts. Most controls of foreign ringed birds also originate from the east with totals as follows: Lithuania (16), the Netherlands (13), Denmark (10), Finland (8), Belgium (7), Germany (6), Poland (5), Sweden (4), Estonia (4), Norway (2), the former Czechoslovakia (2), Spain (2) and Switzerland (1).

	Max count and date	Other counts
Weymouth Bay	20,000 in Jan 1989	15,000–20,000 in both winter periods 1980– 1982; 15,000 in both winter periods 1979, Dec 1991, Dec 1992 and Feb 1993; 10,000–15,000 in Jan and Nov 1975; 10,000 in Jan and Aug 1970
Radipole NR	18,000 in Dec 1985	c.16,000 in Jan 1987; c.15,000 in Nov 1986; c.10,000 in Dec 1982
Lodmoor NR	c.10,000 in Feb 1985 and Nov–Dec 1986	9,000 in Jan 1984 and Jan 1989; 8,000 in Jan 1990
Wareham Channel	30,000 in Dec 1991	22,790 in Jan 1993 (BTO Survey); 20,000 in Sep 1965 and Jan 1992; 15,000 in March 1977 & March 1987; 13,000 in March 1989; 10,000 in both winter periods 1982 & Nov 1984
Lytchett Bay	12,000 in early winter 1982	7,000 in March 1997
Christchurch Hbr	28,000 in Jan 1999	20,000 in Jan 1983; 15,000–20,000 in Dec 1996; 14,500 in Feb 1997; 10,623 in Jan 1993 (BTO Survey); 10,000 in Jan and Feb 1998

Table 289. Roost and pre-roost counts (mainly winter) at the main sites 1965–1999

The Black-headed Gull breeds across much of Eurasia, mainly between 40°N and 65°N. It is mostly migratory over much of the central and eastern parts of the breeding range, but dispersive and partially migratory elsewhere. It winters widely over the more temperate areas of Eurasia south to the northern tropics of Africa and Asia.

Postscript 2000–2002
The breeding population in Poole Harbour was estimated at c.5,200 pairs in 2000 and c.5,128 pairs in 2002. There is evidence of a decline in winter numbers, e.g. only c.3,000–6,000 birds now reported roosting in Weymouth Bay.

Ring-billed Gull   *Larus delawarensis*

A scarce winter visitor and passage migrant

This species was first recorded in 1976 when Radipole NR hosted an adult on 4th February and a second-summer bird on 29th April. There were further records from Radipole NR in 1978 with a first-summer bird moulting into second-winter plumage from 9th to 21st July, and 1980 with a first-winter bird from 5th November to 7th December when it was killed by a passing car! In spring 1981 there was a large influx of Ring-billed Gulls into Great Britain. This resulted in a remarkable total of 12 birds (11 first-years and one adult) being recorded at Radipole NR with two of these individuals wandering to Lodmoor NR and one to the Fleet at Langton Herring. Since then the species has occurred annually with totals ranging from 14 in 1983 to only one in 1999 – see Table 290.

	81	82	83	84	85	86	87	88	89	90	91	92	93	94	95	96	97	98	99
Adult	1	4	8	7	5	2	4	2	3	7	3	8	9	6	3	6	3	4	1
Second-year	2	5	1	1	0	1	0	0	1	0	1	2	0	3	2	1	3	1	0
First-year	11	1	5	1	1	1	2	0	0	1	3	2	1	1	0	0	2	0	0

Table 290. Annual totals for each age group 1981–1999

The 1981 influx seems to have established a residual population of birds on this side of the Atlantic, which influenced the subsequent pattern of occurrence in the county. The preponderance of second-year birds in 1982 and adults subsequently strongly suggests that many of the birds returned in successive years up to at least 1985. There were some new arrivals during this period as shown by the occurrences of first-year birds annually during 1982–1985. After low numbers in the late 1980s, there were more influxes during the 1990s, but not on the same scale as spring 1981, and mainly involving adult and second-year birds.

The seasonal pattern of occurrence is complex – see Table 291. There is a prolonged spring passage extending from early February to late May. The earlier passage consists mainly of adults, which curiously show two distinct peaks, one during the first half of February and the second from mid-March to mid-April. Second-year birds are mainly recorded from mid-March to late April, whilst the later passage is dominated by first-year birds, which peak in May. Although three first-year birds have lingered into the summer, only two new arrivals have occurred between the end of May and mid-October involving a first/second-year bird at Radipole NR from 9th–21st July 1978 and a second-winter bird at Lytchett Bay on 19th–20th September 1997. From mid-October, records consisting mainly of adult birds increase to a distinct peak during the second half of December, with fewer new birds being reported during January.

Jan	Jan	Feb	Feb	Mar	Mar	Apr	Apr	May	May	Jun	Jun
1–15	16–31	1–15	15–28	1–15	16–31	1–15	16–30	1–15	16–31	1–15	16–30
4:2:1	4:1:0	11:0:0	5:2:0	7:1:1	14:2:3	9:2:5	1:4:5	3:1:7	0:0:6	0	0

Jul	Jul	Aug	Aug	Sep	Sep	Oct	Oct	Nov	Nov	Dec	Dec
1–15	16–31	1–15	16–31	1–15	16–30	1–15	16–31	1–15	16–30	1–5	16–31
0:1:0	0	0	0	0	0:1:0	0	1:1:1	5:3:1	5:1:0	6:2:1	12:2:2

Table 291. Half-monthly totals for different age groups (first-years, second-years, adults) 1976–1999

Although certain aspects of this seasonal pattern mirror those of some commoner gulls, others appear to be more unusual. The second spring peak of adult birds and the later peak of first-year birds is very similar to the pattern shown by spring passage Common Gulls, a species with which the Ring-billed Gull closely associates. By contrast, the early spring peak of adults during the first half of February indicates a much earlier start to passage than is the case with other gulls in Dorset, whilst the striking peak in the second half of December does not conform with any recognised feature of gull movements in the county.

Unlike other parts of the British Isles where Ring-billed Gulls regularly overwinter, the species rarely stays for long in Dorset. For example, only 32 (22%) of the 146 birds recorded have remained for a week or more, and only nine of these have overwintered or stayed for a protracted period – all in the Weymouth area as detailed below:

1981	Radipole and Lodmoor NRs: first-year 23rd May to at least 15th August
1981/82	Radipole NR: second-winter/ad. 31st October–1st February
1983/84	Radipole NR: first-year 4th December–22nd July
	Radipole and Lodmoor NRs: ad. 28th December–11th April
1984/85	Radipole and Lodmoor NRs: second-winter 8th November–14th April
1994/95	Weymouth area: second-winter 19th November–21st March; additionally an ad. and another second-winter 2nd January–21st March
1995/96	Weymouth area, ad. 8th November–20th March

Radipole NR is the main site for the species with 58% of the records, and together with Lodmoor NR and Weymouth Bay, account for 71% of the county's total – see Table 292. There are 14 records from the Fleet with ten at Abbotsbury including a mini-influx of four birds during 18th–28th March 1997, and seven records from West Bexington. Birds frequently move between sites in the Weymouth/Fleet area. In the east of the county the Ring-billed Gull is comparatively rare with only eight records from Poole Harbour including four at Lytchett Bay and two at Poole Park, and eight records from Christchurch Harbour. Elsewhere along the coast, a first-winter bird feeding at the Southwell sewer on 13th January 1987 represents the only sighting from Portland, whilst a second-winter bird at Branksome Chine on 1st January 1998 is the only other coastal record. Otherwise there are a few inland reports as follows:

1983 Sutton Bingham: ad. 6th March and first-winter 21st October
1986 Dorchester: ad. 28th–29th December
1989 Near Sydling St Nicholas: ad. 29th March
1990 Dorchester: ad. 12th–15th March
1996 Dorchester/Charminster: ad. 31st January
1999 Sturminster Marshall GP: ad. 20th–23rd March

	Total for sites where birds first recorded	Total for sites including birds first recorded elsewhere
West Bexington	7	–
The Fleet	12	14
Radipole NR	85	88
Lodmoor NR	14	24
Weymouth Bay	4	9
Poole Harbour	7	8
Christchurch Harbour	8	–
inland	7	–

Table 292. Totals at the main sites 1976–1999

The overall distribution of the Ring-billed Gull in Dorset, including inland records, corresponds well with that of the Common Gull, notably the latter species' preference for roosting and pre-roosting sites close to the favoured feeding areas on the chalk downs inland of Weymouth Bay and West Bexington. This is not surprising considering the close association between the two species.

This North American gull breeds in two populations – one based on the prairies, and the other on the Great Lakes and east up the St Lawrence to Labrador and Newfoundland. It winters mainly in the coastal states of the USA south to Mexico. The Ring-billed Gull was not recorded in the British Isles until 1973 but subsequently sightings have increased and after the influx of 1981 the number of records remain high with the total at 614 by 1987.

Postscript 2000–2002
By contrast to the normal distribution of birds in Dorset, all records were from the east of the county. In 2000 there were single adults at Swineham Point, Poole Harbour on 21st February and Sturminster Marshall GP on 26th–27th March, and a second-winter bird at Stanpit Marsh, Christchurch Harbour on 4th November. In 2001 there were reports of an adult, possibly the same individual, in pig fields near Didlington on four dates during 1st February–18th March and nearby at Wimborne Meadows on 1st and 10th April with a second-year bird at the latter site on 11th April. In 2002 there was a second-winter bird at Lytchett Bay on 23rd February, an adult at Corfe Mullen Tip during 5th–15th March with the same bird at Sturminster Marshall GP on 10th March, and second-summer bird at the latter site on 21st April.

Common Gull (Mew Gull) *Larus canus*

A common winter visitor and passage migrant
The status of this species has not changed since the 19th Century when Mansel-Pleydell (1888) described it as "an autumn and winter visitant in some numbers from the north".

Although small breeding populations have become established in some wintering areas, the Common Gull has not bred in Dorset. In fact it is normally rather scarce during the summer with relatively few records between mid-May and mid-July. There is a marked arrival during October with numbers at their highest during the winter when huge roosts develop. In January 1993, the ten-yearly BTO Gull Roost Survey collected data from important sites on the weekend of 23rd/24th producing a county total of over 12,000 birds. Peak counts at most of the individual roost sites have been exceeded on other occasions, notably 20,000 at West Bexington on 22nd March 1976, 12,000 in the Wareham Channel in February 1958 and January 1978, and 10,000 in Weymouth Bay during both winter periods in 1982 – see Table 293. West Bexington has regularly recorded high counts in March when the roost consists mostly of adult birds. The lack of similar increases in March at other coastal sites suggest that most movement occurs overland. Prior to roosting in Weymouth Bay, there are pre-roost gatherings at Radipole and Lodmoor NRs where numbers sometimes exceed 3,000 birds, the highest counts being c.8,100 at Radipole NR in December 1985 and c.3,000–5,000 at Lodmoor NR during the winter periods in 1986 – see Table 293.

	Max count and date	Other counts
West Bexington	20,000 in March 1976	15,000 in Jan 1972; 10,000–15,000 in Feb 1971; 14,000 in March 1977; 10,000 in March 1980, March 1984 and March 1985
The Fleet	4,000 at Abbotsbury in March 1997	2,101 in Nov 1999; 2,000 in Feb 1995
Weymouth Bay	10,000 in both winter periods 1982	5,000–10,000 in both winter periods 1980 and 1981; 6,000–8,000 in March 1991; 5,000 in both winter periods 1979, Jan 1989, Feb 1993 and Jan 1994
Radipole NR	8,100 in Dec 1985	3,900 in Jan 1986; 3,800 in Dec 1984; 3,500 in Dec 1982
Lodmoor NR	3,000–5000 on sev. dates in both winter periods 1986	1,500 in Feb 1996; 1,000 in Jan 1984, Dec 1992 and Nov 1995
Wareham Channel	12,000 in Feb 1958 and Jan 1978	10,000 in Dec 1951; 7,000 in Dec 1992 and both winter periods 1999; 6,930 in Jan 1993 (BTO Survey);
Christchurch Hbr	566 in Dec 1990	560 in Nov 1991; only 20 in Jan 1993 (BTO Survey)

Table 293. Roost and pre-roost counts (mainly winter) at the main sites 1951–1999

Earthworms are the staple food for Common Gulls in winter and the highest worm populations are found in soils formed on calcareous strata such as chalk and limestone. This fact may account for the low numbers roosting in Christchurch Harbour, as roosts further west have easier access to favoured feeding areas, most notably the chalk downs inland of Weymouth Bay and West Bexington. These inland sites often attract large numbers, for example at Puddletown 3,000 on 22nd January 1991, 2,000 on 9th January 1990 and 1,600 on 23rd December 1984, also 3,000–4,000 at Winterborne Houghton in late March 1965, 2,000 in the Batcombe to Clay Pigeon Hill area on 19th March 1983 and 2,000 in the Grimstone to Winterbourne Abbas area on 9th March 1984. It is interesting to note the coincidence between the high counts at inland sites and the West Bexington roost during March.

Like the Black-headed Gull, flocks of Common Gulls, which are often intermixed with the previous species, commute between their roosting sites on the coast and inland feeding areas by following regular flight lines along the river valleys.

Coastal movements are often easterly in spring, but can lack directional bias, and mainly westerly in autumn. Numbers are relatively low with day-totals rarely exceeding 200, the highest being c.1,000SE at Ferrybridge on 28th April 1976, 550W at Portland Bill on 3rd April 1977 and 500E at Hengistbury on 25th March 1987, whilst 700N at Arne NR on 13th April 1974 is also noteworthy. In addition, large feeding flocks have been occasionally recorded at Portland Bill, notably c.1,000 during 1st–5th April 1981 and more recently c.1,000 on 20th February 1996. Coastal movements may also occur during periods of cold weather, for example 1,880 at Portland Bill in February 1986 with 700E there on 22nd–23rd December 1996, and 1,395E at Durlston CP during January–February 1985.

A total of seven birds has been ringed in the county. There have been foreign controls from Denmark (two), and singles from Belgium, the Netherlands, Norway, Poland and Estonia.

The Common Gull breeds mainly north of 50° throughout Eurasia and the western parts of North America, but it is scarce between 50°N and 55°N in Europe, breeding in any numbers only in the north and north-west of the British Isles. In Europe the Common Gull winters mainly along the western seaboard (including the Baltic) south to Brittany and the north Atlantic coast of France to approx 45°N.

Postscript 2000–2002

There is evidence of a decline in winter numbers, e.g. only c.1,000–2,000 birds are now reported roosting in Weymouth Bay.

Lesser Black-backed Gull   *Larus fuscus graellsii*

A scarce resident, and fairly common winter visitor and passage migrant

Mansel-Pleydell (1888) considered this species to be a frequent visitor to the coast, but noted there were no authentic reports of breeding. Blathwayt (1945) described it as a passage migrant, very rare in winter, and mentioned that an occasional pair may breed on coastal cliffs, two pairs being found nesting at Portland in 1944.

The Lesser Black-backed Gull prefers to nest in dense colonies on level ground with short vegetation near the sea. Since Dorset lacks undisturbed areas of this optimal habitat, the species has remained a scarce breeding bird with nesting most frequent on Brownsea with a peak of four pairs in 1981 – see Table 294. Elsewhere evidence of breeding has been recorded from Ballard Down, Durlston CP, the Verne Cliffs at Portland, Portland Dockyard (including a moored landing craft in 1978) and the Portland Harbour Breakwaters. More recently breeding has spread to built-up areas with reports of rooftop nesting from North Portland and Weymouth in 1994, factory roofs near Holes Bay in 1996 and 1997, Christchurch and Mudeford (2–3 pairs) in 1998 and 1999, and Poole Town Centre in 1999.

	1952	1971	1972	1973	1974	1975	1976	1978	1980	1981	1982
Brownsea	0	2+1*	3	2–3	3	2	0	0	1	4	1
elsewhere	1	0	0	1	1	1	1	1	0	0	1

	1985	1986	1990	1991	1992	1994	1996	1997	1998	1999
Brownsea	1+1*	1*	0	1	0	0	0	0	0	0
elsewhere	0	0	1	0	1–2	2–3	1	1	2–3	4

Table 294. Number of breeding pairs 1952–1999. *paired with Herring Gull

Both passage and winter numbers have increased, particularly during the late 1990s. The Lesser Black-backed Gull was a rare winter visitor until the late 1960s, when small numbers started to regularly occur in the county. In January 1993, the ten-yearly BTO Gull Roost Survey collected data from important sites on the weekend of 23rd/24th producing a county total of over 250 birds. Peak counts at most of the individual roost sites have been exceeded on other occasions – see Table 295. Several of these peak counts coincide with spring passage in March and the end of autumn passage in November. Despite the increase in the winter population, the highest numbers typically occur in autumn, the most notable counts being from Lytchett Bay with 2,128 on 14th August 1999, 1,400 in September 1997 and 1,050

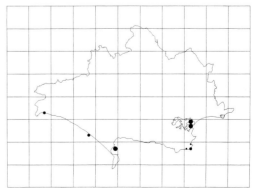

	Max count and date	Other counts
West Bay	121 in Nov 1992	
The Fleet	200 in Nov 1995	
Weymouth Bay	296 in March 1988	264 in March 1998; 222 in March 1995; c.200 in Dec 1983; only 19 in Jan 1993 (BTO Survey)
Radipole NR	340 in Nov 1997	201 in March 1987
Lodmoor Tip/NR	310 in Nov 1995	216 in Feb 1996; 201 in March 1987
Wareham Channel	2,000–3,000 in autumn/ winter 1998 and 1999	500 in Nov 1991 and Dec 1992; 400 in Dec 1996; 197 in Jan 1993 (BTO Survey)
Christchurch Hbr	380 in Jan 1998	260 in Dec 1998; 115 in Jan 1997; only 31 in Jan 1993 (BTO Survey)

Table 295. Roost and pre-roost counts (mainly winter) at the main sites 1968–1999

on 20th September 1995, whilst in September 1988 large numbers were attracted to sprat shoals off the Chesil with 1,500 in the Chesil Cove/Ferrybridge area on 21st–22nd and 600 nearby at Portland Bill on 21st (cf. Herring Gull).

Inland the species was very rare prior to 1980 and remained scarce until the late 1980s after which records increased, mainly during the autumn and winter. In the north of the county, a mid-winter influx of birds occurred in the Sherborne area during 1987–1993 at least with peak counts of 260 in January 1989, 150 in January 1990 and 103 in February 1992. These birds were thought to roost at Chew Valley Lake in Somerset. In the Lower Avon Valley daily movements of up to 250 birds were recorded in 1993 with 800 commuting to and from floodwater there in January 1995. More recently there has been a sudden arrival of birds in the Stour Valley between Corfe Mullen and Sturminster Marshall (incl the gravel pit) with the highest counts recorded during October–December including 160 in October 1994, 210 in December 1996 and 300 in November 1999. This would appear to be a pre-roosting area for birds destined to roost in Poole Harbour (Lytchett Bay). Elsewhere inland 460 at Gillingham on 25th October 1998 with 500 there on 1st November of the same year, 220 at Sherborne Lake in July 1999, 180 at Durweston on 12th December 1992 and 108S over Poyntington Ridge on 4th August 1987 are noteworthy counts. In 1998 autumn observations from the north of the county at Gillingham suggest that birds feeding there during the day sometimes fly south towards Poole Harbour (or perhaps Weymouth Bay), and sometimes north-west towards Chew Valley Lake in Somerset. The latter was the destination for birds wintering in the Sherborne area during the late 1980s and early 1990s. Like other gulls, birds use the river valleys, notable the Stour and Frome, as flight lines for daily commuting.

Coastal movements in spring extend from March to May and mostly involve adults, whilst autumn movements, which are much heavier, extend from July to November and include more young birds. Peak day-totals rarely exceed 200 birds, the highest being from Portland Bill with 575NE on 26th November 1990, 484 on 28th August 1962, 391W on 11th November 1992 and 300W on 14th September 1987, also 300E at Durlston CP on 13th April 1996 and 220S at West Bexington on 23rd March 1980. Coastal movements may also occur during periods of cold weather, the most notable being 1,090 at Portland Bill on 22nd December 1996. It has been shown that adult *L. f. graellsii* have reduced their winter movements, resulting in a greater presence in the British Isles at that season, but young birds continue more or less as before. Avoidance of the rigours of migration is a possible reason for the increase in the British breeding population from 50,100 pairs during 1969–1970 to 64,400 pairs during 1985–1987 when during the same period Herring Gulls have declined.

A total of eight birds has been ringed in the county. There have been four foreign controls of colour-ringed birds from the Netherlands, whilst locally c.11 colour-ringed birds from the Bristol/Bristol Channel area have been observed in Dorset during 1994–1999.

The race of Lesser Black-backed Gull *L. f. graellsii* breeds in Iceland, the British Isles, France and north-west Spain. The wintering range extends along coasts of north-western and western Europe, the western Mediterranean, and north-west and West Africa.

Postscript 2000–2002

Rooftop nesting continued with a minimum of ten pairs at three sites in 2000, four pairs at three sites in 2001 and two pairs at one site in 2002. Inland pig farms in the east of the county attracted high numbers with 400 near Didlington on 6th January 2001, and 400 near Tarrant Keyneston on three dates during 29th July–8th August 2002.

Lesser Black-backed Gull   *Larus fuscus intermedius*

Of uncertain status, possibly an uncommon winter visitor and passage migrant

The race *L. f. intermedius* has been varyingly described as a passage migrant and winter visitor in small numbers (Dorset Bird Report 1996), a rare visitor (Dorset Bird Report 1997) and a scarce migrant (Dorset Bird Report 1998 and 1999). Its status in the county requires clarification. In 1996 at St Aldhelm's Head spring passage totalled 655 with those recorded in March mainly considered to be *L. f. intermedius*, whilst those in April were mainly considered to be *L. f. graellsii*. In 1997 only one of c.2,000 individuals seen in Lytchett Bay was considered to be *L. f. intermedius*. In 1998 and 1999 all reports of birds showing the characteristics of this race are given as follows:

1998   Abbotsbury: 'a few' in February
          Radipole NR: six 11th February and singles 17th February and 7th March
          Portland: four 14th August
          Ferrybridge: five 7th September
1999   Abbotsbury: five 2nd March and three 31st March

The race of Lesser Black-backed Gull *L. f. intermedius* breeds in the Netherlands, Denmark and southern Norway. The wintering range is similar to *L. f. graellsii* extending along the coasts of north-western and western Europe, the western Mediterranean, and north-west and West Africa.

Postscript 2000–2002

Records of this race involved eight birds in 2000, c.11 birds in 2001, but only two birds in 2002.

'Baltic' Gull   *Larus fuscus fuscus*

The race *L. f. fuscus* was considered to be a regular passage migrant in Dorset up to the mid-1980s at least. This race has declined by at least 50% in recent years and the 'Baltic' Gull is now regarded as endangered over most of its breeding range. As a result of recent identification reviews suggesting that *L. f. fuscus* is very difficult to identify, all recent claims of 'Baltic' Gull in the county have been rejected. Indeed there is considerable doubt as to whether this race has ever occurred in Dorset.

This race of Lesser Black-backed Gull, *L. f. fuscus*, breeds from northern Norway and Sweden eastwards to the western Kola peninsula and western White Sea. The main wintering range extends from the eastern Mediterranean and the Black Sea, south through the Nile and Rift Valleys to the Red Sea, Persian Gulf, Arabian Sea and East and south-eastern Africa.

Herring Gull   *Larus argentatus argenteus*

A common resident, and abundant winter visitor and passage migrant

Mansel-Pleydell (1888) considered this species to be the most abundant and generally distributed of the gulls, that bred in every available locality on the chalk, oolite and shale cliffs on the coast. Blathwayt (1945) described it as "a common resident", which bred along the coast, at intervals, from Portland to Old Harry Rocks.

The Herring Gull is principally a breeding bird of the cliffs, only avoiding those areas which are geologically unstable and prone to slumping. In the early 1950s a few pairs also nested on marshy ground in Poole Harbour, whilst during the 1960s and 1970s large numbers bred on Brownsea Lagoon, but not subsequently – see Table 296. During the last 30 or so years, the species has nested on rooftops in increasing numbers. This was first noted in 1969 when nests were present on the roofs of a factory and a house in the Ferrybridge/Wyke Regis area. By 1979 rooftop nesting had spread from North Portland and Wyke Regis westwards to Swyre, West Bexington and the Bridport area. Although rooftop nesting seemingly increased rather slowly during the 1980s, it was well established in Lyme Regis by 1991 when Poole was first colonised. Subsequently there has been a dramatic increase with c.387 pairs nesting on rooftops in 1994 including c.215 pairs in various

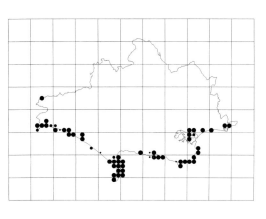

towns and villages between West Bexington and Lyme Regis, 100 pairs at North Portland and 60 pairs at Weymouth – see Table 297. More recently, buildings in the Christchurch and Mudeford area were colonised in the late 1990s. Although the Tetrad Map shows that most breeding occurs along the coastal strip, single pairs have bred well inland at Beaminster in 1983 and Chard Junction GP in 1991.

1964	1968	1971	1972	1973	1974	1975	1978	1980	1981	1985	1991
500**	350	930**	650	450*	250*	200*	50-70*	17-20*	12*	4*	1*

Table 296. umber of breeding pairs on Brownsea 1964–1991; ** whole island *assume reserve/lagoon only

	1978	1980	1981	1983	1984	1985	1986	1992	1994	1995	1998	1999
Bridport	3	2–3	6	12	7	10	nc	nc	78	nc	nc	nc
N Portland	nc	nc	12	nc	nc	nc	20	nc	100	nc	nc	80
Lyme Regis	0	0	0	0	0	0	0	50	66	nc	nc	nc
Poole	0	0	0	0	0	0	0	3	12	c.36	nc	29
Christchurch	0	0	0	0	0	0	0	0	0	0	10	20

Table 297. Increase in rooftop nesting at selected sites 1978–1999

From about 1940 to the early 1970s, the breeding population increased nationally. This was reflected by the 1969/1970 Operation Seafarer Survey, which recorded 2,125 pairs in Dorset. Much of this increase was thought to derive from better enforcement of bird protection legislation, and the species' ability to exploit food sources from a larger and more affluent human population. Subsequently the population has declined both in Dorset and the British Isles as a whole, so that by the time of the NCC/Seabird Group Survey during 1985–1987 breeding numbers in the county had declined by c.76% to 489 pairs – see Table 298. Various reasons have been suggested for this decline including botulism, culling, increased predation by foxes and changes in food availability. The more recent increase in rooftop nesting, however, may herald a recovery in the species' fortunes. Indeed there is a hint of a partial recovery in breeding numbers at some cliff sites by the late 1990s – see Table 298.

Burton Cliffs to West Bay	1969: 247	1994: 38	1999: 90	
Portland Bill	1962: 85	1989: 21	1995: 12	
Verne Cliffs, Portland	1975: 300	1979: decline	1989: deserted	
whole of Portland	1968: 500	1989: c.41		
Portland Harbour Breakwaters	1983: 300	1990: 60	1997: 30	
Durlston CP to St Aldhelm's Head	1969: 387	1975: 99	1989: 46	1999: 77

Table 298. Number of breeding pairs at selected sites 1962–1999

Outside the breeding season numbers are highest in mid-winter when the population is augmented by immigrants from beyond the county. Generally the largest concentrations are recorded at refuse tips, pre-roost and roosting sites. The 'old' tip at Lodmoor was particularly favoured during the early 1980s when counts, involving both the tip and nearby Lodmoor NR, normally ranged between 3,000–5,000 birds, the highest being 7,000+ on 31st January 1984 – see Table 299. After the construction of the 'new' tip in 1985, numbers declined with the best counts in subsequent years being 3,800 in January 1989 and 2,400 in February 1996. The latter count was associated with the presence in the mid-1990s of fishing factory ships and trawlers in nearby Weymouth Bay, which attracted up to 1,200 birds in December 1995. The best counts from other refuse tips are 2,000–3,000 at Warmwell Tip in 1981 and 400–600 at Canford Heath Tip in 1985.

Numbers at the bathing and pre-roost gathering at Radipole NR were at their highest in the late 1970s and early 1980s, presumably reflecting the attractiveness of the 'old' tip at nearby Lodmoor. During this period, peak counts at the Radipole NR pre-roost generally ranged between 2,500–5,500 birds in winter, the highest being 6,900 in December 1978 – see Table 299. As at Lodmoor NR, numbers have declined since the construction of the 'new' tip, the best count in recent years being 1,500 in November 1991. In January 1993, the ten-yearly BTO Gull Roost Survey collected data from important sites on the weekend of 23rd/24th producing a county total of over 3,500 birds. Peak counts at most of the individual roost sites have been exceeded on other occasions – see Table 299. In addition, a study of the roost movement past the Nothe in Weymouth toward Portland Harbour revealed 6,962 birds in autumn 1997.

	Max count and date	Other counts
West Bay– East Bexington	2,000 in Nov 1995	1,403 in Aug 1992
Portland Harbour	3,267 in Sep 1994	2,000 in March 1996
Weymouth Bay	5,000–10,000 in 1978	5,000 in both winter periods 1980
Radipole NR	6,900 in Dec 1978	5,500 in Dec 1977; 5,000 in both winter periods 1980 and Dec 1976; 4,000 in Dec 1982; 3,500 in Dec 1981; 2,500 in Jan 1983; 1,500 in Nov 1991
Lodmoor Tip/NR	7,000 in Jan 1984	5,000 in both winter periods 1980 and in 1983; 4,000 in 1982; 3,800 in Jan 1989; 3,000 in 1981; 2,400 in Feb 1996; 2,000 in 1987
Poole Harbour excl. Wareham Channel	2,000 in Feb–March 1998	
Wareham Channel	1,000 in Dec 1991	
Christchurch Hbr	2,100 in March 1998	1,850 in Oct 1975

Table 299. Roost and pre-roost counts (mainly winter) at the main sites 1968–1999

Opportunistic feeding assemblages of Herring Gulls have been occasionally recorded, most notably in late September 1988 with c.10,000 at Portland Bill on 21st–22nd and c.10,000 at nearby Chesil Cove on 21st (presumably involving some overlap with Portland Bill). Other large gatherings include c.8,000 fishing at Portland Bill on 4th January 1970, c.5,000 feeding on dead fish washed up on Overcombe and Preston Beach on 28th January 1984, c.2,500 around trawlers sheltering in Chesil Cove on 21st January 1984 and c. 2,400 at Hengistbury on 20th January 1999.

Coastal movements are more pronounced in autumn (mainly westerly) than in spring (mainly easterly) with peak day-totals rarely exceeding 1,000 birds. The highest counts in recent years have been at Abbotsbury in November 1991 with 2,175W on 13th and 1,899W on 8th, also 2,000W at Durlston CP on 24th–25th September 1988 and 1,000W at Portland Bill on 9th October 1981 and 14th September 1987. Coastal movements may also occur during periods of cold weather, for example at Durlston CP in early 1985 with 2,800E during 14th-20th January and 1,400E in mid-February, also 2,000E there on 30th December 1996.

Apart from refuse tips, the species is poorly recorded inland. There is, however, evidence of an increase in sightings in recent years with the highest counts often during the autumn and winter (cf Lesser Black-backed Gull) e.g. 1,000 commuting along the Lower Avon Valley in January 1995 with up to 400 doing likewise during 1993, 700W along the North Winterborne Valley on 20th October 1996 and 500 at Compton Valence on 21st August 1992.

A total of 528 birds have been ringed in the county. There is one notable recovery from Jersey, whilst the most interesting controls are two from France, and one each from Guernsey, Scotland and Eire. In addition a colour-ringed bird seen at Radipole NR was subsequently observed at the Pas-de-Calais, France. There is also a record of a female nesting annually on rooftops at North Portland during 1979–1982, which had been ringed at Worthing, West Sussex in December 1975.

The race of Herring Gull *L. a. argenteus* breeds in Iceland, the Faroes, the British Isles, western France and the North Sea coast east to Germany. Outside the breeding season, it is either resident or dispersive to varying degrees.

Postscript 2000–2002

Rooftop nesting continued including 200 nest sites at Portland in 2001, 100 nests at North Portland in 2002 and 68 pairs in the Christchurch and Mudeford area in 2000. At Christchurch Harbour, monthly maxima of 3,000 in January and 2,700 in March 2000 exceed the previous highest counts from this site, whilst 2,500 at Brownsea on 5th January 2000 is seemingly the highest roost count from Poole Harbour. A flock of 2,000 at Bovington in March 2000 is a notably high count from an inland site.

Scandinavian Herring Gull   *Larus argentatus argentatus*

An uncommon winter visitor and passage migrant

This race has been only identified in Dorset since 1993, and the subsequent increase in records undoubtedly reflects improved observer awareness of the identification features – see Table 300.

1993	1994	1995	1996	1997	1998	1999
8	2	16	11	9	6	4

Table 299. Annual totals 1993–1999

Most sightings are from the Weymouth/Fleet area, which accounts for 48 of the 56 birds recorded during 1993–1999. Otherwise all other reports are given below:

1993   Dorchester: 11th January
1995   Lytchett Bay: singles 26th September and 17th October
1998   Brownsea: 28th February
1999   Sturminster Marshall GP: singles 2nd January and 25th September
         Magna Rd, Poole: 2nd–3rd March
         Lytchett Bay, 21st March

All sightings are within the period 25th September to 11th April with most (80%) during November–February.

The Scandinavian race of Herring Gull *L. a. argentatus* breeds in Denmark and Scandinavia east to the northern Kola peninsula. This race is strongly migratory and winters mainly in western Europe.

Postscript 2000–2002

Records of this race involved about nine birds in 2000, six in 2001, and 2–3 in 2002.

American Herring Gull

Larus argentatus smithsonianus

Accidental: one record

2002   Corfe Mullen Tip, lytchett Bay and Sturminster Marshall GP: 4th March–6th May

This first-winter individual was seen mainly at Corfe Mullen Tip, but wandered to Lytchett Bay on at least one occasion and made a minimum of three visits to Sturminster Marshall GP where it was last reported. A full account can be found in the Dorset Bird Report for 2002.

The American Herring Gull *L. a. smithsonianus* breeds in northern North America and winters south to the Gulf coast and Mexico. A vagrant to Great Britain with 10 records up to 2002.

Yellow-legged Gull

Larus cachinnans michahellis

A scarce resident, and locally common passage migrant and winter visitor

The Yellow-legged Gull was formerly considered to be a race of Herring Gull *L. argentatus*, but it is now widely regarded as a separate species. Although overlooked and under-recorded in earlier years, the increase in records since 1980, which has been particularly notable during the 1990s, is undoubtedly genuine and reflected nationally.

Apparently there were occasional reports of yellow-legged 'Herring Gulls' prior to 1980, for example at Portland Bill on 16th April 1976. Although at the time these were described as variants of the local race, they could have referred to this species. The first definite records of Yellow-legged Gull involve single adults at Radipole NR on 11th and 16th January 1980, and Stanpit Marsh, Christchurch Harbour during August–September 1981. Subsequently the species has occurred annually with numbers slowly increasing up to 1990 with a mini-peak of 22 birds in 1988. During this period most birds were recorded from the well-watched gull sites in the Weymouth area, notably Radipole and Lodmoor NRs, which together accounted for 60% of the total – see Table 301. There were scattered sightings from other coastal sites including ten bird-days at Christchurch Harbour during 29th September–12th December 1988 and a long-staying individual, which appeared in Poole Park in successive winters from January 1982 to 1984/85 and again from 1986/87 to December 1988. Inland records were rare with singles in the Stour Valley at Merley on 24th December 1982 and Nether Cerne on 22nd–23rd September 1989.

	1982	1983	1984	1985	1986	1987	1988	1989	1990
Radipole NR	1	1	4	9	5	4	7	5	9
Lodmoor NR	0	0	3	6	6	6	3	0	0
Christchurch Hbr	1	0	1	0	3	3	8	0	2
elsewhere	2	2	1	2	4	4	4	1	8

Table 301. Annual totals at the main sites 1982–1990

Seasonally there was a hint of a late summer/autumn influx with a distinct peak in July, which mainly resulted from two mini-influxes at Radipole NR of six birds in 1985 and four in 1988 – see Table 302. Otherwise most birds were recorded between October and March, which accounted for 61% of the total for the period 1980–1990, with October and December the peak months.

Jan	Feb	Mar	Apr	May	Jun	Jul	Aug	Sep	Oct	Nov	Dec
9	6	8	4	3	2	18	10	5	16	14	16

Table 302. Monthly totals 1980–1990

Since 1991 the status of the Yellow-legged Gull in Dorset has changed dramatically. This has been most evident in Poole Harbour with a late summer/autumn gathering of increasing size becoming a feature of the north-western parts of the harbour, notably Holes and Lytchett Bays. The first indications of this occurred in 1991 with six singles in Holes Bay during 18th August–6th November and three bird-days in Lytchett Bay during August–September. This was followed in 1992 by six in Brand's Bay on 4th September and up to 11 there in early October. In 1993 birds were regularly present in Holes Bay during July–October with a maximum of 39 on 16th August. In subsequent years counts have increased with the peak between mid-August and mid-September, the highest being 210 at Holes Bay in August 1999 – see Table 303. Numbers often remain high through September, but slowly decline during the autumn to a much lower level in winter. The build-up of Yellow-legged Gulls in estuaries and harbours in late summer and autumn is also a recurring phenomenon in the Thames Estuary and Southampton Water, and it has been suggested that the birds favour areas with lower salinity. Smaller numbers are reported at other sites in Poole Harbour, the highest counts being 40 at Keysworth in August 1994 and 18 at Brownsea on 21st August 1999.

	1993	1994	1995	1996	1997	1998	1999
Holes Bay	39	4	53	98	160	177	210
Lytchett Bay	9	11	10	23	65	22	20
Harbour total	nc	nc	64–Aug	121–Sep	nc	nc	nc

Table 303. Peak counts in late summer/autumn at the main sites in Poole Harbour 1993–1999

Another significant event occurred in Poole Harbour in 1995 when two pairs attempted to breed on Brownsea with one chick seen on 14th May, but not subsequently and presumably predated. This possibly constitutes the first British breeding record. Since then breeding has occurred annually during 1996–1999. In 1996 one pair produced two pulli, which were subsequently predated. Breeding was successful in 1997 when two pairs raised two young to flight, and again in 1998 when three young were present on 26th July. In 1999 a pair fledged two young and another adult was paired with a Herring Gull.

Away from Poole Harbour both the seasonal pattern of occurrence and distribution of records are very similar to that prior to 1991 with the majority of sightings from the Weymouth area and Christchurch Harbour – see Table 304. There was one long-staying individual, an adult which summered at Abbotsbury for at least ten successive years up to 1999, whilst the only significant coastal movement involved 4E at Portland Bill on 26th November 1997.

	1991	1992	1993	1994	1995	1996	1997	1998	1999
Abbotsbury	4	0	1	3	2	nc	3	1	6
Radipole NR	13	13	10	8	21 bds	14bds	max 6	max 4	5
Lodmoor NR	0	2	3	7	max 5	nc	max 5	0	0
Weymouth Bay	0	2	0	0	1	nc	max 4	4	0
Christchurch Hbr	4	8	2	13 bds	12 bds	nc	max 10	max 3	20
elsewhere	3	5	4	0	3	nc	7	18	22

Table 304. Annual totals/maxima at the main coastal sites excl Poole Harbour 1991–1999

Although the species remains a rare visitor inland, there has been an increase in sightings with most records from the section of the Stour Valley closest to Poole Harbour:

1993 Canford Heath: 10th March
1995 Stour Valley at Corfe Mullen: two 24th December
      Sturminster Marshall GP: 30th December
1997 Frome Valley at Wool: four on 29th November
      Sturminster Marshall GP: singles 27th October and 16th November
1998 Bardolf Manor, Puddletown: three 15th September
      Sturminster Marshall GP: two 23rd October
      Stour Valley at Corfe Mullen: 3rd November
1999 Sturminster Marshall GP: singles 6th March, 25th and 30th September, 23rd October and
      12th November

The Yellow-legged Gull *L. c. michahellis* breeds widely in south-western Europe and the Mediterranean basin. Although it normally disperses locally, there has been a marked northward expansion in recent years.

Postscript 2000–2002

Breeding continued on Brownsea with two pairs (one successful) in 2000, two pairs (both successful) in 2001, and one pair (unsuccessful) in 2002. In addition, a pair bred unsuccessfully at Sandbanks in 2001 and 2002. Generally numbers continued to increase with the late summer/autumn influx into Holes Bay reaching peaks of 307 in September 2000 and 312 in September 2001. There was also a dramatic increase in the number of inland reports including up to 150 in pig fields near Didlington in late August 2001.

Sponsored by James Lidster

Iceland Gull   *Larus glaucoides glaucoides*

An uncommon winter visitor and passage migrant

This species was a rare winter visitor until comparatively recent times. It was first recorded in 1893 when singles were reported from both Poole Harbour and Weymouth. Subsequently there were records from Swanage on 6th April 1934 and 31st March 1938, Weymouth on 27th December 1943, and Radipole NR on 15th October 1961, 3rd February 1966 and 25th February 1968. These were followed by a mini-influx in spring 1970 involving birds at Portland Bill on 20th April, Brownsea on 1st May and Radipole and Lodmoor NRs on 1st–2nd May.

Since 1974 the Iceland Gull has occurred annually with a marked increase in annual totals during the mid-1980s in association with the high numbers of large gulls attracted to the Weymouth area and particularly Lodmoor Tip (cf Herring and Glaucous Gulls) – see Table 305. Although there was a decrease in sightings during the late 1980s, numbers increased again in the 1990s due in part to the presence of fishing factory ships and trawlers in Weymouth Bay during the middle of the decade. Annual totals were remarkably stable during 1991–1997, ranging between 8–11 birds. National influxes also influence the pattern of occurrence in Dorset, most notably in 1984, which was a record year for the species with a total of 22 birds reported in the county. It should be noted, however, that birds are highly mobile, most notably within the Weymouth/Portland/Fleet area. Consequently it is difficult to establish exactly how many different individuals might be involved, particularly during good years for the species. Reports involving more than single birds are rare, the highest counts being up to four in the Weymouth Bay/Lodmoor Tip/NR area during 24th January–11th February 1984 and four in the Weymouth area during 8th–30th January 1994.

70	71	72	73	74	75	76	77	78	79	80	81	82	83	84
3	0	0	0	6	2	1	2	2	3	3	5	1	7	22

85	86	87	88	89	90	91	92	93	94	95	96	97	98	99
10	6	5	4	2	7	11	8	9	8	10	10	8	15	6

Table 305. Annual totals 1970–1999

The seasonal pattern of occurrence is not as obvious as that for the Glaucous Gull. It seems likely that the high numbers in February involve both winter arrivals and early migrants with spring passage peaking in March, but extending through to May – see Table 306. There are very few records between May and October. In 1979 a second-summer bird was present at Radipole NR during 27th May–20th July with presumably the same individual at Lyme Regis on 1st June, whilst an adult bird lingered at Brownsea from 18th May to 6th June 1981. Otherwise there are only five new arrivals during this period, namely one at Christchurch Harbour on 27th July 1976, an adult at Christchurch Harbour on 27th–28th September 1980, one at Egmont Bight (Purbeck) on 12th July 1987, a second-year bird flying east at Durlston CP on 7th June 1991 and finally a first-summer bird at Holes Bay on 17th June 1999. Autumn passage is negligible with a gradual increase in sightings from October through to January and mid-winter influxes reflected by relatively high numbers during December–January.

Jan	Feb	Mar	Apr	May	Jun	Jul	Aug	Sep	Oct	Nov	Dec
29	33	36	26	22	2	2	0	1	5	9	14

Table 306. Monthly totals 1961–1999

For both Iceland and Glaucous Gulls, the high proportion of records during January–May (82% and 74% respectively) suggests that winter birds arrive late (during January and February) this far south, followed by an extended return passage during the spring.

Most birds have occurred in the Weymouth/Portland/Fleet area, which accounts for 54% of the total since 1961 – see Table 307. Within the Weymouth/Fleet area, the most favoured sites are Radipole NR, Lodmoor Tip/NR and Bowleaze Cove/Weymouth Bay. The species is scarcer in the east of the county where most records are from Christchurch Harbour with fewer sightings from Durlston CP and the Poole Harbour area. Elsewhere along the coast there are reports from St Aldhelm's Head (five), West Bexington (three), two each from Lyme Regis and Winspit, and single records from Redcliff Point, Worbarrow Bay/Kimmeridge, Egmont Bight, Poole Bay and Mudeford. The species is very rare inland, the only record involving a first-year bird at Canford Heath Tip during 8th–10th February 1984.

	Number
Weymouth/Fleet area	70
Portland	26
Durlston CP	18
Poole Harbour area	14
Christchurch Harbour	34
elsewhere	17

Table 307. Totals at the main sites 1961–1999

There are some interesting differences in the seasonal pattern of occurrence at the main sites – see Table 308. The highest proportion of winter records is from the Weymouth/Fleet area, which accounts for 58% of the total for the December–February period and reflects the attractiveness of this area during periods in the 1980s and 1990s for foraging large gulls. As a result, this is the only area to have hosted birds for any length of time, the most notable being the long-staying individual, which arrived as a first-winter bird on 28th November 1986 and returned in successive winters up to 24th January 1993. At the other main sites, the greatest proportion of birds is recorded during spring passage.

	Jan	Feb	Mar	Apr	May	Jun	Jul	Aug	Sep	Oct	Nov	Dec
Weymth area	18	16	7	9	4	0	0	0	0	1	5	10
Portland	1	3	6	6	7	0	0	0	0	1	1	1
Durlston CP	3	3	5	1	1	1	0	0	0	1	1	2
Poole Hbr	0	5	5	1	2	1	0	0	0	0	0	0
Xchurch Hbr	3	4	8	7	6	0	1	0	1	1	2	1

Table 308. Monthly totals at the main sites 1961–1999

The nominate race of Iceland Gull *L. g. glaucoides* breeds exclusively in low arctic Greenland with the more migratory east coast population wintering mainly around Iceland and more sparingly south to the northern parts of the British Isles and east to Scandinavia.

Postscript 2000–2002
In 2000 there were c.15 records, but probably only involving two or three birds, in 2001 there were eight records involving nine birds, and in 2002 most records involved the same two birds that frequented Corfe Mullen Tip/Lytchett Bay during 5th–23rd March wandering to Ham Common on 7th and Sturminster Marshall GP on 10th, with two other birds elsewhere in the county.

Kumlien's Gull   *Larus glaucoides kumlieni*

Accidental: two records

1995   Abbotsbury: ad. found dead 10th April
2001   Corfe Mullen Tip: first-winter 11th April

Usually considered a race of Iceland Gull, Kumlien's Gull *L. g. kumlieni* breeds on Baffin Island and in extreme north-western Quebec in arctic Canada, and winters in north-eastern North America. A vagrant to the British Isles with at least 78 records up to 1998.

Glaucous Gull   *Larus hyperboreus*

A scarce winter visitor and passage migrant

Both Mansel-Pleydell (1888) and Blathwayt (1945) considered this species to be a rare winter visitor with about five records up to 1907 involving three from the Weymouth area including one killed at Lodmoor on 2nd January 1870, one from Poole Harbour in an unspecified year, and one from Portland on 26th February 1907. There were no further reports until 1940 when one was present in Poole Harbour on 29th August with the next sighting in 1952 when one frequented Poole Quay from 24th January to 22nd March.

Subsequently the Glaucous Gull has occurred more frequently with annual records from 1974 onwards except for 1993 – see Fig 33. There was an increase in annual totals during the 1980s in association with the high numbers of large gulls attracted to the Weymouth area and particularly Lodmoor Tip (cf Herring and Iceland Gulls). Numbers then declined to very low levels during 1989–1999 except for a temporary revival in 1994 and 1995, which was partly due to the presence of fishing factory ships and trawlers in Weymouth Bay. National influxes also influence the pattern of occurrence in Dorset and were responsible for the high numbers recorded in 1986, 1987 and again in 1995. It should be noted, however, that birds are highly mobile, most notably within the Weymouth/Portland/Fleet area. Consequently it is difficult to establish exactly how many different individuals might be involved, particularly during good years for the species. Reports involving more than single birds are rare, the highest count being four together at Lodmoor NR on 14th February 1995.

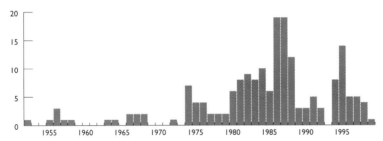

Fig 33. Annual totals 1952–1999

Spring passage is clearly indicated by a distinct peak in sightings in March and April, presumably involving birds returning north from wintering in south-west Great Britain – see Table 309. Although a few individuals have lingered into or indeed remained throughout the summer months, including a second-summer bird at Lodmoor NR from 30th May to 10th June 1985 when it was found dead, the only new arrivals between the end of May and early September involve singles in the Weymouth area on 15th June 1986 and during 22nd July–31st August 1987. There is a small autumn passage with numbers increasing to another distinct peak during December and January reflecting mid-winter influxes into the county.

Jan	Feb	Mar	Apr	May	Jun	Jul	Aug	Sep	Oct	Nov	Dec
42	19	29	36	11	1	1	0	7	8	11	20

Table 309. Monthly totals 1952–1999

Most birds have occurred in the Weymouth/Portland/Fleet area, which accounts for 65% of the total since 1952 – see Table 310. Although Radipole NR and Lodmoor Tip/NR are the main sites within the Weymouth/Fleet area, Glaucous Gulls are frequently reported from Bowleaze Cove/Weymouth Bay, Ferrybridge/East Fleet and Chesil Cove. The species is much scarcer in the east of the county where most records are from Christchurch Harbour and Durlston CP with relatively few from the Poole Harbour area.

Elsewhere along the coast there are four sightings from West Bexington, three from St Aldhelm's Head, one each from Peveril Point and Flag Head Chine and one seen 13km off the Purbeck coast. The species is very rare inland, the only reports involving a first-year bird at Canford Heath Tip on 10th February 1984 and more notably one at Beaminster on 1st October 1989.

	Number
Weymouth/Fleet area	84
Portland	38
Durlston CP	20
Poole Harbour area	13
Christchurch Harbour	20
elsewhere	12

Table 310. Totals at the main sites 1952–1999

There are some interesting differences in the seasonal pattern of occurrence at the main sites – see Table 311. The highest proportion of winter records is from the Weymouth/Fleet area, which accounts for 49% of the total for the December–February period and reflects the attractiveness of this area at times in the 1980s and 1990s for foraging large gulls. As a result, this is the only area to have regularly hosted long-staying individuals, the most notable being a first-year bird during 1st January–3rd July 1982, one during 17th March–19th December 1986 and a fourth-winter/adult from 5th December 1987 to 9th November 1988. In general the Weymouth/Fleet area mirrors the seasonal pattern of the county as a whole with a second peak of sightings during the spring.

By contrast, most reports from Portland and Christchurch Harbour involve birds on spring passage. Rather surprisingly the same is not true for Durlston CP where December is the peak month, perhaps involving birds *en route* to their wintering areas. In the Poole Harbour area most records are for the winter period December to February.

	Jan	Feb	Mar	Apr	May	Jun	Jul	Aug	Sep	Oct	Nov	Dec
Weymth area	24	8	13	14	5	1	1	0	2	1	6	8
Portland	3	4	11	7	3	0	0	0	5	4	1	1
Durlston CP	5	1	1	4	0	0	0	0	0	0	2	7
Poole Hbr	6	2	0	1	0	0	0	0	0	2	0	2
Xchurch Hbr	2	3	2	7	3	0	0	0	0	0	1	2

Table 311. Monthly totals at the main sites 1952–1999

The Glaucous Gull breeds across the Holarctic except for Scandinavia. It winters from the breeding areas south in decreasing numbers to the British Isles.

Postscript 2000–2002
Annual totals involved six birds in 2000, c.7–11 birds in 2001, and c.5–8 birds in 2002.

Great Black-backed Gull   *Larus marinus*

A scarce resident, and fairly common winter visitor and passage migrant

There is some confusion over the early breeding status of the Great Black-backed Gull in Dorset. Mansel-Pleydell (1888) inferred that nesting occurred during the 19th Century by describing this species as being much scarcer than the Herring Gull during the breeding season on the Purbeck cliffs. Blathwayt (1945), however, considered an account of breeding in 1865 as not convincing and suggests a nest at Whitenose (White Nothe) on 25th May 1924 as being probably the first authentic record. Although breeding had not increased much by the mid-1940s, it has become virtually annual since 1948.

Nesting has occurred in a variety of habitats and locations, the most frequently used being Brownsea, the cliffs at Ballard Down including the offshore stacks of Old Harry, the Purbeck cliffs between Durlston

CP and St Aldhelm's Head, and the Portland Harbour Breakwaters – see Table 312. Other breeding sites have included cliffs at Portland and Bat's Head, the Chesil Beach and more recently rooftops at Portland Dockyard/Castletown, Poole and Christchurch. This is reflected by the Tetrad Map. Prior to the mid-1980s the breeding population was small with 16 pairs located by the Operation Seafarer Survey in 1969–1970, and numbers generally ranging from 1–7 pairs during 1971–1985 except for 30–50 pairs on the Portland Harbour Breakwaters in June 1983. Subsequently numbers have generally increased, but breeding is seemingly under-recorded in some years, the true population size being best assessed when counts are available from the Portland Harbour Breakwaters. The five pairs recorded by the NCC/Seabird Group Survey during 1985–1987 is likely to have been an under-estimate.

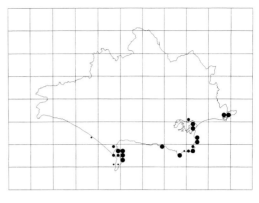

	70	71	72	73	74	75	76	77	78	79	80	81	82	83	84
Brownsea	0	5	4	5	5	3	0	0	2	0	3	2	0	0	0
Ballard Down– Old Harry	0	0	0	0	0	0	0	0	0	0	0	2	0	0	0
Durlston CP– St Aldhelm's	0	0	0	0	0	2	1	0	1	1	0	0	1	1	2
Portland Hbr Breakwaters	0	0	2	0	0	0	0	0	0	0	0	1	3	50	5
other sites	1	1	0	0	0	0	0	0	0	1	0	0	0	0	0

	85	86	87	88	89	90	91	92	93	94	95	96	97	98	99
Brownsea	2	2	0	2	2	2	0	2	0	0	0	2	3	0	2
Ballard Down– Old Harry	2	0	0	0	0	1	1	0	0	0	0	4	0	7	6
Durlston CP– St Aldhelm's	2	2	1	2	2	1	1	0	0	2	0	1	3	3	4
Portland Hbr Breakwaters	8	6	6	12	10	10	0	0	0	0	0	0	40	nc	50
other sites	0	0	3	2	1	0	0	0	0	2	3	1	2	2	4

Table 312. Number of confirmed breeding pairs 1950–1999

The Great Black-backed Gull is most numerous during the winter when, like the other large gulls, high numbers are found at refuse tips, pre-roost and roosting sites. The highest counts were recorded during the 1980s at Lodmoor Tip/NR with 1,150 on 4th January 1987, 1,100 on 31st December 1986, 1,080 on 31st December 1985 and 1,020 on 2nd January 1986. Although these counts occurred after the closure of the 'old' tip in 1985, there was an eventual decline in numbers during the late 1980s and early 1990s with winter maxima reaching very low levels of only 24 in February 1991 and 22 in October 1992. Subsequently there was a marked recovery during the mid-1990s resulting in counts of 700 in January 1995, 950 in November 1995, 550 on 9th February 1996 and 600 on 21st–22nd February 1997. This was associated with the presence in the mid-1990s of fishing factory ships and trawlers in nearby Weymouth Bay, which attracted up to 550+ birds during January–February 1995. Numbers declined again during 1998–1999 with a winter peak of only 85 in January 1998. The only other substantial counts at a refuse tip are from Canford Heath Tip with 500 in January 1995, 220 on 28th January 1985, 130 on 21st December 1984 and 100 on 31st January 1986. In addition, movements up and down the Lower Avon Valley, which probably involve birds heading for refuse tips in Hampshire, include peaks of up to 180 at dawn and dusk in 1995, 110 on 6th January 1984 and up to 100 regularly at dusk during 1987.

Not all birds make their way to roosts, perhaps because of their great size they are safe roosting closer to feeding areas. Nevertheless high counts have been recorded from various coastal sites including those used as pre-roost and roosting sites. In January 1993, the ten-yearly BTO Gull Roost Survey collected data from important sites on the weekend of 23rd/24th producing a county total of over 880 birds. Peak counts at most of the individual roost sites have been exceeded on other occasions – see Table 313. Numbers at Radipole NR were at their highest in the late 1970s and early 1980s, presumably reflecting the attractiveness of the 'old' tip at nearby Lodmoor, with a peak of 500 in December 1978. As at Lodmoor NR, numbers have declined since the construction of the 'new' tip in 1985, the best count in recent years being 100 in November 1991.

	Max Count and date	Other counts
West Bexington	300 in Nov 1974	
The Fleet	557 in Nov 1998	527 in Jan 1999; 500 in Aug 1999
Portland Harbour	600 in Nov 1998	500 in March 1996 and Dec 1974
Weymouth Bay	600 in Feb 1998	550 in Jan–Feb and Sept 1995
Radipole NR	500 in Dec 1978	350 in Jan 1983; 310 in Jan 1981
Lodmoor Tip/NR	1,150 in Jan 1987	1,110 in Dec 1986; 1,080 in Dec 1985; 950 in Nov 1995; 750 in Jan 1984; 700 in Jan 1995; 550 in Feb 1996; 528 in Feb 1988
Poole Harbour	343 in Nov 1980	200 in Jan 1992
Christchurch Hbr	470 in Dec 1998	450 in Sep 1975; 400 in Sep 1974; 380 in Jan 1993

Table 313. Roost and pre-roost counts (mainly winter) at the main sites 1950–1999

During the autumn large flocks gather on the Chesil Beach, mainly opposite Langton Herring, but sometimes at Ferrybridge, with peak counts of 500 on 13th September 1988, 350–400 on 26th September 1981 and 350 on 7th September 1998. These birds presumably roost on the Portland Harbour Breakwaters. In common with Lesser Black-backed and Herring Gulls, very high numbers were recorded during September 1988 in the Chesil Cove/Ferrybridge area reaching a peak of 1,000 on 22nd. Some of the highest counts in Christchurch Harbour have also occurred in autumn with maxima of 450 in September 1975 and 400 in September 1974.

This species is the least inclined of the large gulls to venture inland and, apart from groups attracted to refuse tips, there are relatively few records. Away from the Lower Avon Valley and Canford Heath Tip, the most favoured areas are Puddletown (maximum of 30 on 11th August 1989), the Stour Valley between Merley and Sturminster Marshall (maximum of 17 at Lake Gates floods on 5th January 1983), Bovington (maximum of 14 in January 1990) and Sherborne Lake (maximum of five on 30th November 1989). A gathering of 34 at Hatch Pond, Poole on 26th December 1982 presumably involved birds commuting to Canford Heath Tip.

Coastal movements, like overall passage, are most obvious in autumn when predominantly westerly in direction. Peak day-totals rarely exceed 200 birds, the best being 500W at Portland Bill on 17th October 1987 and 8th November 1998 with 400W there on 17th September 1989, and 387E at Abbotsbury on 1st November 1991, whilst 161E at Hengistbury on 14th May 1994 and 141W at Portland Bill on 12th April 1969 are high counts for spring. In addition, feeding flocks are sometimes recorded at Portland Bill including 600 on 21st September 1988 (cf Chesil/Ferrybridge) and 350 on 26th September 1975. Cold weather may also induce coastal movements, for example at Durlston CP in early 1985 390E during 14th–

18th January with a maximum of 110E on 18th, and 410E during 11th–16th February peaking at 130E on 12th. Other heavy movements in mid-winter include 360W at Portland Bill on 24th January 1984, 350W at Hengistbury on 7th January 1988 and 338W at East Weare, Portland on 22nd December 1974.

A total of 41 birds has been ringed in the county and there has been one foreign control from Norway.

As a breeding bird, the Great Black-backed Gull is confined to the North Atlantic extending from the north-eastern seaboard of North America to Greenland, Iceland and north-western Europe – mainly north-west France, the British Isles and Scandinavia. It is migratory north of the Arctic Circle, but mainly dispersive in southern parts of the range, the main European wintering range extending south to the Bay of Biscay and Atlantic coast of Iberia.

Postscript 2000–2002

At Brownsea a monthly maximum of 576 in January 2000 is seemingly the highest roost count from Poole Harbour. A count of 35 on floodwater at Corfe Mullen on 4th January 2001 is high for an inland site other than refuse tips.

Ross's Gull   *Rhodostethia rosea*

Accidental: two records

    1967   Portland Harbour: ad. 13th August
    1974   Christchurch Harbour: first-summer 16th June–20th August

The 1967 bird was seen from a vessel anchored in Portland Harbour.

The Ross's Gull breeds in north-east Siberia and western and northern Greenland, also in northern Canada (Churchill). It disperses around the edge of the Arctic ice-cap in winter. A vagrant to Great Britain with 83 records up to 2002.

Kittiwake (Black-legged Kittiwake)   *Rissa tridactyla*

An uncommon resident, and fairly common passage migrant and winter visitor

Mansel-Pleydell (1888) considered this species to be very common in autumn and winter at which time hundreds could be seen following shoals of Sprats between Christchurch Beach and Old Harry. Blathwayt (1945) described it as "chiefly a winter visitor and passage migrant".

Although there is some anecdotal evidence that the Kittiwake may have bred in Dorset during the 19th Century, Mansel-Pleydell (1888) stated that "it does not breed on our coast", but fails to specify whether or not it had done so previously. Certainly by the 1880s there was a massive trade in 'tarrock' (immature) skins nationally causing a major decline in the population. The first evidence of breeding during the 20th Century occurred in 1931 when the Dorset Bird Report referred to a pair apparently nesting in the Guillemot colony at Portland Bill. There were no further reports until 1944 when around eight pairs bred at Portland Bill with c.16 pairs there in 1945. Breeding spread to the Purbeck cliffs in 1956 when around ten birds were present and two nests seen at Durlston CP. Subsequently both the Portland and Purbeck colonies increased, reaching peaks of 145–200 pairs on the West Cliffs at Portland during 1969–1974 and 297 pairs between Durlston CP and St Aldhelm's Head in 1982 – see Table 314. The Operation Seafarer Survey found a total of 262 pairs in 1969–1970, whilst the NCC/Seabird Survey recorded 242 pairs during 1985–1987 suggesting that the county population had been relatively stable during the intervening period. Despite this, the Portland colony declined during the late 1970s and early 1980s, stabilising at 15–25 pairs during 1984–1990, with evidence of a slight increase during the rest of the 1990s when numbers generally ranged between 20–30 pairs. The collapse of the Purbeck colonies since 1990 has been dramatic with breeding ceasing at Durlston CP after a reservoir draining operation wiped out the main colony there in 1991. Other reasons for this decline are complex and may relate to the availability of sand-eels, the primary food of young Kittiwakes, and nest parasitism. Certainly in more recent years the resurgence of the Peregrine population is having a direct impact on the species, notably at the last surviving Purbeck colony at Blackers Hole.

	44	45	51	56	59	62	63	64	65	66	67	68	69	70
Portland	8	16	12	nc	nc	19	30	nc	nc	73	100	135	151	nc
Purbeck	0	0	0	2	1	11	19	27	39	42	54	nc	107	101

	71	72	73	74	75	76	77	78	79	80	81	82	83	84
Portland	200	150	145	150	125	nc	nc	nc	72	60	nc	54	40	20
Purbeck	139	152	192	166	190	171	191	196	234	292	250	297	261	215

	85	86	87	88	89	90	91	92	94	95	96	97	98	99
Portland	20	15	25	25	25	15	12	nc	48	25	30	30	9	20
Purbeck	192	159	182	198	162	165	126	129	76	nc	78	31	27	46

Table 313. Number of breeding pairs/nests on Portland West Cliffs and Purbeck (Durleston CP–St Aldhelm's Head) 1944–1999

Coastal movements of Kittiwakes are complex involving passage in spring and autumn, whilst large numbers may also occur either in response to inclement weather or to favourable feeding conditions, particularly in winter. Spring passage is predominantly, but not exclusively, easterly in direction and extends from February to May or even early June. These movements are most prominent at Portland Bill with smaller numbers along the Purbeck coast and at Hengistbury. This suggests that many birds stay well out to sea on their passage up-channel. At Portland Bill peak day-totals rarely exceed 1,000 birds, the highest count being 2,100E on 21st March 1983. Autumn movements, which have a distinct westerly bias, are more widely reported and can be particularly heavy during stormy weather late in the season (October–November). Similarly, inclement weather conditions can result in large movements during mid-winter. Peak day-totals are normally much higher than in spring with several counts of between 1,000–3,500 birds, the best being from Portland Bill with 9,725W on 26th October 1980 and 5,000E on 17th October 1982 (but 3,300W there the previous day); also 4,000S at Chesil Cove on 4th December 1982 and 3,600E at Durlston CP on 5th November 1982 (cf

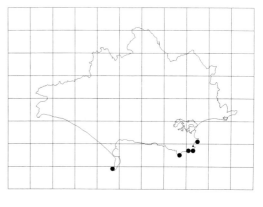

Portland Bill). In addition large shoals of Sprats will attract huge gatherings of Kittiwakes, as for example at Portland Bill in November 1985 with 2,500 on 4th (also 3,500E the same day) increasing to 10,000 on 5th. In general the strength of these movements was higher during the late 1970s and early 1980s than earlier or later. This may reflect the fortunes of the breeding population nationally.

Otherwise there are regular reports, usually involving small numbers, from the more sheltered sections of the coast including Radipole and Lodmoor NRs, Poole Harbour and Christchurch Harbour. The species is rare inland with most sightings after winter storms. Mansel-Pleydell (1888) noted that a considerable number were observed on Charlton Down on 1st December 1886 after a 'hurricane', and mentions three further birds at Whatcombe Down in March 1871 (shot), Kingston Down in spring 1873 and Milton Abbey Lake in autumn 1885 (shot). There are a few inland records in recent years as follows:

1954   All Hallows CBs: 8th December
1957   Near Cranborne: 23rd February
1970   Wynford Eagle: one found exhausted 6th September
1979   River Stour at Merley: 3rd January
1981   Boscombe: one flying north-east 29th March
1983   Chickerell: 13th March
1984   Poole Grammar School: 31st January
1990   Corfe Castle: one flying west 8th February
         Avon Causeway: 24th February
         Sherborne Lake: 4th March

1996 Sherborne Lake: 12th November
1997 Broadstone GC: 26th February
      Branksome Station: 18th July
      Sydling St Nicholas: 30th December
1998 Wyke Down: 20th–30th January
      Sherborne Lake: 1st February

In addition an exceptional flock of 33 flew south into Dorset from Sutton Bingham on 23rd December 1982. A total of five birds has been ringed in the county.

The Kittiwake breeds on coasts within the temperate and arctic zones of Northern Hemisphere and in winter disperses widely throughout the Northern Oceans.

Postscript 2000–2002
On Purbeck at Blackers Hole, there were 49 occupied nests in 2000 and 42 young were raised in 2002. No counts were undertaken of the Portland colony in both years, and the Blackers Hole colony in 2001.

Sponsored by Julian Francis

Ivory Gull
Pagophila eburnea

Accidental: seven or eight records

There are five, possibly six, records of birds obtained in the 19th Century:

1843 shot off Preston Beach, Weymouth
1850 shot at Lodmoor in winter
1857 shot from amongst a flock of Herring Gulls in Portland Roads
1860 killed in Weymouth Bay in November
1884 caught in trap on the Fleet at Abbotsbury

In addition, an undated specimen in the collection of Mr Pike of Wareham was purchased at a sale in Studland out of a collection of local birds and is believed to have been shot in that neighbourhood.

There are two Dorset records in the 20th Century:

1932 Weymouth Bay: 6th June
1980 Chesil Cove: first-winter 22nd January–10th February

The Ivory Gull has a circumpolar breeding range in the high Arctic and usually remains close to the pack ice throughout the year. A vagrant to Great Britain with 121 records up to 2002.

Gull-billed Tern
Sterna nilotica

A very rare passage migrant: ten records involving 11 individuals

Seven of the ten records involve birds passing Portland Bill.

1961 Portland Bill: 21st August
1963 Portland Bill: 20th October
1967 Portland Bill: two flying west 16th September
1974 Portland Bill: 16th May
      Portland Bill: 14th September
1976 Lodmoor NR: 27th April
      Portland Bill: 12th May
1979 Radipole NR: 6th May
1993 Stanpit Marsh, Christchurch Harbour: 5th–6th October
1996 Portland Bill: 5th May

The Gull-billed Tern is a cosmopolitan breeding species with a fragmented distribution including central and southern Eurasia, north-west Africa, the southern USA, the West Indies and parts of South America. The main colonies in the Western Palearctic are located around the Mediterranean and Black Seas with a small breeding population in Denmark. It winters in the tropics and sub-tropics, the wintering range of northern and western European birds extending from Mauritania east to Nigeria and Chad. A vagrant to Great Britain with 269 records up to 2002.

Caspian Tern   *Sterna caspia*

A very rare passage migrant: 14 records involving 16 birds

There are three 19th Century records with two shot at the Weymouth Backwater in autumn 1848, one in Poole Harbour in 1869 and one on the Wareham River in July 1872. Since 1974 there have been 11 reports, including eight between 12th June and 28th July. Christchurch Harbour is the favoured site with six of the 11 recent sightings.

1974	The Chesil at Abbotsbury: 15th June
1980	Stanpit Marsh, Christchurch Harbour: 26th July
1984	Poole Harbour, between Sandbanks and Brownsea: 28th July
1988	Stanpit Marsh, Christchurch Harbour: 15th–17th June and again briefly 21st June
1991	Radipole NR: 30th June
	Weymouth, Portland and the Fleet: ad. feeding a juv. 13th to 15th September
1992	Hengistbury: 15th August
1995	Stanpit Marsh, Christchurch Harbour: 11th July
2001	The Chesil at Ferrybridge: 11th May
	Stanpit Marsh, Christchurch Harbour: 12th June; another on 23rd and 27th July

The Caspian Tern is a cosmopolitan breeding species with a fragmented distribution covering Eurasia, Africa, Australasia and North America, the main colonies in the Western Palearctic being located along the Baltic coasts of Sweden, Finland and Estonia. The European population winters mainly in West Africa, notably the upper Niger inundation and the Gulf of Guinea. A vagrant to Great Britain with 273 records up to 2002.

Lesser Crested Tern   *Sterna bengalensis*

Accidental: one record

1995   Hengistbury: flying west 25th April

A full account of this record can be found in the Dorset Bird Report for 1995.

The Lesser Crested Tern breeds on islands off Libya, in the Red Sea and Persian Gulf, and in New Guinea and northern Australia. The Libyan breeders winter off West Africa. A vagrant to the British Isles with eight records up to 2000.

Sandwich Tern   *Sterna sandvicensis*

An uncommon summer visitor and fairly common passage migrant

Mansel-Pleydell (1888) stated that this species was "a spring and autumn visitant, but does not breed with us, though possibly it may have done so formerly" and referred to a female shot on the Chesil Bank on 12th May 1855 with well-developed eggs in the ovary. Blathwayt (1945) also hinted at the possibility of breeding on the Chesil Beach by reporting that most years a pair or two spent the summer with the Common Terns at Abbotsbury with single eggs found on the beach in July 1923, August 1929 and June 1933–none of which were incubated. Reports of young being fed in 1949 and 1951 may have involved birds bred outside the county. Subsequently birds have regularly summered in the vicinity of the Chesil Beach with recently fledged young reported on a number of occasions, but still there has been no positive proof of successful nesting.

In Poole Harbour birds were present in most summers from 1949 to 1971. Apart from display, the only evidence of breeding during this period concerned a juvenile, which was just able to fly, being fed by its parents in August 1953. Breeding was eventually confirmed in 1972 when a pair nested on Brownsea, but the one (fertile) egg was deserted, whilst the following year 23 pairs raised 25 young. After a gap of two years, regular breeding was established on Brownsea and, despite considerable annual variations in the size of the colony, numbers have increased to peaks of 152 pairs in 1997 and 174 nests in 1999 – see Table 315. In 1987 the colony partially moved to Round/Long Island where 80 pairs raised at least 80 young, but this appears to have been a 'one-off' event with breeding otherwise being exclusive to Brownsea.

	72	73	74	75	76	77	78	79	80	81	82	83	84	85
Breeding pairs	1	23	0	0	53	98	52	120	60	94	60	50	20	110
Fledged young	0	25	0	0	76	31	58	80	80	52	50	25	nc	120

	86	87	88	89	90	91	92	93	94	95	96	97	98	99
Breeding pairs	103	25	68	90	64	75	82	117	75	107	139	152	80	174
Fledged young	nc	35	72	82	30	44	66	92	nc	91	74	71	100	10

Table 315. Number of breeding pairs on Brownsea 1972–1999

Otherwise Sandwich Terns are widely reported along the coast on passage. The first birds of the spring normally arrive during the first half of March, the earliest records of presumed genuine migrants being 21st February 1998 at Lodmoor NR, 23rd February 1990 in Portland Harbour, 23rd February 1995 in Poole Park, 26th–27th February 1997 in Studland and Brand's Bays and 28th February 1998 at Ferrybridge. Since the 1950s, the average date of the first arrivals has gradually become earlier – see Table 316. Although autumn passage is generally finished by mid-October, late migrants often linger well into November, but the latest reports are obscured by wintering birds.

	1950–1959	1960–1969	1970–1979	1980–1989	1990–1999
Range	22nd March– 8th April	8th March– 8th April	12th March– 3rd April	6th–20th March	21st February– 15th March
Average	1st April	21st March	19th March	13th March	5th March

Table 316. Dates for first spring arrivals each decade 1950–1999

	1980	1981	1982	1983	1984	1985	1986	1987	1988	1989
Portland Bill	467	144	195	576	228	300	223	278	524	319
Durlston CP	nc	232	380	244	475	980	552	630	788	846

	1990	1991	1992	1993	1994	1995	1996	1997	1998	1999
Portland Bill	435	282	280	276	356	134	358	138	224	259
Durlston CP	604	629	376	385	nc	714	nc	555	600	370

Table 317. Spring totals for coastal movements at Portland Bill and Durlston CP 1980–1999

	1980	1981	1982	1983	1984	1985	1986	1987	1988	1989
Portland Bill	426	280	309	532	191	232	312	360	259	324
Durlston CP	nc	650	497	1248	788	985	632	873	813	803

	1990	1991	1992	1993	1994	1995	1996	1997	1998	1999
Portland Bill	208	197	308	142	103	129	89	204	172	220
Durlston CP	483	494	893	287	nc	990	nc	830	990	676

Table 318. Autumn totals for coastal movements at Portland Bill and Durlston CP 1980–1999

In general, passage numbers are lower than those for the Common Tern. Coastal movements are predominantly easterly in spring, but westerly during the autumn. Numbers passing the Purbeck coast and Hengistbury are generally higher than those recorded at Portland Bill in both seasons – see Tables 317 and 318. This suggests that Sandwich Terns prefer to move close inshore and, like many species of wader in spring, a substantial proportion of passage birds will overfly the Chesil Beach rather than pass Portland Bill. Peak counts are usually in double figures but rarely exceed 200 birds, the highest being an exceptional 700W at Hengistbury on 19th August 1990 with 300W there on 30th August 1992 and 12th September 1998, 348 at Portland Bill on 20th September 1958 and 331W at Durlston CP on 19th September 1983, whilst on 23rd April 1994, a day of heavy easterly movement resulted in 346 at St Aldhelm's Head, 307 at Hengistbury, but only 139 at Portland Bill. Otherwise passage birds gather at such favoured localities as the Fleet, Lodmoor NR, Poole Harbour and Christchurch Harbour. Numbers are generally small with peak counts rarely exceeding 100 birds, but 248 at Christchurch Harbour on 22nd August 1982 with 230–240 there on 19th–20th August 1999.

The only winter records prior to 1988 were singles at Poole Harbour Entrance from 27th November to 13th December 1970, Portland Harbour/Ferrybridge from 6th December 1981 to 4th January 1982 and Poole Bay on 11th December 1984. Subsequently there has been an increase in sightings, particularly during the mid-1990s, with most reports from the Weymouth and Poole Harbour areas – see Table 319.

	1987/88	1988/89	1989/90	1990/91	1991/92	1992/93
Weymouth area	1	0	1	0	0	0
Poole Harbour area	0	0	0	0	1	2
Christchurch Harbour	0	0	0	0	0	0

	1993/94	1994/95	1995/96	1996/97	1997/98	1998/99
Weymouth area	0	0	1	1	1	0
Poole Harbour area	0	0	1	0	1	0
Christchurch Harbour	0	1	0	0	1	0

Table 319. Wintering birds 1987–1999

Inland, there are frequent sightings from the Lower Avon Valley, notably during 1982–1991 with a maximum of six on 27th April 1988. Elsewhere inland, the species is rare with a few records as follows:

1972   Netherbury: two flying south-west 8th June
1974   Sherborne Lake: two 14th May
1979   Corfe Mullen: two 13th July
1980   River Stour at Iford and Merley: 1–2 birds in April
1982   Hazelbury Bryan: eight flying west 29th August
1983   Parkstone: two flying north 17th September
1984   Milton Abbas Lake: 1st May
1987   Bagber: two 25th September
1988   Radipole School: two flying south-east 7th September
1989   Woolgarston: 14th July
1999   Hartland Moor: six 13th September

A total of 167 birds has been ringed in the county. There have been two foreign recoveries from Ghana, and single recoveries from the Ivory Coast, Angola and South Africa as well as two foreign controls from Eire and one from the Netherlands.

The Sandwich Tern breeds locally on the coasts of western Europe (mainly the British Isles, France, the Netherlands, Denmark and Sweden), the north-west Mediterranean, and the Black and Caspian Seas. Birds from western Europe winter mainly along the west coast of Africa south to the Cape of Good Hope, whilst the Black Sea population winters in the eastern Black Sea and central and south-east Mediterranean, and the Caspian Sea population winters mainly in the Persian Gulf and Arabian Sea.

Postscript 2000–2002

In both 2000 and 2001, birds deserted Brownsea shortly after arrival and failed to breed, but recently fledged young appeared from early July suggesting that they had nested nearby. In 2002, birds returned to nest on Brownsea with 75 pairs rearing 25 young. In 2000 up to four birds were present in the Portland Harbour/Ferrybridge area throughout November with two remaining until 13th December. In 2002 there was a series of sightings in early February involving at least one bird in the Portland Harbour/Fleet area during 4th–6th and one in Poole Harbour on 4th, whilst late in the year unprecedented numbers were present with two at Christchurch Harbour on 26th November, six at Arne NR on 28th November with 1–2 birds in the Poole Harbour/Studland Bay/Swanage Bay area during 13th–30th December, and up to six in the Portland Harbour/Ferrybridge area throughout November with one through December. In addition, there were three notable inland records involving two at Sherborne Lake on 12th May 2001 with one there on 25th May 2002, and two flying north at King's Park, Bournemouth on 2nd July 2001.

Roseate Tern

An uncommon passage migrant – occasionally breeds

Mansel-Pleydell (1888) considered the Roseate Tern to be a rare summer visitor and referred to one at Poole in 1841, no less than seven killed by one shot at Weymouth before the 'Sea-Birds Preservation Act' was passed, and an immature bird shot at Poole in autumn 1874. According to Blathwayt (1945) there were no further records until 1917 when the species was present in summer on the Chesil Beach, which was followed by the first proof of breeding at this site on 13th June 1921. Subsequently a pair or two resided amongst the Common Terns nearly every year up to the mid-1940s with breeding proved several times.

Although Roseate Terns continued to occur on the Chesil Beach at Abbotsbury during most summers from 1946 to 1967, breeding was only confirmed in 1960 when one pair nested. Most records involve only 1–2 birds, but occasionally more were recorded with a maximum of eight on 3rd May 1957. Subsequently the only evidence of breeding from the entire Chesil Beach involves two amongst Common Terns at mid-Fleet on 12th July 1970, and at Abbotsbury one during 8th–13th June 1991, two on 21st July 1992, and singles on 17th June 1993 and 15th June 1997.

Nearby on the Portland Harbour Breakwaters a single amongst the Common Tern colony on 18th July 1982 was the first hint that this was potentially a new nesting site. Breeding was confirmed there in 1986 when one pair raised two young. The following year one pair raised two young and three other pairs may have bred, whilst in 1988 a pair with one chick was seen on a single date. Unfortunately there were no further reports after the Common Tern colony deserted in 1989 and 1990. During 1986–1989, birds from this colony regularly visited nearby Weymouth Bay to feed and rest with sightings from May to September.

In Poole Harbour, one to two pairs have summered amongst the Common Tern colony on Brownsea in 1967, 1968, 1970, almost annually during 1978–1991 and again in 1995, 1996 and 1999 with isolated sightings in other years. Although display has been observed in several years, the only firm evidence of breeding occurred in 1985 when one pair nested, but subsequently deserted. This pattern of a few pairs intermittently summering, but rarely breeding successfully, amongst Common Tern colonies appears to be a feature of the species.

Although passage undoubtedly occurs, it is difficult to distinguish between summering/breeding birds and migrants in the Weymouth/Fleet and Poole Harbour areas. In recent years passage has been most evident at Christchurch Harbour with fewer birds recorded from Portland Bill and the Purbeck coast – see Table 320. Generally numbers are small, usually 1–3 birds, the highest counts being from Hengistbury and Christchurch Harbour with 9W on 15th September 1983, nine on 22nd June 1988, 8E on 23rd May 1976 and eight on 16th July 1995, also 9W at Portland Bill on 21st September 1961. There are a few sightings from West Bexington including six on both 23rd June 1976 and 15th May 1979, but the only report from further west involves two at Charmouth on 17th May 1954.

	70	71	72	73	74	75	76	77	78	79	80	81	82	83	84
Christchurch Hbr	–	–	–	–	7	11	15	15	12	4+	13	7	12	27	nc
Portland Bill	1	2	4	1	10	4	0	0	2	4	10	2	0	8	1
Purbeck sites	2	0	2	0	0	0	0	2	0	0	0	0	1	0	1

	85	86	87	88	89	90	91	92	93	94	95	96	97	98	99
Christchurch Hbr	8	nc	48	35	10	7	8	12	44	11	32	22	11	18	5
Portland Bill	2	2	7	3	1	2	0	1	2	1	3	5	7	4	1
Purbeck sites	6	0	4	9	7	11	1	0	11	4	13	16	6	0	5

Table 320. Annual totals at the main passage sites 1970–1999

There are occasional records during the second half of April, the earliest sightings being 23rd April in five years during 1969–1994. The majority of reports, however, are for the period May to September with a distinct peak in May reflecting spring passage – see Table 321. There are a few October sightings up to the 10th, the latest being two first-winters at Portland Bill on 22nd October 1997.

Apr	May	Jun	Jul	Aug	Sep	Oct
4%	36%	22%	14%	16%	8%	1%

Table 320. Monthly distribution (%) at main passage sites 1970–1999

A total of four birds has been ringed in the county.

The Roseate Tern has a wide, but very local global breeding distribution. The British Isles are the main European breeding area, most colonies being in Ireland. The European population winters exclusively in West Africa.

Postscript 2000–2002

In 2000 c.19 birds were reported from eight sites during 6th May–4th October, in 2001 c.49 were reported from seven sites during 1st May–8th October, and in 2002 c.34 were reported from eight sites during 4th May–11th August.

Common Tern   *Sterna hirundo*

An uncommon summer visitor and common passage migrant

Mansel-Pleydell (1888) considered this species to be a common summer visitor, which bred annually on the Chesil Bank. Blathwayt (1945) also referred to a long-established colony of perhaps 1,000 pairs that bred on the Chesil Beach at Abbotsbury with a few additional pairs along the beach towards Portland.

The Chesil Beach colony was apparently still thriving in the early 1950s with counts of 2,000 birds in May 1950 and 4,000 birds including flying young on 10th July 1952. Subsequently the colony went into rapid decline with only 175 pairs in June 1967 and 140+ pairs in 1975 – see Table 322. Numbers continued to fall, and by 1984 disturbance and predation had taken its toll with no breeding taking place on the Chesil Beach. In 1982 birds, presumably from the Chesil Beach, started to breed on the nearby Portland Harbour Breakwaters and the following year most of the Chesil Beach colony had relocated to this site with numbers increasing to a peak of 60 pairs in 1987 – see Table 323. The relocation to the Portland Harbour Breakwaters was short-lived and in 1989 and again in 1990, after early occupation, the colony deserted due to disturbance from helicopters. Thirty pairs returned to the Chesil Beach at Ferrybridge in 1990, but subsequent breeding has been sporadic (three pairs in 1991, five in 1992 and four in 1996) and unsuccessful. Although small numbers nested in the Portland Harbour area during 1991–1994, most of the breeding colony transferred to artificial islets in the Fleet at Abbotsbury. Two pairs bred at this site in 1982 followed by a single pair throughout the rest of the 1980s increasing to 14 pairs in 1990 and 26–30 pairs during 1992–1994. Although breeding failed after initial occupation of these artificial islets during 1996–1998, eight young fledged from 14 clutches in 1999. It is also pleasing to report that breeding occurred at Lodmoor NR in 1998, when six pairs reared 11 young, and again in 1999 with a maximum count of 46 birds on 20th July.

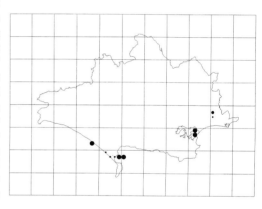

66	67	68	69	70	71	72	73	74	75	76	77	78	79	80	81	82
60	175	70	nc	80	80	65	130	54	140	80	51	60	nc	35	49	25

83	84	85	86	87	88	89	90	91	92	93	94	95	96	97	98	99
8	2	1	1	1	1	0	44	29	35	30	30	0	4	0	0	14

Table 322. Number of breeding pairs on the Chesil Beach including artificial islets at Abbotsbury 1966–1999

1982	1983	1984	1985	1986	1987	1988	1989	1990	1991	1992	1993	1994
9	30–35	35	40	53	60	35	d	d	5	8	5–10	1

Table 323. Number of breeding pairs in the Portland Harbour area 1982–1994; d = colony deserted

In Poole Harbour breeding was suspected in 1949 and confirmed during 1951–1953 when 1–3 pairs nested. Apparently no further breeding attempts were reported until the colony was established on Brownsea in 1963. Subsequently numbers have steadily increased with more than 100 pairs consistently recorded since 1988 peaking at 192 nests in 1999 – see Table 324. There is evidence that breeding has occasionally occurred at other sites within Poole Harbour, for example in 1970 on Keysworth Spit and Wood Bar Looe, in 1971 at Patchins Point and Russell Quay, and more recently in 1996 when territorial behaviour was observed at Poole Yacht Club.

63	64	65	66	67	68	69	70	71	72	73	74	75	76	77	78	79	80
6–7	10	30	22	93	54	74	67	68	65	58	0	65	55	57	60	75	68

81	82	83	84	85	86	87	88	89	90	91	92	93	94	95	96	97	99
68	79	83	28	96	100	82	104	110	131	105	135	126	141	151	160	173	192

Table 324. Number of breeding pairs on Brownsea 1963–1999; (no count in 1998)

Although birds that regularly fish along the lower reaches of the River Stour have been seen displaying and copulating, the only evidence of attempted breeding involved a scrape on a gravel shoal near Wimborne in early May 1973, which was subsequently flooded.

Otherwise passage birds occur widely along the coast. The first spring migrants usually appear during the first half of April, more occasionally in late March, the earliest record being 21st March 1981 with two at Portland Bill. Unlike the Sandwich Tern, there is no evidence that the average date of the first arrivals has become earlier during 1960–1999 – see Table 325. In autumn the last birds are normally recorded in October, more rarely in November with the latest on 1st–2nd December 1960 in Portland Harbour. Although there is only one wintering record involving a bird in Portland Harbour from December 1964 to February 1965, a 'Commic' Tern was seen at Poole Harbour Entrance on 13th December 1986.

	1950–1959	1960–1969	1970–1979	1980–1989	1990–1999
Range	7th– 21st April	24th March– 13th April	30th March– 16th April	21st March– 15th April	26th March– 22nd April
Average	14th April	3rd April	6th April	1st April	4th April

Table 325. Dates for first spring arrivals each decade 1950–1999

This species is the most numerous of the terns on passage and occasionally coastal movements can be spectacularly heavy – see Tables 326 and 327. In some springs, the numbers overflying the Chesil Beach and passing through Portland Harbour and along the Purbeck coast can be higher than those passing Portland Bill (cf Sandwich Tern and certain wader species). Peak movements rarely exceed 500 birds, the best counts being 3,500W at Hengistbury on 19th August 1990, 2,090E at Portland Bill on 3rd May 1974 with 2,000E there on 5th May 1985, and 1,991E at St Aldhelm's Head on 8th May 1981 (only 525 at Portland Bill all May), whilst 'thousands' were reported flying west at Portland Bill on 20th September 1953 with 2,000+ 'Commics' there on 6th September 1992 – a day of particularly heavy sea passage. These coastal movements are predominantly easterly in spring and westerly in autumn. Otherwise birds gather at various coastal sites such as the Fleet, Lodmoor NR, Poole Harbour and Christchurch Harbour in spring and autumn. Some of these gatherings, notably in Poole Harbour, refer to post-breeding flocks, for example 360 at Brownsea on 7th August 1989 and 200 at Arne NR on 22nd July 1992. Other high numbers reflect passage, the best counts being 500 in Christchurch Harbour on 20th August 1975 with 400 there in early September 1977, and 300 at Ferrybridge on 6th September 1992, whilst several thousand terns in Studland Bay on 18th August 1952 involved substantial, but unspecified numbers of Common Terns.

	1980	1981	1982	1983	1984	1985	1986	1987	1988	1989
Portland Bill	3190	573	494	1364	2048	2888	882	373	799	1143
St Aldhelm's	nc	3467	nc	nc	1357	1984	380	589	584	1199
Durlston CP	nc	356	133	129	421	712	407	552	261	694

	1990	1991	1992	1993	1994	1995	1996	1997	1998	1999
Portland Bill	978	895	395	725	273	695	1708	399	1672	724
St Aldhelm's	1637	414	109	747	352	nc	1909	nc	nc	nc
Durlston CP	1673	384	353	nc	nc	1059	1000	819	1070	516

Table 326. Spring totals for coastal movements at the main watch-points 1980–1999

	1980	1981	1982	1983	1984	1985	1986	1987	1988	1989
Portland Bill	402	350	390	384	409	428	620	513	387	515
Durlston CP	nc	560	502	624	254	398	235	480	704	720

	1990	1991	1992	1993	1994	1995	1996	1997	1998	1999
Portland Bill	255	34	2509	240	106	74	48	562	159	250
Durlston CP	417	376	688	nc	nc	694	nc	603	610	497

Table 327. Autumn totals for coastal movements at the main watch-points 1980–1999

Inland, birds regularly fish along the lower reaches of the River Avon upstream to Winkton, and the River Stour upstream to Spetisbury and less frequently to Sturminster Newton. Generally numbers are very small, involving 1–2 birds, but there were 40 along the Lower Avon on 11th May 1993 and 11N at Blandford on 2nd May 1990. There are also several reports from Sherborne Lake (maximum of 19 on 31st August 1998). Away from these areas, inland sightings are scarcer with records from sites scattered throughout the county. In addition there are several reports of inland 'Commic' Terns, notably 50 at Sturminster Newton on 3rd September 1992, 40–50E at Chetnole on 1st May 1984 and a late bird at Bagber on 16th October 1987.

A total of 662 birds has been ringed in the county. There are single foreign recoveries from Senegal, Sierra Leone, Ghana and France, and single foreign controls from Norway and Sweden.

The Common Tern breeds widely across the Northern Hemisphere mainly between 40°N and 70°N with the majority of the Western Palearctic population wintering off the western seaboard of Africa.

Postscript 2000–2002
Breeding numbers increased at Brownsea, Lodmoor NR and Abbotsbury with combined totals of c.241 pairs in 2000 and c.263 pairs in 2001, but declined to 229 pairs in 2002. This included a record count of 203 pairs at Brownsea in 2001. At Sherborne Lake, 44 on 18th August 2001 is a notably high count for an inland site. There was a remarkable ringing recovery in 2000 involving a bird ringed at Brownsea in 1999 and found in Cape Province, South Africa after being hit by a train along with 45 other terns!

Arctic Tern   *Sterna paradisaea*

A fairly common passage migrant – occasionally breeds
The status of the Arctic Tern in the county is obscured, particularly before 1950, due to confusion with the previous species. Although this situation has improved in recent years, many passage birds are still recorded as either Common or Arctic ('Commic') Terns.

Mansel-Pleydell (1888) considered this species to be a spring and autumn visitor, which did not breed in the county, and referred to it being much less numerous than the Common Tern. Blathwayt (1945) described it as "an irregular and scarce passage migrant", but mentioned that possibly a pair or two may have bred on the Chesil Beach with the Common Terns. Apparently a great number appeared in Poole Harbour after a severe gale in October 1883.

Although breeding was suspected on the Chesil Beach at Abbotsbury in 1949 and during the 1950s, it was not confirmed until 1962 when a pair with eggs was present in June. Subsequent breeding attempts have been sporadic and only involve one to two pairs – see Table 328.

	1962	1967	1971	1972	1973	1974	1975	1982	1985	1987	1988
Chesil Beach	1	1	1	2	2	1	2	0	0	0	0
Portland Hbr	0	0	0	0	0	0	0	1	1	1–2	1

Table 328. Breeding records 1962–1988

Otherwise the Arctic Tern is a regular passage migrant with a similar pattern of occurrence to the previous species. Since many birds are recorded as 'Commic' Terns, it is difficult to determine passage totals on a systematic basis. Nevertheless some heavy movements of specifically identified Arctic Terns have been reported in recent years, notably in May 1993 with 1,359E at St Aldhelms Head during 10th–14th including 411 on 12th and 524 on 13th, and 250E at Portland Bill on 11th, and in spring 1994 with 400 at the Chesil on 22nd April and 205E at Portland Bill on 3rd May. Other high counts from Portland Bill include 238E on 29th April 1988 and 200E on 18th May 1991. In autumn, the best count would appear to be c.100 at Ferrybridge on 26th July 1962.

Spring migrants seemingly arrive a little later than the previous species, the earliest record being 1st April 1994 in Portland Harbour. Late autumn migrants occasionally linger well into November, the latest being 23rd November 1981 at Lodmoor NR. The only winter sightings involve one at Worbarrow Bay on 26th December 1968 with the same at Kimmeridge Bay on 27th December, and one at the Nothe, Weymouth on 20th December 1976 with presumably the same bird (recorded as a 'Commic') at Lodmoor NR on 23rd December.

By contrast to the Common Tern, the Arctic Tern is much scarcer inland with relatively few records as follows:

1947 Iwerne Minster: found dead 3rd May
1976 River Stour at Merley: one with Common Terns 13th May
1980 Gussage Hill: flock of 25 flying north-east 5th May–a remarkable record
1982 Modbury FF: three 1st October
1987 Coward's Marsh, Christchurch: two 14th May and three 18th August
1989 Sherborne Lake: 12th May
1990 Sherborne Lake: five 3rd April
1993 Coward's Marsh, Christchurch: two 25th April
1994 Coward's Marsh, Christchurch: 8th–10th May
1996 River Stour at Sturminster Marshall: one 21st–23rd October
1997 Sherborne Lake: 2nd September
1998 Sherborne Lake: 31st August
1999 Sturminster Marshall GP: two 25th September–2nd October with one remaining to 9th October

Only two birds have been ringed in the county.

The Arctic Tern breeds widely in the Northern Hemisphere mainly south to about 55°N and performs the most extensive migration of any bird to its main wintering grounds around Antarctica.

Postscript 2000–2002

There was one notable inland record involving two at Sherborne Lake on 17th May 2001.

Sponsored by G. J. Armstrong

Forster's Tern   *Sterna forsteri*

Accidental: one record

1995 The Fleet and elsewhere: 26th December–10th February 1996

This first-winter bird was first recorded at East Fleet and last seen at West Bexington. Although the bird favoured Ferrybridge and nearby Portland Harbour, it could be elusive at times and wandered widely along the coast from Cogden Beach in the west to Lodmoor NR in the east. It was thought that the bird roosted in Weymouth Bay as it was often seen flying in that direction at dusk. A full account can be found in the Dorset Bird Report for 1995.

The Forster's Tern breeds in North America and winters along the coasts of the southern USA south to Central America. A vagrant to Great Britain with 18 records up to 2002.

Bridled Tern   *Sterna anaethetus*

Accidental: one record

   1984   Lodmoor NR: ad. flying west 11th July

A full account of this record can be found in the Dorset Bird Report for 1984.

The Bridled Tern breeds throughout the tropics and sub-tropics, the nearest breeding populations being in the Caribbean and Mauritania. A vagrant to the British Isles with 21 records up to 2000.

Sooty Tern   *Sterna fuscata*

Accidental: one record

   1935   Abbotsbury: two ads. 24th May

The two birds were seen first by Fred Lexter, the swanherd, and subsequently by Colonel Cyril Saunders and two friends. All particulars of plumage were checked. Interestingly, Sooty Terns were also seen in Kent in June and Norfolk in September of the same year.

The Sooty Tern is a widespread and abundant breeding species throughout the tropical and sub-tropical zones of the Atlantic, Indian and Pacific Oceans, the nearest colonies being in the Caribbean and South Atlantic. A vagrant to the British Isles with 26 records up to 2000.

Little Tern   *Sterna albifrons*

An uncommon summer visitor and locally common passage migrant

Mansel-Pleydell (1888) described this species as "a regular summer visitant", which breeds on the Chesil Bank at Langton Herring and Abbotsbury. Blathwayt (1945) recorded breeding of perhaps 70 pairs in scattered colonies on the Chesil Beach between Abbotsbury and Portland.

Due to the incomplete nature of the surveys, it is difficult to assess the fortunes of this colony during the 1950s and early 1960s, but a complete census of the entire Chesil Beach in 1967 revealed a total of 205 pairs. This would appear to represent a peak with numbers subsequently declining to a relatively low level of 30–40 pairs during the late 1980s. There was a partially recovery during the 1990s peaking at 95 pairs in 1996 – see Table 329. The nesting sites on the Chesil Beach are protected by fencing, and the area is intensively wardened to prevent human disturbance and predation by foxes. The latter can be responsible for very low success rates, for example 45 pairs produced only one young in 1982 and 55 pairs reared only four young in 1992 – see Table 330.

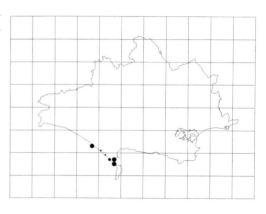

51	56	59	60	62	67	68	70	71	72	74	76	77	78	80	81	82
6	15	25	18+	20	205	100	120	125	85	81	47	54	73	65	61	45

83	84	85	86	87	88	90	91	92	93	94	95	96	97	98	99
49	52	40	39	30	38	39	55	55	50	70	90	95	nc	80	90

Table 329. Number of breeding pairs on the Chesil Beach 1950–1999

1982	1984	1987	1988	1990	1991	1992	1993	1994	1995	1996	1998	1999
1	21	8	20	20	12	4	30	34	37	15	18	40

Table 330. Number of fledged young reared on the Chesil Beach 1982–1999

The Little Tern is more widely reported on passage. The first spring migrants usually arrive in mid-April, the earliest being 28th March 1998 at Ferrybridge and 2nd April 1980 at Christchurch Harbour. Since the 1950s, the average date of the first arrivals has gradually become earlier – see Table 331. The last birds of the autumn are normally recorded between mid-September and mid-October, the latest being a long-staying juvenile at Ferrybridge from 4th October–1st November 1984, and exceptionally late individuals at Lyme Regis on 10th November 1953 and Studland on 13th November 1949.

	1950–1959	1960–1969	1970–1979	1980–1989	1990–1999
Range	8th April–3rd May	12th–30th April	6th–19th April	2nd–19th April	28th March–21st April
Average	20th April	19th April	14th April	13th April	10th April

Table 331. Dates for first spring arrivals each decade 1950–1999

Christchurch Harbour is the premier site for passage birds in Dorset with peak counts often in excess of 50 birds, the highest being 293 including 215W on 4th May 1982, 229 on 10th August 1974 (during a period of heavy sea passage at Hengistbury), 140 on 15th May 1990 and 5th May 1994, 130 in July 1993, 127 on 1st August 1981, 120 on 19th May 1987 and 115 on 1st May 1978.

In the Poole Harbour area the species is most numerous during the autumn, notably August, when small post-breeding gatherings are a regular feature. Arne NR and Brownsea are the most favoured sites, the latter sometimes hosting an evening roost of birds. Peak counts usually range from 10–40 birds, the highest being an exceptional 105 roosting at Brownsea on 21st August 1983 with 71 there on 28th July 1987 and 64 on 8th August 1985. Numbers have been much lower in recent years, e.g. autumn maxima at Brownsea were ten in 1995, nine in 1996 and five in 1999.

In the Weymouth area passage is obscured by the presence of breeding birds on the Chesil Beach with family parties visiting Radipole and Lodmoor NRs during the summer. The highest numbers occur in spring with peak counts usually ranging from 25–60 birds, the best being 250 in Portland Harbour on 16th May 1992 (the largest single flock recorded in Dorset) and 200+ at Ferrybridge on 26th April 1985.

Coastal movements are most prominent at Hengistbury with smaller numbers passing Durlston CP and St Aldhelm's Head, but very few at Portland Bill where it is regarded as somewhat of a rarity. It would appear that in spring at least, the majority of birds overfly the Chesil Beach and continue on their up-channel passage through Portland Harbour and eastwards along the Purbeck coast towards Hengistbury – see Table 332. Away from Hengistbury peak counts are very small, usually <10 birds, the highest being from St Aldhelm's Head with 60E on 4th May 1995, 42E on 1st May 1990 and 40E on 8th May 1989, also on 2nd May 1990 38E at Durlston CP and 21E at Portland Bill.

	1980	1981	1982	1983	1984	1985	1986	1987	1988	1989
Hengistbury	318	93	215	186	159	63	58	195	108	nc
Durlston CP	nc	8	5	43	18	6	10	15	14	26
St Aldhelm's Head	nc	16	nc	nc	16	5	12	49	42	83
Portland Bill	8	1	7	0	3	1	1	15	2	11

	1990	1991	1992	1993	1994	1995	1996	1997	1998	1999
Hengistbury	nc	nc	nc	nc	27	nc	nc	205	nc	nc
Durlston CP	84	15	12	nc	9	43	49	51	46	20
St Aldhelm's Head	175	35	14	27	16	95	29	44	nc	nc
Portland Bill	29	4	4	2	13	9	14	11	5	4

Table 332. Spring totals for coastal movements at the sites 1980–1999

The Little Tern is very rare inland with only five records as follows:

1954   River Stour at Bryanston Weir: 1st May
1978   River Stour at Sturminster Marshall: 9th June

1980   Lodden Lakes: 23rd April
       River Stour at Iford: two 25th and 31st May
1983   Sherborne Lake: 'a few' 8th September

A total of 36 birds has been ringed in the county.

The Little Tern breeds widely in Europe and North Africa east to western Asia, also in southern and eastern Asia south to Australia with an isolated population in west Africa. Western Palearctic breeders winter mainly on the coasts of Africa and Arabia.

Postscript 2000–2002
Poor breeding success continues on the Chesil Beach with 81 pairs rearing 16–25 young in 2000, 65 pairs rearing only five young in 2001, and 65 pairs rearing no young in 2002!

Sponsored by Garry Williams

Whiskered Tern   *Chlidonias hybrida*

Accidental: five records

1836   Lyme Regis: one shot in August
1983   Sutton Bingham: first-summer 29th May
1987   Lodmoor and Radipole NRs: ad. 18th–23rd April; presumed same as the bird present in Devon
           12th–17th April
1988   Stanpit Marsh, Christchurch Harbour: single ads 30th May and 16th June

The Whiskered Tern breeds from Spain and France eastwards through central and southern Europe and discontinuously across central Asia to China, also in the northern Indian sub-continent, south-east Asia and Australia. European birds winter mainly in sub-Saharan Africa. A vagrant to Great Britain with 124 records up to 2002.

Black Tern   *Chlidonias niger*

A locally common passage migrant

Mansel-Pleydell (1888) described this species as "a spring and autumn visitant, but very uncertain in its appearance", which was occasionally seen in the Poole Harbour and Weymouth areas, and referred to inland records from Ensbury in July 1839 and Frampton Court, Dorchester in July 1871. Blathwayt (1945) considered it to be a regular, but not numerous passage migrant.

Subsequently the Black Tern has remained a regular passage migrant with numbers increasing from 1970 onwards – see Figs 34 and 35. During the 1950s and 1960s the species was generally scarce in spring and more numerous in autumn, but this situation has been largely reversed since 1980. Despite the overall increase in records, seasonal totals vary considerably from year to year.

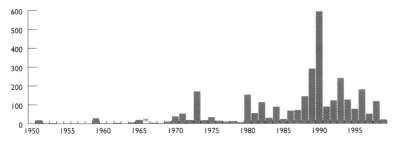

Fig 34. Spring totals 1950–1999

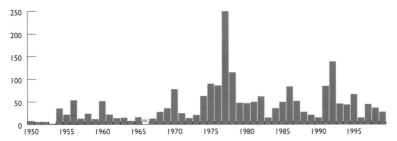

Fig 35. Autumn totals 1950–1999

In spring high seasonal totals are usually the result of heavy coastal movements, the most notable in recent years being in 1989, 1990 and 1993 – see Table 333. Even in the best springs, day-totals rarely exceed 50 birds, the highest counts being from Portland Bill with 150E including a single flock of 129 on 3rd May 1973 and 85E on 11th May 1993, whilst heavy passage in May 1990 produced 63E at the Chesil, 43E at St Aldhelm's Head and 26E at Durlston CP on 3rd, 68E at St Aldhelm's Head and 64E at the Chesil on 5th, and 79E at Portland Bill during 3rd–5th.

	1980	1981	1982	1983	1984	1985	1986	1987	1988	1989
Portland Bill	74	0	8	6	29	10	47	3	28	99
The Chesil	nc	nc	55	5	nc	nc	nc	26	59	62
St Aldhelm's Hd	nc	26	7	nc	2	1	nc	19	2	91
Durlston CP	nc	3	3	5	9	2	1	7	17	37

	1990	1991	1992	1993	1994	1995	1996	1997	1998	1999
Portland Bill	94	22	56	105	27	12	29	21	58	3
The Chesil	191	nc	13	11	33	18	32	7	42	0
St Aldhelm's Hd	224	31	nc	96	12	7	24	3	1	0
Durlston CP	44	9	35	19	4	31	22	15	14	18

Table 333. Spring totals for coastal movements at the main sites 1980–1999

High autumn totals are due to influxes usually associated with inclement weather. During 20th–27th August 1977 a minimum of 250 birds arrived after southerly gales with peak counts of 130 at Brownsea, 64 at Christchurch Harbour and 50 at Lodmoor NR. This 'pales into insignificance', however, when compared to the events of 18th August 1952 when, as part of an unprecedented influx of terns into east Dorset, c.1,000 were assembled on the beach at Studland Bay. At the time, this was the largest concentration ever recorded in the British Isles. Otherwise peak counts are usually between 1–10 and rarely exceed 20 birds, the most notable being 54E in Poole Bay on 31st July 1978 and 36 at Christchurch Harbour on 28th September 1991.

In spring the first birds normally arrive between mid-April and early May, the earliest sightings being 6th April 1980 at Hengistbury and 7th April 1985 at Lodmoor NR. The average date of the first arrivals has been earlier during the 1980s and 1990s than during the previous three decades – see Table 334. Most spring passage takes place in May with a few birds sometimes recorded in June. Autumn migration extends from July to October with August and September the peak months. There are a few reports for November, the latest being 12th–13th November 1981 at Christchurch Harbour and during 8th–13th November 1983 at Radipole NR.

	1950–1959	1960–1969	1970–1979	1980–1989	1990–1999
Range	2nd–16th May	18th April–11th May	21st April–17th May	6th April–5th May	11th–30th April
Average	8th May	28th April	28th April	22nd April	22nd April

Table 334. Dates for first spring arrivals each decade 1950–1999

Black Terns occur widely along the coast from West Bay to Christchurch Harbour. Excluding coastal movements, birds generally favour the Fleet, Radipole and Lodmoor NRs, Poole Harbour and Christchurch Harbour. Inland, the species is frequently recorded from Sherborne Lake (maximum of four on 12th–13th May 1980), the Lower Avon (maxima of seven on 28th April 1988 and six from 27th August–2nd September 1986), and the Lower Stour upstream to Corfe Mullen, but mainly in the vicinity of Wimborne. Otherwise there are a few more inland records as follows:

1959   Crichel Lake: 18th October
1960   Crichel Lake: 4th–11th May
1968   Milton Abbas Lake: 20th May
1981   Morden Decoy Pond: 21st August
        East Farm, Hammoon: one after gales on 12th October was seen feeding on a manure heap
1982   Modbury FF: 30th September and three 1st October
1986   Puddletown: 31st August
1994   Modbury FF: two 16th September

Only four birds have been ringed in the county.

The nominate race of Black Tern breeds locally in marshlands across much of Europe, being more widely distributed in the east and extending into western Asia. It has bred in Great Britain but it is mainly a passage migrant. Eurasian birds winter largely along the west coast of tropical Africa.

Postscript 2000–2002
At the Chesil, 169E on 7th May 2000 is the highest spring day-count for the county.

White-winged Black Tern
(White-winged Tern) *Chlidonias leucopterus*

A very rare passage migrant

This species was known to Mansel-Pleydell (1888), who stated that according to a Mr Hart of Christchurch several had been seen on the Hampshire and Dorset coasts, one of which was preserved in the collection of Sir John Crewe, whilst reference was also made to a Mr Pike of Wareham who shot one in Poole Harbour in June of an unspecified year.

Since 1959 there have been records involving 24 birds of which 15 have occurred in autumn with eight in August, five in September and two in October. The remaining nine sightings have been in spring and summer with three in May, four in June and two in July. The most favoured sites are Radipole and Lodmoor NRs with 11 records and Christchurch Harbour with five.

1959   Ferrybridge: ad. 7th–8th June
        Radipole NR: juv. 19th–22nd August
1964   Brownsea: ad. 3rd June
        Lodmoor and Radipole NRs: ad. 7th–8th June
1967   Portland Bill: 22nd October

1968   Radipole NR: 10th August
1969   Radipole NR: juv. 5th August
1970   Lodmoor and Radipole NRs: ad. 4th–6th May
1976   Radipole NR: ad. 23rd May
       River Avon between Burton and Winkton: juv. 9th–11th October; same at Stanpit Marsh,
           Christchurch Harbour 16th–30th October
1980   Portland Bill: ad. 31st August
1982   Radipole NR: juv. 24th–30th September
1984   River Stour at Longham Bridge: second-summer 18th May
1986   The Nothe, Weymouth: juv. 12th August; same at Radipole NR 13th–14th August
       Christchurch Harbour and Coward's Marsh: juv. 21st–28th August
1988   Weymouth Bay: ad. 27th June
       Hengistbury: juv. 7th September
1991   Stanpit Marsh, Christchurch Harbour: juv. 1st -3rd September
1992   Stanpit Marsh, Christchurch Harbour: ad. 22nd August
       Lodmoor NR: ad. 29th September
1996   Lodmoor and Radipole NRs: second-summer 10th July
       Lodmoor NR: juv. 12th August
1998   Portland Bill: juv. 26th July
1999   Ferrybridge: juv. 19th September

The White-winged Black Tern breeds from eastern Europe discontinuously eastwards across central Asia to China. Western Palearctic populations winter in sub-Saharan Africa. A vagrant to Great Britain with 773 records up to 2002.

Guillemot (Common Guillemot)   *Uria aalge*

A locally common resident, and common winter visitor and passage migrant

This species was well-known in the 19th Century, Mansel-Pleydell (1888) commenting that "during the breeding season the Guillemot resorts to our cliffs in some numbers". Blathwayt (1945) described it as "a common summer resident", which bred at intervals on the coast from Portland to Anvil Point with a very large colony on the east side of St Aldhelm's Head. The 1951 Bird Report refers to the decline of the Portland and Purbeck colonies, for example "far fewer east of St Aldhelm's Head than c.50 years ago, when there were thousands of eggs on the cliffs".

Since 1950 the main Purbeck colonies have been located between Durlston CP and St Aldhelm's Head. Although the lack of comprehensive counts in the early years makes it difficult to assess population trends, there does appear to have been a rather gradual decline from 500 pairs in 1949 to 800 birds in 1964, followed by a sharp fall to 495 birds in 1969. Since then, however, the overall trend in breeding numbers has been relatively stable with counts ranging from 320 birds in 1970 to 567 birds in 1977 and 1994 – see Table 335. A small isolated colony of 24–35 birds survived at Bat's Head up to 1967, but deserted in 1969. Subsequently the only reports of breeding on the Purbeck coast west of St Aldhelm's Head are four birds at Gad Cliff in 1978 and two at Bat's Head in 1982.

64	69	70	71	72	73	74	75	76	77	78	79	80	81	82	83
800	495	320	550	470	500	nc	550	509	567	488	492	561	401	498	356

84	85	86	87	88	89	90	91	92	93	94	95	96	97	98	99
468	408	459	513	458	431	450	529	nc	nc	567	nc	506	495	516	548

Table 335. Number of breeding birds between Durlston CP and St Aldhelm's Head 1964–1999

The colony on the West Cliffs at Portland has generally varied between 20–70 pairs during 1951–1997 except for an estimate of 100 pairs in 1955. It is difficult to distinguish any meaningful population trends, but there is evidence of a slight decline during the 1980s followed by a recovery during the 1990s – see

Table 336. In 1998, however, a boat-based count of the breeding colony, much of which is invisible from the clifftop, revealed the presence of 300 birds ashore on 22nd June. This figure is nearby double any previous count of the colony, and very much higher than suspected by land-based estimates.

	51	55	65	68	70	71	72	73	74	75	76	77	78	79	80	81	82
Pairs	50	100	–	40	50	–	25	40	–	–	–	50	–	40	50	50	35
Birds	–	–	60	–	–	53	–	–	112	120	78	–	80	–	–	–	–

	83	84	85	86	87	88	89	90	91	92	93	94	95	96	97	98	99
Pairs	30	30	25	30	35	30	–	–	–	–	–	45	–	–	–	–	–
Birds	–	–	–	–	–	–	83	80	140	60	100	–	100	100	140	300	147

Table 335. Number of breeding pairs/birds on Portland West Cliffs 1951–1999

In the past breeding success has been difficult to ascertain, but the recent use of camera surveillance at Durlston CP revealed that 76 monitored nests reared 37 young in both 1995 and 1996. At Portland Bill breeding success is sometimes reported as poor, for example in 1976 the hot summer had an adverse effect on the young birds with few fledged, and only four young were seen in 1992 and again in 1993.

Although the breeding ledges are usually deserted by late July, the adults may return as early as October, but more typically between mid-November and mid-December. Numbers rapidly increase during the winter with high counts often reported during January and February, for example 380 at Durlston CP in February 1988 with 350 there on 12th February 1984, and 150 at Portland Bill on 20th February 1962 with 100 there during January–February 1984. Sometimes high numbers are recorded much earlier in the winter, for example 300 at Winspit on 25th November 1971. Despite these early returns, recent studies from Durlston CP suggest that the colony may not be fully established until late April when the first eggs are also laid.

During the winter non-breeding birds, especially first-years, either remain at sea or disperse along the coast where they tend to favour relatively sheltered waters such as Portland Harbour, Weymouth Bay, Poole Harbour and Studland/Poole Bays. Numbers are small, usually involving under ten birds, but there were 21 in Portland Harbour in mid-February 1998 with 15–20 there during November 1985.

Since many auks passing at sea are too distant to identify specifically, movements of Guillemots as detailed below include counts for auks spp. At Portland Bill the vast majority of auk movements (e.g. 95% in 1982) are considered to comprise mainly Guillemots.

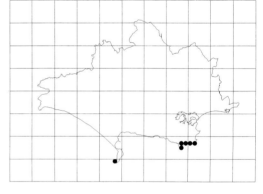

Coastal movements, notably along the Purbeck coast, are complicated by the presence of local breeding colonies. Nevertheless, many of the high counts and heavy movements in mid-winter involve auks attracted to offshore Sprat shoals (cf Kittiwake). This is a particular feature at Portland Bill where counts frequently exceed 1,000 birds and occasionally involve many more, the highest being an exceptional 50,000 (auks) on 30th December 1996, 20,000 (auks) on 9th January 1965 and 3rd January 1996, 10,000 (auks) on 21st December 1970 and 1st January 1971, and up to 9,000 (Guillemots) during 1st–10th January 1983 – see Table 337. Elsewhere winter movements are generally smaller, the best from Durlston CP being 3,000E (auks) during 1st–9th January 1992, 3,000W (Guillemots) during 4th–10th January 1998, 2,500W (Guillemots) during 8th–30th December 1998 (maximum of 1,000 on 27th) and 1,350W (auks) on 14th December 1983, also 1,000 (auks) moving at Winspit on 23rd January 1972. At Hengistbury 1,000E (auks) on 31st December 1980, and 500E (auks) per hour attracted to Sprats between dawn and midday on 1st January 1981 are exceptional counts.

Spring and autumn movements at Portland Bill, where the breeding population is much smaller, are more likely to involve non-local birds and reflect genuine passage. These movements are smaller than in mid-winter with peak counts rarely exceeding 500 birds, the highest being 1,454W (auks) on 26th April

68/69	69/70	70/71	71/72	72/73	73/74	74/75	75/76	76/77
6000	2950	10,000	2000	2000	2500	577	30	300
77/78	80/81	81/82	82/83	84/85	85/86	86/87	87/88	88/89
300	5500	500	10,000	30	few	1000	1000	1500
89/90	90/91	91/92	92/93	93/94	95/96	96/97	97/98	98/99
40	1500	1200	1500	2850	20,000	50,000	5600	5000

Table 337. Winter maxima of feeding movements at Portland Bill 1968–1999

1970, 860W (auks) on 1st May 1969 and 800E (auks) on 17th March 1996. During 1980–1987 movements showed a westerly bias from September to December and an easterly bias during February and March – see Table 338. This suggests that passage at Portland Bill may involve some birds that breed in colonies in the North Sea and beyond. It should be noted, however, that in earlier years autumn movements were mainly easterly in direction. Furthermore ringing records show that non-local wintering birds originate mainly from colonies bordering the Irish Sea.

	Jan	Feb	Mar	Apr	May	Jun	Jul	Aug	Sep	Oct	Nov	Dec
East	901	310	162	65	23	–	–	3	25	161	343	521
West	951	130	18	0	5	–	–	3	110	845	418	1641

Table 338. Average monthly coastal movements (bds) at Portland Bill 1980–1987

The Guillemot is vulnerable to oil pollution, for example nearly 1,000 were found dead or dying in two major oil spills mainly in west Dorset in January 1971, 222 oiled birds were found along the whole Dorset coastline during January and early February 1970, and 208 were found dead between Portland and Lyme Regis on 25th–26th February 1995.

Although there are no inland records, singles at Radipole NR on 23rd February 1981 (oiled), 15th February 1985, 13th December 1986 and 9th September 1989 are unusual.

The 'bridled' form of Guillemot, more numerous further north, is regularly recorded in very small numbers (1–7 birds) from the Purbeck colonies. Otherwise there are occasional reports from Portland Bill and amongst corpses found after oil spills.

A total of 12 birds has been ringed in the county. Although there have been no recoveries, there have been ten controls from colonies bordering the Irish Sea and one from the Western Isles of Scotland.

The Guillemot breeds on cliffs and islands of the northern Pacific and Atlantic Oceans including the North and Baltic Seas mainly between 40°N and 75°N. It winters both offshore and far out to sea.

Postscript 2000–2002

A count of 720 birds along the Purbeck Cliffs between Durlston CP and St Aldhelm's Head on 25th June 2000 represents a marked increase in the breeding population. At Portland Bill, numbers attending the breeding colony were estimated at 200 birds in both 2000 and 2001 with 700 birds in 2002.

Sponsored by Alan Davies

Razorbill

Alca torda

An uncommon resident, and fairly common winter visitor and passage migrant

Apparently the Razorbill was commoner than the Guillemot in the 19th Century; Mansel-Pleydell (1888) commented that during the breeding season the Razorbill frequented the Dorset coast in great numbers. Reference was also made to occasional mortalities caused by stormy weather, for example "in February 1872 the Chesil Bank was strewn with their dead bodies" and "the following winter and that of 1881/82 were equally disastrous; hundreds were then cast ashore on all parts of the coast". Blathwayt (1945) described this species as "a common summer resident", which bred at intervals on the coast from Portland to Anvil Point, especially on the east side of St Aldhelm's Head, but was much less numerous than the Guillemot.

It is clear that the Razorbill decreased markedly during the 20th Century with the main Purbeck colonies supporting 100–250 pairs in 1948 but with only 30 pairs present in 1967 and even fewer by 1970. Subsequently the situation has remained relatively stable with numbers generally varying between 12–30 birds including 6–7 pairs at Durlston CP during 1991–1997 – see Table 339. Since 1948 breeding birds have been limited to the cliffs between Durlston CP and St Aldhelm's Head, except for an isolated colony at Bat's Head, which held three pairs in 1948 and 1949, 18 birds in 1955, but only one pair in 1967 with none in 1969 (cf Guillemot). There are no subsequent reports of breeding on the Purbeck coast to the west of St Aldhelm's Head.

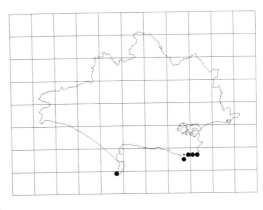

67	69	70	71	72	73	74	75	76	77	78	79	80	81	82	83
60	14	nc	24	31	16	nc	12	14	22	14	12	19	12	12	16

84	85	86	87	88	89	90	91	92	93	94	95	96	97	98	99
24	14	28	23	8	12	nc	20	26	nc	23	nc	21	29	13	15

Table 339. Number of breeding birds between Durlston CP and St Aldhelm's Head 1967–1999

Since 1950 numbers on the West Cliffs at Portland have declined from a peak of 40 pairs in 1958 to 15 pairs in 1967 and 3–5 pairs in several years during 1982–1990 – see Table 340. Subsequently there appears to have been a slight recovery with up to 20 birds present in some years during the 1990s.

	51	58	65	67	70	71	72	73	74	75	76	77	78	79	80	81	82
Pairs	12	40	–	15	10	13	10	12	12	12	12	12	nc	10	14	15	4
Birds	–	–	45	–	–	–	–	–	–	–	–	–	–	–	–	–	–

	83	84	85	86	87	88	89	90	91	92	93	94	95	96	97	98	99
Pairs	10	5	5	6	10	4	5	5	–	–	–	–	–	–	–	–	–
Birds	–	–	–	–	–	–	–	–	18	20	20	17	10	10	10	10	19

Table 339. Number of breeding pairs/birds on Portland West Cliffs 1951–1999

The breeding cycle differs from that of the Guillemot in that young are raised to a greater level of maturity before leaving the cliffs, and the adults return to the breeding ledges later in the winter, usually during February.

In winter the species is widely recorded along the coast favouring relatively sheltered waters such as Portland Harbour, Weymouth Bay, Poole Harbour and Studland/Poole Bays. Numbers are small, usually involving less than ten birds, but peak counts in Portland Harbour/Weymouth Bay have reached 20–30 birds on several occasions. In addition, groups of birds are occasionally recorded in summer fishing on the Hook Sands off Poole Harbour Entrance, for example 20 on 17th May 1990 and again on 23rd May 1995.

Since many auks passing at sea are too distant to identify specifically, the movements of Razorbills are included with those for auk spp and follow the same pattern as described in the species account for Guillemot. At Portland Bill only a small minority of auk movements (e.g. 5% in 1982) are considered to comprise Razorbills. There are, however, a number of substantial counts, involving both winter feeding movements and passage in spring and autumn, which refer specifically to this species. In winter very high numbers were recorded from Portland Bill in January 1983 with up to 8,000 feeding offshore during the second half of the month, 6,000W on 19th and 4,600W on 27th. Otherwise winter counts rarely exceed 100 birds, the best being 400 at Portland Bill on 5th January 1992 with 300 there on 28th December 1968, and 315 fishing at Durlston CP on 8th February 1970 with a peak of 300 there in February 1995, whilst

730 bird-days at Hengistbury in December 1980 is noteworthy. Passage is very small, easterly in direction and often non-existent in spring, but more obvious in autumn with a westerly bias. Counts are generally much smaller than in winter, rarely exceeding 100 birds, so 4,000W at Portland Bill on 24th October 1957 is exceptional. Otherwise the best movements are 400W at Portland Bill on 18th October 1987 and 232W at Durlston CP during 14th–16th October of the same year.

Like all the auks, the Razorbill is vulnerable to oil pollution, for example 60 were found dead between Portland and Lyme Regis on 25th–26th February 1995, and 50 were found dead or dying in two major oil spills mainly in west Dorset in January 1971.

Although there are no inland records, singles at Radipole NR in August 1972 and on 5th February 1980, and an oiled individual at Lodmoor NR on 20th February 1979 are unusual.

A total of seven birds has been ringed in the county. Although there have been no recoveries, there have been four controls from colonies bordering the Irish Sea and one from the Western Isles of Scotland.

The Razorbill breeds on the cliffs and islands of the North Atlantic including the North and Baltic Seas mainly between 45°N and 75°N. The more southerly populations disperse fairly locally in winter, but northern birds move south, some as far as the western Mediterranean.

Postscript 2000–2002

At Portland Bill, the breeding population numbered 15 birds in 2000, 27 birds in 2001 and 30 birds in 2002, whilst along the Purbeck Cliffs between Durlston CP and St Aldhelm's Head 20 birds were counted on 25th June 2000. Otherwise there was a notably high movement of 5,000 birds per hour, mainly Razorbills, at Portland Bill on 3rd February 2000.

Black Guillemot   *Cepphus grylle*

A rare winter visitor and passage migrant

Mansel-Pleydell (1888) regarded this species as a rare visitor and listed three records involving singles shot/killed in Weymouth Bay in the winter of 1855 and again on 10th December 1874, and at Swanage in January 1862. Subsequently one was picked up dead inland on 19th December 1893 and another seen in Poole Harbour on 4th February 1933.

Since 1962 the Black Guillemot has occurred more frequently with Portland Harbour/Newton's Cove and Portland Bill accounting for the vast majority of records – see below. Most sightings from Portland Harbour/Newton's Cove are for the winter period and birds have overwintered in this area on a number of occasions, most notably in four successive years from 1986/87 to 1989/90. By contrast, at Portland Bill the species is mainly recorded on passage in spring (March–May) and autumn (September–October).

Portland Harbour/Weymouth Bay/Newton's Cove records:

1970	27th–28th December
1973	21st January and 9th December
1974	12th–30th January–perhaps same as December 1973
1979	28th January and possibly the same 4th–7th March
1981	15th December

1983	7th January–25th February
1984	4th–8th May–same as one of two at Portland Bill
1986	9th February
1986/87	9th December–12th April, another 16th March–12th April and a third 19th March
1987/88	one–two birds, including presumably one or two of above, 25th December–20th April
1988/89	presumed one of above 27th November–11th March
1989/90	presumed same as above 10th December–25th March
1996	13th January–23rd March with a second 15th January
1997	23rd January–14th February
1997/98	presumed same as above 31st December, 10th and 22nd January, another 5th February–13th March, presumed same in Weymouth Bay 11th February–14th March
2001/02	Weymouth Bay/Newton's Cove, 23rd December–1st January; same at Lodmoor NR 2nd–3rd January – a remarkable location!

Portland Bill records:

1962	singles 3rd–5th May and 21st October
1963	two 28th–29th September and singles 19th and 26th October
1974	31st December
1980	13th May
1983	18th March–possibly same as Portland Harbour
1984	two 30th April–5th May
1985	6th November
1986	4th May
1987	singles 5th April–possibly same as Portland Harbour, and 25th October
1990	one on 24th–25th February
1996	one on 8 dates from 6th April to 29th June–presumed same as Portland Harbour
1997	singles 11th January and 20th March

In the east of the county there are sightings of singles from Hengistbury on 2nd January 1980, 30th October 1983, 1st November 1985, 26th January 1988, 6th January 1991 and 2nd December 1992. Elsewhere there are reports of singles from Peveril Point on 29th January 1968, Durlston CP on 10th August 1975, Kimmeridge Bay on 4th February 1987, Studland Bay on 27th December 1999 and Poole Harbour during 3rd–25th October 2001.

Otherwise the only other record involves one in summer plumage at West Bexington on 18th February 1999.

The Black Guillemot is a fairly sedentary species breeding across much of the Holarctic south to north-east Canada and New England, Scandinavia, the Baltic Sea, and the north-western British Isles. Birds from the Arctic Ocean move south of the ice in winter, whilst it is a scarce and irregular visitor to the southern North Sea and English Channel.

Little Auk   *Alle alle*

An uncommon passage migrant, mainly in autumn, and winter visitor

Both Mansel-Pleydell (1888) and Blathwayt (1945) considered this species to be an irregular winter visitor, most often recorded after storms when birds were sometimes found inland including one shot at Child Okeford prior to 1799, one dead at Blandford in spring 1873, and singles at Corfe Castle on 11th November 1921, 23rd December 1929 and 7th January 1930.

Since 1950 the Little Auk has occurred more frequently, records being virtually annual from 1963 onwards and increasing markedly during the 1980s and 1990s – see Fig 36. The vast majority of sightings are for the period October–February, which accounts for 97% of the total, with November and December the peak months – see Table 341. The species is prone to sporadic influxes during the late autumn (late October–early December), reflecting much larger displacements of Little Auks into the North Sea due to inclement weather further north. The most notable of these late autumn movements involves 55 birds at various sites along the coast from Abbotsbury to Hengistbury during 28th October–25th November

1996, whilst other high totals include 19 birds during 4th–27th November 1984 and again in November 1990, 18 birds during 29th–31st October 1983 and 14 birds during 6th–8th November 1991.

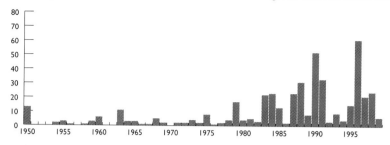

Fig 36. Annual totals 1950–1999

In winter most birds occur during and after severe westerly storms, which on occasions can also produce influxes of birds. The best example is the 'wreck' in mid-February 1950 when c.11 birds were found dead, dying or exhausted at various inland sites including Tincleton, Warmwell, Friar Waddon, Rampisham, Cerne Abbas, Motcombe and Shaftesbury. More recently 22 birds appeared during 2nd January–14th February 1988 including eight at Hengistbury and seven (six of them dead) in Chesil Cove, whilst in December 1990 25 birds were recorded including at least 17 during 27th–31st. Birds rarely stay for long and the only occurrences of overwintering are from Portland Harbour with 2–3 birds from late November 1979 to early March 1980 and one during 1st January–19th February 1994. Otherwise birds have occasionally lingered on the Fleet, for example singles at Abbotsbury during 6th–21st November 1990 and East Fleet during 25th November–17th December 1996.

Jan	Feb	Mar	Apr	May	Jun	Jul	Aug	Sep	Oct	Nov	Dec
44	31	5	5	2	1	0	0	0	67	190	108

Table 341. Monthly totals 1950–1999

Most records involve 1–2 birds with counts rarely exceeding six, the highest being from Portland Bill with 10E on 30th October 1983 and 9W on 29th December 1990. Elsewhere six in Chesil Cove on 11th November 1979, six (one dying) in Portland Harbour on 4th November 1984 and up to four on the Fleet at Abbotsbury during 31st October–3rd November 1996 are noteworthy.

There are few reports for the first half of October, the earliest being 5th October 1981 at Hengistbury and 7th October 1987 at Southbourne. Spring passage is virtually non-existent with 12 sightings during March–May including singles at Portland Bill on 15th April 1959, 4th April 1987, 26th March 1988, 24th March 1990, 3rd May 1991 and 5th April 1997 with 1W at Durlston CP on 5th March 1972 and one in Portland Harbour on 1st March 1998. The other four records all refer to dead birds including one on the Chesil Beach on 6th May 1960. The most exceptional unseasonal report involves a bird in full summer plumage photographed at Peveril Point on 29th June 1990.

Although birds have been recorded along the entire coast from Charmouth to Hengistbury, the most favoured sites are in the Weymouth/Portland/Fleet area, which accounts for 58% of the total – see Table 342. In the east of the county, Christchurch Harbour is the main locality with virtually all sightings at sea off Hengistbury, whilst most of the Purbeck records are from Durlston CP.

	Number
Portland Bill	164
Weymouth/Fleet area	104
Purbeck	59
Poole Harbour area	26
Christchurch Harbour	74
elsewhere	32

Table 342. Totals at the main sites 1950–1999

Severe late autumn and winter gales have resulted in Little Auks occurring in unusual situations, sometimes far inland. Apart from the 'wreck' of February 1950, the following records are of interest:

1955   Bloxworth: one found dying 14th November
1965   Seatown: one found in a bucket of water in a garden 25th January, subsequently released on
           the shore and swam away
1966   Preston, Weymouth: one found 18th October, but died later
1967   Corfe Castle: one found alive 2nd November, but died the same day
1968   Worth Matravers: one found on 27th December
1971   Wyke Regis: one found in a garden 1st December, released at Portland Bill a few days later
1979   Radipole NR: one found in a bramble bush 25th November, died later
1981   Hawkchurch: one found dead in the road 2nd November
1983   Weymouth: one found alive in a garden 31st October
1985   Lodmoor NR: one 7th December following a severe overnight gale
1988   Lodmoor NR: one found dead 17th January

Only one bird has been ringed in the county.

The Little Auk breeds in the high Arctic, mainly between 70°N and 82°N, from west Greenland and northern Iceland east to Svalbard and Franz Joseph Land. It winters in the open sea south to the North Sea and New England.

Postscript 2000–2002
Annual totals involved 12 birds in 2000, c.21 in 2001 and c.32 in 2002. Singles at Durlston CP on 24th and 27th September 2001 are the earliest county records.

Puffin (Atlantic Puffin)   *Fratercula arctica*

An uncommon summer visitor, and rare passage migrant and winter visitor

Mansel-Pleydell (1888) stated that "the Puffin appears almost to the day during the last week of March, and breeds in our cliffs in company with Guillemots and Razorbills", whilst also making reference to singles shot in Poole Harbour on 3rd February 1847 and 26th January 1883, as well as to 30 or more corpses thrown upon the Chesil Bank after a storm in January of an unspecified year. Blathwayt (1945) described this species as "a common summer resident", which bred at intervals from Portland along the cliffs nearly to Anvil Point, but was not as numerous as the Guillemot or Razorbill.

The Puffin suffered the same fate as the Razorbill with a marked decrease in the breeding population during the first half of the 20th Century. This decline has continued with the number of breeding pairs on the Purbeck cliffs falling from less than 100 pairs in 1949 to 37 pairs in 1969, 10–15 pairs during the 1980s and c.2–3 pairs in 1996 and 1997 – see Table 343. Similarly at Portland Bill breeding numbers have declined from 20–25 pairs in 1948 and 1958, to ten or less pairs subsequently with only 2–3 pairs present during 1986–1999 – see Table 344. The relative strength of the breeding colony at Portland Bill in the early 1950s is reflected by summer counts of 87 on 16th July 1951 and 65 on 29th June 1953. At present the breeding status of the species in the county is very precarious.

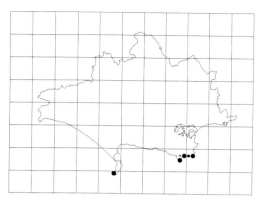

	63	66	67	69	70	71	72	73	74	75	76	77	78	79	80	81	82
Pairs	–	33	30	37	32	–	27	–	nc	–	–	17	–	–	15	–	–
Birds	20	–	–	–	–	47	–	39	nc	34	25	–	22	16	–	15	18

	83	84	85	86	87	88	89	90	91	92	93	94	95	96	97	98	99
Pairs	–	8	12	10	13	nc	15	6	–	6	–	10	–	3	2	–	–
Birds	18	–	–	–	–	nc	–	–	4	–	7	–	9	–	–	12	13

Table 343. Number of breeding pairs/birds between Durlston CP and St Aldhelm's Head 1963–1999

51	58	62	66	67	69	70	71	72	73	74	75	76	77	78	79	80	81
14	25	8	8	10	6	6	10	5	6	4	4	2	3	3	3	5	5

82	83	84	85	86	87	88	89	90	91	92	93	94	95	96	97	98	99
6	6	4	5	3	3	3	3	3	2	2	2	3	2–3	2	2	2	2

Table 344. Number of breeding pairs at Portland Bill 1951–1999

The breeding cliffs are normally occupied from late February or early March, when the adults return, to late July with odd birds occasionally lingering into August. In recent years breeding on Purbeck has been restricted mainly to the cliffs between Dancing Ledge and St Aldhelms Head, but in 1987 a pair bred at Durlston CP for the first time since 1969. In late summer, evening gatherings of Puffins regularly occur at Dancing Ledge where counts have declined along with the breeding population, e.g. 22 on 22nd June 1978, but only 12 on 28th June 1998 and 13 on 19th June 1999. At Portland Bill the species bred on the East Cliffs up to 1951, but subsequently breeding has only occurred in the vicinity of the West Cliffs.

Spring passage is sometimes evident at Portland Bill, e.g. 30W on 12th May 1976, 29W on 9th May 1985, 16W on 11th April 1990 and 12W on 16th April 1977. The presence of local breeding birds obscures spring movements along the Purbeck coast, but there are several reports including 34E at St Aldhelm's Head during 26th April–7th May 1984 with 9E there on 2nd May 1981, which may reflect genuine passage. There are spring and summer sightings from Hengistbury in 14 years during 1974–1993, mainly 1–2 birds each year, but seven in 1984 and four in 1985 and 1990. These presumably involve both migrants and birds wandering from the nearby Purbeck colonies.

Autumn passage is more obvious, but records from the main coastal watch-points have declined since the late 1980s – see Table 345. Most sightings involve only 1–2 birds, the best counts being nine at Portland Bill on 19th October 1979 with six there on 31st October 1983, and 6W at Durlston CP on 12th October 1983. The majority of reports are from Portland Bill and Durlston CP with Hengistbury only recording eight birds in five years during 1974–1984.

Reports in mid-winter were virtually unknown prior to 1980, but have increased subsequently with an isolated peak of 25 bird-days during January–February 1988 including 21 bird-days at Durlston CP – see Table 346. Again most records are from Portland Bill and Durlston CP with Hengistbury recording ten birds in six years during 1978–1993.

1974	1975	1976	1977	1978	1979	1980	1981	1982	1983	1984	1985	1986
4	15	3	10	16	25	2	11	5	29	10	4	5

1987	1988	1989	1990	1991	1992	1993	1994	1995	1996	1997	1998	1999
21	24	6	1	1	1	2	5	4	0	0	2	0

Table 345. Autumn totals for coastal movements and the main watch-points 1974–1999

80	81	82	83	84	85	86	87	88	89	90	91	92	93	94	95	96	97	98	99
1	3	0	1	2	1	1	9	25	3	4	2	0	1	1	5	0	1	1	3

Table 346. Mid-winter totals 1980–1999

Away from the main sites, the Puffin is somewhat of a rarity. In Lyme Bay there are occasional records from the coast between Chesil Cove and West Bexington including 12E+2 at the latter site on 11th May 1997. There are also several reports of corpses from Chesil Cove/Chesil Beach including four found dead during January–February 1995. Elsewhere there are sightings of single birds from Portland Harbour on 2nd December 1991 and 14th February 1997, the Nothe on 27th November 1984, Weymouth Bay on 19th January 1995 (dead), Lulworth Cove on 11th May 1980, Peveril Point on 9th May 1986, Brownsea on 16th August 1974, and Southbourne on 7th October 1987 with perhaps the same bird at Boscombe Pier on 17th October. Perhaps the most unusual record involves one flying north-west along the Fleet at Langton Herring on 26th October 1984.

Only one bird has been ringed in the county.

The Puffin breeds on cliffs and islands of the North Atlantic mainly between 45°N and 80°N. It winters, far out to sea, mainly between 40°N and the pack-ice, but extending south to the Azores, the Canary Islands and the western Mediterranean.

Postscript 2000–2002

The Puffin maintains its precarious status as a breeding bird in the county with 12 pairs (three pairs confirmed breeding) along the Purbeck Cliffs between Durlston CP and St Aldhelm's Head in 2000, whilst at Dancing Ledge there were summer evening peak counts of 16 birds on 9th June 2001 and 15 birds on 21st June 2002. At Portland Bill five birds were present during the breeding season in 2000 and 2002, but only three birds in 2001. Otherwise, one at Hengistbury on 15th May 2002 was the first record from this site since 1993.

Pallas's Sandgrouse   *Syrrhaptes paradoxus*

Accidental

1888   Near Wareham: six 28th May

The above is the only record given in Blathwayt (1945) and subsequent publications, but there are further reports which were published in the *Field* 9th June 1888: 839 and 12th Jan., 1889: 51, and *Zool.*, 1888: 265, 388 namely:

1888   Wimborne: killed 18th June
        Near Wareham: flock late June to early July
1889   Marnhull: male shot 3rd January

The Pallas's Sandgrouse is a bird of the central Asian steppes, which irrupted into western Europe in 1863, 1888–89 and 1908. It is now a very rare vagrant to Europe with only six records (seven birds) for Great Britain since 1909.

Rock Dove (Rock/Feral Pigeon)   *Columba livia*

A fairly common resident (Feral Pigeon)

Mansel-Pleydell (1888) expressed considerable doubt that genuine Rock Doves bred in Dorset in the 19th Century. Subsequently the Rock Dove has been largely ignored and has only been mentioned in the Dorset Bird Reports since 1986. Even then the information is very scanty and refers to the Feral Pigeon rather than the true Rock Dove. The *BTO Atlas* (1968–1972) showed a distinct coastal bias in distribution with evidence of breeding recorded in only ten (27%) 10-km squares (confirmed in two, probable in three and possible in five). It is not certain whether this was a true reflection of the species status in the county at the time.

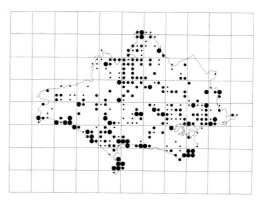

By contrast the Tetrad Survey (1987–1994) found that the Feral Pigeon is widely, if somewhat sparsely, distributed throughout the entire county with evidence of breeding in all but two (95%) of the pre-1974 10-km squares (confirmed in 23, probable in ten and possible in two). Although this startling increase may partly be due to better coverage achieved by the Tetrad Survey, it also seems likely to represent a genuine expansion, particularly into rural areas where the species has taken advantage of recent agricultural changes that have also benefited the Stock Dove and Woodpigeon. The Tetrad Map reflects the habitat preferences of the Feral Pigeon, which includes coastal cliffs with notable concentrations in east Purbeck, on Portland, and in the west between Bridport and Lyme Regis. Intensively urbanised areas are also favoured, particularly the Bournemouth and Poole conurbation where high buildings provide surrogate nesting ledges similar to those found on cliffs. Indeed the Feral Pigeon is particularly common in the town centres of Bournemouth and Poole where it is considered a pest. Since 1991 flocks of 200–330 have been reported from Portland, Weymouth, Lytchett Bay, Poole, Parkstone and Bournemouth with an isolated peak count of 1,091 at Lytchett Bay on 11th December 1992. The species is regularly predated by cliff-nesting Peregrines, particularly at Durlston CP.

It is impossible to claim the existence of totally pure stock in many countries, particularly in western Europe. Feral Pigeons, the descendants of wild Rock Doves, are widely distributed and present in all continents.

Stock Dove (Stock Pigeon) *Columba oenas*

A common resident, winter visitor and passage migrant

Mansel-Pleydell (1888) reported that this species was annually becoming more abundant, especially in the sandy parts bordering Poole Harbour where it bred in rabbit burrows, whilst nesting on cliffs was also recorded. Blathwayt (1945) considered the Stock Dove to be a common resident and winter visitor.

The *BTO Atlas* (1968–1972) revealed evidence of breeding in all 10-km squares (confirmed in 29, probable in seven and possible in one). Subsequently there appears to have been little change in status up to the Tetrad Survey (1987–1994), which found evidence of breeding in all of the pre-1974 10-km squares (confirmed in 33 and probable in four). The Tetrad Map shows that the species is widely distributed throughout most of the county, albeit somewhat patchily in parts of the south and extreme north (ST72 and ST82), whilst it is scarce or absent in the more intensively urbanised areas, notably the Bournemouth and Poole conurbation.

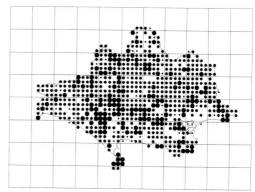

There is relatively little information on breeding densities and population trends. The Bird Reports for 1975–1977 allude to an apparent increase, perhaps reflecting the national recovery, which occurred between 1961 and 1980. This followed the dramatic decline during the 1950s associated with the widespread use of organochlorines as seed dressings. In recent years, there appears to have been a decline in the breeding population, most notably at coastal sites. For example, at Durlston CP the number of breeding pairs increased from eight in 1981 to 15 in 1987 before declining to 6–7 in 1995, two in 1996 with only 1–3 birds present in 1999 – see Table 347. Similarly at Portland Bill, a population of 20–25 pairs in 1967 and 10–15 pairs during the 1980s declined in the early 1990s with no evidence of attempted breeding at the normal West Cliff sites during 1993–1997. More recently, breeding birds were present at several cliff and quarry sites on Portland in 1998 and 1999. Inland, the few CBC sites with long-term records indicate a more stable situation, e.g. 3–5 pairs have bred at Arne NR annually between 1974 and 1993, but increased to ten in 1995.

81	82	83	84	85	86	87	88	89	90	91	92	93	94	95	96
8	10	12	14	14	12	15	12	nc	nc	8	9	nc	nc	6-7	2

Table 347. Number of breeding pairs at Durlston CP 1981–1996

During the non-breeding season flocks form in areas where suitable feeding can be found, e.g. stubble fields. In the 1970s and early 1980s large gatherings were a feature at Portland Bill, particularly between late autumn and early spring (October to March) – see Table 348. The size of these flocks often reached 200–300 birds, but 800 on 20th February 1975 and 420 on 31st October 1976. Since 1982 this winter population declined rapidly and had disappeared by the mid-1990s. This was predicted in the 1981 PBO Report, which observed that the lack of feeding areas, such as stubble fields, may well affect the status of this species in future years! Elsewhere in the county non-breeding flocks of up to 200 birds were frequently reported, and there is a record of 500 at Pentridge on 25th November 1961. Since 1996, however, non-breeding flocks have rarely exceeded 50 birds, the highest being 60 at Middlebere on 27th January 1998, perhaps reflecting the decline in the breeding population.

73/74	74/75	75/76	76/77	77/78	78/79	79/80	80/81	81/82	82/83	83/84
300	800	110	420	nc	200	300	300	200	150	150

84/85	85/86	86/87	87/88	88/89	89/90	90/91	91/92	92/93	93/94	94/95
70	50	35	30	34	25	25	22	56	23	6

Table 348. Winter maxima at Portland Bill 1973–1995

Spring passage between March and early May is generally very small and hardly detected in some years, but occasionally prominent visual movements are recorded, e.g. 186S over Portland Harbour on 8th May 1971, 143N at Radipole NR during 7th–21st April 1991 (with maximum of 85 on 16th) and 94N there on 9th April 1988, and 140E at Durlston CP during 19th–30th April 1984. Visual passage in autumn, which mainly occurs between mid-October and mid-November, is more pronounced but, as in spring, it appears to be virtually non-existent in some years. At Portland Bill and Durlston CP movements, predominantly southerly in direction, have been recorded in most autumns since 1989. Passage was particularly heavy at these sites in November 1994 with peaks of 1,500S at Durlston CP and 850S at Portland Bill on 16th, also 747W at St Aldhelm's Head on the same day. These counts, however, are overshadowed by a remarkable 5,000S at Portland Bill on 28th November 1959. Other notable movements include 660W at West Bexington on 12th November 1996 and 450W at Radipole School during 15th–17th November 1991. Cold weather movements are occasionally reported, e.g. 150E at Durlston CP in January 1982 with 130E there during 6th–9th February 1986.

A total of 180 birds has been ringed in the county.

The Stock Dove breeds in north-west Africa and across much of Europe, but in Scandinavia only in the south-east, extending eastwards into west-central Asia, also in Asia Minor. It is resident in the west and extreme south of its range, but migratory elsewhere.

Postscript 2000–2002

Exceptional passage was reported from Hengistbury in early November 2001 with 3,500W on 1st and 1,500W on 2nd, also 'thousands' recorded from Abbotsbury at the same time. Winter counts of 200 at Dorchester on 9th December 2001, 152 at Sherford Bridge/Morden on 7th March 2000 and 120 at Bardolf Manor, Puddletown on 20th October 2000 are the highest recorded in the county since 1994.

Woodpigeon (Common Wood Pigeon)   *Columba palumbus*

An abundant resident, winter visitor and passage migrant

Both Mansel-Pleydell (1888) and Blathwayt (1945) regarded this species to be a common resident. The *BTO Atlas* (1968–1972) suggested little change in status with breeding confirmed in all 10-km squares except Portland Bill (SY66) where absent. There is some evidence to suggest a population expansion, albeit on a localised basis, during the 1970s. For example, it was considered that the Woodpigeon occurred with increasing regularity in urban and suburban gardens, whilst Portland Bill was colonised in about 1977 – see Table 349. The Tetrad Survey (1987–1994) confirmed breeding in all pre-1974 10-km squares and shows that the species remains widely distributed throughout the county with evidence of breeding in almost all tetrad squares.

Population trends at those few sites with long-term data show no consistent pattern – see Table 350. There have been marked declines at Radipole NR, from c.30 pairs during 1981–1984 to 20 pairs in 1988 and only nine pairs in 1997, and Durlston CP, from 12–16 pairs during 1980–1990 to 6–8 pairs during 1996–1998. At other sites such as the CBC plots at Fontmell Down and Forde Abbey, there is evidence of an increase in populations despite some annual fluctuation in numbers. This upward trend is also shown by figures from Merley Park with 20 pairs in 1995 increasing to 31 pairs in 1997 and 32 pairs in 1999. In 1969 a bird was still brooding young in a nest as late as 10th November.

77	78	79	80	81	82	83	84	85	86	87	88	89	90	91	92	93	94	95	96	97
2	10	12	3	2	2	3	3	3	2	4	4	4	3	6	5	10	4	5	5	6

Table 349. Number of breeding pairs at Portland Bill 1977–1997

	80	81	82	83	84	85	86	87	88	89	90	91	92	93	94	95	96	97	98
Radipole NR	nc	30	30	30	30	25	24	27	20	nc	nc	nc	nc	nc	nc	nc	nc	9	nc
Durlston CP	15	12	15	15	16	15	15	12	16	nc	12	nc	nc	nc	nc	nc	7-8	6-8	6
Fontmell Dn	nc	nc	nc	17	16	17	20	nc	22	29	nc	20	19	15	30	nc	nc	nc	nc
Forde Abbey	7	6	6	nc	6	10	11	nc	15	19	nc	8	13	13	8	14	8	nc	nc

Table 350. Number of breeding pairs at various sites 1980–1998

Although flocks of up to 1,000 or so birds are frequently recorded during the non-breeding season, c.5,000 at Alderholt on 6th November 1953 is noteworthy. Spring migration is small and insignificant, but heavy passage involving 100s and sometimes 1,000s of birds often occurs in the late autumn, mainly between late October and mid-November. The heaviest movements recorded in the county include c.40,000W or SW at Christchurch Harbour during 27th October–20th November 1999, 22,450W at West Bexington during 9th–11th November 1996 with an exceptional peak of 13,000W on 11th, also 15,700W there during 8th–12th November 1999, and 17,822W at nearby Abbotsbury in November 1991 including 12,036W during 16th–17th. Very heavy passage also occurred in late October 1983, most notably on 29th, with 12,000E at St Aldhelm's Head during 25th–29th (maximum of 10,000E on 29th), 10,861E and 982W at Christchurch Harbour between 20th–30th including 9,472 during 28th–29th, 10,600S at Portland Bill during 19th–30th (maximum of 6,300S on 29th), and 9,600E at Durlston CP during 27th October–26th November (maximum of 6,500E on 29th). Other high counts include 10,000N at St Aldhelm's Head on 17th November 1967 and 10,000SW at Portland Bill on 28th November 1959, whilst well inland 7,000N over Cranborne during 13th–15th November 1961 is notable. There is some evidence of cold weather movements, e.g. 450E at Durlston CP in January 1982.

A total of 317 birds has been ringed in the county.

The Woodpigeon breeds in north-west Africa and across much of Europe, except northern Scandinavia, extending eastwards through Asia Minor and the Middle East with isolated populations in south-west and west-central Asia. It is mainly migratory in the north and east of its range, partially migratory elsewhere with the degree of movement declining progressively towards the west and south.

Postscript 2000–2002

Exceptional coastal passage was reported during late autumn 2001 with 52,200W at Hengistbury during

29th October–14th November including a county record peak of 24,000 on 1st November, also 13,300W at West Bexington during 1st–5th November and 7,435W at East Bexington on 10th November.

Sponsored by Julian Francis

Collared Dove (Eurasian Collared Dove)   *Streptopelia decaocto*

A common resident

This species first bred in Great Britain in Norfolk in 1955 after a spectacular spread across Europe, and reached Dorset in 1961 when three were seen at Swanage on 15th May. Although a pair of these birds laid eggs, breeding was unsuccessful. Another pair probably bred in west Dorset in the same year, whilst singles flew in from the sea at Peveril Point on 18th September and Portland Bill on 13th October. There were further reports from Portland Bill and the coastal fringes between West Bay and West Bexington in 1962 and 1963 when breeding was reported at the latter site. By 1964 breeding was established in at least four widely dispersed areas, namely West Bexington, Weymouth, Parkstone and Sherborne with further records from other sites mainly along the coastal fringes including 20 at West Bexington on 22nd October and 18 at Portland Bill on 8th November. The subsequent colonization of the county was rapid and by the *BTO Atlas* (1968–1972) the Collared Dove was widely distributed with evidence of breeding in 33 (89%) 10-km squares (confirmed in 25, probable in five and possible in three), the most notable absence being from the extreme north (ST72).

Although the Dorset Bird Reports for 1973 and 1974 suggest that the Collared Dove was still spreading into new areas, expansion appears to have ceased by the second half of the decade as the population reached its peak. There is some indication of a reduction in numbers during the 1980s. The Bird Report for 1987 comments that the species was declining in many parts of the county and suggested that after the surge of colonisation, numbers had begun to fall back before settling at a lower and more stable level. This is supported by CBC data from Forde Abbey where the number of breeding pairs fell from eight in 1982 to three in 1986, two in 1988 and only one intermittently during 1989–1996. The national trend shows the same pattern with a rapid increase in the population during the 1970s to a peak in 1982, followed by a slight decline to 1977 levels during the 1980s.

The Tetrad Survey (1987–1994) found evidence of breeding in all but one (97%) of the pre-1974 10-km squares (confirmed in 34 and probable in two). The Tetrad Map shows that the Collared Dove is still widely distributed throughout the county, being absent mainly from the tetrads lacking agriculture and/or human habitation. These include areas of heathland and forestry, notably around the south of Poole Harbour (SY88, SY98 and SZ08) and in the extreme east of the county (SU10 and SZ19).

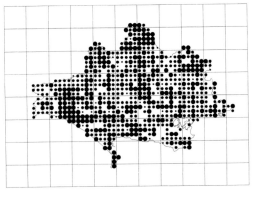

The size of the post-breeding flocks reflect the general pattern of colonisation. By 1967 these flocks had reached treble figures with over 100 often recorded at Weymouth. Subsequently gatherings of 100 or more were frequently recorded throughout the 1970s and early 1980s, notably at Portland Bill where the 'barn flock' reached a maximum of 120 in April and November 1976, and remained a regular feature until 1982 when the practice of storing grain in the barns was discontinued. Other sites hosting regular flocks included West Bexington (maximum of 118 on 20th September 1976), Bagber (maximum of 112 in November 1976 and again in February 1977), Langton Herring (maximum of 105 on 25th September 1973) and near Almer (maximum of 103 in 1974). From 1981 to 1993 the size of post-breeding flocks declined, the only count exceeding 70 birds being 100 at Burton on 1st January 1988. Since 1994 there has been a moderate resurgence in numbers including regular counts of 100–120 at Lodmoor NR throughout 1995 with a maximum of 300 on 26th February, also 100 there on 18th April 1998, whilst nearby at Overcombe counts of 150 were recorded on 10th December 1994, 30th November

1996 and 22nd February 1997. Other recent high counts include 150 at Monkton Up Wimborne on 28th November 1999 and 140 at New Barn Farm near Abbotsbury on 28th January 1999.

Migration is most obvious in the spring, being slight or non-existent in autumn. The strength of the spring movements, which mainly occur in April, increased dramatically during the 1970s to reach a peak during 1979–1985 before diminishing to the point where passage has virtually ceased, except for an isolated count of 42N at Portland Bill during 23rd April–4th June 1998 – see Table 351. Nationally the amount of long-distance movement declined as population densities levelled off during the 1980s.

	72	73	74	75	76	77	78	79	80	81	82	83	84	85
Portland Bill	40	9	20	5	33	48	nc	247	78	288	189	487	87	115
Durlston CP	nc	nc	nc	nc	nc	nc	nc	nc	nc	67	nc	nc	nc	60
Xchurch Hbr	-	-	nc	nc	nc	nc	nc	nc	nc	148	115	nc	68	106

	86	87	88	89	90	91	92	93	94	95	96	97	98	99
Portland Bill	nc	52	49	40	4	41	0	0	0	2	1	0	42	nc
Durlston CP	28	19	0	0	16	10	0	0	0	5	7	3	nc	nc
Xchurch Hbr	nc	24	10	8	9	18	0	nc	nc	nc	nc	nc	nc	nc

Table 351. Spring passage at the main coastal watch-points 1972–1999

A total of 245 birds has been ringed in the county.

Since c.1930 the Collared Dove has spread rapidly north and west to become a widespread breeding resident throughout much of Europe mainly between 40°N and 65°N. There are also large populations in Asia Minor, the Middle East and parts of southern Asia including the Indian sub-continent.

Turtle Dove (European Turtle Dove)　　　*Streptopelia turtur*

An uncommon summer visitor and passage migrant

Mansel-Pleydell (1888) briefly referred to this species as a summer visitor, whilst Blathwayt (1945) described it as "a common summer resident", which is apparently increasing.

The fortunes of the Turtle Dove have declined during the past 50 years. Although a decrease was first reported in the early 1960s, the *BTO Atlas* (1968–1972) found that the species was still widely distributed in the county, apparently being commonest in the north and west. There was evidence of breeding in 32 (86%) 10-km squares (confirmed in 14, probable in 14 and possible in four), the most notable absence being in the extreme north (ST72).

The breeding population continued to diminish during the 1970s. For example, the 1974 Bird Report stated that there was "no sign of the usual pairs at Colehill, Morden Park and Corfe Mullen" and that it was "rarely seen or heard in the north-west and west", whilst the 1976 Bird Report suggested that the species "is declining in Dorset". During the 1980s this decline accelerated and by the time of the Tetrad Survey (1987–1994), the Turtle Dove had retreated east and south across the county, deserting most of its

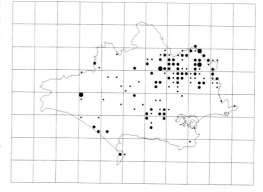

former haunts in the north and west. Since records of possible breeding may refer to late migrants, it is best to use evidence of confirmed or probable breeding when making comparisons between surveys. This reveals a reduction from 28 (76%) 10-km squares during the *BTO Atlas* (1968–1972) to 15 (41%) of the pre-1974 10-km squares during the Tetrad Survey (1987–1994).

The Tetrad Map shows that the northern chalk of Cranborne Chase, mainly to the east of the River Stour, and the neighbouring northern fringes of the Poole Basin are the Turtle Dove's stronghold in the county. In addition, there is a much smaller population based in the centre of the Poole Basin between Wareham and Moreton. Otherwise there are a few occupied tetrad squares scattered throughout the rest of Dorset. Observations made during the Tetrad Survey suggest that the species is still fairly widespread within its stronghold on Cranborne Chase, favouring deciduous woodland and mixed forestry plantations particularly where Ash is present. Indeed most suitable woodlands appeared to hold at least a single pair with occasionally small concentrations of birds, e.g. five singing males in the Harbin Park/Tarrant Gunville area during the summer of 1993.

The Dorset Bird Reports for 1995 and 1996 suggested a further decline in the population with breeding virtually restricted to the north-east of the county. By contrast, there has been an encouraging increase in breeding records during 1997–1999. For example, in 1997 and 1998 evidence of breeding was reported from at least 12 (32%) of the pre-1974 10-km squares. The majority of breeding records during 1997–1999 are from the north-east of the county and the centre of Poole Basin, the most favoured sites being Garston Wood, the Cranborne area, White Sheet Plantation/Holt Heath NNR and Wareham Forest. In 1997 there were breeding reports from two sites in the extreme west (SY39 and SY49) where the species was apparently absent during the Tetrad Survey.

The British population grew steadily during the 1960s and 1970s, before declining sharply during the 1980s to below the level of the early 1960s. This pre-1978 increase was not apparent in western England.

The Turtle Dove's decline as a breeding bird is reflected by the numbers reported on migration at the main coastal watch-points – see Table 352. Peak counts of 50–100 birds were frequently recorded up to 1983, the best being from Portland Bill with 250 on 9th September 1956, 150 on 15th September 1953, 140 on 27th September 1976 and 130 on 2nd October 1976, whilst 100 on 30th April 1973 is very high for spring passage. Elsewhere 100+ near Cranborne on 5th June 1963 is a notable inland gathering. From 1984 to 1989 there were only two reports of 50 birds, both again at Portland Bill on 25th May 1985 and 10th May 1989, whilst during the 1990s peak counts never exceeded 21 birds, and failed to reach double figures during 1994–1999 with the exception of 11 at Portland Bill on 11th May 1998.

	60–64	65–69	70–74	75–79	80–84	85–89	90–94	95–99
Portland Bill	308	366	401	484	384	226	100	51
Durlston CP	nc	nc	nc	nc	121	120	62	42
Xchurch Hbr	–	–	–	nc	68	35	13	9

Table 352. 5-year average annual totals (bds) at the main coastal watch-points 1960–1999

Spring migrants normally arrive during the second half of April, the earliest being 22nd March 1998 at Lodmoor NR and 29th March 1973 at Portland Bill, whilst Blathwayt (1945) referred to an early record on 31st March of an unspecified year. On average, birds arrived later during the 1950s and 1960s than in the three subsequent decades – see Table 353. Although spring passage usually peaks in May, it is sometimes protracted and may continue in some strength through to mid-June and occasionally later. A few early returning migrants appear in July followed by the main autumn passage from late August. Peak movements occur in September and occasionally in early October with late stragglers recorded through to the end of the month. Apart from wintering birds, the latest reports are mainly from Portland Bill with singles on 1st November 1976, 3rd November 1979, 8th November 1966 and 27th November 1983; also one at Hengistbury on 3rd November 1984.

	1950–1959	1960–1969	1970–1979	1980–1989	1990–1999
Range	18th–21st April	12th–29th April	29th March–24th April	9th–30th April	22nd March–23rd April
Average	20th April	20th April	15th April	16th April	16th April

Table 353. Dates for first spring arrivals each decade 1950–1999

Instances of wintering are rare with four records as follows:

1967/68   Portland Bill: a male joined a flock of domesticated Barbary Doves at the Bird Observatory on 17th July and remained until 29th April

1968/69 Portland Bill and Weston: first-winter bird associated with Collared Doves late October–19th
        January
1977/78 Portland Bill: 7th January–15th February probably died in the cold spell
1995/96 French's Farm, Lytchett Bay: first-winter 2nd December–at least 25th February

A total of 51 birds has been ringed in the county and there have been three foreign recoveries from Portugal and one from Spain.

The Turtle Dove breeds from North Africa and across much of Europe, except for Ireland, Scotland and Scandinavia, extending eastwards to Asia Minor, the Middle East and west-central Asia. It winters almost exclusively in a band across sub-Saharan Africa between 10°N and 20°N.

Postscript 2000–2002
One at Lodmoor NR on 3rd November 2001 was unusually late.

Ring-necked Parakeet (Rose-ringed Parakeet)　　*Psittacula krameri*

A scarce feral resident and escapee

The early status of this feral exotic is sketchy. Prior to 1980, the species was known in the county for at least 12 years as an escapee, but detailed records were not kept. All published reports during the 1970s came from Portland Bill with singles on 27th October 1975 and 18th April 1976, followed by an exceptional series of sightings during 1979 involving 14 birds including 11 in August.

Since 1980 the Ring-necked Parakeet has been recorded annually except for 1985 and 1987 – see Table 354. The vast majority of records are from the coastal fringes, the only sightings from well inland being at Woodbury Hill on 13th March 1986, Bagber on 10th and 12th November 1986, Toller Porcorum on 14th August 1991, Catsley Farm, Corscombe during 1st–8th October 1996 and Dorchester Hospital all year in 1998.

80	81	82	83	84	85	86	87	88	89	90	91	92	93	94	95	96	97	98	99
1	2	1	2	2	0	3	0	1	9	2	3	5	4	1	1	10	10	7	4

Table 354. Annual totals 1980–1999 (excluding Studland birds since 1990)

Although the 1987 Bird Report noted that the species was thought to be resident in parts of the Bournemouth and Poole conurbation, there appears to be little evidence to support this statement. Since 1990, however, free-flying captive birds have established a small feral population in Studland Village where there were earlier sightings of singles on 27th October 1983 and 25th March 1989. Although successful breeding apparently occurred during 1990–1993, the only evidence subsequently involves a pair mating on 26th February 1995, birds visiting nesting holes in 1996 and three juveniles seen on 3rd October 1997. Peak counts from this site have varied from 4 to 12 birds during 1993–1999 – see Table 355.

1993	1994	1995	1996	1997	1998	1999
8	8	9	12	7	8	4

Table 355. Annual maxima at Studland Village 1993–1999

The Ring-necked Parakeet, which is mainly an inhabitant of the northern tropics of Africa and the tropical/subtropical areas of south-west Asia and the Indian sub-continent, started breeding ferally in south-east England in 1969. As a result it was subsequently admitted to Category C of the British List.

Postscript 2000–2002
There were reports from the small resident population in Studland Village, which reached a maximum of seven birds in both 2000 and 2001.

Great Spotted Cuckoo   *Clamator glandarius*

Accidental: two records

1989   St Aldhelm's Head: probable first-summer 11th–12th March
1994   Hengistbury: 20th April

The Great Spotted Cuckoo is a summer visitor breeding in Iberia, southern France, parts of Italy, extreme eastern Greece, Asia Minor and parts of the Middle East. It winters mainly in parts of western, central and eastern Africa where it is also resident, being a breeding summer visitor to southern Africa. A vagrant to Great Britain with 42 records up to 2002.

Sponsored by Ivor Sargent

Cuckoo (Common Cuckoo)   *Cuculus canorus*

A common summer visitor and passage migrant

The Cuckoo was a "well-known summer visitant" to Mansel-Pleydell (1888), whilst Blathwayt (1945) considered it to be a common and well-distributed summer resident.

The *BTO Atlas* (1968–1972) suggests little change in status with evidence of breeding in all but two (95%) 10-km squares (confirmed in 24 and probable in 11). Despite reports during the mid-1970s of apparent scarcity in the extreme west and north, the Tetrad Survey (1987–1994) found evidence of breeding in all but two (95%) of the pre-1974 10-km squares (confirmed in 19, probable in 13 and possible in three). The Tetrad Map shows the Cuckoo is widely distributed, seemingly favouring parts of the Poole Basin and the Blackmore Vale, being scarcer on the chalk and in the west of the county, and largely absent from intensively urban areas such as the Bournemouth and Poole conurbation.

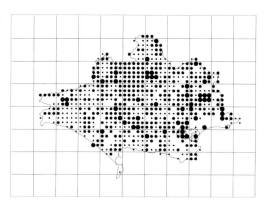

Although the little information there is available on breeding numbers suggests that the population is relatively stable, there is some evidence of a reduction during the 1990s. For example the Bird Report for 1996 states that many observers noted an ongoing decline, whilst in the Toller area the number of calling males fell from 20 in 1990 to 5–6 in 1993.

Blathwayt (1945) gave a list of the less usual hosts including Woodlark, Grey Wagtail, Grasshopper Warbler, Marsh Warbler, Dartford Warbler, Blackcap, Wood Warbler, Redpoll and Corn Bunting, whilst the Dorset Bird Report for 1950 adds Whitethroat, Spotted Flycatcher, Greenfinch and Cirl Bunting. Very little information has been published on this subject subsequently.

Passage at the main coastal watch-points is usually stronger in the spring than the autumn – see Tables 356 and 357. Peak counts at these and other sites occasionally exceed five but rarely ten birds, the highest being 15 at Radipole NR on 26th August 1980 and 11 tired birds flying north low over Cranborne Common at dawn on 30th April 1964.

	1980	1981	1982	1983	1984	1985	1986	1987	1988	1989
Portland Bill	26	26	25	7	40	26	14	20	4	34
Durlston CP	nc	37	17	14	19	24	5	13	18	21
Christchurch Hbr	21	25	16	14	37	30	28	36	24	33

	1990	1991	1992	1993	1994	1995	1996	1997	1998	1999
Portland Bill	24	39	19	25	6	10	14	nc	12	11
Durlston CP	6	24	37	8	nc	nc	22	20	nc	8
Christchurch Hbr	35	32	21	12	nc	nc	18	59	30	21

Table 356. Spring totals (bds) at the main coastal watch-points 1980–1999

	1980	1981	1982	1983	1984	1985	1986	1987	1988	1989
Portland Bill	3	16	20	78	13	0	21	21	31	5
Durlston CP	nc	6	10	10	10	1	17	21	18	35
Christchurch Hbr	3	12	14	12	7	9	7	14	25	2

	1990	1991	1992	1993	1994	1995	1996	1997	1998	1999
Portland Bill	6	4	33	3	8	6	1	nc	2	3
Durlston CP	13	9	10	15	nc	nc	37	25	nc	7
Christchurch Hbr	8	1	2	6	nc	nc	10	17	nc	3

Table 357. Autumn totals (bds) at the main coastal watch-points 1980–1999

Although early migrants are occasionally recorded in March, the earliest being 16th March 1977 at Canford Heath and 19th March 1970 at Shipton, the first birds of the spring normally occur during the first half of April, the average first arrival date over the past 50 years being 6th April – see Table 358. The last birds are usually seen in August or September with occasional late stragglers remaining into October, the latest being 27th October 1969 at St Aldhelm's Head and 31st October 1992 at Christchurch Harbour. Mansel-Pleydell (1888) reported that he flushed a Cuckoo on the coast in the month of November.

	1950–1959	1960–1969	1970–1979	1980–1989	1990–1999
Range	2nd– 14th April	29th March– 11th April	16th March– 17th April	26th March– 15th April	1st–16th April
Average	8th April	4th April	3rd April	6th April	9th April

Table 358. Dates for first spring arrivals each decade 1950–1999

Rather surprisingly there are only five published records of hepatic phase birds with singles at Burton Mere in early June 1969, Portland Bill on 12th May 1978, 29th May 1984 and 17th April 1987, and Radipole NR on 18th August 1978.

A total of 52 birds has been ringed in the county.

The Cuckoo breeds from north-west Africa, across virtually the whole of Europe and Asia Minor, extending eastwards throughout Asia except for the extreme north and much of the south-west and south including most of the Indian sub-continent. It winters in Africa south of the equator and in parts of south-east Asia.

Postscript 2000–2002
There was a very early record of two at Stanpit Marsh, Christchurch Harbour on 20th March 2000.

Yellow-billed Cuckoo   *Coccyzus americanus*

Accidental: three records

    1895   Near Bridport: found dead 5th October
    1979   Portland Bill: first-year 24th–28th September, wounded, probably fatally, by a Kestrel
    1991   Budworth School, Weymouth: found moribund 7th October, died 8th October. (Not yet
             submitted to BBRC)

The Yellow-billed Cuckoo is a summer visitor breeding from southern Canada south through the USA to the Gulf Coast, Mexico and the Caribbean. It winters from Panama south through South America to Argentina. A vagrant to Great Britain with 58 records up to 2002.

Barn Owl   *Tyto alba*

A locally common resident

This species was known to Mansel-Pleydell (1888), but no comment was made regarding its status in Dorset. Blathwayt (1945) considered it to be not uncommon and apparently generally distributed, but scarcer in the east and south-east of the county.

Nationally the Barn Owl has declined during the last 30–40 years. In the 1960s this was caused by agricultural pesticides, but the main concerns in recent years have been changes in farming practices, loss of nesting sites and road casualties. Dorset, however, has seemingly suffered less than many counties. The *BTO Atlas* (1968–1972) found evidence of breeding in 32 (86%) 10-km squares (confirmed in 23, probable in six and possible in three), the most notable absence being in the far north (ST72). Encouragingly the Tetrad Survey (1987–1994) revealed only a slight decline with evidence of breeding in 30 (81%) of the pre-1974 10-km squares (confirmed in 20, probable in eight and possible in two), the most notable absences being in the west (SY39), the north (ST72) and the east (SZ08). The Tetrad Map shows that the species prefers the central and northern chalk areas with a notable concentration on Cranborne Chase, whilst it is rather scarce in the west, far north, and south-east of the county. This is virtually identical to the distribution of sightings recorded by a special survey undertaken during the mid-1960s.

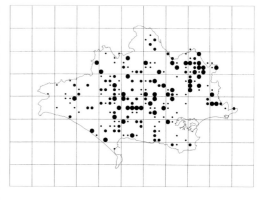

There is very little meaningful information to quantify changes in population levels in Dorset. Although there is some evidence to suggest that numbers were high in 1949–1950, population levels subsequently declined to a very low ebb in the mid-1960s as shown by a continuous survey which recorded only 3–4 breeding pairs annually during 1964–1968. There were reports of a marked recovery during the 1970s, whilst the number of breeding pairs given in the Dorset Bird Reports from 1980 to 1999 have varied between 3 and 12 pairs with no obvious trend.

Dispersing individuals are occasionally recorded from Portland, the Purbeck coast and Christchurch Harbour. At Portland Bill most of the c.22 reports during 1967–1990 are for the autumn with October the peak month – see Table 357. Unusually a bird was recorded intermittently at Portland Bill from 13th November 1989 to 25th April 1990.

Jan	Feb	Mar	Apr	May	Jun	Jul	Aug	Sep	Oct	Nov	Dec
2	3	0	0	1	1	1	0	4	8	2	0

Table 359. Monthly totals at Portland Bill 1967–1990

From autumn 1949 to spring 1950 "a quite outstanding number" were seen hunting in daylight in various parts of the county including Yetminster where it was described as "an epidemic of daylight hunting".

Evidently this was widespread throughout south-west England and presumably related to either a scarcity of nocturnal prey or an unusual abundance of diurnal prey, and not solely to the abundance of Barn Owls.

There are two or three claims of the dark-breasted continental race, *T. a. guttata*, in the county. A specimen in the Dorchester Museum obtained from Came in 1908 appears to belong to the continental race. In 1986 a bird trapped at Portland Bill on 30th September, which remained to 3rd October, was on measurement too large to be a British bird and showed plumage characteristics intermediate between *T. a. alba* and *T. a. guttata*. Another bird found badly injured at Fortuneswell, Portland on the same day was even darker and greyer.

A total of 72 birds has been ringed in the county. Published recoveries are few, the most interesting being two birds ringed at East Lulworth in June 1976 with one recovered in East Sussex in December 1977 and the other locally at Corfe Castle in February 1984, whilst another ringed at Povington in June 1983 was recovered in Surrey in March 1984.

The Barn Owl is a cosmopolitan species breeding over large parts of all five continents, but there are also large areas of absence, notably much of Asia except for the Indian sub-continent and the south-east. It is resident in Europe north to Scotland and Denmark and east to the Ukraine, being scarce in the Balkans.

Sponsored by Eileen Bowman and N. R. Green

Scops Owl (Eurasian Scops Owl)   *Otus scops*

Accidental: one confirmed record

Mansel-Pleydell (1888) referred to one killed at Buckland Ripers prior to 1873, but Blathwayt (1945) cast doubt upon the record. More recently:

1990   Off Portland Bill: 20th March

This record (the earliest date for the British Isles) involved a bird caught aboard a fishing boat c.2.5km off Portland Bill and released at Portland Bird Observatory later the same day. A full account can be found in the Dorset Bird report for 1990.

The Scops Owl is a summer visitor breeding from north-west Africa, across much of southern and eastern Europe, but generally declining further north, extending eastwards to Asia Minor, west-central Asia to about 100°E, and locally in the Middle East. Although some remain in Mediterranean areas, most winter in the northern tropics of Africa. A vagrant to Great Britain with a total of 92 records up to 2002.

Little Owl   *Athene noctua*

A fairly common resident

Blathwayt (1945) recorded that the species reached Dorset in c.1900 and bred at Abbotsbury in about 1902. Subsequently there were reports from Lyme Regis in 1911, Canford in 1912, Dorchester and Weymouth by 1917, east Dorset in 1918, Swanage in 1920, and Melbury Osmond and Netherbury in 1921. A rapid and widespread increase followed so that by the 1930s the Little Owl was quite common in the county.

The *BTO Atlas* (1968–1972) found evidence of breeding in 34 (92%) 10-km squares (confirmed in 20, probable in 11 and possible in three), the most notable absence being SY58. Subsequently there has been little change in distribution with the Tetrad Survey (1987–1994) revealing evidence of breeding in all but two (95%) of the pre-1974 10-km squares (confirmed in 30 and probable in five), the most notable absence being SZ08. The Tetrad Map shows that the species favours the north of the county including parts of the Blackmore Vale and the northern chalk of Cranborne Chase with isolated concentrations on

Portland and Purbeck, whilst it is scarce in the south-east and largely absent from the Bournemouth and Poole conurbation.

The only long-term information on population trends in Dorset comes from Portland Bill – see Table 360. This shows a relatively stable population of 2–3 pairs for much of the period from 1967 to 1985, declining to 0–1 pairs most years during 1986–1994, followed by a partial recovery to 1–2 pairs during 1995–1998. Population estimates for the whole of Portland reveal that the decline occurred later during 1991–1995 with a 'best-guess' estimate of about ten pairs in 1998 suggesting a full recovery – see Table 361. Although the reasons for the decline of the breeding population on Portland may be due to local factors, they could reflect the national trend which shows a cyclical pattern. This national pattern may also explain the trend shown by number of breeding pairs given in the Bird Reports from 1980 to 1999, but it is doubtful whether this data is really meaningful – see Table 360.

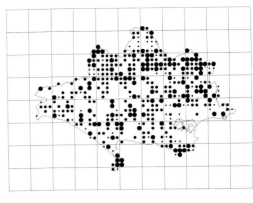

67	68	69	70	71	72	73	74	75	76	77	78	79	80	81	82
2	4	2	nc	nc	nc	nc	1	2	3	3	3	3	3	3	2–3

83	84	85	86	87	88	89	90	91	92	93	94	95	96	97	98
2-3	3	3	1	1	0	0	0	1	2	0	1	2	2	2	1

Table 360. Number of breeding territories at Portland Bill 1967–1998

1968	1983	1990	1991	1992	1993	1994	1995	1996	1997	1998
7	9	7	2	3	1	2	3	4	3	c.10

Table 361. Number of breeding territories on Portland 1968–1998

80	81	82	83	84	85	86	87	88	89	90	91	92	93	94	95	96	97	98	99
15	12	12	24	17	8	6	11	10	24	12	6	16	5	17	6	12	18	6	6

Table 362. Number of breeding pairs given in Bird Reports 1980–1999

There is some evidence of local dispersal during the autumn from several coastal sites including Portland Bill (maximum of ten on 22nd October 1955), Radipole and Lodmoor NRs, St Aldhelm's Head with up to five in October 1985, and Christchurch Harbour.

A total of 238 birds has been ringed in the county. Although there are very few recoveries, five are noteworthy for the long distances involved: from Swanage in May 1927 to Herefordshire in June 1928, a journey worthy of special mention in *Birds of the Western Palearctic* (Cramp *et al.* (eds) 1977-1994); from Portland Bill in September 1964 to near Oxford in November 1966; from Marnhull in September 1985 to Bristol in June 1990; from St Aldhelm's Head in October 1993 to Warwickshire in June 1994; and finally from St Aldhelm's Head in October 1995 to Warwickshire in June 1999. The coincidence of the last two reports is remarkable.

The Little Owl is a resident breeding throughout Europe, except Ireland and Scandinavia, also in Asia Minor, the Middle East, Arabia, central Asia as well as parts of northern Africa. It was introduced into Kent and Northamptonshire in the late 19th Century and spread quite rapidly to most of England and Wales by the 1940s, but more slowly into southern Scotland in subsequent years.

Postscript 2000–2002

In 2001 this species was resident at 15 sites on Portland, which suggests that the local population is increasing and has fully recovered from the apparent decline in the early 1990s.

Sponsored by Imogen Davenport and John Stobart

Tawny Owl

Strix aluco

A common resident

Mansel-Pleydell (1888) described this species as "abundant in the wooded districts and parks of the county", whilst Blathwayt (1945) considered it to be a generally distributed resident.

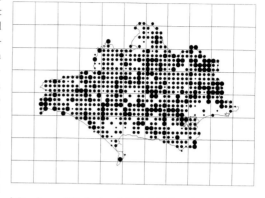

Little has changed since then, the *BTO Atlas* (1968–1972) found evidence of breeding in all but two (95%) 10-km squares (confirmed in 30 and probable in five), whilst the Tetrad Survey (1987–1994) produced almost the identical result with evidence of breeding in all but one (97%) of the pre-1974 10-km squares (confirmed in 30, probable in five and possible in one). Although the Tetrad Map shows that the Tawny Owl is widely distributed throughout much of the county, it is seemingly scarce or absent in the Bournemouth and Poole conurbation.

The limited information available on long-term population trends suggests a relatively stable situation in recent years with three pairs at both Arne NR and Durlston CP during 1974–1993 and 1984–1999 respectively. There is some evidence, however, to indicate increases in some areas, e.g. Milton Abbas, three

pairs in 1969 to eight pairs in 1974, and Radipole NR, one pair in 1980 to four pairs in 1984. The number of breeding pairs given in the Bird Reports from 1980 to 1999 have varied between five and 40 pairs, but it is doubtful whether this data is really meaningful. There a few reports of notable concentrations of calling males including eight at Milton Abbas in 1974, seven at Puncknowle in 1971, six at Oakers Wood in 1996 and five at Sutton Waldron in 1992.

Although evidence of dispersal is hard to detect at coastal sites such as North Portland, Durlston CP and Hengistbury where breeding birds are either present or residing in the close vicinity, occasional records from Portland Bill must refer to individuals that have moved at least a few kilometres.

A total of 76 birds has been ringed in the county.

The Tawny Owl is a common resident breeding from north-west Africa and across much of Europe, except Ireland, all but the southern parts of Scandinavia and most Mediterranean islands, and extending eastwards to west-central Asia, Asia Minor and parts of the Middle East. There are further populations in central and eastern Asia.

Sponsored by Julian Francis

Long-eared Owl

Asio otus

A rare resident, and scarce passage migrant and winter visitor

Mansel-Pleydell (1888) considered this species to be less abundant than the Barn and Tawny Owls, being more restricted to the wooded districts of the county, notably the Chase Woods, Milton, Houghton and Middlemarsh Grange Woods. Blathwayt (1945) referred to it as a local, but not very uncommon resident, being more numerous amongst fir-clumps on the eastern heaths than in the west.

Since 1950 breeding has occurred intermittently with most records from downland pinewoods and plantations on the northern chalk of Cranborne Chase. Birds were reported from this favoured area annually during 1953–1964 and breeding, involving one to three and possibly up to five pairs, was confirmed in at least six years – see Table 363. Subsequently confirmed or probable breeding was recorded in 1966, at least once during the *BTO Atlas* (1968–1972), again in 1981 and 1982, and at two sites during the Tetrad Survey (1987–1994). Despite the sporadic nature of these records, it seems likely that a small population of Long-eared Owls have regularly bred in this area, possibly since Mansel-Pleydell's time. Elsewhere there are a few isolated occurrences of breeding from widely scattered sites in the south and east of the county – see Table 362.

	1953	1954	1955	1956	1957	1958	1959	1960	1961
Confirmed	1	1	0	1	2	1	0	1	0
Probable	0	0	0	0	0	1	2	1	0
Possible	0	0	1	0	0	1	0	0	5

	1962	1963	1964	1966	1968–1972	1981	1982	1987–1994
Confirmed	0	0	0	1	1	1	0	0
Probable	0	0	0	0	0	0	1	2
Possible	1	1	1	0	0	0	0	0

Table 363. Number of pairs recorded during breeding season on NE chalk 1950–1994

	1950	1953	1954	1959	1961	1988	1989	1990	1992	1993	1998	1999
Confirmed	0	0	0	1	1	1	2	1	1	0	1	0
Probable	0	0	0	0	0	0	0	0	0	0	0	0
Possible	1	1	1	1	1	0	0	0	0	1	0	1

Table 364. Number of pairs recorded during the breeding season elsewhere 1950–1999

Winter roosts were rarely reported until the late 1990s. As a result of a national influx during the winter of 1975/76, three roosted in small bushes at Wootton Fitzpaine for ten days from 11th January and six were present at Marnhull Ham during February–March. In early 1984 a chalk downland roost held up to five birds from 27th January to 13th March with one on 6th April. More recently up to three roosted at a site in the east of the county from 22nd November 1996 to 2nd May 1997 and one remained at Sutton Waldron from November 1997 to April 1998, whilst at Verne Common, Portland birds have roosted in at least three consecutive winters with three during 1997/98, one during 1998/99, and at least three during 1999/2000. Otherwise there are occasional sightings in mid-winter (December–February) mainly involving single birds on a single date only – see Table 365. Some of these records are from coastal sites, the most notable being one at Hengistbury on 18th February 1979 with two there on 22nd, one at Portland Bill on 1st January 1991, one at East Fleet from 30th December 1996 to 4th January 1997 with two nearby at Littlesea on 21st January 1998, whilst one at Ferrybridge on 22nd and 25th February 1999 was considered to be from the roost at nearby Verne Common.

Jan	Feb	Mar	Apr	May	Jun	Jul	Aug	Sep	Oct	Nov	Dec
7	7	9	4	11	0	0	1	7	29	25	7

Table 365. Monthly totals of non-breeding birds (excluding winter roosts) 1950–1999

Since 1974 the species has occurred with increasing frequency as a scarce migrant, mostly in the autumn. In spring there are records from early March to the peak month of May, the latest being 27th May 1981 at Radipole NR. Early autumn migrants have been reported in late August and September, the earliest being from 29th August to 4th September 1994 at West Bexington, with the main passage peaking during October–November – see Table 365. Although most sightings are from Portland, Durlston CP and Christchurch Harbour, migrant Long-eared Owls have been noted at other coastal sites notably West

Bexington (one), Abbotsbury (two), Langton Herring (one), Littlesea (one), Melcombe Regis (one), Radipole NR (two), Lodmoor NR (two), Coombe Bottom near Worth Matravers (one) and Fitzworth (one) – see Table 366. There are also a few reports from widely scattered inland sites involving presumed migrants. Most passage records involve single birds, very occasionally more, the best count being four at Town Common, Christchurch on 17th November 1991.

Portland	Durlston CP	Christchurch Hbr	elsewhere
34	9	15	12

Table 366. Distribution of coastal migrants at the main sites 1950–1999

A total of 14 birds has been ringed in the county. There are no foreign recoveries, but there are single foreign controls from Lithuania and Latvia. Within Great Britain, there is one local recovery from Marnhull in February 1976 to Hinton St Mary in May 1976, and one control from Suffolk in November 1983 to Whitcombe in April 1984.

The Long-eared Owl breeds widely across most of Europe, central Asia and North America mainly between 35°N and 65°N, also in north-west Africa and Asia Minor with isolated populations in East Africa. It is a summer visitor to northern forests, resident to about 60°N with some birds wintering well south of the breeding range.

Postscript 2000–2002

There were breeding reports from three sites in 2000 and one site in 2001. At the Verne Common roost on Portland at least 3–4 birds were present during winter 2000/01 and one bird during 2001/02. There were seven migrants (six in autumn and one in spring) reported in 2001, one autumn migrant in 2002, but none in 2000.

Short-eared Owl   *Asio flammeus*

An uncommon passage migrant and winter visitor

Mansel-Pleydell (1888) referred to this species as an autumn visitor arriving at the end of October and mentions its local name the 'Woodcock Owl'. Blathwayt (1945) considered it to be a scarce winter visitor and listed only four records between 1927 and 1944 when six were seen at Blandford on 13th November.

Since 1951 the Short-eared Owl has occurred annually, mainly as an autumn migrant – see Figs 37 to 39. Although there has been a marked increase in records since the early 1970s, numbers can vary considerably from year to year, particularly during the autumn when the species is prone to sporadic influxes. These may be reflected by a corresponding increase in reports during the following winter and spring. For example, the record influx of autumn 1982 (c.108 bird-days) resulted in high totals for the following winter (23 bird-days) and spring (32 bird-days).

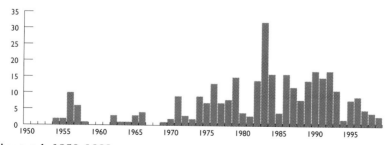

Fig 37. Spring totals 1950–1999

Although autumn migrants have been recorded from mid-August through to early December, most passage occurs during October–November. There is an exceptionally early record on 21st July 1990 at Hengistbury, whilst one at Christchurch Harbour on 5th August 1989 is also noteworthy. Many reports involve 1–2 and rarely exceed six birds, the highest counts being from Portland Bill with 10 on 15th October 1973, 20th October 1978 and 9th October 1982.

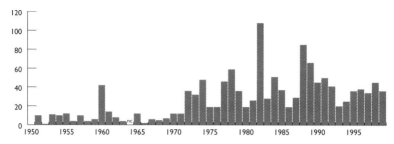

Fig 38. Autumn totals 1950–1999

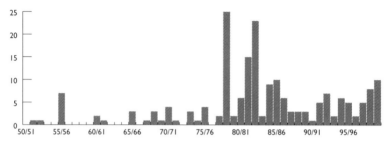

Fig 39. Winter totals 1950–1999

Spring passage, which has only been reported annually since 1969, is normally much smaller and extends from perhaps as early as late February to mid-May with a distinct peak in April. There are several reports during the latter part of May with exceptionally late individuals at Godlingston Heath on 1st June 1975 and 27th June 1988, and Portland Bill on 12th June 1986. Spring totals are often dependent on the strength of the previous autumn's passage and most records refer to singles, the highest counts being up to five at Christchurch Harbour during 22nd April–13th May 1978, four at Portland Bill on 1st May 1991 and 3–4 at Lodmoor NR on 3rd March 1966.

Winter reports were rare until the late 1970s. Despite an increase in records subsequently, which involves annual sightings since 1977/78, the Short-eared Owl remains a scarce and erratic visitor during this season. Most occurrences refer to birds on one or two dates only, and until the late 1990s evidence of genuine overwintering was sparse. In recent years birds have wintered in the East Fleet area and at Martinstown – see Table 367, whilst up to three at Portland Bill from 9th January to 30th April 1999 is noteworthy. Winter sightings usually refer to 1–2 birds rarely more, the best counts being up to six at Coward's Marsh, Christchurch during January 1993 and up to four at Martinstown from 19th December 1997 to 24th March 1998.

	96/97	97/98	98/99	99/00
East Fleet area	1	0	3	2
Martinstown	0	4	2	2

Table 367. Winter maxima in the East Fleet area and at Martinstown 1996–1999

In 1984 the species was recorded on the Fleet throughout the year including the summer months, whilst the only other hint of summering involves a single at Arne NR from April to June 1983.

The majority of birds occur at coastal sites, mainly at Portland and Durlston CP, which together account for 60% of the records since 1980 – see Table 368. Otherwise there are reports from Cogden Beach/West Bexington, the Fleet, Radipole and Lodmoor NRs, elsewhere on Purbeck, the Poole Harbour area and Christchurch Harbour. Generally the Short-eared Owl is very rare inland with the Lower Avon Valley the most favoured area in recent years.

Only one bird has been ringed in the county. There is one control from Dumfries in June 1976 to West Compton (dead) in November 1976.

	%
The Fleet	7%
Portland	41%
Durlston CP	19%
Poole Harbour	9%
Christchurch Harbour	8%
other coastal sites	10%
inland	6%

Table 368. Distribution (%) of birds 1980–1999

The Short-eared Owl breeds across much of Eurasia, mainly between 50°N and 70°N, and North America, mainly between 40°N and 70°N. It is widespread over much of Scandinavia and Russia, but breeds more locally elsewhere in northern Europe including northern and eastern Great Britain, France and the Low Countries, Germany, Denmark and Iceland. Generally wintering occurs well south of the breeding areas including the northern tropics of Africa and much of southern and eastern Asia, but there are some areas of overlap, most notably in north-western Europe. There are also resident populations in the Caribbean and South America.

Postscript 2000–2002
In 2002, there was a remarkable influx at Portland Bill late in the year involving peaks of 11 on 2nd November and 22nd December with birds remaining into 2003. There is only one previous record of overwintering at Portland. Nearby 3–4 birds were also wintering at Lodmoor NR during 2002/03.

Nightjar (European Nightjar) *Caprimulgus europaeus*

A locally common summer visitor and scarce passage migrant

Mansel-Pleydell (1888) considered this species to be a summer visitor which bred freely on the heathlands, whilst Blathwayt (1945) commented that it also bred sparingly in woodlands throughout the county.

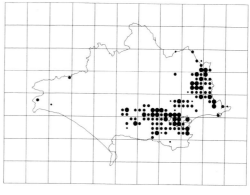

The *BTO Atlas* (1968–1972) suggests little change in distribution with evidence of breeding in 19 (51%) 10-km squares (confirmed in nine, probable in eight and possible in two). Although the population was concentrated in the heathland and forest areas of the Poole Basin, breeding was recorded from other sites, mainly on the chalk, but also in the north and west of Dorset. Prior to the *BTO Atlas* (1968–1972), breeding had been reported from SY49 and SY68 in 1962, and Portland in 1951. The Tetrad Survey (1987–1994) revealed that the population had become increasingly concentrated within the Poole Basin with very few reports from elsewhere. Although there was still evidence of breeding from 16 (43%) of the pre-1974 10-km squares (confirmed in ten, probable in three and possible in three), the species had disappeared from most of its previous haunts on the chalk, but seemingly survived in at least two, possibly three sites in the west.

Despite this contraction in range, population levels have seemingly increased. Special Surveys in 1958 (described as fragmentary), 1962 and 1970 produced 14, 53 and 74 churring males respectively. More recent surveys, however, have shown an increase from 225 pairs in 1981 to 547 pairs in 1992, which represented about 17% of the British population of c.3,000 pairs. This improvement in population levels is also reflected by data from the Arne NR, which shows an increase in territories from 15 in 1978 to a peak of 27 in 1992 followed by a decline to 22 in 1998 and 1999 – see Table 369.

There are several possible and potentially interacting causes for the decline in population levels observed during the earlier years of the 20th Century. Immediately after the First World War, many of the Poole

299

1978	1979	1980	1981	1982	1983	1984	1985	1986	1987	1988
15	14	17	16	18	12	16	16	15	16	16

1989	1990	1991	1992	1993	1994	1995	1996	1997	1998	1999
16	18	22	27	25	24	22	22	20	22	22

Table 368. Number of territories at Arne NR 1978–1999

Basin heaths were planted with commercial conifer forests. More recently, in the 50 years up to 1978, c.12,000ha of heathland were lost, mainly to urban expansion, mineral extraction and agricultural intensification. In addition, a reduction in the traditional management of key habitats and the increasing use of agricultural pesticides may also be contributory factors in this decline. The recent improvement in the Nightjar's fortunes locally is due to the increase of new conifer plantations and clear-felled areas, which have resulted from the felling of the commercial conifer forests on reaching maturity in the late 1970s.

Due to the species' silent and almost completely nocturnal habits away from the nesting areas, there are relatively few reports of migrants from coastal sites. The exception to this is where tape-luring has been used, for example at St Aldhelm's Head in the mid-1980s with a peak of 21 bird-days (13 trapped) during 26th August–23rd September 1985, and more recently at Keysworth with nine trapped during 26th July– 31st August 1993. Otherwise passage birds have occurred most frequently at Hengistbury, Durlston CP and Portland, whilst there are also records from other localities along the coast including West Bexington, the Fleet, the Chesil, Radipole and Lodmoor NRs, and the Poole Harbour area – see Table 370. Amongst the more interesting sightings, a female was mobbed by Little Terns at Ferrybridge on 7th June 1984.

	1980	1981	1982	1983	1984	1985	1986	1987	1988	1989
Christchurch Hbr	3	4	1	2	2	5	2	3	2	4
Durlston CP	2	1	0	1	1	0	1	1	0	0
St Aldhelm's Head	0	0	0	7	5	21	1	0	2	1
Portland	0	0	0	0	0	1	0	1	0	2
other coastal sites	0	0	2	0	2	0	0	1	0	0

	1990	1991	1992	1993	1994	1995	1996	1997	1998	1999
Christchurch Hbr	1	5	1	0	2	1	1	0	2	0
Durlston CP	1	0	0	2	4	5	3	5	0	2
St Aldhelm's Head	1	0	0	0	1	0	0	0	0	0
Portland	1	3	1	0	1	0	1	1	0	2
other coastal sites	1	3	1	11	8	3	4	1	1	0

Table 370. Annual totals of coastal migrants 1980–1999

Spring passage normally extends from late April or early May through to late June and peaks during May. There is an exceptionally early record on 2nd April 1996 at Studland NNR, which is 19 days earlier than singles at Rodden and East Fleet on 21st April of the same year. There appears to be relatively little variation and no obvious trend in the average date of the first arrivals during the past five decades – see Table 370. Autumn passage starts from mid-July and mainly takes place during August–September. The last individuals of the year are usually recorded between late August and late September with occasional sightings into early October, the latest being singles at Hengistbury on 16th and 23rd October 1994.

	1950–1959	1960–1969	1970–1979	1980–1989	1990–1999
Range	3rd–4th May	28th April– 11th May	30th April– 13th May	24th April– 12th May	2nd April– 6th May
Average	4th May	4th May	7th May	3rd May	1st May*

Table 371. Dates for first spring arrivals each decade 1950–1999; *excludes 2nd April 1996

Mostly as a result of extensive studies by the Stour Ringing Group, a total of 834 birds has been ringed in the county. There are single foreign recoveries from France and Morocco. In addition, a bird ringed in

Wareham Forest in June 1981 and controlled in the same place in June 1992 is a new British longevity record, more than doubling the previous one of five years.

The Nightjar breeds from north-west Africa northwards over most of Europe to southern Scandinavia and eastwards to Asia Minor and central Asia to about 110°E. It winters in sub-Saharan Africa.

Sponsored by Brian Cresswell and Stour Ringing Group

Egyptian Nightjar   *Caprimulgus aegyptius*

Accidental: one record

1984   Portland Bill: 10th June

This is the most recent of Great Britain's two records of this extreme rarity, the first being in Nottinghamshire on 23rd June 1883. A full account of the Portland bird can be found in the Dorset Bird Report for 1984 and *British Birds* Vol. 92, Number 3, March 1999.

The Egyptian Nightjar is a summer visitor breeding in the desert areas of north-west Africa, Egypt, and parts of the Middle East and south-west Asia. It winters mainly in the Sahel zone of sub-Saharan Africa.

Common Nighthawk   *Chordeiles minor*

Accidental: one record

1983   Studland Village: 23rd October

A full account of this record, which involved a bird seen briefly flying over the village, can be found in the Dorset Bird Report for 1983.

The Common Nighthawk is a summer visitor breeding across much of southern Canada south through the USA to Central America and the West Indies. It winters mainly in South America. A vagrant to Great Britain with 19 records up to 2002.

Sponsored by Michael Massey

Swift (Common Swift)   *Apus apus*

A common summer visitor and passage migrant

Both Mansel-Pleydell (1888) and Blathwayt (1945) considered this species to be a common summer visitor, a situation which has changed little subsequently.

The *BTO Atlas* (1968–1972) found evidence of breeding in 35 (95%) 10-km squares (confirmed in 32, probable in two and possible in one), whilst the Tetrad Survey (1987–1994) produced almost an identical result with evidence of breeding in 35 (95%) of the pre-1974 10-km squares (confirmed in 32 and probable in three).

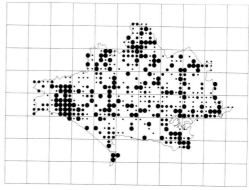

Although the Tetrad Map shows that breeding occurs widely throughout the county, there are several distinct clusters of population, most notably in the Bridport and Beaminster areas, parts of the Blackmore Vale, on Purbeck and perhaps less obviously in the Bournemouth and Poole conurbation, along the Allen and Cerne Valleys, and on Portland. This distribution reflects the presence of suitable nesting sites, which are normally associated with old buildings irrespective of whether they are located in large intensively urbanised conurbations, small market towns, villages, hamlets or farms. Birds will also nest in single buildings and old ruins. The presence of cliff-nesting birds on Purbeck is noteworthy. Breeding apparently occurred at up to three sites, including the Winspit quarries, between 1964 and at least 1975. In 1979 two pairs returned to Durlston CP, a much used site prior to 1910, and subsequently up to six pairs bred on the cliffs there up to at least

1990, whilst nearby at Dancing Ledge 13 pairs were breeding in 1984. Cliff-nesting has also been reported from Portland in 1967, 1969 (six pairs at Blacknor) and 1970, but not apparently since.

There are two exceptionally early records, both in March 1990, involving two at Hengistbury on 19th and one at Branksome Chine on 23rd. Otherwise the first birds appear during April, usually during the second half of the month. There appears to be a slight trend of birds arriving earlier between the 1950s and the 1980s, which is much more pronounced during the 1990s – see Table 372.

	1950–1959	1960–1969	1970–1979	1980–1989	1990–1999
Range	17th–29th April	4th–25th April	10th–26th April	10th–27th April	19th March–23rd April
Average	23rd April	18th April	21st April	19th April	12th April

Table 372. Dates for first spring arrivals each decade 1950–1999

Generally migration in April is relatively small, the heaviest passage taking place during May when peak movements at coastal watch-points can be spectacular – see Table 373. For example, during 1976–1981 large flocks of between 2,500–6,000 birds were a regular feature at Radipole NR in May with exceptional numbers present in late April 1980 including c.10,000 on 28th. Other high counts in spring include 3,646W at East Bexington on 9th May 1992, 3,500 at Hengistbury on 24th May 1997 and 3,000N at Christchurch Harbour on 20th May 1985.

Large gatherings and movements, often associated with advancing weather fronts, are frequently recorded in mid-summer when numbers can reach four figures, e.g. 7,000N at Portland Bill during 26th–29th June 1997, 5,220E at Christchurch Harbour on 28th June 1981, 5,000 at Came Down on 21st June 1989, 3,665W at East Bexington on 6th July 1992, 3,500NNE at Studland Bay on 23rd June 1951 and 3,000+ at Langton Herring on 29th June 1975 and 19th June 1977.

Autumn migration mainly occurs from mid-July to early September with large flocks sometimes forming prior to departure – see Table 373. Again numbers often exceed 1,000 birds, the highest counts being 4,600 at Portland Bill and 4,500N at Radipole School on 20th July 1987, 3,000+ at Christchurch on 3rd August 1976 and 3,000+ at Portland Bill on 6th August 1975. Most birds have left by early September, but stragglers often occur later in the autumn. Since the mid-1970s there have been near annual records in October, whilst there are several sightings for November, the latest being 14th November 1951 at Durlston CP with two there during 25th–27th November 1994, and 30th November 1984 at Radipole NR.

	Apr	May	Jun	Jul	Aug	Sep	Oct
Portland Bill	85	1331	1717	1809	943	14	<1
Durlston CP	15	1855	1811	3730	1413	16	<1

Table 373. Average monthly totals at Portland Bill 1986–1999 and Durlston CP 1986–1997

A total of 444 birds has been ringed in the county. Although there have been no foreign recoveries, there has been one foreign control from France.

The Swift breeds in north-west Africa and throughout most of Europe, except Iceland and northern Scandinavia, eastwards through Asia Minor, parts of the Middle East and across central Asia to about 120°E. It winters in Africa south of the equator.

Postscript 2000–2002
There was an exceptionally late report of one at Easton, Portland on 27th November 2000.

Sponsored by Mark S. Andrews F.C.C.A, Jillian Bale and David Russell

Pallid Swift   *Apus pallidus*

Accidental: two records involving three individuals

Both records were typically late in the autumn.

    1984   Portland Bill: 10th November; relocated together with a second bird at the Grove, Portland later the same day

2002   Stanpit Marsh, Christchurch Harbour: 22nd November

The Pallid Swift is a summer visitor breeding in north-west Africa, southern Iberia and more locally in other countries fringing the Mediterranean extending eastwards to Arabia and western Pakistan. It winters in the northern tropics of Africa. A vagrant to Great Britain with 39 records up to 2002.

Alpine Swift   *Apus melba*

A rare passage migrant

A report of one shot near Bishop's Caundle prior to 1854 is mentioned by Blathwayt (1945), but not by Mansel-Pleydell (1888). The first generally accepted record for the county involved one over the River Frome at Moreton on 25th–26th May 1925.

Since 1950 a total of 37 birds have occurred with annual sightings during 1984–1998 except for 1991, 1993 and 1994. In spring 25 birds have been recorded on dates ranging between 24th March and 29th May – see Table 374. There are two reports of singles in late June and one in late July, whilst there are nine autumn records between 24th August and 12th October. A mini-influx of four birds during 29th March–11th April 1988 is particularly notable.

Portland is undoubtedly the premier site for the species accounting for 18 birds (49%), whilst Durlston CP/Swanage is another favoured area with ten birds (27%) including one seen previously at Portland. All but one of the records come from the coastal fringes.

Mar	Apr	May	Jun	Jul	Aug	Sep	Oct
6	8	11	2	1	3	4	2

Table 374. Monthly totals 1950–2002

All records are given below:

1950   Durlston CP: 22nd May
         Wareham: 29th May
1963   Portland Bill: 3rd–5th April
         Swanage: 2nd–3rd September
1967   East Weare, Portland: 24th–25th March
1969   Portland Bill: 18th September
1970   Swanage: 18th April; same at Durlston CP 23rd–24th April
1973   Portland Bill: 7th October
1977   Portland Bill: 20th May
1981   Easton, Portland: 11th–12th September; same at Durlston CP 12th

303

1984   Durlston CP: 16th April
1985   Portland Bill: 26th June
        Weston, Portland: 28th August
        Durlston CP: 31st August
1986   Portland Bill/Southwell: 24th August
1987   Portland Bill: 28th April; presumed same at Studland NNR and Christchurch Harbour 1st May
        Portland Bill: 5th May
1988   The Grove, Portland: 29th March–2nd April; same at Wyke Regis, Weymouth on 29th March
        Swanage, two 30th March; one of the same at Durlston CP 31st March
        Overcombe: 11th April
1989   Dorchester: 18th May
1990   Rope Lake Head: 26th March
1992   Branksome Chine: 26th April
        Chesil Cove: 12th May
1995   Wick, Christchurch: 12th October
1996   Yates Corner, Portland: 15th April
1997   Weston, Portland: 27th May
        Durlston CP: 29th July
1998   Portland Bill: two 11th May with another 13th May
        Hengistbury: 5th September
2002   Studland: one flying south 31st March
        Lodmoor NR: 21st April; same briefly at Portland Bill during its stay
        Radipole NR: 18th May
        Peveril Point: 15th–17th June

The Alpine Swift is a summer visitor breeding from north-west Africa, across much of southern Europe eastwards to Asia Minor and south-west Asia; also more locally in parts of the Middle East. It winters mainly in eastern and southern Africa where it is also locally resident, whilst there is also a resident population in the Indian sub-continent. A vagrant to Great Britain with 482 records up to 2002.

Little Swift   *Apus affinis*

Accidental: two records

1983   Shell Bay, Studland NNR: 26th November
1997   Hengistbury: 5th June

The Little Swift breeds in north-west Africa, locally in the Middle East, and more widely over sub-Saharan Africa, the Indian sub-continent and southern Asia. It is mainly resident, but migratory or partially migratory in the northern parts of its range. A vagrant to Great Britain with 18 records up to 2002.

Kingfisher (Common Kingfisher)   *Alcedo atthis*

A fairly common resident

Both Mansel-Pleydell (1888) and Blathwayt (1945) considered the Kingfisher to be a generally distributed resident.

Subsequently there has been very little change in status. The *BTO Atlas* (1968–1972) found evidence of breeding in 31 (84%) 10-km squares (confirmed in 24, probable in two and possible in five), whilst the Tetrad Survey (1987–1994) produced virtually the same result with evidence of breeding in 31 (84%) of the pre-1974 10-km squares (confirmed in 25, probable in two and possible in four).

Not surprisingly the Tetrad Map reveals a distribution closely correlated with the county's network of rivers. The species shows a preference for the major lowland river systems in the centre and east of the county, namely the Lower Avon, Stour, Frome and Piddle, rather than the shorter watercourses that typify west Dorset. The River Stour is particularly favoured as it offers the ideal habitat for breeding.

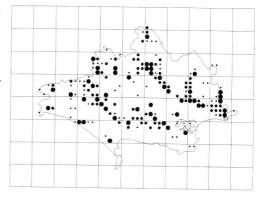

Unlike the neighbouring chalk rivers, the Stour is rather 'spatey' resulting in the widespread development of vertical earth banks suitable for nest sites. The RSPB Survey in 1979 recorded that earth banks occurred along 46% of the survey length of the River Stour compared to only 2% of the survey length of the River Avon.

Although the breeding population was reduced by the severe winter of 1962/63, numbers apparently recovered by 1967. Smaller reductions following severe winters have been reported subsequently. In 1979 the RSPB Survey found 17 confirmed and two possible territories along the River Stour with most between Muscliff (Bournemouth) and Sturminster Newton. A similar pattern of distribution along the River Stour is shown by the Tetrad Map. The only data relating to long-term trends comes from the River Allen where annual surveys during 1989–1999 reveal a population fluctuating between three and seven territories – see Table 375.

1989	1990	1991	1992	1993	1994	1995	1996	1997	1998	1999
4	5	5	7	5	3	5	5	3	4	5

Table 375. Number of territories along River Allen 1989–1999

During the non-breeding season there is a general dispersal of birds to the lower reaches of rivers and the coast. The extent to which birds desert the rivers depends on the severity of the weather. In mild winters good numbers may remain on the rivers, e.g. 29 along the Stour between Christchurch and Blandford during 1st–3rd February 1989. The movement of birds to the coast has been detected by ringing activities. For example, 14 were trapped at Radipole NR in autumn 1976, whilst more recently 11 were trapped at Keysworth between 29th July–14th September 1991 and 14 likewise between 1st August–18th September 1992 with only four retraps indicating some through passage.

On the coast, birds mainly frequent the estuaries, harbours and sheltered bays, notably in the Weymouth/ Portland Harbour/Fleet area, and Poole and Christchurch Harbours. Numbers are small, usually between one and six birds, although 11 were counted during the Poole Harbour WeBS Survey on 11th September 1999, with peak counts during the autumn in August and September. Although the species occurs much less frequently along the more exposed rocky coastlines, it is virtually an annual visitor to Portland Bill in the autumn with most sightings in August and September. It is also a scarce visitor to the Purbeck coast where it is most often observed in the vicinity of St Aldhelm's Head with the first records from Durlston CP as recently as 1985.

A total of 595 birds has been ringed in the county.

The Kingfisher breeds from north-west Africa and across most of Europe north to southern Scandinavia, also locally in Asia Minor and more widely in parts of central, eastern and southern Asia including the Indian sub-continent. It is a summer visitor to eastern Europe, central and eastern Asia, being a resident and winter visitor elsewhere. Small numbers also winter south of the breeding range.

Sponsored by Kingfisher Birding

Bee-eater (European Bee-eater) *Merops apiaster*

A rare migrant, mainly in spring and summer

There are two reports from the 19th Century involving singles shot at Chideock prior to 1843 and Swanage prior to 1888. In 1929 a party of 5–6 birds occurred in the Dorset part of Bournemouth on 11th May with one at Hampreston on the same day.

Since 1964 there have been c.31 records involving a total of c.46 birds, of which 25 records (81%) have been from the Portland and Weymouth areas. Although reports extend from the earliest on 18th April to the latest on 21st August, the vast majority (83%) have occurred between early May and mid-June

– see Table 374. Most sightings involve one or two birds, so flocks of six at Studland NNR in 1988 and Durlston CP/Swanage in 1997 are noteworthy.

Apr 16–30	May 1–15	May 16–31	Jun 1–15	Jun 16–30	Jul 1–15	Jul 16–31	Aug 1–15	Aug 16–31
1	12	11	15	5	1	0	0	1

Table 376. Half-monthly totals 1964–2002

All records are given below:

1964	Portland Bill: 27th–30th May
1972	Upwey: two 9th–10th June
1973	Lodmoor NR: 25th June
1976	Portland Bill: 11th May
1982	The Grove, Portland: two 14th June
1983	Verne Common, Portland: 23rd May flew north over Portland Harbour and relocated at Radipole Village 24th–25th May
1986	Weymouth: two 8th–9th May; same two at Portland Bill 9th May Portland Bill: 22nd May
1987	Durlston CP: 18th April
1988	Studland NNR: flock of six 7th May
1990	Portland Bill: 1st May
1993	Portland Bill: 1st June
1994	Portland Bill: 12th June
1996	Portland Bill and Verne Common: 2nd June
1997	Durlston CP and Swanage: flock of six 31st May Portland Bill: 19th June
1998	Ballard Down: 9th May Portland: 13th May
1999	Durlston CP: 22nd May Weston and Fortuneswell, Portland: 9th June Weston, Portland: three 11th June
2001	Portland Bill: singles, 24th May and 15th July
2002	Portland Bill: singles on 8th, 10th, 11th, 15th, 23rd and 24th June Weston, Portland: one flying north 27th June Stanpit Marsh, Christchurch Harbour: 21st August

The Bee-eater is a summer visitor breeding from north-west Africa, across much of southern Europe eastwards to Asia Minor and parts of south-west Asia. It winters in western Africa and much of southern Africa where it is also resident in the extreme south. A rare but increasing visitor to the British Isles with 666 records up to 1990.

Roller (European Roller)   *Coracias garrulus*

Accidental: five records

There is one 19th Century record of one shot near Dorchester in 1868. More recently:

1955	Near Yetminster: 7th April
1966	Sugar Hill, Wareham Forest: 13th–14th June
1967	Hartland Moor: 8th June
1975	West Milton: three dates between 16th–21st June

The Roller is a summer visitor breeding from north-west Africa, across southern and eastern Europe eastwards to Asia Minor and parts of west-central and south-west Asia; also locally in the Middle East. It winters in eastern Africa. A vagrant to Great Britain with 230 records up to 2002.

Hoopoe   *Upupa epops*

An uncommon passage migrant, mainly in spring

Mansel-Pleydell (1888) stated that "the Hoopoe is an irregular summer visitant, and would be seen much oftener if allowed to remain and breed, which it doubtless would do, but its conspicuous plumage is fatal; for as soon at it appears, it attracts the attention of every thoughtless gunner"! He also recorded that "according to the observations of Mr Turner of Sherborne, Dorsetshire, the nest has been taken on three or four occasions by the schoolboys from pollard willows, on the banks of the river Lenthay". Blathwayt (1945) considered this species to be a fairly regular passage migrant in small numbers and commented "would probably breed if unmolested, and perhaps has nested on rare occasions". There is also a diary record of breeding at Canford prior to 1904.

Since 1950 the Hoopoe has occurred annually as an uncommon passage migrant in spring, but only as an occasional visitor in autumn – see Figs 40 and 41. Spring totals generally vary between 1–5 birds in 'poor' years and 10–15 birds in 'good years' with notable influxes in 1958 (26), 1964 (c.20–30) and 1996 (25). There are exceptionally early records on 13th February 1954 at Charmouth and from 28th February to 5th March 1997 at Durlston CP, but the possibility of the former bird having overwintered cannot be excluded. In 1998 reports from Bridport on 15th February and Abbotsbury on an unspecified date in the same month may have involved the same early or wintering bird that was present at Chickerell from 16th February to 11th March. Other early birds have arrived during the first half of March, notably in 1977 with records from Portland Bill on 7th, Chickerell on 12th and well inland at Hazelbury Bryan on 14th, whilst there are also sightings from Preston, Weymouth during 12th–15th March 1957, and Lodmoor NR on 13th–14th March 1983. Most spring migrants occur between mid-March and late May with a distinct peak during the second half of April – see Table 377. A few late stragglers have appeared through to late June. Overall spring records account for 81% of the total migrants recorded during 1950–1999.

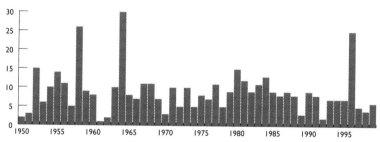

Fig 40. Spring totals 1950–1999

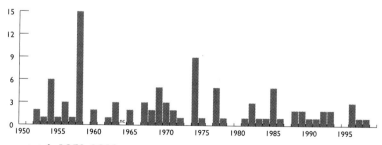

Fig 41. Autumn totals 1950–1999

In those autumns when the species is recorded, totals usually range from 1–3 and rarely exceed five birds, the best counts being 15 in 1958 and nine in 1974. Although there are records for the period from early July to mid-November, most birds occur between mid-August and late September with a distinct peak during the first half of September – see Table 377. A surprising number of late birds have occurred during the first half of November with reports from West Parley on 3rd November 1958 (two birds), Studland on 8th November 1970, Sandbanks/Lilliput up to 13th November 1972, and various sites on Portland during 1st–15th November 1982. The only report of genuine overwintering concerns a bird at Avonbourne, Bournemouth from 7th December 1992 to 22nd March 1993. One seen on a birdtable at Thorncombe on 24th January 1976 was thought to be an escape.

Feb 1–15	Feb 16–28	Mar 1–15	Mar 16–31	Apr 1–15	Apr 16–30	May 1–15	May 16–31	Jun 1–15	Jun 16–30
1	2	5	35	87	126	77	36	12	4

Jul 1–15	Jul 16–31	Aug 1–15	Aug 16–31	Sep 1–15	Sep 16–30	Oct 1–15	Oct 16–31	Nov 1–15	Nov 16–30
7	3	8	14	24	14	9	5	5	0

Table 377. Half-monthly totals of migrants 1950–1999

Although the majority of birds have been recorded from the coastal fringes, there are a surprising number of sightings from inland sites, which account for 24% of the total – see Table 378. It is interesting to note that inland reports were most frequent during the 1950s and have steadily declined during subsequent decades – see Table 379. Portland is undoubtedly the premier coastal site for this species with 173 birds (138 in spring and 35 in autumn) representing 33% of the total. As a proportion of birds that have occurred during 1974–1999, Christchurch Harbour accounts for 15% of the total.

	Spring		Autumn		Total	
Portland	138	32%	35	36%	173	33%
Weymouth and the Fleet	41	9%	17	18%	58	11%
Purbeck and Poole Harbour	83	19%	14	15%	97	18%
Christchurch Harbour	34	8%	7	7%	41	8%
Christchurch, Bournemouth & Poole	13	3%	1	1%	14	3%
west coast	17	4%	4	4%	21	4%
inland	108	25%	18	19%	126	24%

Table 378. Distribution of migrants 1950–1999

1950–1959	1960–1969	1970–1979	1980–1989	1990–1999
31%	28%	23%	18%	14%

Table 379. Proportion (%) of inland birds per decade 1950–1999

Most records refer to single birds with occasional reports of two, rarely more. At Portland Bill the spring influxes of 1958 and 1964 resulted in counts of four on 15th and 17th April and 11th and 13th April respectively, whilst during 11th–19th September 1974 at least four birds were present in the Weston/Portland Bill area. More recently four birds were reported from various sites on Portland on 22nd April 1996. The only counts of three birds are from Winterborne Herringston in early May 1952, together in the same tree at Abbotsbury on 2nd August 1964, and at Christchurch Harbour on 10th May 1993.

Since 1950 there have been only two reports suggestive of breeding. In 1954 the species was heard calling from an upland oakwood in the west of the county on 2nd and 18th June, whilst more recently a pair was observed entering a suitable nesting hole near Weymouth for seven weeks during the summer of 1983, but apparently without success.

Two birds have been ringed in the county.

The Hoopoe breeds over much of central and southern Eurasia, and north-west and sub-Saharan Africa. It is a summer visitor to most of Europe and central Asia, but a resident and winter visitor in southern Iberia, over most of its African range and in southern Asia.

Postscript 2000–2002
There were two records of single birds in spring 2000, and three records of single birds in both spring 2001 and spring 2002. A single at Coombe and Arne Farm on 5th September 2002 was the only autumn sighting.

Wryneck (Eurasian Wryneck) *Jynx torquilla*

An uncommon passage migrant, mainly in autumn

The status of this species has changed dramatically since the 19th Century when Mansel-Pleydell (1888) described it as "a well-known visitant in summer, when its singular cry may be heard frequently in woods and orchards". Blathwayt (1945) referred to the Wryneck as a bird of the east of the county where it is not uncommon, but said to be decreasing. Certainly it was lost as a regular breeding species by 1950 when the last nest (unsuccessful) was reported from a site in the Poole Basin on 21st May. Although there were a few records of calling birds during the 1950s and 1960s, the only hint of breeding involved a pair at Canford Heath during 12th–28th April 1953 and one at a site in the Poole Basin during 30th April–28th May 1956. Subsequently the Wryneck has occurred exclusively as an uncommon passage migrant, mainly in the autumn.

There was an initial decline in spring records from the 1950s through to the 1970s, presumably reflecting the fortunes of this species as a breeding bird nationally. Since 1980, however, this trend has been reversed with spring sightings in all but six years including mini-influxes in 1980 (five birds) and 1990 (eight birds) – see Fig 42. Spring passage extends from early April to late May and reaches its peak during the second half of April – see Table 380. The extreme dates for coastal migrants are 3rd April 1960 at Portland Bill and 23rd–24th May 1991 at Durlston CP, there being a later report of a calling bird inland at Bovington on 28th May 1958.

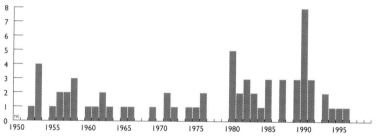

Fig 42. Spring totals 1950–1999

Mar 1–15	Mar 16–31	Apr 1–15	Apr 16–30	May 1–15	May 16–31	Jun 1–15	Jun 16–30
0	0	16	25	18	6	0	1

Jul 1–15	Jul 16–31	Aug 1–15	Aug 16–31	Sep 1–15	Sep 16–30	Oct 1–15	Oct 16–31
2	1	8	82	151	108	38	12

Table 380. Half-monthly totals of migrants 1950–1999

There are very few records in mid-summer, the most notable being a long-staying individual at Portland Bill from 30th June to 2nd September 1997. The remaining reports involve one seen and heard at Buckland Newton on 11th July 1952 and one at Abbotsbury on 6th July 1970.

The number of autumn migrants recorded increased during the late 1960s with annual sightings since 1967 – see Fig 43. Subsequent seasonal totals have varied from as low as three birds in 1985 to marked influxes in 1976 (26), 1981 (20), 1992 (31), 1993 (34), 1995 (22) and 1998 (21). The main passage period extends from mid-August to late September with a peak during the first half of September – see Table 380. Early migrants have occurred at Christchurch Harbour in late July 1988 and on 1st August 1987, whilst the latest reports are 29th October 1976 at Portland Bill with a long-staying bird there from 16th October to 4th November 1991.

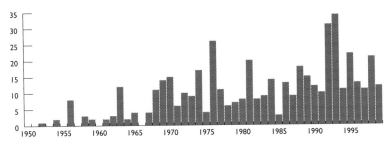

Fig 43. Autumn totals 1950–1999

The vast majority of migrants are recorded from the coastal fringes, Portland being the most favoured site with 215 birds (23 in spring and 192 in autumn) representing 40% of the total – see Table 381. Elsewhere, Purbeck and the Poole Harbour area accounts for 125 birds (12 in spring and 113 in autumn) which is 23% of the total, whilst as a proportion of birds that have occurred during 1974-1999, Christchurch Harbour accounts for 11%. Inland records represent 14% of the total with widely scattered sightings as far north and west as Shaftesbury, Bradford Abbas, Yetminster and Beaminster.

	Spring		Autumn		Total	
Portland	23	35%	192	41%	215	40%
Weymouth and the Fleet	11	17%	42	9%	53	10%
Purbeck and Poole Harbour	12	18%	113	24%	125	23%
Christchurch Harbour	5	8%	38	8%	43	8%
Christchurch, Bournemouth & Poole	2	3%	5	1%	7	1%
west coast	0	0	20	4%	20	4%
inland	13	20%	63	13%	76	14%

Table 380. Distribution of migrants 1950–1999

Most records refer to single birds with occasional reports of two, rarely more. The autumn influx of 1992 resulted in peak counts of five at Portland Bill on 23rd September and four at Durlston CP on several dates during 13th September–4th October, whilst up to four were present at Portland Bill from 31st August–5th September 1981 with four also there on 12th September 1963.

A total of 64 birds has been ringed in the county. There is one local recovery from Portland Bill in August 1990 to Southampton Docks, Hampshire in September of the same year.

The Wryneck breeds in declining numbers throughout most of Europe except for the British Isles, where it is now virtually extinct, much of central and southern Iberia, and Greece. It also breeds across most of central Asia eastwards to Japan. European breeders winter in the northern tropics of Africa, whilst Asiatic breeders winter in the Indian sub-continent and south-east Asia.

Postscript 2000–2002

In 2000 there were reports of four birds in spring and 19 in autumn, in 2001 there were reports involving one bird in spring and 26 in autumn, and in 2002 there were two birds in spring and 24 in autumn. In 2000 reports included singles at West Bexington on 27th–28th March and Lodmoor NR on 17th November, which are the earliest and latest records for the county.

Sponsored by John Blackwell

Green Woodpecker   *Picus viridis*

A common breeding resident

The status of the Green Woodpecker has apparently changed little since the 19th Century when Mansel-Pleydell (1888) referred to it as a well-known and abundant resident of the wooded districts of the county. The species was still considered to be common by Blathwayt (1945).

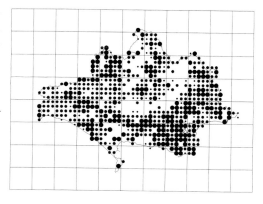

More recently the *BTO Atlas* (1968–1972) confirmed breeding in all but two (95%) 10-km squares, whilst the Tetrad Survey (1987–1994) found evidence of breeding in all but one (97%) of the pre-1974 10-km squares (confirmed in 31, probable in four and possible in one).

The Tetrad Map reveals an absence from large areas of the chalk downs, reflecting the scarcity of suitable feeding areas, notably short grass sward supporting rich and diverse ant populations. This is due to the increase in arable farming and corresponding decline in sheep husbandry plus a decrease in the extent and intensity of grazing by rabbits. Elsewhere the Green Woodpecker is widely distributed, particularly throughout the Poole Basin and much of the west of the county.

There was a marked decrease in breeding numbers for a few years following the severe winter of 1962/63, but the population had seemingly recovered by the time of the *BTO Atlas* (1968–1972). The limited data available on population levels suggest these have been relatively stable in recent years – see Table 382.

	1978	1979	1980	1981	1982	1983	1984	1985	1986	1987	1988
Arne NR	4	nc	5	4	4	4	4	4	4	4	nc
Studland NNR	3	1	1	2	1	3	2	3	3	1	1
Fontmell Down	nc	nc	nc	3	2	3	2	nc	2	nc	3

	1989	1990	1991	1992	1993	1994	1995	1996	1997	1998	1999
Arne NR	nc	nc	4	nc	3	nc	nc	4	2-3	nc	6
Studland NNR	2	1	1	1	1	2	2	nc	nc	nc	nc
Fontmell Down	2	nc	2	2	2	5	nc	nc	nc	nc	nc

Table 382. Number of breeding territories at selected sites 1978–1999

Although breeding was reported to be regular on Portland at Church Ope Cove up to 1951 at least, there were no further reports until 1977 when one pair bred successfully in central Portland. Subsequently regular breeding has been re-established, mainly in the East Weare/Pennsylvania Castle area, with at least three pairs present in 1983.

There is no evidence of cross-Channel passage, but local dispersal is indicated by reports from Portland Bill and other coastal sites where it does not breed. Otherwise a bird flying along the coast c.100 yards offshore at Durlston CP in January 1982 and another flying towards Lodmoor NR from the sea in company with a Great Spotted Woodpecker on 6th October 1983 are curious observations.

A total of 211 birds has been ringed in the county.

The Green Woodpecker breeds throughout much of Europe and Asia Minor, except for Ireland, the tundra regions of Norway and Sweden, Finland and the north and east of European Russia.

Sponsored by David Fogden

Great Spotted Woodpecker   *Dendrocopos major*

A common resident and rare passage migrant

Mansel-Pleydell (1888) referred to the Great Spotted Woodpecker as the rarest of the resident *Picidae* in Dorset and listed only five records, all involving birds shot. The fortunes of this species improved considerably during the 20th Century with Blathwayt (1945) describing it as "not uncommon and well distributed and increasing".

The *BTO Atlas* (1968–1972) found evidence of breeding in 34 (92%) 10-km squares (confirmed in 33 and probable in one), whilst the Tetrad Survey (1987–1994) produced an almost identical result with

evidence of breeding in 35 (95%) of the pre-1974 10-km squares (confirmed in 32, probable in one and possible in two).

The Tetrad Map shows that the Great Spotted Woodpecker is widely if unevenly distributed with most absences occurring on chalk downland, particularly in the centre and south of the county. The limited data available on breeding numbers suggests a decline in population levels during the late 1990s – see Table 383.

	1980	1981	1982	1983	1984	1985	1986	1987	1988	1989
Arne NR	4	3	3	3–4	4	3–4	4	3	nc	nc
Studland NNR	1	1	2	nc	2	1	0	0	0	1
Brackett's Copse	2	1	1	nc	2	2	2	nc	2	3

	1990	1991	1992	1993	1994	1995	1996	1997	1998	1999
Arne NR	nc	3	nc	4	nc	nc	nc	1	1	1
Studland NNR	0	0	0	1	1	1	0	nc	nc	1
Brackett's Copse	nc	3	2	2	1	nc	nc	nc	nc	nc

Table 383. Number of breeding territories at selected sites 1980–1999

Although the occasional records from coastal sites in spring and autumn mainly refer to locally dispersing birds, some genuine migrants may also be involved. At Portland Bill c.31 birds have occurred during 1957–1999 with most records in autumn – see Table 384. A number of these have been observed flying north, e.g. singles on 10th and 15th October 1957, 22nd October 1983 and 29th September 1995 with two on 15th September 1988. Other reports suggesting genuine immigration include one flying towards Lodmoor NR from the sea in company with a Green Woodpecker on 6th October 1983, and at Hengistbury – 5N on 22nd October 1987, 1N on 27th September 1993, three new birds on 27th September 1994 and an exhausted bird near the beach huts on 22nd August 1997.

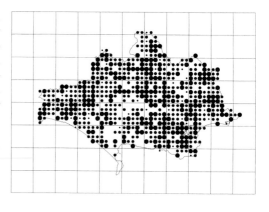

Jan	Feb	Mar	Apr	May	Jun	Jul	Aug	Sep	Oct	Nov	Dec
0	0	1	5	0	1	1	6	8	7	2	0

Table 384. Monthly totals at Portland Bill 1957–1999

A total of 250 birds has been ringed in the county.

The Great Spotted Woodpecker breeds throughout most of Europe, except Ireland, northern Scandinavia and much of Greece. It also breeds widely across north-central and eastern Asia, also in parts of North Africa and Asia Minor. The northern populations are subject to occasional eruptions.

Lesser Spotted Woodpecker   *Dendrocopos minor*

A uncommon resident

Mansel-Pleydell (1888) considered the Lesser Spotted Woodpecker to be a generally distributed resident in suitable localities and commoner than the previous species. This situation was reversed during the 20th

Century with Blathwayt (1945) describing it as "sparingly distributed throughout the county" and "the least common of the three British species".

The *BTO Atlas* (1968–1972) revealed that breeding occurred in 26 (70%) 10-km squares (confirmed in six, probable in four and possible in 16), whilst the Tetrad Survey (1987–1994) found evidence of breeding in 24 (65%) of the pre-1974 10-km squares (confirmed in eight, probable in nine and possible in seven). The Tetrad Map shows that the species is restricted mainly to the Poole Basin and the north and west of Dorset, being absent from large areas of the county, notably the chalk downs. The most favoured localities are centred in and around Wareham Forest, the western fringes of Poole Harbour, Holt Heath NNR and the Lower Avon Valley.

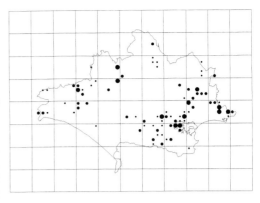

The only record from Portland Bill involves a single bird on 17th October 1987, whilst occasional reports from Durlston CP and Christchurch Harbour apparently indicate some dispersal of local birds.

A total of 11 birds has been ringed in the county.

The Lesser Spotted Woodpecker breeds throughout most of Europe, except Ireland, Scotland and much of Iberia. It also breeds widely across north-central Asia, also in parts of North Africa and Asia Minor.

Postscript 2000–2002
One flying in off the sea at Hengistbury on 16th April 2001 is an intriguing record.

Sponsored by Danny Alder

Calandra Lark *Melanocorypha calandra*

Accidental: one record

1961   Portland Bill: 2nd April

This bird, which spent most of its one-day stay in Portland Bill's Top Fields, constituted the first British record.

The Calandra Lark breeds from north-west Africa and Iberia eastwards through southern Europe, Asia Minor and the Middle East to west-central Asia, being mainly resident in the west of its range, but more migratory in the east. A vagrant to Great Britain with only ten records up to 2002.

Short-toed Lark
(Greater Short-toed Lark) *Calandrella brachydactyla*

A very rare passage migrant: 13 records

Rather surprisingly this species was not recorded in the county until 1985. Since then there have been 12 further sightings in eight years during 1987–2000. Of the nine spring records, eight have occurred during the relatively short period of 29th April–13th May. Portland is the main site with ten birds, the remaining three being recorded from Christchurch Harbour. All records are listed below:

1985   Portland Bill: 7th–19th October
1987   Portland Bill: 19th September
1989   Portland Bill: 5th May
          Weston, Portland: 10th May
1990   Weston, Portland: 7th May
1991   Weston, Portland: 5th May
          Stanpit Marsh, Christchurch Harbour: 17th October
          Hengistbury: 29th October
1993   Portland Bill: 13th May

1995   Hengistbury: 29th April
        Portland Bill: 4th May
1997   Portland Bill: 30th May–1st June
2000   Portland Bill: 3rd May

The Short-toed Lark is a summer visitor breeding locally in France, but more widely from north-west Africa and Iberia east through southern Europe, Asia Minor and the Middle East to central Asia. European populations winter mainly in the northern tropics of Africa between 14°N–17°N. A vagrant to the British Isles with 512 records up to 1993.

Lesser Short-toed Lark   *Calandrella rufescens*

Accidental: one record

1992   Portland Bill: 2nd May

This bird, seen in the Top Fields at Portland Bill, constituted the first and only record for Great Britain. A full account can be found in *Birding World* Vol. 5, Number 5, June 1992 and *British Birds* Vol. 88, Number 12, December 1995.

The Lesser Short-toed Lark breeds from southern and eastern Spain eastwards through North Africa, Asia Minor, the Middle East and southern Russia to central Asia, being mainly resident in the west of its range, but migratory in the east where it winters south to Pakistan.

Woodlark (Wood Lark)   *Lullula arborea*

A locally common resident and scarce passage migrant

Mansel-Pleydell (1888) described this species as "resident in the wooded districts of the county, where it is not uncommon". There was little change in status during the first half of the 20th Century, Blathwayt (1945) referring to the Woodlark as a characteristic bird of the county with many widely scattered breeding colonies, which were not confined to any special type of country, being found on the heaths, downs and vales.

In 1950 and 1951 there were numerous records from many parts of Dorset including the Marshwood Vale where a marked increase had taken place since 1946. Although still widely distributed in 1954 and 1955 with reports from the Marshwood and Blackmore Vales, northern chalk and the Poole Basin, some areas recorded a decline. This decline became more widespread during the late 1950s and in 1960 a special survey located 24 pairs in 12 10-km squares. Despite this decrease, the Woodlark could still be found in widely scattered sites throughout the county including the same areas as 1954 and 1955 plus the central chalk. During the 1960s the population fell to very low levels, particularly after the severe winter of 1962/63. In 1965 another special survey recorded a mere seven singing males with a total absence from the Marshwood Vale, and the coast between Abbotsbury and Lyme Regis where the species had been well distributed in the 1950s.

Although only two pairs were reported in 1967, a marked recovery occurred by the time of the *BTO Atlas* (1968–1972) with evidence of breeding in 17 (46%) 10-km squares (confirmed in five and probable in 12), which were distributed in the west (Marshwood Vale), north (Blackmore Vale) and east (Poole Basin) of Dorset. A total of 12 singing males were recorded in 1971 and again in 1972. Subsequent reports of breeding during the 1970s and 1980s were rather sparse and incomplete, but clearly showed that the Woodlark had rapidly disappeared from its haunts in the west and north of the county, and become confined to the heaths of the Poole Basin where the main strongholds were Wareham Forest and Canford Heath. During this period the best counts were c.12 pairs in 1981, 14 pairs in 1987 and 17 pairs in 1988.

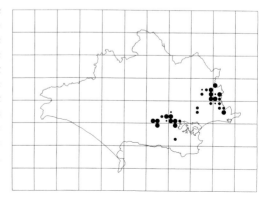

The Tetrad Survey (1987–1994) revealed evidence of breeding in only seven (19%) of the pre-1974 10-km squares (confirmed in five and probable in two), whilst the Tetrad Map shows that the species was still confined to the heaths of the Poole Basin with concentrations in Wareham Forest and the extreme east of Dorset. Although the Woodlark's distribution was more limited than in earlier years, full surveys undertaken by the RSPB Dorset Heathland Project during the 1990s found a dramatic increase in the breeding population with 41 territories in 1991, 64 territories in 1994 and 105 territories in 1997. Despite this, the distribution remains very similar to that shown by the Tetrad Map, except for a slight westwards expansion to Warmwell Heath. This remarkable increase in population levels is attributed to the lack of harsh winters and the creation of new habitats resulting in particular from improved heathland management.

The number of autumn and winter records reflect the breeding fortunes of the Woodlark in the county. During the 1950s there were occasional reports of large flocks with 30 near Holt on 11th October 1955, 30 near Cripplestyle on 29th November 1958 and up to 25 roosting in stubble near Cranborne in November 1958. The next significant report involves a flock of 17 near Holes Bay in December 1976, whilst during 1980–1985 autumn and winter flocks of 12–17 birds were recorded from Canford Heath and the eastern heaths. More recently the largest flocks have been reported from West Holme with 26 in maize stubble on 30th January 1998, 'set-aside' stubble near Holton Heath with 23 in January 1994 and 18 during January–February 1995, Chamberlayne's Heath with 19 in stubble on 1st January 1999 and East Holme with 18 on 1st February 1998.

Coastal passage has also reflected the changes in the strength of the breeding population. For example, at Portland Bill there were frequent records from 1951 to 1962 including 14N on 4th November 1956 and 16 birds during 27th–30th March 1958, none reported during 1963–1970, sightings in five years from 1971 to 1979 and near-annual reports subsequently. Since 1980 small numbers of migrants have been recorded from all the main coastal watch-points with evidence of an increase in recent years – see Table 385. Most records are for the autumn with a distinct peak in October, whilst March is the peak month for spring migrants – see Table 386. Day-totals are very small and rarely exceed four birds, the best counts in recent years being seven at Hengistbury on 4th November 1984, seven at Durlston CP on 23rd October 1995, seven at Stanpit Marsh, Christchurch Harbour on 5th October 1996 and 7W at East Bexington on 1st November 1998.

	1980	1981	1982	1983	1984	1985	1986	1987	1988	1989
Portland	3	2	4	2	4	1	2	3	0	2
Durlston CP	0	1	1	1	0	2	4	3	5	3
Hengistbury	1	6	8	4	19	3	1	5	10	7

	1990	1991	1992	1993	1994	1995	1996	1997	1998	1999
Portland	3	1	4	6	13	2	6	12	4	4
Durlston CP	11	6	7	4	2	21	8	9	10	7
Hengistbury	4	8	2	0	1	2	10	3	2	4

Table 385. Totals at the main coastal watch-points 1980–1999

Jan	Feb	Mar	Apr	May	Jun	Jul	Aug	Sep	Oct	Nov	Dec
4	2	37	18	2	1	2	2	12	138	48	2

Table 386. Monthly totals at the main coastal watch-points 1980–1999

A total of 25 birds has been ringed in the county.

The Woodlark breeds throughout most of Europe north to south-east England and southern Scandinavia and eastwards through Russia to about 50°E, also in north-west Africa, Asia Minor and the Middle East. It is largely resident in the western part of its range, but a summer visitor in the east. These eastern birds appear to move south and west to winter.

Postscript 2000–2002

Despite the lack of full surveys, the breeding population is still considered to be increasing. This resulted in breeding well away from traditional heathland sites on 'set-aside' grassland at Edmondsham with single pairs in 2000 and 2001, and four pairs in 2002. Otherwise 24 at West Knighton on 6th January 2001 and 14W at East Bexington on 17th October 2002 are high counts for winter and autumn passage respectively.

Skylark (Sky Lark)   *Alauda arvensis*

A common resident, winter visitor and passage migrant

Both Mansel-Pleydell (1888) and Blathwayt (1945) considered this species to be a common resident, winter visitor and passage migrant.

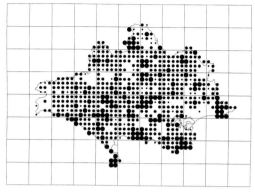

More recently the *BTO Atlas* (1968–1972) revealed evidence of breeding in all but one (97%) 10-km squares (confirmed in 33 and probable in three), whilst the Tetrad Survey (1987–1994) found evidence of breeding in all of the pre-1974 10-km squares (confirmed in 30 and probable in 7). The Tetrad Map shows that the Skylark is widely distributed, albeit patchily in parts of north-west and south-east Dorset. The population is most widespread on the chalk downs and limestone areas, which support the drier grassland habitats particularly favoured by this species, whilst it is scarce or absent from the damper pastures of the Blackmore Vale, extensive forestry plantations, particularly in the east of the county, and large intensively urbanised areas, notably the Bournemouth and Poole conurbation.

This widespread distribution obscures a decrease in the breeding population. At those sites with long-term data, the timing and extent of this decline varies considerably – see Table 387. At Portland Bill the population fell from 45 pairs in 1968 to 15 in 1980, but numbers then recovered to 17–30 pairs during 1983–1993 before declining to 15–19 during 1994–1999. Further east along the coast at Durlston CP, numbers diminished from 6–9 pairs in the early 1980s to 3–5 in the 1990s, whilst at Lodmoor NR the population declined from c.20 pairs in 1972 to only two by 1989. The pattern from inland sites such as the Stour Valley at Corfe Mullen and Fontmell Down NR seems to reflect the national trend more closely with a decrease from the early 1980s followed by a modest recovery in the 1990s.

	68	71	72	73	74	75	76	77	78	79	80	81	82	83	84
Portland Bill	45	nc	nc	nc	nc	nc	nc	nc	nc	nc	15	nc	nc	25	19
Durlston CP	nc	nc	nc	nc	nc	nc	nc	nc	nc	nc	9	8	6	9	7
Lodmoor NR	nc	17	20	14	11	13	nc	nc	10	11	6	4	3	9	7
Corfe Mullen	nc	nc	5	nc	4	nc	nc	nc	10	5	5	5	3	3	1
Fontmell Dwn	nc	nc	nc	nc	nc	nc	nc	nc	nc	nc	nc	4	nc	5	4

	85	86	87	88	89	90	91	92	93	94	95	96	97	98	99
Portland Bill	17	25	25	22	30	25	20	20	20	16	16	15	15	18	19
Durlston CP	5	6	7	4	nc	5	3	5	nc	nc	nc	nc	5	nc	nc
Lodmoor NR	4	6	4	2	2	nc	nc	nc	nc	nc	nc	nc	nc	nc	nc
Corfe Mullen	3	nc	3	2	3	3	3	5	5	3	nc	nc	nc	nc	nc
Fontmell Dwn	nc	4	nc	2	1	nc	3	3	2	3	nc	nc	nc	nc	nc

Table 387. Number of breeding territories at selected sites 1968–1999

Nationally this decline, which is considered to be as much as 50% since the early 1980s, is mainly attributed to changes in agricultural policy. This has resulted in a reduction in the pattern of mixed farming, which was well represented across rural Dorset, particularly on the free-draining chalk and limestone areas where arable fields were interspersed with pockets of semi-natural downland. In addition, there has been a shift from spring sown to autumn sown cereals, which has largely removed untilled winter stubbles from the agricultural landscape. Consequently there has been a massive reduction in the weed seeds and grain available to Skylarks in winter and early spring. There is some evidence of a recent improvement in population levels due to another change in agrarian policy, which encourages a reduction in intensive arable farming by means of 'set-aside' schemes. These provide some, albeit as yet small-scale, benefits in terms of nesting and wintering habitats.

Coastal migration, including visual movements, is largely confined to the autumn and extends from mid-September to mid-November with a peak normally in late October. Passage is generally heavier on the Purbeck coast and at Hengistbury than at Portland Bill – see Table 388. Peak day-totals rarely exceed 300 birds, the highest counts being 900SW at Hengistbury on 22nd October 1987 and 700E at Durlston CP on 12th October 1991 apart from an exceptional 2,588W at East Bexington on 31st October 1992. At Portland Bill passage is predominantly to the south in most autumns, but inward movements to the north occasionally dominate – see Table 389. Furthermore, the size of the off-passage flock at Portland Bill has diminished in recent years, perhaps reflecting the decline in the British breeding population – see Table 390. Passage flocks are recorded elsewhere along the coast, 660 at West Bexington in October 1975 being particularly high.

	1980	1981	1982	1983	1984	1985	1986	1987	1988	1989
Portland Bill	319	230	559	33	180	308	63	390	708	401
Durlston CP	nc	267	971	420	525	760	430	540	1080	nc
Hengistbury	268	246	129	278	nc	373	nc	1110	310	nc

	1990	1991	1992	1993	1994	1995	1996	1997	1998	1999
Portland Bill	299	16	131	331	237	461	225	116	99	68
Durlston CP	1282	2760	740	nc	130	1168	1140	1545	930	875
Hengistbury	293	444	283	1084	nc	626	820	239	594	409

Table 388. Totals for autumn movements at the main coastal watch-points 1980–1999

	1980	1981	1982	1983	1984	1985	1986	1987	1988	1989
south	319	87	389	24	180	130	63	390	636	377
north	nc	143	170	9	0	178	0	0	72	24

	1990	1991	1992	1993	1994	1995	1996	1997	1998	1999
south	202	16	108	60	237	461	225	37	99	48
north	97	0	23	271	0	0	0	79	0	20

Table 389. Totals for inward and outward autumn movements at Portland Bill 1980–1999

1980	1981	1982	1983	1984	1985	1986	1987	1988	1989
600	160	550	350	250	100	55	40	nc	200

1990	1991	1992	1993	1994	1995	1996	1997	1998	1999
110	70	250	40	110	50	nc	nc	nc	70

Table 390. Peak counts for off-passage autumn flock at Portland Bill 1980–1999

Spring passage is small and not detected in some years with most records from Durlston CP – see Table 391. An isolated record of 200N at Hengistbury on 24th March 1974 is most unusual, the next highest day-total in spring being 70N at Durlston CP on 1st April 1988.

	1980	1981	1982	1983	1984	1985	1986	1987	1988	1989
Portland Bill	3	21	0	16	0	0	0	0	1	0
Durlston CP	nc	83	small	195	170	150	280	nc	250	nc

	1990	1991	1992	1993	1994	1995	1996	1997	1998	1999
Portland Bill	0	0	0	0	0	0	0	0	1	0
Durlston CP	0	nc	93	0	0	nc	113	205	90	150

Table 391. Spring totals at Portland Bill and Durlston CP 1980–1999

Cold weather movements during severe winter weather can be spectacular both on the coast and inland. Sometimes passage is so heavy that numeration is virtually impossible. The heaviest movements recorded occurred on 31st December 1961 at several sites including c.100,000 observed from Sandbanks flying west over Poole Bay and c.10,000 per hour at Colehill. Other notable westerly movements took place in late December 1978 and early January 1979 including c.38,000 at Christchurch Harbour during 31st December–2nd January, and c.24,000 at Radipole NR on 1st–2nd January with 2,000 per hour there on 31st December. Similarly in January 1982 westerly passage in the Weymouth/Portland area peaked on 10th with 15,000 at Weymouth and 10,000 at Radipole NR (presumably involving a considerable overlap of birds). During these heavy cold weather movements, counts of grounded flocks sometimes reach several thousands of birds, notably at Portland Bill with 4,000 on 10th January 1982, 2,000 on 31st December 1962, 1,100 on 14th January 1987 and 1,000 in late December 1970, whilst inland there are counts of 1,000 at Shillingstone on 5th January 1962 and 500–1,000 at Woodsford on 26th December 1981. In such severe conditions, birds are frequently driven to seek refuge in gardens where they sometimes feed on bird-tables.

Otherwise winter counts are much more modest with the highest counts rarely exceeding 300 birds, particularly in recent years. At Portland Bill, the regular wintering flock has also declined in recent years thus mirroring the situation with the off-passage autumn flock – see Table 392.

80/81	81/82	82/83	83/84	84/85	85/86	86/87	87/88	88/89
300	4000	200	270	700	200	1100	20	20

89/90	90/91	91/92	92/93	93/94	94/95	95/96	96/97	97/98
120	160	40	120	25	100	50	10	21

Table 392. Peak counts for winter flock at Portland Bill 1980–1998

A total of 869 birds has been ringed in the county.

The Skylark breeds throughout most of Europe and northern Asia as well as north-west Africa and Asia Minor, being a summer visitor in the north and east of its range. The west European population is more sedentary and augmented by migrants in the winter. The Asiatic populations winter mainly to the south of the breeding range.

Postscript 2000–2002
Counts of 850W at West Bexington on 13th October 2000 and 800 at Durlston CP on 21st October 2001 are particularly high for autumn passage.

Shore Lark (Horned Lark)   *Eremophila alpestris*

A very rare winter visitor and passage migrant

There are a few 19th Century records from the Weymouth area, the last in 1895, with no further sightings until four were seen at Abbotsbury on 23rd December 1939 and one at Portland Bill from 18th to 20th October 1951.

Since 1968 there have been 20 records involving 25 birds, most of which have occurred within two distinct periods of time with ten records (15 birds) during 1968-1974 and a further five records of single birds during 1983–1988. Apart from an exceptional June sighting at Portland Bill in 1988, all birds have occurred between October and March. The peak months are November and December with six reports each, two of the December reports involving birds that have subsequently overwintered. Christchurch Harbour and Portland Bill are the most favoured sites with seven and six sightings respectively. All records since 1968 are listed below:

1968　Langton Herring: 4th November
　　　Portland Bill: 9th November
1969　Ferrybridge: two 23rd November
1970　Portland Bill: 26th October
1972　Portland Bill: two 14th–17th October with four 18th October
1973　Studland Bay: 18th February and 18th March
　　　Studland Bay: 15th and 29th December and 2nd January–23rd February 1974
　　　Brownsea: two 15th December
　　　Portland Bill: 28th December, 1st–28th January and 17th February 1974

1974 Hengistbury: 3rd November
1983 Lodmoor NR: 24th October
1984 Stanpit Marsh, Christchurch Harbour: 3rd–4th November
1986 Portland Bill: 16th October
1988 Portland Bill: 16th–18th June
     Stanpit Marsh, Christchurch Harbour: 12th December
1992 Stanpit Marsh, Christchurch Harbour: 26th October
     Hengistbury: 20th December
1996 Stanpit Marsh, Christchurch Harbour: 15th November
1997 Stanpit Marsh, Christchurch Harbour: 16th January
     Durlston CP: 20th December

The Shore Lark is a breeding summer visitor to the sub-arctic and arctic regions of Eurasia including Scandinavia, wintering on the coasts of the southern North Sea and Baltic, locally inland in north-central Europe and more widely across central Asia east to northern China. Other more isolated populations in Morocco, south-eastern Europe, Asia Minor, the Middle East and south-central Asia are basically resident. Similarly in North America, the northern populations are migratory, but those from the upland and desert areas are mainly resident.

Sand Martin   *Riparia riparia*

A fairly common summer visitor and passage migrant

Mansel-Pleydell (1888) described this species as "a summer migrant, more local in its distribution than its congeners", whilst Blathwayt (1945) considered it to be a common summer resident breeding where suitable nesting haunts can be found.

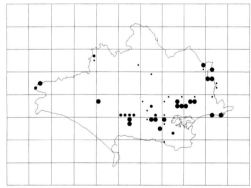

Subsequently there was little change in status up to the *BTO Atlas* (1968–1972), which revealed confirmed or probable breeding in 20 (54%) 10-km squares throughout the county including the Blackmore Vale and the extreme west. Since then there has been a marked reduction in range so that the Tetrad Survey (1987–1994) only found confirmed or probable breeding in 11 (30%) of the pre-1974 10-km squares. The Tetrad Map shows that the Sand Martin has deserted many of its former haunts in the north and west of Dorset with most breeding colonies now confined to the Poole Basin.

The transient nature of the breeding colonies, and lack of consistent counting of occupied nest holes at many sites, makes it difficult to determine long-term population trends. The impact of the widespread population crash during 1968–1969 is not clear, the *BTO Atlas* (1968–1972) indicating that the species was still widely distributed in the county. During the 1970s the population in Dorset appeared reasonably healthy with several large colonies supporting in excess of 100 pairs, notably at West Knighton GP (400 in 1971), Moreton Heath (255 at three colonies in 1970), Henbury GP (245 at two colonies in 1971), Stokeford Heath (220 in 1970), Canford Heath (200 in 1978), Carey (115 in 1975) and Chard Junction GP (100 in 1971). These counts were eclipsed, however, by the discovery of a huge colony of c.6,000–7,500 pairs at a previously inaccessible site near West Knighton during 1979–1980, which rapidly diminished subsequently.

The impact of the next national population crash during 1983–1984 was much more dramatic with a total absence at some colonies, e.g. Upton Heath, Canford Heath and Chsard Junction GP, and drastically reduced numbers at others, e.g. Povington Claypits, Stokeford Heath and Bovington. Subsequently breeding numbers have recovered with several large colonies of more than 100 pairs recorded during 1989–1999 including Warmwell (600–700 during 1997–1999), Chard Junction GP (254 in 1996), Carey (250 in 1989), Povington Claypits (200 in 1996), Black Hill near Bere Regis (138 in 1996) and Stokeford Heath (128 in 1995). This recovery is also well illustrated by counts for Chard Junction GP during 1984–1999 – see Table 393.

1984	1986	1988	1989	1990	1991	1992	1993	1994	1995	1996	1997	1998	1999
0	21	50	50	30	66	95	88	117	222	254	170	60	70

Table 393. Number of nests at Chard Junction GP 1984–1999

The recovery in breeding numbers was not reflected by the Tetrad Survey (1987–1994), which revealed a marked contraction in distribution since the *BTO Atlas* (1968–1972), particularly in the north and west of the county. Although the population crash of the mid-1980s may have contributed to this, it seems that other factors are involved, which have resulted in the permanent loss of suitable breeding sites. These may include disturbance of river-bank and sea-cliff colonies.

The majority of colonies are located in artificial cliffs created in gravel, sand and clay quarries, which are found mainly in the central and southern areas of the Poole Basin. Natural breeding sites are relatively scarce in Dorset. The longest established sea-cliff colony is at Hengistbury with 92 nests in 1991, whilst during the Tetrad Survey (1987–1994) breeding occurred nearby in cliffs at Southbourne. Sea-cliff colonies have also been reported from Canford Cliffs in 1968, Burton Bradstock during 1969–1973 (maximum of 30–50 nests in 1969 and 1970), Shipstal Point, Arne NR in the late 1960s and again in 1990, and Bournemouth East Cliff in 1977. River-bank nesting has been recorded from a number of rivers, mainly in the west of the county. The most persistent attempts of river-bank nesting in recent years has occurred on the River Frome at Frome Vauchurch with reports of successful or attempted breeding from 1986 to at least 1995.

There are two exceptionally early records, both in 1998, involving one flying along the West Cliffs at Portland on 20th February and another at Durlston CP on an unspecified date in February. Otherwise the first spring migrants normally arrive during March, other early reports being 1st March 1992 with 2N at Radipole School, 2nd March 1990 at the Grove, Portland and Nether Cerne, 2nd March 1994 at West Bexington and 3rd March 1989 at Radipole NR. Since the 1950s the average date of the first arrivals has gradually become earlier – see Table 394.

	1950–1959	1960–1969	1970–1979	1980–1989	1990–1999
Range	10th March–21st April	17th March–5th April	5th–28th March	3rd–28th March	20th February–16th March
Average	30th March	23rd March	17th March	15th March	7th March

Table 394. Dates for first spring arrivals each decade 1950–1999

Generally migration at the main coastal watch-points is relatively small in March with passage building up to peak during April and early May, spring totals being typically rather modest but highly variable – see Table 395. There was a general decline in spring totals during the mid-1980s reflecting the population crash at that time, whilst passage was particularly weak at both Portland Bill and Durlston CP during 1992–1994. Peak movements are usually small, often in double figures and rarely exceeding 150 birds, the best counts being 439N at Portland Bill on 15th April 1968, 350N at Christchurch Harbour on 2nd May 1987 with 300N there on 15th May 1988, and 254N at Weston, Portland on 25th March 1989.

During the 1970s and early 1980s, there were several large counts from Radipole NR including 1,000 on 18th April 1970, 1,750 on 20th April 1977, 1,800 on 29th April 1980 rising to an exceptional 7,500 on 3rd May, and 900 on 17th April 1981. Elsewhere spring gatherings rarely exceed 300–400 birds, the highest being 1,000 at Coward's Marsh, Christchurch during 1st–5th April 1994 and 800 at Longham in April 1966.

	1980	1981	1982	1983	1984	1985	1986	1987	1988	1989
Portland Bill	193	112	425	268	152	133	100	91	212	620
Durlston CP	245	68	184	138	258	89	95	191	181	515
Christchurch Hbr	406	138	77	77	nc	120	nc	640	720	623

	1990	1991	1992	1993	1994	1995	1996	1997	1998	1999
Portland Bill	308	165	141	89	82	345	306	390	139	407
Durlston CP	243	337	117	140	nc	441	872	840	321	370
Christchurch Hbr	nc	nc	nc	1166	258	935	8928	3294	4226	764

Table 395. Spring totals (bds) at the main coastal watch-points 1980–1999

Autumn passage occurs mainly from early July to late September with small numbers through to mid-October. Although autumn totals at the main coastal watch-points are larger than in spring, they are still highly variable – see Table 396. Like the spring, the population crash of the mid-1980s was reflected in diminished autumn totals, notably at Portland Bill in 1984. Peak movements usually range up to 300 birds and rarely exceed 600 birds, the best counts being 2,000 at Portland Bill on 29th August 1962, a minimum of 1,000 assembled over Portland on 21st August 1968 and 1,000E at Christchurch Harbour on 5th September 1982.

	1980	1981	1982	1983	1984	1985	1986	1987	1988	1989
Portland Bill	2236	1130	1314	821	190	710	648	1251	1089	4119
Durlston CP	nc	1315	3155	2481	1566	1040	1309	1551	1839	1106
Christchurch Hbr	nc	410	1540	nc	nc	182	200	314	275	nc

	1990	1991	1992	1993	1994	1995	1996	1997	1998	1999
Portland Bill	1471	1065	880	1342	755	919	882	590	791	1350
Durlston CP	1744	807	2102	1050	nc	1650	1585	4303	1621	1802
Christchurch Hbr	nc	nc	nc	1876	341	4189	5306	3893	5383	2865

Table 396. Autumn totals (bds) at the main coastal watch-points 1980–1999

Large gatherings, often in association with post-breeding roosts in reedbeds, sometimes form prior to departure. These are most frequently recorded from Christchurch Harbour, Lytchett Bay, Arne NR, Radipole and Lodmoor NRs, and Abbotsbury. Peak counts usually occur in July and often reach 1,000–2,000 birds, the highest being 5,000 at Lytchett Bay on 18th July 1996, 4,000 at Lodmoor NR on 17th July 1970 and 3,500 at Radipole NR on 28th July 1977. Elsewhere autumn gatherings rarely exceed 500 birds, the best being 900 at Tuckton, Christchurch in July 1976.

The last birds are usually recorded during late October, more exceptionally in November, the latest being 19th November 1985 at Radipole NR, 20th November 1976 with three at Radipole NR, and 21st November 1964 with two at Cowgrove near Wimborne.

A total of 9,509 birds has been ringed in the county. There have been seven foreign recoveries from Spain, six from France, two from Senegal and one from Portugal. In addition there been six foreign controls from France and one each from Spain and Senegal.

The Sand Martin is a summer visitor breeding widely across most of Europe, Asia Minor, Asia north of 20°N and North America; also locally in the Middle East and the Nile Valley of Egypt. It winters mainly in sub-Saharan Africa and in parts of southern Asia.

Postscript 2000–2002

One at Durlston CP on 25th February 2000 is only the third Dorset record for that month. At Hengistbury, 1,500 on 26th August 2001 is a high count for autumn passage.

Sponsored by Stephen Hales, Maureen Spencer and Imerys Minerals Ltd

Swallow (Barn Swallow)   *Hirundo rustica*

A common summer visitor and passage migrant

Mansel-Pleydell (1888) described this species as "one of our best known and familiar summer visitants", whilst Blathwayt (1945) referred to it as a common summer resident.

Little has changed subsequently, both the *BTO Atlas* (1968–1972) and the Tetrad Survey (1987–1994) confirmed breeding in all but one of the pre-1974 10-km squares. Although the Tetrad Map shows that breeding occurs widely throughout much of the county, it is virtually absent from the Bournemouth and Poole conurbation and those areas comprising large tracts of open heathland and forest.

There appears to be a gradual long-term decline in population levels, but the little information there is available on breeding numbers makes it difficult to quantify this with certainty. There were, however, noticeable declines in 1974 and the early 1980s, perhaps due to adverse conditions in Africa, but recoveries soon followed.

There are several records for February, but one at Gussage on 14th February 1979 may have been overwintering. The earliest presumed migrant occurred on 23rd February 1989 at Poole, whilst there are reports for 24th February 1990 at Lulworth Ranges, 24th February 1998 at Portland Harbour, 27th February 1975 at Stour Row and 29th February 1988 at Canford Park. Otherwise the first birds usually appear during March, occasionally in early April. Like the previous species, the average date of the first arrivals has gradually become earlier since the 1950s – see Table 397.

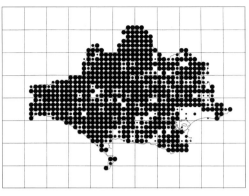

	1950–1959	1960–1969	1970–1979	1980–1989	1990–1999
Range	23rd March– 4th April	15th March– 3rd April	27th February– 4th April	23rd February– 31st March	24th February– 26th March
Average	27th March	25th March	22nd March	17th March	10th March

Table 397. Dates for first spring arrivals each decade 1950–1999

Spring migration rapidly builds up during April to peak in May. Passage is apparently stronger at Portland Bill than at the other main coastal watch-points – see Table 398. The heaviest movements frequently reach 1,000 birds, occasionally more, the best occurring on 3rd May 1980 with 15,000 at Radipole NR and 6,000 at Portland Bill.

	1980	1981	1982	1983	1984	1985	1986	1987	1988	1989
Portland Bill	9881	5700	5008	4117	nc	5799	3986	5278	5845	10998
Durlston CP	1200	930	1605	932	1560	2541	1255	945	1682	5579
Christchurch Hbr	630	343	326	219	809	1175	nc	1790	3122	595

	1990	1991	1992	1993	1994	1995	1996	1997	1998	1999
Portland Bill	6307	8750	4506	7147	3893	6083	6181	7580	5016	9898
Durlston CP	3062	3033	1098	nc	nc	3010	nc	2826	6729	4310
Christchurch Hbr	nc	nc	nc	4157	4204	117	1522	746	886	435

Table 398. Spring totals (bds) at the main coastal watch-points 1980–1999

	1980	1981	1982	1983	1984	1985	1986	1987	1988	1989
Portland Bill	17933	17917	10665	18128	nc	22970	46499	14380	23027	25121
Durlston CP	nc	11462	11548	18483	23547	20383	33784	15982	17283	32132
Christchurch Hbr	nc	2950	11370	2140	1600	13870	nc	11920	21033	nc

	1990	1991	1992	1993	1994	1995	1996	1997	1998	1999
Portland Bill	11084	14408	12854	13295	12215	19202	6022	23438	18094	nc
Durlston CP	24571	25903	39685	nc	nc	27450	nc	26080	24431	8058
Christchurch Hbr	nc	nc	8556	57496	nc	22105	51135	56706	38359	34824

Table 399. Autumn totals (bds) at the main coastal watch-points 1980–1999

Although autumn passage extends from late July through to early November, peak numbers usually occur during September and occasionally early October. Unlike the spring, autumn totals are seemingly more evenly balanced between the main coastal watch-points – see Table 399. Movements can be spectacularly heavy, the most notable being 75,000 bird-days at North Portland over seven dates during 18th–28th September 1997 (maximum of 20,000S on 23rd), 25,000 at Christchurch Harbour on an unspecified date in September 1993 with 15,000 there on 25th September 1997 (cf North Portland),

22,730E at East Bexington on an unspecified date in September 1992, and 16,000E at Durlston CP on 16th September 1984 with 15,000 there on 7th September 1989. Otherwise day-counts of up to 10,000 birds are not infrequent.

Like the Sand Martin, large reedbed roosts sometimes form prior to departure. Peak counts often involve several thousands of birds, the highest being 10,000 at Arne NR on 12th September 1971, 10,000 at Keysworth on 16th September 1992 and 7,750 at Radipole NR on 1st September 1979.

Although the last birds are usually recorded during the second half of November, there are at least 19 records for December since 1950, the latest being 24th–25th December 1988 at Portland Bill. There are also five mid-winter reports as follows:

1960   Durweston: 3rd January
1975   Radipole NR: 11th and 15th January
1979   Colehill, Wimborne: 8th January
1993   Kinson, Bournemouth: 9th January
1996   Stanpit Marsh, Christchurch Harbour: 15th January

A total of 32,307 birds has been ringed in the county. There have been six foreign recoveries from France, four from South Africa, two each from Spain, Morocco and Algeria, and one each from Italy, Western Sahara, Nigeria, Uganda and Namibia. In addition there have been two foreign controls from France and one from Spain.

The Swallow is the most cosmopolitan of the hirundines, breeding as a summer visitor over most of Europe, Asia Minor, Asia except for the Indian sub-continent and the south-east, and North America; also in parts of North Africa and the Middle East. It winters over much of sub-Saharan Africa, the Indian sub-continent and south-east Asia, and northern South America. Most British birds winter in South Africa.

Postscript 2000–2002
There was an exceptional passage on 23rd September 2000 with 30,000S at North Portland, 25,000S at Hengistbury and c.13,500E at East Bexington. Heavy passage was again reported from North Portland in autumn 2001 with 20,000S on 21st–22nd September, and again in autumn 2002 with 25,000S on 21st September, also 20,000S at Hengistbury on 12th September 2002.

Red-rumped Swallow   *Hirundo daurica*

A rare migrant, mainly in spring and summer

Since the first at Radipole NR in 1972, there have been 26 further records involving 27 birds. Occurrences have increased in recent years with annual sightings from 1987 to 1992 involving 11 records (12 birds) and again from 1995 to 2000 involving nine records. All but two of the birds have appeared during the spring and summer on dates ranging from 9th April to 29th July with May the peak month – see Table 400. There is an exceptionally early record for 26th February, whilst the only autumn sighting involves a late bird on 11th–12th November. Portland is undoubtedly the most favoured site for the species accounting for 14 birds (50% of the total).

Feb	Mar	Apr	May	Jun	Jul	Aug	Sep	Oct	Nov
1	0	7	12	4	3	0	0	0	1

Table 400. Monthly totals 1972–2002

All records are given below:

1972   Radipole NR: 6th May
1973   Portland Bill: 29th July
1975   Radipole NR: 22nd–25th May
1980   Portland Bill: 20th April
1983   Verne Common and Portland Bill: 14th–15th May
      Easton, Portland: 26th June

1987   Arne NR: 19th April
        Stanpit Marsh, Christchurch Harbour: two 2nd May
        Hengistbury: 6th May, considered different to above
1988   Portland Bill: 27th April
        Corfe Mullen: 18th July–10th September – see below
1989   Stanpit Marsh, Christchurch Harbour: 9th April
        Weston, Portland: 20th May
        Blacknor, Portland: 1st July
1990   Swanage: 11th November; same at Durlston CP 12th November
1991   Southwell, Portland: 17th June
1992   Portland Bill: 29th April
1995   Chesil Beach: 3rd May
        Portland Bill: 7th May
1996   The Fleet at Littlesea and Budmouth School, Weymouth: 11th April; same at Radipole NR
          12th April
        Portland Bill: 2nd June
1997   Blacknor, Portland: 27th May
1998   Hengistbury: 26th February
        Lodmoor NR: 25th April
1999   Verne Common, Portland: 28th–29th June
2000   Lodmoor NR: 3rd–4th May
2002   Blacknor, Portland: 3rd May

Special mention must be made of the unique event of 1988 when a male held territory amongst a House Martin colony in Corfe Mullen for almost two months, possibly longer if its discovery was delayed. It was frequently observed acting as a 'helper' by aggressively defending a House Martin's nest and attempting to feed the occupants.

The Red-rumped Swallow is a summer visitor breeding mainly in Morocco, Iberia, south-eastern Europe, parts of Asia Minor and the Middle East, and more extensively in eastern Asia. It is both a breeding species and a winter visitor to the Indian sub-continent and locally across tropical Africa. Although not common in southern France, Italy and the northern Balkans, there has been a gradual northward spread in recent years. A vagrant to Great Britain with 389 records up to 2002.

Cliff Swallow   *Hirundo pyrrhonota*

Accidental: one record

   2000   Verne Common, Portland: juv. 29th–30th September

A full account of this record can be found in the Dorset Bird Report for 2000.

The Cliff Swallow is a summer visitor breeding throughout much of North America south to Mexico. It winters in southern South America. A vagrant to Great Britain with 9 records up to 2002.

House Martin   *Delichon urbica*

A common summer visitor and passage migrant

Both Mansel-Pleydell (1888) and Blathwayt (1945) considered this species to be a common summer visitor.

There has been little change in status subsequently. The *BTO Atlas* (1968–1972) confirmed breeding in 34 (92%) 10-km squares, whilst the Tetrad Survey (1987–1994) produced virtually the same result with breeding confirmed in 35 (95%) of the pre-1974 10-km squares. The Tetrad Map shows that breeding occurs widely throughout much of the county, any absences reflecting the lack of suitable nesting sites, which are almost entirely artificial and associated with human habitation. Its apparent scarcity in the Bournemouth and Poole conurbation may be due to difficulties in finding sources of nesting material.

Cliff-nesting has been reported spasmodically from Purbeck since before 1894 when it occurred at Arish Mell. Since then breeding has occurred at Lulworth Cove in 1934 and subsequent years (1–2 pairs),

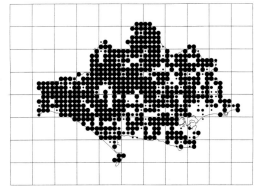

Arish Mell in 1935 and 1936 (8–10 pairs), Worbarrow Tout in 1936 (many nests), one or two sites along the limestone cliffs between Kimmeridge and Swanage, and more recently at Handfast Point (Old Harry Rocks) intermittently between 1963 and at least 1996 – see Table 401. There are also reports of nesting on the cliffs at Portland.

The limited data available on breeding numbers show different patterns, which makes it difficult to assess long-term trends in the county with any certainty – see Tables 401–404. For example, the population at Canford School has been relatively stable despite some fluctuation in numbers, but at AEE Winfrith and Bardolf Manor there is evidence of a decline during the 1990s. Elsewhere, occasional counts from the cliff-nesting colony at Handfast Point (Old Harry Rocks) indicate a highly variable situation.

1963	1965	1967	1968	1982	1985	1986	1994	1996
1	12	7	1	55	55	53	1	20

Table 401. Number of nests at Handfast Point (Old Harry Rocks) 1963–1996

1962	1963	1967	1968	1994	1995	1996	1997	1998	1999
64	153	87	62	47	46	71	60	76	68

Table 402. Number of nests at Canford School 1962–1999

1979	1989	1990	1992	1993
170	179	178	98	62

Table 403. Number of nests at AEE Winfrith 1979–1993

1990	1991	1993	1994	1995	1996	1997	1998
82	65	65	56	62	49	50	49

Table 402. Number of nests at Bardolf Manor, Puddletown 1990–1998

There is an exceptionally early record on 18th February 1998 at Briantspuddle. Otherwise the first spring migrants usually arrive during late March or early April, other early reports being 1st–2nd March 1960 at Weymouth and 11th March 1990 and 1992–both at Radipole NR. The average date of the first arrivals was earlier during the 1990s than during the previous four decades – see Table 405.

	1950–1959	1960–1969	1970–1979	1980–1989	1990–1999
Range	26th March– 15th April	1st March– 18th April	12th March– 7th April	22nd March– 7th April	18th February– 2nd April
Average	2nd April	2nd April	27th March	31st March	20th March

Table 403. Dates for first spring arrivals each decade 1950–1999

Spring passage gradually increases during April to peak in May, totals at the main coastal watch-points being highly variable (cf Sand Martin) – see Table 406. The heaviest movements are usually less than 500 and rarely exceed 1,000 birds, the best counts being 5,000 at Radipole NR on 3rd May 1980 (cf Swallow) and 3,000 at Christchurch Harbour on an unspecified date in May 1993.

Autumn passage extends from late July through to early November with peak numbers usually occurring during September and early October. Like the spring, autumn totals at the main coastal watch-points are highly variable – see Table 407. Movements can be spectacularly heavy, particularly in the vicinity of St

	1980	1981	1982	1983	1984	1985	1986	1987	1988	1989
Portland Bill	2730	668	663	1021	nc	1176	520	3028	1160	2624
Durlston CP	910	615	877	476	558	450	393	661	nc	2080
Christchurch Hbr	262	228	93	116	423	335	nc	460	1010	204

	1990	1991	1992	1993	1994	1995	1996	1997	1998	1999
Portland Bill	1376	3670	746	1919	1079	1086	698	2316	792	1577
Durlston CP	1523	1496	1107	nc	nc	720	615	1039	2000	1140
Christchurch Hbr	nc	nc	nc	3322	133	nc	921	373	64	144

Table 406. Spring totals (bds) at the main coastal watch-points 1980–1999

Aldhelm's Head with 65,833 bird-days during August–October 1986 (maximum of 20,000 on 2nd October), 64,177 bird-days during August–October 1987 (maximum of 20,000 in 18th September) and 15,000 on 24th September 1985. Elsewhere the highest counts are 24,000E at Durlston CP on 16th September 1984 (cf Swallow), 16,000 at Christchurch Harbour on 25th September 1997 and 15,000 at Portland Bill on 20th September 1985. Otherwise day-counts of up to 10,000 birds are not uncommon.

	1980	1981	1982	1983	1984	1985	1986	1987	1988	1989
Portland Bill	4156	1600	4162	16850	nc	47894	38796	15261	15462	7721
Durlston CP	2400	9030	15620	15989	33066	16593	18019	15950	nc	12829
Christchurch Hbr	2000	4970	9530	3740	1560	15630	nc	5280	10200	nc

	1990	1991	1992	1993	1994	1995	1996	1997	1998	1999
Portland Bill	6340	7761	7223	5688	4147	5005	2667	13293	11016	nc
Durlston CP	11930	10789	31963	nc	nc	5450	25420	21556	12657	13170
Christchurch Hbr	nc	nc	3463	14375	9262	46364	69756	33058	25034	3615

Table 407. Autumn totals (bds) at the main coastal watch-points 1980–1999

Although the last birds are usually recorded during the second half of November, there are at least 19 records for December since 1950, the latest being 20th–21st December 1972 at Bucknowle and 21st December 1986 at Brownsea. There is also one mid-winter report involving two at Christchurch on 6th January 1981.

A total of 29,423 birds has been ringed in the county. There have been two foreign recoveries from France and one from Algeria, but no reports of any foreign controls.

The House Martin is a summer visitor breeding throughout Europe and much of northern and central Asia; also in north-west Africa, parts of Asia Minor and the Middle East. It winters throughout sub-Saharan Africa and in parts of south-east Asia.

Postscript 2000–2002
One at Portland Bill on 28th February 2000 is the second earliest record for the county.

Sponsored by Rosemary Rooke

Richard's Pipit   *Anthus novaeseelandiae*

A scarce passage migrant, mainly in autumn

There are two 19th Century records involving singles shot at Ringstead in autumn 1882 and near Weymouth in early January 1883.

The first report in recent times concerns three at Portland Bill on 22nd April 1957 with no further sightings for another ten years. Since 1967 the species has become increasingly recorded as a scarce autumn migrant with annual sightings during 1982–1999 including marked influxes in 1985 (11), 1988 (ten), 1994 (15) and 1995 (nine) – see Table 408. Although autumn records extend from 12th September 1969 at Portland Bill to 27th November 1998 at Easton and Weston, Portland, October is the peak month with 72 birds (65%) – see Table 409.

67	68	69	70	71	72	73	74	75	76	77	78	79	80	81	82	83
2	1	1	1	0	1	0	1	3	0	1	0	0	1	0	3	6

84	85	86	87	88	89	90	91	92	93	94	95	96	97	98	99
1	11	3	5	10	6	2	2	3	4	15	9	7	5	4	2

Table 408. Autumn totals 1967–1999

Jan	Feb	Mar	Apr	May	Jun	Jul	Aug	Sep	Oct	Nov	Dec
1	0	2	7	4	0	0	0	19	72	19	2

Table 409. Monthly totals 1957–1999

Portland is by far the most regular site for autumn migrants with 64 birds (58%) – see Table 410. Durlston CP and Christchurch Harbour did not record their first birds until 1985, but 20 and 17 birds respectively have occurred subsequently with annual reports from the latter site up to 1994. There are very few autumn sightings away from these sites with singles at Abbotsbury from 15th to 19th November 1994, Lodmoor NR on 1st October 1967, 11th November 1975, 21st November 1983 and 7th October 1994, and on Purbeck at Redcliff Point on 3rd October 1994, St Aldhelm's Head on 30th September 1992 and from 14th to 21st October 1995, and Winspit on 23rd October 1982.

	Spring		Autumn		Total	
Portland	10	77%	64	58%	74	60%
Durlston CP	1	8%	20	18%	21	17%
Christchurch Harbour	1	8%	17	15%	18	15%
elsewhere	1	8%	9	8%	10	8%

Table 410. Distribution of migrants 1957–1999

Although most reports in autumn involve single birds, there are five records of two birds and one of three, at Southwell, Portland on 27th October 1983, whilst in 1994 up to four birds were present at Portland Bill during 2nd–9th November with a peak of five birds on 4th.

The Richard's Pipit is a very rare visitor in spring. There are records for 1957 (see above) and 1976 with no further occurrences until a flurry of sightings, involving four in 1989, two in 1990 and one in 1991, followed by single reports in 1995 and 1997. These spring migrants occurred between the extreme dates of 19th March 1989 at Dancing Ledge and 15th May 1990 at Portland Bill with most birds recorded in April – see Table 409. Like the autumn, Portland is the favoured locality accounting for ten birds, whilst the other spring birds all occurred in 1989 at Dancing Ledge from 19th to 27th March, Durlston CP on 27th March and Hengistbury on 11th May.

Since 1957, there have been three winter records involving singles at Portland Bill from 19th to 24th December 1970, Wick Fields, Christchurch Harbour from 23rd December 1994 to 6th January 1995, and Weston, Portland on 16th January 1995.

The race *A. n. richardi* is a summer visitor breeding in east-central Asia, and wintering mainly in the Indian sub-continent and south-east Asia. It also migrates in small numbers through Europe to winter in sub-Saharan Africa and even southern Spain. Other races are resident in southern and eastern Africa, the Indian sub-continent, south-east Asia and Australasia.

Postscript 2000–2002

One by the Fleet at the Bridging Camp from 1st to 6th January 2000 is only the fourth winter record for the county since 1957. Otherwise there were five autumn reports involving singles at Hengistbury on 22nd October 2000, St Aldhelm's Head on 22nd September 2001, Portland on 27th September and 5th October 2001, and Christchurch Harbour on 19th–20th October 2001.

Blyth's Pipit   *Anthus godlewskii*

Accidental: one record involving two individuals

1998   Portland Bill: two 22nd–24th November, one until 6th December

Two birds were present in the Top Fields at Portland Bill from 22nd to 24th November 1998 with one remaining until 6th December. Both birds were trapped and ringed and they represent Great Britain's first multiple arrival! A full account can be found in the Dorset Bird Report for 1998.

In addition, a controversial large pipit at Portland Bill from 16th March to at least 27th April 1989 was considered by some observers to be this species.

The Blyth's Pipit is a summer visitor breeding from southern Siberia and China south to north-east India and winters in the Indian sub-continent including Sri Lanka. A vagrant to Great Britain with 12 records up to 2002.

Tawny Pipit *Anthus campestris*

A scarce passage migrant, mainly in autumn

The first county record occurred in 1953 when two birds were present at Portland Bill on 17th September. Subsequently the species has become increasingly regular and it is now a scarce autumn migrant with annual sightings during 1979–1999 including marked influxes in 1983 (19), 1986 (13), 1989 (17), 1992 (11) and 1993 (11) – see Fig 44. Apart from an exceptionally early bird at Portland Bill on 24th July 1990, autumn records extend from 18th August 1977 to 24th October – 1st November 1990–both at Portland Bill. The first half of September is the peak time for autumn migrants and accounts for 41%, whilst the month as a whole accounts for 72% – see Table 411.

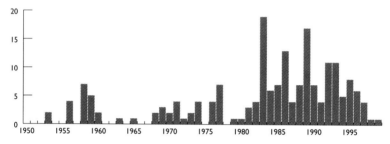

Fig 44. Autumn totals 1953–1999

May 1–15	May 16–31	June 1–15	June 16–30	July 1–15	July 16–31	Aug 1–15	Aug 16–31	Sept 1–15	Sept 16–30	Oct 1–15	Oct 16–31
11	1	0	0	0	1	0	29	73	53	16	4

Table 411. Half-monthly totals 1953–1999

Like the Richard's Pipit, Portland is the main site for Tawny Pipits in autumn with 137 birds (72%) – see Table 412. Although the species was not recorded with any frequency at Durlston CP and Christchurch Harbour until the mid-1980s, 20 and 24 birds respectively have occurred at these sites. The relatively few autumn sightings away from the main coastal watch-points involve singles by the Fleet at Langton Herring on 16th September 1971, Moonfleet on 21st August 1984, and Ferrybridge from 12th to 15th September 1974, at Lodmoor NR on 19th August 1986 and from 29th September to 9th October 1995, and on Purbeck at Kingston Matravers on 15th September 1984, St Aldhelm's Head on 10th September 1993 and 25th August 1995, and Winspit on 11th September 1992. One at Coward's Marsh, Christchurch on 25th September 1983 is the only inland record.

	Spring		Autumn		Total	
Portland	6	50%	137	72%	143	70%
Durlston CP	2	17%	20	10%	22	11%
Christchurch Harbour	2	17%	24	13%	26	13%
elsewhere	2	17%	10	5%	12	6%

Table 412. Distribution of migrants 1953–1999

The majority of reports in autumn involve one or occasionally two birds, but three have been recorded on at least four occasions at Portland. In addition, there were four at Portland Bill on 23rd September 1983 during an influx, which may have involved as many as nine birds in the Bill/Weston/Southwell area during 23rd–26th September.

Spring migrants are rarely recorded with the first at Weston, Portland on 2nd–3rd May 1971. There are no further sightings until a flurry of reports involving seven birds during 1987–1990 followed by singles in 1993, 1995, 1996 and 1998 (cf Richard's Pipit). All records have occurred between 2nd May 1971 at Weston, Portland and 17th May 1998 at Easton, Portland. Portland accounts for six of the birds with two each at both Durlston CP and Christchurch Harbour, whilst the remaining two reports involve singles at Cogden Beach on 7th May 1988 and nearby at Burton Bradstock on 13th May 1996 – see Table 412.

A total of three birds have been ringed in the county.

The Tawny Pipit is a summer visitor breeding from north-west Africa and Iberia eastwards across much of Europe except the north, Asia Minor and central Asia to about 118°E. It is local and declining over much the western, northern and central parts of its European range. The Tawny Pipit winters mainly in the northern tropics of Africa, Arabia and the Indian sub-continent.

Postscript 2000–2002

The recent decline continued with singles at Ower, Poole Harbour on 6th August 2000 and Hengistbury on 14th November 2001 the only reports. The Hengistbury record is the latest date that this species has been recorded in the British Isles.

Olive-backed Pipit　　　　　　　　　*Anthus hodgsoni*

Accidental: five records involving six birds

All records are from Portland:

1970	Portland Bill: 2nd–4th May; trapped on 2nd; relocated 10th May
1990	Portland Bill: two 14th October; same at Top Fields/Southwell 22nd October
1991	Verne Common, Portland: 12th April
	Easton, Portland: 13th October
1992	Southwell, Portland: 5th October

The race *A. h. yunnanensis*, which occurs as a vagrant, is a summer visitor breeding from the Urals east across Siberia to the Pacific, whilst the nominate race *A. h. hodgsoni* is a summer visitor breeding from the Himalayas east to eastern China and Japan. Wintering occurs in the Indian sub-continent and south-east Asia. A vagrant to Great Britain with 249 records up to 2002.

Tree Pipit　　　　　　　　　　　　　*Anthus trivialis*

A locally common summer visitor and fairly common passage migrant

Mansel-Pleydell (1888) simply described this species as "a summer visitant", which inhabited timbered hedgerows and the outskirts of woods. Blathwayt (1945) considered it to be a not very common summer visitor, being well-known in some districts, but absent in others.

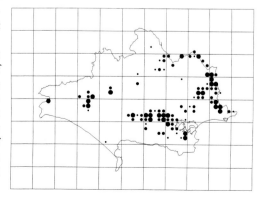

The *BTO Atlas* (1968–1972) found that the Tree Pipit was widely distributed with evidence of breeding in 27 (73%) 10-km squares (confirmed in seven and probable in 20). Like the Woodlark, this species subsequently disappeared from many sites in the north and west of the county. As a result the Tetrad Survey (1987–1994) revealed evidence of breeding in only 19 (51%) of the pre-1974 10-km squares (confirmed in 11, probable in four and possible in four).

The Tetrad Map shows that breeding is now largely confined to the Poole Basin, the two main strongholds being in the centre from Wareham Forest west to Puddletown Forest, and in the east from Christchurch north to Ringwood Forest including Holt Heath NNR and its environs. It is scarce on the Purbeck heathlands, being seemingly absent from some well-known sites such as Arne NR and Studland NNR. Elsewhere the Tree Pipit is a very local breeding bird mostly inhabiting woodlands and forestry plantations on the steeper slopes of the chalk scarp. There is also a small, but notable population centred in the Powerstock/Kingcombe area of the western downs, whilst confirmed breeding at Lambert's Castle was the only tetrad record from the far west.

Population trends are difficult to assess due to variable coverage from year to year, but there is evidence of a genuine increase in breeding numbers during the late 1990s – see Table 413. Notable population concentrations have been reported from the Lower Avon Valley with 26 pairs/territories in 1990, and Bovington with 20 pairs/territories in 1998 and 19 in 1999.

	86	87	88	89	90	91	92	93	94	95	96	97	98	99
Pairs	42	50	50	21	51	73	48	nc	78	79	62	104	59	135
Sites	–	–	16	11	–	–	–	–	–	16	13	21	13	26

Table 413. Number of breeding pairs/territories in Dorset 1986–1999

There is a very early record of two birds at the Nothe, Weymouth on 10th March 1990 but otherwise the first spring migrants usually appear during late March or early April, other early reports being from Portland Bill on 17th March 1989 and 20th March 1977. Since the 1950s the average date of the first arrivals has gradually become earlier – see Table 414.

	1950–1959	1960–1969	1970–1979	1980–1989	1990–1999
Range	2nd–21st April	3rd–14th April	20th March–16th April	17th March–6th April	10th March–9th April
Average	11th April	8th April	5th April	31st March	29th March

Table 414. Dates for first spring arrivals each decade 1950–1999

Spring passage mostly occurs between mid-April and mid-May, the numbers recorded at the main coastal watch-points being relatively small – see Table 415. Peak counts are usually less than 30 and rarely exceed 50 birds, the highest being 100N at Hengistbury on 24th April 1990 and 100+ at St Aldhelm's Head on 3rd May 1980. Autumn migration is generally much heavier and occurs mainly between mid-August and late September – see Table 416. Peak counts sometimes exceed 50 but rarely 100 birds, the highest being 200 at Radipole NR on 31st August 1976, 156 at Portland Bill on 16th–17th August 1971 with 150 there on 25th–26th August 1979, and 150 at Durlston CP on 18th August 1992. Since 1980 there has been a marked decline in the strength of both spring and autumn passage at Portland Bill, which is not evident at Durlston CP – see Tables 417 and 418. A few migrants are noted inland during spring and autumn, but 100–150 heard over Beaminster on 24th August 1982 is an exceptional count.

	1980	1981	1982	1983	1984	1985	1986	1987	1988	1989
Portland Bill	230	130	171	154	267	132	68	264	137	154
Durlston CP	50	42	50	35	91	43	46	122	74	120
Christchurch Hbr	165	178	nc	nc	nc	112	nc	87	36	101

	1990	1991	1992	1993	1994	1995	1996	1997	1998	1999
Portland Bill	165	76	52	71	30	86	71	83	76	92
Durlston CP	104	85	46	22	129	96	90	180	120	61
Christchurch Hbr	233	245	9	15	52	37	13	58	nc	19

Table 415. Spring totals (bds) at the main coastal watch-points 1980–1999

	1980	1981	1982	1983	1984	1985	1986	1987	1988	1989
Portland Bill	937	600	370	533	542	948	630	727	588	298
Durlston CP	204	166	268	212	422	322	277	475	433	456
Christchurch Hbr	nc	nc	nc	nc	nc	352	nc	574	250	244

	1990	1991	1992	1993	1994	1995	1996	1997	1998	1999
Portland Bill	229	232	217	237	239	395	286	289	339	124
Durlston CP	450	229	1010	234	432	616	310	444	287	320
Christchurch Hbr	173	68	209	302	45	116	56	78	163	101

Table 416. Autumn totals (bds) at the main coastal watch-points 1980–1999

	1980–84	1985–89	1990–94	1995–99
Portland Bill	190	151	79	82
Durlston CP	54	81	77	109

Table 417. 5-year average spring totals (bds) at Portland Bill and Durlston CP 1980–1999

	1980–84	1985–89	1990–94	1995–99
Portland Bill	596	638	231	287
Durlston CP	254	393	471	395

Table 418. 5-year average autumn totals (bds) at Portland Bill and Durlston CP 1980–1999

The last birds are usually reported during October, the latest records being from Portland Bill with one on 1st November 1981 and two on 1st November 1985, and Newton's Cove, Weymouth with two on 2nd–3rd November 1981 (cf Portland Bill).

A total of 344 birds has been ringed in the county. There is one foreign recovery from the Netherlands, but there are no reports of any foreign controls.

The Tree Pipit is a summer visitor breeding over most of Europe, except Ireland and the more arid parts of Iberia and the Mediterranean countries; also across much of north-central Asia (boreal regions) and northern Asia Minor. It winters in a broad band across sub-Saharan Africa from Guinea to Ethiopia and south through east Africa to Natal and Transvaal, also throughout much of the Indian sub-continent.

Postscript 2000–2002

The breeding population increased in 2000 with 167 pairs/territories at 20 sites, but then declined with 110 pairs/territories at 22 sites in 2001 and only 55 pairs/territories at 18 sites in 2002.

Sponsored by D. S. Dicker

Pechora Pipit   *Anthus gustavi*

Accidental: two records

1983   Portland Bill: 27th September
1990   Wide Street, Portland: 20th October

The Pechora Pipit is a summer visitor breeding in a narrow band from the Pechora River eastwards across Siberia. It winters in the islands of the Phillipines, Borneo and Sulawesi. A vagrant to Great Britain with 72 records up to 2002.

Meadow Pipit   *Anthus pratensis*

A fairly common resident, and common passage migrant and winter visitor

Mansel-Pleydell (1888) described this species as "resident, and common on the heaths and dry moors". Blathwayt (1945) referred to it as a common resident, passage migrant and winter visitor.

The *BTO Atlas* (1968–1972) found evidence of breeding in all 10-km squares (confirmed in 30, probable in six and possible in one). There is a suggestion of a slight contraction in range subsequently, the

Tetrad Survey (1987–1994) recording breeding in 34 (92%) of the pre-1974 10-km squares (confirmed in 25, probable in six and possible in three).

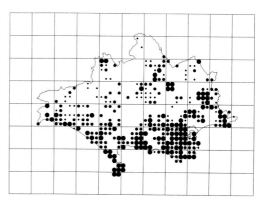

The Tetrad Map shows that the bulk of the breeding population occurs on the heathlands of Poole Basin and the rough grasslands of the coastal fringes. The Meadow Pipit is more sparsely distributed in the west and over much of the chalk where it is restricted to areas of uncultivated downland, notably on steep slopes such as those along the chalk scarp. The small concentration of breeding birds on the relatively flat downland around Blandford Camp is noteworthy. Elsewhere, there is a small isolated population associated with the North Dorset Limestone Ridges around Sherborne, and a few scattered reports of breeding from the nearby Blackmore Vale.

The relatively little information available on long term population levels shows different trends – see Table 419. At Arne NR numbers have fluctuated between 20–35 pairs during 1973–1993, but the overall trend has been relatively stable. At Portland Bill the population declined during the early 1980s, but then recovered to remain relatively stable during the 1990s. By contrast numbers at Durlston CP and Lodmoor NR show a steady decline, which is particularly dramatic at the latter site with a decrease from 14 pairs in 1974 to a single pair in 1989 with no further reports subsequently. More recently a decline has been recorded at Canford Heath from 32 pairs in 1995 to 17 pairs in 1999.

	70	71	72	73	74	75	76	77	78	79	80	81	82	83	84
Portland Bill	nc	nc	nc	nc	nc	nc	nc	nc	nc	20	23	20	15	14	17
Durlston CP	nc	nc	nc	nc	nc	nc	nc	nc	nc	21	14	10	8	7	9
Lodmoor NR	3	9	5	13	14	12	nc	nc	3	nc	nc	nc	nc	nc	5
Arne NR	nc	nc	nc	25	30	32	35	25	20	nc	25	30	25	20	20

	85	86	87	88	89	90	91	92	93	94	95	96	97	98	99
Portland Bill	13	20	17	17	18	23	20	24	20	22	20	20	20	27	nc
Durlston CP	7	5	6	nc	nc	4	5	6	nc	nc	5	5	5	nc	4
Lodmoor NR	3	nc	0	0	1	0	0	0	0	0	0	0	0	0	0
Arne NR	20	25	25	nc	25	25	25	26	29	nc	nc	nc	nc	nc	nc

Table 419. Number of breeding territories at selected sites 1970–1999

The species is particularly numerous on migration when visual movements at the main coastal watch-points, such as Portland Bill, are frequently conspicuous – see Tables 420 and 421. In spring the first migrants may appear as early as late February with peak passage between mid-March and mid-April, which is followed by smaller numbers through to the end of the month and occasionally into early May. Several thousand birds often occur at the main coastal watch-points with daily maxima often in excess of 500 and occasionally up to 1,600 birds, but at Portland Bill a total of 3,688 during 11th–13th April 1971 and counts of 2,500N on 24th March 1985 and 2,000N on 24th April 1996 are notably high. Visual passage is predominantly northerly in direction in spring.

1980	1981	1982	1983	1984	1985	1986	1987	1988	1989
1380	771	1060	2244	4017	5788	2070	1900	1218	2603

1990	1991	1992	1993	1994	1995	1996	1997	1998	1999
2568	3043	1575	257	116	444	3853	950	970	2048

Table 420. Totals for spring movements (northerly) at Portland Bill 1980–1999

Migration is even heavier in the autumn. Although a few birds may occur in August, passage usually peaks between mid-September and mid-October when movements can be spectacular and often involve daily counts of 1,000–2,000 occasionally as many as 4,000 birds, but 10,300S at Portland Bill on 7th October 1985 and 9,000SE at Christchurch Harbour on 2nd October 1993 are exceptional. Visual movements are generally to the south, but substantial northerly passage often occurs later in the autumn. For example, in 1985 at Portland Bill 20,900 flew south during 15th September–11th October followed by 4,000N during 12th–31st October.

	1980	1981	1982	1983	1984	1985	1986	1987	1988	1989
South	1374	4842	5790	7041	5766	20,907	7000	7860	3552	5400
North	0	435	289	132	0	4000	2070	1860	3069	985

	1990	1991	1992	1993	1994	1995	1996	1997	1998	1999
South	3697	3042	10,439	4592	2600	6662	4666	3180	nc	3650
North	719	715	616	2670	1170	200	200	6500	nc	0

Table 421. Totals for autumn movements at Portland Bill 1980–1999

Off-passage flocks are often a feature of the autumn migration, notably at Portland Bill where peak counts generally vary between 500–2,000 birds, but 4,000 on 8th October 1985 during a period of heavy passage with 3,000 in September 1988 and on 26th September 1993 – see Table 422.

1980	1981	1982	1983	1984	1985	1986	1987	1988	1989
900	200	2500	1000	400	4000	1000	1000	3000	600

1990	1991	1992	1993	1994	1995	1996	1997	1998	1999
500	1500	700	3000	400	600	2000	700	1000	600

Table 422. Peak counts for off-passage autumn flock at Portland Bill 1980–1999

Relatively small numbers are present during the winter with maxima usually less than 100 and rarely exceeding 200 birds. The highest counts are normally associated with cold weather, notably 'vast numbers' on Upton Heath in January 1979 and 450 at Radipole NR in February 1978.

A total of 3,064 birds has been ringed in the county. There are three foreign recoveries from Portugal, two from Spain and one from France, but there are no reports of any foreign controls.

The Meadow Pipit breeds mainly in northern and north-central Europe including Iceland, being a summer visitor to the northern and eastern parts of its range. It winters mostly in western and southern Europe, North Africa, Asia Minor, the Middle East and parts of south-west Asia.

Postscript 2000–2002
At Hengistbury, 8,000S on 30th September 2000 is a very high count for autumn passage.

Red-throated Pipit　　　　　　　　　　　*Anthus cervinus*

A very rare passage migrant, mainly in autumn: ten records
Since the first at Portland Bill in 1961, there have been nine further records with two each in 1979, 1992 and 2000. All but two of the birds have appeared during the autumn on dates ranging from 24th August to 13th November, the two remaining sightings being in May. Portland accounts for six birds.

1961	Portland Bill: 13th November
1979	The Fleet at Herbury Gore: 9th September
	Portland Bill: 13th October
1987	Hengistbury: 25th May
1989	Portland Bill: 27th September
1992	Lodmoor NR: 1st–2nd October
	Easton, Portland: 4th October
1998	Weston, Portland: 14th October
2000	Weston, Portland: 12th May
	Hengistbury: 24th August

The Red-throated Pipit is a summer visitor breeding almost entirely within the Arctic circle from northern Scandinavia east across Siberia to Alaska. It winters mainly in the northern tropics of Africa and south-east Asia, but also locally in parts of North Africa, Asia Minor and the Middle East. A vagrant to Great Britain with 423 records up to 2002.

Rock Pipit   *Anthus petrosus*

A locally common resident, winter visitor and passage migrant

Both Mansel-Pleydell (1888) and Blathwayt (1945) considered this species to be a common resident on the coast from which it seldom wanders.

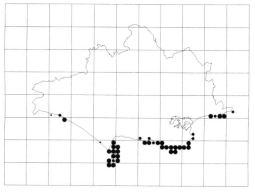

The *BTO Atlas* (1968–1972) established confirmed or probable breeding in all but two of the 10-km squares along the coast from Studland in the east to Lyme Regis in the west. The exceptions were SY58 and SY68, which involve the relatively low-lying section of coast along the Chesil Beach, where breeding was recorded as possible. The Tetrad Survey (1987–1994) found that there was little change in distribution with breeding confirmed or probable in all of the pre-1974 coastline 10-km squares except for absences in west Purbeck (SY78) and along the Chesil Beach (SY58 and SY68). The Tetrad Map reveals that breeding is concentrated along four sections of the coast, namely Highcliffe to Southbourne including Hengistbury, the Purbeck coast from Ballard Down to Durdle Door, the Weymouth and Portland area, and finally Burton Bradstock to Lyme Regis in the west.

During the last 20 years, population levels have been relatively stable – see Table 423. In earlier years numbers at Portland Bill ranged from 5–8 pairs during 1962–1971 with ten pairs there in 1973. Other counts of breeding birds from the Purbeck coast include from 2–6 pairs between Winspit and St Aldhelm's Head during 1981–1984, six pairs at Worbarrow Bay in 1981, and 11 pairs between Ballard Down and Seacombe in 1988. Elsewhere ten pairs bred at Portland Harbour in 1986 and 1987 with 15 pairs there in 1989.

	1979	1980	1981	1982	1983	1984	1985	1986	1987	1988	1989
Portland Bill	12 (6)	nc	nc	nc	nc	(5)	(3)	10 (6)	9 (6)	8 (5)	12
Durlston CP	3	2	2	3	3	3	3	4	3	nc	4
Hengistbury	2	nc	nc	nc	nc	3	3	3	3	3	nc

	1990	1991	1992	1993	1994	1995	1996	1997	1998	1999
Portland Bill	10	10	12	11	10	(6)	nc	nc	nc	nc
Durlston CP	6	6	4	nc	nc	6	5	6	5	4
Hengistbury	4	nc	nc	1	nc	3	nc	3	1	nc

Table 423. Number of breeding pairs at Portland Bill, Durlston CP and Hengistbury 1979–1999; () = East Cliffs only

Rock Pipits are more widely distributed during the winter when birds disperse to the lower-lying parts of the coast, the saltings and marshes of Poole and Christchurch Harbours being particularly favoured. Numbers are generally small with winter maxima usually less than 20 and rarely exceeding 30 birds, the highest counts being 60 at Swineham, on 26th November 1989 with 50 nearby at Keysworth on 4th November 1990, 48 between Swanage Pier and Anvil Point on 4th January 1997, and 45 at Portland Dockyard on 9th November 1990.

Spring passage is rarely detected with occasional reports of migrants from the main coastal watch-points, e.g. in 1983 with 10E at Durlston CP on 15th April and 4N at Christchurch Harbour on 30th March. Autumn migration, albeit small, is more obvious with most passage during September and October. At Portland Bill numbers increase to a peak in October when up to 50 birds have been recorded. Visual movements, which are predominantly easterly in direction, occur most frequently at Christchurch Harbour where peak daily counts usually range between 30–45 birds.

Away from the coast, the species is very rare and all inland records are given below:

1976   Sherborne Lake: 7th March after strong southerlies
1982   Coward's Marsh, Christchurch: 28th March
1984   Christchurch Water-meadows: 7th March
1993   Fordington, Dorchester: 24th October

A total of 324 birds has been ringed in the county.

The status of the highly migratory Scandinavian race *A. p. littoralis* in Dorset is unclear, but reports suggest that it is a scarce passage migrant, mainly in spring. All published records are given:

1975   Portland Bill: 16th April
       Stanpit Marsh, Christchurch Harbour: 6 in November
1988   Hengistbury: 8th April
1992   Portland Bill: recorded in spring
       Christchurch Harbour: recorded in spring
1996   Stanpit Marsh, Christchurch Harbour: one overwintering with Rock Pipits
1997   Hengistbury: two 6th March
1999   Portland Bill: 23rd March
       Christchurch Harbour: 30th March

The race of Rock Pipit *A. p. petrosus*, which is largely resident, breeds in the British Isles and north-western and western France, whilst the Scandinavian race *A. p. littoralis* breeding in Scandinavia and north-west Russia is a summer visitor and winters mainly in western and southern Europe.

Postscript 2000–2002
Birds of the 'Scandinavian' race *A. p. littoralis* were recorded at Christchurch Harbour on 7th and 13th March 2000.

Water Pipit   *Anthus spinoletta*

An uncommon winter visitor and passage migrant

The status of this species has changed dramatically during the 20th Century. First recorded in the county on 4th April 1925 at Lodmoor NR, a few were seen at the same site in subsequent years up to 1929 on dates ranging between 4th March and 19th April. One was also identified near Weymouth on 29th August 1929. Based on this early series of records, Blathwayt (1945) described the Water Pipit as "apparently a fairly regular spring visitor, and also probably passes in autumn, but then more rarely observed". This assessment appears to be been rather premature, since there were no further reports until 1953 when one was present at Lodmoor NR on 13th March. This was followed by two more birds in 1958 involving singles at Portland Bill on 12th April and 2nd September. Although there was an increase in sightings during the 1960s, the species remained a scarce visitor until late in the decade – see Table 424. All but one of the records during 1963–1966 referred to presumably the same individual, which wintered at Cranborne CBs in four successive years.

1960	1961	1962	1963	1964	1965	1966	1967	1968	1969
0	0	2	1	2	1	1	5	0	8

Table 424. Annual totals 1960–1969

During the 1970s the Water Pipit became firmly established as a regular winter visitor and migrant in small numbers, being most obvious on passage during the spring. Birds show a marked preference for two distinct type of habitats, namely watercress beds, and marshes/wet meadows along the lower river valleys and coast. During the last 30 years the vast majority of records have come from cress-beds mainly in the Frome and Piddle Valleys – notably those at Bere Regis, Waddock Cross and Tincleton, the Lower Avon Valley, and favoured coastal sites such as Christchurch Harbour, the western fringes of Poole Harbour including Lytchett Bay, and Lodmoor NR.

Elsewhere the species is very scarce. For example, there are only three reports from the Fleet at Abbotsbury and only three sightings from the west of the county involving singles at West Bexington on 31st March 1981, Charmouth on 31st January 1991 and Lyme Regis on 6th January 1999. A mere total of eight birds have occurred at Portland Bill with two in 1958, two in 1962 and more recently singles on 28th November 1976, 13th February 1986, 20th April 1989 and 7th March 1991. The only records from the Purbeck coast involve two at Durlston CP during 1st–3rd April 1987 with one there on 17th March 1988, and singles at Peveril Down on 16th March 1964 and Osmington on 31st January 1996. Otherwise there is a scatter of reports from other sites mainly in the Weymouth area, along the southern fringes of Poole Harbour, and along the lower reaches of the Frome and Stour Valleys. Well inland, it is very rare away from cress-bed sites with two by the River Stour at Sturminster Marshall on 20th–21st April 1979, and singles at Clifton Wood on 28th March 1982, Sugar Hill in Wareham Forest on 14th January 1990 and Sherborne STW on 1st January 1997 the only sightings.

The first birds usually arrive from the second week of October onwards, the earliest report being from Lodmoor NR on an unspecified date in September 1996. Autumn migration is generally poorly defined and obscured by wintering birds, but occasional peak counts at regular sites and other isolated records during October – early November suggest some through passage. Spring migration between early March and mid-April is much more obvious with a marked increase in birds particularly at wintering sites in the Lower Avon Valley and along the coast. Birds are rarely recorded after the third week of April, the latest sightings being all from Christchurch Harbour on 3rd May 1988, 4th May 1975 and 4th May 1984.

70/71	71/72	72/73	73/74	74/75	75/76	76/77	77/78	78/79	79/80
5	3	15	10	6	6	2	2	10	10

80/81	81/82	82/83	83/84	84/85	85/86	86/87	87/88	88/89	89/90
10	10	18	25	5	14	5	3	2	3

90/91	91/92	92/93	93/94	94/95	95/96	96/97	97/98	98/99	99/00
2	3	1	2	6	3	6	14	3	1

Table 425. Winter maxima at Lodmoor NR 1970–1999

Winter	Lytchett Bay	Christchurch Harbour	Lower Avon Valley	Bere Regis CBs	Waddock Cross CBs	Tincleton CBs
1980/81	–	4	–	–	1	–
1981/82	6	1	–	–	–	–
1982/83	8	0	–	–	2	–
1983/84	8	11	–	–	6	2
1984/85	15	4	–	2	15	10
1985/86	20	2	10	6	5	8
1986/87	2	0	3	3	4	1
1987/88	1	4	10	3	5	2
1988/89	0	1	6	1	5	1
1989/90	0	2	10	–	3	5
1990/91	1	2	13	6	3	5
1991/92	1	7	2	5	3	–
1992/93	1	–	5	–	2	4
1993/94	5	5	25	–	3	5
1994/95	4	4	15	1	3	1
1995/96	2	4	14	1	6	1
1996/97	12	3	21	1	10	–
1997/98	2	2	1	1	3	–
1998/99	4	1	–	5	1	–

Table 426. Winter maxima at the other main sites 1980–1999

Wintering numbers increased during the 1970s, when maxima frequently reached but rarely exceeded ten birds, to peak during the mid-1980s when counts at some favoured sites ranged from 15–25 birds, the highest being an exceptional 50 at Wareham Water-meadows on 9th December 1984 – see Tables 425 and 426. Subsequently wintering numbers declined during the late 1980s and early 1990s, only to increase again in the mid-1990s with maxima reaching double figures at several sites, the highest counts being from the Lower Avon Valley with 25 on 28th January 1994 and 21 on 9th February 1997. This was followed by yet another decline during the late 1990s.

In spring, peak counts occur in March and frequently reach 20 birds, the highest being 35 at Lodmoor NR on 9th March 1984, although there is an unsubstantiated claim of 68 flying off the sea at this site in 15 minutes on 6th April 1974 – see Table 427. There is some evidence to suggest a decline in spring maxima since a peak in the mid-1980s with a hint of a recovery in the early/mid-1990s.

	71	72	73	74	75	76	77	78	79	80	81	82	83	84	85
Lodmoor NR	10	20	20	12	6	nc	–	20	nc	15	20	20	20	35	6
Lytchett Bay	–	–	–	–	–	–	–	–	–	–	–	1	nc	20	16
Christchurch Hbr	–	–	–	5	4	6	4	4	nc	4	7	6	5	15	15
Lower Avon Valley	–	–	–	–	–	–	–	16	–	7	–	10	2	4	2

	86	87	88	89	90	91	92	93	94	95	96	97	98	99
Lodmoor NR	14	4	nc	nc	nc	2	21	4	nc	4	nc	13	nc	0
Lytchett Bay	–	1	–	1	–	–	–	15	8	4	4	11	2	0
Christchurch Hbr	7	2	9	3	1	2	21	4	–	2	4	1	3	9
Lower Avon Valley	12	5	19	nc	11	4	nc	20	nc	nc	9	1	0	0

Table 427. Spring maxima at the main sites 1971–1999

A total of 15 birds has been ringed in the county.

The Water Pipit breeds in the mountains of southern, central and eastern Europe, eastwards through Asia Minor to central Asia. In winter it extends over much of western and southern Europe, north-west Africa, Asia Minor, the Middle East, Arabia and south-west Asia.

Postscript 2000–2002
At Lodmoor NR, 30 on 22nd March 2001 is the second highest spring count for Dorset. Despite this, there appears to be a continuing decline in numbers with no reports from any cress-bed sites in 2001.

Yellow Wagtail   *Motacilla flava flavissima*

A fairly common passage migrant
Mansel-Pleydell (1888) described this species as "a summer visitant, frequenting the pastures and marshes on the sea-coast". Blathwayt (1945) considered it to be a local summer resident, perhaps breeding more numerously in the east of the county where it nests on the heaths as well as the water-meadows.

During the 1950s the Yellow Wagtail remained a very local breeding bird with most records from Lodmoor NR and the Stour and Allen Valleys in the vicinity of Wimborne. With the exception of an isolated report in 1971, breeding last occurred in the Allen Valley in 1962, but continued in the nearby Stour Valley and at Lodmoor NR throughout the 1960s. The *BTO Atlas* (1968–1972) confirmed the relative scarcity of this species with evidence of breeding recorded from 13 (35%) 10-km squares (confirmed in seven, probable in two and possible in four). The reports of confirmed and probable breeding were mainly confined to Lodmoor NR and river valleys in the south and east of the county. The sole exception was that of confirmed breeding in the Blackmore Vale (ST71).

Subsequently the fortunes of this fragile population declined, so that by 1992 the species had become extinct as a breeding bird in Dorset. Regular breeding ceased in Christchurch Harbour in 1979 and the Stour Valley near Wimborne in 1980, continued in the Lower Avon Valley up to 1990 and, apart from absences during 1973–1976 and in 1989, occurred at Lodmoor NR up to 1991 – see Table 428. Otherwise there were isolated breeding records from the Frome Valley in 1981, the Stour Valley at Corfe Mullen in

1985, Abbotsbury in 1986, Radipole NR in 1988, and Christchurch Harbour in 1989 and 1990. The Tetrad Survey (1987–1994) reflected the parlous status of the breeding population immediately prior to extinction.

	51	55	59	60	69	70	71	72	73	74	75	76	77	78
Lodmoor NR	1	2	6	1	5*	4*	2*	1	0	0	0	0	1	2*
Stour Valley	4	4	5	3	4	4	4	2	0	1	8	6	6	2
Lower Avon	–	–	–	–	–	–	–	–	–	nc	nc	nc	nc	nc
elsewhere	sev	sev	0	sev	0	0	1	1	0	5	4	sev	sev	0

	79	80	81	82	83	84	85	86	87	88	89	90	91	92
Lodmoor NR	1	3	1	1	3	3	3	4	1	1	0	1	1	1*
Stour Valley	1	2	0	0	0	0	1	0	0	0	0	0	0	0
Lower Avon	7	2	nc	9	3	3	1	3	4	2	4	3	0	0
elsewhere	3	0	1	0	0	0	0	1	0	1	2	2	0	0

Table 428. Number of breeding pairs at the main sites 1951–1992; *including mixed or pure pairs of other races

The first spring migrants arrive during late March or early April with the earliest being 15th March 1975 at Portland Bill and 16th March 1998 at Stanpit Marsh, Christchurch Harbour. Since 1950 the average date of the first arrivals has gradually become earlier – see Table 429.

	1950–1959	1960–1969	1970–1979	1980–1989	1990–1999
Range	2nd–18th April	28th March– 13th April	15th March– 14th April	29th March– 9th April	16th March– 11th April
Average	11th April	6th April	4th April	2nd April	29th March

Table 429. Dates for first spring arrivals each decade 1950–1999

The main passage occurs from mid-April to the end of May. Numbers recorded at the main coastal watch-points are generally small with peak counts usually ranging from 10–30 and rarely exceeding 50 birds, so 178N at Portland Bill on 1st May 1965, 120N at Hengistbury on 24th April 1990 and 100 at Portland Bill on 3rd May 1980 are unusually high – see Table 430.

	1980	1981	1982	1983	1984	1985	1986	1987	1988	1989
Portland Bill	239	161	206	303	170	150	180	223	145	223
Durlston CP	13	38	72	47	61	45	33	54	88	173

	1990	1991	1992	1993	1994	1995	1996	1997	1998	1999
Portland Bill	257	224	104	104	55	94	130	116	158	106
Durlston CP	153	113	58	nc	60	68	115	240	89	100
Christchurch Hbr	356	474	44	93	nc	85	111	63	37	25

Table 430. Spring totals (bds) at the main coastal watch-points 1980–1999

After a few mid-summer records and a trickle of birds in July, most autumn passage, which is much stronger than in spring, occurs during August and September – see Table 431. Peak counts of coastal migrants, including those involved in visual movements and off-passage flocks, rarely exceed 500 birds, the highest being 1,000 at Chickerell on 25th August 1990 and 975 at Portland Bill on 25th August 1968. Much larger numbers were recorded at reedbed roosts, which were such a notable feature of the 1970s and 1980s. Until recently Radipole NR was a particularly favoured site, the highest counts being up to 7,000 during 30th August–1st September 1982 and 6,500 on 29th August 1976 – see Table 432. The best counts from other reedbed roosts are 2,000 at Abbotsbury on 7th September 1983, 1,000 at Lodmoor NR in late August–early September 1982, 500 at Christchurch Harbour in early August–September 1978, and 400 at Keysworth on 29th August 1987. During the early 1950s birds roosted in reedbeds at Charmouth in the west of the county with a maximum of 300 on 8th September 1952.

A few birds are seen on passage at inland sites, most notably along river valleys. Numbers are very small, usually in single figures and very rarely exceeding 50 birds, so counts of 300 at Charminster on 28th–29th August 1988, 300W in the Crane Valley on 15th August 1961 and 225 at Coward's Marsh, Christchurch on 3rd September 1987 are remarkable.

	1980	1981	1982	1983	1984	1985	1986	1987	1988	1989
Portland Bill	2048	nc	2488	2262	1583	2559	2960	2978	nc	1836
Durlston CP	379	149	554	443	327	1680	582	887	1016	600

	1990	1991	1992	1993	1994	1995	1996	1997	1998	1999
Portland Bill	1548	1623	1273	1108	1212	1382	1107	1137	1714	1250
Durlston CP	676	713	888	nc	254	414	478	724	618	681
Christchurch Hbr	1202	720	395	964	nc	842	820	320	618	713

Table 431. Autumn totals (bds) at the main coastal watch-points 1980–1999

Overall, there appears to have been a decrease in the numbers recorded on passage during the 1990s compared to the 1980s. This is most evident in the apparent decline of the main autumn reedbed roosts and at Portland Bill – see Tables 432–434. Peak counts in autumn have rarely exceeded 150 birds since 1992, the highest being 350 at Abbotsbury on 31st August 1999 and 300 at Portland Bill on 30th August 1998.

1971	1972	1973	1974	1975	1976	1977	1978	1979	1980	1981	1982	1983	1984
200	600	nc	300	1500	6500	450	1100	2800	2800	1600	7000	1750	2100

1985	1986	1987	1988	1989	1990	1991	1992	1993	1994	1995	1996	1997	1998
600	670	1000	400	1100	350	300	29	nc	45	nc	nc	nc	150

Table 432. Peak counts at Radipole NR autumn reedbed roost 1971–1998

	1970–74	1975–79	1980–84	1985–89	1990–94	1995–99
Portland Bill	82	109	216	184	149	121
Durlston CP	nc	nc	46	79	96	122

Table 433. 5–year average spring totals (bds) at Portland Bill and Durlston CP 1970–1999

	1970–74	1975–79	1980–84	1985–89	1990–94	1995–99
Portland Bill	1851	1964	2095	2414	1389	1209
Durlston CP	nc	nc	370	953	633	583

Table 434. 5-year average autumn totals (bds) at Portland Bill and Durlston CP 1970–1999

The last birds are usually reported during the second half of October and the first few days of November. The latest sightings have been 14th November 1988 at Christchurch Harbour, 16th November 1999 at Portland Bill, 21st–22nd November 1998 at Wakeham, Portland, 30th November 1997 at Radipole NR, and more exceptionally from 26th November to 7th December 1953 at the Nothe, Weymouth and on 10th December 1977 at Studland NNR.

There is one winter record involving a single bird at Coward's Marsh, Christchurch from at least 1st to 30th January 1993.

A total of 13,062 birds has been ringed in the county. There have been nine foreign recoveries from Morocco, six from Portugal, three from Senegal, two from Spain and one from Guinea-Bissau, but there are no reports of any foreign controls.

This complex species comprises many races, which are breeding summer visitors to most of northern Eurasia. The race *M. f. flavissima* breeds mainly in Great Britain and locally along the adjacent coasts of north-western Europe. Birds of this race winter in western Africa.

Blue-headed Wagtail   *Motacilla flava flava*

A scarce passage migrant, mainly in spring – has bred

Although not mentioned by Mansel-Pleydell (1888), Blathwayt (1945) referred to a few specimens in the Dorchester Museum, including one adult from Weymouth and one from Wareham dated 4th June 1903, as well as one seen in Poole Park on 17th October 1913.

Since 1950 this race has been recorded with increasing frequency so that by the late 1960s it had become a regular but scarce passage migrant in small numbers, annual totals rarely exceeding ten birds except for notable spring influxes in 1983 and 1984 – see Figs 45 and 46. The seasonal distribution of records has changed since the 1950s when all reports were restricted to the autumn. There was a more even distribution in sightings between the seasons during the 1960s and 1970s, whilst during the 1980s and 1990s spring was clearly the main passage period, almost exclusively so between 1989 and 1997 when only one autumn bird was recorded.

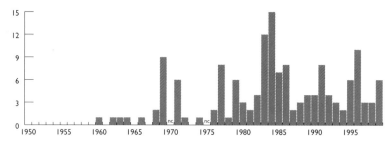

Fig 45. Spring totals 1952–1999

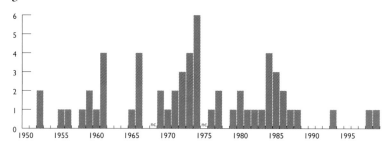

Fig 46. Autumn totals 1952–1999

Spring reports extend from early April, the earliest being 3rd April 1977 at Lodmoor NR and 4th April 1996 at Christchurch Harbour, through to mid-June with most sightings between mid-April and mid-May. Autumn migrants have been recorded from late June to early October, the latest being from Portland Bill on 9th–10th October 1958 and 10th October 1979, with August and September the peak months – see Table 435.

Jan	Feb	Mar	Apr	May	Jun	Jul	Aug	Sep	Oct	Nov	Dec
0	0	0	64	73	7	4	15	25	7	0	0

Table 435. Monthly totals 1952–1999

The main sites for migrants are Portland Bill, Christchurch Harbour and Lodmoor NR, which together account for 80% of the total – see Table 436. There are several records from Radipole NR, but elsewhere in the county this race is a rare visitor with most sites accounting for no more than 1–2 birds. Reports typically involve 1–2 birds, the highest counts being five at Christchurch Harbour on 19th April 1983 and four at Portland Bill on 7th October 1966.

Single 'pure' pairs bred at Lodmoor NR in 1978 and 1992. In addition, a female paired with a male Yellow Wagtail also bred at Lodmoor NR in 1978, whilst another female, paired with a male Yellow

	Spring		Autumn		Total	
Portland	53	35%	30	52%	83	40%
Radipole NR	9	6%	5	9%	14	7%
Lodmoor NR	30	20%	4	7%	34	16%
Christchurch Harbour	39	26%	11	19%	50	24%
elsewhere	19	13%	8	14%	27	13%

Table 436. Distribution of migrants 1952–1999

Wagtail, bred at Coward's Marsh, Christchurch in 1987. The 1992 report is the last breeding record for the '*flava*' wagtail species in Dorset.

The Blue-headed Wagtail *M. f. flava* breeds over much of Europe from western France to the Urals, north to southern Sweden and south to the Pyrennes, Alps, northern Balkans and lower Volga. It winters in sub-Saharan Africa.

Postscript 2000–2002

In 2000 there were reports involving about six birds in spring and one in autumn, in 2001 there was one bird in spring and two in autumn, and in 2002 there was one bird reported in spring and one in autumn.

Grey-headed Wagtail *Motacilla flava thunbergi*

Accidental: five records – has bred

In 1990 a male, apparently breeding with a female Yellow Wagtail, was present at Lodmoor NR from 25th May to 16th August. There are four other records:

1977   Portland Bill: 24th September
1978   Lodmoor NR: 28th August
1996   Stanpit Marsh, Christchurch Harbour: 8th–11th September
2001   Stanpit Marsh, Christchurch Harbour: 23rd May

The Grey-headed Wagtail *M. f. thunbergi* breeds in Scandinavia and northern Russia and winters in sub-Saharan Africa and the Indian sub-continent.

Ashy-headed Wagtail *Motacilla flava cinereocapilla*

Accidental: four records – has bred

In 1970 a male arrived at Lodmoor NR on 26th April and subsequently paired and bred successfully with a female Yellow Wagtail, whilst a second male appeared on 24th May and attempted to invade the territory of an established pair of Yellow Wagtails, but was driven off. There are two further records:

1984   Christchurch Harbour: 3rd May
       Upton CP: 5th October

The Ashy-headed Wagtail *M. f. cinereocapilla* breeds in Italy, Sardinia, Sicily and the north-west Balkans and winters in central Africa.

Grey Wagtail *Motacilla cinerea*

A locally common resident, passage migrant and winter visitor

Although Mansel-Pleydell (1888) only knew this species as a winter visitor in the 19th Century, Blathwayt (1945) referred to it as a resident, which bred by streams throughout the county. Unfortunately there are no details of its colonisation of Dorset as a breeding bird.

The *BTO Atlas* (1968–1972) found evidence of breeding in 32 (86%) 10-km squares (confirmed in 29, probable in two and possible in one), the most notable absences being in the south-east of the county (SY97 and SZ08). The Tetrad Survey (1987–1994) revealed little change in status, evidence of breeding being recorded in 31 (84%) of the pre-1974 10-km squares (confirmed in 27 and probable in four), the most notable absences being in the north (ST91), south (SY67) and south-east (SZ08). The Tetrad Map shows that breeding is closely associated with rivers and streams throughout the county. As in much of lowland Britain, this bird is heavily dependent on man-made structures such as bridges, weirs, sluices, mills and other riverside buildings to provide suitable nesting sites.

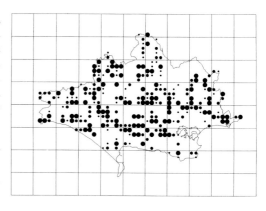

There is little information on population trends. Although there was a considerable reduction after the severe winter of 1962/63, there are no subsequent comments regarding the species' fortunes after the bad winters of the mid-1980s. Annual surveys of the River Allen during 1989–1999 reveal a dramatic decline in numbers from a peak of 11 pairs – see Table 437. Nearby from 3–6 pairs bred at Canford Park during 1992–1997, and six pairs were present along the River Stour between Wimborne and Little Canford in 1969, whilst the RSPB Survey located 16 territories along the River Stour in 1979. Elsewhere six pairs were found along the River Hooke between Maiden Newton and Hooke in 1984, and five pairs were present along the River Frome between Dorchester and Lower Bockhampton in 1978.

1989	1990	1991	1992	1993	1994	1995	1996	1997	1998	1999
9	11	5	5	7	11	11	8	1	2	2

Table 437. Number of breeding pairs along River Allen 1989–1999

Spring passage at the main coastal watch-points is generally very small with seasonal totals rarely reaching double figures at Portland Bill and Christchurch Harbour, but there has been a marked increase in numbers at Durlston CP during 1996–1999 – see Table 438. Although March is typically the peak month for migrants, records extent from February through to June.

	1980	1981	1982	1983	1984	1985	1986	1987	1988	1989
Portland Bill	12	3	5	9	15	3	5	2	5	16
Durlston CP	nc	10	6	15	14	6	4	4	7	6

	1990	1991	1992	1993	1994	1995	1996	1997	1998	1999
Portland Bill	9	4	2	6	2	4	3	3	4	2
Durlston CP	16	7	12	11	4	17	38	47	43	81
Christchurch Hbr	8	4	1	0	1	0	1	nc	3	4

Table 438. Spring totals (bds) at the main coastal watch-points 1980–1999

Autumn migration is much heavier involving several hundreds of birds – see Table 439. Passage extends from July to November with a distinct peak in September. Peak counts rarely exceed 50 birds, so 134W at East Bexington on 9th September 1992, and 120 at Portland Bill on 14th September 1989 and 13th September 1995 are exceptional.

	1980	1981	1982	1983	1984	1985	1986	1987	1988	1989
Portland Bill	548	338	334	461	249	297	393	344	300	451
Durlston CP	129	94	133	181	138	291	186	184	306	321

	1990	1991	1992	1993	1994	1995	1996	1997	1998	1999
Portland Bill	228	159	205	230	296	364	167	214	162	308
Durlston CP	152	70	234	296	98	231	232	271	284	281
Christchurch Hbr	195	68	206	269	136	315	156	nc	114	45

Table 439. Autumn totals (bds) at the main coastal watch-points 1980–1999

The Grey Wagtail is more widely distributed in winter with watercress beds and small sewage works particularly favoured haunts. A few birds also frequent suitable sites along the coast, while there are occasional reports from gardens. Winter gatherings are small, generally in single figures, ten at Waddock Cross CBs on 13th January 1985 being the highest count.

A total of 661 birds has been ringed in the county.

The Grey Wagtail breeds over much of Europe north to southern Scandinavia and east to Poland, the Ukraine and Rumania; also in north-west Africa, Asia Minor and the Caucasus. It is largely resident except for the more northern and eastern parts of its range where it is a summer visitor. Birds from these populations also winter in parts of north and east Africa, and the Middle East. There are also breeding populations in northern and central Asia, including Japan, which winter mainly in the Indian sub-continent and south-east Asia.

Sponsored by Julian Francis and David & Margaret Seward

Pied Wagtail   *Motacilla alba yarrellii*

A common resident, passage migrant and winter visitor

Both Mansel-Pleydell (1888) and Blathwayt (1945) considered this species to be a common resident and passage migrant with large parties assembling on the coast in autumn.

There has been little change in status subsequently. The *BTO Atlas* (1968–1972) confirmed breeding in all but two (95%) 10-km squares, whilst the Tetrad Survey (1987–1994) confirmed breeding in all but one (97%) of the pre-1974 10-km squares. The Tetrad Map shows that breeding occurs widely throughout the county, most absences coinciding with areas of heathland and chalk, and rather surprisingly parts of the Blackmore Vale. There is relatively little information on long-term population trends and densities. At Canford Park the number of breeding pairs ranged from 6–8 pairs during 1967–1971 with five pairs in 1986, six pairs in 1996, four pairs in 1997 and 3–4 pairs in 1998. Surveys along the River Frome revealed eight pairs along two 2.5km

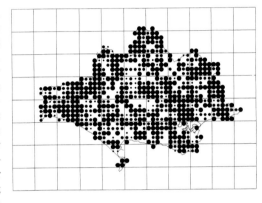

stretches of the river in 1976 and five pairs between East Burton and Wool in 1978, whilst seven pairs were located along a 3km stretch of the River Asker at Bridport in 1981. In 1989 ten pairs were found in Central Portland.

Spring passage extends from March to May with a distinct peak in the first month. Numbers at the main coastal watch-points are modest – see Table 440. Peak counts are usually in single figures and rarely exceed 20–30 birds, the highest being 120 at Radipole NR on 19th March 1998. Otherwise the next highest counts are all from Christchurch Harbour with 73N on 28th March 1985, 70 on 15th March 1998 and 70+ on an unspecified date in March 1999. Visual movements are predominantly northerly in direction.

	1980	1981	1982	1983	1984	1985	1986	1987	1988	1989
Portland Bill	nc	163	246	272	499	435	387	305	345	583
Durlston CP	17	34	93	51	112	36	108	179	574	448

	1990	1991	1992	1993	1994	1995	1996	1997	1998	1999
Portland Bill	414	474	236	286	216	345	132	347	288	272
Durlston CP	275	96	176	nc	nc	63	602	583	520	452

Table 440. Spring totals (bds) at Portland Bill and Durlston CP 1980–1999

Passage in autumn is much heavier, extending from August to November with October overwhelmingly the peak month for movement – see Table 441. Peak counts sometimes reach 500–600 birds, the highest in recent years being 850S at Portland Bill on 9th October 1985 with 720S there two days later, 800E at

Durlston CP on 12th October 1991 with 715 there on 3rd October 1989, and 700E at Hengistbury on 3rd October 1988. Visual passage is more complex during the autumn. At Portland Bill movements are mainly to the south, but in some years substantial passage to the north is also recorded, e.g. 590N in October 1992 and 550N on 12th October 1985 a day after 720 had departed south. It is suggested this may be due to birds returning from an abortive attempt to move south rather than a true immigration. By contrast visual passage at Durlston CP and Christchurch Harbour is mainly easterly in direction, but with occasional heavy movements in other directions – notably the south and west.

	1980	1981	1982	1983	1984	1985	1986	1987	1988	1989
Portland Bill	nc	2413	4206	4510	3263	6195	5010	2558	3571	3059
Durlston CP	215	540	1286	953	1438	1545	3725	1439	3301	3156

	1990	1991	1992	1993	1994	1995	1996	1997	1998	1999
Portland Bill	3186	2411	2196	3588	3629	5826	3800	2263	1019	2162
Durlston CP	4663	5467	1834	nc	nc	2955	4541	5417	2888	3028

Table 441. Autumn totals (bds) at Portland Bill and Durlston CP 1980–1999

During the autumn large roosts form, particularly in reedbeds, with the highest counts often coinciding with peak passage in October. Maxima often reach 300–600 birds, but 1,000 were present at Radipole NR on 12th October 1970. During the early 1950s birds roosted in reedbeds at Charmouth in the west of the county with a maximum of 500 in mid-September 1952 (cf Yellow Wagtail). There is some evidence to suggest that these autumn reedbed roosts have declined in size since the late 1980s. Numbers at these reedbed sites are usually smaller during the winter when roosts are more closely associated with buildings in urban areas, most reports in recent years being from the Dorchester, Weymouth and Portland Dockyard areas. Again numbers at these urban sites often reach peaks of 300–500 birds, the highest counts being from Boscombe Hospital with 759 on 31st December 1981 and 681 on 21st January of the same year, and from the vicinity of the Weymouth Harbour roundabout with 850 on 30th December 1998, 700 on 16th January 1993 and 650 in February 1996.

A total of 6,114 birds has been ringed in the county. There are two foreign recoveries from France, and one each from Spain, Portugal, Morocco and Algeria, but there are no reports of any foreign controls.

The Pied Wagtail *M. a. yarrellii* breeds in the British Isles and locally on the coasts of western Europe. It is largely resident, but some birds move south, the main wintering areas being Brittany, western Iberia and Morocco.

Postscript 2000–2002

At the Tesco supermarket in Blandford, 1,000 on 16th January 2000 is a county record count for a winter roost. Otherwise, 800S at Hengistbury on 22nd October 2000 is a notably high count for visual passage in autumn.

White Wagtail   *Motacilla alba alba*

A fairly common passage migrant

This race was recognised by Mansel-Pleydell (1888) who described it as "an annual summer visitant" and listed one obtained from Poole in March 1861 and several shot in Kimmeridge Bay in May 1877. Blathwayt (1945) referred to the White Wagtail as a regular passage migrant.

Although the numbers recorded on passage since 1950 are generally small, birds of this race are undoubtedly overlooked amongst the larger movements of 'Pied/White' Wagtails – see Table 442. There is some evidence to suggest that the passage of 'Whites' is much heavier in some autumns at least. For example, at Portland Bill c.450 birds on 27th September 1979, and the majority of 'Pied/White' Wagtails in September and early October 1981 and September 1985 were considered to be probably of this race.

Early migrants have occurred on 11th February 1999 at Stanpit Marsh, Christchurch Harbour, 20th February 1998 at Portland Bill and the Fleet (three birds), and 27th February 1984 at Radipole NR (two birds). Otherwise spring records extend from early March to mid-June with most passage occurring between late March and early May. Autumn migrants occur between July and October with September the peak month. The latest reports are from Portland Bill with two on 2nd November 1994 and one on an unspecified date in November 1990, and Canford Heath with one on 23rd November 1999. Peak counts rarely reach double figures, the highest being 25 at Christchurch Harbour on 13th April 1996, 21 at Lodmoor NR on 10th April 1982 and 20 at Durlston CP on 29th October 1998. Although most records are from coastal sites, Portland Bill, Lodmoor NR and Christchurch Harbour being particularly favoured, there is a scattering of sightings from inland localities.

	1976	1977	1978	1979	1980	1981	1982	1983	1984	1985	1986	1987
Spring	29	9	12	29	20	nc	16	40	25	53	116	32
Autumn	10	19	17	28	12	nc	102	75	9	77	18	28

	1988	1989	1990	1991	1992	1993	1994	1995	1996	1997	1998	1999
Spring	19	43	33	19	3	17	13	24	46	12	29	77
Autumn	100	23	11	3	3	4	3	0	0	0	5	2

Table 442. Annual totals at Portland Bill 1976–1999

The only reported occurrence of summering involves one at Balaclava Bay, Portland from 2nd June–2nd July 1992, whilst there have been five winter records as follows:

1974 Newton's Cove, Weymouth: early February
1990 Christchurch Harbour: 17th January
1993 Christchurch Harbour: 13th January
1998 Easton/Weston, Portland: autumn 1998–26th January 1999
1999 Branksome: two 6th December

The White Wagtail *M. a. alba* breeds over much of Europe, except the British Isles, as well as Asia Minor and the Middle East, being mainly resident in the west and south of its range, but a summer visitor in the north and east. Its winter range extends south over much of Africa north of the equator, as well as the Middle East and Arabia. Other races occur in north-west Africa and throughout Asia.

Postscript 2000–2002
At Portland Bill, one was paired with a Pied Wagtail in 2000. Otherwise there was an unusual winter record from Canford Heath on 9th January 2000, and a late autumn report from Upton CP on 10th November 2002.

Waxwing (Bohemian Waxwing) *Bombycilla garrulus*

A rare winter visitor and passage migrant, subject to occasional irruptions

Mansel-Pleydell (1888) described this distinctive and attractive species as "an occasional winter visitant from the north, arriving spasmodically and in some numbers" and mentioned five records with one killed near Shaftesbury in 1785, singles shot at Bexington in an unspecified year and Abbotsbury in January 1850, one frequenting the garden of Little Bridy Rectory during the winter of 1855, and two in a hedgerow adjoining Weymouth Cemetery on 10th December 1858, one of which was shot! There was no change in status during the first half of the 20th Century with Blathwayt (1945) referring to it as an irregular winter visitor and listing four further reports involving two near Wareham on 21st March 1906, and singles near Poole on 12th March 1911, near Parkstone in spring 1931 and at Charmouth in February 1942.

Since 1950 the pattern of occurrence has involved a period during 1957–1975 when from 1–5 birds were recorded in nine winters with a massive irruption in 1965/66 involving at least 133 birds including c.80 during 22nd November–12th December. Apart from further notable irruptions during the winters of 1988/89 (33 birds) and 1995/96 (141 birds), the Waxwing has been a very rare visitor with reports of 1–2 birds in only four other winters between 1976/77 and 1996/97. The largest flocks and counts have occurred in irruption years, notably in early 1996 with a minimum of 40 birds at Wareham during 5th February–7th March including a regular flock at Northmoor, 30 at Verwood during 24th March–7th April and flocks of 20–23 in the Canford Heath/Broadstone/Merley area on various dates during 22nd February–24th March. The only other high counts are 24 at Sturminster Newton during late November–

early December 1965 and 22E at Southbourne on 18th December 1988. All other records, except for those during the irruption years, involve 1–2 birds.

Although there are reports from sites scattered throughout the county, the suburban areas of Bournemouth, Poole and Weymouth are particularly favoured. Most sightings have occurred on dates between mid-November and mid-April, the earliest being 4th November 1961 at Broadmayne and 4th November 1982 at Portland Bill with a very late bird at the Grove, Portland on 11th May 1996.

The Waxwing is largely a summer visitor breeding in north-eastern Scandinavia, Siberia and north-western North America. In winter the Eurasian population moves west and south into the rest of Scandinavia, eastern Europe and central Asia. A few reach eastern Great Britain in most winters, but there are occasional major irruptions reaching further south and west. The North American population winters south and east of the breeding range across southern Canada and the northern USA.

Postscript 2000–2002
Singles at Portland Bill on 12th November 2000 and Radipole Village on 27th–28th January 2001 are the only records.

Dipper (White-throated Dipper)   *Cinclus cinclus gularis*

An uncommon resident

Mansel-Pleydell (1888) stated that this species "is only known on the western side of Dorsetshire", and listed a mere five records between 1830 and 1887 including a pair which nested in the Bride Valley for three consecutive years from 1883 to 1885. Blathwayt (1945) considered it to be resident in small numbers, mainly in the west, but suggested an extension of range eastwards, referring to reports of breeding in the vicinity of Wareham in 1896 and 1913 with a sighting from Corfe Castle in 1908.

Since 1950 the Dipper has remained an un-common breeding resident of rivers and streams in the west of the county. The *BTO Atlas* (1968–1972) confirmed breeding in 12 10-km squares to the west of a line between Weymouth and Sherborne (SY7080 to ST7010) with possible breeding in three 10-km squares to the east of this line – namely SY79, SY89 and ST81. Subsequently there appears to have been little change in overall distribution, the Tetrad Survey (1987–1994) revealing evidence of breeding in 12 10-km squares to the west of the Weymouth/Sherborne line (confirmed in nine, probable in one and possible in two) with possible breeding in one 10-km square to the east of this line – namely ST81.

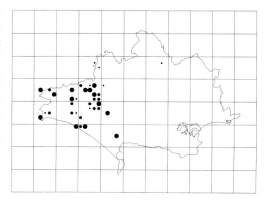

In the years between these surveys, isolated occur-rences of breeding were reported at a site in the east of the county (probably in SY88) in 1980 and possibly again during the mid-1980s, near Shaftesbury in 1982 and unsuccessfully at Charborough Park in 1983.

During the Tetrad Survey (1987–1994) reports were received from the River Axe and its tributaries, the River Lim, the River Char and its tributaries, the River Brit and its tributaries the Asker and Mangerton Stream, the River Bride, the River Wey, the River Frome upstream of Dorchester and its major upper tributaries the River Hooke and Rampisham Stream, and the River Yeo and its tributaries to the south of Yeovil. The greatest concentration of breeding birds occurred within the upper catchment of the River Frome and along the neighbouring southern tributaries of the upper River Yeo in ST50 and SY59. In fact the Frome and Yeo Catchments accounted for 18 (51%) of the 35 tetrad records.

A slight contraction of range westwards appears to have occurred since the early 1980s with the species disappearing from some its most easterly haunts, notably the River Cerne (last recorded in 1983) and the Sydling Brook (last recorded in 1980). On the positive side, birds returned to the River Wey in 1991 after an absence of ten years with reports in most subsequent years including confirmed breeding in 1996 and 1998. Since the Tetrad Survey (1987–1994), all breeding reports have come from traditional sites in the west of the county.

There is relatively little information on breeding numbers. In 1969 the county population was estimated as c.16 pairs, whilst the results of the Tetrad Survey (1987–1994) suggest a minimum of 25–30 pairs. In spring 1984 a comprehensive survey of the River Hooke between Maiden Newton and Lower Kingcombe located five pairs.

Apart from the isolated breeding attempts, the Dipper is a rare wanderer to the east of Dorset with all records since 1950 listed below:

1953   Morden: 31st January
1956   River Tarrant: December
1964   Holwell CBs: 26th August
          River Stour at Canford School: 10th November
1966   River Stour at Canford School: 31st July–30th September
          River Allen at Wimborne: 14th September – possibly same as above
1978   River Divelish: one reported during the year
          Winterborne Stickland: one reported during the year
1979   Milton Abbas: two for two weeks in January
1981   Milton Abbas: one during the cold weather in December
1985   Fontmell Brook at Fontmell Magna: 27th October
1986   Cranborne CBs: 26th February
1997   Corfe Castle: 6th March
1999   River Stour at Cowgrove near Wimborne: 21st June

In addition, one at Portland Bill on 9th April 1993 is an exceptional record and coincided with a good fall of migrants.

A total of 14 birds has been ringed in the county.

The Dipper is a breeding resident of the upland regions of Europe, north-west Africa, Asia Minor and central Asia. The race *C. c. gularis* is restricted to the west and north of Great Britain with the exception of western Scotland.

Postscript 2000–2002
One at Lodmoor NR on 15th September 2002, an unusual locality for the species.
Sponsored by Reginald Christian and Bernard & Elizabeth Watts

Black-bellied Dipper   *Cinclus cinclus cinclus*

Accidental: one record

1965   River Stour: January, same on River Allen until 11th February

One spent two days on the River Stour at Canford School in January 1965, then moving to Witchampton paper mills on the River Allen where it remained until 11th February.

The Black-bellied Dipper *C. c. cinclus* breeds mainly in Scandinavia, north-western Russia, central France, the Pyrenees and north-west Iberia. It is a rare winter visitor to Great Britain, mainly recorded in the east.

Wren (Winter Wren)   *Troglodytes troglodytes*

An abundant resident and passage migrant

Both Mansel-Pleydell (1888) and Blathwayt (1945) considered this species to be a common and widely distributed resident.

There has been little change in status subsequently, both the *BTO Atlas* (1968–1972) and the Tetrad Survey (1987–1994) confirmed breeding in all of the pre-1974 10-km squares. The Tetrad Survey also shows the Wren is widely distributed throughout the county with evidence of breeding in almost all tetrad squares. The Common Bird Census Index for Dorset during 1981–1994 clearly indicates the species vulnerability to cold winters, notably those of 1981/82, 1984/85 and 1990/91 – see Table 443. Although a full recovery in population levels occurred subsequent to the 1981/82 and 1984/85 to 1986/87 winters,

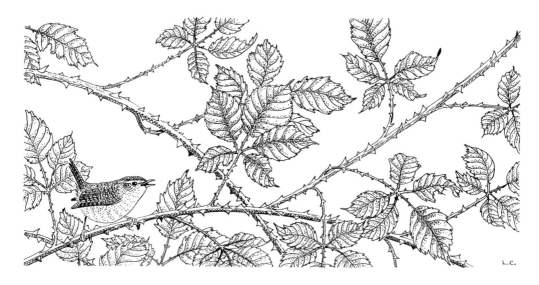

recovery after the 1990/91 winter was only partial. In earlier years a 75% decline in population levels was reported as the result of the severe 1962/63 winter. This was followed by a rapid recovery.

1981	1982	1983	1984	1985	1986	1987	1988	1989	1990	1991	1992	1993	1994
100	62	80	101	61	65	–	78	100	89	60	68	79	78

Table 441. The Common Bird Census Index for Dorset 1981–1994

Spring passage at the main coastal watch-points is sometimes detected during March–April, but numbers are very small with peak counts rarely reaching double figures, the highest being 15 at Portland Bill in early April 1984, on 9th April 1985 and during 25th–27th April 1990. Migration is much more pronounced in the autumn, mainly in October, when peak counts generally vary between 20–80 birds, the highest being 129 at Hengistbury on 4th November 1984 with 120 there on 19th October 1975, and 120 at Portland Bill on 20th October 1987.

High numbers are sometimes recorded during the winter, particularly at roost sites, the best counts being from Studland NNR during the 1987 and 1988 winter periods with 250 and 300 respectively.

A total of 10,101 birds has been ringed in the county.

The Wren breeds over much of Europe, except the far north and east. It also breeds in parts of North Africa, Asia Minor and the Middle East, and more widely in central and eastern Asia and northern North America. In Europe it is mainly resident except in the north where it is a summer visitor.

Brown Thrasher   *Toxostoma rufum*

Accidental: one record

1966   Durlston CP: 18th November–5th February 1967

This bird was trapped, ringed and photographed on 23rd November. During its stay it frequented the dense cover of Holm Oaks opposite Durlston Castle. On some occasions it could be very skulking, but on others it took little notice of observers and could be watched at close ranges as it fed under trees or on the cliff path. This remains the only record of one of the more unexpected species to have occurred in the British Isles and the Western Palearctic. A full account can be found in *British Birds* Vol. 61, Number 12, December 1968.

The Brown Thrasher breeds in central and eastern North America from southern Canada to the Gulf of Mexico, and winters in the southern half of this region.

Sponsored by John V. Boys

Dunnock (Hedge Accentor)   *Prunella modularis*

An abundant resident and passage migrant

Mansel-Pleydell (1888) stated that "this familiar little bird is a constant resident with us, and generally distributed", whilst Blathwayt (1945) simply referred to it as a common resident.

Little has changed subsequently, both the *BTO Atlas* (1968–1972) and the Tetrad Survey (1987–1994) found evidence of breeding in all of the pre-1974 10-km squares (confirmed in 36 and probable in one). The Tetrad Survey also shows that the Dunnock is widely distributed throughout the county with evidence of breeding in almost all tetrad squares. Despite this, the Common Bird Census Index for Dorset during 1981–1994 reveals a decline in population levels during this period – see Table 444. Cold winters are clearly implicated in this decline, most notably after 1981/82, 1984/85 and 1990/91 (cf Wren).

1981	1982	1983	1984	1985	1986	1987	1988	1989	1990	1991	1992	1993	1994
100	84	88	84	45	80	–	80	78	77	49	56	50	66

Table 444. The Common Bird Census Index for Dorset 1981–1994

Spring migration at the main coastal watch-points is occasionally detected in very small numbers during March–April, so an influx of 54 at Christchurch Harbour on 30th March 1974 is noteworthy. Passage is more obvious in autumn, mainly during September–October, when numbers are higher, but still rather modest. Peak counts rarely exceed 60 birds, the highest being an exceptional 365 at Durlston CP on 2nd October 1983, also 180 at Portland Bill on 20th–21st September 1961 and 142 at Christchurch Harbour on 3rd October 1982. There is also evidence that the species is sometimes involved in cold weather movements, e.g. 90E at Durlston CP during 9th–15th January 1982 with a maximum of 42E on 11th.

A total of 8,912 birds has been ringed in the county.

The Dunnock breeds over much of central and northern Europe, also in parts of Asia Minor. It is largely resident in the west and south of its range, but a summer visitor in the east and north. The migratory populations winter south to the Mediterranean.

Sponsored by Calluna Books

Alpine Accentor   *Prunella collaris*

Accidental: one record

1978   Portland Bill: 8th–30th April

This individual remained around the quarries at Portland Bill during its protracted stay and was trapped, ringed and photographed on 11th.

The Alpine Accentor is a montane species breeding in the Alps, Pyrenees and other mountain ranges of southern and eastern Europe, also in north-west Africa, Asia Minor and widely in central and eastern Asia. A vagrant to Great Britain with 43 records up to 2002.

Robin (European Robin)   *Erithacus rubecula*

An abundant resident, passage migrant and winter visitor

This species was well-known to Mansel-Pleydell (1888), who referred to it as the 'Redbreast' and further recorded that many young birds migrated southwards to the Continent. Blathwayt (1945) described it simply as "a common resident".

There has been no change in status subsequently. The *BTO Atlas* (1968–1972) found evidence of breeding in all but one (97%) 10-km squares (confirmed in 35 and probable in one), whilst the Tetrad Survey (1987–1994) produced almost the identical result with evidence of breeding in all but one (97%) of the pre-1974 10-km squares (confirmed in all 36). The Tetrad Survey also shows that the Robin is widely distributed throughout the county with evidence of breeding in almost all tetrad squares. The Common Bird Census Index for Dorset during 1981–1994 reveals a series of declines resulting from the cold winters of 1981/82, 1984/85, 1985/86 and 1990/91 followed by substantial recoveries in 1984, 1990 and 1994 – see Table 445.

1981	1982	1983	1984	1985	1986	1987	1988	1989	1990	1991	1992	1993	1994
100	68	71	92	61	47	–	75	82	97	74	72	88	103

Table 445. The Common Bird Census Index for Dorset 1981–1994

Although spring passage at the main coastal watch-points extends from March to May, most migrants occur in April. Generally numbers are very small with peak counts rarely reaching double figures, the highest being from Durlston CP with 43 on 14th April 1984, 32 on 30th March 1983, 30 on 10th April 1981 and 28 on 10th April 1985, also 25 at Portland Bill on 29th March 1958. Autumn migration is much heavier as northern breeders migrate to southern winter quarters, and extends from August to early November with most passage occurring between mid-September and late October. Numbers vary from year to year with peak counts usually ranging between 20–100 birds. Occasionally there are marked influxes resulting in much higher counts, notably 500+ at Hengistbury on 12th October 1995 with 300 there on 30th September 1996, 500 at Portland on 27th September 1992, 400 at Christchurch Harbour on 27th September 1994, and 300 at Portland Bill on 30th September 1979, 22nd October 1990 and 11th October 1995. Passage in both spring and autumn regularly involves varying numbers of the continental (nominate) race *E. r. rubecula*.

A total of 12,893 birds has been ringed in the county. There have been five foreign recoveries from France, and one each from the Netherlands, Spain and the Channel Islands, as well as two foreign controls from the Netherlands, and one each from Belgium, Poland and Finland.

The Robin breeds throughout much of Europe extending eastwards into north-west Asia, also in parts of north-west Africa and Asia Minor. It is mainly resident in the west and south of its range, but a summer visitor to the north and east. The wintering range extends from western and southern Europe south to North Africa and the Middle East.

Thrush Nightingale   *Luscinia luscinia*

Accidental: two records

    1994   Portland Bill: first-summer trapped 11th June
    1996   Abbotsbury: first-summer male singing and subsequently trapped 25th May

The Thrush Nightingale is a summer visitor, breeding from southern Norway and Denmark eastwards across eastern Europe and west-central Asia and wintering in eastern Africa. A vagrant to Great Britain with 147 records up to 2002.

Nightingale (Common Nightingale)   *Luscinia megarhynchos*

An uncommon summer visitor and passage migrant

Mansel-Pleydell (1888) described this well-known songster as "a common summer visitant on the eastern side, rarer on the western side of the county, which is nearly the limits of its range". Blathwayt (1945) considered it to be a locally common summer resident, probably more numerous in the east than the west, but frequent around Sherborne and found westwards towards Beaminster and beyond.

There was a westward spread around 1950 when the species was described as locally numerous in the Marshwood Vale and the west of the Blackmore Vale. A special survey in 1965 reported a decrease, notably in the Marshwood Vale and around Sherborne. Despite this, the Nightingale remained a widespread breeding bird throughout the 1960s, whilst the *BTO Atlas* (1968–1972) revealed evidence of confirmed or probable breeding in 31 (84%) 10-km squares. Subsequently there has been a marked decline in the breeding population. The BTO Survey in 1980,

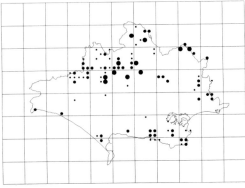

which achieved good coverage, found breeding birds in only c.20 (54%) of the pre-1974 10-km squares mainly distributed in the north of the county and on Purbeck. Nearly half of the 120 singing males located by this survey were found in the Blackmore Vale with a notable concentration of 27 males on Rooksmoor, Lydlinch, Deadmoor and Okeford Commons, which are all situated close together in ST71. The other major concentration, which involved 22 males, was present on the Lulworth Ranges in SY87 and SY88. The Tetrad Survey (1987–1994) produced a similar result to the BTO Survey of 1980 with confirmed or probable breeding in 22 (59%) of the pre-1974 10-km squares. The Tetrad Map shows that the population was still mainly concentrated in the Blackmore Vale and on Purbeck, with smaller populations in east Dorset and along the Hampshire border in the extreme north-east of the chalk downs. Another BTO Survey in 1999 revealed a continuing decline with evidence of confirmed or probable breeding in only nine (24%) of the pre-1974 10-km squares. The 68 singing males located by this survey represents a 43% decline since 1980 with the population becoming increasing restricted to favoured haunts in the Blackmore Vale, mainly in ST71, and on the Purbeck coast in the Tyneham area. On a more positive note, an additional pair bred successfully at Verne Common, Portland in 1999, the first breeding record for this site since 1968! Dorset is now at the western limit of the species breeding range in Great Britain.

The first migrants usually appear during the second half of April, the earliest being 3rd April 1985 at Coward's Marsh, Christchurch, 4th April 1993 at Stanpit Marsh, Christchurch Harbour and 5th April 1961 at Portland Bill. Since the 1950s the average date of the first arrivals has generally remained very similar, ranging from 14th–16th April for all decades except the 1970s – see Table 446.

	1950–1959	1960–1969	1970–1979	1980–1989	1990–1999
Range	8th–26th April	5th–21st April	14th–27th April	3rd–21st April	4th–22nd April
Average	16th April	16th April	20th April	14th April	15th April

Table 446. Dates for first spring arrivals each decade 1950–1999

Passage typically occurs from mid-April to mid-May and from early August to mid-September, but numbers are generally very small even at the main coastal watch-points with peak counts rarely exceeding five birds, the highest being nine at Portland Bill on 16th April 1988 and eight at Durlston CP on 16th August 1988. There is clear evidence that passage numbers have diminished during the 1990s, reflecting the decline in the breeding population – see Table 447 and 448.

	1980	1981	1982	1983	1984	1985	1986	1987	1988	1989
Portland Bill	29	12	1	1	2	4	8	3	21	8
Durlston CP	7	23	0	br	br	12	5	6	10	4
Christchurch Hbr	10	7	3	1	9	9	1	2	3	3

	1990	1991	1992	1993	1994	1995	1996	1997	1998	1999
Portland Bill	5	5	3	2	2	5	4	3	1	3
Durlston CP	3	5	0	4	3	6	5	7	7	1
Christchurch Hbr	3	1	1	11	3	3	2	1	0	0

Table 447. Spring totals (bds) at the main coastal watch-points 1980–1999; br = breeding

	1980	1981	1982	1983	1984	1985	1986	1987	1988	1989
Portland Bill	3	11	2	5	>6	3	10	4	0	1
Durlston CP	2	3	6	15	10	12	6	5	29	20
Christchurch Hbr	1	6	3	2	3	8	8	9	2	1

	1990	1991	1992	1993	1994	1995	1996	1997	1998	1999
Portland Bill	0	1	3	2	3	2	1	3	0	0
Durlston CP	17	4	0	7	1	4	3	10	1	2
Christchurch Hbr	1	1	1	0	0	2	0	0	0	3

Table 448. Autumn totals (bds) at the main coastal watch-points 1980–1999

There are relatively few records for October, the latest being 20th October 1984 at Portland Bill and 27th October 1985 at St Aldhelm's Head, also two at Sherborne Lake on 5th October 1974 is a notably late report for an inland site.

There is an exceptional winter sighting of one in the front garden of Portland Bird Observatory on 2nd–3rd December 1968.

A total of 285 birds has been ringed in the county. There has been one foreign recovery from Germany, but no reports of any foreign controls.

The Nightingale is a summer visitor breeding from north-west Africa and across much of western, southern and central Europe eastwards through parts of Asia Minor and the Middle East to west-central Asia. It winters mainly within the northern tropics of Africa.

Sponsored by Dr and Mrs J. A. Larkin

Siberian Rubythroat   *Luscinia calliope*

Accidental: one record

1997   Osmington Mills: 19th October

This first-winter male was found in a hedge in the early afternoon and remained there until dusk. Although generally elusive, it did show well to the increasing crowd of admirers for half an hour during the late afternoon. A full account can be found in *Birding World*, Vol. 10, Number 10, November 1997 and the Dorset Bird Report for 1997.

The Siberian Rubythroat is a summer visitor breeding across much of northern Asia from the Urals to the Pacific and wintering in south-east Asia. A vagrant to Great Britain with only three records up to 2002.

Bluethroat   *Luscinia svecica*

A scarce passage migrant

Although Mansel-Pleydell (1888) referred to a bird of the race *L. s. svecica* said to have been obtained in Dorset prior to 1837, the only reliable old record concerns one near Weymouth on 2nd May 1914.

There were no further sightings until 1954 when singles were reported at Radipole NR on 27th September and Portland Bill on 6th October. Subsequently the species has become a scarce passage migrant, mainly in autumn, with records in every year since 1959 except for 1962, 1976, 1982 and 1998.

A total of 98 birds have occurred in autumn since 1954 with small influxes in 1969 (seven), 1970 (eight) and 1972 (nine) – see Fig 47. Apart from an exceptionally early bird inland at Littlebredy on 31st July 1987, records extend from 19th August 1971 at Portland Bill to 13th November 1994 when a male was found dead at Chickerell. There is only one other November record involving a male at Portland Bill during 5th–10th November 1994 (considered different to the Chickerell bird). The first half of September is the peak time for autumn migrants and accounts for 40%, whilst the month as a whole accounts for 66% – see Table 449.

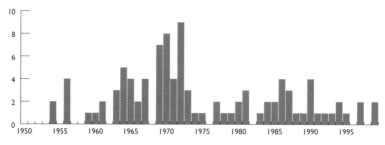

Fig 47. Autumn totals 1954–1999

Portland (40 birds) and the reedbeds at Radipole NR (28 birds) are the main sites for the Bluethroat in autumn and together account for 69% – see Table 450. At the latter site no less than 20 birds occurred during the ten years 1963–1972 including five in 1972. Otherwise there is a scatter of sightings from other coastal sites including nine birds at Christchurch Harbour and six at Lodmoor NR. The only inland record in autumn involves the early bird at Littlebredy already mentioned above. Although seasonal totals of up to five birds have been recorded at some sites, the majority of autumn reports refer to single birds, the highest count on a single day being three at Portland Bill on 9th September 1956.

Mar 16–31	Apr 1–15	Apr 16–30	May 1–15	May 16–31	Jun 1–15	Jun 16–30	Jul 1–15
2	5	3	1	9	1	0	0

Jul 16–31	Aug 1–15	Aug 16–31	Sep 1–15	Sep 16–30	Oct 1–15	Oct 16–31	Nov 1–15
1	0	10	39	26	15	5	2

Table 449. Half-monthly totals 1954–1999

	Spring		Autumn		Total	
The Fleet and west coast	0	0	7	7%	7	6%
Portland	12	57%	40	41%	52	44%
Radipole NR	2	10%	28	29%	30	25%
Lodmoor NR	1	5%	6	6%	7	6%
Purbeck coast	2	10%	3	3%	5	4%
Poole Harbour area	2	10%	4	4%	6	5%
Christchurch Harbour	0	0	9	9%	9	8%
inland	2	10%	1	1%	3	3%

Table 450. Distribution of migrants 1954–1999

Spring migrants have become more frequent in recent years with only six birds during 1956–1978 compared to 15 birds during 1980–1999 – see Fig 48. Records extend from late March 1983 at Stalbridge and 29th March 1996 at Durlston CP to 13th June 1987 at Radipole NR. There is only one other June report involving one at Lodmoor NR on 1st June 1983 (seen earlier on 19th–20th May). There appears to be two peaks of occurrence, the first during the first half of April (five birds) and the second during the second half of May (nine birds) – see Table 449.

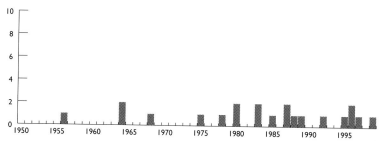

Fig 48. Spring totals 1954–1999

The main site in spring is Portland Bill (12 birds), which accounts for 57% – see Table 450. The most notable of the remaining spring records involve single males in a garden at Serpentine Road, Poole on 13th April 1968, well inland at Chalbury during 8th–12th April 1975, and also well inland at Stalbridge from late March to early May 1983. Otherwise there are sightings from Radipole NR (two birds), Lodmoor NR, Worth Matravers, Durlston CP and Arne NR.

All records where it has been possible to determine the race have involved the 'red-spotted' nominate form *L. s. svecica*.

A total of 40 birds has been ringed in the county.

The nominate 'red-spotted' race *L. s. svecica* is a summer visitor breeding from Scandinavia eastwards through northern Siberia to western Alaska, whilst the 'white-spotted' race *L. s. cyanecula* is a summer visitor breeding locally in Spain and more widely over central and eastern Europe. Another race *L. s. namnetum* is a summer visitor breeding in western France. There are other races, which are breeding summer visitors to various parts of eastern Europe, central and eastern Asia. The west Palearctic populations have a large wintering area extending from the Mediterranean Basin south to the northern tropics of Africa and east to the Indian sub-continent.

Postscript 2000–2002
There were three records involving a male at Cogden Beach on 26th August 2000, a first-summer female at Weston, Portland on 4th June 2002 and a late first-winter male at Church Ope Cove, Portland on 7th November 2002.

Red-flanked Bluetail   *Tarsiger cyanurus*

Accidental: one record

1993   Winspit Valley: first-winter male 30th October–8th November

This individual provided the first real opportunity for most British birdwatchers to enjoy this attractive Siberian vagrant. A full account can be found in *Birding World* Vol. 6, Number 11, December 1993 and the Dorset Bird Report for 1993.

The nominate race *T. c. cyanurus* is a summer visitor breeding mainly from north-west Russia eastwards across much of northern Asia to Japan, but in recent years it has expanded westwards to breed in Finland. Birds winter mainly in south-east Asia. A vagrant to Great Britain with 29 records up to 2002.

Black Redstart   *Phoenicurus ochruros*

An uncommon passage migrant and winter visitor – occasionally breeds

Both Mansel-Pleydell (1888) and Blathwayt (1945) considered this species to be a winter visitor that occurred regularly on the coast in small numbers between late October and mid-March, but rarely inland. Blathwayt (1945) also mentioned that Weymouth was a favourite haunt and further recorded that six were seen together at Swanage on 11th December 1931.

Since 1950 the Black Redstart has also become a regular passage migrant, especially in autumn, whilst there have been increasing but sporadic reports of attempted or successful breeding, particularly during the late 1980s and throughout the 1990s.

Although spring migration extends from early March to mid-May with late stragglers occasionally recorded into June, most passage occurs between mid-March and mid-April. Numbers at the main coastal watch-points are generally small with peak counts rarely reaching double figures, the highest being 15 at Durlston CP on 4th April 1987 and Portland Bill on 18th March 1997 – see Table 451. There are occasional reports of early autumn migrants from July to early September, but passage normally extends from late September through to early December with the peak between mid-October and mid-November. Numbers are higher than in spring with peak counts often reaching 20–35 birds, the highest being from Portland Bill with 100 on 31st October 1984, 60 the next day and 50 on 25th October 1976 – see Table 452.

	1980	1981	1982	1983	1984	1985	1986	1987	1988	1989
Portland Bill	40	50	49	57	61	58	70	62	43	26
Durlston CP	5	30	25	18	18	12	10	36	14	20
Christchurch Hbr	4	3	10	15	8	15	10	11	6	nc

	1990	1991	1992	1993	1994	1995	1996	1997	1998	1999
Portland Bill	22	17	40	103	26	63	91	95	70	95
Durlston CP	27	16	29	54	27	45	38	45	33	54
Christchurch Hbr	nc	33	1	8	12	5	15	nc	8	nc

Table 451. Spring totals (bds) at the main coastal watch-points 1980–1999

	1980	1981	1982	1983	1984	1985	1986	1987	1988	1989
Portland Bill	116	50	>135	63	>207	124	90	171	207	80
Durlston CP	18	22	38	15	57	22	45	37	60	43
Christchurch Hbr	4	3	34	4	78	10	16	23	27	nc

	1990	1991	1992	1993	1994	1995	1996	1997	1998	1999
Portland Bill	144	>120	47	104	178	169	108	69	44	90
Durlston CP	40	33	44	44	35	76	35	46	25	52
Christchurch Hbr	nc	0	23	6	11	39	20	nc	nc	nc

Table 452. Autumn totals (bds) at the main coastal watch-points 1980–1999

The wintering population is usually small with most records involving 1–2 birds and rarely exceeding six, the best counts being eight at North Portland during November–December 1981 and seven at the Nothe, Weymouth on 7th January 1985.

The species shows a preference for coastal sites with cliffs, quarries and rocky shorelines such as Portland, the Purbeck coast and to a lesser extent Christchurch Harbour, whilst the Weymouth area, notably the Nothe, is particularly favoured in winter.

Although scarce away from the coast, there are reports from inland sites scattered widely throughout the county. Most sightings involve 1–3 birds, but 15 in the Bride Valley on 3rd November 1984, also up to five at Sherborne Abbey on 30th–31st October 1989 were notable counts for so far inland.

Breeding has occurred successfully at Portland in 1965, 1977 and 1996, Weymouth in 1987, and Durlston CP in 1993 and 1995. There are also several other records suggestive of breeding, mainly from Portland and Durlston CP with further reports from Poole (twice), Weymouth, Christchurch and Mapperton (all once). In addition, the Tetrad Survey (1987–1994) found evidence of breeding in three tetrads in the south-east corner of Purbeck (SZ07), being probable in one and possible in the remaining two. Other records for June and July are likely to refer to late spring or early autumn migrants.

A total of 98 birds has been ringed in the county.

The Black Redstart breeds over much of Europe north to south-east England and southern Scandinavia and east to south-west Russia, also in Asia Minor and central Asia with small populations in north-west Africa and the Middle East. It is resident in the south-western part of its range, but a summer visitor elsewhere. It mainly winters in the Mediterranean Basin, in north-east Africa, Arabia and eastwards through south-west Asia to the Indian sub-continent and Burma.

Postscript 2000–2002

There was a notably high wintering population of 20–30 birds at Portland in December 2000. A bird ringed at Portland Bill in November 1999 and found dead in Germany in April 2000 represents the first foreign recovery of a Dorset-ringed bird.

Sponsored by Jamie McMillan

Redstart (Common Redstart)   *Phoenicurus phoenicurus*

A scarce summer visitor and fairly common passage migrant

Mansel-Pleydell (1888) described this species as "a summer migrant by no means common in the county", whilst Blathwayt (1945) considered it to be more common as a passage migrant than a breeding bird.

Since 1950 the Redstart has remained a rather scarce and erratic summer visitor with isolated occurrences of breeding reported from sites scattered throughout the county. The *BTO Atlas* (1968–1972) found evidence of breeding in 20 (54%) 10-km squares (confirmed in 10, probable in six and possible in four), whilst the Tetrad Survey (1987–1994) revealed evidence of breeding in 19 (51%) of the pre-1974 10-km squares (confirmed in eight, probable in one and possible in 10). During the *BTO Atlas* (1968–1972) breeding occurred mostly in the north and west of the county, but the Tetrad Map shows that breeding is now concentrated mainly in the Poole Basin area. There are a few sites where breeding has occurred fairly regularly over a number of years, notably Lambert's Castle in the extreme west of the county with up to six pairs during 1952–1964, but intermittent reports subsequently, Green Hill Down in the late 1960s, and the Wareham Forest area since 1980. Population numbers seemingly declined between the *BTO Atlas*

(1968–1972) and the Tetrad Survey (1987–1994) as indicated by the number of pre-1974 10-km squares recording confirmed or probable breeding, i.e from 16 to 9. Since the Tetrad Survey, the species has maintained its precarious status as a breeding bird in the county with most records from its favoured haunts in the Wareham Forest area.

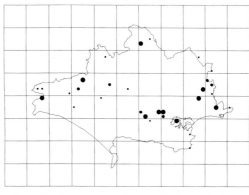

There are two very early records on 23rd February 1996 at Portland Bill (a female) and 5th March 1995 at Ham Common, Poole. Otherwise the first spring migrants usually appear during late March or early April, other early reports being 13th March 1991 at the Grove, Portland, 20th March 1992 at Hengistbury (three birds) and 22nd March 1993 at Portland Bill. The average date of the first arrivals was considerably earlier in the 1990s than during the previous four decades – see Table 453.

	1950–1959	1960–1969	1970–1979	1980–1989	1990–1999
Range	29th March–23rd April	31st March–10th April	26th March–18th April	27th March–9th April	23rd February–1st April
Average	9th April	5th April	4th April	3rd April	20th March

Table 453. Dates for first spring arrivals each decade 1950–1999

Most spring passage occurs from the second week of April through to mid-May with occasional stragglers into June. Peak counts usually range from 20–60 and rarely exceed 100 birds, the highest being an exceptional 320 at Hengistbury on 24th April 1990 (cf Tree Pipit) with 130 there the next day, 250 at Central Portland on 24th April 1989 with 130 there on 24th–25th April 1990, and 110 at Portland Bill on 25th April 1985 with 100 there on 3rd May 1980. Although there are occasional sightings of early returning migrants in July, the main autumn passage months are August and September. Peak counts during this period are rather modest, mostly ranging from 20–40 and rarely exceeding 50 birds, the highest being 79 at Christchurch Harbour on 6th September 1988.

	1980	1981	1982	1983	1984	1985	1986	1987	1988	1989
Portland Bill	>320	206	239	194	239	270	119	196	217	342
Durlston CP	70	29	39	33	54	65	26	60	78	109
Christchurch Hbr	272	168	104	28	196	186	33	54	51	63

	1990	1991	1992	1993	1994	1995	1996	1997	1998	1999
Portland Bill	345	377	93	163	58	270	386	238	111	127
Durlston CP	102	65	17	32	21	67	146	123	55	97
Christchurch Hbr	598	117	18	30	59	18	25	103	31	15

Table 454. Spring totals (bds) at the main coastal watch-points 1980–1999

	1980	1981	1982	1983	1984	1985	1986	1987	1988	1989
Portland Bill	123	93	108	152	147	114	311	148	188	233
Durlston CP	129	113	186	209	130	255	312	401	270	395
Christchurch Hbr	74	72	56	86	nc	81	102	87	162	46

	1990	1991	1992	1993	1994	1995	1996	1997	1998	1999
Portland Bill	97	133	109	152	78	151	87	108	96	38
Durlston CP	260	217	407	226	168	302	180	214	239	194
Christchurch Hbr	36	28	37	80	16	14	32	23	28	20

Table 455. Autumn totals (bds) at the main coastal watch-points 1980–1999

At Portland Bill and Christchurch Harbour spring passage is usually heavier than in autumn, but curiously the reverse is true at Durlston CP where autumn numbers are much higher than in spring – see Tables 454 and 455. As a result numbers at Durlston CP are much lower in spring, but generally higher in autumn than those recorded at Portland Bill. Inland, there are widely scattered records in spring and autumn, usually involving 1–3 and rarely more than five birds.

A few birds occur in October when the last birds are normally reported, the latest of several November records being 22nd November 1978 well inland at Beaulieu Wood, 23rd November 1982 at Langton Herring and from 22nd to 24th November 1984 in a Bournemouth garden.

There is an exceptional record of a very late migrant or wintering bird at the Nothe, Weymouth from 4th to 23rd December 1976.

Individuals at Portland Bill on 4th November 1991 and Hengistbury on 20th September 1992 showed the characteristics of the eastern race *P. p. samamisicus*.

A total of 2,872 birds has been ringed in the county. There have been two foreign recoveries from Morocco, and one each from Spain and Portugal, but no reports of any foreign controls.

The Redstart is a summer visitor breeding over much of Europe and north-central Asia eastwards to about 105°E, also in north-west Africa, Asia Minor and south-west Asia. It mainly winters in the northern tropics of Africa and southern Arabia.

Postscript 2000–2002
There were no reports of confirmed breeding in 2000 and 2001, but at least one pair bred in 2002.

Whinchat   *Saxicola rubetra*

A fairly common passage migrant – occasionally breeds

Mansel-Pleydell (1888) simply described this species as "a summer migrant", but gave no clear indication of breeding status, whilst Blathwayt (1945) stated that it was chiefly a passage migrant, which had been found breeding near Swanage, but apparently rarely nested in Dorset.

The Whinchat has remained a rare and sporadic breeder, the only occurrences of successful nesting being near Bradford Abbas during 1947–1949, at a undisclosed site in Poole Basin North in 1956, at Cranborne Common in 1964, at one or two un-disclosed sites involving two pairs in 1966, near Holt in 1968, near Blandford Camp in 1980, at Christ-church Harbour in 1988 and near Sixpenny Handley in 1991. The *BTO Atlas* (1968–1972) provided two additional reports of confirmed breeding in ST80 and SY89 with probable breeding recorded in five 10-km squares, whilst the Tetrad Survey (1987–1994) found probable breeding in two pre-1974 10-km squares. Although nesting has been suspected on several other occasions, some cases must be treated with caution because this species begins its autumn dispersal very early and remains in family parties, so reports of juveniles in July may not refer to locally-bred birds. Records of birds holding territory may be a better indication of probable breeding, whilst reports of possible breeding almost certainly refer to unseasonal migrants.

There are very early records on 5th March 1977 at Christchurch Harbour, 9th March 1961 at Morden Bog, and 12th March 1977 and 18th March 1978 at Studland NNR. Otherwise the first spring migrants usually appear between late March and late April, the average date of the first arrivals being earlier during 1960s–1980s than in the 1950s and 1990s – see Table 456.

	1950–1959	1960–1969	1970–1979	1980–1989	1990–1999
Range	9th–29th April	9th March– 2nd May	5th March– 23rd April	28th March– 17th April	4th–22nd April
Average	20th April	10th April	5th April	9th April	15th April

Table 456. Dates for first spring arrivals each decade 1950–1999

Spring passage mostly occurs from mid-April to mid-May, but often extends into early June. Peak counts generally range from 30–60 but rarely exceed 100 birds, the highest being 150 at Central Portland on 24th April 1989 (cf Redstart) with 130 there on 30th April 1990, and 110 at Christchurch Harbour on 10th May 1993. Although early dispersing migrants are regularly reported in very small numbers during July, the main passage period in autumn extends from August to mid-October with September the peak month. Peak counts normally range from 30–70 but rarely exceed 100 birds, the highest being from Portland Bill with 300 on 2nd September 1981, 175 on 22nd September 1980 and 150 on 23rd–24th August 1973.

Spring passage is generally, and often substantially heavier at Portland Bill than at the other main coastal watch-points, whilst spring totals at Christchurch Harbour are seemingly highly variable with very few birds recorded in some years, e.g. 1983 and 1992 – see Table 457. Again Portland Bill usually records higher autumn totals than the other main coastal watch-points, but not to the same degree as in spring – see Table 458. The reasons for these differences may reflect habitat preferences for migrant Whinchats.

	1980	1981	1982	1983	1984	1985	1986	1987	1988	1989
Portland Bill	216	164	106	198	253	418	123	275	179	343
Durlston CP	47	25	12	28	104	59	17	53	80	68
Christchurch Hbr	315	64	53	8	242	162	18	164	75	44

	1990	1991	1992	1993	1994	1995	1996	1997	1998	1999
Portland Bill	257	431	130	174	72	230	228	103	166	158
Durlston CP	60	98	30	nc	13	27	65	89	56	51
Christchurch Hbr	130	214	7	209	27	20	13	nc	37	12

Table 457. Spring totals (bds) at the main coastal watch-points 1980–1999

	1980	1981	1982	1983	1984	1985	1986	1987	1988	1989
Portland Bill	>650	1768	349	556	432	324	671	353	337	358
Durlston CP	104	173	112	173	210	196	255	226	175	260
Christchurch Hbr	84	94	88	125	346	135	172	286	172	97

	1990	1991	1992	1993	1994	1995	1996	1997	1998	1999
Portland Bill	228	486	435	342	284	378	200	289	156	136
Durlston CP	227	124	329	nc	58	195	214	169	188	117
Christchurch Hbr	133	93	346	228	43	140	126	nc	92	108

Table 458. Autumn totals (bds) at the main coastal watch-points 1980–1999

The species is widely recorded inland on passage, particularly in autumn when reasonable numbers sometimes occur, e.g. 51 bird-days at Puddletown in September 1992, 34 bird-days at Cranborne Common during 21st August–3rd October 1999 and 31 bird-days in the Stour Valley between Corfe Mullen and Sturminster Marshall in September 1984. Counts of up to 12 birds are not infrequent, the highest being an exceptional 25 in the Stour Valley at Wimborne on 5th May 1976 and c.20 at Long Bredy on 30th September 1976.

The last birds are usually reported in October, more occasionally in November, the latest being 25th November 1989 well inland at Holcombe Bottom near Piddlehinton, 5th December 1998 at Langton Herring, and in 1984 one at Ballard Down on 24th November was presumably the same individual recorded nearby at Studland NNR on 25th November and 15th December.

A total of 570 birds has been ringed in the county.

The Whinchat is a summer visitor breeding over much of Europe, except the far south, extending east into west-central Asia, also in eastern Asia Minor. It winters mainly in the northern tropics of Africa with smaller numbers further south in East Africa.

Postscript 2000–2002
There were very late birds at Lytchett Bay from 4th to 22nd November 2001 and Swineham GP on 30th November 2002.

Stonechat
Saxicola torquata

A fairly common resident, passage migrant and winter visitor

Mansel-Pleydell (1888) described this species as "a constant resident with us, frequenting the open downs and heaths". Blathwayt (1945) also considered it to be resident, breeding commonly on heathland and along the coast as well as in many inland areas.

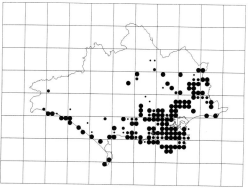

There has been little change in breeding status. The *BTO Atlas* (1968–1972) revealed evidence of breeding in 26 (70%) 10-km squares, (confirmed in 20, probable in three and possible in three), whilst the Tetrad Survey (1987–1994) found evidence of breeding in 25 (68%) of the pre-1974 10-km squares (confirmed in 21, probable in three and possible in one). Both surveys show that breeding is widespread on the heaths of the Poole Basin and along the coast, but occurs very locally elsewhere. Away from the main breeding areas, there have been some minor changes in distribution since the *BTO Atlas* (1968–1972) with the species disappearing from the Blackmore Vale, but spreading to sites in river valleys and on chalk downland.

The breeding population is very vulnerable to severe winters with numbers markedly depleted after those of 1946/47, 1962/63 and the mid-1980s, but subsequent recovery has been rapid. This is demonstrated by long-term population figures from Arne NR, which show sharp declines after the 1981/82 and 1984/85 winters – see Table 459. Despite this, population numbers have increased considerably at this site since the 1960s and 1970s. This healthy situation is further illustrated by population estimates for the county as a whole during the 1990s with a peak of 300 pairs (incomplete census) in 1994 – see Table 460. Sites with notable breeding populations include Studland NNR with 55 pairs in 1994 and 1995, Canford Heath with 39 pairs in 1994, 1995 and 1998, and Holt Heath NNR with 24 pairs in 1997. At the last site there were 36 pairs in 1971, but only four pairs in 1986.

67	74	75	76	77	78	80	81	82	83	84	85	86	91	92	93	94	95	96	97	98	99
7	6	8	7	7	7	9	11	8	12	13	5	4	13	17	24	21	20	17	20	29	25

Table 459. Number of breeding pairs at Arne NR 1967–1999

1990	1991	1992	1994	1995	1996	1997	1998	1999
127	161*	138	300	288	220	247	272	252

Table 460. Breeding population estimates for Dorset 1990–1999; *RSPB Dorset Heathland Project

Although spring migration, which extends from February to April, is usually small and only just detectable at the main coastal watch-points, heavy passage occasionally occurs, e.g. at Portland Bill with 154 bird-days in March 1981 and 201 bird-days during March–April 1984. Peak counts rarely exceed 10 birds, the best being from Portland Bill with 25 in March 1984 and 22 on 18th March 1976. Autumn passage is also variable and mainly occurs during September–October, but sometimes from August to November or even into early December. Peak counts normally range from 20–40 birds, the highest being 80 at Christchurch

Harbour on 7th October 1990. Although birds disperse widely in winter, most are recorded in coastal areas.

A total of 1,456 birds has been ringed in the county of which five have been recovered in Spain (including one from Mallorca), and one from France, but there are no reports of any foreign controls.

The various races of Stonechat breed over much of western, southern and central Europe as well as northern and central Asia, also in north-west Africa, Asia Minor and in sub-Saharan Africa, mainly in the east and south. The European races *S. t. rubicola* and *S. t. hibernans*, (which occurs in the British Isles) winter in the west and south of their breeding range. Eastern populations are more migratory and winter mainly in the north-eastern tropics of Africa, Arabia, the Indian sub-continent and south-east Asia.

Postscript 2000–2002
Spring passage was particularly conspicuous at Portland Bill with peak counts of 23 on 6th March 2000, 28 on 22nd February 2001 and 34 on 4th March 2002.

Sponsored by Kevin Sayer

Siberian Stonechat *Saxicola torquata maura*

A very rare autumn migrant: ten records

All records of this distinctive form of Stonechat have occurred between 30th September and 9th November, with all but one of the sightings from Portland:

1974	Portland Bill: 21st October
1975	Portland Bill: 24th October
1979	Portland Bill: female/first-winter 11th October
1987	Portland Bill: female/first-winter 3rd–4th October
1990	Hengistbury: male 7th October
1994	Portland Bill: first-winter male 30th September–4th October
	Portland Bill: first-winter female 7th–9th November
1998	Portland Bill: female/first-winter 17th–18th October
1999	Southwell, Portland: female/first-winter 19th October
	Weston, Portland: female/first-winter 23rd October

Most records are considered to belong to the race *S. t. maura*, which breeds across much of Siberia, but is replaced in the Far East by *S. t. stejnegeri*. A vagrant to Great Britain with 302 records up to 2002.

Wheatear (Northern Wheatear) *Oenanthe oenanthe*

A scarce summer visitor and common passage migrant

There is an interesting reference in Pulteney (1799) regarding great numbers of this species, including over thirty dozen in one day, trapped on Portland where it was locally known as the 'Snorter'. A person who disposed of the Wheatears as a delicacy in Weymouth market paid £30 to one man in 1794 for birds at one shilling a dozen, and is said to have been supplied with fifty dozen more than could be sold. Another reference mentions that 7,800 birds were caught by one man in 1794! Not surprisingly Mansel-Pleydell (1888) noted that this species was less plentiful than in Pulteney's time, but recorded that it still bred freely on the downs and appeared in large numbers on migration, particularly in September. Blathwayt (1945) consider-ed the Wheatear to be a passage migrant and summer resident that bred sparingly on the coast and downs.

Since 1950, as elsewhere in lowland Great Britain, the population declined dramatically so that by the 1960s it had become a scarce and erratic breed-ing species in the county. During the 1950s and early 1960s the population apparently remained fairly stable at 11–12 pairs, but subsequently diminished

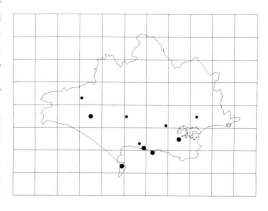

to very low levels with reports of confirmed breeding becoming increasingly infrequent during the 1970s and non-existent during 1980–1988 – see Table 461. There has been a recovery in recent years, notably during the late 1990s, with 25 of the 32 breeding records during 1989–1999 from Portland and the Purbeck coast. It is interesting to note that apparent revivals in the breeding fortunes of this species during 1968–1970 and 1989–1993 coincided with the *BTO Atlas* (1968–1972) when breeding was confirmed in four and considered probable in seven 10-km squares, and the Tetrad Survey (1987–1994) when breeding was confirmed in five and thought probable in four of the pre-1974 10-km squares.

	50	61	62	63	64	65	66	67	68	69	70	71	72	73	74	75	76	77	78	79
Confirmed	6	4	1	nc	1	2	1	0	2	2	3	0	0	1	1	0	1	0	1	3
Probable	5	8	1	nc	0	0	0	1	4	1	0	0	2	0	2	0	0	4	2	0
Total	11	12	2	nc	1	2	1	1	6	3	3	0	2	1	3	0	1	4	3	3

	80	81	82	83	84	85	86	87	88	89	90	91	92	93	94	95	96	97	98	99
Confirmed	0	0	0	0	0	0	0	0	0	1	1	1	3	0	0	0	2	4	2	2
Probable	0	1	0	0	0	1	0	0	0	0	0	1	1	3	0	0	2	2	6	1
Total	0	1	0	0	0	1	0	0	0	1	1	2	4	3	0	0	4	6	8	3

Table 461. Number of breeding pairs in Dorset 1950–1999

There is a very early spring record on 14th February 1965 at Worth Matravers, whilst there are other February sightings from Portland Bill during 22nd–28th February 1998, Stourpaine on 27th February 1971, Wyke Regis, Weymouth on 27th February 1993, Studland on 28th February 1995, North Portland on 28th February 1998 and Durlston CP on an unspecified date in 1998. Otherwise the first spring migrants usually appear in early March, the average date of the first arrivals being earlier in the 1990s than during the previous four decades – see Table 462.

	1950–1959	1960–1969	1970–1979	1980–1989	1990–1999
Range	7th– 23rd March	14th February– 19th March	27th February– 18th March	4th– 16th March	22nd February– 9th March
Average	13th March	9th March	12th March	9th March	2nd March

Table 462. Dates for first spring arrivals each decade 1950–1999

In spring, the main passage period extends from mid-March to mid-May with April the peak month, whilst late migrants sometimes occur through to mid-June. Peak counts generally range from 100–250 but rarely exceed 350 birds, the highest being an exceptional 1,100 at Central Portland on 24th April 1989 (cf Whinchat and Redstart) with 400 at Portland Bill the same day. Although early dispersing migrants occur in small numbers during July, the main autumn passage extends from August to mid-October with August and September the peak months. Peak counts normally range from 100–250 but rarely exceed 300 birds, the best being from Portland Bill with 800 on 25th August 1987 and 500 on 2nd September 1981.

Passage is usually, and often substantially, heavier at Portland Bill than at the other main coastal watch-points – see Tables 463 and 464. The reasons for these differences may reflect habitat preferences for migrant Wheatears (cf Whinchat).

	1980	1981	1982	1983	1984	1985	1986	1987	1988	1989
Portland Bill	1453	1072	851	1535	1258	1384	2666	1493	1667	1636
Durlston CP	146	158	130	200	424	213	252	346	308	393
Christchurch Hbr	1129	538	>252	nc	1386	996	525	268	873	559

	1990	1991	1992	1993	1994	1995	1996	1997	1998	1999
Portland Bill	1462	1553	1118	998	781	1215	1650	1637	2049	1101
Durlston CP	426	390	307	465	nc	572	568	807	471	523
Christchurch Hbr	950	665	360	431	315	220	184	476	379	236

Table 463. Spring totals (bds) at the main coastal watch-points 1980–1999

	1980	1981	1982	1983	1984	1985	1986	1987	1988	1989
Portland Bill	2936	2346	2289	2676	>1620	2084	3010	4315	2688	1761
Durlston CP	304	249	315	664	399	574	437	749	802	606
Christchurch Hbr	582	504	447	401	958	772	486	1375	791	309

	1990	1991	1992	1993	1994	1995	1996	1997	1998	1999
Portland Bill	2052	2746	1063	1213	1736	2063	2078	1865	1817	1837
Durlston CP	562	667	1026	476	nc	404	616	805	560	497
Christchurch Hbr	599	387	980	491	89	301	277	108	379	344

Table 464. Autumn totals (bds) at the main coastal watch-points 1980–1999

Passage birds are widely recorded inland, usually in small numbers involving under 12 birds, the highest counts being from Coward's Marsh, Christchurch with 40+ on 10th April 1984 and 25 on 2nd April 1986.

The last birds are usually reported in late October or early November, the latest being 23rd November 1998 at Portland Castle, 24th November 1997 between Burton Bradstock and West Bay, 24th November 1983 at Portland Bill, 25th November 1972 at Central Portland, 26th November 1984 at Brenscombe Hill, and 1st December 1990 at Portland Bill.

The Greenland Wheatear *O. o. leucorhoa* regularly occurs on passage in small numbers. Birds are most often recorded later in spring from late April and through May, but one at Portland Bill on 2nd April 1956 was unusually early. In autumn most birds are reported during September and October.

A total of 550 birds has been ringed in the county with one foreign recovery from France, but no reports of any foreign controls.

The Wheatear is a summer visitor breeding from north-west Africa, across most of Europe, Asia Minor, and north and central Asia east to Alaska. It winters in the northern tropics of Africa extending south of the equator in the east. The Greenland race *O. o leucorhoa* breeds in north-east Canada, Greenland and Iceland, and winters in West Africa.

Postscript 2000–2002
There was a huge fall on 17th–18th March 2001 along almost the entire Dorset coast involving many thousands of birds including 1,000 at Portland on 17th and 1,200 there the next day. At Portland counts of 500 on 26th August in both 2000 and 2001 are high for autumn passage. In 2000 early migrants were reported from Portland Bill from 25th to 28th February and Durlston CP also on 25th February, whilst one at Radipole NR on 7th December 2001 is the latest record for Dorset. Breeding continues in the county with three pairs in 2000, and two in both 2001 and 2002.

Sponsored by Anne and Henry Wheatcroft

Pied Wheatear   *Oenanthe pleschanka*

Accidental: two records

   1954   Portland Bill: first-winter female 17th–19th October, trapped on 18th
   1996   West Weare, Portland, male of uncertain age 25th October

The Pied Wheatear is a summer visitor breeding from south-eastern Europe eastwards across central Asia to about 120°E. It winters in East Africa. A vagrant to Great Britain with 44 records up to 2002.

Black-eared Wheatear   *Oenanthe hispanica*

Accidental: four records

   1975   Portland Bill: first-summer male race *O. h. melanoleuca* 14th June; same at St Aldhelm's Head
          the next day
   1985   Blacknor, Portland: first-summer male race *O. h. melanoleuca* 27th–28th May
   1998   Winspit Valley: female 16th May
   2000   Upton Heath: first-summer male race *O. h. melanoleuca* 25th–26th June

The nominate race *O. h. hispanica* is a summer visitor breeding in north-west Africa, Iberia, southern France, north and central Italy and the north-western Balkans. The eastern race *O. h. melanoleuca* is a summer visitor breeding in southern Italy and the Balkans east through Asia Minor and parts of the Middle East to extreme south-west Asia. Both races winter in the northern tropics of Africa. A vagrant to the British Isles with 61 records up to 2000.

Desert Wheatear   *Oenanthe deserti*

Accidental: three records

1991   Portland Bill: first-winter female 9th–12th October, trapped on 11th
1994   Southwell, Portland: first-winter male 11th October
1997   Knoll Beach, Studland: first-winter male 5th–6th March

The race *O. d. homochroa* breeds across North Africa, the nominate race *O. d. deserti* breeds in the Middle East, whilst the races *O. d. atrogularis* and *O. d. oreophila* breed in south-west and central Asia. It is resident in the southern and eastern parts of its North African range, being a summer visitor elsewhere. It winters mainly in the Sahara and Sahel areas of Africa, east through Arabia to the north-western part of the Indian sub-continent. A vagrant to Great Britain with 77 records up to 2002.

Rock Thrush (Rufous-tailed Rock Thrush)   *Monticola saxatilis*

Accidental: two records

It is an amazing coincidence that the first county record should be followed so promptly by the second at the same location a year later!

1988   Portland: male at various locations 16th–24th April
1989   Portland Bill: male 6th May

The Rock Thrush is a summer visitor breeding in mountains from north-west Africa and Iberia east through southern Europe and Asia Minor to central Asia. It winters mainly in the northern tropics of Africa extending south of the equator in the east. A vagrant to the British Isles with 28 records up to 2000.

Ring Ouzel   *Turdus torquatus*

An uncommon passage migrant

Both Mansel-Pleydell (1888) and Blathwayt (1945) considered this species to be a passage migrant, but the former referred to a pair which wintered at Turnworth in 1878. According to Pulteney (1799), Ring Ouzels were known as 'Michaelmas Blackbirds' on Portland.

Since 1950 the species has remained a regular passage migrant in small numbers, particularly favouring those coastal areas with scrub, cliffs and disused quarries such as Portland and Purbeck.

Exceptionally early records on 2nd February 1996 at Portland Bill, 10th February 1984 at Ballard Down, 11th February 1986 at Easton, Portland and 15th February 1986 at St Aldhelm's Head may possibly refer to wintering birds rather than genuine migrants. Otherwise the first birds usually appear during March, the earliest being 3rd March 1970 at Chapman's Pool, 3rd March 1990 at the Grove, Portland and 5th March 1977 at various sites on Portland. Since the 1950s the average date of the first arrivals has become earlier – see Table 465.

	1960–1969	1970–1979	1980–1989	1990–1999
Range	15th March–3rd April	3rd–28th March	10th February–25th March	2nd February–24th March
Average	25th March	18th March	12th March	11th March

Table 465. Dates for first spring arrivals each decade 1960–1999

In spring, the main passage period extends from mid-March to mid-May with April the peak month. Seasonal totals are normally small to modest and day-counts have only apparently exceeded 12 birds once, an exceptional 32 at Portland Bill on 12th April 1970, whilst ten at East Fleet on 3rd April 1988 is a notably high number away from the main haunts – see Table 466. There is a remarkable report of one at Chapman's Pool on the unseasonal date of 8th July 1973. Otherwise early autumn migrants occasionally occur during August and early September, but the main passage generally starts during the second half of September and peaks in October. Autumn totals are highly variable with passage notably heavy in 1972 (190 sightings from Portland during 28th August–27th October), 1988 and 1991 – see Table 467. Some of the highest counts were recorded during October 1988 including an exceptional 100 at St Aldhelm's Head on 14th with 46 at Durlston CP on 15th, 27 at Winspit on 14th, 20 at Central/North Portland on 19th and 19 at Christchurch Harbour on 18th. In October 1991 peak numbers included 25 at Durlston CP on 14th, 15 at North Portland and 12 at Portland Bill on 13th, and 11 at Christchurch Harbour on 12th. Other notable counts include 31 at Portland on 13th October 1972 with 29 there on 18th October 1999, and 31 at Portland Bill on 16th October 1980 with 30 there on 4th October 1998 and 27 on 15th October 1986.

	1980	1981	1982	1983	1984	1985	1986	1987	1988	1989
Portland	47	46	13	27	38	20	32	34	35	36
Durlston CP	19	9	4	8	10	2	4	14	5	24
rest of Purbeck	5	4	0	0	1	3	4	0	nc	6
Christchurch Hbr	4	19	20	8	12	17	8	5	16	12

	1990	1991	1992	1993	1994	1995	1996	1997	1998	1999
Portland Bill	86	13	16	29	10	35	37	>50	35	8
Durlston CP	22	8	8	10	10	11	19	19	10	10
rest of Purbeck	4	1	2	1	1	2	5	2	3	1
Christchurch Hbr	8	6	7	6	1	16	5	4	2	6

Table 466. Spring totals (bds) at the main coastal watch-points and Purbeck 1980–1999

	1980	1981	1982	1983	1984	1985	1986	1987	1988	1989
Portland Bill	80	9	7	10	2	50	55	66	111	20
Durlston CP	19	23	20	5	5	30	17	26	159	32
rest of Purbeck	6	8	2	4	5	30	8	33	>323	23
Christchurch Hbr	3	4	3	5	1	35	6	34	92	1

	1990	1991	1992	1993	1994	1995	1996	1997	1998	1999
Portland Bill	34	171	16	41	32	3	32	>85	133	>37
Durlston CP	37	120	21	35	12	19	13	42	44	33
rest of Purbeck	33	38	3	11	14	3	8	17	22	4
Christchurch Hbr	15	26	5	21	11	1	11	3	8	6

Table 467. Autumn totals (bds) at the main coastal watch-points and Purbeck 1980–1999

Although scarce away from the coast and near-coastal fringes, there are widely scattered reports from well inland with sites on heathland and downland particularly favoured. Most sightings involve 1–3 birds but there were 5N at Maiden Castle on 27th April 1984 and four at Charminster on the remarkably late date of 23rd November 1992.

Late stragglers are frequently recorded well into November, the latest being 30th November 1968 inland at Minterne Magna and 30th November 1990 at Durlston CP, but several December records may also refer to late migrants rather than wintering birds.

There are a surprising number of reports for the winter period, some of which may refer to late autumn or early spring migrants rather than genuine overwintering birds.

1951 Doghouse Hill near Seatown: male 20th December
1967 Verne Common, Portland: 2nd December

1968	Portland Bill: male 8th December
	Winspit: imm. 30th December
1982	East Stoke: 10th–17th December
1984	Southwell, Portland: male 13th January
1986	Wimborne: 19th December
1987	Nether Cerne: 21st January
1991	Chideock: 25th–27th January
1998	Chalbury Common: 4th December

A total of 106 birds has been ringed in the county.

The nominate race *T. t. torquatus* is a summer visitor breeding in Brittany, the north and west of the British Isles and in Scandinavia and winters in Spain and north-west Africa. The distinctive Alpine race *T. t. alpestris* is mainly a summer visitor breeding in the mountains of central and southern Europe and western Turkey. It winters mainly in the south of the breeding range as well as north-west Africa. Another race *T. t. amicorum* is a summer visitor breeding in the Caucasus and eastern Turkey eastwards into south-west Asia and winter in the latter area.

Postscript 2000–2002

Spring passage was notably strong at Portland in mid-April 2000 with counts of 23 on 15th and 26 on 16th, whilst 35 on 10th October 2002 would appear to be the highest autumn count from the island, in recent years at least. There was a remarkable series of winter records with singles at Sturminster Newton from 31st December 2000 to January 2001, Bestwall near Wareham on 1st January 2001, Marnhull from 1st January to 4th March 2001 and Verne Mount, Portland on 17th January 2001. Otherwise there was a very late migrant at Southwell, Portland from 25th November to 9th December 2002.

Sponsored by John Lunt

Blackbird (Common Blackbird)   *Turdus merula*

An abundant resident, winter visitor and passage migrant

Mansel-Pleydell (1888) referred to this species as being resident, but migratory in autumn and remarked that "this has been abundantly proved by the numbers which have been observed at the lighthouses and lightships during the period of migration". Blathwayt (1945) described it as "a very common resident", a status which has not changed subsequently.

The *BTO Atlas* (1968–1972) confirmed breeding in all 10-km squares, whilst the Tetrad Survey (1987–1994) produced almost the identical result with evidence of breeding in all of the pre-1974 10-km squares (confirmed in 36 and probable in one). The Tetrad Survey also shows that the Blackbird is widely distributed throughout the county with evidence of breeding in almost all tetrad squares. The Common Bird Census Index for Dorset during 1981–1994 clearly indicates the species vulnerability to cold winters, notably those of 1981/82, 1984/85 and 1990/91 – see Table 468. Although there were good recoveries in population levels after the 1981/82 and 1984/85 to 1986/87 winters, evidence for recovery after the 1990/91 winter was non-existent up to at least 1994. At Portland Bill there appears to have been a long-term decline in the breeding population, which is not totally related to the effects of cold winters – see Table 469.

1981	1982	1983	1984	1985	1986	1987	1988	1989	1990	1991	1992	1993	1994
100	90	108	108	83	82	–	99	94	99	73	79	71	74

Table 468. The Common Bird Census Index for Dorset 1981–1994

80	81	82	83	84	85	86	87	88	89	90	91	92	93	94	95	96	97	98	99
25	27	25	33	18	18	20	20	29	25	21	15	17	14	11	10	10	10	nc	10

Table 469. Number of breeding pairs at Portland Bill 1980–1999

Spring migration during March–April at the main coastal watch-points is small and sometimes non-existent with peak counts rarely exceeding 50 birds, the highest being 80 at Hengistbury on 6th April 1975 with 76 there on 30th March 1974, and 80 at Portland Bill on 3rd March 1987. Passage is much more obvious during the autumn and occurs mainly in October when peak counts generally vary between 50–300 birds, the highest being from Portland Bill with 1,000 on 15th October 1974, 525 on 30th October 1974 and 500 on 24th October 1958. The species is also sometimes involved in cold weather movements, e.g. 250 at Durlston CP on 29th December 1997 with 225E there on 9th–10th January 1982.

A total of 16,467 birds has been ringed in the county. There have been foreign recoveries from Germany (c. 11), France (nine), three each from the Netherlands and Sweden, two each from Denmark and Eire, and one each from Belgium, Norway and Finland. Four foreign controls have been recorded from Belgium, two from the Netherlands and one from Germany. These reflect the movement of birds between summer breeding areas in Scandinavia and eastern Europe, and their wintering areas in western Europe, notably France.

The Blackbird breeds widely throughout much of Europe, except the far north, also in north-west Africa, Asia Minor and parts of the Middle East with other breeding populations in southern Asia including the Indian sub-continent. It is largely resident in the west and south of its European range, being a summer visitor in the north and east. These migratory populations winter mainly in western and southern Europe and north-west Africa.

Sponsored by Terence David Sims

Black-throated Thrush (race of Dark-throated Thrush)   *Turdus ruficollis atrogularis*

Accidental: one record

1994   Berry Hill, near Throop, Bournemouth: 7th January

The above record involved a fine male of the Black-throated race *T. r. atrogularis* seen well, but all too briefly amongst a flock of Redwings. A full account can be found in the Dorset Bird Report for 1994.

The Dark-throated Thrush is a summer visitor breeding from the Urals across much of western and central Asia with a small population in the Caucasus. The Black-throated race *T. r. atrogularis* breeds mainly in the north-west of the species' range, being replaced by the nominate Red-throated race *T. r. ruficollis* in the south-east. It winters from eastern Arabia eastwards through parts of south-west, central and south-east Asia including the northern Indian sub-continent. A vagrant to Great Britain with 51 records up to 2002 – all but one belonging to the Black-throated race.

Fieldfare   *Turdus pilaris*

A common winter visitor and passage migrant

Mansel-Pleydell (1888) was rather vague regarding this species, only mentioning that it arrives later than the Redwing, whilst Blathwayt (1945) referred to it as a common winter visitor.

Although there are early autumn records on 31st August 1981 at Southwell, Portland, 1st September 1975 at Verne Common, Portland and 7th September 1968 at the Fleet (three birds), the first migrants normally appear between mid-September and mid-October. Since the 1970s the average date of the first arrivals has gradually become later – see Table 470.

	1970–1979	1980–1989	1990–1999
Range	1st September–23rd October	31st August–14th October	23rd September–16th October
Average	25th September	28th September	4th October

Table 470. Dates for first autumn arrivals each decade 1970–1999

Autumn passage, which is often well marked both along the coast and inland, increases during late October, peaks in November and sometimes extends into early December. Seasonal totals can vary considerably from year to year – see Table 471. Peak day-counts rarely exceed 300–400 birds, the highest being recorded during autumn 1991 with an exceptional 3,100 at Durlston CP on 1st December and 1,000W at Christchurch Harbour on 15th November, also 800N at Portland Bill on 21st October 1970. Heavy passage occurred inland in November 1981 with 750S at Gillingham on 22nd and 500SW at Upton Heath on 21st.

	1980	1981	1982	1983	1984	1985	1986	1987	1988	1989
Portland Bill	nc	379	68	274	152	157	78	256	237	155
Durlston CP	nc	nc	102	154	489	157	30	300	669	353
Christchurch Hbr	nc	nc	3	16	19	64	18	21	31	3

	1990	1991	1992	1993	1994	1995	1996	1997	1998	1999
Portland Bill	191	360	35	327	182	12	104	136	122	293
Durlston CP	895	5191	31	nc	nc	1035	1042	1040	nc	386
Christchurch Hbr	10	>1000	nc	104	43	2	45	nc	nc	35

Table 471. Autumn totals (bds) at the main coastal watch-points 1980–1999

The Fieldfare occurs widely during the winter in flocks of up to 500 birds or so. Much larger numbers are occasionally reported, usually during periods of severe cold when movements can be spectacular and involve several thousand birds. For example, in January 1963 immense numbers were recorded passing west over the south-east of the county, whilst on 20th February 1969 a massive movement included c.20,000E at Arne NR and c.10,000N at Portland Bill. More recently various counts of c.10,000–15,000 were made at sites in the Weymouth/Fleet area on 8th–9th January 1982, and widespread heavy movements during 7th–9th February 1991 included c.20,000W on 9th at Christchurch Harbour. Finally 'thousands' were present at Abbotsbury with 'tens of thousands' elsewhere on the Fleet on 20th February 1996.

Otherwise very large numbers roosted at Duncliffe Wood between 1967 and 1979. During the winter of 1967/68 vast numbers of this species and Redwing reached a total possibly in excess of 100,000 birds. In other winters more modest numbers of Fieldfares were recorded, the highest being 14,000 on 16th March 1979, 12,000 in February 1977, whilst the joint total with Redwing reached 10,000 in early 1975.

	1980	1981	1982	1983	1984	1985	1986	1987	1988	1989
Portland Bill	21	33	17	10	22	43	258	107	6	24
Durlston CP	nc	nc	nc	160	20	nc	29	11	20	45
Christchurch Hbr	nc	nc	14	3	4	nc	45	3	1	2

	1990	1991	1992	1993	1994	1995	1996	1997	1998	1999
Portland Bill	7	3	10	7	2	17	17	2	55	6
Durlston CP	21	30	18	nc	nc	50	60	43	nc	4
Christchurch Hbr	nc	nc	nc	0	1	nc	17	nc	nc	2

Table 472. Spring totals (bds) at the main coastal watch-points 1980–1999

Spring migration is most evident from inland sites, being seldom conspicuous at the main coastal watch-points, the exceptions being 160N at Durlston CP on 2nd April 1983, and at Portland Bill in spring 1986 and 1987 – see Table 472. Although passage may start as early as late February, peak numbers usually occur in March and April when flocks of up to 250 birds are frequently recorded at inland sites, the highest counts being 1,000 at Woodsford on 3rd March 1968, Sherborne on 13th March 1984, East Holme on

18th March 1988 and Coward's Marsh, Christchurch on 10th April 1988, also 400 in the Allen Valley on 28th April 1951 is notable considering the late date.

Cold springs tend to prolong passage, which sometimes extends into early May, the latest dates being 17th May 1988 at Stalbridge, 19th May 1968 at Upton Heath and 3rd June 1979 at Portland Bill. There is an exceptional mid-summer record of one at Durlston CP on 7th July 1999.

A total of 641 birds has been ringed in the county and there have been two foreign recoveries from France, and one each from Sweden and Latvia, but there are no reports of any foreign controls.

The Fieldfare breeds from northern Great Britain and eastern France eastwards across central and northern Europe and northern Asia to about 135E, being a summer visitor to the northern and eastern parts of its range. It winters mainly in Europe except for the north, also in Asia Minor, parts of the Middle East and west-central Asia.

Postscript 2000–2002

Exceptionally for the second year running there was a mid-summer record from Durlston CP with one on 29th June 2000. A report of 12+ at Badbury Rings on 10th September 2001 is unusually early.

Song Thrush   *Turdus philomelos*

A common resident, winter visitor and passage migrant

Mansel-Pleydell (1888) referred to this species as being resident, but partially migratory in autumn, whilst Blathwayt (1945) described it as "a common resident" and stated that some emigrate.

Little has changed subsequently. The *BTO Atlas* (1968–1972) confirmed breeding in all 10-km squares, whilst the Tetrad Survey (1987–1994) produced similar results with evidence of breeding in all of the pre-1974 10-km squares (confirmed in 36 and probable in one). The Tetrad Map shows that the Song Thrush remains a widespread breeding bird throughout the county. Although the Common Bird Census Index for Dorset during 1981–1994 shows a marked decline during the mid-1980s, this does not appear to be so closely correlated with the cold winters as other common breeding birds such as the Blackbird – see Table 473. There was a full recovery in the population by 1989 followed by a period of relative stability at a moderately reduced level during 1990–1994. At Portland Bill there has been a rapid decline in the breeding population during the mid-1990s (cf Blackbird) – see Table 474.

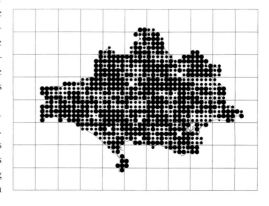

Spring migration during March–April is sometimes detected at the main coastal watch-points. Numbers are normally very small with peak counts rarely exceeding 30 birds, but heavier passage is occasionally recorded, e.g. at Portland Bill during the night of 8th–9th March 1986 with 65 there on

27th March 1975, and 140N at Durlston CP during 6th–9th March 1991. Autumn passage is much more obvious and occurs mainly in October when peak counts usually range between 50–150 birds, the highest being an exceptional 1,100 at Durlston CP on 30th October 1989 and 300 at Portland Bill on 29th October 1976. The species is also sometimes involved in cold weather movements, e.g. 500 at Portland Bill on 27th December 1970 with 300 there on 9th December 1967, 11th January 1982 and 14th January 1987, also 290E at Durlston CP on 9th–10th January 1982. Continental birds of the nominate race *T. p. philomelos* are often recorded during these autumn and cold weather influxes, e.g. at Durlston CP in 1995 with 320 bird-days in October, 490 bird-days in November and 1,650 bird-days in December.

1981	1982	1983	1984	1985	1986	1987	1988	1989	1990	1991	1992	1993	1994
100	80	100	69	43	54	–	74	100	80	83	69	83	83

Table 473. The Common Bird Census Index for Dorset 1981–1994

80	81	82	83	84	85	86	87	88	89	90	91	92	93	94	95	96	97	98	99
5	12	5	6	4	5	7	7	8	6	4	4	6	6	3	2	1	nc	0	1

Table 474. Number of breeding pairs at Portland Bill 1980–1999

A total of 6,275 birds has been ringed in the county. There have been seven foreign recoveries from France, four from Portugal and one from the Netherlands, and two foreign controls from Belgium and one from Sweden. These reflect the movement of birds between summer breeding areas in Scandinavia and eastern Europe, and their wintering areas in western Europe, notably France.

The Song Thrush breeds throughout most of Europe, except southern and central Iberia and the Mediterranean fringes, extending eastwards into west-central Asia, also in northern Asia Minor. It is largely resident in the west and south of its range, being a summer visitor in the north and east. These migratory populations winter mainly in western and southern Europe, north-west Africa, Asia Minor, the Middle East, parts of Arabia and extreme south-west Asia.

Postscript 2000–2002
At Portland Bill 80 on 15th April 2000 is a high count for spring passage, whilst 550N in 20 minutes at Southwell, Portland on 10th October 2002 is a high count for autumn passage.

Redwing   *Turdus iliacus*

A common winter visitor and passage migrant
Mansel-Pleydell (1888) was rather vague regarding this species, referring to it as only an autumn visitor, whilst Blathwayt (1945) considered it to be a common winter visitor.

Although there are early autumn records on 4th September 1980 at Stanpit Marsh, Christchurch Harbour, 6th September 1982 at Portland Bill and 8th September 1973 at Stalbridge (15 birds), the first migrants usually appear during late September and early October. The average date of the first arrivals was considerably earlier in the 1980s than during the 1970s and 1990s – see Table 475.

	1970–1979	1980–1989	1990–1999
Range	8th September–8th October	4th September–3rd October	22nd September–8th October
Average	27th September	19th September	29th September

Table 475. Dates for first autumn arrivals each decade 1970–1999

The main autumn passage, which is often well marked both along the coast and inland, occurs earlier than that for Fieldfare and normally peaks during late October and early November, but may extend into early December. Seasonal totals can vary considerably from year to year – see Table 476. Massive nocturnal movements involving thousands of birds sometimes occur and may be followed by large falls of 'grounded' birds, e.g. at Durlston CP in late October/early November 1983 with a fall of 2,200 on 8th November. Heavy diurnal passage also occurs, the most notable being an exceptional 15,000N over Portland on 11th

October 1973 including 8,000N at the Bill, also 3,500S at Portland Bill on 12th October 1972. Otherwise there are several records of day-counts ranging from 1,000 to 2,200 birds.

The Redwing is widely reported during the winter in flocks of up to 500 birds or so. Much larger numbers occasionally occur, usually during periods of severe cold when movements can be spectacular and involve several thousands of birds. For example, in January 1963 a large westerly passage occurred, whilst on 20th February 1969 heavy movements included 7,000 at Portland Bill, 6,000 at Arne NR and 4,000 at Radipole Village. More recently 6,000 flew west at Radipole NR on 12th December 1981 followed by various counts of c.4,000-15,000 at sites in the Weymouth/Fleet area on 9th January 1982 with 3,300 at Christchurch Harbour the previous day. There were widespread heavy movements during 6th–10th February 1991 including 10,760W at Christchurch Harbour (maximum of 9,000W on 9th). Finally in early 1996, 4,000 were present on Portland on 27th January, 3,000 at East Fleet on 8th February and 4,000 at Hengistbury on 20th February.

	1980	1981	1982	1983	1984	1985	1986	1987	1988	1989
Portland Bill	749	513	429	1656	1720	1016	745	784	809	1270
Durlston CP	nc	nc	1162	nc	2468	2350	373	704	3070	3387

	1990	1991	1992	1993	1994	1995	1996	1997	1998	1999
Portland Bill	568	926	1990	3379	1009	545	700	736	450	604
Durlston CP	3510	3647	953	nc	nc	3605	2900	3576	nc	580

Table 476. Autumn totals (bds) at Portland Bill and Durlston CP 1980–1999

Otherwise there was a very large roost at Duncliffe Wood between 1967 and 1979. During the winter of 1967/68 vast numbers of this species and Fieldfare perhaps reached totals in excess of 100,000 birds. In other winters more modest totals of Redwings were recorded, the highest being 10,000 in February 1977 and 5,000 on 8th February 1978, whilst the joint total with Fieldfare reached 10,000 in early 1975. Other large roost counts include c.10,000 at Shillingstone in January 1964 and c.7,500 at Radipole NR on 23rd January 1977.

Spring migration is more evident at the coastal watch-points than for the Fieldfare, but seasonal totals can vary considerably from year to year – see Table 477. Heavy nocturnal movements may occur during the main passage period in March, e.g. at Portland Bill during 1st–10th March 1981, Hengistbury during 15th February–31st March 1998, and Durlston CP in March 1999 with c.2,000 there during 18th–25th March 1983 and again during 5th–25th March 1984 (reaching a maximum of 700 on 5th). Diurnal passage is generally more modest, the highest day-count being an exceptional 1,000+ at Portland Bill on 13th March 1955 with other peak counts rarely exceeding 100 birds, the best being 350N at Durlston CP on 14th March 1991 with 200W there on 5th March 1990.

	1980	1981	1982	1983	1984	1985	1986	1987	1988	1989
Portland Bill	64	99	110	49	319	159	886	489	120	20
Durlston CP	nc	nc	119	nc	nc	nc	173	120	8	614

	1990	1991	1992	1993	1994	1995	1996	1997	1998	1999
Portland Bill	33	32	51	103	35	92	128	14	225	47
Durlston CP	425	1200	1004	nc	nc	147	531	320	nc	nc

Table 477. Spring totals (bds) at Portland Bill and Durlston CP 1980–1999

The last birds are normally recorded in April, the latest of several May reports being all from Hengistbury/Christchurch Harbour on 12th May 1991, 13th May 1984 and 15th May 1996. There is an exceptional mid-summer record of one at Radipole NR on 7th July 1986.

Icelandic birds of the race *T. i. coburni* have been recorded on a number of occasions either trapped on passage or found dead in severe cold weather.

A total of 3,417 birds has been ringed in the county. There have been four foreign recoveries each from France and Portugal, three from Spain, and one each from Belgium, Sweden, Finland, Poland and Georgia, as well as one foreign control from Sweden.

The Redwing is a summer visitor breeding across most of northern Eurasia including Iceland and very locally in northern Scotland. It winters mainly in western and southern Europe, north-west Africa, Asia Minor and parts of the Middle East.

Mistle Thrush

Turdus viscivorus

A common resident, winter visitor and passage migrant

Although reported to be extremely scarce at the end of the 18th Century, Mansel-Pleydell (1888) considered this species to be common. Blathwayt (1945) described the Mistle Thrush as "a common resident" and noted that it had been recorded on passage.

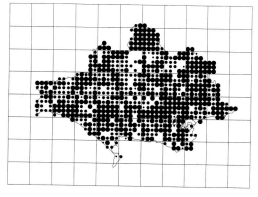

There has been little change in status subsequently. The *BTO Atlas* (1968–1972) found evidence of breeding in 35 (95%) 10-km squares (confirmed in 33 and probable in two), whilst the Tetrad Survey (1987–1994) produced an almost identical result with evidence of breeding in 35 (95%) of the pre-1974 10-km squares (confirmed in 34 and probable in one). The Tetrad Map shows that this species is a widely distributed breeding bird throughout the county. There is insufficient information to comment meaningfully on long-term population trends.

Passage is often negligible at the main coastal watch-points with seasonal totals ranging from 0–12 birds in spring, mainly March–April, and rarely exceeding 25 birds in autumn, mainly October–November, but exceptional numbers were recorded from Portland Bill in 1961 with 267 bird-days during 7th August–13th November (reaching a maximum of 90 on 30th October), and Durlston CP in 1982 with 207 bird-days during September–December. Birds are occasionally involved in cold weather movements, e.g. 60 at Radipole NR in mid-February 1979, 60 at Lytchett Bay on 9th February 1991, 37W at Christchurch Harbour on 8th–9th February 1991 with 36W at Hengistbury on 28th January 1979, and 26S at Portland Bill during 12th–24th December 1981.

Post-breeding flocks are a regular feature of the late summer and autumn with gatherings of up to 50 birds frequently reported, the highest counts being 150–200 at Pentridge on 9th September 1967, 152 at Sherborne Lake on 26th August 1975 and 100 at Uddens on 28th August 1974.

A total of 312 birds has been ringed in the county.

The Mistle Thrush breeds throughout most of Europe, except the far north, extending eastwards into west-central Asia, also in north-west Africa and Asia Minor. It is largely resident in the west and south of its range, being a summer visitor in the north and east. These migratory populations winter in western and southern Europe, north-west Africa, Asia Minor, the Middle East and extreme south-west Asia.

American Robin

Turdus migratorius

Accidental: one record

1966   Brand's Bay: 15th–16th January; same at Canford Cliffs 18th January–10th March

After foraging along the shore of Brand's Bay, this individual then moved to a Canford Cliffs garden where it remained until early March.

The American Robin breeds across most of North America south into Mexico, and winters mainly in the USA, Mexico, Guatemala, Cuba and the Bahamas. A vagrant to the British Isles with 32 records up to 2000.

Cetti's Warbler

Cettia cetti

A locally common resident and rare passage migrant

This recent colonist first bred in Great Britain in 1972, the same year as Dorset's first record which involved a singing bird at Radipole NR on 21st October. There were no further reports until another at Radipole NR on 29th September 1974, which was followed in 1975 by 1–2 birds intermittently at Lodmoor NR from 25th April to 29th October and one at Hengistbury on 18th May. There was a mini-influx in autumn 1976 involving at least nine birds recorded from Radipole NR, Lodmoor NR, Portland Bill, Chapman's Pool and Burton near Christchurch. These records were the precursors to breeding being confirmed at Radipole NR in 1977 with at least 11 birds present in the Weymouth area during that autumn. Elsewhere during 1977, there were reports from the Lower Avon Valley, Christchurch Harbour, Brownsea and Wimborne.

Colonisation was rapid along the coastal strip between Weymouth and Cogden Beach with the bulk of the population based at Radipole and Lodmoor NRs – see Table 478. The lack of consistent population data from some key sites makes interpretation of long-term trends tentative, but there is evidence of a decline in numbers after the initial colonisation, which peaked at 25 singing males in 1981. This is supported by a slight contraction in range in the west with regular breeding ceasing at Cogden Beach during 1982–1993, West Bexington during 1982–1986 and Abbotsbury during 1987–1993. Since the early 1990s, this trend has been reversed as shown by a marked increase in the breeding population. This is reflected by the number of singing males at the main sites, e.g. at Radipole NR from seven in 1980 to 21 in 1996 and at Lodmoor NR from three in 1980 to 11 in 1993. In addition, the sites to the west of Weymouth have been recolonised with singing males reaching counts of five at Abbotsbury, four at West Bexington and one at Cogden Beach in 1995. There has also been a recent slight expansion eastwards along the coast to the Osmington Mills/Ringstead Bay area with 1–2 singing males recorded regularly since 1991.

78	79	80	81	82	83	84	85	86	87	88	89	90	91	92	93	94	95
12	nc	20	25	16	22	nc	nc	nc	12	nc	nc	nc	17	14	29	32	39

Table 478. Number of singing males Weymouth to Cogden Beach 1978–1995

The Cetti's Warbler remained relatively scarce in the rest of Dorset until 1982 when there was a marked increase in reports from the western fringes of Poole Harbour and breeding was first confirmed at Christchurch Harbour. Subsequent expansion in the east of the county was almost instantaneous, the main centres of population being the western fringes of Poole Harbour between Wareham and Lytchett Bay, Christchurch Harbour and the Lower Avon Valley – see Table 479. As in the Weymouth area, the population in the east initially increased to a peak and then declined with evidence of a resurgence in the mid-1990s. The total of 27–33 singing males located along the western fringes of Poole Harbour during the 1996 National Survey suggest that earlier population counts from this area were under-estimated.

	83	84	85	86	87	88	89	90	91	92	93	94	95	96
Poole Harbour (west)	12	7	9	c6	c7	7	>3	8	2	nc	c4	c8	6	33
Christchurch Harbour	6	8	10	nc	1	3	4	1	sev	3	3	0	5	nc
Lower Avon Valley	2	4	6	3	5	10	11	4	5	2	2	2	5	nc

Table 479. Number of singing males at the main sites in east Dorset 1983–1996

Away from the Lower Avon Valley, the species has attempted to colonise other river valleys, as shown by a scattering of breeding season reports from various sites along the Stour, Moors, Allen, Frome, Piddle and Cerne, but there has been little permanent success. The exception to this is the River Frome between Woodsford and Dorchester where breeding appears to have become established since it was first proven at Woodsford in 1991.

Although the breeding population has increased since the Tetrad Survey (1987–1994), there has been little change in the overall distribution as shown by the Tetrad Map. The 1996 National Survey estimated

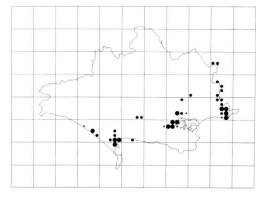

the county population to be in the region of 89–97 singing males, which amounts to 16% of the national population. Prior to this survey the highest Dorset population was 67 singing males in 1984, which fell to 37 singing males in 1986. Although some decreases can be attributed to cold winters, notably in 1985/86 and 1986/87, other declines cannot be linked to this factor. Although coverage has been incomplete during 1997–1999, there is no evidence to suggest any significant change in the county's breeding population during this period.

Migrants and/or locally dispersing birds are occasionally recorded from coastal watch-points at Portland and along the Purbeck coast, which are well away from the main breeding sites – see Table 480. Most of the Purbeck records come from the St Aldhelm's Head/Chapman's Pool area with only three reports from Durlston CP on 9th–10th November 1987, 16th May 1997 and 30th October 1999.

	76	77	78	79	80	81	82	83	84	85	86	87
Portland	1	3	0	1	1	1	0	0	0	0	0	0
Purbeck coast	3	0	0	0	0	0	3	4	3	0	0	2

	88	89	90	91	92	93	94	95	96	97	98	99
Portland	1	3	0	0	0	4	0	0	1	1	0	0
Purbeck coast	0	0	0	0	0	2	1	0	2	1	0	1

Table 480. Totals of migrants/dispersing birds at Portland and the Purbeck coast 1976–1999

The Cetti's Warbler is rare in the north of the county with most reports from Sherborne Lake involving singles on 10th December 1989, 14th and 20th December 1997, during 10th January–15th April 1998 and on 31st December 1999, also singles at Marnhull on 1st December 1979, Hammoon on 25th September 1982 and Lodden Lakes near Gillingham in 1996.

A total of 555 birds has been ringed in the county. Four birds ringed in Hampshire have been controlled in Dorset suggesting a westerly dispersal after the breeding season, whilst one Dorset ringed bird has made the reverse journey. There are other recoveries of Dorset ringed birds from Glamorgan, Somerset and more locally St Aldhelm's Head. In addition a bird ringed in Devon was controlled at Portland Bill.

It may be significant that eight birds ringed and controlled in Dorset at distances over 10km were females and only one of them was over one year old. Sound records, however, clearly indicate that males wander in search of new territories in spring. Studies at Radipole NR showed that, while most birds were sedentary, a minority of adult males and females regularly left their breeding territories in September and returned in April. It was also noted that influxes of Cetti's Warblers coincided with arrivals of *Phylloscopus* warblers suggesting a common origin for the species concerned.

The Cetti's Warbler breeds in western Europe from southern Great Britain and the Netherlands south through France and Iberia to north-west Africa and east through southern Europe to Asia Minor and the Middle East, reaching the eastern limit of its range in west-central Asia. The nominate western race *C. c. cetti* is mainly sedentary.

Sponsored by Colin Raymond

Fan-tailed Warbler (Zitting Cisticola)　　　*Cisticola juncidis*

Accidental: three records

Dorset can boast a near-monopoly of this rarity with no less than three of the four British records. Remarkably 23 years after the first county record in 1977, two arrived almost simultaneously in May 2000.

1977　Lodmoor NR: singing male 24th–28th June
2000　Portland Bill: singing male 15th–16th May
　　　　Hengistbury: singing male 20th–31st May, visiting Stanpit Marsh on a couple of occasions

A short account of the Lodmoor bird can be found in *British Birds*, Vol. 73, Number 1, January 1980. Accounts of the 2000 records can be found in *Birding World*, Vol. 13, Number 5, June 2000.

The Fan-tailed Warbler breeds from the Netherlands and the Channel coast of France south to Iberia and north-west Africa, and east through southern Europe to parts of Asia Minor, the Middle East and Egypt. There are other populations in sub-Saharan Africa, the Indian sub-continent, south-east Asia and Australia.

It has spread west and north in Europe during the 20th Century reaching the Channel coast of France and the Netherlands by the mid-1970s. Although almost extinct in these areas after the severe winters of the mid-1980s, it had recolonised by the late 1990s. A vagrant to Great Britain with only 4 records up to 2002.

Pallas's Grasshopper Warbler *Locustella certhiola*

Accidental: one record

 1996   Portland Bird Observatory: trapped 13th September

Since most records of this species occur in the Northern Isles, mainly Shetland, this first-winter bird trapped at Portland Bird Observatory is particularly noteworthy. A brief account can be found in the Dorset Bird Report for 1996.

 The Pallas's Grasshopper Warbler is a summer visitor breeding from western Siberia and central Asia east to Japan, and south to Mongolia and northern China. It winters in the Indian sub-continent and south-east Asia. A vagrant to Great Britain with 29 records up to 2002.

Grasshopper Warbler
(Common Grasshopper Warbler) *Locustella naevia*

A scarce summer visitor and uncommon passage migrant

This species was known to Mansel-Pleydell (1888) as a breeding summer visitor and to Blathwayt (1945) as a local and somewhat irregular summer visitor, widely distributed in the county, but more frequent in the eastern half, especially around Poole Harbour.

There is evidence of a growing and expanding breeding population during the 1950s and 1960s, associated in particular with the spread of young forestry plantations as reported from the Marshwood Vale in 1957 and the Cranborne area in 1960. This was reflected by the *BTO Atlas* (1968–1972), which revealed evidence of breeding in all but one (97%) of the 10-km squares (confirmed in 19, probable in 16 and possible in one). A decrease in breeding numbers was suggested from the mid-1970s and became more apparent during the 1980s. This decline was shown by the Tetrad Survey (1987–1994), which found evidence of breeding in 26 (70%) of the pre-

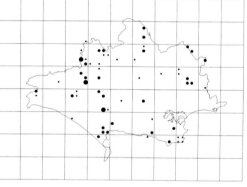

1974 10-km squares, but more significantly breeding was confirmed in only three, being probable in 15 and possible in eight. The Tetrad Map shows that it had become very sparsely distributed across the county.

 Due to the Grasshopper Warbler's secretive behaviour and the fact that males sing on spring migration, it is difficult to accurately assess the strength of the breeding population. During 1970–1972 estimates varied between 40–57 pairs, whilst the subsequent decline is reflected by the number of singing males reported since 1980 – see Table 481. Although there appears to have been a revival in the mid-1990s, most of these records apparently refer to migrants. Indeed breeding was last confirmed in 1990, whilst since 1994 there has been little evidence of birds holding territory long enough to indicate breeding.

80	81	82	83	84	85	86	87	88	89	90	91	92	93	94	95	96	97	98	99
25	29	17	15	7	18	27	31	20	17	18	8	8	6	13	1–2	c17	14	16	4

Table 481. Number of singing males in Dorset 1980–1999

 The decline in Dorset is reflected nationally, there being a large reduction in the British population since a peak in the 1960s. The reasons for this decline are uncertain. Although there has been some loss of habitat from land drainage, scrub and hedgerow clearance, and the maturing of young conifer plantations, there are still many suitable sites in Dorset which remain unoccupied. Numbers fluctuate widely at the most favoured haunts, whilst many other sites are occupied only intermittently. A more likely cause of the decline is drought in the Sahel region resulting in greater mortality on migration.

The earliest spring record is 24th March 1996 at Easton, Portland. Otherwise the first spring migrants usually appear during the first half of April with the average date of the first arrivals gradually becoming earlier since the 1950s – see Table 482.

	1950–1959	1960–1969	1970–1979	1980–1989	1990–1999
Range	12th–22nd April	29th March–23rd April	5th–17th April	29th March–14th April	24th March–12th April
Average	15th April	11th April	12th April	8th April	4th April

Table 482. Dates for first spring arrivals each decade 1950–1999

In spring, the main migration period extends from mid-April to early May with peak passage often recorded during the last ten days of April. A few late stragglers may occur through to the end of May. Autumn migrants first appear during July with the main passage extending through August to mid-September.

Numbers of migrants recorded at the main coastal watch-points are highly variable, the general pattern of passage being occasionally interspersed by exceptional influxes, which are often limited to a single site – see Tables 483 and 484. The most notable of these occurred at Portland Bill in spring 1967 (140), spring 1970 (122), autumn 1970 (177), spring 1980 (140) and spring 1989 (163), Portland (whole island) in spring 1972 (140) and Durlston CP in autumn 1992 (152). Not surprisingly the highest day-totals often coincide with the periodic spring influxes at Portland Bill, notably 40 on 24th April 1989, and 35 on 27th April 1967 and 23rd April 1981, whilst the best counts in autumn are 20 at Portland Bill on 6th August 1970 and 11 at Durlston CP on 29th September 1992. Otherwise peak counts in spring rarely exceed 20 birds and those in autumn rarely exceed ten.

	1980	1981	1982	1983	1984	1985	1986	1987	1988	1989
Portland Bill	140	nc	60	21	20	48	11	32	52	163
Durlston CP	32	13	19	15	32	17	12	13	30	37
Christchurch Hbr	25	38	16	4	12	18	5	9	10	32
	1990	1991	1992	1993	1994	1995	1996	1997	1998	1999
Portland Bill	65	58	41	30	20	79	55	43	38	28
Durlston CP	22	26	27	16	8	29	24	33	31	29
Christchurch Hbr	nc	31	4	10	25	3	10	14	9	11

Table 483. Spring totals (bds) at the main coastal watch-points 1980–1999

	1980	1981	1982	1983	1984	1985	1986	1987	1988	1989
Portland Bill	31	44	15	28	5	13	3	12	20	19
Durlston CP	nc	39	28	46	46	38	56	42	57	65
Christchurch Hbr	nc	2	4	6	19	7	3	7	4	1
	1990	1991	1992	1993	1994	1995	1996	1997	1998	1999
Portland Bill	20	21	28	25	16	9	15	31	24	5
Durlston CP	54	40	152	76	35	44	42	54	43	49
Christchurch Hbr	nc	1	1	10	4	6	7	3	5	2

Table 484. Autumn totals (bds) at the main coastal watch-points 1980–1999

Although there is clear evidence that the decline in the breeding population is reflected by diminishing numbers of migrants at Portland Bill, this is not so evident at Durlston CP – see Tables 485 and 486.

	1965–69	1970–74	1975–79	1980–84	1985–89	1990–94	1995–99
Spring	76	91	34	60	61	43	49
Autumn	50	63	37	25	13	22	17

Table 485. 5-year average seasonal totals (bds) at Portland Bill 1965–1999

	1980–84	1985–89	1990–94	1995–99
Spring	22	22	20	29
Autumn	40	52	71	46

Table 486. 5-year average seasonal totals (bds) at Durlston CP 1980–1999

Spring totals at Portland Bill and Christchurch Harbour are generally much higher than in autumn, but the situation is reversed at Durlston CP. Indeed the numbers of autumn migrants at some sites may be under-recorded due to the species' secretive behaviour. Recent ringing totals resulting from systematic trapping in reedbeds at Keysworth are perhaps a more realistic reflection of the true strength of autumn passage through the county – see Table 487.

1991	1992	1993	1994	1995	1996	1997	1998	1999
60	30	54	107	125	19	36	15	nc

Table 487. Totals trapped in autumn at Keysworth 1991–1999

The last birds usually occur in late September or during October, the latest records being 25th October 1979 at Portland Bill and 2nd November 1988 at Durlston CP.

A total of 1,068 birds has been ringed in the county and although there has been one foreign control from Eire, there are no reports of any foreign recoveries.

The Grasshopper Warbler is a summer visitor breeding across western and central Europe extending north to southern Scandinavia and south to northern Spain, and eastwards into west-central Asia to about 100°E. The wintering quarters of the western nominate race *L. n. naevia* are not well-known, but apparently lie mainly in tropical West Africa, whilst the eastern race *L. n. straminea* winters mainly in the Indian sub-continent.

Postscript 2000–2002
The decline continues, the only evidence of breeding involving a reeling bird at Lodmoor NR from 20th April to 20th August 2000.

Savi's Warbler   *Locustella luscinioides*

A rare passage migrant and summer visitor – has bred

The status of the Savi's Warbler in Dorset very much mirrors the fortunes of this species in Great Britain as a whole since 1960, when recolonisation occurred in Kent after a 100 years of extinction. Nationally numbers increased from 1965 to reach a peak in the 1980s, but subsequently declined to reach very low levels during the 1990s.

The first county records involved one trapped at Radipole NR on 20th August 1973 followed by a singing male at Portland Bill on 29th April 1974. There were three reports in 1975 and, after an absence in 1976, from 1–6 birds were recorded annually up to 1989 – see Table 488. Subsequently there have been only five records in three years during the 1990s.

1973	1974	1975	1976	1977	1978	1979	1980	1981	1982	1983	1984	1985	1986
1	1	3	0	1	4	1	2	6	6	2	4	4	3

1987	1988	1989	1990	1991	1992	1993	1994	1995	1996	1997	1998	1999	2000
4	3	1	0	2	0	0	1	0	2	0	0	0	0

Table 488. Annual totals 1973–2000

The majority of birds have been reported in spring and early summer with April and May accounting for 76% of the total – see Table 489. Although records extend from 15th April 1985 to 13th–14th June 1987 – both at Radipole NR, some birds have held territory throughout the summer into July, and as late as 22nd August at Lodmoor NR in 1977. Excluding these long-staying individuals, there are six additional records for the early autumn. The two July birds both occurred in 1996, the first at Radipole NR from 11th–21st July is perhaps best considered a late arrival, whilst the second at Christchurch Harbour on 21st July should be considered an autumn migrant, together with the four August reports on dates ranging between 2nd and 20th.

April	May	June	July	August
15	17	6	2	4

Table 489. Monthly totals 1973–1999

Not surprisingly, records are mainly from localities with extensive reedbeds – see Table 490. Radipole NR is the most favoured of these sites and accounts for 37% of the total, the other main haunts being the reedbeds fringing the western side of Poole Harbour between Arne NR and Lytchett Bay, Lodmoor NR and Christchurch Harbour. There are three spring reports from Portland Bill, whilst the remaining records involve one singing by the River Stour at Wimborne during 9th–18th May 1975 and one at Durlston CP on 2nd–3rd August 1981.

	Spring/Summer		Autumn		Total	
Portland Bill	3	7%	0	0	3	6%
Radipole NR	17	38%	2	33%	19	37%
Lodmoor NR	9	20%	0	0	9	18%
Poole Harbour (west)	11	24%	1	17%	12	24%
Christchurch Harbour	4	9%	2	33%	6	12%
elsewhere	1	2%	1	17%	2	4%

Table 490. Distribution of birds including migrants 1973–1999

Although many of the spring and summer records involve singing males holding territory for up to 15 days, breeding has been either suspected or proven on only four occasions as follows:

1977   Lodmoor NR: singing male 9th May–22nd August, trapped 26th May
1978   Lodmoor NR: up to three singing males 28th April–July
1981   Holton Shore: three singing males during the breeding season
1982   Holton Shore: two pairs bred but success unknown

A total of four birds has been ringed in the county.

The Savi's Warbler is a summer visitor breeding from north-west Africa, Iberia and France locally across much of central and southern Europe, and more widely from eastern Europe into west-central Asia, also locally in Asia Minor and the Middle East. It winters in a narrow band across the northern tropics of Africa. After temporarily recolonising southern England in the 1960s, it has declined to become a vagrant again to Great Britain with 614 records during 1958–2002.

Aquatic Warbler   *Acrocephalus paludicola*

A scarce autumn passage migrant

The first Dorset record involved a bird by the River Stour at Bryanston on 16th September 1953. This was followed by reports of 12 birds in eight years during 1955–1970 – see Fig 49. Since 1971 the species has occurred annually in much higher numbers. This is mainly the result of intensive ringing activities, most notably at Radipole NR during 1971–1979 and more recently at Keysworth during 1991–1998, with trapped birds accounting for 65% of the total records. Indeed, the true extent of passage through the county's reedbeds would go largely undetected but for these ringing operations.

Records extend from 26th July 1976 at Brownsea to 11th–12th October 1955 at Portland Bill and 12th October 1982 at Lodmoor NR with an exceptionally late bird at West Bexington on 1st–2nd November 1985. Peak passage occurs during the second half of August with 64% of the total, the month as a whole accounting for 74% – see Table 491.

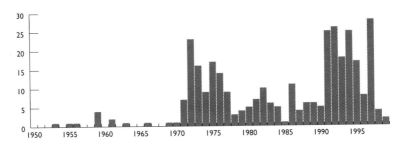

Fig 49. Autumn totals 1950–1999

Jul	Aug	Aug	Aug	Sep	Sep	Sep	Oct	Oct	Oct	Nov
21–31	1–10	11–20	21–31	1–10	11–20	21–30	1–10	11–20	21–31	1–10
<1%	10%	36%	28%	11%	8%	5%	2%	<1%	0%	<1%

Table 491. Proportion (%) of autumn migrants in 10-day periods during autumn 1953–1999

The annual totals generally reflect the amount of ringing effort, the high counts during the 1970s and 1990s are mainly due to the number of birds trapped at Radipole NR and Keysworth – see Table 492. It is not surprising that these two sites account for 31% and 23% respectively of the total records, whilst the only other localities to attract substantial numbers are Christchurch Harbour and Lodmoor NR each with 14% – see Table 493.

Prior to the start of intensive ringing activities at reedbed locations, Portland Bill was the main site accounting for 11 of the 12 birds recorded during 1955–1970. Radipole NR was by far the premier site for Aquatic Warblers during 1971–1979 with 81% of the total for this period. Nearby Lodmoor NR became the main locality in the 1980s based on both birds trapped and sight records during 1980–1986, which together accounted for 49% of the total for the decade. Finally Keysworth has been the most favoured site during the 1990s with 49% of the total for this period.

	1971	1972	1973	1974	1975	1976	1977	1978
Radipole NR	6	22	16	8	11	10	3	3

	1991	1992	1993	1994	1995	1996	1997	1998
Keysworth	21	13	7	17	5	4	11	0

Table 492. Ringing totals from Radipole NR 1971–1978 and Keysworth 1991–1998

Away from the four main sites, reedbeds adjacent to the Fleet and Chesil Beach have recorded good numbers during the 1990s with 15 birds at Abbotsbury during 1992–1997 including six in 1993, and nine birds at West Bexington during 9th–12th August 1997. Most of the remaining birds have occurred at Portland Bill (22), where birds have been observed in cereal crops, and Durlston CP (six). There are also reports from Brownsea on 26th July 1976, Lytchett Bay (trapped) on 22nd August 1983 and Langton Herring on 19th–20th September 1987, whilst the location of the county's first record is not without precedent with further inland records from Sutton Bingham on 25th September 1986 and Puddletown on 22nd August 1988.

	Total	
Cogden Beach/West Bexington	12	4%
Abbotsbury	15	4%
Portland Bill	22	7%
Radipole NR	102	31%
Lodmoor NR	46	14%
Durlston CP	6	2%
Keysworth	78	23%
Christchurch Harbour	47	14%
elsewhere	6	2%

Table 493. Distribution of migrants 1953–1999

The majority of reports involve singles, very occasionally two or more birds, the highest counts being a minimum of five at West Bexington on 11th August 1997, which coincided with a large movement of *Acrocephalus* warblers that morning, four trapped at Radipole NR on 15th and 17th August 1972, and four in corn crops at Portland Bill on 14th August 1977.

A total of 217 birds has been ringed in the county.

The Aquatic Warbler is a summer visitor to eastern Europe, which has undergone a considerable decline during the 20th Century. The species now breeds in a few isolated colonies, mainly in eastern Germany and Hungary, with the bulk of the population occurring in eastern Poland, the Baltic States, Belarus, the Ukraine and west-central Russia. Its winter quarters are poorly known, but are thought to lie mainly in the Sahel region of West Africa. Migration is circular with birds moving west or south-west in autumn along a narrow corridor through the Netherlands, Belgium, northern France and southern England and then south to leave Europe via Iberia. Return migration in spring is more direct.

Postscript 2000–2002

A total of eight birds, including four trapped at Keysworth, occurred during August 2000, but only two single birds were reported in both autumn 2001 and autumn 2002.

Sponsored by Ian Lewis

Sedge Warbler   *Acrocephalus schoenobaenus*

A common summer visitor and passage migrant

Both Mansel-Pleydell (1888) and Blathwayt (1945) referred to this species as a common summer visitor, a status which has not changed subsequently.

The *BTO Atlas* (1968–1972) revealed evidence of breeding in 33 (89%) 10-km squares (confirmed in 25, probable in seven and possible in one), the most notable absence being ST40. The Tetrad Survey (1987–1994) produced a similar result with evidence of breeding in 32 (86%) of the pre-1974 10-km squares (confirmed in 21, probable in six and possible in five), the most notable absences being SY39 and ST91. The Tetrad Map reflects the Sedge Warbler's habitat preference for dense wetland and riverine scrub with breeding concentrated in the river valleys and coastal marshes with just a scatter of records elsewhere.

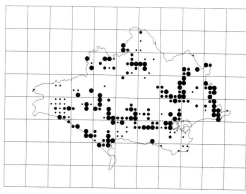

The limited available data suggests that since 1980, despite some fluctuation, the breeding population has been relatively stable overall – see Tables 494 to 496. The exception to this was in 1984 when numbers fell dramatically at Radipole and Lodmoor NRs. This decrease was also recorded on the River Stour between Corfe Mullen and Sturminster Marshall in 1983 and 1984. The reason for this decline was extreme drought conditions in some wintering areas in West Africa during 1983/84, resulting in the survival of only c.5% of adult Sedge Warblers to return to their breeding grounds.

Subsequent recovery in the breeding population was rapid. During the late 1970s breeding numbers at Radipole NR varied between 70–120 territories with the peak in 1977.

	1980	1981	1982	1983	1984	1985	1986	1987	1988	1989
Radipole NR	84	73	80	70	22	65	84	94	81	nc
Lodmoor NR	n	nc	47	61	6	84	67	75	58	68

Table 494. Number of breeding territories at Radipole and Lodmoor NRs 1980–1989

78	79	80	81	82	83	84	85	86	87	88	89	90	91	92	93	94	95	96	97	98
12	15	26	17	20	12	11	14	21	17	21	23	29	28	21	14	12	20	17	11	9

Table 495. Number of breeding territories along River Stour between Corfe Mullen and Sturminster Marshall 1978–1998

1989	1990	1991	1992	1993	1994	1995	1996	1997	1998	1999
83	72	78	95	78	78	102	122	84	89	100

Table 496. Number of breeding territories along River Allen 1989–1999

There is a very early record on 2nd March 1974 at the Fleet Coastguard Cottages at Langton Herring with other early reports on 15th March 1997 at Radipole NR and 22nd March 1991 at Christchurch Harbour. Otherwise the first spring migrants usually appear from late March to mid-April with the average date of the first arrivals gradually becoming earlier since the 1950s – see Table 497.

	1950–1959	1960–1969	1970–1979	1980–1989	1990–1999
Range	5th–21st April	29th March–17th April	2nd March–16th April	26th March–18th April	15th March–6th April
Average	14th April	10th April	5th April	3rd April	29th March

Table 497. Dates for first spring arrivals each decade 1950–1999

	1980	1981	1982	1983	1984	1985	1986	1987	1988	1989
Portland Bill	85	76	71	34	166	102	38	101	93	183
Durlston CP	23	17	17	15	49	38	19	43	36	94

	1990	1991	1992	1993	1994	1995	1996	1997	1998	1999
Portland Bill	63	310	39	57	61	99	160	61	67	60
Durlston CP	61	99	22	43	14	39	51	70	43	49

Table 498. Spring totals (bds) at Portland Bill and Durlston CP 1980–1999

	1980	1981	1982	1983	1984	1985	1986	1987	1988	1989
Portland Bill	249	489	120	213	113	76	85	104	104	158
Durlston CP	15	43	30	49	98	59	46	87	88	100

	1990	1991	1992	1993	1994	1995	1996	1997	1998	1999
Portland Bill	94	107	86	116	152	183	268	161	91	53
Durlston CP	83	74	116	64	22	69	114	109	85	94

Table 499. Autumn totals (bds) at Portland Bill and Durlston CP 1980–1999

Although spring migration extends through April and May with a few late stragglers occasionally reported in early June, peak passage normally occurs from late April to mid-May. Seasonal totals from coastal watch-points such as Portland Bill and Durlston CP are highly variable – see Table 498. Peak counts generally range from 10–60 birds, the best being 80 at Portland Bill on 9th May 1967 and 9th May 1968, and 75 at Christchurch Harbour on 10th May 1993, but there is an exceptional record of c.300 at Portland

Bill on 29th April 1955. Autumn passage begins in July, builds up rapidly to peak during August and subsequently declines through September. Again seasonal totals from coastal watch-points such as Portland Bill and Durlston CP are highly variable – see Table 499. Peak counts generally range from 10–40 and rarely exceed 50 birds, the best being 70 at Portland Bill on 6th August 1970. Good numbers have also been recorded from St Aldhelm's Head in some years, notably 221 bird-days in 1990, 160 bird-days in 1989 and 125 bird-days in 1983.

Large numbers of migrants pass through coastal reedbeds during the late summer and autumn, particularly in years when the Plum-reed Aphid is plentiful. Consequently, the true strength of autumn passage is better reflected by counts, mainly as a result of systematic trapping, from such sites. For example, ringing totals from Radipole NR include 3,363 in 1972, 2,869 in 1975 and 1,551 in 1997, whilst at Keysworth impressive numbers were caught during the early 1990s with a large arrival of c.500 birds on 6th August 1995 – see Table 500. At Christchurch Harbour, there are frequent three-figure counts during late July and August, the highest being 400 in August 1983 and on 15th & 16th August 1991.

1991	1992	1993	1994	1995	1996	1997
3444	1903	2659	4327	1808	679	593

Table 500. Totals trapped in autumn at Keysworth 1991–1997

The last migrants are usually reported in October, the latest being 30th October 1974 at Christchurch Harbour except for an exceptionally late bird at Little Sea on 28th November 1984.

A total of 64,754 birds has been ringed in the county. There have been recoveries and controls from many parts of the British Isles including Orkney, Northern Ireland and southern Eire with a regular interchange of birds between Keysworth and Icklesham in East Sussex. Further afield there have been seven recoveries from Senegal, two from Mali and one each from Liberia and Ghana, plus one control from Senegal clearly indicating that our birds winter in sub-Saharan West Africa. There have been c.52 recoveries from France – many from the Etang du Trunvel in Finisterre, as well as the Channel Islands (14), Spain (five), Portugal (two) and Morocco (two) plus controls from France (c.10) and the Channel Islands (one) suggesting that a direct route is taken during migration. In addition there have been five recoveries and two controls from Belgium, and one control from Switzerland.

The Sedge Warbler is a summer visitor breeding throughout much of Europe from northern Scandinavia south to south-west France, northern Italy and the Balkans, and eastwards into western Asia; also in parts of Asia Minor. It winters throughout much of sub-Saharan Africa.

Postscript 2000–2002

The largest ever fall occurred at Portland on 5th May 2002 with 100 at the Bill and at least 50 at other sites in the centre of the island.

Blyth's Reed Warbler   *Acrocephalus dumetorum*

Accidental: three records

    1989   Portland Bill: trapped 12th June
    2001   Portland Bill: 16th October–3rd November, trapped 16th
           Portland Bill: trapped 12th November

The Blyth's Reed Warbler is a summer visitor breeding from southern Finland and the Baltic States eastwards across Russia to west-central Asia. It winters in the Indian sub-continent and Burma. A vagrant to Great Britain with 56 records up to 2002.

Marsh Warbler   *Acrocephalus palustris*

A rare passage migrant and summer visitor – has bred

This species probably bred annually at Abbotsbury up to 1954. Otherwise breeding reports from earlier years are sporadic. Blathwayt (1945) referred to breeding near Shillingstone in 1893, near Sherborne in

1897 and 1925, near Blandford in 1904 and in some numbers there in 1919, and in south-west Dorset in 1908 where there were haunts supporting several pairs every year. In the late 1940s birds sang in the Yeo Valley during 1948–1950 and a colony of 6–8 pairs was present in east Dorset in 1949.

Since the mid-1950s evidence of breeding has been very scarce. Although singing males occurred at the traditional site at Abbotsbury in at least five years during 1965–1985, most only remained for 1 or 2 days and perhaps should be considered as spring migrants. During the *BTO Atlas* (1968–1972) breeding was confirmed in SY88, whilst singing males were present at East Weare, Portland from 8th–20th June 1969 and Bridport for two weeks in July 1970. During 1977–1980 up to three, possibly four, males held territory at various sites in the Weymouth area with breeding reported to have been successful at Lodmoor NR in 1977 and strongly suspected at Chafey's Lake, Radipole NR in 1978. The most recent indication of breeding occurred in 1982 with long-staying singing males at Wick Fields, Christchurch Harbour during 18th May–24th July and Radipole NR during 4th–30th June.

Otherwise most of the spring and summer records, including some of the above, refer to migrants – see Table 501. Reports are infrequent and extend from mid-May, the earliest being 15th May 1972 at Winspit and 15th May 1994 at East Fleet, to late July in the case of long-staying individuals. The peak time for spring migrants is late May–early June, which accounts for 61% of the total – see Table 502. Most reports are from Portland with ten birds including five at the Bill, and Abbotsbury with eight birds. The remaining records are from Radipole NR (five excluding breeding birds), Winspit (three), Christchurch Harbour (two), and singles at Bridport, East Fleet and well inland at Shillingstone.

58	60	65	67	68	69	70	71	72	74	76	77	80	82	83	85	87	88	91	93	94	96
1	1	1	1	0	2	1	2	1	1	2	1	1	2	1	2	1	1	3	1	3	2

Table 501. Annual totals of spring and summer birds 1950–1999

May 1–10	May 11–20	May 21–31	Jun 1–10	Jun 11–20	Jun 21–30
0	3	9	10	5	3

Table 502. Totals in 10-day periods during spring and summer 1950–1999

Autumn migrants are rare with only 14 records in 11 years during 1956–1993 as follows:

1956   Portland Bill: three trapped 4th–14th September
1958   Portland Bill: trapped 3rd September
1968   Abbotsbury: singing male 17th August
1969   Portland Bill: trapped 9th September
1978   Abbotsbury: first-year bird in mid-July
1979   Abbotsbury: ad. trapped 13th September
1986   Portland Bill: 22nd–23rd September
1987   Portland Bill: 9th–10th October
       Hengistbury: 13th October
1988   Hengistbury: 12th October
1990   Portland Bill: trapped 19th October
1993   Winspit: a late bird 3rd–8th November

A total of 17 birds has been ringed in the county.

The Marsh Warbler in a summer visitor breeding in Europe from southern Scandinavia, extreme south-east Great Britain, eastern France, northern Italy and the Balkans east to west-central Asia. It winters in eastern Africa, mainly south of the equator.

Postscript 2000–2002

One singing at Abbotsbury on 11th June 2000 is the first county record since 1996.

Reed Warbler (Eurasian Reed Warbler)   *Acrocephalus scirpaceus*

A common summer visitor and passage migrant

Both Mansel-Pleydell (1888) and Blathwayt (1945) simply referred to this species as a summer visitor, the latter adding that it is well distributed where reed and osier beds are found, a status which has not since changed.

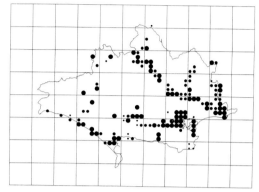

The *BTO Atlas* (1968–1972) revealed evidence of breeding in 27 (73%) 10-km squares (confirmed in 20, probable in six and possible in one), whilst the Tetrad Survey (1987–1994) produced a similar result with evidence of breeding in 27 (73%) of the pre-1974 10-km squares (confirmed in 21, probable in five and possible in one). The Tetrad Map reflects the Reed Warbler's habitat preference for *Phragmites* reedbeds with a breeding distribution even more closely associated with the river valleys and coastal marshes than that for the Sedge Warbler.

The limited available data on breeding numbers suggest that population levels, despite fluctuating, are relatively stable at some sites – see Tables 503 to 506. The exceptions to this include a dramatic decline at Radipole NR between 1990 and 1998, and a steady increase along the River Allen during the 1990s. The changes at Radipole NR and along the River Allen are likely to relate to local changes rather than reflect general population trends. Other reedbeds supporting notable breeding populations include Abbotsbury with 200 pairs in 1986, Keysworth with 200 pairs in 1986 and Lytchett Bay with 60 pairs in 1984.

1967 & 1971	1973–1975	1980–1983	1986–1990	1991	1993–1994
30–35	25	40–50	30	15	25

Table 503. Number of breeding territories at Arne NR 1967–1994

	1980	1981	1982	1983	1984	1985	1986	1987	1988	1989	1990	1998
Radipole NR	450	500	450	380	465	433	560	470	549	nc	375	37
Lodmoor NR	nc	nc	nc	96	90	107	90	113	110	71	nc	nc

Table 504. Number of breeding territories at Radipole and Lodmoor NRs 1980–1990 and 1998

78	79	80	81	82	83	84	85	86	87	88	89	90	91	92	93	94	95	96	97	98
37	26	23	25	28	23	29	31	29	29	40	42	38	50	36	31	28	36	33	31	34

Table 505. Number of breeding territories along River Stour between Corfe Mullen and Sturminster Marshall 1978–1998

1989	1990	1991	1992	1993	1994	1995	1996	1997	1998	1999
23	31	35	20	39	41	50	44	68	77	80

Table 506. Number of breeding territories along River Allen 1989–1999

The earliest spring records are from Radipole NR on 1st April 1989 and Christchurch Harbour on 1st April 1997, 2nd April 1981 and 4th April 1974. Otherwise the first migrants usually appear later in April with the average date of the first arrivals gradually becoming earlier since the 1950s – see Table 507.

	1950–1959	1960–1969	1970–1979	1980–1989	1990–1999
Range	17th–26th April	13th–26th April	4th–23rd April	1st–18th April	1st–19th April
Average	20th April	19th April	16th April	10th April	10th April

Table 507. Dates for first spring arrivals each decade 1950–1999

Spring migration is very protracted, extending from mid-April through to late June and occasionally into early July. Furthermore, in some years the main passage can be late, e.g. 41% of the spring and summer migrants recorded at Portland Bill since 1980 occurred in June as compare with 48% in May – see Table 508. This late passage is also reflected at breeding sites with new birds establishing territories well into June. The seasonal totals at coastal watch-points such as Portland Bill and Durlston CP fluctuate from year to year – see Table 509. Peak counts rarely reach double figures, the best being from Portland Bill with an exceptional 60 on 20th May 1987, the next highest being 20 on 6th June 1998, 18 on 29th June 1997 and 16 on 14th June 1995. Not surprisingly, spring passage is heavier at reedbed sites as suggested by peak counts from Christchurch Harbour, e.g. 64 on 28th May 1983, 43 on 29th April 1982, 36 on 17th May 1984 and 31 on 12th May 1980. Autumn migrants start to appear during the second half of July with the bulk of the migration taking place through August and September. There is evidence to suggest that peak passage occurs during August at the reedbed sites, but a little later in September at such coastal watch-points as Portland Bill and Durlston CP – see Table 508. Seasonal totals at Portland Bill and Durlston CP are variable, but generally rather small, with peak counts apparently never exceeding eight birds – see Table 510. By comparison, numbers recorded at St Aldhelm's Head in some autumns are higher, e.g. 132 bird-days in 1990 and 79 bird-days in 1989 with a maximum of 24 on 24th September.

Apr	May	Jun	Jul	Aug	Sep	Oct	Nov
96:5%	608:34%	526:30%	49:3%	161:9%	241:14%	90:5%	2:<1%

Table 508. Monthly totals at Portland Bill 1981–1999

	1980	1981	1982	1983	1984	1985	1986	1987	1988	1989
Portland Bill	>56	55	23	37	59	86	44	148	75	71
Durlston CP	nc	2	5	7	48	15	8	36	50	62

	1990	1991	1992	1993	1994	1995	1996	1997	1998	1999
Portland Bill	62	105	27	44	34	114	74	77	82	59
Durlston CP	64	68	21	43	15	46	53	76	56	61

Table 509. Spring totals (bds) at Portland Bill and Durlston CP 1980–1999

	1980	1981	1982	1983	1984	1985	1986	1987	1988	1989
Portland Bill	19	43	18	35	13	20	27	12	25	9
Durlston CP	nc	5	1	10	21	44	36	48	51	31

	1990	1991	1992	1993	1994	1995	1996	1997	1998	1999
Portland Bill	21	16	30	38	30	38	50	29	25	18
Durlston CP	18	27	77	64	19	45	38	45	42	31

Table 510. Autumn totals (bds) at Portland Bill and Durlston CP 1980–1999

Like the Sedge Warbler, the true strength of autumn passage is better reflected by counts, resulting from systematic trapping, at reedbed sites. For example, ringing totals from Radipole NR include 984 in 1972, 700 in 1975, 927 (new birds) in 1976 and 751 in 1997, whilst at Keysworth good numbers were caught during the early 1990s including a peak count of 150 birds on 3rd August 1996 – see Table 511. At Christ-church Harbour, there are also several high counts, the best being 200 on 15th August 1991, 150 in August 1983 and 116 on 31st August 1993. Elsewhere 150 at Lodmoor NR on 3rd August 1980 is a notable count.

1991	1992	1993	1994	1995	1996	1997
983	462	819	1409	394	364	339

Table 511. Totals trapped in autumn at Keysworth 1991–1997

The last migrants are usually reported in October, more exceptionally in early November, the latest being 10th November 1984 at Winspit, 11th November 1998 at Durlston CP and 16th November 1999 at Abbotsbury.

A total of 27,131 birds has been ringed in the county. There have been recoveries and controls from many parts of the British Isles north to Lancashire, Yorkshire and the Isle of Man, including one control from southern Eire, with a frequent interchange of birds between reedbeds in Dorset and others in southern England including Icklesham in East Sussex and Chew Valley Lake in Somerset. Further afield, four recoveries from Senegal indicate that some of our birds winter in sub-Saharan West Africa. Seven recoveries from the Channel Islands, five from France, four from Spain, and three each from Portugal and Morocco plus two controls from the Channel Islands and France, and one each from Portugal and Morocco suggest that a direct route is taken during migration. Three recoveries from Belgium, two from the Netherlands and one each from Sweden and Estonia plus three controls from the Netherlands and one each from Denmark and Poland show that Continental birds as well as British birds pass through Dorset. One of the more interesting movements involves a bird ringed at St Aldhelm's Head in September 1988, controlled in Belgium in July 1989 and again in Spain in August of the same year.

The Reed Warbler is a summer visitor breeding from north-west Africa and across much of Europe north to southern Great Britain and southern Scandinavia, and extending eastwards through parts of Asia Minor and the Middle East to south-west and west-central Asia. It winters throughout much of tropical Africa.

Postscript 2000–2002
One at Christchurch Harbour on 1st April 2002 equals the earliest record for the county, whilst one at Portland Bill on the exceptional date of 6th December 2000 is by far the latest record for Dorset.

Great Reed Warbler   *Acrocephalus arundinaceus*

A very rare passage migrant and summer visitor: eight records

Not surprisingly, four of the eight records are from Radipole NR.

1959	Portland Bill: 15th May
1967	Radipole NR: singing male 3rd June
1969	Little Sea: singing male 6th–26th June
1971	Radipole NR: trapped 2nd September
1978	River Stour at Corfe Mullen: 19th June
1989	Radipole NR: singing male 21st May
	Hengistbury: 24th September–2nd October, trapped on 24th
2002	Radipole NR: singing male 31st May

The Great Reed Warbler is a summer visitor breeding in north-west Africa and throughout much of Europe north to north-east France, the Low Countries and southern Scandinavia, and extending east across Asia Minor and most of central Asia to Japan and the Philippines. It winters in sub-Saharan Africa and south-east Asia. A vagrant to Great Britain with 218 records up to 2002.

Eastern Olivaceous Warbler   *Hippolais pallida*

Accidental: one record

1999	Portland Bill: 4th–5th July

The only confirmed Dorset record involves an unseasonal bird trapped at Portland Bird Observatory. After release the bird remained in the general vicinity of the Observatory Quarry and Hut Field until early afternoon the following day. A full account can be found in *Birding World*, Vol. 12, Number 7, August 1999 and the Dorset Bird Report for 1999.

Three old records of 'Olivaceous Warbler' from Portland Bill on 16th August 1956, Easton, Portland on 5th September 1962 and Portland Bill on 27th August 1967 have been reassessed by the BBRC and the BOURC and are no longer considered acceptable.

The former 'Olivaceous Warbler' has recently been split into two full species; the Eastern *H. pallida* and the Western *H. opaca*. The Eastern Olivaceous Warbler is a summer visitor breeding over much of south-eastern Europe and Asia Minor, and parts of the Middle East and south-west Asia. It winters mainly in north-east and East Africa extending to just south of the equator. A vagrant Great Britain with 10 records up to 2002.

Booted Warbler   *Hippolais caligata*

Accidental: five records

Four of the five records are from Portland.

1980   Portland Bill: 22nd–23rd September, trapped 23rd
1984   St Aldhelm's Head: trapped 23rd October and released next day
1987   Portland Bill: trapped 13th September
1999   Weston, Portland: 13th–14th September
2002   Portland Bill: 15th–19th August, trapped 15th

The 2002 bird is the earliest autumn record for Great Britain.

The Booted Warbler is a summer visitor breeding from north-west Russia east across central Asia to Mongolia and north-west China and wintering in the Indian sub-continent. A vagrant to Great Britain with 87 records up to 2002.

Sykes's Warbler   *Hippolais rama*

Accidental: one record

2000   Portland Bill: trapped 1st July

This individual was trapped at the Portland Bird Observatory and after release in the Observatory Quarry, it later showed well along the edge of the Observatory garden. A full account can be found in *Birding World*, Vol. 13, Number 7, August 2000 and the Dorset Bird Report for 2000.

Sykes's Warbler, which has only been recently 'split' from Booted Warbler, is a summer visitor breeding in south-central and south-west Asia, and winters in the southern Indian sub-continent. A vagrant to Great Britain with only four records up to 2002.

Icterine Warbler   *Hippolais icterina*

A scarce passage migrant, mainly in autumn

The first record for the county occurred in 1958 when one was trapped and ringed at Portland Bill on 1st September. Although this was followed by annual reports involving 11 birds up to 1962, the only subsequent autumn records until 1971 were a single in 1965 and two birds in 1967 – see Fig 50. Since then the species has been recorded annually except for 1976 but, unlike the Melodious Warbler, there has been no long-term trend in the number of occurrences with annual totals varying considerably from year to year, the highest being in 1983 (12), 1993 (10) and 1997 (11).

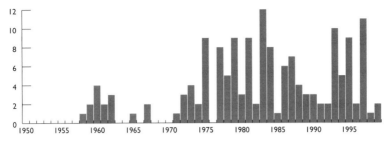

Fig 50. Autumn totals 1958–1999

Although autumn records extend from 24th July 1987 at Portland Bill to 21st-23rd October 1987 at Durlston CP, there is a distinct peak during the second half of August and the first half of September, which accounts for 71% of the total – see Table 512. This is a little later than the peak time for Melodious Warblers.

Jul 1–15	Jul 16–31	Aug 1–15	Aug 16–31	Sep 1–15	Sep 16–30	Oct 1–15	Oct 16–31
0	<1%	12%	35%	37%	10%	4%	1%

Table 512. Proportion (%) of autumn migrants half-monthly 1958–1999

Portland Bill is by far the most favoured site for autumn Icterine Warblers and accounts for 61% of the total, but the species is scarce elsewhere on Portland with only 12 records – see Table 513. The other main haunts are Christchurch Harbour with 19 birds (12%) and Durlston CP with 14 birds (9%), whilst five birds have been recorded at St Aldhelm's Head. In the Weymouth/Fleet area, there are sightings of single birds from Radipole NR on 13th August 1984 and 20th August 1997, East Fleet on 3rd August 1979, and Abbotsbury on 14th August 1984 and 6th September 1997. The remaining records are from Studland NNR on 9th September 1962, Brownsea on 31st August–1st September 1979, and Ballard Down with singles on 2nd September and 5th–6th September 1997, whilst two at Row near Holt on 7th September 1960 represent the only inland report of a specifically identified *Hippolais* warbler. Most records refer to singles, only very occasionally are two birds reported.

	Total	
Portland Bill	97	61%
elsewhere on Portland	12	8%
St Aldhelm's Head	5	3%
Durlston CP	14	9%
Christchurch Harbour	19	12%
elsewhere	11	7%

Table 513. Distribution of autumn migrants 1958–1999

It is a rare visitor in spring with only six records including two long-staying individuals:

1966	Portland Bill: 31st May
1968	Kimmeridge: 25th May
1970	Southwell, Portland: 25th–26th May
1979	Portland Bill: singing male 12th–31st May
1991	Portland Bill: 26th May
1993	Stanpit Marsh, Christchurch Harbour: singing male 22nd May–29th June

A total of 43 birds has been ringed in the county.

The Icterine Warbler is a summer visitor breeding in Europe eastwards from Scandinavia, the Low Countries, eastern France, Switzerland and the Balkans into west-central Asia. It winters in southern Africa.

Postscript 2000–2002
There was one at Stanpit Marsh, Christchurch Harbour on 4th August 2000 and at least four, possibly five singles at Portland Bill during 17th August–5th September 2002. As a consequence, 2001 is the first year without reports in Dorset since 1976!

Melodious Warbler   *Hippolais polyglotta*

A scarce passage migrant, mainly in autumn

The first county record occurred in 1954 when one was trapped and ringed at Portland Bill on 4th September. The next reports followed in 1957, since when the species has been recorded annually except for 1964 – see Fig 51. There was an increase in sightings during the 1970s with numbers at their highest during 1977–1984 including peaks of c.17 birds in 1979 and 16 birds in 1981. Subsequently there has been a marked decline with only 1–4 birds reported in most autumns during 1987–1999 except for isolated peaks in 1990 (13), 1992 (eight) and 1994 (ten).

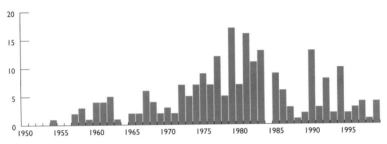

Fig 51. Autumn totals 1954–1999

Apart from an early bird at Portland Bill during 5th–7th July 1997, autumn records extend from late July to mid-October. The second half of August is the peak time for autumn migrants and accounts for 36% of the total, whilst the month as a whole accounts for 62% – see Table 514. The remaining July sightings are for the period 24th–30th with all but one occurring after 1981 including all four county records in 1997. There are relatively few reports for October, the latest involving long-staying individuals at Easton, Portland during 13th–18th October 1994 and Portland Bill during 1st–19th October 1990.

Jul 1–15	Jul 16–31	Aug 1–15	Aug 16–31	Sep 1–15	Sep 16–30	Oct 1–15	Oct 16–31
<1%	5%	26%	36%	19%	9%	5%	0

Table 514. Proportion (%) of autumn migrants half-monthly 1954–1999

	Total	
Portland Bill	167	70%
elsewhere on Portland	9	4%
St Aldhelm's Head	3	1%
Winspit	3	1%
Durlston CP	19	8%
Christchurch Harbour	30	13%
elsewhere	7	3%

Table 515. Distribution of autumn migrants 1954–1999

Portland Bill is by far the most favoured haunt for autumn Melodious Warblers and accounts for 70% of the total, but the species is very scarce elsewhere on Portland with only nine records – see Table 514. The other main sites are Christchurch Harbour with 30 birds (13%) and Durlston CP with 19 birds (8%), whilst St Aldhelm's Head and Winspit have hosted three birds each. In the Weymouth/Fleet area, there are sightings of singles from Lodmoor NR on 14th August 1986, Radipole NR on 24th August 1975 and 8th October

1990, East Fleet on 9th August 1986 and Langton Herring and Moonfleet on 4th–5th September 1979. The remaining records are from East Lulworth on 25th August 1992 and Little Sea on 1st August 1977.

Most autumn reports involve singles or occasionally two birds, the highest counts being from Portland Bill with five on 13th August 1977 and 1st and 5th September 1979, and four on 1st September 1974.

It is a rare visitor in spring and summer with only eight records, all from Portland Bill, including six during 1993–1999:

1976	Portland Bill: 22nd May
1979	Portland Bill: 5th May with an unidentified *Hippolais*, presumably the same bird, seen the previous day
1993	Portland Bill: singing male 23rd May
1995	Portland Bill: singing male 1st June
1998	Portland Bill: singles 15th and 27th May
1999	Portland Bill: singing male 30th May and one on 19th June

A total of 92 birds has been ringed in the county.

The western counterpart of the Icterine Warbler, the Melodious Warbler is a summer visitor breeding from the Channel coast of France south and east to Belgium, Luxembourg, extreme western Germany, Switzerland, Croatia, Italy, Iberia and north-west Africa. It winters in tropical west Africa.

Postscript 2000–2002

In 2000 five birds, all trapped at Portland Bill, were recorded during 28th July–9th September. In 2001 a total of 11 birds occurred during 30th July–2nd September including six at Portland and singles at Abbotsbury, Worth Matravers, Ballard Down, Swineham GP and Stanpit Marsh, Christchurch Harbour. In 2002, there was a spring bird at Portland Bill on 12th May, and eight birds in autumn during 31st July–11th September with five trapped at Portland Bill (maximum of three on 16th August), and singles at Durlston CP, Ballard Down and Hengistbury.

Hippolais spp – either Icterine or Melodious Warbler

There are a small number of reports of unidentified *Hippolais* warblers, either Icterine or Melodious, which have all occurred in autumn between early August and mid-October. The most interesting of these records involves one at Dorchester on 10th September 1986–only the second inland report of a *Hippolais* warbler for Dorset. The remaining sightings are from Portland Bill (seven), elsewhere on Portland (four), Winspit (one) and Christchurch Harbour (seven).

Dartford Warbler   *Sylvia undata*

A locally common resident

Mansel-Pleydell (1888) described this species as "a resident, confining itself to the heathy districts of the county", but added that after the severe winters of 1880/81 and 1886/87 "it is doubtful whether we shall any longer see our heaths enlivened by this active little bird". Despite this prophesy, the Dartford Warbler survived into the 20th Century with Blathwayt (1945) reporting that numbers on the heaths of east and south-east Dorset reached a high peak for several years up to 1939, but became scarce in 1940 and had not made a good recovery in the few years after.

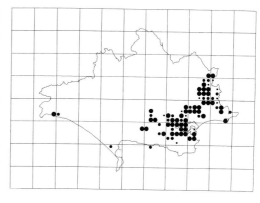

Since 1950 the species has remained vulnerable to habitat destruction and cold winters, particularly when glazing of vegetation by freezing fog or lying snow persists for more than two or three days. Indeed the severe conditions experienced during the winter of 1962/63 almost resulted in the extermination of the breeding population with only four pairs present in 1963. Despite this and other setbacks, numbers have steadily increased, most notably during the

1980s and 1990s – see Table 516. This increase is also reflected by the Tetrad Survey (1987–1994), which found confirmed or probable breeding in 13 (35%) of the pre-1974 10-km squares compared to ten (27%) during the *BTO Atlas* (1968–1972). Not surprisingly the Tetrad Map shows that breeding is concentrated on the heathlands of the Poole Basin.

1960	1963	1964	1967	1968	1969	1970	1971	1972	1973	1974	1975	1978	1980
63	4	4	<20	31	38	48	73	>100	120	286*	300	18	35

1981	1982	1983	1984	1985	1986	1988	1989	1990	1991	1992	1994	1997	1998
46	28	55	127*	97	76	100	115	216*	221*	315*	650*	>300	400

Table 516. Breeding population estimates for Dorset 1960–1998; *= systematic surveys

A more detailed examination of population trends shows that numbers generally increased during the 1950s, despite the severe cold spells of January–February 1954 and February 1956, with 63 pairs recorded in 1960. After the severe winter of 1962/63 caused the dramatic 'crash' to four pairs during 1963–1964, numbers slowly recovered again to reach a peak of c.300 pairs in 1975. The blizzard of February 1978 resulted in another population reduction to c.18 territories in 1978. Apart from a setback due to the cold winter of 1981/82, the subsequent recovery was strong with 127 pairs located at 42 sites in 1984. Numbers continued to rise, particularly during the 1990s when a county peak of 650 territories was recorded in 1994 representing 39% of the total population nationally. Although no systematic surveys were conducted after 1994, there is evidence of a 10–50% reduction in 1996 due to the cold spell in February of that year, followed by a recovery with c.400 pairs recorded in 1998. During the recent peak in the population, the highest counts of breeding territories/pairs from the main breeding sites are Studland NNR – 127 in 1998, Arne NR – 50+ in 1999, Holt Heath NNR – 45 in 1994, and Canford Heath–41 in 1992 and 1994.

When populations are high, birds spread away from the traditional heathland sites to areas of gorse on chalk downland and more notably along the coast. Mansel-Pleydell (1888) referred to reports from Black Down, Houghton Stubbs and Fairmile between Blandford and Stickland, whilst Blathwayt (1945) recorded its presence in west Dorset at Black Down in 1862, Lyme Regis during 1868–1880, and between Abbotsbury and Bridport as late as 1927. Breeding was reported in 1950 from near Blandford, west of Weymouth and on coastal downland, and in 1962 from the central chalk and west Dorset where up to four pairs bred during 1972–1977. During the Tetrad Survey (1987–1994) there were records from the Purbeck coast (SY87), the shores of the Fleet (SY67) and coastal west Dorset (SY39 and SY49). Subsequently this trend has continued, e.g. nine territories along the Purbeck Ridge from Ballard Down to Grange Arch in 1994, breeding reports from three sites on the Purbeck coast in 1995, and successful breeding recorded at Durlston CP and Chickerell Rifle Range in 1996. By 1999 small numbers were breeding at various sites along the entire Dorset coastline from Christchurch Harbour in the east to Stonebarrow Hill in the west.

Since 1980, there has been an increase in the autumn dispersal of juveniles away from the breeding areas to mainly coastal sites, where birds may also spend the winter – see Table 517. This obviously reflects the recent revival in the breeding population. In spring, occasional records from the main coastal watch-points gives support to the theory that some British Dartford Warblers may winter across the Channel, but this is yet to be proven – see Table 518.

	1980	1981	1982	1983	1984	1985	1986	1987	1988	1989
Portland Bill	1	1	5	2	0	7	1	1	4	2
Durlston CP	0	0	0	1	3	32 bds	1	1	1	1
Christchurch Hbr	3	0	2	7	3	7	6	5	mx 5	2

	1990	1991	1992	1993	1994	1995	1996	1997	1998	1999
Portland Bill	3	5	5	10	8	10	0	15	9	12
Durlston CP	3	24	28 bds	nc	12 bds	29 bds	br	nc	br	25 bds
Christchurch Hbr	5	20 bds	nc	mx 15	mx 6	20 bds	41 bds	br	nc	nc

Table 517. Autumn totals at the main coastal watch-points 1980–1999; bds = bird-days, mx = maximum count, br = breeding

80	81	82	83	84	85	86	87	88	89	90	91	92	93	94	95	96	97	98	99
0	1	0	0	4	0	0	2	0	0	0	0	0	0	2	1	1	1	4	1

Table 518. Spring totals at Portland Bill 1980–1999

A total of 278 birds has been ringed in the county.

The Dartford Warbler breeds from southern England south through western and southern France to Iberia, Corsica, Sardinia, southern Italy and north-west Africa. Some continental birds winter south of their breeding range, but in Great Britain adult birds are sedentary with dispersal by juveniles mainly along the south coast.

Sponsored by Bob & Ivor Kemp and RSPB Arne-based Reserves

Subalpine Warbler   *Sylvia cantillans*

A very rare passage migrant: 21 records

Since the first at Portland Bill in 1964, there have been 20 further records. Occurrences have increased in recent years with 16 sightings in eight years during 1987–1997. All but one of the birds have appeared during the spring and early summer on dates ranging from 9th April to 5th June with records spread fairly evenly throughout this period – see Table 519. There is one autumn report for October. Portland Bill is undoubtedly the most favoured site for the species accounting for 13 birds (62% of the total).

Apr 1–15	Apr 16–30	May 1–15	May 16–31	Jun 1–15
5	4	5	4	2

Table 519. Half- monthly totals 1964–2001

All records are given below:

1964	Portland Bill: male 19th–23rd April, trapped on an unspecified date
1975	Portland Bill: male 15th April–7th May, trapped 16th April
1981	Portland Bill: male 12th–13th May, trapped 12th
1987	Verne Common, Portland: male showing characteristics of eastern race *S. c. albistriata* 20th–29th May
	Portland Bill, male showing characteristics of western race *S. c. cantillans* trapped 21st May
1988	Wick Fields, Christchurch Harbour male 3rd–4th June
1989	Portland Bill: 3 single males 20th April, 3rd–4th May and 9th May; first two showing characteristics of eastern race *S. c. albistriata*, third showing characteristics of western race *S. c. cantillans*
	Durlston CP: male 3rd May
1992	Redcliff Point near Weymouth: male 5th–6th June
1993	Portland Bill: male 9th April
	Hengistbury: male 10th–15th April
	Easton, Portland: male showing characteristics of eastern race *S. c. albistriata* 24th May
1995	Portland Bill: male 24th April
	St Aldhelm's Head: male 4th May
1996	Portland Bill: male showing characteristics of western race *S. c. cantillans* 11th April
	Portland Bill: male showing characteristics of eastern race *S. c. albistriata* 7th–27th October, trapped on 7th
1997	Portland Bill: male 25th May
2001	Portland Bill: first-summer female trapped 12th April
	Southwell, Portland: first-summer male 17th April

A total of six birds has been ringed in the county

The Subalpine Warbler is a summer visitor breeding in north-west Africa, southern Europe and western Turkey with the nominate race *S. c. cantillans* from Italy westwards and *S. c. albistriata* further to the east. Both races winter in Africa chiefly along the southern edge of the Sahara. A vagrant Great Britain with 493 records up to 2002.

Sardinian Warbler   *Sylvia melanocephala*

Accidental: four records

Two of the four records occurred in 1995.

> 1988   Cogden Beach: singing male 2nd–8th May
> 1993   Portland Bill: female 2nd June
> 1995   Weston, Portland: first-summer male 10th–11th April
>   Weston, Portland: female or first-winter 12th October

The Sardinian Warbler breeds in north-west Africa, southern Europe, western Turkey and the Middle East. Many birds are sedentary but others winter south of the breeding range, notably in the western Sahara, southern Turkey, Cyprus, the Middle East and Egypt. A vagrant to Great Britain with 63 records up to 2002.

Desert Warbler   *Sylvia nana*

Accidental: one record

> 1970   Portland: 16th December–2nd January 1971

This bird, the first record of this species for Great Britain and Dorset, was trapped at Weston and taken for examination at Portland Bird Observatory where it was roosted overnight and released the following morning. It remained in the general vicinity of the Observatory up to 2nd January 1971. Like all subsequent British records, the bird belonged to the nominate race *S. n. nana*. A full account can be found in *British Birds*, Vol. 65, Number 11, November 1972.

There are two discrete populations of Desert Warbler which are often now considered distinct species. The nominate race *S. n. nana* is a summer visitor breeding from the Caspian Sea eastwards across the deserts of central Asia. It winters from north-east Africa eastwards across much of Arabia and the Middle East to the north-western Indian sub-continent. The African race *S. n. deserti* breeds in semi-desert areas of the western Sahara and is mainly sedentary. A vagrant to Great Britain with 11 records up to 2002.

Orphean Warbler   *Sylvia hortensis*

Accidental: one record

> 1955   Portland Bill: 20th September

The only Dorset record involves a first-winter male trapped at Culverwell.

The Orphean Warbler is a summer visitor breeding in north-west Africa, southern Europe, Asia Minor, the Middle East and parts of south-west Asia. It winters in Africa chiefly along the southern edge of the Sahara, also in southern Arabia, south-west Asia and the Indian sub-continent. A vagrant to Great Britain with only five records up to 2002.

Barred Warbler   *Sylvia nisoria*

A scarce autumn migrant

This species first occurred in Dorset in the mid-1950s with a flurry of records from Portland Bill involving two singles in 1955 and three singles in 1956. Apart from a long-staying individual at Portland Bill from 3rd October–4th November 1962, there were no further reports until 1968. Subsequently, from 1–6 birds have been recorded in all but seven autumns up to 1999 – see Table 520.

68	69	70	71	72	73	74	75	76	77	78	79	80	81	82	83
2	0	0	1	6	4	1	0	2	1	4	5	0	1	0	2

84	85	86	87	88	89	90	91	92	93	94	95	96	97	98	99
1	3	6	2	3	3	0	0	3	2	4	3	1	1	1	1

Table 520. Autumn totals 1968–1999

Although records extend from mid-August to early November, September is the peak month with 56% of the total – see Table 521. The earliest autumn sightings are 10th August 1973 at Winspit and 10th August 1978 at Portland Bill, whilst the latest reports are from Portland Bill on 5th November 1994 and 9th November 1983.

Aug 1–15	Aug 16–31	Sep 1–15	Sep 16–30	Oct 1–15	Oct 16–31	Nov 1–15
3	8	19	19	11	6	2

Table 521. Half-monthly totals 1955–1999

Portland Bill is by far the most favoured site and accounts for 59% of the total – see Table 522. Rather surprisingly, there are only two records from the rest of Portland involving one at Easton on 21st October 1985 and one at Suckthumb Quarry on 6th October 1998. The only other site to attract significant numbers is Christchurch Harbour with 13 birds (19%), which have all occurred since 1986. On Purbeck, there have been sightings from Winspit (four) and Durlston CP (three) with singles at Ringstead Bay on 2nd September 1971, Worbarrow Bay on an unspecified date in 1986 and St Aldhelm's Head on 30th September 1979. The remaining records are from Radipole NR on 22nd August 1972, Lodmoor NR during 17th–23rd October 1973 and Studland NNR on 20th September and 3rd October 1981. Reports mainly involve singles, very occasionally two birds.

	Total	
Portland Bill	41	59%
elsewhere on Portland	2	3%
Winspit	4	6%
Durlston CP	3	4%
Christchurch Harbour	13	19%
elsewhere	6	9%

Table 522. Distribution of migrants 1955–1999

A total of 23 birds has been ringed in the county.

The Barred Warbler is a summer visitor breeding in Europe from southern Scandinavia, Germany, Switzerland, northern Italy and the Balkans eastwards into west-central Asia. It winters in tropical East Africa, mainly in Kenya.

Postscript 2000–2002

One at Avalanche Road and Suckthumb Quarry, Portland on 14th November 2000 is the latest record for the county. There was a good series of reports in autumn 2001 with singles at Hengistbury during 25th–28th August, Barleycrates Lane, Portland on 28th–29th August, and Portland Bill on 4th September, and during 14th–16th October with possibly the same bird again on 20th October.

Lesser Whitethroat   *Sylvia curruca curruca*

A fairly common summer visitor and passage migrant

Mansel-Pleydell (1888) considered this species to be a generally distributed summer visitor, though less common than the Whitethroat. Blathwayt (1945) referred to it as being fairly well distributed and numerous in some localities, e.g. near Sherborne, but scarcer on heathland.

There is little evidence to suggest any substantial change in status since with the *BTO Atlas* (1968–1972) showing evidence of breeding in 33 (89%) 10-km squares (confirmed in 19, probable in 11 and possible in three), the most notable absence being SY99. The Tetrad Survey (1987–1994) suggests a slight increase with evidence of breeding found in all but one (97%) of the pre-1974 10-km squares (confirmed in 28, probable in seven and possible in one). The Tetrad Map shows a widespread but rather patchy distribution, being sparse in some areas, but fairly common in the north from Sherborne through the Blackmore Vale to Gillingham. This reflects the species' habitat preference for dense bramble and thorn scrub, and overgrown thick hedgerows with at least three years growth since trimming.

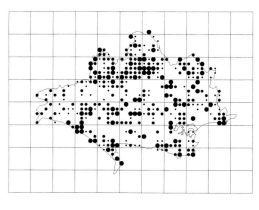

The little information available on breeding numbers offers no clear indication of any long-term population trends – see Tables 523 and 524. The considerable fluctuations at Radipole NR probably reflect adverse climatic conditions in the wintering areas.

1980	1981	1982	1983	1984	1985	1986	1987	1988
8	13	5	3	5	15	13	13	12

Table 523. Number of breeding territories at Radipole NR 1980–1988

1980	1981	1982	1983	1984	1985	1986	1987	1991	1992	1996	1997	1998	1999
4	4	4	5	5	5	6	6	7	4	6	5	6	7

Table 524. Number of breeding territories at Durlston CP 1980–1999

There is a very early record on 23rd March 1995 at Hengistbury (two birds), the next earliest being 3rd April 1987 at Verne Common, Portland and 7th April 1989 at Portland Bill. Otherwise the first spring migrants usually appear during the second half of April with the average date of the first arrivals gradually becoming earlier since the 1950s – see Table 525.

	1950–1959	1960–1969	1970–1979	1980–1989	1990–1999
Range	17th April– 1st May	16th–29th April	10th–26th April	3rd–25th April	23rd March– 22nd April
Average	24th April	23rd April	20th April	16th April	12th April

Table 525. Dates for first spring arrivals each decade 1950–1999

Although spring migration extends through April and May with a few late stragglers occasionally reported in early June, peak passage normally occurs during late April and the first half of May. Seasonal totals from the main coastal watch-points are highly variable, ranging at Portland Bill from only seven birds in 1997 to an exceptional 305 in 1987 – see Table 526. Peak counts are generally small, often in single figures and rarely exceed 20 birds, the highest being at Portland Bill during the exceptional passage in May 1987 with 140 on 5th and 65 on 20th, also 50 there on 15th May 1984. Elsewhere 30–40 daily at Radipole NR during 1st–3rd May 1980 and 30 at Durlston CP on 3rd May 1990 are notable counts. Autumn migration starts during late July with most passage taking place during August and September, often peaking during the former month. Seasonal totals are variable, but considerably higher at Durlston CP in comparison with the other main coastal watch-points (cf Grasshopper Warbler) – see Table 527. This may reflect the species' preferred habitat on migration. Not surprisingly the highest peak counts have been recorded from Durlston CP with 60 on 15th August 1992, 44 on 20th August 1989, and 35 in August 1996 and on 18th August 1984. Elsewhere peak counts are generally small, often in single figures and rarely exceeding 12 birds, the best being 26 at Christchurch Harbour on 22nd September 1987 with 25 there on 4th August 1988, and 20 at Studland NNR on 28th August 1986.

	1980	1981	1982	1983	1984	1985	1986	1987	1988	1989
Portland Bill	59	31	25	67	128	89	36	305	35	108
Durlston CP	25	49	35	32	157	58	52	59	72	163
Christchurch Hbr	34	19	22	11	69	48	10	37	30	25

	1990	1991	1992	1993	1994	1995	1996	1997	1998	1999
Portland Bill	24	67	34	45	15	19	82	7	72	18
Durlston CP	166	117	26	19	nc	71	60	49	52	78
Christchurch Hbr	34	39	29	29	40	42	78	nc	9	16

Table 526. Spring totals (bds) at the main coastal watch-points 1980–1999

	1980	1981	1982	1983	1984	1985	1986	1987	1988	1989
Portland Bill	65	30	>12	43	69	55	>32	87	58	46
Durlston CP	99	173	252	322	257	228	131	274	338	419
Christchurch Hbr	14	61	24	42	56	60	72	238	123	26

	1990	1991	1992	1993	1994	1995	1996	1997	1998	1999
Portland Bill	23	48	28	59	14	34	39	22	27	23
Durlston CP	264	375	629	174	nc	265	354	202	239	175
Christchurch Hbr	67	22	56	115	13	41	47	nc	55	38

Table 527. Autumn totals (bds) at the main coastal watch-points 1980–1999

The last migrants usually occur in October, the latest being from Portland Bill on 29th–30th October 1991 and 30th October 1982, and Melcombe Regis Cemetery, Weymouth on 4th November 1984.

There are three records of very late migrant and/or wintering birds:

1974   Hazelbury Bryan: 21st–29th November
1991   West Bexington: 28th December
1996   Easton, Portland: 19th–20th January

A total of 1,422 birds has been ringed in the county and there has been one foreign control from Belgium, but no reports of any foreign recoveries.

The nominate race *S. c. curruca* is a summer visitor breeding from Great Britain and central France east through most of central and northern Europe, except northern Scandinavia, to western Siberia. It winters mainly in the north-eastern tropics of Africa with small numbers in Arabia. Other races are breeding summer visitors to south-east Europe, Asia Minor, parts of the Middle East, and much of north and central Asia to about 120°E. These more easterly races mainly winter in Arabia, south-west Asia and the Indian sub-continent.

Siberian Lesser Whitethroat   *Sylvia curruca blythi*

A very rare autumn migrant

Typically individuals showing characteristics of this race occur later than the nominate form with most reports from mid-October to late November:

1968   Portland Bill: trapped, 25th September–7th October
1984   Portland Bill: 3rd November
1987   Portland Bill: trapped 19th October
         St Aldhelm's Head: 23rd October
         Durlston CP: two in October
1988   Durlston CP: 21st–23rd October
1994   Portland Bill: trapped, 11th October–2nd November
         Winspit: 29th November, coinciding with a Hume's Warbler
1998   Pennsylvania Castle, Portland: 20th–25th November

This race breeds in eastern Siberia and winters in the Indian sub-continent.

Postscript 2000–2002
One at Hengistbury on 14th October 2000 showed the characteristics of the race *S. c. blythi*. At Portland in 2000, birds showing characteristics of one or other of the 'eastern' races were present at the Bill during 15th–19th October and Perryfields on 7th–8th November. Although both birds were examined in the hand, conclusive assignment to a particular subspecies was not possible in either case.

Whitethroat (Common Whitethroat) *Sylvia communis*

A common summer visitor and passage migrant

Both Mansel-Pleydell (1888) and Blathwayt (1945) referred to this species as a common summer visitor.

Despite a major population 'crash' in 1969, the overall status of this species has remained much the same. The *BTO Atlas* (1968–1972) confirmed breeding in all 10-km squares except two where it was probable, whilst the Tetrad Survey (1987–1994) showed similar results with breeding confirmed in all of the pre-1974 10-km squares except one where it was probable. The Tetrad Map shows that breeding occurs widely throughout the county except for the urban and heathland areas of the Poole Basin, where the distribution is rather more patchy. Otherwise there are concentrations of population along the coastal fringes from Bridport to Purbeck, and in the north from Sherborne through the Blackmore Vale to Shaftesbury (cf Lesser Whitethroat).

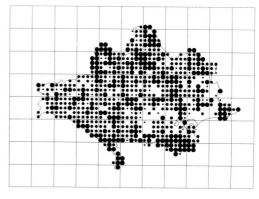

The *BTO Atlas* (1968–1972) did not reflect the impact of the catastrophic decline in breeding numbers in 1969 following severe drought in the Sahel wintering area. It was suggested that only a third of the 1968 population returned to Great Britain the following year. Although nationally the breeding population fluctuated around this lower level throughout the 1970s and much of the 1980s, with troughs in 1974 and 1985 and a peak in 1977, there is evidence of a more sustained recovery since the late 1980s. This is reflected by the limited but sometimes contradictory information available on long-term population trends in Dorset – see Tables 528 to 532. At Portland Bill breeding ceased in 1969 and did not occur regularly again until 1985, since when the population has increased to peak in the mid-1990s. Studland NNR and Arne NR supported good breeding numbers immediately prior to 1969. Although the initial decrease was small at Arne NR, the population at both these sites has steadily declined to the point of extinction. The reason for the lack of recovery at these sites is not obvious. More recent data suggests that in the county as a whole the population is increasing and perhaps beginning to reach pre-1969 levels, e.g. c.100 pairs at Portland in 1997 with 66 there in 1999, and 37–38 pairs at Christchurch Harbour in 1997 and 1999.

1985	1986	1987	1988	1989	1990	1991	1992	1993	1994	1995	1996	1997	1998	1999
1	3	2	3	2	2	3	4	10	14	14	15	12	9	10

Table 528. Number of breeding territories at Portland Bill 1985–1999

1980	1981	1982	1983	1984	1985	1986	1987	1988
14	13	13	nc	6	18	19	23	18

Table 529. Number of breeding territories at Radipole NR 1980–1988

1980	1982	1984	1985	1986	1987	1988	1990	1991	1992	1993	1996	1997	1999
23	26	21	24	25	24	26	30	30	32	32	30	30	30

Table 530. Number of breeding territories at Durlston CP 1980–1999

1964	1965	1967	1968	1972	1973	1975	1976	1977	1978	1982	1987	1993	1996
33	23	30	c34	8	5	4	4	7	7	8	0	0	0

Table 531. Number of breeding territories at Studland NNR 1964–1996

1968	1969	1971	1972	1973	1974	1975	1976	1977	1978	1984	1987	1991
25	22	13	6	2	1	0	c5	3	3	1	1	0

Table 532. Number of breeding territories at Arne NR 1968–1991

There are very early records on 10th March 1996 at Christchurch Harbour and 11th March 1961 at Portland Bill, the next earliest being 19th March 1992 at Christchurch Harbour, 27th March 1985 at Bridport and 30th March 1971 at Nether Cerne. Otherwise the first spring migrants usually appear during the first three weeks of April, the average date of the first arrivals being considerably earlier in the 1990s than during the previous four decades – see Table 533.

	1950–1959	1960–1969	1970–1979	1980–1989	1990–1999
Range	2nd–19th April	11th March–17th April	30th March–19th April	27th March–22nd April	10th March–12th April
Average	12th April	10th April	11th April	10th April	3rd April

Table 533. Dates for first spring arrivals each decade 1950–1999

The main migration period in spring extends from mid-April to late May with peak passage often recorded during the first half of May. Autumn migrants first appear during July with most passage taking place during August and the first half of September. The 1969 population 'crash' is clearly reflected by the numbers recorded on migration – see Table 534 and 535. Since then, the strength of passage over the longer term has mirrored the fortunes of the breeding population with annual fluctuations in the seasonal totals associated with climatic conditions in the wintering areas. In recent years, the presence of local breeding birds at the main coastal watch-points has obscured the seasonal totals of migrants, more particularly with the increase in the population since the late 1980s.

1963	1964	1965	1966	1967	1968	1969	1970	1971	1972	1973	1974
347	238	431	461	282	700	47	107	121	208	144	73

1975	1976	1977	1978	1979	1980	1981	1982	1983	1984	1985	1986
233	296	193	277	nc	394	226	>320	198	>252	279	100

Table 534. Spring totals (bds) at Portland Bill 1963–1986

1963	1964	1965	1966	1967	1968	1969	1970	1971	1972	1973	1974
729	889	589	1001	851	1443	284	346	374	386	218	208

1975	1976	1977	1978	1979	1980	1981	1982	1983	1984	1985	1986
239	407	538	269	590	460	406	329	307	>171	220	nc

Table 535. Autumn totals (bds) at Portland Bill 1963–1986

Peak counts are probably a better indication of passage strength which, like the breeding population, appears to be showing some signs of recovering to the levels recorded prior to 1969. During the 1950s and 1960s, there were frequent counts in excess of 100 birds at Portland Bill, notably 500+ on 16th September 1958, 400 on 8th May 1962 and 9th May 1968, and 300 on 5th May 1957. These totals are overshadowed by the massive 'fall' on 29th April 1955 involving many hundreds of thousands, if not several millions of birds throughout the county as a whole. This included c.1,000+ at Portland Bill, whilst extraordinary numbers "all over the place" were reported well inland between Cranborne and Alderholt. From 1970 to 1988, peak counts apparently reached or exceeded 100 birds at the main coastal watch-points on only four occasions, mainly at Portland Bill with 170 on 5th May 1976, 140 on 6th May 1982 and 100 on 3rd May 1980, also 150 at Christchurch Harbour on 18th May 1975. Since 1989 there is a hint of a recovery with at least nine counts of 100 or more birds including 230 at Durlston CP on 15th August 1992, and 'falls' of 200 at Christchurch Harbour and 120 at Portland Bill on 10th May 1993, and 150 at Central Portland and 100 at Portland Bill on 24th April 1989. Despite this, the annual totals of Whitethroats ringed at Portland Bird Observatory during 1959–1999 strongly suggest that the numbers of migrants have not recovered to the level prior 1969.

The last birds are usually recorded during October, more exceptionally in early November, the latest being 9th November 1972 in a Dorchester garden, 8th November 1987 and 10th November 1968 at Portland Bill, with exceptionally late birds in a garden at Parkstone, Poole on 25th November 1951 and at Sixpenny Handley on 29th November 1992. There is also one winter record involving a bird in a Weymouth garden on 2nd January 1983.

A total of 9,843 birds has been ringed in the county and there have been four foreign recoveries from Spain and one from Eire, but there have been no reports of any foreign controls.

The Whitethroat is a summer visitor breeding across most of Europe, except the far north, and extending eastwards to Asia Minor and west-central Asia; also in north-west Africa and parts of the Middle East. It winters in sub-Saharan Africa.

Postscript 2000–2002
At Portland a 'fall' of between 500 and 700 birds on 5th May 2002 is the highest count since 29th April 1955! In 2001 there were early birds at Lodmoor NR with two on 24th March and five on 31st March.

Garden Warbler   *Sylvia borin*

A fairly common summer visitor and passage migrant

Mansel-Pleydell (1888) described this species as "a late summer visitor, frequenting shrubberies, woods, plantations, and gardens, where its sweet soft song may often be heard in May". Blathwayt (1945) referred to it as a summer resident, apparently more numerous than the Blackcap, though more local.

Although there is little evidence to suggest any substantial change in status since, it is now regarded as being both less numerous and more local than the Blackcap. The *BTO Atlas* (1968–1972) revealed evidence of breeding in 34 (92%) 10-km squares (confirmed in 21, probable in 12 and possible in one). The Tetrad Survey (1987–1994) produced an almost identical result with evidence of breeding in 34 (92%) of the pre-1974 10-km squares (confirmed in 27, probable in four and possible in three). The Tetrad Map shows that as a breeding bird the Garden Warbler is fairly well distributed, but more densely so in the northern half of the county, being rather sparse over much of the south-west, in the more open parts of the chalk downs, and in the urban areas of the south-east.

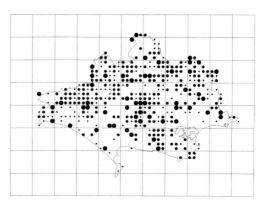

There is no useful data available on long-term population trends, whilst notable reports of population concentrations include an exceptional 25 singing males in Milborne Wood in 1987, this being a site where traditional hazel coppicing is still practiced for hurdle making, and 12 pairs in Clifton Wood in 1982 and 1987.

The earliest spring records are 29th March 1981 at Radipole NR and 30th March 1974 at Winspit. Otherwise the first migrants usually appear in April, the average date of the first arrivals being later in the 1950s than during the following four decades – see Table 536.

The main migration period in spring extends from mid-April to late May with peak passage normally recorded during the first half of May. Seasonal totals from the main coastal watch-points are highly variable, ranging at Portland Bill from a mere 65 birds in 1992 to notably high numbers in 1984 (419), 1987 (350) and 1991 (404) – see Table 537. Peak counts rarely exceed 50 birds, the highest being from Portland Bill with 120 on 16th May 1972 and 6th May 1982, and 100 on 15th May 1970, 16th May 1984 and 10th

	1950–1959	1960–1969	1970–1979	1980–1989	1990–1999
Range	16th–25th April	6th April– 3rd May	30th March– 24th April	29th March– 21st April	1st–23rd April
Average	21st April	15th April	11th April	13th April	14th April

Table 536. Dates for first spring arrivals each decade 1950–1999

May 1989. The first autumn migrants appear during late July with the main passage period extending through August (often the peak month), and September into early October. Again seasonal totals are highly variable at the main coastal watch-points – see Table 538. Peak counts usually range from 10–25 and rarely exceed 30 birds, the highest being 60 at Portland Bill on 8th August 1997 and 50 at St Aldhelm's Head on 17th August 1985, Durlston CP on 20th August 1992 and Christchurch Harbour in August 1996. During the 1990s there has been a marked decline in the strength of both spring and autumn passage at Portland Bill, which is not evident at Durlston CP – see Tables 539 and 540.

	1980	1981	1982	1983	1984	1985	1986	1987	1988	1989
Portland Bill	171	118	180	131	419	229	81	350	149	204
Durlston CP	24	26	41	29	44	34	30	31	39	44
Christchurch Hbr	38	68	38	17	217	96	40	82	82	78

	1990	1991	1992	1993	1994	1995	1996	1997	1998	1999
Portland Bill	105	404	65	128	69	157	149	93	264	78
Durlston CP	122	87	27	nc	10	55	63	69	48	30
Christchurch Hbr	39	156	15	173	69	11	45	8	28	10

Table 537. Spring totals (bds) at the main coastal watch-points 1980–1999

	1980	1981	1982	1983	1984	1985	1986	1987	1988	1989
Portland Bill	379	241	186	334	200	138	272	411	329	113
Durlston CP	103	130	93	212	202	178	207	248	221	171
Christchurch Hbr	78	78	47	44	107	112	88	263	160	31

	1990	1991	1992	1993	1994	1995	1996	1997	1998	1999
Portland Bill	107	84	149	133	159	116	89	107	77	65
Durlston CP	357	116	320	nc	138	183	248	234	193	155
Christchurch Hbr	12	13	38	114	23	19	222	31	46	26

Table 538. Autumn totals (bds) at the main coastal watch-points 1980–1999

	1980–84	1985–89	1990–94	1995–99
Portland Bill	204	203	154	148
Durlston CP	33	36	62	53

Table 539. 5-year average spring totals (bds) at Portland Bill and Durlston CP 1980–1999

	1980–84	1985–89	1990–94	1995–99
Portland Bill	268	253	126	91
Durlston CP	148	205	233	203

Table 540. 5-year average autumn totals (bds) at Portland Bill and Durlston CP 1980–1999

The last birds usually occur during the second half of October and occasionally in early November, the latest being from Portland Bill on 16th November 1985 and 17th November 1981, and Easton, Portland with very late individuals on 26th November 1998 and 28th–29th November 1987. There are also two exceptional winter records involving singles in a Ferndown garden on 29th December 1974 and at Sydling St Nicholas on 14th February 1976.

A total of 5,712 birds has been ringed in the county and there have been four foreign recoveries from France, two from Morocco, and one each from Ghana, Belgium, the Netherlands, Spain, Portugal and the Channel Islands, as well as one foreign control from Belgium.

The Garden Warbler is a summer visitor breeding over most of Europe, except for much of the Mediterranean region and the extreme north, and extending eastwards to north-west Asia; also in northern Asia Minor. It winters in sub-Saharan Africa.

Blackcap   *Sylvia atricapilla*

A common summer visitor and passage migrant, and uncommon winter visitor

Mansel-Pleydell (1888) described this species as "a common and regular summer visitant, vieing with the Nightingale in the power and sweetness of its song". Blathwayt (1945) referred to it as a common and well-distributed summer resident.

In recent years, small but increasing numbers have overwintered, but its status as a breeding summer visitor and passage migrant has remained largely unchanged. The *BTO Atlas* (1968–1972) revealed evidence of breeding in 35 (95%) 10-km squares (confirmed in 31 and probable in four). The Tetrad Survey (1987–1994) produced a similar result with evidence of breeding in all but one (97%) of the pre-1974 10-km squares (confirmed in 34, probable in one and possible in one). The Tetrad Map shows that the Blackcap is a widespread breeding bird throughout the county except for localised absences from parts of the Bournemouth and Poole conurbation and the downland area to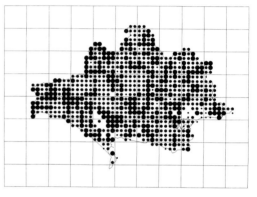

the west of Dorchester. The Common Bird Census Index for Dorset during 1981–1994 reveals higher, albeit fluctuating population levels for most of the 1980s, followed by a modest decline to a relatively stable situation during 1989–1993 with evidence of a recovery in 1994 – see Table 541.

1981	1982	1983	1984	1985	1986	1987	1988	1989	1990	1991	1992	1993	1994
100	139	–	118	132	86	–	121	93	93	86	79	93	111

Table 541. The Common Bird Census Index for Dorset 1981–1994

The start and finish of true migration is obscured by the presence of wintering birds and consequently extreme passage dates cannot be ascertained. In spring, the first genuine migrants normally arrive between mid-March and early April with the main passage period extending through April to late May, followed by occasional stragglers into early June. Seasonal totals from the main coastal watch-points are variable with peak counts usually ranging from 20–60 and rarely exceeding 100 birds, the highest being 200 at Christchurch Harbour on 24th April 1990 with 140 there on 10th May 1993, and 150 at Portland Bill on 27th April 1972 – see Table 542.

	1980	1981	1982	1983	1984	1985	1986	1987	1988	1989
Portland Bill	490	268	342	219	371	395	197	271	265	469
Durlston CP	80	78	183	142	104	115	109	89	122	175
Christchurch Hbr	178	158	>128	23	209	275	79	94	133	150

	1990	1991	1992	1993	1994	1995	1996	1997	1998	1999
Portland Bill	254	587	70	181	151	408	418	218	321	448
Durlston CP	178	182	106	nc	nc	137	113	203	150	196
Christchurch Hbr	350	201	66	260	207	133	121	256	132	187

Table 542. Spring totals (bds) at the main coastal watch-points 1980–1999

Overall autumn migration is particularly lengthy and extends from late July to early December. The timing and extent of passage, however, seemingly varies between the main coastal watch-points – see Table 543. At Durlston CP, other Purbeck sites and Christchurch Harbour migrants first appear in August, followed by the main passage during September and October with peak numbers in the former month. At Portland Bill passage is later and normally starts in early September, with very few migrants recorded prior to this time, and builds up to the main peak in October. Indeed the percentages of migrants recorded in September and October are almost transposed at Portland Bill and Durlston CP. One possible explanation is that the Purbeck sites and Christchurch Harbour attract a larger proportion of British birds, which migrate earlier than birds of Continental origin, the latter making up the majority of migrants recorded later in the autumn during October and November.

	Aug	Sep	Oct	Nov
Portland Bill	1%	29%	61%	9%
Durlston CP	6%	59%	32%	4%

Table 543. Proportion (%) of autumn migrants monthly at Portland Bill and Durlston CP 1986–1999

Although the autumn totals are variable, they are consistently and considerably higher at Durlston CP than at the other main coastal watch-points (cf Grasshopper Warbler and Lesser Whitethroat) – see Table 544. This is also reflected by autumn counts from elsewhere on Purbeck, notably at St Aldhelm's Head where peak counts have frequently exceeded 100 birds, the highest being 400 on 29th September 1989, 250 on 6th September 1983, and 200 on 28th September 1990 and 19th September 1991. At Durlston CP there are fewer counts in excess of 100 birds, the best being 250 on 11th September 1993. Elsewhere peak counts are more modest and rarely exceed 50 birds. At Christchurch Harbour 210 on 8th September 1987 and 138 on 26th September 1992 are exceptional, the next highest count for this site being 65 on 6th September 1981, whilst at Portland Bill the best autumn counts are 60 on 21st September and 11th–12th October 1995, and 3rd October 1998. Although numbers are small, passage extends well into November and occasionally even into early December as exemplified by an influx of 15 at Verne Common, Portland on 3rd December 1995. Some of these late migrants may be destined to winter in Great Britain.

	1980	1981	1982	1983	1984	1985	1986	1987	1988	1989
Portland Bill	357	189	312	nc	334	224	292	397	381	171
Durlston CP	616	459	720	631	750	632	643	834	992	1297
Christchurch Hbr	238	456	188	201	248	432	368	563	471	90

	1990	1991	1992	1993	1994	1995	1996	1997	1998	1999
Portland Bill	143	214	364	416	269	543	387	123	448	225
Durlston CP	1016	727	1631	1254	nc	1716	1231	776	1327	988
Christchurch Hbr	108	77	358	323	134	181	79	152	378	253

Table 544. Autumn totals (bds) at the main coastal watch-points 1980–1999

Wintering was apparently first recorded in 1952 when a pair frequented a bird-table at Bridport from 1st to 21st January. There were no further reports until 1959 when single males were present at Morecombe-lake from 8th February to 2nd April and Dorchester on 23rd February. Since then wintering has occurred annually, initially involving relatively few birds, but with notable increases in 1969 and 1981 culminating in a remarkable peak of 160 birds in 1996, which included 125 birds during the first winter period – see Fig 52. Although winter birds have been widely reported, the majority of sightings come from suburban gardens and parks in the built-up areas of the south-east, namely Christchurch, Bournemouth, Poole, Broadstone, Corfe Mullen, Wimborne and Ferndown, as well as Swanage and the Weymouth and Portland areas. Most records involve 1-2 birds, notable concentrations including 16 in the Weymouth area and 12 in the Bournemouth and Poole area in the first winter period of 1985, 16 in various Broadstone gardens in the first winter period of 1986 with a minimum of seven visiting one Broadstone garden in the first winter period of 1995, 14 in the Bournemouth, Poole and Wimborne areas in the first winter period of 1983, at least ten at Weston, Portland and the same number at Verne Common, Portland on 7th January 1996, and nine at Radipole NR in December 1984 with seven there in the second winter period of 1986.

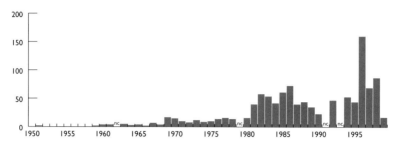

Fig 52. Winter totals 1950–1999

A total of 22,360 birds has been ringed in the county. Most foreign recoveries are from Iberia and north-west Africa, the main wintering area for British Blackcaps. Ringed birds have been recovered from Morocco (13), Spain (eight), Algeria (four) and Portugal (one). A bird recovered from Mallorca was unusually far east for a British or indeed West European Blackcap. Otherwise there are foreign recoveries from France (two), and one each from Germany, the Channel Islands and Eire, whilst there are two foreign controls from Belgium, and one each from France, Germany, Morocco and the Channel Islands.

The Blackcap breeds from north-west Africa and across most of Europe except the far north, extending eastwards into northern Asia Minor and west-central Asia. It is largely a summer visitor except in the west and extreme south of its breeding range. It winters from the British Isles, the Low Countries and Denmark south through western and southern Europe to north-west Africa and separate areas of West and East sub-Saharan Africa.

Postscript 2000–2002
At North Portland, 100 on 20th September 2002 is a high autumn count for the island.

Greenish Warbler   *Phylloscopus trochiloides*

A very rare passage migrant: nine records

Although the first four birds occurred in autumn between 20th August and 1st October, the last five have appeared in late spring and summer between 1st June and 1st July. All but one of the records are from Portland.

    1975   Portland Bill: imm. trapped 5th September with another on 13th September
    1977   Verne Common, Portland: 20th August
    1985   Hengistbury: 1st–3rd October, trapped 2nd
    1988   Portland Bill: trapped 13th June
    1990   Portland Bill: 15th–16th June, trapped on 15th
    1992   Portland Bill: singing male 10th June
    1993   Verne Common, Portland: singing male 1st June
    2001   Weston, Portland: singing male 1st–2nd July

The Greenish Warbler is a summer visitor breeding in north-eastern Europe, locally as far west as Sweden, Denmark and Germany, but mainly eastwards from southern Finland and the Baltic States through Belarus and Russia, and extending into central Asia as far east as China. It winters in the Indian sub-continent and south-east Asia. A vagrant to Great Britain with 371 records up to 2002.

Arctic Warbler   *Phylloscopus borealis*

Accidental: one record

    1984   Portland Bill: 6th September

The single Dorset record involves a first-winter bird trapped at Portland Bird Observatory. After release it was seen intermittently in the Observatory garden throughout the remainder of the day. A full account can be found in the Dorset Bird Report for 1984.

The Arctic Warbler is a summer visitor breeding from northern Scandinavia eastwards across Siberia to Japan and Alaska. It winters in south-east Asia. A vagrant to Great Britain with 250 records up to 2002.

Pallas's Warbler (Pallas's Leaf Warbler) *Phylloscopus proregulus*

A scarce autumn migrant

This attractive little 'gem' from Siberia first occurred in Dorset on 25th October 1965 at Portland Bill. This site hosted further birds on 14th October 1974 and during 29th–31st October 1975 with possibly the same individual nearby at East Weare, Portland on 1st November. Since 1979, this species has been recorded almost every year with absences only in 1980, 1983 and 1990. Annual totals ranged between 1–6 birds up to 1993, but more recently there have been notable influxes in 1996 (13) and 1998 (12) – see Table 545.

79	80	81	82	83	84	85	86	87	88	89	90	91	92	93	94	95	96	97	98	99
1	0	1	4	0	3	2	1	5	6	3	0	1	1	1	9	2	13	5	12	8

Table 545. Annual totals 1979–1999

Although records extend from mid-October to late November, there is a distinct peak during the last ten days of October, which accounts for 51% of the total – see Table 546. Indeed 61 birds (74%) have occurred during the relatively short period between 18th October and 8th November. There is evidence of a secondary peak in late November, but this is largely accounted for by the late influx of 11 birds during 19th–26th November 1998 and the late arrival of three birds during 21st–30th November 1997. The earliest autumn records are from Portland Bill on 14th October 1974 and 15th October 1979, and Verne Common, Portland on 14th October 1996, whilst the latest reports are from Pennsylvania Castle, Portland in November 1997 with one during 25th–30th and a second bird on 27th.

Oct 1–10	Oct 11–20	Oct 21–31	Nov 1–10	Nov 11–20	Nov 21–30
0	7	42	16	6	11

Table 546. Totals in 10-day periods during late autumn 1965–1999

Portland is the main site and accounts for 60% of the total – see Table 547. Although 20 birds have been recorded from the Bill, the species tends to favour the more wooded areas in the centre and north of the island, which have attracted some 29 birds. The other main sites are Hengistbury and Durlston CP, whilst there are four sightings from Winspit. The remaining records are from Radipole NR on 31st October 1982, the Nothe, Weymouth on 23rd–24th October 1988, St Aldhelm's Head on 5th November 1994 and Pilot's Point, Studland NNR on 25th October 1999.

	Total	
Portland Bill	20	24%
elsewhere on Portland	29	35%
Winspit	4	5%
Durlston CP	10	12%
Hengistbury	15	18%
elsewhere	4	5%

Table 547. Distribution of migrants 1965–1999

Most reports involve singles or very occasionally two or more birds. On 25th October 1996 there were at least seven birds at various sites on Portland including four at Verne Common, whilst there were three birds nearby at the Grove the following day. During the influx in late November 1998, there were four at Hengistbury on 23rd and three at Pennsylvania Castle, Portland during 21st–24th.

A total of eight birds has been ringed in the county.

The nominate race *P. p. proregulus* breeds from the Siberian taiga south to northern Mongolia, whilst other races breed in China and the Himalayas. The nominate race winters mainly in China and it is vagrants from this population which now reach the British Isles annually each autumn, with over 548 records up to 1990.

Postscript 2000–2002

In 2000 four singles were reported from various sites on Portland during 15th October–23rd November, whilst two at Hengistbury on 5th–6th December constitutes the latest record for the county. There were only two sightings in 2001 involving singles at Southwell, Portland on 29th October and Hengistbury on 14th November, and again there were only two sightings in 2002 involving singles at Hengistbury on 23rd October and more notably at Lulworth Cove on 1st November.

Sponsored by Dr George Green

Yellow-browed Warbler   *Phylloscopus inornatus*

An uncommon autumn passage migrant

The first Dorset records involve singles at Portland Bill on 30th September and 1st October 1960 and 21st October 1964. Subsequently the species has occurred more frequently with 1–2 birds reported in six years during 1968–1977 – see Table 548. Since 1979 records have been annual and increased markedly in 1985, with much higher numbers occurring in most autumns during the late 1980s and throughout the 1990s.

68	69	70	71	72	73	74	75	76	77	78	79	80	81	82	83
1	2	0	1	0	0	1	1	0	2	0	1	1	2	1	4

84	85	86	87	88	89	90	91	92	93	94	95	96	97	98	99
5	21	26	21	29	8	25	18	8	14	20	6	27	21	10	9

Table 548. Autumn totals 1968–1999

Yellow-browed Warblers arrive about two weeks earlier in the autumn than Pallas's Warblers. Although there are reports from mid-September through to early December, the main passage period extends from late September to the end of October, which accounts for 93% of the total, with the peak (34%) in the middle of October – see Table 549. There is a very early record on 13th September 1997 at Durlston CP, the next earliest being from Central Portland on 19th September 1993 and 20th September 1988. All but one of the September reports have occurred since 1985. Very few have been recorded during November, which accounts for only 6% of the total compared with 40% for Pallas's Warbler. The latest records are from Easton, Portland on 26th November 1997, and Hengistbury on 22nd–23rd November 1998, 26th November 1991 and 6th–7th December 1980.

Nearly half of the birds (49%) have been recorded from Portland and, like the Pallas's Warbler, the more wooded areas in the centre and north of the island have attracted more birds (81) than the Bill (60) – see Table 550. The other main sites are Hengistbury and Durlston CP followed by St Aldhelm's Head.

A total of 29 birds have occurred at other sites, mainly along the coastal and near-coastal fringes of the county. In the west, there is a single sighting from West Bexington, whilst along the Fleet four singles have occurred at Abbotsbury since 1993 with further singles reported from Langton Herring, East Fleet and Littlesea. In the Weymouth area six birds have been recorded involving two singles at Lodmoor CP in 1998, two singles at Radipole School and single birds at Radipole Park and Melcombe Regis Cemetery. Elsewhere on Purbeck, there are reports of singles from Osmington Mills, Ringstead, Tyneham, Winspit, Worth Matravers and well inland at Church Knowle on 11th October 1997, whilst the fringes of Poole Harbour have produced five singles at Studland NNR (three in 1994) and one at Ham Common, Poole. There are three additional inland records, at East Stoke on 12th October 1992, at Winterbourne Steepleton Pond on 29th October 1995 and at Bovington on 1st November 1999.

Sep 11–20	Sep 21–30	Oct 1–10	Oct 11–20	Oct 21–31	Nov 1–10	Nov 11–20	Nov 21–30	Dec 1–10
3	32	67	92	58	10	3	3	1

Table 549. Totals in 10-day periods during autumn 1960–1999

	Total	
Portland Bill	60	21%
elsewhere on Portland	81	28%
St Aldhelm's Head	16	6%
Durlston CP	40	14%
Hengistbury	61	21%
elsewhere	29	10%

Table 550. Distribution of migrants 1960–1999

Most records involve single birds, occasionally two or three with the highest counts being five at Hengistbury on 19th October 1990 with four there on 2nd October 1994, four at Portland Bill on 19th October 1985 and four at Verne Common, Portland on 14th October 1996.

A total of 30 birds has been ringed in the county. There is one recovery involving a bird ringed at Portland Bill on 21st October 1988 and controlled on Guernsey the following day.

The Yellow-browed Warbler is a summer visitor breeding in Siberia from the northern Urals east to far-eastern Russia and south to the Sayan mountains. It winters mainly in the north of the Indian sub-continent and south-east Asia.

Postscript 2000–2002

In 2000 a total of nine single birds were reported during 30th September–21st October including six at various sites on Portland, whilst one at Radipole NR from 3rd–14th December is the latest record for the county. In 2001 eight singles occurred during 29th September–24th October including three at Durlston CP. In 2002, there were records of eight singles from September to 11th November including three at various sites on Portland.

Hume's Warbler
(Hume's Leaf Warbler)   *Phylloscopus humei*

Accidental: four records

This species, which has been recently 'split' from the Yellow-browed Warbler, has been recorded from Portland in three successive years from 1999 to 2001. All birds have arrived on typically late dates in November and December.

1994   Winspit: 26th November–3rd December
1999   Southwell, Portland: 4th–6th November
2000   Portland Bill: 4th–9th December, trapped 7th
2001   Portland Bill:15th–17th November, trapped 15th

This recently recognised species is a summer visitor breeding in central Asia from the Sayan and Altai mountains south to the north-west Himalayas. It winters mainly in the northern and central Indian sub-continent with smaller numbers west to eastern Arabia. A vagrant to Great Britain with 49 records up to 2002.

Radde's Warbler   *Phylloscopus schwarzi*

A very rare autumn migrant: nine records

Apart from the first at St Aldhelm's Head in 1976, all the remaining birds have been recorded since 1989 including six during 1995–2001. There are seven records from Portland and two from Purbeck. This species generally occurs earlier than the Dusky Warbler and has been recorded on dates ranging from 24th September to 26th October.

    1976   St Aldhelm's Head: trapped 10th October
    1989   Easton, Portland: 18th–19th October
            Portland Bill: trapped 26th October
    1995   Winspit: 12th–13th October
    1997   Portland Bill: trapped 22nd October
    1999   Portland Bill: singles trapped 12th and 14th October
    2000   Portland Bill: trapped 1st October
    2001   Portland Bill: trapped 24th September

The Radde's Warbler is a summer visitor breeding from west-central Siberia east to the Pacific and winters in south-east Asia. A vagrant to Great Britain with 240 records up to 2002.

Dusky Warbler   *Phylloscopus fuscatus*

A very rare autumn migrant – has overwintered: 12 records

Apart from the first at Portland Bill in 1984, all the remaining records have occurred since 1991 including eight in the five years 1997–2001. Nine of the 11 autumn birds have been recorded on typically late dates between 27th October and 30th November including three during 23rd–30th November. There is one report of wintering.

    1984   Portland Bill: trapped 27th October
    1991   Hengistbury: 29th October
    1994   Easton, Portland: 5th November
            Verne Common, Portland: 26th November
    1997   Winspit: 23rd–24th November
            Wick Fields, Christchurch Harbour: 30th November
    1998   Lodmoor NR/Tip area: 23rd–26th January, again 18th February–23rd March
            Abbotsbury Swannery: 4th–7th November
    1999   Abbotsbury Beach: 14th–15th November
    2000   Southwell, Portland: 15th–17th October
            Portland Bill: trapped 16th November
    2001   Southwell, Portland: 13th–14th October

The Dusky Warbler is a summer visitor breeding from central and north-east Siberia to China and the eastern Himalayas. It winters from the north of the Indian sub-continent east to southern China and south-east Asia. A vagrant to Great Britain with 249 records up to 2002.

Western Bonelli's Warbler   *Phylloscopus bonelli*

A very rare passage migrant: eight records

Four of the eight records occurred during the five-year period 1972–1976. Based on a review undertaken by the BBRC, the following records are accepted as proven Western Bonelli's Warblers:

1955   Portland Bill: trapped 29th August
1965   Portland Bill: 10th–20th August, trapped 10th
1972   Weston, Portland: 9th September
1976   Portland Bill: 13th August–3rd September, trapped 14th and 26th
1984   Hengistbury: singing male 24th–25th May

Although it seems likely that the following records also refer to Western rather than Eastern Bonelli's Warblers, they are considered to be indeterminate:

1974   Brownsea: 19th August
1975   Hengistbury: singing male 31st May
1989   Hengistbury: 29th–31st August

The Western Bonelli's Warbler is a summer visitor breeding in north-west Africa, Iberia and much of France east to Austria, Croatia and Italy. It winters in Africa along the southern edge of the Sahara. A vagrant to Great Britain with 63 records up to 2002. There were 136 records of 'Bonelli's Warbler' up to 1995 prior to the split into Western Bonelli's Warbler *P. bonelli* and Eastern Bonelli's Warbler *P. orientalis* in 1996.

Wood Warbler   *Phylloscopus sibilatrix*

An uncommon summer visitor and passage migrant

Mansel-Pleydell (1888) referred to this species as a summer visitor that frequented the wooded districts of the county, whilst Blathwayt (1945) considered it to be a summer resident, somewhat local and scarce in some areas, but widely distributed and preferring large woods of oak and beech.

The *BTO Atlas* (1968–1972) found evidence of breeding in 23 (62%) 10-km squares (confirmed in six, probable in 15 and possible in two), whilst the Tetrad Survey (1987–1994) revealed evidence of breeding in 24 (65%) of the pre-1974 10-km squares (confirmed in six, probable in ten and possible in eight). Since records of possible breeding may refer to migrants, it is perhaps better to use evidence of confirmed or probable breeding when making comparisons between surveys. This reveals a reduction from 21 (57%) 10-km squares during *BTO Atlas* (1968–1972) to 16 (43%) of the pre-1974 10-km squares during the Tetrad Survey (1987–1994). Since the earlier survey, the Wood Warbler has seemingly disappeared from many of its former haunts in

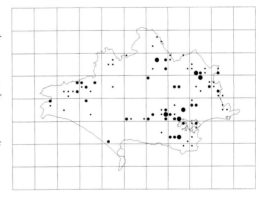

the centre and north of the county, which has been partially balanced by a slight expansion into south-east Purbeck. The Tetrad Map shows a localised breeding distribution, the most favoured sites being woodlands within the Poole Basin, notably Wareham Forest, and in west Dorset. It is also evident that many sites are used irregularly and both surveys may well overstate the breeding population. Since 1980, the number of pairs and singing males reported annually has varied considerably ranging from less than five in poor years to 20–30 in good ones with a peak of 32 in 1988.

There is a very early record on 23rd March 1995 at Hengistbury (cf Lesser Whitethroat), the next earliest being 4th April 1975 at Chapman's Pool, 10th April 1983 at East Fleet and 12th April 1991 at the Grove, Portland. Otherwise the first spring migrants usually appear during the second half of April, the average date of the first arrivals during 1950–1999 being 18th April.

The migration period extends from mid-April to late May with peak passage often recorded during the first half of May. Autumn migrants appear from mid-July through to mid-September with peak passage in August. The numbers of migrants recorded at the main coastal watch-points are very low – see Tables 551 and 552. In view of the sizeable breeding populations further north and west in Great Britain, and in northern Europe, it is surprising that migration through Dorset is so light. Although spring passage is typically more prominent than in autumn, totals for each season have only occasionally reached double figures, the best being 29 bird-days at Hengistbury in spring 1991 with 26 bird-days there in spring 1984. Not surprisingly day-totals are generally very small and normally range from 1–4 birds, the highest being 15 at Hengistbury on 11th May 1991 with 14 there on 17th May 1984, and 12 at Portland Bill on 5th May 1987. Elsewhere there are scattered reports of migrants from other coastal sites, the most favoured being Studland NNR, Brownsea, St Aldhelm's Head, Radipole NR with a remarkable count of 12 on 1st May 1980, Radipole School, the Nothe in Weymouth and East Fleet.

	1980	1981	1982	1983	1984	1985	1986	1987	1988	1989
Portland Bill	1	4	1	3	8	4	4	18	4	3
rest of Portland	nc	0	1	0	4	1	1	13	5	10
Durlston CP	>4	4	10	12	10	3	3	10	6	8
Christchurch Hbr	1	4	2	0	26	16	4	4	4	14

	1990	1991	1992	1993	1994	1995	1996	1997	1998	1999
Portland Bill	0	4	6	8	2	1	2	0	4	4
rest of Portland	22	13	4	5	5	2	1	1	5	9
Durlston CP	6	6	5	6	2	8	8	5	3	7
Christchurch Hbr	12	29	4	11	0	3	2	0	4	5

Table 551. Spring totals (bds) at the main coastal watch-points 1980–1999

	1980	1981	1982	1983	1984	1985	1986	1987	1988	1989
Portland Bill	2	8	7	4	5	2	5	12	4	4
rest of Portland	1	0	2	0	1	1	3	1	2	4
Durlston CP	7	8	10	5	4	3	9	5	6	8
Christchurch Hbr	0	3	1	7	10	4	5	9	4	4

	1990	1991	1992	1993	1994	1995	1996	1997	1998	1999
Portland Bill	1	1	0	2	1	6	1	0	0	1
rest of Portland	1	0	0	0	0	1	2	4	0	0
Durlston CP	1	5	3	3	1	14	3	5	4	5
Christchurch Hbr	1	0	3	15	1	3	2	0	3	2

Table 552. Autumn totals (bds) at the main coastal watch-points 1980–1999

The last birds usually occur in September, more rarely in October, the latest records being 20th October 1983 at Winspit and 21st October 1996 at Pennsylvania Castle, Portland.

A total of 120 birds has been ringed in the county.

The Wood Warbler is a summer visitor breeding across much of Europe, except for north and central Scandinavia, Ireland, most of Iberia and the Mediterranean fringes, extending eastwards into west-central Asia. It winters in equatorial West and central Africa.

Chiffchaff (Common Chiffchaff)   *Phylloscopus collybita*

An abundant summer visitor and passage migrant, and uncommon winter visitor

Mansel-Pleydell (1888) simply referred to this species as a very early visitor in spring, whilst Blathwayt (1945) considered it to be a generally distributed and common summer resident and further mentioned that it had been recorded in January.

There has been little change in status subsequently except for an increase in the wintering population. The *BTO Atlas* (1968–1972) revealed evidence of breeding in 35 (95%) 10-km squares (confirmed in 31 and probable in four). The Tetrad Survey (1987–1994) produced a similar result with evidence of breeding in all but one (97%) of the pre-1974 10-km squares (confirmed in 33, probable in two and possible in one). The Tetrad Map shows that the Chiffchaff breeds throughout the county except for a few tetrads in the Bournemouth and Poole conurbation, and in open country south-west of Dorchester and north-east of Blandford. The Common Bird Census Index for Dorset during 1981–1994 shows marked fluctuations including a major decline in 1983 and peaks in 1988 and 1994, interspersed with periods of relative stability during 1984–1986 and 1989–1992 – see Table 553.

1981	1982	1983	1984	1985	1986	1987	1988	1989	1990	1991	1992	1993	1994
100	91	41	75	72	72	–	119	106	103	106	106	81	125

Table 553. The Common Bird Census Index for Dorset 1981–1994

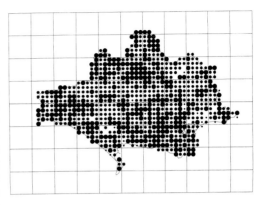

The start of spring migration is obscured by wintering birds, but the first genuine migrants usually arrive during the first ten days of March, perhaps a little earlier in some years, e.g. 15th February 1998 at Portland Bill. Although passage can be prolonged with new arrivals sometimes reported as late as July, the main migration period extends from mid-March to the end of May. Peak numbers normally occur in April, occasionally in March and exceptionally in May. Seasonal totals from the main coastal watch-points are highly variable – see Table 554. Peak counts usually range from 30–100 and rarely exceed 250 birds, the highest being an exceptional 1,200 at Radipole NR on 9th April 1985 with 700 there on 8th April 1981, when there were also 500 at Portland Bill and 800 'Willowchiffs' at Christchurch Harbour. Autumn migration is also prolonged. A few migrants occur in August, but the main passage starts in early September and extends through to late October with smaller numbers recorded into early December. These later individuals may involve Continental birds destined to winter in southern Great Britain (cf Blackcap). Seasonal totals are highly variable and like some other small migrants, Durlston CP attracts larger numbers than the other main coastal watch-points (cf Grasshopper Warbler and Lesser Whitethroat) – see Table 553. Peak counts usually range from 40–150 and rarely exceed 250 birds, the highest being 470 at Durlston CP on 14th September 1989, and 400 at Portland Bill on 16th September 1958, Christchurch Harbour on 19th September 1988 and Chapman's Pool on 1st–2nd October 1994.

	1980	1981	1982	1983	1984	1985	1986	1987	1988	1989
Portland Bill	nc	c1000	>250	645	335	281	543	755	1289	772
Durlston CP	nc	142	347	323	266	264	203	177	182	607
Christchurch Hbr	nc	nc	nc	nc	nc	nc	nc	91	nc	nc

	1990	1991	1992	1993	1994	1995	1996	1997	1998	1999
Portland Bill	679	526	499	770	830	708	1043	661	1781	865
Durlston CP	439	143	439	nc	nc	130	320	577	315	440
Christchurch Hbr	271	198	111	248	385	nc	712	535	1120	761

Table 554. Spring totals (bds) at the main coastal watch-points 1980–1999

	1980	1981	1982	1983	1984	1985	1986	1987	1988	1989
Portland Bill	435	163	466	380	275	649	1099	728	863	1016
Durlston CP	nc	1055	949	879	987	804	1159	1425	2264	1979
Christchurch Hbr	nc	nc	nc	nc	nc	nc	nc	756	nc	nc

	1990	1991	1992	1993	1994	1995	1996	1997	1998	1999
Portland Bill	652	542	849	566	823	894	1045	703	1676	530
Durlston CP	1059	898	1554	nc	nc	1447	1227	1317	1384	1060
Christchurch Hbr	906	507	936	738	240	nc	894	581	1549	481

Table 555. Autumn totals (bds) at the main coastal watch-points 1980–1999

Since 1950 the number of wintering birds has steadily increased, most notably in the late 1960s and again in the late 1970s with peaks in 1981 (90), 1983 (72), 1984 (88), 1993 (79) and 1994 (76) – see Fig 53. Although winter birds have been widely reported, the majority of sightings come from the coastal fringes, most notably the Weymouth and Portland areas, whilst river valleys, cress-beds and small sewage works are particularly favoured inland. Most records involve 1–10 birds, notable concentrations including 20 at Kinson in the first winter period of 1983 with 12 there in the first winter period of 1993, 15 at Sandsfoot Castle and 12 at Newton's Cove in the first winter period of 1981, 15 at Verne Common, Portland in December 1994, 14 at Lower Bockhampton and 12 at Radipole NR in 1977, 10–13 at Studland NNR in December 1991 and 12 at Waddock Cross CBs on 17th January 1994.

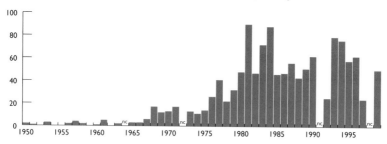

Fig 53. Winter totals 1950–1999

'Northern' or 'Scandinavian' Chiffchaffs *P. c. abietinus* have undoubtedly occurred with most claims from the main coastal watch-points. Records of the 'Siberian' Chiffchaff *P. c. tristis* are given separately.

A total of 28,279 birds has been ringed in the county. Many foreign recoveries have been from the main migration routes and wintering areas for British Chiffchaffs in the extreme west of Europe, the western Mediterranean and west Africa. There have been five recoveries from Spain, three from Portugal, two each from France, Morocco and Senegal, and one each from Algeria, Western Sahara and the Channel Islands. This pattern is also shown by foreign controls, e.g. three from the Channel Islands, two from Senegal and one from Spain, whilst single controls from Belgium, Germany and Sweden reflect the movement of Continental birds into Great Britain. There is one recovery from Eire.

The nominate race *P. c. collybita* is mainly a summer visitor breeding throughout most of western and central Europe north to Denmark and southern Sweden, south to the Pyrenees, Italy and Greece, and east to Bulgaria, Rumania, Hungary and Poland. It is replaced throughout most of Scandinavia and eastern Europe east to the Urals, also in the Caucasus, Transcaucasia and northern Iran by *P. c. abietinus*, whilst *P. c. tristis* breeds to the east of *P. c. abietinus*. The European races *P. c. collybita* and *P. c. abietinus* winter in western and southern Europe, north-west Africa, the northern tropics of Africa, Arabia and south-west Asia.

Siberian Chiffchaff   *Phylloscopus collybita tristis*

A scarce autumn migrant and winter visitor

All records of this race since 1995 have been assessed by the Dorset Bird Club Records Panel – see Dorset Bird Report for 2002 for full details. During 1995–2002 a total of 17 birds were accepted on plumage features and vocalisations, and a further eight showed plumage features indicative of *P. c. tristis*, but were not heard to call.

Although records span the period from 30th October to 25th April, most (40%) arrived in November – see Table 556. Overwintering is shown by the ten sightings during December–February, which include a number of long-staying individuals. Two singing at Radipole NR during 5th–20th April 2002 are particularly noteworthy.

Oct	Nov	Dec	Jan	Feb	Mar	Apr
2	10	2	3	5	1	2

Table 556. Monthly totals 1995–2002

Reports are widely distributed along the coastal strip from West Bexington to Christchurch Harbour including seven from the Weymouth area, six from Portland, four from Abbotsbury, three from Christchurch Harbour, two from Winspit and singles at West Bexington, Lulworth and Studland NNR.

Prior to 1995, the first Dorset reports were from Portland Bill involving one trapped on 14th October 1955 followed by sightings of singles on 2nd September and 7th–8th November 1956. Apart from one inland at Merley on 16th December 1977, all subsequent records occurred during 1982–1985 (nine birds) and in 1994 (one bird). The months of October and November accounted for 11 individuals, with two early birds in September and one December sighting. No less than eight of these 14 pre-1995 birds were recorded from Portland Bill, the remainder being three from Christchurch Harbour, two from St Aldhelm's Head and one from Merley. At present pre-1995 records have not been assessed and should be regarded as 'unproven'.

The Siberian Chiffchaff *P. c. tristis* is a summer visitor breeding in Siberia east of the Urals and winters mainly in the Middle East, Arabia, south-west Asia and the northern Indian sub-continent.

Iberian Chiffchaff   *Phylloscopus ibericus*

Accidental: one record

1999 Verne Common, Portland: 25th April–8th July

A singing male held territory at Verne Common, Portland from late April to early July 1999. The bird was trapped and ringed on 9th May and identification was confirmed by biometrics and examination of sonograms. This was the first ever to be 'twitchable' in Great Britain. A full account can be found in *Birding World* Vol. 12, Number 5, June 1999 and the Dorset Bird Report for 1999.

There is one previous record claimed for Dorset involving a singing bird at Lodmoor NR on 17th April 1983, whilst one trapped at Portland Bird Observatory on 11th May 2000 is still awaiting adjudication by the BBRC.

This recently recognised species breeds mainly in Iberia, except for large parts of the south and east, also locally in south-west France and north-west Africa. There is a narrow zone of overlap with the Common Chiffchaff *P. c. collybita* in south-west France and north-east Spain. The Iberian Chiffchaff winters in sub-Saharan Africa but the range is little-known. A vagrant to Great Britain with six records up to 2002.

Sponsored by C. E. Richards

Willow Warbler   *Phylloscopus trochilus*

A common summer visitor and passage migrant

Both Mansel-Pleydell (1888) and Blathwayt (1945) referred to this species as a common summer visitor.

There was little change in status until the population 'crash' of the late 1980s and early 1990s. The *BTO Atlas* (1968–1972) revealed evidence of breeding in 35 (95%) 10-km squares (confirmed in 33 and probable in two). The Tetrad Survey (1987–1994) produced a similar result with evidence of breeding in all of the pre-1974 10-km squares (confirmed in 34, probable in two and possible in one). Although the Tetrad Map shows that breeding occurs widely throughout the county, it is absent from a few more tetrads than the Chiffchaff. Most of these absences occurred in the more intensively farmed areas of the chalk downs including west Purbeck. The Common Bird Census Index for Dorset during 1981–1994 shows a dramatic decline since a peak in 1983 with population levels during 1992–1994 around a quarter of that in 1981 – see Table 557. Concern over this decline resulted in a special survey being organised during 1996–1999. This showed the county population to average c.3,000 pairs during this period, which is a low figure by comparison with the national population of about two million birds.

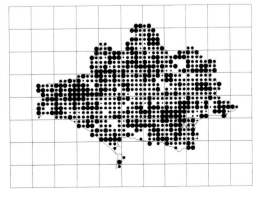

411

1981	1982	1983	1984	1985	1986	1987	1988	1989	1990	1991	1992	1993	1994
100	50	117	97	86	78	–	59	52	48	31	22	27	27

Table 557. The Common Bird Census Index for Dorset 1981–1994

There are very early records from Swanage on 2nd March 1975, Christchurch Harbour on 6th March 1992, 8th March 1995 and 9th March 1998, and the Fleet at Butterstreet Cove also on 9th March 1998. Otherwise the first spring migrants usually appear during the second half of March, the average date of the first arrivals being considerably earlier in the 1990s than during the previous four decades – see Table 558.

	1950–1959	1960–1969	1970–1979	1980–1989	1990–1999
Range	24th March–8th April	18th March–6th April	2nd March–5th April	15th–31st March	6th–27th March
Average	30th March	29th March	25th March	26th March	16th March

Table 558. Dates for first spring arrivals each decade 1950–1999

Although spring migration extends from mid-March to late May with a few late stragglers through into early June, peak passage normally occurs in April and early May. Seasonal totals at the main coastal watch-points are highly variable, ranging at Portland Bill from 1,000–2,000 in poor years to over 4,000 birds in good years – see Table 559. Peak counts are usually in the 100–600 range, but there are occasional heavy 'falls' when numbers may well exceed 1,000 birds. The heaviest of these occurred on 24th April 1989 with 3,500 at Central Portland, 1,000 at Portland Bill and 500 at St Aldhelm's Head, also 1,100 at Christchurch Harbour the previous day; on 24th April 1990 with 3,500 at Christchurch Harbour and 500 at St Aldhelm's Head; and during 1st–7th May 1980 with 1,450 at Radipole NR on 1st, 1,200 at Portland Bill on 3rd, 1,000 at North Portland during 1st–3rd and 500–600 at Christchurch Harbour during 5th–7th. There are several other high counts both from Portland Bill with 1,500 on 19th April 1997, and 1,000 on 8th April 1981 and 26th April 1995, and Christchurch Harbour with 1,500 on 11th May 1975 and 25th April 1985, and 1,000 on 22nd April 1997. Spring passage at Durlston CP is seemingly lighter than at the other main coastal watch-points – see Table 559. Autumn migration starts during the second half of July with most passage taking place during August and the first half of September, often peaking during the former month. Seasonal totals are variable with peak counts usually ranging from 100–350 and apparently only once exceeding 500 birds, i.e. 700 at Christchurch Harbour on 8th August 1977 – see Table 560.

	1980	1981	1982	1983	1984	1985	1986	1987	1988	1989
Portland Bill	>3000	3366	>2300	1094	1938	2995	1098	1628	3252	4278
Durlston CP	nc	277	507	272	324	1260	223	290	988	1169
Christchurch Hbr	nc	nc	nc	nc	nc	3610	nc	721	nc	nc

	1990	1991	1992	1993	1994	1995	1996	1997	1998	1999
Portland Bill	1727	2242	1001	2647	1665	4552	3445	4107	2248	4958
Durlston CP	723	548	258	nc	nc	614	881	577	582	584
Christchurch Hbr	5572	2496	nc	527	nc	nc	1406	2808	461	1009

Table 559. Spring totals (bds) at the main coastal watch-points 1980–1999

	1980	1981	1982	1983	1984	1985	1986	1987	1988	1989
Portland Bill	1319	2128	1269	1960	2484	1505	1880	2912	1390	1110
Durlston CP	nc	789	1464	967	1080	1463	1675	1520	1367	1306
Christchurch Hbr	nc	nc	nc	nc	nc	nc	nc	430	nc	nc

	1990	1991	1992	1993	1994	1995	1996	1997	1998	1999
Portland Bill	1226	1725	874	909	1270	1622	1230	1850	1298	1160
Durlston CP	1216	649	1468	nc	nc	915	1158	1015	727	1098
Christchurch Hbr	611	943	745	342	nc	nc	173	1115	417	744

Table 560. Autumn totals (bds) at the main coastal watch-points 1980–1999

Very few birds occur after the end of September. The last migrants are usually reported in October, but during the 1990s there has been an increase in November records, the latest being 20th November 1993 at Christchurch Harbour, 25th November 1997 at North Portland and 27th November 1996 at Pennsylvania Castle, Portland. There is also a report from West Bexington on 13th November 1983.

There are four records for the winter period:

1975   Burton Bradstock: one in song from 1975 remained until 8th January 1976
1980   Winspit: 9th–10th December, possibly a very late migrant
1988   Lodmoor NR: singing male 21st February, possibly a very early migrant
1997   Winspit: 20th November–5th January 1998

The 'Northern' race *P. t. acredula* has been claimed in spring from Portland Bill on a number of occasions, mainly during the late 1950s and early 1960s.

A total of 54,122 birds has been ringed in the county. All foreign recoveries are from the main migration route through Iberia with six from Spain and two from Portugal, whilst there are also two recoveries from the Channel Islands. One from the Netherlands is the only foreign control. Otherwise there are many reports of recoveries and controls from within the British Isles, including Eire, reflecting the wide origins/destinations of Willow Warblers passing through Dorset. The most interesting of these involves one ringed at St Aldhelm's Head on 21st October 1987, which was killed by a cat at Warrington, Cheshire on 2nd December of the same year presumably attempting to overwinter!

The Willow Warbler is a summer visitor breeding across much of northern Eurasia and wintering throughout much of sub-Saharan Africa.

Postscript 2000–2002
There was a very late bird at the Nothe, Weymouth on 4th December 2000.

Goldcrest   *Regulus regulus*

A common resident, winter visitor and passage migrant

Both Mansel-Pleydell (1888) and Blathwayt (1945) referred to this species as a common resident.

Despite suffering heavily from severe winters, notably in 1962/63, the Goldcrest has remained a widespread breeding bird. The *BTO Atlas* (1968–1972) found evidence of breeding in 35 (95%) 10-km squares (confirmed in 33 and probable in two), whilst the Tetrad Survey (1987–1994) produced a similar result with evidence of breeding in all but one (97%) of the pre-1974 10-km squares (confirmed in 30, probable in five and possible in one). The Tetrad Map shows that the breeding population is concentrated in west Dorset, the Sherborne area, parts of the northern chalk, and the east of the county, notably the Poole Basin. It is particularly scarce in the far north, the central and southern chalk areas, and the coastal fringes from the Fleet east to the Purbecks. This distribution reflects the species preference for coniferous and mixed woodlands, as well as parks and gardens with coniferous trees. The Common Bird Census Index for Dorset during 1981–1994 clearly indicates the Goldcrest's vulnerability to cold winters, notably those of 1984/85,

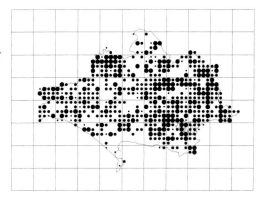

1985/86 and 1990/91 – see Table 561. Although there was a slight reduction after the 1981/82 winter, numbers recovered rapidly to high levels in 1983 and 1984. There was a dramatic decline resulting from the severe winters of the mid-1980s with the subsequent partial recovery interrupted by another cold winter in 1990/91. As a result, the population only recovered to 48% and 40% of the 1983 peak by 1990 and 1994 respectively. In earlier years, the very severe winter of 1962/63 also resulted in a catastrophic decline with only one report of a breeding pair the following summer. There was, however, a rapid recovery with the population reported to be at a very high level in 1972.

1981	1982	1983	1984	1985	1986	1987	1988	1989	1990	1991	1992	1993	1994
100	84	132	111	53	0	–	21	53	63	11	11	21	53

Table 561. The Common Bird Census Index for Dorset 1981–1994

The species' vulnerability to cold winters is reflected by the numbers recorded on passage at the main coastal watch-points. There is a dramatic illustration of this at Portland Bill in the springs following the winters of 1984/85, 1985/86, 1986/87, 1990/91 and 1996/97 with only nine birds in 1987 and three birds in 1992 – see Table 562. The impact on autumn passage is not so obvious, but very low numbers occurred in 1986, 1991 and 1996 – see Table 563.

Spring migration is generally lighter than that in autumn and extends from early March to early May with peak passage usually between mid-March and mid-April. Seasonal totals are highly variable and, as mentioned above, reflect the fortunes of the breeding population with respect to cold winters – see Table 562. Peak counts are rather modest, typically ranging from 20–50 and rarely exceeding 60 birds, the highest being from Christchurch Harbour with 250 in March 1998, 150 on 25th March 1974 and 130 on 15th April 1984, and from Portland Bill with 150 on 28th March 1971 and 28th March 1998. Autumn passage is much stronger and extends from late August to early December with peak numbers usually recorded in October. Seasonal totals are variable and generally higher at Durlston CP than Portland Bill see Table 563. Prior to the mid-1980s peak counts usually ranged from 30–150 birds, but in recent years they have increased and included several spectacular 'falls', most notably 1,500 at St Aldhelm's Head on 20th October 1988, 1,000 at Central Portland on 23rd October 1990 and 1,000 at Christchurch Harbour on 8th October 1993. It is interesting to contrast the autumn peak counts recorded in 1990 and 1991 at Portland Bill (250 and eight), St Aldhelm's Head (500 and four), Durlston CP (130 and four), and Christchurch Harbour (600 and two), which reflect the impact of the severe cold weather during the 1990/91 winter. Occasionally high autumn counts are recorded at other sites including Radipole NR with a maximum of several 100 in October 1984, and inland at Bovington peaking at 350 also in October 1984.

	1980	1981	1982	1983	1984	1985	1986	1987	1988	1989
Portland Bill	12	247	124	336	278	51	88	9	396	515
Durlston CP	0	nc	79	267	206	62	69	56	114	453
Christchurch Hbr	nc	nc	nc	nc	nc	59	nc	nc	nc	nc

	1990	1991	1992	1993	1994	1995	1996	1997	1998	1999
Portland Bill	338	133	3	88	53	71	330	53	856	277
Durlston CP	244	97	25	48	nc	215	378	290	205	128
Christchurch Hbr	nc	nc	2	14	nc	27	nc	nc	nc	60

Table 562. Spring totals (bds) at the main coastal watch-points 1980–1999

	1980	1981	1982	1983	1984	1985	1986	1987	1988	1989
Portland Bill	638	255	138	1246	218	660	21	821	996	1149
Durlston CP	378	697	905	2896	856	1000	34	2084	2857	2609
Christchurch Hbr	nc	nc	nc	nc	nc	nc	nc	791	nc	nc

	1990	1991	1992	1993	1994	1995	1996	1997	1998	1999
Portland Bill	1443	64	359	537	806	692	62	1250	394	610
Durlston CP	1757	40	721	1157	nc	3280	1958	2233	1120	1580
Christchurch Hbr	nc	2	225	1557	nc	1015	nc	648	nc	1640

Table 563. Autumn totals (bds) at the main coastal watch-points 1980–1999

There is very little information on winter numbers except from Bovington where the highest count was 400–500 during November and December 1984.

A total of 16,477 birds has been ringed in the county and there have been two foreign recoveries from Denmark, and one each from Norway and France, as well as two foreign controls from Sweden and one each from Denmark, Poland and Eire. These largely reflect the movement of birds between breeding areas in Scandinavia and eastern Europe, and wintering areas in western Europe including Great Britain.

The nominate race *R. r. regulus* breeds over most of north and central Europe, but it is restricted to mountainous areas further south in Iberia, Italy and the Balkans, also in Asia Minor. It is a summer visitor to the northern part of its breeding range with wintering extending south to the Mediterranean. Other races breed in the Caucasus and Asia.

Postscript 2000–2002

A family party at Easton on 8th July 2000 constitutes the first breeding record for Portland.

Sponsored by Brian G. Smith

Firecrest   *Regulus ignicapilla*

An uncommon passage migrant and winter visitor – occasionally breeds

Mansel-Pleydell (1888) described this species as "an occasional visitant" and referred to single birds shot at Parkstone and Cerne. Blathwayt (1945) considered it to be a scarce winter visitor and listed only four records involving one at Charmouth on 28th March 1906, four near Studland on 29th March 1936 with one there on 26th March 1937, and one at Swanage on 4th December 1941.

The Firecrest continued to be a rare visitor until the mid-1950s with only one sighting during 1950–1954. Since 1955, however, records have increased substantially and the species has become a regular, but uncommon passage migrant, with annual wintering established by the late 1960s. There have also been sporadic reports of breeding.

Although spring passage mainly occurs between mid-March and mid-April, late stragglers are frequently recorded through to mid-May and exceptionally into June. Numbers at the main coastal watch-points are generally modest, but can vary with seasonal totals at Portland Bill ranging from as low as a single bird in 1991 and four in 1996, to highs of 77 in 1984 and 68 in 1999 – see Table 564. Peak counts rarely exceed six birds, the highest being 15 at Portland Bill on 28th March 1998 with at least 12 there on 27th March 1958, nine at Durlston CP on 26th March 1989, 7–9 at Christchurch Harbour on 28th March 1981 with eight there on 10th April 1979, and eight at Verne Common, Portland in spring 1999. There are occasional reports of early autumn migrants from July to early September, but passage normally extends from mid-September through to early December with the peak usually during the second half of October, but occasionally as early as late September. Seasonal totals are higher than in spring and vary considerably from year to year, ranging at Portland Bill from only three in 1991 (cf spring) to 274 in 1996 – see Table 565. Peak counts generally range from 5–15 and rarely exceed 20 birds, the highest being 45 at Christchurch Harbour in October 1996 with 35 there on 31st October 1982, and 40 at Portland Bill on 20th–21st October 1967 with 30 there on 14th October 1996.

Away from the main coastal watch-points, most records of migrants are from the coast and coastal fringes. Despite this, there are a good number of reports from inland sites scattered throughout the county including the far north. Most sightings involve only 1–2 birds, the highest counts being five at White Sheet on 5th November 1967, five near a reservoir at Corfe Mullen on 30th October 1972 and five at Beaminster on 17th March 1984.

Regular wintering became established in the late 1960s with relatively high totals recorded during 1967–1969 – see Fig 54. Numbers were relatively low during much of the 1970s, but increased again at the beginning of the 1980s to reach a peak during 1982–1984 before declining to a more modest level

	1980	1981	1982	1983	1984	1985	1986	1987	1988	1989
Portland Bill	50	44	34	47	77	15	11	34	20	49
Durlston CP	20	27	12	13	21	0	1	13	17	24
Christchurch Hbr	2	9	9	12	25	12	6	19	28	15

	1990	1991	1992	1993	1994	1995	1996	1997	1998	1999
Portland Bill	31	1	42	23	24	59	4	36	61	68
Durlston CP	19	1	11	33	10	9	13	7	12	22
Christchurch Hbr	14	8	1	5	6	11	7	5	nc	nc

Table 564. Spring totals (bds) at the main coastal watch-points 1980–1999

	1980	1981	1982	1983	1984	1985	1986	1987	1988	1989
Portland Bill	153	49	200	143	167	38	74	110	120	112
Durlston CP	12	30	88	40	39	21	30	70	105	39
Christchurch Hbr	6	13	93	30	74	29	61	84	96	32

	1990	1991	1992	1993	1994	1995	1996	1997	1998	1999
Portland Bill	160	3	45	99	68	140	274	36	204	120
Durlston CP	120	57	52	84	35	61	66	70	50	60
Christchurch Hbr	39	0	20	28	8	32	163	3	nc	nc

Table 565. Autumn totals (bds) at the main coastal watch-points 1980–1999

subsequently. The majority of winter records are from the coastal fringes, the Weymouth and Portland areas, Purbeck and Christchurch Harbour being particularly favoured. Most reports involve 1–2 birds and rarely exceed five, the most notable concentration being 30 in the Weymouth and Portland areas during the first winter period of 1983.

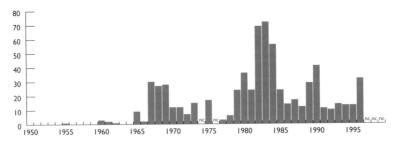

Fig 54. Winter totals 1950–1999

There are only six reports of confirmed breeding of which four occurred during the Tetrad Survey (1987–1994). This suggests that this species may well be overlooked as a breeding bird in the county. All records confirming or suggestive of breeding are given below:

1970   Undisclosed site in SZ08: pair reared five young

1973   Purbeck coastal site: pair feeding at least four young 30th July

1974   Undisclosed site in Purbeck: pair probably bred

1980   Ferndown: one on 15th July

1981   Hengistbury: pair throughout May and a single on three dates in June
      Two undisclosed sites: single singing males in May

1987   Undisclosed site A: adult feeding two, perhaps six fledged juvs 29th May
      Undisclosed site B: one juv. 1st August

1988   Undisclosed site: singing male 5th–14th May

1989   Colehill: pair feeding six recently fledged juvs 13th August
      Undisclosed site: one on 10th May

1990   Undisclosed site: pair bred

1994   Bovington: singing male on one date in May

1997   Canford Heath: one on 8th June

A total of 1,113 birds has been ringed in the county. There have been no reports of any foreign recoveries or controls, but there has been a control from the Channel Islands.

The Firecrest breeds in north-west Africa and throughout much of central and southern Europe as far north as southern England and Denmark, and as far east as Belarus, the Ukraine, Rumania and Bulgaria, also locally in Asia Minor and southern Russia. It is a summer visitor in the north-east of its range and winters mainly in western and southern Europe and north-west Africa.

Postscript 2000–2002

There was evidence of breeding in 2000 with one territory established at Bovington. Spring passage was notably strong at Portland Bill in 2001 with 100 bird-days.

Sponsored by Jean Southworth

Spotted Flycatcher   *Muscicapa striata*

A fairly common summer visitor and passage migrant

Although the Spotted Flycatcher was known to Mansel-Pleydell (1888), no mention was made regarding its early status in the county. Blathwayt (1945), however, referred to the species as a common and generally distributed summer resident.

There has been little change in status subsequently. The *BTO Atlas* (1968–1972) confirmed breeding in 34 (92%) 10-km squares, whilst the Tetrad Survey (1987–1994) produced a similar result with evidence of breeding in 35 (95%) of the pre-1974 10-km squares (confirmed in 30, probable in one and possible in four). The Tetrad Map shows that breeding occurs widely in the county except in the Weymouth and Portland areas, and the extreme south-east including most the Bournemouth and Poole conurbation. Although there is little meaningful information on population trends, there is some evidence to indicate that breeding numbers have declined in recent years. For example, at Canford Park the population ranged from 12–20 pairs during 1964–1968, but only from 4–10 pairs during 1985–1998.

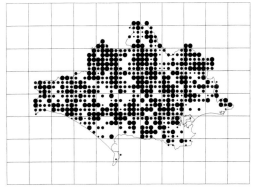

There are very early records on 7th April 1970 well inland at Hammoon and 8th April 1981 at Portland Bill. Otherwise the first spring migrants usually appear during the second half of April, the average date of the first arrivals being later in the 1950s than during the following four decades – see Table 566.

	1950–1959	1960–1969	1970–1979	1980–1989	1990–1999
Range	27th April– 8th May	15th April– 9th May	7th April– 3rd May	8th April– 2nd May	15th April– 1st May
Average	3rd May	27th April	22nd April	22nd April	25th April

Table 566. Dates for first spring arrivals each decade 1950–1999

The main migration period normally extends from early May to early June with peak passage often recorded during the second half of May. Seasonal totals from the main coastal watch-points are highly variable, ranging at Portland Bill from a mere 42 birds in 1982 to notably high numbers in 1987 (517), 1991 (361) and 1998 (368) – see Table 567. Generally spring totals are lower at Durlston CP than at the other main coastal watch-points. Peak counts generally range from 10–50 and rarely exceed 100 birds. The highest numbers are sometimes associated with widespread 'falls', the most notable being 180 at Portland Bill on 15th May 1987 with 100 at Christchurch Harbour the previous day, 120 at Christchurch

Harbour and 100 at Verne Common, Portland on 10th May 1993, and 150 at Portland Bill and 100 at Central Portland on 11th May 1998. Other high counts include 173 at Christchurch Harbour on 9th May 1988, 123 at Central Portland on 21st May 1998 and 110 at Portland Bill on 25th May 1977. Although autumn migration extends from late July or early August through to early October, peak passage usually occurs between mid-August and mid-September. Seasonal totals are variable, but generally higher at Durlston CP in comparison with the other main coastal watch-points (cf other small migrants) – see Table 568. Peak counts tend to be a little lower than in spring, normally ranging from 10–40 and rarely exceeding 50 birds, the highest being 100 at Portland Bill on 22nd August 1993 with 80 there on 21st August 1971. There are, however, some remarkably high autumn counts from inland sites including 150 by the River Stour at Canford Park on 31st August 1976 with 80+ there on 25th August 1983, and 150 at Sherford Bridge, Wareham Forest on 20th August 1977. There are several reports from other inland sites involving counts of up to 50 birds.

	1980	1981	1982	1983	1984	1985	1986	1987	1988	1989
Portland Bill	200	111	42	140	233	137	99	571	265	164
Durlston CP	75	28	57	85	107	46	19	190	124	56
Christchurch Hbr	146	94	25	62	337	35	96	344	229	37

	1990	1991	1992	1993	1994	1995	1996	1997	1998	1999
Portland Bill	87	361	74	157	90	106	102	164	368	107
Durlston CP	38	85	24	37	16	29	56	28	nc	nc
Christchurch Hbr	79	212	26	148	97	36	30	11	nc	nc

Table 567. Spring totals (bds) at the main coastal watch-points 1980–1999

	1980	1981	1982	1983	1984	1985	1986	1987	1988	1989
Portland Bill	147	141	102	255	183	112	415	265	162	167
Durlston CP	223	181	224	209	241	239	459	315	270	281
Christchurch Hbr	42	nc	42	138	137	72	91	207	55	58

	1990	1991	1992	1993	1994	1995	1996	1997	1998	1999
Portland Bill	90	111	122	250	93	118	83	51	46	56
Durlston CP	291	147	453	346	96	330	108	285	nc	nc
Christchurch Hbr	44	52	33	39	15	86	68	14	nc	nc

Table 568. Autumn totals (bds) at the main coastal watch-points 1980–1999

The last birds usually occur in October, the latest being 31st October 1996 at Pennsylvania Castle, Portland, and 5th November 1988 at Radipole School.

A total of 3,417 birds has been ringed in the county. There have been four foreign recoveries from Spain and one each from Portugal, Morocco and Eire, but there have been no reports of any foreign controls.

The Spotted Flycatcher is a summer visitor breeding in north-west Africa and across most of Europe eastwards into central Asia to about 115°E, also in northern Asia Minor and locally in the Middle East. It winters in tropical and southern Africa.

Sponsored by Roger H. Peart

Red-breasted Flycatcher *Ficedula parva*

A scarce passage migrant, mainly in autumn

This species first occurred in Dorset in the mid-1950s with singles at Portland Bill on 12th and 14th October 1954, 23rd October 1955 and 1st–2nd October 1956. There were further sightings in 1958, 1961, 1962, 1964 and 1966 after which birds were recorded almost annually in autumn with the exceptions of 1973 and 1981 – see Fig 55. Annual totals mostly ranged from 1–3 birds up to 1983, but then increased and subsequently ranged from 2–8 birds. The influx of nine in 1968 was a remarkable event at the time.

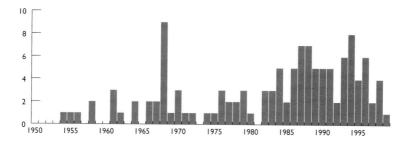

Fig 55. Autumn totals 1954–1999

Although records extend from late August to early November, the first half of October is the peak period with 38% of the total, the month as a whole accounting for 66% – see Table 569. The earliest sightings are 22nd August 1993 at Stanpit Marsh, Christchurch Harbour and 31st August 1976 at St Aldhelm's Head, whilst the latest reports are from Purbeck with singles at Winspit during 2nd–8th November 1982 and on 3rd November 1984, and St Aldhelm's Head on 4th November 1984.

Aug 1–15	Aug 16–31	Sep 1–15	Sep 16–30	Oct 1–15	Oct 16–31	Nov 1–15
0	2	15	21	47	34	4

Table 569. Half-monthly totals 1954–1999

Portland Bill is by far the most favoured site and accounts for 46% of the total, whilst the rest of Portland has attracted a further 27 birds (22%) – see Table 570. The only other site to record significant numbers is Christchurch Harbour with 15 birds (12%), which have all occurred since 1982. On Purbeck, seven birds have been recorded from each of St Aldhelm's Head, the Winspit/Worth Matravers area and Durlston CP. There are only three sightings from elsewhere involving singles at East Fleet on 19th October 1990 and 9th September 1999, and Radipole NR on 8th October 1978. In addition, there is an interesting report from the Channel Island Ferry of two birds which left just before it docked at Weymouth on 13th October 1980. Coincidentally, a bird appeared at Portland Bill the following day.

	Total	
Portland Bill	57	46%
elsewhere on Portland	27	22%
St Aldhelm's Head	7	6%
Winspit	7	6%
Durlston CP	7	6%
Christchurch Harbour	15	12%
elsewhere	3	2%

Table 570. Distribution of migrants 1954–1999

Most records involve singles, very occasionally two birds, the highest count being four at Portland Bill on 20th October 1987. The vast majority of sightings refer to immature birds, the only reports of adult males being from Hengistbury on 12th October 1988 and Southwell, Portland during 19th–23rd September 1996.

It is an exceedingly rare visitor in spring with only three records as follows:

1961   Lyme Regis: 24th April
1984   Portland Bill: first-summer 9th June
       Portland Bill: first-summer 14th–15th June, different from above

A total of 28 birds has been ringed in the county.

The Red-breasted Flycatcher is a summer visitor breeding from southern Finland, southern Sweden,

Ger-many, Austria and the northern Balkans across eastern Europe to about 65°E in west Siberia, also locally in Turkey, the Caucasus and Iran. It winters mainly in the Indian sub-continent.

Postscript 2000–2002

In 2000, one at Portland Bill on 2nd November was the only record. By contrast, a total of six single birds were reported during October 2001 with five at various sites on Portland and one at Winspit. In 2002, an adult male at Pennsylvania Castle, Portland on 17th–18th November was the only sighting and represents the latest record for the county.

Pied Flycatcher   *Ficedula hypoleuca*

An uncommon passage migrant – has bred

Mansel-Pleydell (1888) described this species as "a rare visitor" and only referred to seven birds, all of which had been shot including a pair in the grounds of Corfe Castle Rectory in May 1879. Its status improved during the early part of the 20th Century as Blathwayt (1945) considered it to be a passage migrant most frequently seen in spring, but with no record of nesting in the county.

There has been little change in status subsequently, except that it is now more numerous on autumn passage and breeding has occurred.

The earliest spring records are 30th March 1965 at Bere Heath and 30th March 1994 at Nether Cerne, whilst on 1st April 1998 there was a notable early arrival on Portland with four birds at the Bill and one at Weston. Otherwise the first migrants usually appear later in April with the average date of the first arrivals gradually becoming earlier since the 1950s – see Table 571.

	1950–1959	1960–1969	1970–1979	1980–1989	1990–1999
Range	13th April– 2nd May	30th March– 26th April	4th–20th April	8th–18th April	30th March– 22nd April
Average	19th April	16th April	15th April	13th April	7th April

Table 571. Dates for first spring arrivals each decade 1950–1999

Spring passage mainly occurs between mid-April and mid-May with late stragglers recorded through to late May and exceptionally into June. Numbers at the main coastal watch-points are generally modest, but can vary, with seasonal totals at Portland Bill ranging from a low of ten in 1994 to a high of 78 in 1995 – see Table 572. Peak counts rarely exceed 15 birds, the highest being 45 at Portland Bill on 5th May 1987 and 35 at Central Portland on 24th April 1989. Although occasional early autumn migrants occur in late July, most passage takes place from early August to mid-September with a few late birds recorded into October. Autumn totals are higher than in spring and vary considerably from year to year, ranging at Portland Bill from only 20 in 1998 to between 200 and 300 in 1983, 1984, 1986 and 1995 – see Table 573. Peak counts usually range from 5–15 and rarely exceed 25 birds, the highest being reported during August 1984 with 60 at Portland Bill on 17th, 50 at North Portland on 26th and 47 at Christchurch Harbour on 28th, also 50 at Christchurch Harbour on 16th August 1975, and 40 at Portland Bill on 9th September 1956, 14th August 1975 and 11th August 1983.

	1980	1981	1982	1983	1984	1985	1986	1987	1988	1989
Portland Bill	59	26	30	20	26	46	28	69	32	46
Durlston CP	10	5	12	14	19	14	10	22	16	32
Christchurch Hbr	54	36	26	1	49	35	9	31	19	22

	1990	1991	1992	1993	1994	1995	1996	1997	1998	1999
Portland Bill	12	41	12	21	10	78	25	19	16	18
Durlston CP	11	23	7	13	9	23	38	41	14	20
Christchurch Hbr	32	58	4	6	44	6	8	19	13	nc

Table 572. Spring totals (bds) at the main coastal watch-points 1980–1999

	1980	1981	1982	1983	1984	1985	1986	1987	1988	1989
Portland Bill	88	102	72	201	282	50	274	67	74	56
Durlston CP	15	30	16	45	94	38	64	60	61	30
Christchurch Hbr	6	38	20	31	102	34	35	39	19	15

	1990	1991	1992	1993	1994	1995	1996	1997	1998	1999
Portland Bill	60	40	41	122	72	267	80	123	20	53
Durlston CP	33	40	56	29	32	62	47	57	30	45
Christchurch Hbr	5	4	5	5	6	9	12	11	9	nc

Table 573. Autumn totals (bds) at the main coastal watch-points 1980–1999

Elsewhere most reports are from the coast and near-coastal fringes where sightings usually involve 1–3 and rarely more than ten birds, 20+ at Arne NR on 11th August 1977 being a notably high count. Otherwise there is a scattering of inland records throughout the county, mainly involving 1–3 and never more than five birds.

The last birds are usually recorded during October, the latest being 30th October 1982 at East Weare, Portland and 5th November 1991 at Portland Bill.

Breeding occurred successfully in 1991, but failed in 1996. These and other records suggestive of breeding are given below:

1954   Ulwell near Swanage: one on 20th June
1967   Charmouth: female carrying flies on several days including 21st June
1972   Radipole School: pair with male singing 28th April–3rd May
       Bucknowle: female 12th July
1973   Long Bredy: one on 2nd July
1976   Brackett's Copse: singing male 8th May
       Upton House: male 6th June
1980   Blandford: female 22nd June
1991   Near Blandford: pair bred in a nest-box
       Lambert's Castle: two singing males in late May
1996   Brackett's Copse: female incubating seven eggs from 17th May, but eggs failed to hatch

A total of 1,225 birds has been ringed in the county. There have been single foreign recoveries from France and Norway, but there have been no reports of any foreign controls.

The Pied Flycatcher is a summer visitor breeding widely in central, eastern and northern Europe eastwards into north-west Asia, but more locally in western and south-western Europe and north-west Africa. It winters in tropical West Africa.

Bearded Tit   *Panurus biarmicus*

A scarce resident, and uncommon passage migrant and winter visitor

Mansel-Pleydell (1888) described this species as "a rare and very exceptional visitor to Dorsetshire" and referred to several on the Fleet at Abbotsbury where five or six were said to have been shot!

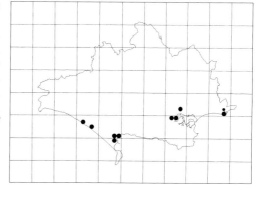

There were no further reports until 1964 when seven appeared at Radipole NR in the late autumn. In the next few years a large influx of birds from the newly created polders in the Netherlands reached Great Britain and this, aided by mild winters and successful breeding in East Anglia and Kent, resulted in an expansion of range along the south coast of England. At Radipole NR birds were present throughout 1965 and 1966 with up to 20–30 birds during November–December of the latter year. Breeding was first confirmed at this site in 1967 and has continued ever since – see Table 574. Initially the population increased steadily to a peak of 34 pairs in 1978 and then declined before being decimated by the cold winter of 1981/82. Numbers remained at a perilously low level during 1982–1984 before recovering to another peak of 30 pairs in 1989. Subsequently the population has declined again with numbers fluctuating from 5–15 pairs during the 1990s. Although nearby Lodmoor NR was not colonised until 1978, breeding is thought to have occurred there in most subsequent years up to 1998, with the population surviving the initial impact of the 1981/82 cold winter better than that at Radipole NR – see Table 575. Sadly, there was no evidence of breeding at Lodmoor NR in 1999.

	1976	1977	1978	1979	1980	1981	1982	1983	1984	1985	1986	1987
Pairs	15	24	34	27	16	16	2	2	2	7	7	13
Young	140	150	160	45	nc	40	16	12	6	30	30	100

	1988	1989	1990	1991	1992	1993	1994	1995	1996	1997	1998	1999
Pairs	15	30	15	8	br	12	8–9	5	7	10	br	br
Young	90	110	40	nc	nc	19	nc	nc	nc	nc	nc	nc

Table 574. Number of breeding pairs and young reared at Radipole NR 1976–1999; br = no count, but bred

1978	1979	1980	1981	1982	1983	1984	1985	1986	1987	1988
1–2	sev	8	5	3	5–6	4	8	5–7	6	8

1989	1990	1991	1992	1993	1994	1995	1996	1997	1998	1999
5	br	br	br	3	4	4	4	br	br	0

Table 575. Number of breeding pairs at Lodmoor NR 1978–1999; br = no count, but bred

Further west, sporadic breeding has been recorded from reedbeds at Codgen Beach, West Bexington and Abbotsbury. In earlier years breeding reports were understandably vague and generally referred to undisclosed sites. Confirmed breeding certainly occurred at Abbotsbury and another site in west Dorset in 1971, and probably took place at one or more of these sites in other years during the late 1960s and early to mid-1970s. There were no further published records of breeding from this area until the early 1990s with up to four pairs at Abbotsbury during 1990–1992 and at least one pair at West Bexington in 1993 and 1994. No breeding has occurred at the traditional sites in west Dorset during 1995–1999.

The reedbeds along the west side of Poole Harbour were apparently colonised during the 1970s, but the only specific report refers to 2–3 pairs breeding at a site in the east of the county in 1974. There are also records of 5–6 pairs breeding at undisclosed sites during 1976–1978, which may also refer to Poole Harbour. Since 1980 breeding has occurred intermittently at a number of sites between Swineham and Holes Bay – see Table 576. The best year was 1981 when 8 -9 pairs bred at three sites with one present at a fourth site in July. It seems that due to the inaccessibility of some sites, confirmed breeding is difficult to establish and may be more frequent than records suggest. For example in 1987, 1993, 1994 and 1995 the presence of birds at Keysworth throughout the year was strongly suggestive of breeding, but this was not proven. Elsewhere in the east of the county, Christchurch Harbour has also occasionally hosted breeding birds with one pair in 1982, two pairs in 1987, single pairs in 1988 and 1989, and an adult with two juveniles on 19th May 1998.

1980	1981	1982	1983	1984	1985	1986	1987	1988	1989
3	8–9	0	0	1	1	3	p	0	0

1990	1991	1992	1993	1994	1995	1996	1997	1998	1999
1	1	br	p	p	1–2	1	2–3	1	1

Table 576. Number of breeding pairs at Poole Harbour 1980–1999; p = present during the breeding season

At the main breeding sites, notably Radipole and Lodmoor NRs, birds are usually present throughout the year with numbers building up to a post-breeding peak during August to December. Generally these autumn/late winter peaks reflect the success of the breeding season with counts at Radipole and Lodmoor NRs ranging from 40–70 birds in good years. When numbers are particularly high after a good breeding season, eruptive behaviour and movements occur during the autumn. This dispersal will account for a proportion of the autumn and winter records from other sites in the county.

Autumn movements and the local wintering population are also enhanced by the arrival of birds dispersing from breeding sites further afield in eastern Great Britain and the near Continent. Such irruptions were particularly prominent during the mid-1960s and early 1970s, and resulted in the original colonisation of the county. In October 1972 there was a particularly massive influx of 700 or more birds including an exceptional count of 500 at Radipole NR on 31st.

The vast majority of autumn and winter records are from coastal reedbed sites, including those where breeding has occurred either regularly or more intermittently. These include Cogden Beach and West Bexington, Abbotsbury, Radipole and Lodmoor NRs, the west side of Poole Harbour from Arne NR to Holes Bay, Studland NNR, Brownsea and Christchurch Harbour. The presence of wintering birds at several of these sites often depends of the success of the local breeding population and strength of any autumn irruption. Away from Radipole NR, winter counts of 10–20 birds are not unexpected in good years, but counts of 110 at Lytchett Bay on 6th January and 22nd February 1985 are exceptionally high.

In the east of the county, autumn passage is fairly regular at Christchurch Harbour with notable influxes in 1985 (179 bird-days), which was not reflected elsewhere in the county, and 1994 (94 bird-days) – see Table 577. During the influx of October 1985, notable sightings included 40 flying in off the sea at Hengistbury on 14th with 30 doing likewise on 20th, also 23 there on 18th, whilst other high counts from Christchurch Harbour include 37E on 19th October 1990, 29E on 19th October 1988 and 21 on 30th September 1982. There are fewer reports from Portland, mainly the Bill area, with marked influxes in 1972 involving 76 birds during 19th–30th October (maximum of 49N on 19th), and 1980 involving 39 birds during 30th September–18th October (maximum of 18 on 30th September). It is a very scarce visitor to the Purbeck watch-points with only five records from Durlston CP including 16 on 15th October 1992, and only two records from St Aldhelm's Head.

	1980	1981	1982	1983	1984	1985	1986	1987	1988	1989
Christchurch Hbr	16	7	32	12	12	179	11	9	35	0
Portland	39	0	p	0	2	4	3	0	4	0

	1990	1991	1992	1993	1994	1995	1996	1997	1998	1999
Christchurch Hbr	37	39	94	12	12	5	>8	28	41	3
Portland	1	2	2	12	0	2	0	0	0	0

Table 577. Autumn totals from Christchurch Harbour and Portland 1980–1999; pr = present

There are a few reports from inland areas, most of which come from the upper part of the Stour Valley in the vicinity of Marnhull and Gillingham:

1965 Shillingstone: an unspecified date in late autumn
1970 Dorchester: 12th October – a control of a bird ringed at Radipole NR on 6th September
1971 Gillingham: five 28th October–7th November
1972 Gillingham: ten 12th November–3rd December
1977 Marnhull: up to three in November
1980 Lodden Lakes near Gillingham: four 20th–21st October
        Marnhull: 2nd November

A total of 1,218 birds has been ringed in the county. During the influxes of 1971 and 1972 at least four Dutch-ringed birds were controlled at Radipole NR and two likewise at Arne NR, whilst there is one notable recovery from the Channel Islands. Other reports of recoveries and controls confirm the movement of birds between reedbed sites in southern England, including five recoveries from Somerset (three at Chew Valley Lake and two from Berrow), and more locally within the county, e.g. between Lytchett Bay and Radipole NR.

The Bearded Tit breeds very locally across much of Europe, except Scandinavia, also in Asia Minor and much more widely through central Asia to China.

Postscript 2000–2002

Breeding was reported from Radipole NR in all years with nine pairs rearing 49 young in 2000, a peak count of 16 on 20th October 2001, and six pairs (three confirmed) in 2002. Elsewhere one pair bred at Lytchett Bay in 2000 and 2002, and at least one pair reared four young at Arne NR in 2001.

Sponsored by RSPB Weymouth Reserves

Long-tailed Tit   *Aegithalos caudatus*

A common resident

Mansel-Pleydell (1888) simply referred to this species as being resident, whilst Blathwayt (1945) described it as "a numerous resident".

Little has changed subsequently, the *BTO Atlas* (1968–1972) confirmed breeding in 35 (95%) 10-km squares, whilst the Tetrad Survey (1987–1994) produced evidence of breeding in 35 (95%) of the pre-1974 10-km squares (confirmed in 33, probable in one and possible in one). Although the Tetrad Map shows

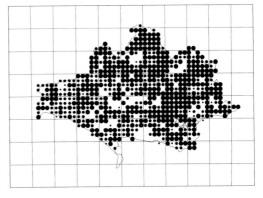

that breeding occurs widely throughout the county, there are notable absences from the centre of the Blackmore Vale and parts of the chalk downs, mostly in the central and southern areas. Despite the lack of Tetrad records from Portland, breeding has been reported on several occasions including 1962, 1975 and more recently at Verne Common during 1997–1999.

Long-term population data is rather limited, consequently any interpretation has to be tentative. Nevertheless, it is clear that the Long-tailed Tit is particularly vulnerable to hard weather with greatly reduced numbers reported after the 1946/47 and 1962/63 winters. For example, after 1962/63, the population in a Poole Basin North study area fell from 30 to two pairs. Recovery from the mid-1960s was rapid and by the early 1970s the population was considered to be at a high level as reflected by peak numbers at Studland NNR and Arne NR – see Tables 578 and 579. Subsequently the populations at these sites declined, but remained relatively stable at a lower level during the remainder of the 1970s and 1980s before a slight decline at Studland NNR during the 1990s. The Common Bird Census Index for Dorset during 1981–1994 shows that 1985/86 was the only cold winter during the 1980s to significantly impact on the population, which otherwise was relatively stable during this decade except for an isolated peak in 1983 – see Table 580. More recently, there was a marked decline in 1992 and 1993, which does not appear to be associated with a cold winter, followed by a recovery in 1994.

1967	1972	1973	1975	1976	1979	1980	1981	1982	1983	1984	1985	1986
5–6	15	13	5	5–6	5	5	3	4	5	4	5	3

1987	1988	1989	1990	1991	1992	1993	1994	1995	1996	1997	1998	1999
3	4	4	3	2	0	1	3	3	1	nc	2	2

Table 578. Number of breeding territories at Studland NNR 1967–1999

1968	1973	1974	1975	1976	1977	1978	1979	1981	1982	1983	1986	1987	1991
6	12	10	10	10	8	8	10	10	6–7	10	10	10	10

Table 579. Number of breeding territories at Arne NR 1968–1991

1981	1982	1983	1984	1985	1986	1987	1988	1989	1990	1991	1992	1993	1994
100	110	160	120	130	50	–	110	120	–	110	80	40	120

Table 580. The Common Bird Census Index for Dorset 1981–1994

Outside the breeding season, the species is commonly reported in flocks of up to 40–50 birds, the highest counts being 80 at Turnerspuddle in September 1974, 79 at Stubhampton Bottom on 16th July 1967 and 72 on Brownsea on 21st September 1967.

There is some evidence of autumn dispersal and perhaps genuine passage, mainly during October and November, at the main coastal watch-points. Numbers at Durlston CP and Christchurch Harbour can reach peaks of up to 40 birds, the highest being 58 at Durlston CP on 23rd October 1992. The Long-tailed Tit occurs less frequently at Portland, mainly in the more wooded and vegetated central and northern parts of the island with relatively few reports from Portland Bill – see Table 581. The only evidence of spring passage involves the occasional record from Portland Bill during March–April. A flock of 15 at Pennsylvania Castle, Portland on an unspecified date in 1996 included at least one of the North European race *A. c. caudatus*.

80	81	82	83	84	85	86	87	88	89	90	91	92	93	94	95	96	97	98	99
0	1	0	8	0	0	0	0	0	0	6	0	9	0	0	0	0	4	1	12

Table 581. Autumn totals at Portland Bill 1980–1999

A total of 4,119 birds has been ringed in the county. Two birds ringed together at Great Yarmouth, Norfolk on 7th October 1973 and controlled, still together, at Brownsea on 22nd October of the smae year was a notable event.

The Long-tailed Tit breeds throughout most of Europe, Asia Minor and north-central Asia eastwards to Japan and extending south to China in the far east.

Postscript 2000–2002
A pale-headed bird considered to be an intergrade between *A. c. caudatus* (northern Europe) and *A. c. rosaceus* (British Isles) was present in the Southdown Av/Lodmoor NR area during 12th–15th February 2000. Remarkably a bird of the northern race *A. c. caudatus* was reported from Lodmoor NR on 1st April 2001.

Sponsored by J. R. Spencer

Marsh Tit   *Parus palustris*

A fairly common resident

Mansel-Pleydell (1888) described this species as "resident and locally abundant, frequenting well-timbered parks and shrubberies without reference to the neighbourhood of water, although equally partial to marshy places and river-sides". Blathwayt (1945) considered it to be a common resident, somewhat local and partial to large woodlands. It should be remembered, however, that prior to 1897 the Marsh Tit was confused with the very similar Willow Tit and the distributions of these two species only became disentangled gradually during the first half of the 20th Century.

The *BTO Atlas* (1968–1972) found evidence of breeding in 35 (95%) 10-km squares (confirmed in 34 and possible in one), whilst the Tetrad Survey (1987–1994) produced a similar result with evidence of breeding in 34 (92%) of the pre-1974 10-km squares (confirmed in 32 and probable in two). The Tetrad Map shows breeding to be widespread in the county with the greatest densities in the well-wooded west, the Blackmore Vale, the wooded areas of the north-east, and the central and southern parts of the Poole Basin. It is rather sparsely distributed across the chalk downs and coastal lowlands around Weymouth, whilst it is absent from Portland and much of the urban areas and coniferous forestry in the south-east.

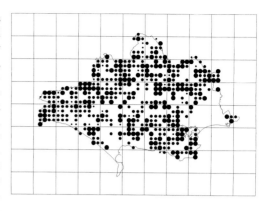

With so little population data, it is difficult to assess long-term trends. At Studland NNR, the population seems to have mainly fluctuated between 3–5 pairs during 1968–1998 with isolated peaks in 1972, 1976 and 1995 and low points in 1971, 1980 and 1999 – see Table 582. Nearby at Arne NR, an increase in numbers between 1968 and 1978 was followed by a period of relative stability until another apparent increase in 1993 – see Table 583. Data from other CBC sites suggests a gradual decline in numbers during the 1980s and 1990s.

1967	1968	1971	1972	1973	1975	1976	1977	1978	1980	1981	1982	1983	1984
6	5	2	7	5	4	8	5	5	2	4	4	4	3

1985	1986	1987	1988	1989	1990	1991	1992	1993	1994	1995	1996	1998	1999
3	5	4	5	5	3	5	3	3	3	7	4	3	1

Table 582. Number of breeding territories at Studland NNR 1967–1999

68	73	74	75	76	78	79	80	81	82	83	84	86	87	91	93
2	6	6	6	6	10	8	8–10	8–10	9	10	10	10	10	10	15

Table 583. Number of breeding territories at Arne NR 1968–1993

There is very little evidence of autumn dispersal at the main coastal watch-points, which reflects the largely sedentary nature of this species. A bird at Easton on 5th October 1987 is seemingly the only occurrence from Portland. Otherwise most records are from Christchurch Harbour, Durlston CP and St Aldhelm's Head, which are all close to known breeding sites. The only report of a large count outside the breeding season involves 25 at Sherford Bridge, Wareham Forest on 5th January 1986.

A total of 669 birds has been ringed in the county.

The Marsh Tit breeds over much of Europe from southern Scandinavia and Great Britain south to northern Spain, Italy and the Balkans, and east across southern Russia to the Urals, also in northern Asia Minor. There is a widely separated population in eastern Asia.

Postscript 2000–2002
One at Easton on 6th December 2001 is only the second record from Portland.

Willow Tit   *Parus montanus*

A scarce resident

The early status of this species in the county is 'shrouded in mystery'. Prior to 1897 the Willow Tit was confused with the very similar Marsh Tit and the distributions of these two species only became disentangled gradually during the first half of the 20th Century. Blathwayt (1945) considered the Willow Tit to be a local resident, which is overlooked, and listed reports in only three years, namely 1897 when it was supposed to have been seen near Sherborne, in 1915 when two pairs are said to have been satisfactorily identified nesting at Canford, and in 1935 when it bred at Studland.

Since 1948 the status of this species in Dorset has become clearer. During the 1950s it was known mainly from the east Purbecks and near the Hampshire border in the extreme north-east of the county, but subsequently it has spread westwards. The *BTO Atlas* (1968–1972) found evidence of breeding in 25 (68%) 10-km squares (confirmed in 11, probable in 11 and possible in three), whilst the Tetrad Survey (1987–1994) also revealed evidence of breeding in 25 (68%) of the pre-1974 10-km squares (confirmed in 12, probable in nine and possible in four). Although the number of occupied pre-1974 10-km squares has remained the same between the two surveys, the Willow Tit has seemingly deserted its breeding haunts in the south of the county including such traditional sites as West Bexington and Studland NNR.

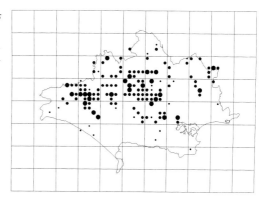

The Tetrad Map shows the breeding distribution in more detail. The main stronghold lies within a strip of countryside about 15km wide stretching from Beaminster in the west to almost Blandford in the east. This mainly follows the northern part of the chalk downs and the north scarp hills, but extends into the west Dorset farmland and the Blackmore Vale. There are also scattered territories spreading out from this area, particularly into the central chalk. Elsewhere there are isolated populations in the Wareham Forest area and the traditional area near the Hampshire border in the extreme north-east. There are a few reports from the south of the county, but no proof of breeding south of a line from Burton Bradstock through Dorchester to Poole. It is also scarce or absent from the western, northern and eastern extremities of the county.

During the late 1990s, there has been a worrying decline in the number of records, particularly those relating to breeding. It is not certain whether this reflects a genuine reduction in the population or lack of observer coverage in its traditional haunts.

Although largely sedentary like the previous species, it would appear that the Willow Tit is prone to dispersing more widely. There are six records from Portland involving singles at the Bill during 8th–10th October 1966, on 29th June 1981, 8th November 1983 and 21st June 1984, and during 29th April–29th May 1994, with one at Suckthumb Quarry on 21st May 1998. There are also several reports from Christchurch Harbour, Durlston CP and other coastal localities.

A total of 159 birds has been ringed in the county.

The Willow Tit breeds from Great Britain and the eastern half of France eastwards through much of central and northern Europe and across northern Asia to the Pacific coast and Japan.

Postscript 2000–2002

The status of the Willow Tit in Dorset continues to cause concern with only ten records in 2000, six records in 2001 and five records from only three sites in 2002.

Sponsored by Major J. M. N. Powell

Coal Tit

Parus ater

A common breeding resident and scarce passage migrant

This species was known to Mansel-Pleydell (1888) as an abundant resident, whilst Blathwayt (1945) described it as "a common resident especially in districts where conifers abound".

There has been little subsequent change in status with the *BTO Atlas* (1968–1972) finding evidence of breeding in 35 (95%) 10-km squares (confirmed in 32 and probable in three), and the Tetrad Survey (1987–1994) producing evidence of breeding in 34 (92%) of the pre-1974 10-km squares (confirmed in 32 and probable in two). Although the Tetrad Map shows that the Coal Tit breeds widely in the county, it is more sparsely distributed over most of the chalk downs, particularly towards the south-west, scarce along much of the coastal strip from Charmouth to St Aldhelm's Head, and absent from Portland. The densest populations occur in the Poole Basin, around Sherborne and Blandford in the north, and in the far west. The increase in conifer plantations during the 20th Century, particularly in the Poole Basin, has undoubtedly been to the benefit of this species.

There is very little useful information on long-term population trends. Although it is stated that numbers declined sharply after severe winters in earlier years, the population appears to have been relatively stable since 1980 with no indication of a decline after the cold winters of the early and mid-1980s.

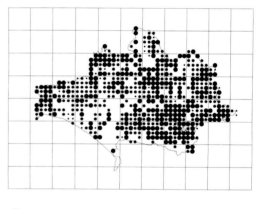

Outside the breeding season flocks of up to 40–50 birds are commonly reported, the highest counts being from Bovington with 200 in August 1984 followed by 100 during September–December of the same year, and 110 in December 1985.

Passage is recorded most years from coastal sites, mainly late in the autumn from mid-September to mid-November. The occurrence of birds of both the British race *P. a. britannicus* and the Continental race *P. a. ater* show that these movements involve both local dispersal and genuine cross-channel immigration. Generally numbers are small and passage can be virtually non-existent in some years with marked influxes in others – see Table 584. In earlier years there were marked autumn influxes in 1957 involving 41 bird-days at Portland Bill from mid-September to early November (cf Blue and Great Tits), 1966 including 15–20 which arrived at St Aldhelm's Head on 8th October, 1969 including 18 on Portland in October, 1971 including 43 at Chapman's Pool plus a flock of ten which "dropped from the sky" at St Aldhelm's Head on 28th September, 1975 including 18W at West Bexington on 7th October and 20 at Hengistbury on 16th October, and 1977 including 15 'Continental' birds at the Grove, Portland on 9th October and 18 at Portland Bill on 19th October. Birds, including the 'Continental' race, occasionally appear on spring passage. There are also some claims of 'Continental' birds well inland during the winter, notably 20 at Horton in December 1971 and 9–10 at Organford on 20th January 1974.

	1980	1981	1982	1983	1984	1985	1986	1987	1988	1989
Portland	0	2	0	3	0	5	0	2	4	21
Durlston CP	0	0	0	4	p	17	p	5	20	47
St Aldhelm's Hd	0	0	0	4	0	27	0	1	30	4
Christchurch Hbr	8	4	2	0	0	9	0	2	6	8

	1990	1991	1992	1993	1994	1995	1996	1997	1998	1999
Portland	0	0	9	1	>8	0	>19	16	1	0
Durlston CP	3	8	115	4	4	101	5	6	6	40
St Aldhelm's Hd	1	0	5	0	6	0	4	0	0	0
Christchurch Hbr	0	0	>25	0	27	6	3	0	0	4

Table 584. Autumn totals at the main coastal sites 1980–1999; p = present

A total of 1,833 birds has been ringed in the county.

Various races of Coal Tit breed in north-west Africa and throughout most of Europe, except the far north, extending eastwards to Asia Minor and across north-central Asia to the Pacific coast and Japan, and then south to China and west to the Himalayas.

Sponsored by Peter Barron

Blue Tit   *Parus caeruleus*

An abundant resident and uncommon passage migrant

Both Mansel-Pleydell (1888) and Blathwayt (1945) considered this species to be a common resident.

There has been no subsequent change in status. The *BTO Atlas* (1968–1972) confirmed breeding in all 10-km squares, whilst the Tetrad Survey (1987–1994) showed evidence of breeding in all of the pre-1974 10-km squares (confirmed in 36 and probable in one). The Tetrad Survey also shows that the Blue Tit is widely distributed throughout the county with evidence of breeding in almost all tetrad squares. The Common Bird Census Index for Dorset during 1981–1993 reveals a fluctuating but generally stable situation and, with the possible exception of 1981/82, shows no strong correlation between population declines and cold winters – see Table 585. Long-term trends at individual sites can be more complex and sometimes differ. For example, the population at Studland NNR appears to have declined from generally between 15–20 pairs during 1964–1980 to vary between 8–14 pairs during 1981–1999. By contrast, at Brackett's Copse the population increased rapidly during the early 1970s as the result of the presence of newly erected nest-boxes, but then remained relatively stable during 1981–1994 despite marked fluctuations from year to year – see Tables 586 and 587.

1981	1982	1983	1984	1985	1986	1987	1988	1989	1990	1991	1992	1993
100	82	96	78	90	91	–	85	112	95	99	86	100

Table 585. The Common Bird Census Index for Dorset 1981–1993

1964	1967	1968	1972	1973	1975	1976	1977	1978	1980	1981	1982	1983	1984
17	15	20	30	20	18	17	19	17	19	14	12	14	13

1985	1986	1987	1988	1989	1990	1991	1992	1993	1994	1995	1996	1998	1999
11	13	10	12	14	11	13	12	14	nc	13	12	10	8

Table 586. Number of breeding territories at Studland NNR 1964–1999

1970	1971	1972	1974	1975	1976	1977	1978	1979	1980	1981	1982	1983
12	20	28	27	26	21	33	27	23	26	40	33	37

1984	1985	1986	1987	1988	1989	1990	1991	1992	1993	1994	1996
32	36	39	nc	32	49	38	43	38	46	36	32

Table 587. Number of breeding territories at Brackett's Copse 1970–1996

Outside the breeding season flocks of up to 50–60 birds commonly occur, the highest count being 240 at Radipole NR in November 1978. Autumn passage/dispersal is a regular feature at the main coastal watch-points, varying from very few birds in some years to substantial numbers in others when peak counts can reach 50 or more birds, the highest in recent years being 150 at Christchurch Harbour on 15th September 1993. Visual movements are sometimes reported, for example at Portland Bill c.70 mainly N on 13th October 1981, 51S on 14th October 1968 and 40N on 11th October 1985. Nothing compares, however, with the exceptional influx at Portland Bill in 1957 when over 2,200 bird-days were recorded during 17th September–12th November including peaks of 460 on 28th September and 300 on 7th October. There was a notable return passage at Portland Bill in spring 1958 with c.240 bird-days from March to mid-May with a maximum of 60 on 30th March. A bird ringed in Germany on 25th June 1957 and controlled at Portland Bill on 28th April 1958 provides direct evidence of the source of at least part of the previous autumn's influx. Generally spring passage is small and sporadic, so 60 at North Portland on 9th April 1997 is notable.

A total of 28,873 birds has been ringed in the county. There has been one foreign control from Germany (see above), the only other notable control being from Guernsey.

The Blue Tit breeds over most of Europe except the far north, in Asia Minor and extreme south-west Asia. The race breeding in north-west Africa is considered a full species by some authorities.

Great Tit   *Parus major*

An abundant resident and scarce passage migrant

Both Mansel-Pleydell (1888) and Blathwayt (1945) considered this species to be a common resident.

Its status has not changed subsequently, both the *BTO Atlas* (1968–1972) and the Tetrad Survey (1987–1994) found evidence of breeding in all pre-1974 10-km squares (confirmed in 36 and probable in one). The Tetrad Survey also shows that the Great Tit is widely distributed throughout the county with evidence of breeding in almost all tetrad squares. The Common Bird Census Index for Dorset during 1981–1994 shows a sharp decline after the cold winter of 1981/82, followed by a fluctuating but relatively stable situation subsequently with the population failing to fully recover and generally remaining c.10–35% below the 1981 level – see Table 588. Apart from 1981/82 and possibly 1986/87, there appears to be no strong relationship between population declines and cold winters. Long-term trends at individual sites can be more complex and sometimes differ. For example, at Studland NNR the population has seemingly declined from ranging between 12–21 pairs during 1967–1986 to ranging between 8–12 pairs during 1987–1999. By contrast, at Brackett's Copse the population increased initially in the early 1970s as the result of the presence of newly erected nest-boxes, then remained relatively stable during 1971–1975,

fluctuated widely during 1976–1978, increased to a peak in 1981, declined markedly after the cold winter of 1981/82, recovered in 1983 and finally stabilised during 1984–1994 – see Tables 589 and 590.

1981	1982	1983	1984	1985	1986	1987	1988	1989	1990	1991	1992	1993	1994
100	69	88	76	93	87	nc	64	64	67	69	55	76	70

Table 588. The Common Bird Census Index for Dorset 1981–1994

1967	1968	1972	1973	1975	1976	1977	1978	1980	1981	1982	1983	1984	1985
12	14	15	15	18	17	19	21	19	18	17	14	14	17

1986	1987	1988	1989	1990	1991	1992	1993	1994	1995	1996	1998	1999
19	11	10	10	9	12	8	9	11	10	8	10	10

Table 589. Number of breeding territories at Studland NNR 1967–1999

1970	1971	1972	1973	1974	1975	1976	1977	1978	1979	1980	1981	1982
4	14	11	13	11	10	5	19	10	10	22	25	12

1983	1984	1985	1986	1987	1988	1989	1990	1991	1992	1993	1994
19	16	20	18	nc	16	17	21	18	15	21	20

Table 590. Number of breeding territories at Brackett's Copse 1970–1994

Outside the breeding season flocks of up to 50 birds commonly occur. Autumn passage/dispersal at the main coastal watch-points is much less obvious than for the Blue Tit and in some years virtually non-existent. Numbers are generally very small with peak counts typically less than 25 and rarely exceeding 50 birds, the highest in recent years being 100 at Christchurch Harbour on 15th September 1993. Visual movements are very occasionally reported, for example 58N at Portland Bill on 18th October 1983. Nothing compares, however, with the exceptional influx at Portland Bill in 1957 when over 500 bird-days were recorded during 25th September–12th November with a peak of 150 on 7th October. There was a modest return passage at Portland Bill in spring 1958 with a peak of 12 on 30th March. Otherwise spring passage is rarely recorded, so 60 at North Portland on 9th April 1997 is most unusual.

A total of 10,345 birds has been ringed in the county.

Various races of Great Tit breed in north-west Africa, over most of Europe except the far north-east, in Asia Minor, parts of the Middle East, and large areas of central, eastern and southern Asia including the Indian sub-continent.

Nuthatch (Wood Nuthatch)   *Sitta europaea*

A fairly common resident

Mansel-Pleydell (1888) considered this species to be an extremely common breeding resident, whilst Blathwayt (1945) described it as "resident and well distributed in all suitable districts".

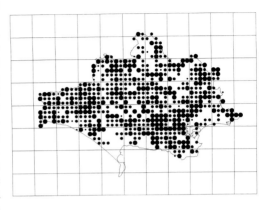

Little has changed subsequently, the *BTO Atlas* (1968–1972) revealed evidence of breeding in 35 (95%) 10-km squares (confirmed in 28, probable in five and possible in two), whilst the Tetrad Survey (1987–1994) found evidence of breeding in 33 (89%) of the pre-1974 10-km squares (confirmed in 31, probable in one and possible in one). The Tetrad Map shows breeding to be widespread in the county with the greatest density of population in the well-wooded west, parts of the Blackmore Vale, and the wooded areas of the Poole Basin and east Purbeck. It is rather sparsely distributed across much of the chalk downs and in the Bournemouth and Poole conurbation, whilst it is very scarce in the area between Weymouth and Dorchester, and absent from Portland. There seems to have been a slight expansion of range during the last 50 years. For example, the Swanage area was first colonised in the late 1940s, whilst more recently breeding was first confirmed at Arne NR in 1979 with up to five pairs there during the late 1980s and early 1990s. There were reports of breeding at new sites as recently as 1991. Although the rather limited CBC data indicates a stable population since 1980, the breeding numbers at Canford Park appear to have declined from between 5–12 pairs during 1965–1968 to between 1–4 pairs during 1996–1998. There are two reports of unusual nest sites, the first in a crevice in a sandstone cliff at Ridge in 1990, and the second in a hole in a garden wall at Compton Valence in 1991.

Essentially a sedentary species, the Nuthatch seldom disperses to coastal sites. For example, there are only five records from Portland involving singles at Pennsylvania Castle on 5th November 1964, Easton on 28th February 1988, the Bill on 12th October 1989 and 16th April 1994, and Verne Common on 2nd May 1999, whilst c.11 birds have been reported from Christchurch Harbour since the first in 1980. Elsewhere there are reports from West Bexington, East Fleet, Radipole and Lodmoor NRs, Swineham and Ham Common. More numerous records from Durlston CP and St Aldhelm's Head may involve local breeders. Even inland, birds rarely wander away from their breeding territories. For example, there have been only two records from a regularly watched area of the Stour Valley between Corfe Mullen and Sturminster Marshall since 1978.

A total of 368 birds has been ringed in the county.

Various races of Nuthatch breed in north-west Africa and throughout most of Europe north to southern Great Britain and southern Scandinavia, extending eastwards to Asia Minor and across much of northern Asia to the Pacific coast and Japan, and then south throughout east and south-east Asia west to the Indian sub-continent.

Postscript 2000–2002

One at Verne Common, Portland on 29th June 2002 is only the sixth record for the island.

Sponsored by John Hammick and Mrs Jo Hammick

Wallcreeper   *Tichodroma muraria*

Accidental: two records

    1920   Chilfrome: 24th April
    1969   Winspit/Seacombe/Dancing Ledge: 19th November–18th April 1970

Dorset can boast two records of this striking and colourful species. The first was seen at close range at Chilfrome and an account can be found in *British Birds* Vol. 14. The second individual, which must rate as one of the county's most famous rarities, frequented the Purbeck cliffs and quarries between Winspit and Dancing Ledge and during its stay was watched by hundreds of birdwatchers. Behavioural notes included a spiralling display flight and an observation of the bird clinging to the flat, horizontal roof of a cave. There is a short note "Analysis of pellet from Dorset Wallcreeper" in *British Birds* Vol. 64, Number 2, February 1971.

The Wallcreeper breeds in high mountains from northern Spain and the Pyrenees eastwards across southern Europe to Asia Minor, the Caucasus, Iran and the mountains of south-central Asia including the Himalayas. It disperses to lower altitudes in winter. A vagrant to Great Britain with only ten records between 1792 and 1985.

Treecreeper (Eurasian Treecreeper) *Certhia familiaris*

A common resident

Mansel-Pleydell (1888) referred to this species as a generally distributed resident in the parks, shrubberies and wooded districts of the county, whilst Blathwayt (1945) simply described it as "a common resident".

There has been little change in status sub-sequently with the *BTO Atlas* (1968–1972) revealing evidence of breeding in 35 (95%) 10-km squares (confirmed in 30, probable in three and possible in two), whilst the Tetrad Survey (1987–1994) showed evidence of breeding in 36 (97%) of the pre-1974 10-km squares (confirmed in 31, probable in two and possible in three). The Tetrad Map reveals a breeding distribution closely resembling that for the Nuthatch, which reflects the similar habitat pre-ferences of these two species. The greatest density of population occurs in the well-wooded far west, parts of the Blackmore Vale, and the wooded areas of the Poole Basin and east Purbeck. It is rather sparsely distributed across much of the chalk downs

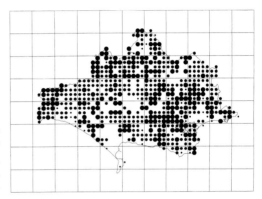

and in the Bournemouth and Poole conurbation, whilst it is very scarce in the area between Weymouth and Dorchester, and virtually absent from Portland. Although the rather limited CBC data indicates a stable population since 1980, the longer-term trends at two individual sites appear to be contradictory. At Studland NNR the population appears to have declined slightly from between 3–7 pairs during 1975–1989 to between 1–4 pairs during 1990–1999, whilst at Arne NR there has been a steady increase from 5 pairs in 1978 and 1979 to 15 pairs in 1993 – see Tables 591 and 592.

1975	1976	1977	1978	1979	1980	1981	1982	1983	1984	1985	1986
5	5–6	7	5	4	5	3	3	3	5	4	6

1987	1988	1989	1990	1991	1992	1993	1994	1995	1996	1998	1999
4	4	5	2	2	2	4	3	2	2	2	1

Table 591. Number of breeding territories at Studland NNR 1975–1999

1978	1979	1980	1981	1983	1984	1985	1986	1987	1991	1992	1993
5	5	8	8	8	8–10	10	10	10	10	5	15

Table 592. Number of breeding territories at Arne NR 1978–1993

Outside the breeding season, the species often joins mixed flocks of tits, the largest winter count being 30 at Sherford Bridge, Wareham Forest on 11th December 1983. Reports from coastal sites suggest the Treecreeper disperses more widely than the Nuthatch. At Portland Bill there are records from as long ago as 1957 with near-annual occurrences since at least the mid-1970s – see Table 593. There are also several sightings from the more wooded areas of Portland, notably Pennsylvania Castle where reports include a pair in 1977 and one throughout the year in 1983. Elsewhere dispersing birds have been recorded from various other coastal sites including West Bexington, East Fleet, Radipole and Lodmoor NRs, St Aldhelm's Head including 28 bird-days during August–October 1989, Winspit, Durlston CP and Christchurch Harbour.

	1977	1978	1979	1980	1981	1982	1983	1984	1985	1986	1987	1988
Spring	1	0	0	0	1	0	0	1	1	0	0	0
Autumn	1	2	0	2	0	2	1	2	0	1	3	0

	1989	1990	1991	1992	1993	1994	1995	1996	1997	1998	1999	2000
Spring	0	1	0	0	0	1	0	0	0	0	2	1
Autumn	8	3	1	1	0	0	1	0	0	0	4	0

Table 593. Spring and autumn totals at Portland Bill 1977–2000

A total of 870 birds has been ringed in the county.

The various races of Treecreeper breed very locally in western Europe south to northern Spain, but more widely in Great Britain, Scandinavia, central, south-eastern and eastern Europe, extending eastwards to parts of Asia Minor and widely across north-central Asia to the Pacific coast and Japan with a separate population in the Himalayas. It is largely replaced by the Short-toed Treecreeper in western Europe.

Short-toed Treecreeper   *Certhia brachydactyla*

Accidental: two records

The first county record was originally rejected, but re-evaluated 30 years later and accepted.

    1970   Pennsylvania Castle, Portland: 23rd November–21st March 1971
    1979   Portland Bill: trapped 7th May

Claims of birds, including a breeding pair at Branksome, Poole in 1971 and up to five pairs breeding at another site in east Dorset during 1972–1975, were not substantiated.

The Short-toed Treecreeper breeds in north-west Africa and over most of Europe north to the Channel coast of France, the Low Countries and Denmark, and east to Poland, western Ukraine, western Rumania, the Balkans and Asia Minor. A vagrant to Great Britain with 21 records up to 2002 of which only four have been outside Kent.

Penduline Tit (Eurasian Penduline Tit)   *Remiz pendulinus*

A very rare autumn migrant and winter visitor: six records involving seven individuals

    1988   Stanpit Marsh, Christchurch Harbour: juv. 21st–22nd October
    1989   Swineham: 10th January
    1990   Radipole NR: ad. 28th October
    1996   Hengistbury: two juvs 9th October
    1998   Lytchett Bay: ad. male 20th January–13th February
    2000   Hengistbury: 4th November

The Penduline Tit breeds from Iberia, southern France, the Low Countries and south Sweden eastwards across southern and central Europe to Asia Minor and through much of central Asia to China. It is a summer visitor to central Europe and most of Asia, and winters mainly in the southern part of its breeding range in Europe, and to the south-west and south of its breeding range in Asia. There has been considerable expansion in its breeding range to the north and west in recent years resulting in more frequent occurrences in Great Britain with 157 records up to 2002.

Golden Oriole (Eurasian Golden Oriole)   *Oriolus oriolus*

A scarce passage migrant, mainly in spring and summer – has bred

There is a published record of breeding in the county early in the 19th Century with unpublished ones for 1892 and 1893. Otherwise Mansel-Pleydell (1888) described this species as "a rare summer visitant" and listed seven occurrences involving eight birds between 1854 and 1885. Blathwayt (1945) referred to it as a somewhat frequent spring visitor, which has probably nested, but gave no details. In 1939 a pair produced young just inside Devon, but the family party was seen in Dorset.

During the 1950s and 1960s the Golden Oriole was an occasional visitor mainly in spring and summer. An increase in reports during the 1970s was a precursor to a marked increase from 1980 onwards with 126 birds recorded during 1980–1999 compared with only 30 during 1950–1979 – see Fig 56. Most birds have occurred between mid-April and mid-June with a distinct peak during the second half of May, the month as a whole accounting for 63% of the spring and summer records – see Table 594. There are exceptionally early reports on 5th April 1955 in a wood on the southern fringes of the

Blackmore Vale, and 13th April 1975 at Rodden. Autumn migrants are very rare with only five records involving singles at Abbotsbury on 6th September 1964, between Witchampton and Tarrant Rushton on the very late date of 24th October 1972, at Portland Bill on 27th September 1985 and 5th–6th September 1991, and in quarries at Easton, Portland on 14th September 1997.

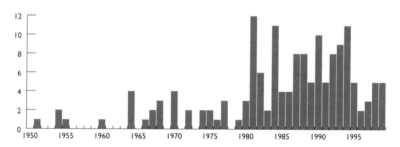

Fig 56. Annual totals for spring and summer birds 1950–1999

Apr 1–15	Apr 16–30	May 1–15	May 16–31	Jun 1–15	Jun 16–30	Jul 1–15	Jul 16–31
2	17	35	58	25	5	4	2

Table 594. Half-monthly totals of spring and summer birds 1950–1999

The marked increase in records since 1980 is associated with an upsurge in the number of birds reported from the main coastal watch-points – see Table 595. For example, there were only six records from Portland during 1950–1979 compared with 64 birds during 1980–1999. Overall, coastal migrants accounted for 93% of all spring and summer records during 1980–1999 compared with 63% for the period 1950–1979. Since 1980, the main site for spring and summer migrants has been Portland, which accounts for 51% of the total.

There have been several mini-influxes during 1980–1999, mainly in late May. These have been most evident at Portland Bill, the most notable being six birds during 19th–24th May 1981 (maximum of three during 21st–23rd), at least five birds during 11th–27th May 1982, up to three birds during 24th–27th May 1985 and three on 22nd May 1993, whilst five birds were recorded at various sites on Portland during 24th May–2nd June 1994. In 1984 there was a very early influx into the county during 21st April–3rd May involving a total of ten birds, which included up to four frequenting the reedbeds at Lodmoor NR from 28th April to 3rd May.

	1950–1979		1980–1999	
Portland Bill	2	7%	41	33%
elsewhere on Portland	4	13%	23	18%
Radipole NR/Radipole School	0	0	8	6%
Durlston CP	0	0	13	10%
Christchurch Harbour	0	0	15	12%
other coastal or near coastal sites	13	43%	17	13%
well inland	11	37%	9	7%

Table 595. Distribution of spring and summer birds 1950–1999

Since 1950 evidence of breeding has been very tentative and mainly involves single birds reported from suitable woodland sites on single dates only. The more interesting records involve a male near the 1939 breeding site on the Devon/Dorset border during 30th June–2nd July 1951, a pair in woodland near Arne NR on 23rd May 1968 and at least one in Wareham Forest from 13th May to 4th July 1988–the latter being the best evidence of breeding in recent years.

A total of three birds has been ringed in the county.

The Golden Oriole is a summer visitor breeding in north-west Africa and across most of southern, central and eastern Europe north to eastern England and southern Scandinavia, extending eastwards to Asia Minor and west and central Asia south to the northern Indian sub-continent. It winters in the southern half of Africa and throughout the Indian sub-continent.

Postscript 2000–2002

In 2000, a total of 11 birds were recorded during 3rd May–23rd June including nine from various sites on Portland, the other two reports being from Durlston CP and Weymouth. By contrast, there were only two records in 2001 involving singles at Durlston CP on 8th May and Lodmoor NR on 13th May, and only two records in 2002 involving singles at Portland Bill on 19th and 21st May.

Isabelline Shrike   *Lanius isabellinus*

Accidental: four records

    1959   Portland Bill: 10th September
    1978   Winspit: 14th–24th October, trapped 16th
    1985   Portland Bill: first-winter 15th–23rd September, trapped 19th
    1988   Durlston CP: first-winter 12th–22nd October

The Winspit bird was considered to be probably an adult female of the race *L. i. phoenicuroides*, sometimes known as the 'Turkestan Shrike', whilst the 1985 and 1988 individuals probably belonged to the race *L. i. isabellinus*, sometimes referred to as the 'Daurian Shrike'. An in-depth study of the racial attribution of all British records is in progress.

The various races of Isabelline Shrike are summer visitors breeding in south-west and south-central Asia from Iran in the west to Mongolia and China in the east. They winter in the eastern tropics of Africa, southern Arabia and south-west Asia including the north-western Indian sub-continent. A vagrant to Great Britain with 59 records up to 2002.

Sponsored by John Valentine

Red-backed Shrike   *Lanius collurio*

A scarce passage migrant – formerly bred

Mansel-Pleydell (1888) described this species as "one of our latest summer visitants" and further commented "it breeds here regularly, and may often be seen in our orchards and hedgerows; very seldom in woods, preferring the open county". Blathwayt (1945) referred to it as a summer resident, which was local and absent from many parts of the county and decidedly more numerous in the east than the west, but nested at Bridport in 1927.

By 1950 the status of the Red-backed Shrike in Dorset was very precarious with regular breeding only recorded up to 1955, the last of three successive years that a pair nested successfully near Bradford Abbas. Subsequently single pairs bred on a Poole Basin heath in 1960, near Milton Abbas during 1960–1962 and at Black Down during 1966–1968. There was also evidence of breeding at other sites in 1956 and during 1960–1962.

Since the demise of the breeding population, the species has only occurred as a scarce passage migrant, mainly in the autumn. With the exception of 1982, there have been annual records in autumn since 1968, but spring sightings are less frequent with absences in nine years during the same period – see Figs 57 and 58. Spring totals normally vary from 0–3 birds, but there was a notable influx in 1987 (nine) and smaller ones in 1988 (four) and 1998 (five). Autumn totals generally range from 1–5 birds except for influxes in 1977 (eight) and 1998 (nine), the latter being a record year for Red-backed Shrikes in the county in recent years.

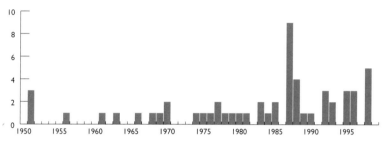

Fig 57. Spring totals of migrants 1950–1999

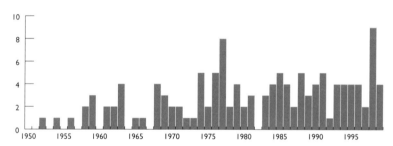

Fig 58. Autumn totals of migrants 1950–1999

There is an exceptionally early record of a male at Portland Bill during 12th–14th April 1956, whilst Blathwayt (1945) referred to an early arrival on 25th April 1909. In more recent years, the earliest report is 1st May 1990 at Stanpit Marsh, Christchurch Harbour. Spring birds are recorded mainly between mid-May and mid-June with a distinct peak during the second half of May, which accounts for 55% of the total – see Table 596. There are a few reports for mid-summer including a long-staying male at Durlston CP during 13th July–8th August 1997. Most autumn passage occurs between mid-August and mid-October with an even spread of records during September and the first half of October – see Table 596. The latest sightings are from Weston, Portland on 4th November 1998, and Portland Bill on 9th November 1975 and the exceptionally late date of 25th November 1998.

Apr 1–15	Apr 16–30	May 1–15	May 16–31	Jun 1–15	Jun 16–30	Jul 1–15	Jul 16–31
1	0	4	30	15	5	3	1

Aug 1–15	Aug 16–31	Sep 1–15	Sep 16–30	Oct 1–15	Oct 16–31	Nov 1–15	Nov 16–30
2	23	31	30	30	7	2	1

Table 596. Half-monthly totals of migrants 1950–1999

Portland Bill is the main site for both spring and autumn migrants, Portland as a whole accounting for 49% of the total – see Table 597. Durlston CP is the next most favoured locality with 14% of the total, whilst most of the remaining sightings are from other sites scattered along the coast from West Bexington in the west to Christchurch Harbour in the east. Inland reports account for 10% of the total, which is surprisingly high for a scarce passage migrant. Most records of migrants involve one, or very rarely two birds, the highest count being three well inland at Compton Valence on 22nd August 1974.

	Spring		Autumn		Total	
Portland Bill	15	27%	50	39%	65	35%
elsewhere on Portland	8	14%	17	13%	25	14%
Fleet/west Dorset coast	4	7%	8	6%	12	6%
Radipole NR	3	5%	6	5%	9	5%
Lodmoor NR	2	4%	1	1%	3	2%
Durlston CP	6	11%	20	16%	26	14%
elsewhere on Purbeck	2	4%	9	7%	11	6%
Poole Harbour	2	4%	3	2%	5	3%
Christchurch Harbour	7	13%	4	3%	11	6%
inland	7	13%	11	9%	18	10%

Table 597. Distribution of migrants 1950–1999

A total of 16 birds has been ringed in the county.

The Red-backed Shrike is a summer visitor breeding over much of Europe from southern Scandinavia south to northern Spain, Italy and the Balkans, extending eastwards to Asia Minor and north-western Asia. In Europe it has disappeared from Great Britain and much of northern France, and declined in some other regions. It winters in Africa south of the equator.

Postscript 2000–2002

In 2000, there was a spring bird at Portland Bill on 4th June, and autumn singles at Durlston CP on 13th, 25th and 30th September. In 2001, singles at Portland Bill on 28th–29th August and Durlston CP on 29th September were the only records. Similarly there were only two records in 2002 involving singles at Durlston CP on 11th and 13th September and Seacombe Bottom from 15th–17th September.

Lesser Grey Shrike   *Lanius minor*

Accidental: three records

1965	Between Bere Regis and Wareham: ad. 23rd August
1988	The Nothe, Weymouth: 18th October
1989	Stoford, on the Somerset border: male 20th May

The Lesser Grey Shrike is a summer visitor breeding in southern and eastern Europe, Asia Minor and west-central Asia. It winters in southern Africa. A vagrant to Great Britain with 160 records up to 2002.

Great Grey Shrike   *Lanius excubitor*

A scarce passage migrant and winter visitor

Mansel-Pleydell (1888) described this species as "a rare winter visitant" and listed several records up to the last, which was shot at Lytchett Matravers in 1872. Blathwayt (1945) referred to it as a scarce winter visitor and reported that a dozen or more had been recorded from various parts of the county including several near Cranborne in the winter of 1906/07.

Since 1951 the Great Grey Shrike has occurred annually except for 1959. It is difficult to assess exact numbers since some overwintering birds are prone to wander over large areas, which may result in some duplication. Despite this, there is evidence to show that numbers increased to peak during the 1970s and 1980s, followed by a marked decline during much of the 1990s with a hint of a revival in 1998–1999 – see Fig 59. The best annual totals in 1982 and 1998 were due to late autumn influxes involving seven and nine birds respectively.

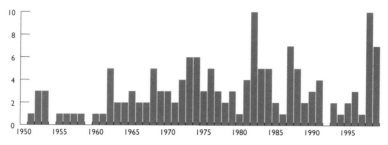

Fig 59. Annual totals excluding returning wintering birds 1950–1999

Although it is clear that a few individuals over-winter and sometimes return to traditional haunts in successive winters, many records are for single dates or relatively short stays and may refer either to overwintering individuals wandering between widely scattered sites, or to transient birds. Certainly a significant number of reports in late autumn and early spring are genuine migrants, which is reflected by a marked peak in occurrences between mid-October and mid-November, and a much smaller peak during the first half of April – see Table 598. There is an exceptionally early record on 9th September 1990 at Bere Regis, the next earliest being 3rd October 1977 at West Bexington. Sightings after mid-April

are rare, the latest being 13th May 1990 at Holt Heath NNR and 18th May 1987 near Blandford, whilst there is a remarkable mid-summer report from Turnerspuddle Heath on 16th June 1974.

Jan 1–15	Jan 16–31	Feb 1–15	Feb 16–28	Mar 1–15	Mar 16–31	Apr 1–15	Apr 16–30	May 1–15	May 16–31	Jun 1–5	Jun 16–30
14	11	11	7	8	6	7	0	1	1	0	1

Jul 1–15	Jul 16–31	Aug 1–15	Aug 16–31	Sep 1–15	Sep 16–30	Oct 1–15	Oct 16–31	Nov 1–15	Nov 16–30	Dec 1–15	Dec 16–31
0	0	0	0	1	0	9	22	17	11	12	9

Table 598. Half-monthly totals 1950–1999

The majority of records are from the heathlands and forestry areas of the Poole Basin, notably Wareham Forest where birds have sometimes overwintered, occasionally in successive years, e.g. Morden Bog from 1997/98 to 1999/2000. Other favoured sites within Poole Basin include Studland NNR, Hartland Moor, Arne NR, Turnerspuddle Heath, Holt Heath NNR and Cranborne Common. All of these have attracted overwintering birds, most notably Holt Heath NNR in recent years. Elsewhere there are scattered sightings from other areas of the county, but reports from coastal sites are relatively few. For example, Portland has only hosted 11 birds during 1957–1999 with eight in October, two in November and one in March, whilst on Purbeck there are two reports from Winspit and single sightings from Durlston CP and St Aldhelm's Head, the latter involving a bird flying in off the sea on 26th October 1968. Almost all occurrences refer to singles, the only exceptions being two at Studland NNR in January 1963, two in the Clouds Hill area on 12th January 1968 and two at Holt Heath NNR during 23rd–25th January 1996.

The Great Grey Shrike breeds over much of northern and central Europe, excluding the Britain Isles, south to central France, the Alps and Carpathian Mountains, extending eastwards across northern Asia to northern North America. It is a summer visitor in the northern parts of its range with birds wintering to the west and south.

Postscript 2000–2002

The only reports refer to the regular wintering bird in the Morden Bog/Wareham Forest area from 1999 to 24th January 2000, from November 2001 to March 2002 and during November–December 2002.

Southern Grey Shrike   *Lanius meridionalis pallidirostris*

Accidental: one record

　　1989　Portland Bill: 1st November

Dorset's only record of this species involved a first-winter bird of the distinctive migratory race, colloquially known as the Steppe Grey Shrike.

The Southern Grey Shrike breeds in Iberia, southern France and North Africa, and eastwards across the Middle East and Arabia to the Indian sub-continent and central Asia. It is mainly sedentary, but the race *L. m. pallidirostris* from central Asia is migratory and winters in south-west Asia, Arabia and north-east Africa. A vagrant to Great Britain with 16 records up to 2002.

Woodchat Shrike   *Lanius senator*

A scarce passage migrant

Pulteney (1799) stated "I have not seen the Woodchat, but am assured it has now and then been shot in Dorsetshire", whilst Mansel-Pleydell (1888) gave records of one killed at Bloxworth in an unspecified year and another seen at Lyme Regis on 22nd June 1876. Blathwayt (1945) referred to further reports involving one at Corfe Castle on 21st April 1893 and a female shot at Portland on 23rd June 1928.

Since 1952 there have been 68 records of which 44 have occurred in spring and 24 in autumn – see Figs 60 and 61. It is interesting to note that during 1952–1974 autumn birds outnumbered spring birds by 15 to five, but subsequently the situation has been reversed with spring birds outnumbering autumn birds by 39 to nine during 1975–1999. An exceptionally early individual was present at Portland Bill from 17th March to 8th April 1990, the next earliest being 12th April 1981 at Southwell, Portland. Otherwise the remaining spring birds have appeared between 20th April and 28th June with a distinct peak during the second half of May (18), the month as a whole accounting for 66% of the spring total since 1952 – see Table 599. There are two July records involving single adults at Lodmoor NR on 5th–6th July 1966 and Portland Bill on 21st July 1968. Autumn birds have been reported from 7th August 1980 at Portland Bill, with the latest a long-staying individual also at Portland Bill from 7th to 23rd October 1958. There is a small peak of occurrences during the second half of August – see Table 599. Apart from adults at Portland Bill on 29th August 1965 and Durlston CP on 9th August 1988, all autumn sightings have referred to immature birds.

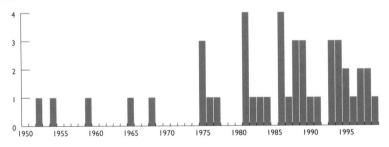

Fig 60. Spring totals 1952–1999

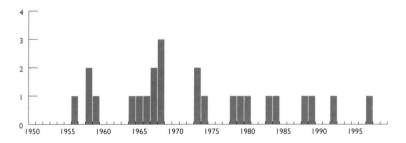

Fig 61. Autumn totals 1956–1999

Mar 1–15	Mar 16–31	Apr 1–15	Apr 16–30	May 1–15	May 16–31	Jun 1–15	Jun 16–30
0	1	1	3	11	18	7	3

Jul 1–15	Jul 16–31	Aug 1–15	Aug 16–31	Sep 1–15	Sep 16–30	Oct 1–15	Oct 16–31
1	1	4	7	4	5	2	0

Table 599. Half-monthly totals 1952–1999

Although there is a greater spread of records in spring than in autumn, Portland Bill is the main site for the species in both seasons – see Table 600. There are a further eight spring sightings from other sites on Portland, but surprisingly none in autumn. The remaining spring reports are from the Purbeck coast with three at Durlston CP and singles at Winspit and Ballard Down, Christchurch Harbour (two), Lodmoor NR (two), Abbotsbury, Langton Herring, Arne NR, Wytch Farm and well inland at East Chaldon on 2nd May 1959, Charborough Park during 2nd–9th June 1989 and Monkton Up Wimborne on 31st May 1994. There are very few autumn records away from Portland Bill involving single birds at West Bexington, Wyke Regis, Melcombe Regis Cemetery, Lodmoor NR and Durlston CP. An adult at Grove Point, Portland on 10th May 1986 showed characteristics of the West Mediterranean Island subspecies *L. s. badius*.

	Spring		Autumn		Total	
Portland Bill	20	45%	19	79%	39	57%
elsewhere on Portland	8	18%	0	0	8	12%
Purbeck coast	5	11%	1	4%	6	9%
Christchurch Harbour	2	5%	0	0	2	3%
other coastal or near coastal sites	6	14%	4	17%	10	15%
well inland	3	7%	0	0	3	4%

Table 600. Distribution of migrants 1952–1999

A total of 12 birds has been ringed in the county.

The Woodchat Shrike is a summer visitor breeding in north-west Africa, southern and central Europe as far north as central France, central Germany and Poland, extending eastwards to Asia Minor, parts of the Middle East and extreme south-west Asia. It winters in the northern tropics of Africa. A rare visitor to the British Isles with 587 records up to 1990.

Postscript 2000–2002

In 2000, there were singles at Portland Bill on 7th May and Abbotsbury on 14th May, whilst 2002 produced singles at Weston, Portland from 7th to 10th May, Portland Bill on 21st August and 21st September, and unusually inland at Winfrith Heath on 16th July. There were no reports during 2001, making it only the second 'blank' year since 1972.

Jay (Eurasian Jay)   *Garrulus glandarius*

A common resident and scarce passage migrant, subject to autumn influxes

Mansel-Pleydell (1888) described this species as "a constant resident" and commented that it suffered from persecution. Blathwayt (1945) simply referred to it as a common resident which prefers woodland districts.

There has subsequently been little change in status with the *BTO Atlas* (1968–1972) revealing evidence of breeding in 35 (95%) 10-km squares (confirmed in 33, probable in one and possible in one), whilst the Tetrad Survey (1987–1994) found evidence of breeding in 33 (89%) of the pre-1974 10-km squares (confirmed in 31 and probable in two). The Tetrad Map reveals a breeding distribution similar to some other woodland birds such as the Nuthatch and Treecreeper. The greatest population densities in the county occur in the west, the north, Poole Basin and east Purbeck. It is rather sparsely distributed across most of the chalk downs and in the area between Weymouth and Dorchester, whilst it is absent from Portland. The population was considered to be increasing during the late 1960s and early 1970s, but the relatively little information available on subsequent long-term trends indicates a relatively stable situation. For example, numbers at Studland NNR have varied between 1–3 pairs during 1968–1999, whilst the population at nearby Arne NR has generally remained steady at 10 pairs from 1973 to 1993 – see Tables 601 and 602.

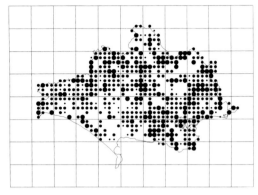

67	68	80	81	82	83	84	85	86	87	88	89	90	91	92	93	94	95	96	98	99
3	3	2	2	2	2	2	1	2	1	2	1	1	1	1	2	2	2	2	1	1

Table 601. Number of breeding territories at Studland NNR 1967–1999

73	74	75	76	78	79	80	81	82	83	84	85	86	87	91	93
10	10	10	10	10	10	10	10	10	10	10	10	10	10	7	10

Table 602. Number of breeding territories at Arne NR 1973–1993

Coastal passage/dispersal occasionally occurs in spring when any visual movements are frequently easterly in direction. Although numbers are generally very small, passage can be quite marked in some years, most notably in 1958 and more recently in 1982, 1984 (after the exceptional autumn influx in 1983), 1985 and 1987 – see Table 603. During these good springs, peak counts sometimes reach double figures, the highest being 24 at Durlston CP and 20E at Lodmoor NR on 10th May 1958 with presumably the same flock of 24 at Portland Bill the following day, 19 at Portland Bill on 28th May 1982, and in May 1984 30 at Shell Bay on 13th with 20NE nearby on 20th, 27E at Durlston CP on 20th and 18 at Portland Bill on 14th. Although movements involving both local dispersal and occasional immigration are more evident in autumn, mainly late September–October, numbers vary considerably with virtually no birds recorded in some years – see Table

604. In most autumns, peak counts rarely exceed 20 birds, but food shortages in some years can produce more remarkable movements including 100 well inland at Cranborne on 2nd October 1961 with 50 there on 20th October 1963, and 60 at both Radipole NR and Chapman's Pool in mid-October 1977. Durlston CP is the main coastal site for autumn birds.

	1980	1981	1982	1983	1984	1985	1986	1987	1988	1989
Portland Bill	1	1	41	0	54	4	0	0	0	1
Durlston CP	10	nc	63	0	306	36	0	26	0	0
Christchurch Hbr	3	2	22	1	58	3	0	0	0	1

	1990	1991	1992	1993	1994	1995	1996	1997	1998	1999
Portland Bill	0	0	0	7	0	0	0	3	0	0
Durlston CP	0	9	nc	0	0	0	0	nc	0	nc
Christchurch Hbr	0	1	0	0	0	0	1	nc	0	0

Table 603. Spring totals (bds) at the main coastal watch-points 1980–1999

	1980	1981	1982	1983	1984	1985	1986	1987	1988	1989
Portland Bill	0	0	0	17	1	0	0	0	0	0
Durlston CP	0	39	15	1057	p	3	23	36	mx20	0
Christchurch Hbr	0	14	2	9	0	3	25	2	2	0

	1990	1991	1992	1993	1994	1995	1996	1997	1998	1999
Portland Bill	1	0	0	0	0	0	0	0	0	0
Durlston CP	mx12	30	237	18	0	400	mx30	mx35	mx18	mx8
Christchurch Hbr	6	3	3	0	11	0	mx15	47	nc	nc

Table 604. Autumn totals (bds) at the main coastal watch-points 1980–1999; mx = maximum

During the late autumn of 1983 an unparalleled invasion took place across southern Great Britain and neighbouring Europe with large numbers of birds moving through Dorset in late September and throughout October. Initially the highest counts were reported well inland in late September with 46 at Compton Valence on 22nd and up to 32 at Puddletown, whilst birds first reached the coast on 29th at Christchurch Harbour (two), and 30th at Durlston CP (8E) and St Aldhelm's Head (two). In October there were two main influxes from the 4th and again from the 17th. Along the coast the largest numbers occurred in the Weymouth/Fleet area involving many hundreds on 4th including 100W in one hour at West Fleet, also at Radipole School 304 bird-days (265W) during the month with a maximum of 100W on 6th and 126W on 19th, with smaller counts of 20–36 birds reported from Radipole and Lodmoor NRs and Preston. On Purbeck, Durlston CP recorded 580 bird-days during October (maximum of 68 (49E) on 25th) with 76 bird-days at nearby St Aldhelm's Head (maximum of 20 on 5th), and 40 at Winspit on 21st. Much smaller numbers were noted from Portland with only 19 bird-days during 20th October–4th November, and Christchurch Harbour including up to five on Hengistbury from 20th October. Elsewhere there were several notable counts during October with 61W in the Stour Valley near Sturminster Marshall on 4th, 48SE at Bincombe Hill and 37SW at Boscombe on 5th, 115 at Clifton Wood on 7th and 55N at Studland NNR on 25th. There was evidence that some numbers remained in the county during November with 477 bird-days at Durlston CP.

In winter flocks of up to 30 birds has been recorded, whilst in January 1982 a cold weather movement occurred at Durlston CP with 30E on 9th–10th.

A total of 187 birds have been ringed in the county.

The Jay breeds in north-west Africa and throughout most of Europe, except the far north, extending eastwards to Asia Minor, parts of the Middle East and across north-central Asia to the Pacific coast and Japan, and then south to China and west to the Himalayas.

Magpie (Black-billed Magpie) *Pica pica*

A common resident

Both Mansel-Pleydell (1888) and Blathwayt (1945) referred to this species as a common resident, which was much persecuted by gamekeepers.

Despite continuing persecution in some areas, the Magpie has remained a common and widespread resident. The *BTO Atlas* (1968–1972) confirmed breeding in 35 (95%) 10-km squares, being absent in the remaining two, which cover the coastal fringes of Portland. By the time of the Tetrad Survey (1987–1994), these coastal fringes had been colonised and consequently breeding was confirmed in all of the pre-1974 10-km squares. The Tetrad Map shows that the species breeds throughout the entire county except for a few tetrads on the chalk downs of Cranborne Chase, where its absence may be due to persecution in game-rearing areas. Population numbers were reported to be increasing during the 1960s and 1970s with birds spreading into suburban areas. Breeding was first reported from North Portland in 1977 and Portland Bill in 1983, and subsequently the Magpie has become well established on Portland with a resident population of 40–60

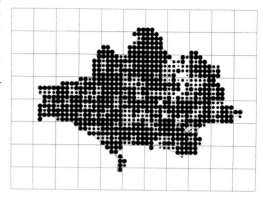

birds in 1993. Otherwise the relatively little information available on long-term trends suggest that, apart from some localised declines such as at Studland NNR, population numbers at most sites have been relatively stable during the 1980s and 1990s – see Tables 605 and 606.

67	68	81	82	83	84	85	86	87	88	89	90	91	92	93	94	95	96	97	98	99
5	5	4	2	1	2	2	2	3	2	2	2	1	1	3	4	1	1	nc	1	1

Table 605. Number of breeding territories at Studland NNR 1967–1999

1973	1974	1975	1978	1979	1980	1981	1982	1983	1986	1987	1991
6	6	6	6	6	7	5	5	5	5	5	5

Table 606. Number of breeding territories at Arne NR 1973–1991

During the winter, counts at roost sites normally range between 20–50 birds, the highest being 76 at Motcombe on 11th February 1982 with 70 there on 4th February 1984, 74 at Hatch Pond, Poole on 29th January 1995 with 72 there on 20th February 1996, and 70 at Durlston CP in several winters during 1984–1990.

There are occasional reports from coastal sites in spring and autumn indicative of local dispersal if not genuine passage. For example, there was a small influx at Portland Bill during 25th October–20th November 1983 (maximum of 13 on 7th November) with 11W at Christchurch Harbour on 20th October of the same year, also 20SE at Christchurch Harbour on 27th September 1994.

A total of 160 birds has been ringed in the county.

The Magpie breeds in north-west Africa, Europe, Asia Minor, large areas of central and eastern Asia, extreme eastern Siberia, and eastern North America.

Postscript 2000–2002

Numbers at the winter roost at Hatch Pond, Poole increased with peaks of 87 on 21st January 2000, 105 on 25th February 2001 and 117 on 10th December 2002, the latter being the highest recorded count for Dorset.

Sponsored by Lorna K. J. Bale

Nutcracker (Spotted Nutcracker) *Nucifraga caryocatactes*

Accidental: seven records all in 1968

Apart from an old report of one at Bingham's Melcombe in November 1906, which was considered to be unsubstantiated by Blathwayt (1945), all records refer to the famous irruption of the Slender-billed race *N. c. macrorhynchos* in September 1968. A total of seven birds were recorded in Dorset as follows:

> 1968 Encombe House (Purbeck): one in a private wood for a few days from 9th September
> Portland Bill: one flying south apparently out to sea 11th September
> Brownsea: 13th–21st September
> Morden: 20th September
> Little Minterne Hill, Cerne Abbas: 20th September and 6th October–9th November
> Netherbury: one in a cider apple orchard 29th September
> Tollard Royal area: one on the county boundary with Wiltshire 21st October–15th January 1969

The various races of Nutcracker breed from the Alps and mountains of central and south-eastern Europe, and the forests of southern Scandinavia eastwards across northern Asia to the Pacific coast and Japan, and then south to China and west to the Himalayas. There are occasional irruptions of the Siberian or Slender-billed race *N. c. macrorhynchos* into western Europe. A vagrant to the British Isles with 400 records up to 2000 of which c.315 occurred during the autumn of 1968.

Chough (Red-billed Chough) *Pyrrhocorax pyrrhocorax*

An extinct resident – otherwise accidental visitor with perhaps four birds seen in 2001

Mansel-Pleydell (1888) recognised the parlous status of this species during the 19th Century with the following comments. "There is much reason to fear that in the county of Dorset this interesting bird is on the eve of extinction. Fifty years ago it used to be abundant on the Purbeck coast, but has gradually become scarcer, and is now quite a rare bird". Several pairs were still present near Lulworth in 1865, whilst subsequent reports include five trapped during the summer of 1885 near Swanage where one was shot the following January, a pair with young at Seacombe in May 1885 and a pair at Studland in April 1887. Blathwayt (1945) stated that a nest at Lulworth Cove in about 1890 was probably the last breeding record and lists three occurrences for the 20th Century as follows: Wyke Regis about 10th October 1906, Osmington Mills with Jackdaws in February 1908 and Winspit during 25th–30th April 1925.

The Chough breeds on coastal cliffs in the west of the British Isles and north-west France, but also in mostly mountain areas from north-west Africa and Iberia eastwards across southern Europe to Asia Minor, and south-west and central Asia. There are also two isolated populations in East Africa.

Postscript 2000–2002

There was a most unexpected series of records from Portland in spring 2001. On 21st March one was first seen flying south over Penn's Weare and later found settled at the Bill, where it remained until the next day. Later in the spring, there were singles at the Bill on 3rd and 8th April, and 5th–6th May. Plumage and bare-part differences, as well as circumstantial evidence, indicated that the records might have involved different individuals. This was undoubtedly the ornithological highlight of the year!

Jackdaw (Eurasian Jackdaw) *Corvus monedula*

A common resident, winter visitor and passage migrant

Mansel-Pleydell (1888) described this species as "resident, and extremely numerous on our sea-cliffs, where, according to some authorities, its increase has operated to drive away the weaker and less combative Chough". Blathwayt (1945) referred to the Jackdaw as a locally common resident, which bred commonly along the sea-cliffs and throughout the county in suitable localities.

There has been little change in status subsequently with both the *BTO Atlas* (1968–1972) and the Tetrad Survey (1987–1994) confirming breeding in all of the pre-1974 10-km squares. The Tetrad Map shows that the species is widely distributed as a breeding bird throughout the county, except for parts of the south-east where it is absent from large tracts of coniferous forestry and open heath, as well as some urban areas, which presumably lack older buildings to provide suitable nest sites. The little information available on long-term population trends suggests a reduction in breeding numbers at some coastal sites. For example, there has been a decline at Portland Bill from 40 pairs in 1962 to 25–30 pairs in 1983 and ten pairs in 1990, whilst at Durlston CP the population remained relatively stable during the 1980s, but then declined during the 1990s – see Table 607. In 1981, the population at Worbarrow Bay was estimated to be c.100 pairs.

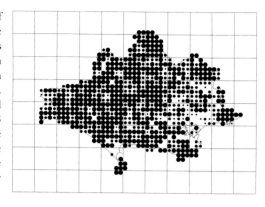

1981	1982	1983	1984	1985	1986	1987	1988	1990	1991	1992	1996	1997	1998
30	38	40	40	35	40	30	30	30	30	28	10	15	14

Table 607. Number of breeding territories at Durlston CP 1981–1998

Outside the breeding season and particularly during the winter, large feeding flocks and roosts commonly occur, sometimes in association with other corvids. Numbers often reach 200–600 birds, occasionally more, the highest counts being 3,000 at St Aldhelm's Head on 12th September 1972, 3,000 at Corfe Mullen on 30th October 1988 with up to 2,000 there during both winter periods of 1990, 1991 and 1992, 2,500 at Two Mile Copse, Weymouth on 28th August 1998, 2,000 at Central Portland on 1st August 1968 and 2,000 at Arne NR on 6th February 1988.

Although there is some difficulty in distinguishing between genuine migratory movements and local feeding flocks following the coast, there is some evidence of passage in spring, mainly during April and May, and sometimes more obviously in autumn, mainly during October and November. The sporadic nature of this passage is shown by data from Portland Bill – see Table 608. Occasionally these movements can reach treble figures, for example 250S at Portland Bill on 29th October 1983 with 170N there on 20th October 1985, 200NE at Lodmoor NR on 4th November 1983, and 150N at Durlston CP on 5th April 1983 with 180E there on 16th October 1986. In recent autumns much larger numbers have been recorded moving at West Bexington with 1,540W during the last week of October 1997 and 2,890W during 18th October–4th November 1998 reaching a maximum of 1,700W on 18th October.

	80	81	82	83	84	85	86	87	88	89	90	91	92	93	94	95	96	97	98	99
Spring	4	5	21	19	17	2	7	0	4	0	0	0	0	0	0	0	0	0	0	0
Autumn	2	45	68	250	0	210	0	0	0	0	0	0	0	1	52	0	80	29	90	0	16

Table 608. Totals of birds involved in visual movements at Portland Bill 1980–1999

A total of 214 birds has been ringed in the county.

The Jackdaw breeds in north-west Africa and across most of Europe as far north as southern Scandinavia, extending eastwards to Asia Minor and west-central Asia, also locally in the Middle East. It is a summer visitor in the more northern and eastern parts of its range with birds wintering mainly in western Europe.

Rook   *Corvus frugilegus*

A common resident, winter visitor and passage migrant

Mansel-Pleydell (1888) and Blathwayt (1945) both considered this species to be a common resident.

There has been little change in status. The *BTO Atlas* (1968–1972) confirmed breeding in 34 (92%) 10-km squares, whilst the Tetrad Survey (1987–1994) produced an almost identical result with confirmed breeding in 35 (95%) of the pre-1974 10-km squares. The Tetrad Map shows that rookeries are widely distributed throughout the county, except for large areas of the east where their absence coincides with coniferous forestry, open heath and the Bournemouth and Poole conurbation. Elsewhere in the county, the absence of rookeries is associated with higher downland.

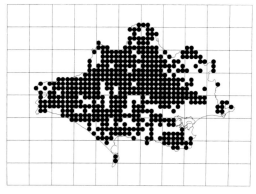

The long-term population trend is reflected by surveys undertaken in 1975, 1976, 1980 and more recently during 1992–1994. In 1975 a BTO Survey found 732 rookeries and 16,427 nests, whilst a further but less comprehensive census in 1976 recorded 581 rookeries and 15,403 nests. The overall conclusion was that the loss of elm trees through disease had not impacted adversely on the county population. In 1980 the BTO organised a partial repeat of the 1975 survey based on a sample of eight 10-km squares. The results suggested that the county population had increased by 27% compared to the 1975 survey with massive increases in three squares, smaller increases in two squares and small decreases in three squares. Although some dead elms were still used for nesting, it was apparent that many rookeries had found suitable alternatives, including hedges, without any diminution in breeding numbers. Only in SU01 was there evidence of a decline due to the lack of suitable nesting trees. The decline in two main urban areas (SY68 and SZ09) may have also been associated with building development. Finally a three-year, county-wide survey completed in 1994 located 589 rookeries containing 24,895 nests with a population at the end of the breeding season estimated to be c.107,000 birds. This shows that the county population has continued to thrive with an overall increase of 52% compared to the 1975 survey, albeit in fewer individual rookeries, which declined by 20%. Obviously any loss of breeding sites has been more than compensated for by increases in the size of individual rookeries. It is interesting to note that at Sherborne Lake, the Rooks have moved away from their original breeding site at the Old Castle since Ravens started to nest in an adjacent tree in 1997. Raven predation has been observed on nestling Rooks.

Outside the breeding season and particularly during the winter, large feeding flocks and roosts commonly occur, sometimes in association with other corvids. These flocks and roosts often number up to 600 birds, occasionally more, the highest counts being from Corfe Mullen with 3,000–4,000 in late summer/autumn 1980, 3,000 on 30th October 1988 and up to 2,000 during both winter periods of 1990, 1991 and 1992, also 2,500 at Two Mile Copse, Weymouth on 28th August 1998, 2,000 at Arne NR on 6th February 1988 and 2,000 at Studland NNR in winter 1993.

There is some evidence of migration in spring, during February–May, and less obviously in autumn, mainly during September–early November. The sporadic nature of this passage is shown by data from Portland Bill – see Table 609. These movements rarely reach double figures, so 280 arriving from the sea at Studland NNR on 14th November 1958 and 161N at St Aldhelm's Head on 27th September 1965 are exceptional counts. A total of 1,023W inland at Merley on 29th September 1976 presumably involved feeding or roosting birds.

	80	81	82	83	84	85	86	87	88	89	90	91	92	93	94	95	96	97	98	99
Spring	17	26	31	26	3	45	0	3	7	8	7	2	0	0	0	0	0	0	0	0
Autumn	0	10	0	5	0	14	2	0	0	14	0	0	0	0	0	45	0	0	0	0

Table 609. Totals of birds involved in visual movements at Portland Bill 1980–1999

A total of 51 Rooks has been ringed in the county.

The Rook breeds throughout much of western and central Europe, more locally north to southern Scandinavia and south to Spain and Greece, extending eastwards to Asia Minor and across north-central Asia to the Pacific coast, and then south to China. It is a summer visitor in eastern Europe and throughout much of Asia. It winters throughout Europe, except the east, south to the Mediterranean, also in Asia Minor and parts of the Middle East, and within and to the south of the breeding range in Asia.

Carrion Crow

Corvus corone

A common resident, winter visitor and passage migrant

Mansel-Pleydell (1888) described this species as "a resident, and holds its own with greater success than does the Raven" and further commented "it is abundant in the Poole estuary, where many may be seen together at low tide, feeding along its margin". Blathwayt (1945) simply referred to it as a common resident.

There has been little change in its status subsequently with both the *BTO Atlas* (1968–1972) and the Tetrad Survey (1987–1994) confirming breeding in all of the pre-1974 10-km squares. The Tetrad Map shows that breeding occurs throughout the entire county except perhaps for a few well-keepered tetrads on the chalk downs of Cranborne Chase. The little information available on long-term trends suggests a relatively stable population – see Tables 610 to 612.

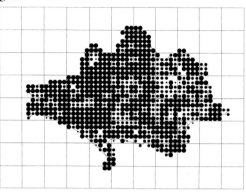

67	68	80	81	82	85	86	87	88	89	90	91	92	93	94	95	96	98	99
2	2	3	1	2	4	2	2	2	2	2	1	1	2	2	2	1	2	2

Table 610. Number of breeding territories at Studland NNR 1967–1999

1974	1980	1981	1982	1983	1984	1985	1986	1987	1991	1993
5	6	6	6	6	6	6	6	5	5	5

Table 611. Number of breeding territories at Arne NR 1974–1993

80	81	82	83	84	85	86	87	88	89	90	91	92	93	94	95	96	97
3–4	2–3	3–4	4	3	2–3	3	3	4	3	3	5	2	1	2	4	4	3

Table 612. Number of breeding territories at Portland Bill 1980–1997

Outside the breeding season, feeding flocks and roosts are smaller than those of other corvids with counts usually ranging up to 50, but rarely exceeding 100 birds, the highest being an exceptional 600 at Canford Heath on 17th December 1994, 400 at Motcombe during January–February 1982, 200 at Gillingham on 24th September 1981 and 200 at Sutton Waldron during 1st–5th February 1993.

Passage is sometimes detected at the main coastal watch-points, more particularly in spring, during February–May, than autumn, during September–November. The sporadic nature of these movements is shown by data from Portland Bill – see Table 613. Counts rarely reach double figures, so the arrival of 130 with other corvids at Portland Bill on 3rd November 1995 is exceptional.

	80	81	82	83	84	85	86	87	88	89	90	91	92	93	94	95	96	97	98	99
Spring	66	123	83	55	23	35	8	25	68	63	2	2	1	0	10	2	0	0	0	0
Autumn	47	5	56	5	0	0	0	0	0	0	0	0	0	45	0	160	0	0	0	0

Table 613. Totals of birds involved in visual movements at Portland Bill 1980–1999

A total of 77 birds has been ringed in the county.

The nominate race of Carrion Crow *C. c. corone* breeds in western Europe from England, Wales and S. Scotland south to Iberia and northern Italy, and east to Denmark, Germany, the Czech Republic and Austria. In the east of its range, there is a zone of overlap with the Hooded Crow, which has only been recently considered a separate species. Another race *C. c. orientalis* occurs in eastern Asia.

Hooded Crow

Corvus cornix

A scarce passage migrant and winter visitor

This recently 'split' species was recognised by Mansel-Pleydell (1888) who described it as "a casual winter visitant, occasionally seen on the Poole estuary, where it is a more frequent visitor than in any other part of the county". Blathwayt (1945) also considered the Hooded Crow to be a scarce winter visitor, but mentioned that it is sometimes seen on spring passage and referred to reports from Portland Bill on 1st May 1919, 10th April 1939 and 28th May 1946.

Since 1950 'Hoodies' have been recorded almost annually in small numbers, usually 1–3 birds, very occasionally more, the best years being 1953 with eight and 1983 with nine – see Fig 62. The majority of birds occur in spring with a distinct peak in April, the months of March to May accounting for 64% of the total records – see Table 614. This mirrors Carrion Crow passage, which is generally more obvious in spring than autumn. The much smaller autumn passage peaks in October. There are relatively few reports in winter, whilst occurrences of genuine overwintering are very rare, namely two at Lodmoor NR from December 1952 to March 1953 and one at Sandbanks from 6th January to 15th March 1953. The only other long-stayers involve one wandering around Portland and visiting Ferrybridge during 25th April–14th June 1971, another individual on Portland during 29th May 1994–4th April 1995 and one in Christchurch Harbour from March to June 1997. All but one of the reports involve 1–2 birds, the exception being three at Lodmoor NR on 20th March 1953.

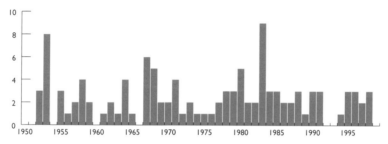

Fig 62. Annual totals excluding hybrids 1950–1998

Jan	Feb	Mar	Apr	May	Jun	Jul	Aug	Sep	Oct	Nov	Dec
6	8	15	37	20	5	3	2	0	8	5	3

Table 614. Monthly totals 1950–1999

Portland is by far the premier site for the species and accounts for 50% of the total records with 38% at the Bill – see Table 615. The rest of the sightings are distributed mainly amongst other coastal sites with 11 birds (10%) reported from inland localities.

	Total	
The Fleet/west Dorset coast	11	10%
Portland Bill	43	38%
elsewhere on Portland	13	12%
Radipole NR	2	2%
Lodmoor NR	8	7%
Purbeck	6	5%
Poole Harbour	7	6%
Christchurch Harbour	11	10%
inland	11	10%

Table 615. Distribution of birds 1950–1999

During the 1970s and early 1980s several hybrids resulting from inter-breeding in 1969 were resident in the Christchurch Harbour area. These have not been included in the totals above. Occasionally these hybrids were reported from further afield with sightings from Bournemouth, Parkstone, Peveril Point and Durlston CP.

The Hooded Crow replaces the Carrion Crow *C. c. corone* in northern and eastern Europe breeding in Ireland, northern Scotland, and eastwards from Scandinavia, Germany, the Czech Republic, Austria, Italy and the Balkans to Asia Minor, the Middle East and much of western Asia.

Raven (Common Raven)   *Corvus corax*

An uncommon resident

The fortunes of the Raven have fluctuated considerably during the past 200 years. Towards the end of the 19th Century the species was almost extinct, Mansel-Pleydell (1888) commenting that this was due to persistent persecution and that fifty years earlier it had bred on the Purbecks at St Aldhelm's Head and Gad Cliff. There were seemingly isolated records of breeding in 1865 at Lulworth and probably c.1887–1888 inland at Whatcombe Woods, whilst it also bred at Badbury Rings up to 1895. Subsequently the situation improved during first half of the 20th Century. Blathwayt (1945) reported that about six pairs, sometimes more, bred on the coastal cliffs where it was increasing, and one or two pairs nested annually in trees inland. Mention was also made that the species formerly nested commonly in trees and that it had done so regularly again in one district since 1926.

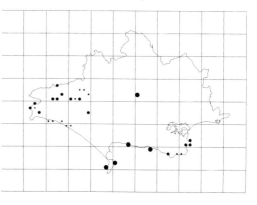

In the early 1950s the county population remained relatively healthy at c.8–9 pairs – see Table 616. Although there was an apparent decline in numbers by the mid-1960s, this may have been unduly pessimistic since the *BTO Atlas* (1968–1972) found evidence of breeding in 11 (30%) 10-km squares (confirmed in six, probable in three and possible in two) with a population of six pairs in 1969 and seven pairs in 1972. Subsequently there was a catastrophic decline with no reports of breeding during 1976–1982. The reasons for this demise are not clear, but on Purbeck both disturbance from the opening of the coastal footpath and at least three instances of poisoning were considered to be important factors. After an increase in records, breeding commenced again on the Purbeck cliffs in 1983. Despite this, the population remained in a precarious state until the 1990s when numbers increased dramatically with a minimum of 11 breeding pairs present in the county in 1996, 1998 and 1999. An encouraging feature of this improvement is the number of pairs breeding at inland localities with seven pairs in 1999, which outnumbered the four pairs at coastal sites. The start of this revival is also reflected by the Tetrad Survey (1987–1994) which revealed evidence of breeding in 15 (41%) of the pre-1974 10-km squares (confirmed in five, probable in six and possible in four). The Tetrad Map shows that breeding occurs mainly in west Dorset, both on the coastal cliffs and inland, and on the cliffs of Portland and Purbeck. Since the Tetrad Survey (1987–1994), however, breeding has spread into inland parts of east Dorset with reports from Wareham Forest during 1997–1999, and Middlebere Farm in 1998.

50	51	62	63	64	65	66	67	68	69	70	71	72	73	74	75	76	77	78	79
8	8–9	3	2	6	1	0	2	4	6	3	5	7	1	2	1	0	0	0	0
0	(1)	0	(1)	0	0	0	(1)	0	0	0	0	0	0	(1)	0	0	0	0	0

80	81	82	83	84	85	86	87	88	89	90	91	92	93	94	95	96	97	98	99
0	0	0	1	1	0	1	1	1	2	3	7	7	6	8	8	11	9	11	11
0	0	0	0	0	0	0	0	0	0	0	0	(1)	(1)	(1)	(2)	–	(4)	(6)	(7)

Table 616. Number of breeding pairs 1950–1999 (inland breeding in brackets)

As the fortunes of the breeding population has improved, so the number of records in total have increased from both coastal and inland sites, most notably in the east of the county where the Raven was traditionally a rare visitor. For example, the Stour Valley between Corfe Mullen and Sturminster Marshall, which has been a well-watched site since 1978, recorded its first birds in 1996. Outside the breeding season small gatherings of up to ten birds sometimes occur, more frequently in recent years, the highest counts being in 1999 with 26E at St Aldhelm's Head on 13th August, 21 at Portland Bill on 27th October and 17 roosting at Blacknor Point, Portland on 24th December.

The Raven breeds in North Africa, Europe except for lowland areas in the west and centre of the continent, Asia Minor, the Middle East, most of north and central Asia, and much of northern and western North America south to Central America.

Postscript 2000–2002

The Raven continues to thrive in the county with breeding reports involving c.13 pairs (nine inland) in 2000, c.14 pairs (nine inland) in 2001 and c.20 pairs (ten inland) in 2002. The highest counts were 18 at Middlebere on 3rd September 2000 and 20 at West Compton on 9th October 2001.

Starling (Common Starling)   *Sturnus vulgaris*

An abundant resident, winter visitor and passage migrant

Mansel-Pleydell (1888) described this species as "resident, and essentially gregarious, congregating in large flocks as soon as the breeding season is over". Blathwayt (1945) considered it to be a very common resident, and also a winter visitor and passage migrant.

Its status has changed little subsequently but there is evidence of a disturbing decline in more recent years. The *BTO Atlas* (1968–1972) confirmed breeding in all 10-km squares, whilst the Tetrad Survey (1987–1994) produced similar results with evidence of breeding in all but one (97%) of the pre-1974 10-km squares (confirmed in 35 and probable in one). Although the Tetrad Map shows that the Starling breeds throughout the entire county, it is absent from a few tetrads, most notably in areas of heathland and forestry in the south-east (mainly SZ08). The very limited information available on long-term population trends supports the assertion that breeding numbers have declined during the 1980s and 1990s – see Table 617.

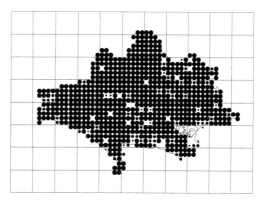

1981	1982	1983	1984	1985	1986	1988	1989	1991	1992	1993	1994	1995	1996
8	7	6	8	6	4	6	4	3	1	6	4	5	3

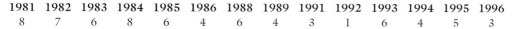

Table 617. Number of breeding territories at Forde Abbey 1981–1996

Post-breeding flocks and roosts build up during the summer and autumn, most notably at reedbed sites such as West Bexington (maximum of 5,000–10,000 in autumn 1999), Abbotsbury (maximum of several thousand in November 1999), Radipole NR (maxima of 12,000 in early October 1976 and 10,000–15,000 on 30th October 1993), Lodmoor NR (maximum of 3,000 during August–September 1985), Arne NR (maximum of 5,000 in October 1975), Lytchett Bay (maximum of 35,000 in October 1984) and Christchurch Harbour (maximum of 15,000–20,000 during late July–August 1975). Many of these roosts have seemingly become smaller in recent years, which is also reflected by the decline in the size of the post-breeding flock at Portland Bill – see Table 618.

1980	1981	1982	1983	1984	1985	1986	1987	1988	1989
800	800	600	1000	600	500	800	800	600	3000

1990	1991	1992	1993	1994	1995	1996	1997	1998	1999
1500	750	500	800	300	500	500	nc	nc	300

Table 618. Peak counts for post breeding flocks at Portland Bill 1980–1999

During the late autumn and winter much larger numbers, involving local birds augmented by continental immigrants, congregate at widely scattered roosts throughout the county. In January 1958 a roost at Jubilee Wood near Badbury Rings was estimated at between one and three million birds with counts of between 100,000 and 300,000 at this site during the autumn and winter in subsequent years up to 1970 at least. In the 1970s large roosts were located at Marnhull and nearby at Duncliffe Wood with peaks of one million birds on 8th March 1974 and from late February to mid-March 1975 respectively. During the 1980s and early 1990s peak counts at winter roosts rarely exceeded 25,000 birds, the highest being 100,000 near Wareham on 12th December 1985, at Studland Village on 24th January 1987 and at Hinton St Mary during late January–March 1993. Since 1995 numbers have diminished dramatically with peak counts at winter roosts during 1997–1999 only ranging between 1,000 and 5,000 birds. The decline in both the post-breeding and winter roosts confirm the disturbing reduction in the breeding population.

	1980	1981	1982	1983	1984	1985	1986	1987	1988	1989
South	252	116	168	0	5	86	540	0	0	12
North	0	13	14	0	3	4	0	0	24	674

	1990	1991	1992	1993	1994	1995	1996	1997	1998	1999
South	0	0	0	0	0	0	0	0	0	0
North	0	0	0	0	0	0	0	0	0	0

Table 619. Spring movements at Portland Bill 1980–1999

	1980	1981	1982	1983	1984	1985	1986	1987	1988	1989
South	900	230	2500	1500	1995	640	440	450	0	1834
North	0	1200	120	400	25	1095	75	150	25	30

	1990	1991	1992	1993	1994	1995	1996	1997	1998	1999
South	2005	12	49	30	400	720	0	0	0	0
North	435	80	269	2757	2075	180	0	1050	505	2100

Table 620. Autumn movements at Portland Bill 1980–1999

Passage is most evident as visual movements. Durlston CP recorded heavy spring passage during the early 1980s, most notably 7,200S during March–April 1981 (maximum of 2,500S on 11th March), and 8,000E during April–May 1984. Subsequently spring movements at this site have become less conspicuous, the last notable count being 590E during 21st–23rd April 1993. By comparison, spring migration at Portland Bill was generally rather modest and occasionally non-existent, the best counts being 540S on 30th March 1986 and 400N on 21st March 1973, whilst passage has seemingly ceased altogether at this site during the 1990s. The direction of these movements was predominantly to the south during 1980–1986, but to the north during 1988–1989 – see Table 619. Autumn migration is generally much heavier, extending from late September to mid-November with peak movements during October. At Portland Bill the strength of passage has varied considerably and, like the spring, the predominant direction of these movements has changed, sometimes between years, but generally from a southerly bias during 1980–1990 to a northerly bias during 1991–1999 – see Table 620. Occasionally these coastal movements reach day-totals of 1,000 or more birds, the highest being 3,000W at West Bexington on 30th October 1976 with 2,625W there on 19th October 1993, and 2,000N at Portland Bill on 13th October 1994 with 2,000 there on 24th October 1976, whilst 5,400S at Portland Bill during the first week of November 1978 and 2,200N at Durlston CP during 10th–11th November 1991 are also noteworthy.

Heavy cold weather movements sometimes occur, the most notable being 100,000 roosting on cliffs at Chideock on 28th December 1962, and more recently 10,000 over Christchurch Harbour on 6th January 1979 and 4,000S at North Portland on 1st January 1996.

A total of 13,305 birds has been ringed in the county. The foreign recoveries and controls reflect the long distance movements of wintering birds from mainly eastern and northern Europe including Russia. There have been 27 recoveries from the Netherlands, 12 each from Germany, Poland and Russia, eight from Belgium, five each from France and Sweden, three each from Finland and Belarus, and one each from Denmark, Estonia and Latvia. There have also been five controls from Belgium, three from Lithuania, two from the Netherlands and one each from France, Denmark, Poland and Belarus.

The Starling breeds throughout Europe except for much of Iberia and the extreme south, extending eastwards to Asia Minor and north-central Asia. It is a summer visitor throughout much of the north and east of its range and winters westwards to the British Isles and south to the Mediterranean countries, north-west Africa, the Middle East, northern Arabia and the northern part of the Indian sub-continent. There are introduced populations throughout North America and in parts of South Africa, Australia and New Zealand.

Sponsored by Shaun George Gartshore

Rose-coloured Starling (Rosy Starling) *Sturnus roseus*

A very rare passage migrant

There are a few old records including two prior to 1799 at Crichel and Charmouth, and at least four during the 19th Century, the last being from Shapwick in autumn 1898. Since 1959 there have been 22 records involving c.14–18 adult birds, c.10–14 in June and four during 15th–30th August, and ten juveniles, one in August, three in September and six in October. Portland is the main site with 13 records.

1959	Portland Bill: juv. 6th September
1964	Lodmoor NR: ad. 21st August
1970	Dorchester: ad. 15th–16th August
1982	Portland Bill: juv. 22nd–23rd October; presumed same at Verne Common, Portland 30th October
1989	Portland various sites: ad. 30th August–22nd April 1990; presumed same at Weymouth 26th January–7th February 1990
	Portland Bill: juv. 24th October
1994	The Grove, Portland: ad. 8th June
	West Bexington: ad. 10th June
	Portland Bill: juv. 23rd–28th September
1995	Portland Bill: ad. 23rd–30th August
	Wareham: juv. 17th October
1996	Easton, Portland: juv. 23rd October
1999	St Aldhelm's Head: ad. 25th June
2000	Portland Bill: ad. 4th–5th June; presumed same at Southwell, Portland 11th June and Weston, Portland 16th June
	Swanage: ad. 5th June
	Lodmoor NR: juv. 27th–28th August
	Portland Bill: juv. 16th October
	The Grove, Portland: juv. 16th October – different from above

2001   Bridport and Cogden Beach: ad. 15th–18th June

Portland Heights/The Grove, Portland: juv. 7th September–24th October; same at Portland
Bill 9th–12th October and again 17th October

2002   Portland Bill/Southwell: at least three possibly up to seven ad./first-summer birds 5th–15th
June, maximum of three together on 14th

Swanage: ad. 5th and 19th June

The Rose-coloured Starling is a summer visitor breeding in the steppe and semi-desert areas of south-eastern Europe and west-central Asia between the Black Sea and western China. Irruptions into Europe are quite frequent and breeding has occurred in some years as far west as Slovakia, Hungary, the Balkans and even Italy. It winters mainly in the Indian sub-continent with small numbers in Oman. A vagrant to Great Britain with 623 records up to 2001.

House Sparrow   *Passer domesticus*

An abundant resident

Both Mansel-Pleydell (1888) and Blathwayt (1945) considered this species to be a common resident.

There has been little change in status, both the *BTO Atlas* (1968–1972) and the Tetrad Survey (1987–1994) confirmed breeding in all of the pre-1974 10-km squares. Although the Tetrad Map shows that the House Sparrow breeds throughout the entire county, it is absent from a few tetrads. This may reflect both the lack of suitable habitat, the species is particularly scarce in modern housing estates with well manicured gardens, and a recent decline in the population, probably due to changes in farming practices and increased numbers of predators. The population at Portland Bill was estimated to be 60–70 pairs in 1987 and 50 pairs in 1988, whilst a cliff-nesting colony was reported from this site in at least 1967. At Durlston CP from 4–6 pairs nested during 1981–1992.

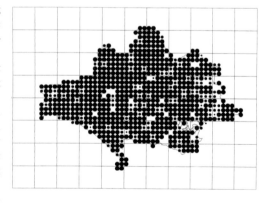

Due to the very limited information available on long-term population trends, the recently reported decline in breeding numbers is best illustrated by the size of the post-breeding feeding flocks at Portland Bill and Durlston CP, as well as ringing totals from the former site – see Tables 621 to 623. Elsewhere, post-breeding and winter flocks of up to 500 birds were still being recorded until 1990, but subsequently counts have steadily declined, the highest in 1999 being 210 at Sutton Waldron in August and 120 at Verne Common, Portland on 21st August. Counts of 890 at Durlston CP on 8th August 1981 and 790 at Portland Bill on 7th August 1973 are exceptional by recent standards.

1973	1974	1975	1986	1989	1990	1991	1993	1994	1999
790	400	300	250	250	400	140	100	200	65

Table 621. Peak counts for post-breeding flock at Portland Bill 1973–1999

1981	1982	1983	1986	1987	1988	1990	1991	1992	1995	1998
890	460	100	100	200	120	200	400	110	120	25

Table 622. Peak counts for post-breeding flock at Durlston CP 1981–1998

1978	1979	1980	1981	1982	1983	1984	1985	1986	1987	1988
1124	716	445	531	386	156	147	51	61	67	49

1989	1990	1991	1992	1993	1994	1995	1996	1997	1998	1999
97	44	35	51	14	69	73	258	116	46	46

Table 623. Ringing totals at Portland Bill 1978–1999

Passage, almost exclusively involving local movements and dispersal, is occasionally recorded from the main coastal watch-points. This is most evident as visual movements in autumn, mainly during October. Exceptional numbers were reported from Portland Bill in the late 1950s and early 1960s with 607N, 130S during 28th September–10th November 1957, 425N, 7S during 19th September–15th November 1959 and 250N, 37S during 25th September–6th November 1960. Since then, the best movements occurred in 1993 with 92SE at Christchurch Harbour on 2nd–3rd October and 80N at Portland Bill during 22nd October–21st November. Other notable movements from Christchurch Harbour are 48W on 4th October 1975, 50W on 17th March 1984 and 53E, 12W during 9th–23rd October 1985.

A total of 8,745 birds has been ringed in the county. The most remarkable recovery involves a female ringed at Portland Bill on 26th July 1959 and recovered on 6th February 1960 at Cherbourg in France, killed by a cat! Apparently the first foreign recovery of a British ringed bird.

The House Sparrow breeds in North Africa, Europe, Asia Minor, the Middle East, Arabia and large areas of northern, central, south-west and southern Asia including the Indian sub-continent. There are introduced populations in southern Africa, eastern Australia, New Zealand and North and South America.

Postscript 2000–2002
The decline of this species in the county apparently continues as exemplified by only a single record from Brownsea in 2000 and no reports from Ham Common, Poole in 2001.

Sponsored by Neil and Yuki Gartshore

Tree Sparrow (Eurasian Tree Sparrow) *Passer montanus*

An uncommon passage migrant and winter visitor – formerly bred

Mansel-Pleydell (1888) simply referred to this species as a resident and noted that it prefers the wild and open parts of the county. By contrast, Blathwayt (1945) considered the Tree Sparrow to be chiefly an uncommon passage migrant and winter visitor, and casts some doubt on breeding reports from Abbotsbury, Ferndown, Wareham and near Dorchester.

There was no immediate change to its uncommon status with only six sightings during 1950–1955. Confirmed breeding at Hammoon in 1956 was the prelude for an increase in records during the latter part of the decade.

Autumn passage at Portland Bill involving 22 birds between 3rd October and 16th November 1957 was considered to be unprecedented at the time. However, this was followed by a larger and

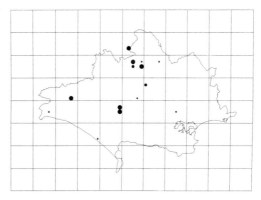

more widespread influx in the autumn and late winter of 1959, which included c.70 at Portland Bill during 13th October–1st November, with a maximum of 35 on 25th October, and a flock of 20 at Tarrant Rawston on 4th November.

This remarkable increase continued into the 1960s during which breeding became established in the county. Initially this was mainly centred at two sites in the Blackmore Vale, namely Hammoon with almost annual reports during 1961–1970 including four pairs in 1964 and 6–8 pairs in 1970, and Stour Provost with up to four pairs in six years during 1963–1973. There were also breeding records from Tarrant Monkton in 1963 and Whatcombe in 1964. By the time of the *BTO Atlas* (1968–1972) there had been a considerable spread throughout central, north and west Dorset with evidence of breeding in 21 (57%) 10-km squares (confirmed in 13, probable in three and possible in five). An equally sharp decline followed with evidence of breeding in only three years during 1974–1981, namely at Bagber in 1976 (almost certain), and Hammoon in 1978 (12 birds present during May–June, but no nesting site located) and 1980 (attempted). There was a mini-revival in fortunes during 1982–1985 with breeding/summer reports from Bagber in 1982 and 1983, Okeford Fitzpaine in 1983 and 1984, Ryme Intrinseca in 1984 and Marnhull in 1985. After an absence of records in 1986 and 1987, the Tetrad Survey (1987–1994) found evidence of breeding in ten (27%) of the pre-1974 10-km squares (confirmed in four, probable in one and possible in five). The Tetrad Map shows that confirmed or probable breeding occurred in eight tetrads mainly in the traditional areas of the Blackmore Vale and on downland north of Dorchester. During this period, the only established colony was located at Holcombe Bottom near Piddlehinton, where breeding occurred regularly during 1990–1996 – see Table 624. There have been no reports of breeding from anywhere in the county during 1997–1999.

1990	1991	1992	1993	1994	1995	1996
3	6	5	6–8	6	3	2

Table 624. Number of breeding pairs at Holcombe Bottom 1990–1996

The 1960s also saw the Tree Sparrow established as a winter visitor and regular passage migrant, mainly in autumn. Despite considerable fluctuations in numbers, this situation remained largely unchanged until the mid-1980s, after which a steady decline ensued so that by the late 1990s the species has virtually reverted to its pre-1955 status as an uncommon visitor.

The strength of coastal passage varied considerably during 1960–1985 with occasional autumn influxes often resulting in high wintering numbers – see Tables 625 and 626. In earlier years, the most notable of these influxes were recorded at Portland Bill with 703 bird-days during 2nd October–13th November 1961 (maxima of 142 on 14th October and 100 on 29th October), and exceptional numbers during mid-October 1970 with 200–250 birds on 8th–9th rising to an astonishing peak of 700 on 12th. A further, more widely reported influx took place at various coastal sites in autumn 1976 with 894 bird-days at Portland Bill during 10th October–5th November (maxima of 160 on 26th October and 250 on 28th October), 550E and 210W at Christchurch Harbour during 3rd–26th October, 221W at West Bexington on 10th October with 79W there on 24th October, and 124S at Verne Common, Portland on 19th October. Other high autumn counts from Portland Bill during the 1960s and 1970s include 100 on 23rd October 1971, 98 on 28th October 1973 and 90 on 31st October 1964. Since the mid-1970s, peak numbers at the main coastal watch-points have rarely exceeded 20 birds, the best being in 1981 at Portland Bill with 50S on 29th September and 40 on 12th October. More recently peak counts have only reached double figures twice since 1986, the best being 25W at Christchurch Harbour on 12th October 1987. Although autumn migrants have been recorded from August through to November, most passage occurs during October.

70	71	72	73	74	75	76	77	78	79	80	81	82	83	84
1000+	250+	117	199	nc	82	895	71	7	23	30	171	10	69	34

85	86	87	88	89	90	91	92	93	94	95	96	97	98	99
27	11	5	0	4	3	0	1	1	1	0	1	0	1	0

Table 625. Autumn totals at Portland Bill 1970–1999

	1980	1981	1982	1983	1984	1985	1986	1987	1988	1989
Durlston CP	44	4	0	2	0	0	1	7	0	3
Christchurch Hbr	10	11	9	32	26	67	9	39	17	2

	1990	1991	1992	1993	1994	1995	1996	1997	1998	1999
Durlston CP	2	2	2	0	0	13	0	4	6	4
Christchurch Hbr	5	6	2	13	10	3	3	0	7	0

Table 626. Autumn totals at Durlston CP and Christchurch Harbour 1980–1999

Spring passage has always been light, but since the mid-1980s it has become virtually non-existent – see Tables 627 and 628. The best seasonal totals and peak counts were recorded from Portland Bill prior to 1986 with 46 bird-days during 11th April–23rd May 1961 and 41 bird-days during 17th April–9th June 1985 (maximum of 21 on 1st June), also 11 on 17th May 1970 and ten on 11th May 1975. Spring migrants have occurred over a particularly prolonged period extending from early March to mid-July with peak passage normally occurring in May, often during the second half of the month. This reflects the late breeding season of the species.

70	71	72	73	74	75	76	77	78	79	80	81	82	83	84
31	16	3	2	10	21	22	28	3	0	23	17	3	5	3

85	86	87	88	89	90	91	92	93	94	95	96	97	98	99
41	4	0	0	0	1	1	0	0	1	1	1	3	3	1

Table 627. Spring totals at Portland Bill 1970–1999

	1980	1981	1982	1983	1984	1985	1986	1987	1988	1989
Durlston CP	0	2	5	0	1	2	1	3	4	9
Christchurch Hbr	0	1	4	1	0	0	0	0	2	2

	1990	1991	1992	1993	1994	1995	1996	1997	1998	1999
Durlston CP	2	0	0	0	1	0	0	0	0	0
Christchurch Hbr	2	0	0	0	0	0	0	0	0	0

Table 628. Spring totals at Durlston CP and Christchurch Harbour 1980–1999

During the peak years 1960–1985, winter flocks were frequently recorded with sites along the Frome Valley such as Winterborne Came and Woodsford particularly favoured. As mentioned earlier, wintering numbers were often high after heavy autumn passage. The influx of October 1961 resulted in several counts of 100 or more birds during the winter of 1961/62, the highest being 250 at Potterne Farm, Verwood on 16th December, 200 at Bellows Cross on 29th October and 200 along the River Allen on 24th February. Counts of 100 at Littledown Reserve during January–February 1972, West Morden in February 1977 and Tarrant Crawford in March 1977 also followed heavy passage the previous autumns. Oddly, the highest count after the exceptional autumn influx of 1970 was a modest 65 at Radipole NR in late December. Furthermore high counts of 100 at Badbury Rings on 8th January 1981 and Woodsford on 5th February of the same year were not preceded by heavy passage at coastal sites the previous autumn. Otherwise peak counts in winters not influenced by heavy autumn passage never exceeded 50 birds. Since 1985, there has been a dramatic decline in wintering numbers to the extent that by the late 1990s there were virtually no reports during this season. The one exception was the presence a winter flock of up to 50 birds in the vicinity of the breeding colony at Holcombe Bottom near Piddlehinton during 1989–1996, but even this appears to have all but disappeared during 1997–1999.

A total of 239 birds has been ringed in the county.

The Tree Sparrow breeds throughout most of Europe north to eastern Great Britain and southern Scandinavia, and eastwards to Asia Minor and across much of Asia except for parts of the south-west and the Indian sub-continent. It is a summer visitor to more northern areas. There is some short-distance migration with occasional larger irruptive movements from the more northerly parts of the breeding range.

Postscript 2000–2002

In 2000, there were nine records involving 20 birds including up to two birds at the traditional haunt of Holcombe Bottom on 13th and 15th January and six at Shroton Lines on 25th December. In 2001, there were ten records involving 11 birds. In 2002, there were seven records involving seven birds.

Red-eyed Vireo   *Vireo olivaceus*

Accidental: three records

    1987   Hengistbury: 12th October
    1988   Southwell, Portland: 3rd–5th October
    1995   Littlesea Holiday Park near Weymouth: 10th October

The Red-eyed Vireo is a summer visitor breeding in northern and eastern North America and wintering in South America. A vagrant to Great Britain with 97 records up to 2002.

Chaffinch   *Fringilla coelebs*

An abundant resident, winter visitor and passage migrant

Mansel-Pleydell (1888) referred to this species as a well-known and generally distributed resident, whilst Blathwayt (1945) considered it to be a very common resident as well as a passage migrant and winter visitor.

There has been little subsequent change in status. The *BTO Atlas* (1968–1972) found evidence of breeding in all 10-km squares (confirmed in 35, probable in one and possible in one), whilst the Tetrad Survey (1987–1994) produced an almost identical result with evidence of breeding in all of the pre-1974 10-km squares (confirmed in 36 and probable in one). The Tetrad Survey also shows the Chaffinch to be widely distributed throughout the county with evidence of breeding in almost all tetrad squares. The Common Bird Census Index for Dorset during 1981–1994 clearly indicates the species vulnerability to the cold winters of 1981/82, 1984/85 to 1986/87 and 1990/91 – see Table 629. Although the population recovered well by 1984 and again by 1989, the cold winter of 1990/91 resulted in another decline with the population remaining at 68-79% of the 1981 level during 1992–1994.

1981	1982	1983	1984	1985	1986	1987	1988	1989	1990	1991	1992	1993	1994
100	62	80	101	61	65	–	78	100	89	60	68	79	78

Table 629. The Common Bird Census Index for Dorset 1981–1994

    Although spring passage is normally rather modest, good numbers are occasionally recorded, notably from Durlston CP, e.g. 400N during 20th March–17th April 1984 and 300W during 20th March–6th April 1983. Autumn passage is much stronger and typically extends from mid-September to mid-November with peak movements during October. Seasonal totals during 1980–1999 generally varied between 1,000–2,000 birds at Portland Bill, but rarely exceeded 1,000 birds at other coastal watch-points – see Table 630. Peak movements usually range up to 500 birds, but rarely exceed 1,000, so counts of 2,028NW and 1,024NW per hour at Radipole School on 22nd–23rd October 1981 are noteworthy. These counts are over-shadowed by the exceptionally heavy movements recorded on 28th October 1993 involving 7,000N at Portland Bill and 2,500N at Chapman's Pool. These day-totals are not without precedent, however, since 8,000 moved north at Portland Bill on 24th October 1955. The directional bias of these movements at Portland Bill varies considerably from year to year – see Table 630. Generally outward passage to the south occurs earlier, usually during the first half of October, whilst inward movements to the north tend to predominate during the second half of October and early November.

	1980	1981	1982	1983	1984	1985	1986	1987	1988	1989
	1738	1340	1147	1874	1133	3728	1620	2006	957	1411
South	nc	0	nc	270	nc	408	480	990	36	1293
North	nc	1300	nc	1400	nc	2521	525	640	35	73
	1990	1991	1992	1993	1994	1995	1996	1997	1998	1999
	874	1642	2421	9836	1867	1061	1308	1597	1746	1450
South	249	1	120	7	1050	465	1308	890	nc	nc
North	240	458	1720	9152	373	0	0	632	nc	nc

Table 630. Autumn passage at Portland Bill 1980–1999

Winter flocks occur widely throughout the county. Peak counts usually range from 100–250 birds and rarely exceed 500, the highest being 1,500 at Came on 5th January 1986, 1,250 at Bulbarrow on 3rd January 1995 and 1,000 at Woodsford on 13th January 1981, Badbury Rings during January–February 1988 and at West Hants Water Company, Christchurch on 16th January 1989.

A total of 7,955 birds has been ringed in the county. There have been three recoveries from Belgium, two from Sweden and one each from the Netherlands, Norway and Finland, as well as three controls from Belgium and one each from the Netherlands and Norway. These largely reflect the movement of birds between breeding areas in Scandinavia and wintering areas in western Europe including the Britain Isles.

The Chaffinch breeds from North Africa and across most of Europe extending eastwards to Asia Minor, the Middle East and north-central Asia to about 105°E. It is a summer visitor to the northern and eastern parts of its range. These populations mainly winter within the breeding range in Europe, but further south in Asia. It is now established in New Zealand after introduction.

Brambling   *Fringilla montifringilla*

A locally common winter visitor and passage migrant

Mansel-Pleydell (1888) described this species as "a winter visitant, arriving late in autumn, and in some years in great numbers", and referred to Pulteney (1799) who recorded that Bramblings were particularly abundant throughout the county in the winter of 1789/90 and very plentiful in the nursery-garden at Blandford in the winter of 1795. Blathwayt (1945) considered it to be a numerous winter visitor.

Since 1950 the Brambling has occurred as a passage migrant and winter visitor in fluctuating numbers. The first birds of the autumn appear during late September and early October, the earliest reports being from Christchurch Harbour on 20th September 1980 and 21st September 1994. Passage normally peaks during the second half of October, more occasionally in early November, and sometimes extends into December. Seasonal totals vary considerably from year to year, 896 bird-days at Durlston CP in 1994 being particularly noteworthy – see Table 631. Peak counts usually range between 10–50 birds and rarely exceed 100, the highest being an exceptional 300 at Durlston CP on 11th November 1994, 150 at Portland Bill on 30th October 1996 and 115 at Christchurch Harbour on 5th November 1994.

	1980	1981	1982	1983	1984	1985	1986	1987	1988	1989
Portland Bill	148	152	45	551	43	340	366	59	192	96
Durlston CP	11	24	30	95	22	124	159	84	120	172
Christchurch Hbr	18	9	2	117	6	138	2	60	56	66
	1990	1991	1992	1993	1994	1995	1996	1997	1998	1999
Portland Bill	20	155	380	401	126	37	386	197	135	148
Durlston CP	111	256	418	181	896	220	249	436	153	43
Christchurch Hbr	28	200	83	230	129	nc	159	43	141	170

Table 631. Autumn totals (bds) at the main coastal watch-points 1980–1999

Winter numbers also fluctuate markedly; in some years the species can be very scarce and almost absent, but in others it can be widely reported, often as a result of a good crop of beech mast or cold weather. Although there are records from all parts of the county, there are a number of favoured localities which often attract large flocks, the most notable being the 'beech avenue' at Badbury Rings and sites along the Frome Valley such as Winterborne Came and Woodsford. Normally peak counts range up to 50 birds and rarely exceed 200, the highest being 800 at Badbury Rings on 22nd January 1994 and 700 at Came Wood on 5th January 1986. Cold weather can also result in high numbers and visual movements at coastal sites, the most notable being the arrival of 800 at Portland Bill on 25th January 1979. Furthermore cold weather often results in birds seeking refuge in suburban gardens, most notably during the severe weather in early 1963 with up to 105 at Canford Cliffs during 11th–19th January and 70 in a Branksome garden on 3rd January. More recently, there has been an increasing trend of birds visiting feeding stations in suburban gardens. For example, up to 30 have been attracted to a Broadstone garden by large quantities of crushed peanuts, whilst peak counts from other garden locations include 60–100 at Ashley Heath in December 1999, 60 at Verwood on 8th March 1997 with 50 there on 27th March 1998, 43 at Sandford on 26th February 1998 and 41 at West Moors on 15th March 1998.

Although wintering birds rarely linger beyond March, it is interesting to note that in 1998 birds feeding in some of the suburban gardens remained as late as 21st April. Reports of 20 at Bere Regis on 4th April 1993 and 55 at Tarrant Rushton on 24th April 1974 are notably high counts for such late dates. Spring passage at the main coastal watch-points is very light and virtually non-existent in some years with most records during March and April – see Table 632.

	1980	1981	1982	1983	1984	1985	1986	1987	1988	1989
Portland Bill	2	17	4	5	23	1	12	15	1	5
Durlston CP	0	0	2	2	8	2	2	7	10	6
Christchurch Hbr	2	7	9	0	1	2	2	2	0	1

	1990	1991	1992	1993	1994	1995	1996	1997	1998	1999
Portland Bill	10	2	4	16	9	8	5	18	7	9
Durlston CP	11	10	6	9	4	8	nc	22	9	8
Christchurch Hbr	1	1	1	0	1	nc	nc	4	7	6

Table 632. Spring totals (bds) at the main coastal watch-points 1980–1999

There are very few sightings in May, the latest being from near Holt on 7th May 1950, Radipole School on 7th May 1986, and Portland Bill on 7th May 1999 and 8th May 1984.

A total of 284 birds has been ringed in the county.

The Brambling is a summer visitor breeding throughout most of northern Eurasia from Scandinavia to eastern Siberia. It winters mainly in western, central and southern Europe as far north as southern Scandinavia, in Asia Minor, parts of the Middle East and south-west, central and eastern Asia.

Postscript 2000–2002

There was exceptional autumn passage at Hengistbury during October–November 2001 involving 1,000 birds (maximum 450W on 1st November), the latter being the highest ever autumn day-count from a coastal site. At Cranborne Common, 130 on 9th April 2000 is a notably high count for such a late date. Finally, one at Portland Bill on 21st May 2001 is by far the latest date for the county.

Sponsored by Ewan Brodie

Serin (European Serin) *Serinus serinus*

An uncommon passage migrant, rare summer visitor and very rare winter visitor – has bred

The first record for Dorset was at Portland Bill on 12th November 1960, when one flew north over the Old Lower Light and was later seen in fields above the West Cliffs. This was followed by a male at Bincleaves, Weymouth from 18th April to 8th July 1962–perhaps the first indication of breeding. Subsequently there were singles at Portland Bill on 1st November 1964, 5th July 1965 and 26th October of the same year, and Durlston CP on 17th December 1966.

Breeding was first confirmed in Great Britain at Swanage, where a pair resided in a garden from the end of April to 27th May 1967 and successfully reared two young. A full account can be found in *British Birds*, Vol. 61, Number 2, February 1968. During the *BTO Atlas* (1968–1972) probable breeding was also recorded in SZ07 (the same square as Swanage) and SZ09 (Parkstone in 1969). At this time, there was considerable speculation that these records heralded the long-awaited colonisation of southern England. Unfortunately these optimistic expectations have not been fulfilled and the Serin has failed to establish itself as any more than a sporadic breeder. This is despite a steady increase in reports, most notably since the mid-1980s – see Table 633. Although breeding has been confirmed in Dorset only on one further occasion, namely at the Grove, Portland in 1990, it has been suspected in several other years as follows:

1983   Portland Bill: 13th July–a very young bird, still in juv. plumage, its origin is a matter of some conjecture

1984   Portland Bill: up to four birds 8th April–4th May, two of which showed intentions of breeding locally, nesting material being carried by the female on two occasions at the end of April

1985   Near Wareham: pair during the breeding season and mating observed on at least one occasion

1988   Weymouth: up to three birds including a singing male 22nd February–22nd March
Portland Bill, female 13th–22nd May with two males briefly on 14th May, then single birds on 25th June and five dates up to mid-July

1991   Portland Bill: singing male on 3rd, 4th, 6th and 17th June

1996   Portland Bill: singing male from 27th June–5th July and a first-year bird 30th July–2nd August

It is clear that Portland is the most favoured site for any future breeding attempts.

60	61	62	63	64	65	66	67	68	69	70	71	72	73	74	75	76	77	78	79
1	0	1	0	1	2	1	5	2	3	1	1	1	3	1	7	2	2	2	4

80	81	82	83	84	85	86	87	88	89	90	91	92	93	94	95	96	97	98	99
2	2	6	8	11	17	6	17	27	29	32	26	13	26	15	29	31	25	27	5

Table 633. Annual totals 1960–1999

The species occurs mainly as a scarce migrant, mostly in spring which accounts for 77% of the total reported on passage. Although there are records of presumed migrants from as early as mid-February, the main spring passage period extends from mid-March to mid-June with a distinct peak in April, which accounts for 43% of the total migrants and 55% of the spring total – see Table 634. Mid-summer and early autumn reports are few, but evenly distributed from mid-June through to the end of August (4–5 birds in each half-month) and culminating in a small peak (11 birds) during the first half of September. Rather surprisingly there are only four records for the period mid-September to mid-October. This is followed by a second and larger peak representing the main passage late in the autumn between mid-October and mid-November, and accounts for 10% of the total migrants and 45% of the autumn total – see Table 634. There is also evidence of another small peak in early December. Perhaps the reports in mid-summer and early autumn involve dispersing birds from the near Continent, whilst the main passage later in the autumn refers to individuals from further afield. It is possible that some of the February and December sightings refer to wintering birds, but since most involve records on single dates at coastal watch-points, these are presumed to be early or late migrants respectively.

Jan 1–15	Jan 16–31	Feb 1–15	Feb 16–28	Mar 1–15	Mar 16–31	Apr 1–15	Apr 16–30	May 1–15	May 16–31	Jun 1–15	Jun 16–30
0	0	<1%	2%	2%	9%	21%	22%	10%	7%	3%	2%

Jul 1–15	Jul 16–31	Aug 1–15	Aug 16–31	Sep 1–15	Sep 16–30	Oct 1–15	Oct 16–31	Nov 1–15	Nov 16–30	Dec 1–15	Dec 16–31
1%	2%	1%	1%	3%	<1%	1%	6%	4%	<1%	2%	0

Table 634. Proportion (%) of migrants half-monthly 1960–1999 (excluding all breeding reports)

By far the most favoured site for migrants is Portland Bill, which accounts for 50% of the total, Portland as a whole accounting for 66% – see Table 635. Much smaller numbers have occurred at the other main coastal watch-points, Durlston CP (11%) and Christchurch Harbour (12%), whilst there is a scattering of records from other coastal sites, namely Cogden Beach (one), West Bexington (five), Abbotsbury (three records involving five birds), Langton Herring (three), Moonfleet Manor (one), East Fleet (one), Bincleaves, Weymouth (two), Radipole NR (four), Lodmoor NR (four), St Aldhelm's Head (3–4 birds), Worth Matravers (one), Winspit (two birds once), Wareham (one) and Bournemouth (one). The vast majority of reports involve single birds often 'flying-over' although there are several sightings of two together. The highest counts come from Portland Bill with three together on 19th–20th April 1975, three on 15th and 21st April 1987, 2–3 on 7th May 1990, three on 5th May 1993 and 3N on 7th April 1998, whilst there were three at Weston, Portland on 25th March 1996. Some breeding reports involve up to four birds. Although there may be some duplication in spring records at Portland Bill involving the same individual, genuine reports of long-staying migrants are very rare, the most notable being one at Lodmoor CP from 17th August to 15th September 1997.

	Spring		Autumn		Total	
Portland Bill	147	51%	35	47%	182	50%
elsewhere on Portland	49	17%	9	12%	58	16%
Durlston CP	38	13%	3	4%	41	11%
Christchurch Harbour	32	11%	11	15%	43	12%
other coastal sites	18	6%	17	23%	35	10%
inland	2	1%	0	0	2	1%

Table 635. Distribution of migrants 1960–1999

There is only one occurrence of overwintering in the county involving a pair at Stanpit Tip on 23rd December 1979, the male remaining until 23rd March 1980, but two at Radipole NR from 9th to 15th February 1968 and one at Weston, Portland from 12th November to 24th December 1989, with perhaps the same bird on 18th February 1990, may have also involved wintering birds. Otherwise there are two mid-winter reports of singles at Lodmoor NR on 28th January 1987 and the Grove, Portland on 22nd January 1989.

Inland, the species is surprisingly rare considering the number of records from the coastal areas. Singles at Knapp Mill/Coward's Marsh, Christchurch from 1st to 4th April 1984 and Sandford in early May 1992 were at sites relatively close to the coast, the only record far inland being in 1993 with one at Sutton Waldron on 27th April and nearby at Iwerne Minster on 1st May.

Only two birds have been ringed in the county.

Although the range of the Serin expanded northwards in Europe during the 20th Century, it failed to establish itself in southern Great Britain where it remains a sporadic breeder. Otherwise it breeds in north-west Africa, across much of Europe north to northern France, Denmark and the Baltic States, and east to western Russia, Belarus and the Ukraine, also in Asia Minor and parts of the Middle East. It is a summer visitor to central and eastern Europe, and winters mainly in north-west Africa, western and southern Europe, Asia Minor and the Middle East.

Postscript 2000–2002

A total of 16 birds were recorded in 2000 with ten at Portland, three at Hengistbury, two at Durlston CP, and one inland at Norden in June. In 2001, there were reports involving 15 birds with ten at Portland, three at Durlston CP, and singles at Christchurch Harbour and Lodmoor NR. In 2002, there were nine records of single birds with seven at Portland, one at Hengistbury, and most notably one well inland at Stalbridge on 16th March.

Greenfinch (European Greenfinch) *Carduelis chloris*

An abundant resident, winter visitor and passage migrant

Both Mansel-Pleydell (1888) and Blathwayt (1945) considered this species to be a common and generally distributed resident, whilst the latter also refers to it being a winter visitor.

There has been little change in status subsequently with both the *BTO Atlas* (1968–1972) and the Tetrad Survey (1987–1994) finding evidence of breeding in all of the pre-1974 10-km squares (confirmed in 36 and probable in one). The Tetrad Survey also shows that breeding occurs throughout the entire county, the few absences coinciding with areas of extensive forestry and treeless farmland. The limited information available on long-term population trends suggests that numbers have generally increased during the last three decades, but a decline was evident at one site – see Tables 636 to 639.

1976	1977	1978	1981	1982	1983	1984	1985	1986	1987	1988
4	12	14	13	19	18	16	15	13	20	21

Table 636. Number of breeding territories at Radipole NR 1976–1988

1981	1982	1984	1985	1986	1987	1988	1990	1991	1996	1997	1998	1999
2	3	4	7	8	10	10	8	12	12	11	14	9

Table 637. Number of breeding territories at Durlston CP 1981–1999

68	73	74	75	76	78	81	82	83	84	85	86	87	91	93
3	5	6	6	9	5	5	8	6	7	7	5	5	5	10

Table 638. Number of breeding territories at Arne NR 1968–1993

77	78	81	82	83	85	86	88	89	91	92	93	94	95	96
10	6	2	6	11	9	9	5	4	3	4	5	4	8	3

Table 639. Number of breeding territories at Forde Abbey 1977–1996

Spring passage is occasionally reported from the main coastal watch-points, but numbers are normally very small, so counts from Portland Bill of 300 during March–April 1975, and 100 on 12th March 1962 and 18th April 1982 are unusually high.

Although autumn passage is generally more obvious, it is virtually non-existent in some years and often confused by the dispersal of local birds. For example, it seems likely that in some years the post-breeding flock at Portland Bill is enhanced by the arrival of late autumn migrants with peak counts generally ranging from 100–300 birds, but 450 on 28th October 1961 and an exceptional 1,000 on 8th October 1977. Visual movements occur mainly between mid-September and mid-November with the peak in October. Numbers are rather modest and highly variable with seasonal totals generally ranging from 0–300 birds and peak counts rarely exceeding 100. There are a few exceptions, however, the most notable being 1,141S at Portland Bill during late October–early November 1975, 1,028SE well inland in the Crane Valley in four hours on 2nd September 1960, perhaps only a local movement, 658W at East Bexington during 29th October–14th November 1998 (with maxima of 221 on 29th October and 376 on 1st November), and 400E at East Fleet on 9th October 1995. The directional bias of movements at Portland Bill varies from year to year – see Table 640.

	1980	1981	1982	1983	1984	1985	1986	1987	1988	1989
South	0	44	80	124	45	64	0	165	0	32
North	0	102	0	140	0	103	0	0	0	22

	1990	1991	1992	1993	1994	1995	1996	1997	1998	1999
South	184	6	0	0	188	0	nc	nc	nc	222
North	3	0	0	167	50	0	nc	nc	nc	0

Table 640. Autumn movements at Portland Bill 1980–1999

Winter flocks occur widely throughout the county. Peak counts usually range up to 200 birds and rarely exceed 300, the highest being 700 near Wareham on 19th February 1960, 500 at Hurn Airport on 26th March 1983, 485 at Boscombe Overcliff on 7th March 1986 and 400 at Wimborne on 10th December 1967.

A total of 23,705 birds has been ringed in the county. There have been only two foreign recoveries, both from France, but no less than six from Guernsey. There have been no foreign controls. The most notable of many recoveries from the southern and eastern counties of England involved two birds ringed from the same flock ten days apart in March 1995 at Canford Park, and killed by the same cat within six days of each other in May of the same year at Faversham in Kent!

The Greenfinch breeds in north-west Africa and throughout Europe, except the far north, extending eastwards to Asia Minor and parts of the Middle East and west-central Asia. It is a summer visitor in the extreme north with birds wintering mainly within the breeding range, but extending a little further south into Egypt and extreme south-west Asia. There are introduced populations in south-east Australia and New Zealand.

Postscript 2000–2002

Heavy late autumn movements were recorded at East Bexington in 2000 involving 1,811W during 26th October–13th November (maximum of 578 on 26th October), at Hengistbury in 2001 involving 2,460 during October–November (maxima of 400S on 12th October and 500S on 17th October), and again at Hengistbury in 2002 involving 3,635 during October–November.

Goldfinch (European Goldfinch)　　　　　　　　*Carduelis carduelis*

A common summer visitor and passage migrant, and fairly common winter visitor

Mansel-Pleydell (1888) simply described this species as "resident", but commented that it had become more numerous since the Wild Birds Preservation Act came into force. Blathwayt (1945) considered it to be a numerous resident.

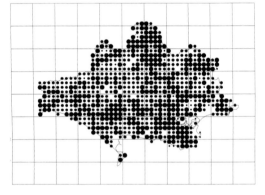

There has been little change in status subsequently. The *BTO Atlas* (1968–1972) found evidence of breeding in all but one (97%) 10-km squares (confirmed in 35 and probable in one), whilst the Tetrad Survey (1987–1994) produced almost an identical result with evidence of breeding in the same number of pre-1974 10-km squares (confirmed in 34 and probable in two). The Tetrad Map shows that the Goldfinch breeds throughout the entire county except for the more built-up areas of the Bournemouth and Poole conurbation and Weymouth. The limited information available on long-term trends suggests, despite some marked fluctuations at one site, a relatively stable population overall during the past two decades – see Tables 641 to 643.

1981	1982	1983	1984	1985	1986	1987	1988	1990	1991	1992	1997	1998	1999
3	3	4	5	4	5	4	3	3	3	4	3	3–4	3

Table 641. Number of breeding territories at Durlston CP 1981–1999

1974	1975	1981	1982	1983	1984	1985	1986	1987	1991	1993
1	1	3	3	3	3	3	2	2	3	3

Table 642. Number of breeding territories at Arne NR 1974–1993

1981	1982	1983	1984	1985	1986	1988	1989	1991	1992	1993	1994	1995	1996
6	5	5	4	5	1	3	1	4	1	3	4	5	3

Table 643. Number of breeding territories at Forde Abbey 1981–1996

Spring passage is prominent at the main coastal watch-points and generally extends from mid-March to mid-May with the peak usually during April. Although seasonal totals fluctuate from year to year, there is some evidence to suggest that these have increased overall since 1989 – see Tables 644 to 646. At

Portland Bill, the directional bias of visual movements can be confusing in some years, but inward passage to the north normally predominates. It is notable that high seasonal totals at this site occurred in years when particularly strong northerly movements were recorded, e.g. during 1989–1991 and in 1995. Peak counts rarely exceed 200 birds, the highest being from Portland Bill with 735 on 20th April 1990, 450N on 8th April and 4th May 1996, 425 on 20th April 1976 and 400 on 23rd April 1991, also 380E at Durlston CP on 23rd April 1984.

	1980	1981	1982	1983	1984	1985	1986	1987	1988	1989
	804	nc	885	879	nc	613	631	631	634	1527
South	100	80	39	261	77	33	0	nc	28	170
North	nc	525	403	103	526	319	0	175	264	598

	1990	1991	1992	1993	1994	1995	1996	1997	1998	1999
	2050	1622	682	978	882	1600	nc	nc	nc	nc
South	nc	62	63	306	206	48	40	nc	nc	nc
North	1549	613	54	285	205	1187	900	1353	376	542

Table 644. Spring passage at Portland Bill 1980–1999

1980	1981	1982	1983	1984	1985	1986	1987	1988	1989
nc	365	437	305	1644	820	501	810	662	1144

1990	1991	1992	1993	1994	1995	1996	1997	1998	1999
1460	972	647	140	nc	1000	980	2400	1510	108

Table 645. Spring totals (bds) at Durlston CP 1980–1999

1980	1981	1982	1983	1984	1985	1986	1987	1988	1989
nc	109	56	77	328	60	nc	40	210	nc

1990	1991	1992	1993	1994	1995	1996	1997	1998	1999
100	175	nc	493	515	nc	nc	200	nc	80

Table 646. Spring totals (bds) at Christchurch Harbour 1980–1999

Autumn passage is much stronger and extends from mid-August to late November or early December with peak movements normally occurring in October, more occasionally in early November. Although seasonal totals have remained fairly stable at Portland Bill since 1980, numbers have increased at the other main coastal watch-points, most notably at Durlston CP with a peak of 29,200 bird-days in 1997 including 22,000 in October – see Tables 647 to 649. Not surprisingly the highest peak counts have been recorded from Durlston CP with an exceptional 7,000 on 22nd October 1997, also 2,705E on 17th October 1988, 2,600 on 4th October 1998, 2,500 on 6th October 1994 and 13th October 1995, and 2,200 on 17th October 1996. At the other main coastal watch-points, the best counts are 2,500E at Christchurch Harbour on 17th October 1988 (cf Durlston CP) and 1,500S at Portland Bill on 8th October 1995. Like the spring, the directional bias of visual movements at Portland Bill can be confusing in some years, but outward passage to the south generally predominates – see Table 647.

	1980	1981	1982	1983	1984	1985	1986	1987	1988	1989
	2035	1079	3264	3786	1364	2598	2110	2850	2996	4944
South	nc	714	603	859	1214	1040	680	1200	440	1590
North	nc	190	0	113	0	114	50	nc	0	167

	1990	1991	1992	1993	1994	1995	1996	1997	1998	1999
	4869	2409	2502	2748	3926	5149	nc	nc	nc	nc
South	1985	346	791	251	1900	2660	2000	808	1923	830
North	207	15	39	498	180	nc	nc	838	90	nc

Table 647. Autumn passage at Portland Bill 1980–1999

1980	1981	1982	1983	1984	1985	1986	1987	1988	1989
1018	1789	4800	2030	5234	5280	3065	4095	14268	9981

1990	1991	1992	1993	1994	1995	1996	1997	1998	1999
15130	14181	14962	7864	nc	16830	16450	29200	13382	2320

Table 648. Autumn totals (bds) at Durlston CP 1980–1999

1980	1981	1982	1983	1984	1985	1986	1987	1988	1989
805	916	536	983	484	2612	nc	2146	5760	nc

1990	1991	1992	1993	1994	1995	1996	1997	1998	1999
2900	2700	2679	3618	4422	2073	2968	nc	nc	2642

Table 649. Autumn totals (bds) at Christchurch Harbour 1980–1999

Post-breeding and winter flocks are widely recorded with numbers generally at their highest during the autumn. Excluding off-passage flocks at the main coastal watch-points, peak counts rarely exceed 250 birds, the highest being 400 at Christchurch Harbour in August 1974 and 326 at Coward's Marsh, Christchurch on 5th October 1990, whilst a roost of 300 at Blagdon on 3rd February 1962 is a particularly high number for mid-winter.

A total of 5,754 birds has been ringed in the county. There have been fourteen foreign recoveries from Spain and seven from France, and single foreign controls from France and the Channel Islands clearly indicating the wintering destination of birds either passing through or bred in the Britain Isles.

The Goldfinch breeds in North Africa and throughout Europe north to southern Scandinavia, extending eastwards to Asia Minor, parts of the Middle East, and west-central and south-west Asia. It is a summer visitor in the extreme north with birds wintering mainly within the breeding range, but extending a little further south in the Middle East. There are introduced populations in southern Australia and New Zealand.

Postscript 2000–2002

In 2002, autumn movements at Portland Bill were the highest ever recorded with 6,008S and 425N during 5th October–30th November.

Sponsored by Sylvia King

Siskin (Eurasian Siskin)   *Carduelis spinus*

A locally common resident, and fairly common winter visitor and passage migrant

Mansel-Pleydell (1888) described this species as "a winter visitant, and one of the rarest of our Finches" and listed a mere handful of records including one claim of breeding. Blathwayt (1945) simply referred to it as an irregular visitor and commented that it was numerous in 1919 from November onwards.

The Siskin remained a scarce passage migrant and winter visitor for much of the 1950s with, for example, no records in 1953 and only single reports in 1955 and 1956. Some increase was evident towards the end of the decade, involving what at the time were considered remarkable autumn passages at Portland Bill in 1957 with 61 birds during 19th September–12th November and 1959 with 93 birds during 7th October–8th November. During the 1960s and 1970s the species steadily became more numerous with marked increases during 1967–1970 in particular. This general increase is perhaps best demonstrated by the peak winter counts recorded for the years 1960 to 1979 – see Table 650.

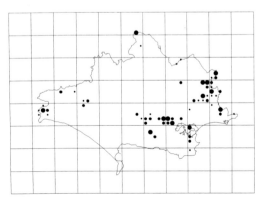

1960	1961	1962	1963	1964	1965	1966	1967	1968	1969
30	23	30	21	25	24	47	30	70	78

1970	1971	1972	1973	1974	1975	1976	1977	1978	1979
30	150	60	30	120	130	100	nc	150	200

Table 650. Peak winter counts 1960–1979

Apart from occasional reports of singing males in the early spring, the only hint of breeding during the 1960s involved eight at Wareham Heath on 31st July 1961 and up to seven on Brownsea during May 1966. Breeding probably occurred first at Ferndown in 1970 and was subsequently confirmed at Dorchester in 1972. Although there was no further evidence of confirmed or probable breeding during the remainder of the 1970s, birds frequently lingered well into May and there were summer records in June 1976 and July 1978. Breeding was next confirmed in 1980 involving around five pairs in Wareham Forest where the population steadily increased in subsequent years to 15–18 singing males by 1984. There was a marked spread into other areas of forestry during 1984 and 1985, and by the time of the Tetrad Survey (1987–1994) evidence of breeding was found in 59 tetrads, (confirmed in 13, probable in 24 and possible in 22). The Tetrad Map shows that most breeding occurs in the central and eastern parts of the Poole Basin, the main centres of population being Wareham Forest and Ringwood Forest. In addition, there are small populations in the extreme west near the Devon border and in the Hooke Park/Rampisham Hill area, with further breeding reports from a few isolated tetrads in the west and north of the county. Since the Tetrad Survey (1987–1994), the breeding population appears have expanded further, mainly into previously unoccupied sites within the Poole Basin.

Although autumn passage at the main coastal watch-points has been generally heavier since 1980, it remains highly variable and occasionally involves massive influxes such as those recorded in 1985, 1988, 1991, 1993 and 1997 – see Table 651. Prior to 1980, passage typically extended from late September to mid-November with the peak in October. Since then, migrants have gradually appeared earlier in the autumn, notably at Durlston CP where first arrivals, presumably involving locally bred birds, have occurred during August throughout much of the 1990s. Typically the main migration period now extends from early or mid-September to late November with occasional stragglers through into December. Normally October remains the peak passage month, but in those autumns with massive influxes the highest numbers sometimes occur in September, most notably in 1988, 1991 and 1997. Not surprisingly, the highest peak counts have been recorded during these influx years, the best being 2,300 at Christchurch Harbour on 27th September 1997 with 1,500E there on 11th October 1991, 2,000 at Durlston CP on 14th October 1993 and 750 at Portland Bill on 13th September 1997. During the 1990s in particular, seasonal totals were generally higher at Durlston CP and Christchurch Harbour than at Portland Bill.

	1980	1981	1982	1983	1984	1985	1986	1987	1988	1989
Portland Bill	265	342	119	121	97	2006	430	187	1215	181
Durlston CP	93	142	99	69	72	2977	618	668	2100	1492
Christchurch Hbr	346	42	9	59	35	1687	130	551	1173	203

	1990	1991	1992	1993	1994	1995	1996	1997	1998	1999
Portland Bill	184	1187	152	855	532	120	248	5574	163	459
Durlston CP	325	3510	550	4014	nc	1428	nc	6087	710	360
Christchurch Hbr	213	3133	125	2009	1645	nc	167	8817	419	700

Table 651. Autumn totals (bds) at the main coastal watch-points 1980–1999

Since the initial increase during the late 1960s, winter flocks have been regularly reported, typically favouring sites within the Poole Basin and along the main river valleys. The largest numbers usually occur at these favoured sites with peak counts ranging up to 100, but rarely exceeding 150 birds, the highest being from Sherford Bridge, Wareham Forest with 300 on 31st December 1985 and 200 on 1st January 1986 and 8th December 1979; also 200 at Sherborne on 9th February 1991 and 180 at Matchams on 14th January 1984. The first occurrence of birds visiting gardens to feed on peanuts seemingly came from Colehill in 1969. By 1973 this habit was being widely reported and subsequently it has become a regular feature of the winter months. The results of ringing at two garden sites in 1994 revealed hitherto unsuspected numbers. For example, at Upton where never more than 20 were present in the observer's garden at any one time, a total of 142 were ringed between 30th January and mid-March. Likewise a total of 222 birds were ringed in a Canford garden between January and March.

Generally spring passage at the main coastal watch-points is negligible and often non-existent – see Table 652. The exception to this is Durlston CP where there has been a steady increase in numbers, perhaps involving local breeding birds. The total of 234 bird-days at this site in spring 1995 is exceptional.

	1980	1981	1982	1983	1984	1985	1986	1987	1988	1989
Portland Bill	0	6	1	0	7	2	11	1	1	8
Durlston CP	0	18	9	6	13	23	40	18	25	35
Christchurch Hbr	2	6	22	0	5	3	11	0	0	0

	1990	1991	1992	1993	1994	1995	1996	1997	1998	1999
Portland Bill	0	0	2	19	3	5	0	1	3	2
Durlston CP	22	9	43	10	nc	234	nc	51	71	nc
Christchurch Hbr	1	0	0	0	0	nc	nc	3	25	nc

Table 652. Spring totals (bds) at the main coastal watch-points 1980–1999

A total of 1,507 birds has been ringed in the county and although there have been no reports of foreign recoveries, there have been single foreign controls from Belgium and Germany.

The Siskin is a summer visitor breeding in the forest zone from Scandinavia eastwards across northern Asia to the Pacific coast and northern Japan; it is also a resident and partial migrant breeding in central Europe and more locally in other parts of Europe, including the British Isles. It winters throughout most of Europe from southern Scandinavia to the Mediterranean, also in parts of north-west Africa, the Middle East and extreme south-west Asia. Eastern populations winter in Japan and eastern China.

Linnet (Common Linnet)   *Carduelis cannabina*

A common resident, winter visitor and passage migrant

Both Mansel-Pleydell (1888) and Blathwayt (1945) considered this species to be a common and generally distributed resident, whilst the latter also refers to it being a winter visitor.

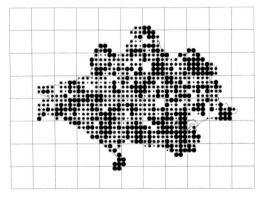

Its status has changed little subsequently, but there is evidence of a decline in more recent years. The *BTO Atlas* (1968–1972) confirmed breeding in all 10-km squares, whilst the Tetrad Survey (1987–1994) produced an almost identical result with evidence of breeding in all of the pre-1974 10-km squares (confirmed in 36 and probable in one). The Tetrad Map shows that breeding occurs widely throughout the county, but reveals absences in some parts of the Bournemouth and Poole conurbation and a few areas of farmland where conditions have become less suitable. The limited information available on long-term trends is contradictory, but generally reflects the recently reported decline in the breeding population – see Tables 653 to 655. Assuming this limited information is representative, the decline appears to have occurred earlier on the chalk downs than the heathlands, whilst at one coastal site at least, numbers appear to have remained relatively stable throughout the last two decades.

80	81	82	83	84	85	86	87	88	90	91	92	97	98	99
21	20	20	23	24	22	20	21	18	24	25	28	20	20	18

Table 653. Number of breeding territories at Durlston CP 1980–1999

73	74	75	76	77	80	81	82	83	84	85	86	87	91	92	93	96	97	98
20	35	25	30	30	30	30	24	25	25	25	20	20	20	20	20	19	15	9

Table 654. Number of breeding territories at Arne NR 1973–1998

1981	1982	1983	1984	1985	1986	1988	1989	1991	1992	1993	1994
5	6	10	11	10	11	6	6	4	2	3	6

Table 655. Number of breeding territories at Fontmell Down 1981–1994

Although spring migration at the main coastal watch-points can extend from mid-March to mid-May, visual passage is often restricted to April. Seasonal totals fluctuate from year to year with inward movements to the north generally predominating at Portland Bill – see Tables 656 to 658. The strength of spring passage appears to have declined since the 1970s when seasonal totals of 1,967N, 395S during 30th March–9th May 1971 and 1,869N, 522S during 30th March–19th May 1974 (maximum of 515N on 7th April) were recorded at Portland Bill; also 350NE at Christchurch Harbour on 19th April 1976. Since 1980 peak movements have rarely exceeded 200 birds, so 1,500N at Portland on 7th April 1997 is exceptional, the next highest being 320N at Portland Bill on 9th April 1988. In addition to these visual movements, off-passage flocks are sometimes recorded with peak numbers generally ranging from 100–300 birds, the highest being 500 at Christchurch Harbour on 7th and 9th April 1975, and 1st April 1998.

	1980	1981	1982	1983	1984	1985	1986	1987	1988	1989
South	270	212	98	302	220	530	232	40	25	227
North	850	265	457	128	375	370	200	300	606	679

	1990	1991	1992	1993	1994	1995	1996	1997	1998	1999
South	186	273	34	111	216	15	35	nc	nc	61
North	542	632	77	215	8	447	868	1535	614	548

Table 656. Spring movements at Portland Bill 1980–1999

1980	1981	1982	1983	1984	1985	1986	1987	1988	1989
nc	180	nc	260	200	390	440	410	70	nc

1990	1991	1992	1993	1994	1995	1996	1997	1998	1999
70	1055	nc	nc	nc	nc	nc	nc	nc	22

Table 657. Spring totals (bds) at Durlston CP 1980–1999

1980	1981	1982	1983	1984	1985	1986	1987	1988	1989
nc	183	242	463	350	216	59	nc	242	nc

1990	1991	1992	1993	1994	1995	1996	1997	1998	1999
200	415	nc	nc	nc	80	nc	275	680	417

Table 658. Spring totals (bds) at Christchurch Harbour 1980–1999

Autumn migration is much heavier and usually extends from early September to mid-November with peak passage occurring in October. Visual movements at Portland Bill, which are predominantly to the south, have declined since the mid-1980s and perhaps earlier, the best counts being 4,500S on 7th October 1957, 3,700S on 10th October 1987 and 3,593S on 6th October 1973 – see Table 659. Similarly the size of the off-passage flock at this site has also declined from peaks of 9,000 on 6th October 1962, 6,000 on 9th–10th October 1970 and 5,000 on 9th October 1986 to only 200–250 during the late 1990s – see Table 660. By contrast, seasonal totals at the other main coastal watch-points have increased since the late 1980s, most notably at Durlston CP with counts of over 20,000 bird-days in 1990, 1993 and 1997 – see Tables 661 and 662. Not surprisingly the highest peak counts in recent years have been recorded from Durlston CP with 12,550E on 21st October 1990 and 8,000 on 14th October 1993 with several records of 1,000–3,500 birds. Elsewhere along the coast, the best counts are 5,500 at Central Portland on 1st October 1988, 4,000 at St Aldhelm's Head on 7th October 1977, 3,000E at Christchurch Harbour on 18th October 1990 and 2,457W at Abbotsbury on 5th November 1991.

	1980	1981	1982	1983	1984	1985	1986	1987	1988	1989
South	1200	1550	1865	4680	3390	8468	5000	8320	5991	6312
North	nc	790	180	120	nc	784	300	470	0	628

	1990	1991	1992	1993	1994	1995	1996	1997	1998	1999
South	4720	736	1065	1910	1799	8360	2790	2623	2000	2370
North	215	282	299	1088	500	nc	nc	600	nc	nc

Table 659. Autumn movements at Portland Bill 1980–1999

1980	1981	1982	1983	1984	1985	1986	1987	1988	1989
3000	2000	1500	2000	nc	2500	5000	1500	2500	3000

1990	1991	1992	1993	1994	1995	1996	1997	1998	1999
250	1000	80	200	350	400	500	250	200	200

Table 660. Peak counts for off-passage autumn flock at Portland Bill 1980–1999

1980	1981	1982	1983	1984	1985	1986	1987	1988	1989
nc	870	2000	1340	1590	4235	2900	2660	12040	11920

1990	1991	1992	1993	1994	1995	1996	1997	1998	1999
20700	14200	19381	20060	nc	1950	nc	22090	10310	2750

Table 661. Autumn totals (bds) at Durlston CP 1980–1999

1980	1981	1982	1983	1984	1985	1986	1987	1988	1989
655	105	578	736	964	2652	nc	2800	5350	nc

1990	1991	1992	1993	1994	1995	1996	1997	1998	1999
4560	nc	2197	3848	nc	nc	nc	3467	950	2655

Table 662. Autumn totals (bds) at Christchurch Harbour 1980–1999

Winter flocks occur widely throughout the county. Peak counts usually range from 100–250 birds and rarely exceed 400, the highest being 2,000 at Tarrant Keyneston on 20th February 1964, 1,000 at Warmwell on 23rd December 1968, 500–1,000 at Woodsford on 26th December 1981, 650 at Witchampton in December 1978, 500 at East Holme on 5th January 1986 and 500 at Holcombe Bottom during the second winter period of 1991. A roost of 1,500–1,800 at St Aldhelm's Head on 5th March 1965 was seemingly too early to involve spring migrants, but northward passage was noted here on that date. Cold weather influxes/movements are occasionally reported, the most notable being from Portland Bill with 2,500 in late January 1979, 1,500 on 20th January 1987 and 1,000 on 10th–11th January 1968; also 1,000 at Christchurch Harbour in February 1978.

A total of 17,121 birds has been ringed in the county. Seventeen foriegn recoveries from France, six from Spain and one each from Morocco and the Channel Islands, and oddly two controls from Sark in the Channel Islands, clearly indicate the wintering destination of birds either passing through or bred in the British Isles (cf Goldfinch).

The Linnet breeds in north-west Africa and throughout Europe north to southern Scandinavia, extending eastwards to Asia Minor, parts of the Middle East, and west-central and south-west Asia. It is a summer visitor in the north and east with birds wintering mainly within and slightly to the south of the breeding range.

Postscript 2000–2002

In 2002, spring movements were notably high, particularly by recent standards, with 2,009N at Portland

Bill during 23rd March–12th April, 500N at North Portland on 23rd March and 1,000W at Ham Common, Poole during April–May, whilst heavy movements occurred at Hengistbury in the autumn with 9,766 during October–November.

Twite   *Carduelis flavirostris*

A scarce passage migrant and rare winter visitor

Mansel-Pleydell (1888) referred to this species as a winter visitor, which was somewhat irregular in occurrence and could sometimes be found with flocks of Linnets. Blathwayt (1945) considered it to be a very scarce winter visitor and gives only two records, namely one seen flocking with Cirl Buntings at Lyme Regis in February 1895 and one picked up dead near Chideock on 28th December 1927. The latter is seemingly the only report for the 20th Century until one at Swanage on 8th and 10th March 1956. This was followed by two at Studland NNR on 6th January 1963, which remained for much of the month with three present on 23rd.

Since 1967 there has been a marked increase in occurrences with records in every year except for 1969, 1972 and 1974 – see Table 663. Generally annual totals have been small, ranging from 1–10 birds in most years, but numbers were much higher during 1983–1990 mainly as a result of autumn influxes, notably in 1985, 1987, 1988 and 1990.

60	61	62	63	64	65	66	67	68	69	70	71	72	73	74	75	76	77	78	79
0	0	0	3	0	0	0	1	4	0	4	2	0	2	0	3	4	6	4	9

80	81	82	83	84	85	86	87	88	89	90	91	92	93	94	95	96	97	98	99
3	8	1	16	14	80	12	37	51	3	38	10	6	8	1	2	4	6	8	3

Table 663. Annual totals 1960–1999

The Twite occurs mainly as a scarce migrant in the autumn, which accounts for 81% of the total. There are two records for September, the first being an exceptionally early bird on 3rd September 1984 at Southwell, Portland and the second on 23rd September 1981 at Durlston CP. Most passage occurs during October and November with a distinct peak during the second half of October, the month as a whole accounting for 67% of the autumn total – see Table 664. The species is occasionally reported during the winter with a peak during the first half of January. Spring passage is suggested by an increase in records from mid-February to mid-March with late birds on 1st April 1978 and 6th April 1984 at Christchurch Harbour, and 18th April 1984 at Durlston CP.

Jan 1–15	Jan 16–31	Feb 1–15	Feb 16–28	Mar 1–15	Mar 16–31	Apr 1–15	Apr 16–30
30	10	5	11	10	0	2	1

Sep 1–15	Sep 16–30	Oct 1–15	Oct 16–31	Nov 1–15	Nov 16–30	Dec 1–15	Dec 16–31
1	1	56	134	26	60	2	5

Table 664. Half-monthly totals 1950–1999

Christchurch Harbour is the main site the species in Dorset and accounts for 60% of the total – see Table 665. Birds have been recorded at this site in all but five autumns since 1979 with notable passage in 1983 (12), 1985 (30 including 24E during 18th–28th October), 1988 (33 including 21E during 16th–28th October) and 1990 (35 including 32E during 15th–23rd October with a maximum of 16E on 17th). Most of the winter records are also from Christchurch Harbour with evidence of genuine overwintering in early 1977 involving presumably the same bird on three dates during 22nd January–7th February, in early 1979 with up to eight birds on three dates during 1st–29th January, and in early 1987 with two birds throughout January and an exceptional 20W on 14th January. The only other report of overwintering was at Studland NNR in January 1963 as mentioned earlier.

Durlston CP and Portland Bill are the next most favoured sites with occurrences almost exclusively restricted to the autumn period – see Table 665. Otherwise there is a scattering of records, again mainly in autumn, from other coastal sites, namely singles at West Bexington, Abbotsbury and Langton Herring, 46 at Ferrybridge/Chesil Beach (including an exceptional 45 on 28th November 1985 – Dorset's highest ever count), one at Radipole NR, 12 at Lodmoor NR (including eight on 24th February 1986 and up to three from 27th October to early November 1984), five at Worth Matravers (including four on 6th February 1970), single records at Winspit and Swanage, three at Studland NNR and three at Lytchett Bay (including one trapped on 20th and 21st November 1983). The scarcity of records from the Poole Harbour area is surprising considering the amount of apparently suitable habitat for this species.

	Autumn		**Winter**		**Spring**		**Total**	
Christchurch Harbour	159	57%	40	80%	13	54%	212	60%
Durlston CP	39	14%	0	0	1	4%	40	11%
Portland Bill	20	7%	2	4%	0	0	22	6%
elsewhere on Portland	5	2%	0	0	0	0	5	1%
other coastal sites	57	20%	8	16%	10	42%	75	21%

Table 665. Distribution of birds 1950–1999

Only two birds have been ringed in the county.

In Europe, the Twite breeds in western and northern Norway and adjacent areas of north Sweden, Finland and Russia (Kola Peninsula), and in the British Isles in north-west Scotland, western Ireland and in England in the Pennines. Scandinavian populations are migratory and winter mainly in northern and eastern Europe whilst British breeders are more sedentary, but birds from the upland areas of Scotland winter along coasts, and those from the Pennines winter along the east coast from Lincolnshire to Kent. There are other breeding populations in Asia Minor, the Caucasus and central Asia.

Postscript 2000–2002

There was only one record involving eight at Hengistbury on 3rd November 2001. As a consequence, 2000 and 2002 are the first years without reports in Dorset since 1974!

Lesser Redpoll   *Carduelis cabaret*

A scarce resident, and fairly common winter visitor and passage migrant

Mansel-Pleydell (1888) considered this species to be mainly a winter visitor, but reported that a nest and eggs were found at Thorncombe near Blandford, and further quoted Mr A. G. More (1865) who stated that it occasionally nests in the county. Blathwayt (1945) referred to the Lesser Redpoll as a winter visitor and local resident, breeding sparingly in the heathland districts of east Dorset, but scarcer in summer in the west.

There has been relatively little change in status subsequently. The *BTO Atlas* (1968–1972) revealed evidence of breeding in 11 (30%) 10-km squares, (confirmed in three, probable in five and possible in three). Of these 11 occupied 10-km squares, six were located within the Poole Basin, three in the Blackmore Vale and two in the far west of the county. There appears to have been a modest expansion in the breeding population during the 1980s. This is reflected by the results of the Tetrad Survey (1987–1994), which found evidence of breeding in 16 (43%) of the pre-1974 10-km squares (confirmed in five, probable in six and possible in five). The Tetrad Map shows a very similar breeding distribution to that suggested by the earlier *BTO Atlas* (1968–1972) with the bulk of the population located within the Poole Basin. In addition, there were breeding reports from a few isolated tetrads in the north and west of

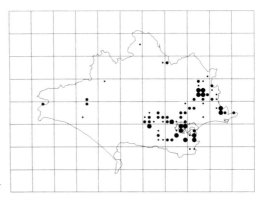

Dorset including the Lower Kingcombe/Rampisham Hill area. Again, most breeding reports between the *BTO Atlas* (1968–1972) and the Tetrad Survey (1987–1994) were from the Poole Basin, but amongst the few records from other areas of the county, the most notable involved two pairs which bred successfully at Radipole NR in 1982.

Studland NNR and Arne NR provide the only information on long-term population trends, which are highly fluctuating at both sites – see Tables 666 and 667. This is particularly evident at Studland NNR between 1997 and 1998, the latter being an extremely poor year for breeding in Dorset with a singing male at Canford Heath on 25th May the only record.

1963	1964	1965	1967	1971	1972	1975	1976	1977	1978	1979	1980	1981
3	11	10	6	8	3	12	11	9	2	6	8	11

1982	1983	1984	1985	1986	1987	1989	1990	1992	1994	1997	1998	1999
3	2	4	4	8	10	4	3	5	1	15	0	nc

Table 666. Number of breeding territories at Studland NNR 1963–1999

76	79	80	81	82	83	84	85	86	87	89	90	91	92	93	94	98
3	1	3	5	3	1	5	3	3	3	8	8	8	7	5	5	0

Table 667. Number of breeding territories at Arne NR 1976–1998

Autumn passage at the main coastal watch-points is highly variable and like the Siskin prone to occasional massive influxes, the most notable being in 1985, during 1987–1989, and in 1997 – see Table 668. Although migrants have been recorded from August through to December, the main passage period typically extends from late September to mid-November with peak numbers usually occurring in October. Seasonal totals are generally higher at Durlston CP and Christchurch Harbour than at Portland Bill. Indeed, most of the highest peak counts are from Christchurch Harbour with several records in excess of 100 birds, the best being 480 on 27th September 1997, up to 250 daily during 8th–12th October 1975 and 235E on 18th October 1985. At the other main coastal watch-points peak counts are generally more modest and rarely exceed 50 birds, the best being 170 at Durlston CP on an unspecified date in October 1997 and 124 at Portland Bill on 30th October 1980. Occasionally high numbers are recorded at other coastal sites during the autumn, the most notable being from Studland NNR with 128 on 11th October 1987 and 120 on 14th October 1973.

	1980	1981	1982	1983	1984	1985	1986	1987	1988	1989
Portland Bill	172	141	22	76	19	278	79	64	208	79
Durlston CP	69	141	114	24	19	316	78	390	269	948
Christchurch Hbr	351	131	59	151	173	808	188	753	311	115

	1990	1991	1992	1993	1994	1995	1996	1997	1998	1999
Portland Bill	37	87	22	17	80	38	49	358	56	117
Durlston CP	336	197	127	322	389	658	nc	966	208	160
Christchurch Hbr	182	288	78	149	80	88	160	1406	116	245

Table 668. Autumn totals (bds) at the main coastal watch-points 1980–1999

Although rather scarce during the 1950s, winter flocks have been regularly reported since and, like the Siskin, typically favour sites within the Poole Basin and along the main river valleys. Peak numbers tend to be lower than for the Siskin, generally ranging up to 50 and rarely exceeding 100 birds, the highest being 200 at Fontmell Magna on 24th December 1995 and 120 at Hurn during January–February 1976.

Spring migration at the main coastal watch-points is very light and sometimes virtually non-existent – see Table 669. Although migrants have been recorded from March through to June, April and May are the main months. Peak counts in recent years have been typically in single figures, the highest being 12E at Durlston CP on 10th April 1984 and 12 at Christchurch Harbour on 2nd May 1986. There is some evidence to suggest that passage was higher at Portland Bill during the early 1970s, e.g. 40 bird-days during 11th April–15th May 1971 (maximum of 17 on 14th April), and 46 bird-days during 9th April–20th May 1972 (maximum of 20 on 13th May).

	1980	1981	1982	1983	1984	1985	1986	1987	1988	1989
Portland Bill	10	17	11	4	8	4	9	23	10	18
Durlston CP	nc	8	6	23	22	0	8	2	7	7
Christchurch Hbr	nc	15	12	6	4	8	63	4	8	1

	1990	1991	1992	1993	1994	1995	1996	1997	1998	1999
Portland Bill	5	2	4	3	0	6	3	0	13	6
Durlston CP	4	4	6	2	1	35	nc	15	14	nc
Christchurch Hbr	4	11	6	5	4	nc	nc	4	2	nc

Table 669. Spring totals (bds) at the main coastal watch-points 1980–1999

A total of 343* birds has been ringed in the county (*incl Mealy Redpolls).

The Lesser Redpoll breeds mainly in the British Isles and the Alps, but in recent years it has spread along the North Sea coast from northern France to Denmark, southern Sweden and south-west Norway, and inland to parts of central Europe. The British and Irish population winters mainly within the Britain Isles with small numbers south and east to France, Belgium, the Netherlands and West Germany. Alpine populations are largely resident.

Postscript 2000–2002

Disturbingly there were no reports of breeding in 2001 and 2002. Heavy movements occurred at Hengistbury with 1,149 during October–November 2001, with a maximum of 350W on 1st November, and 1,622 during October–November 2002.

Mealy Redpoll   *Carduelis flammea*

A very rare winter visitor and passage migrant

Since this species was long regarded as the nominate race of Redpoll, it may well have been under-recorded in the county. The 1996 sightings formed part of a huge nationwide influx during the 1995/96 winter and also coincided with Dorset's first Arctic Redpolls.

1955 Bradford Abbas: 2–3 with six Lesser Redpolls 27th March
1962 Verwood: two ringed 7th January and one ringed 13th January
1972 Portland Bill: trapped 2nd November
1974 Powerstock Common: 23rd January
1985 Studland NNR: 31st October
      Hengistbury: two 24th November
1986 Hengistbury: 9th–12th February
1987 Coward's Marsh, Christchurch: 17th February
1994 Portland Bill: 5th November
1995 Studland NNR: 21st December
1996 Wareham: male 6th February
      Studland NNR: 5–10 birds for two weeks following 20th February; a further three at the same
        site on 26th March
1997 Easton, Portland: 1st November
2002 Studland NNR: 2–3 1st January into early March

The Mealy Redpoll breeds across northern Eurasia and northern North America, being a summer visitor to the northernmost parts of its range. The Scandinavian populations winter mainly in European Russia, but variable numbers remain in Scandinavia with smaller numbers wintering further south in Europe as far west as eastern Great Britain. There are sporadic autumn and winter irruptions into central and western Europe.

Arctic Redpoll

Carduelis hornemanni

Accidental: two records

> 1996   Studland NNR: 20th February
> Studland NNR: 24th–26th March

The two Dorset records occurred as a result of a huge nationwide influx of Arctic Redpolls during the 1995/96 winter (cf Mealy Redpoll). A full account of both records can be found in the Dorset Bird Report for 1996.

The Arctic Redpoll breeds across the Holarctic where it is a relatively short-distance migrant, usually to lower latitudes in winter. A vagrant to Great Britain with 799 records up to 2002.

Two-barred Crossbill

Loxia leucoptera

Accidental: one record

> 1966   Arne NR: male 7th July

Blathwayt (1945) expressed doubt concerning earlier records of two near Weymouth on 4th June 1917 and one at Sherborne on 19th January 1922 and the above occurrence is the sole accepted record for Dorset.

The Two-barred Crossbill breeds in coniferous forests from Finland (where irregular) eastwards across Siberia to the Pacific coast, also in northern North America and, unexpectedly, the mountains of Hispaniola. It is both dispersive and eruptive being a vagrant to Great Britain with 140 records up to 2002.

Crossbill (Common Crossbill)

Loxia curvirostra

An uncommon resident, and irruptive passage migrant and winter visitor

Mansel-Pleydell (1888) described this species as "a spring and autumn migrant, arriving irregularly in large flocks" and further mentioned that it had been known to breed in Holt Forest, near Bournemouth and in the adjoining county of Hampshire. Blathwayt (1945) referred to the Crossbill as a periodic visitor, which occasionally nested, and listed breeding records for 1895, 1911, 1928, 1931 (many) and 1936 – all from the east of the county.

Breeding occurred irregularly during the 1940s and 1950s, but more frequently during 1960s. Apart from 1973, there was little evidence of breeding in the 1970s, other than occasional spring and summer sightings. Since 1980 there has been a general increase in breeding records. Despite this, its status as a regular breeding bird in the county remains precarious and still largely depends on the periodic irruptions which are so characteristic of the species. In years between influxes, the resident population can fall to a very low ebb. For example, between the irruptions of 1966 and 1972, there were only six records during 1970 and 1971, and more recently, between the irruptions of 1990 and 1997, there were only five records in 1996. Population estimates for good years are difficult to assess, but in 1984 8–18 pairs were present in Wareham Forest where post-breeding flocks have reached peaks of 66 in the Sherford Bridge/Morden Bog area on 26th May 1986 and 45 at Sherford Bridge on 11th May 1991.

The *BTO Atlas* (1968–1972) showed evidence of breeding in only eight (22%) 10-km squares (confirmed in three, probable in three and possible in two), whilst the Tetrad Survey (1987–1994) found evidence of breeding in ten (27%) of the pre-1974 10-km squares (confirmed in five, probable in one and possible in four). Both surveys showed that breeding occurs almost exclusively within the Poole Basin. In earlier years, many of the breeding reports came from residential areas such as Colehill, Broadstone, Branksome Chine, Parkstone and Canford Cliffs. More recently, as illustrated by the

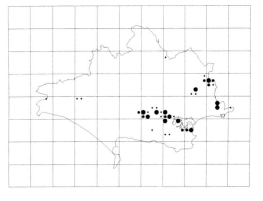

Tetrad Map, Wareham Forest and the extensive tracts of forestry immediately to the west between Bovington and Briantspuddle have been the main areas for breeding, other favoured sites being Arne NR, Rempstone Forest, St Catherine's Hill and Ringwood Forest. Perhaps the most interesting breeding record of recent years involves a pair with a juvenile at Stubhampton Bottom on 25th May 1994, a locality on the chalk of Cranborne Chase some distance from the more traditional haunts.

Since 1950 there have been several classic late summer and autumn irruptions, the most notable being in 1953, 1958, 1962, 1966, 1972, 1985, 1990 and 1997. In some years there is evidence of two influxes, the first in the late summer, usually starting in late June or July, which is followed by another in October, perhaps involving birds moving further west in Great Britain. Although these irruptions have resulted in reports from all parts of the county, including the main coastal watch-points, the majority of records still come from the Poole Basin. Flocks of up to 30 birds are frequent, but counts in excess of 50 are rare, the highest being 100 at Holnest in late October 1953, at least 100 in the vicinity of Canford Cliffs and Parkstone GC on 9th July 1958, 100 at Bovington during the irruption of July 1972, 75–100 at Brownsea from 9th July 1972 and up to 75 at unspecified sites during July 1966. After some influxes, birds have dispersed rapidly during the subsequent autumn with very few reports after November, but in other years numbers have remained high throughout the following winter. For example, in early 1991 there were peak counts of 70 at Sherborne Park on 17th February and 50 at Manswood on 7th March, whilst in early 1998 high numbers were present in Wareham Forest with an aggregate count of 130 on 29th January, and individual counts of 75 at Lawson Clump on 10th January and 70 at Sherford Bridge on 23rd January.

Records from the main coastal watch-points, even in irruption years, are infrequent and generally involve small numbers. The main exception was in 1997 with 194 bird-days at Durlston CP during July–November, and 114 bird-days at Portland and 62 bird-days at Christchurch Harbour during July–August and in October. Otherwise, 82 bird-days at Portland Bill during October–early November 1985 included an exceptional day-count of 50 on 10th November, the next highest being 24 at Durlston CP on 16th June 1990.

A total of five birds has been ringed in the county.

The Crossbill breeds in the coniferous forests of north-west Africa, Europe, Asia Minor, north-central and parts of central Asia, and North America. Its behaviour is dispersive and eruptive so that breeding is sporadic throughout much of the west and south of the Western Palearctic.

Postscript 2000–2002

In 2000, 200+ at Bovington on 20th August would appear to be the highest ever count for Dorset. Other high counts in 2000 include 100+ at Wareham and Rempstone Forests in January–February.

Common Rosefinch   *Carpodacus erythrinus*

Rare passage migrant

Since the first at Portland Bill in 1967, there have been 27 further records, all of single birds. The earlier occurrences during 1967–1985 involved female or immature birds in autumn. Since 1989 there has been a marked increase in reports of singing males in late spring and early summer, coinciding with the westward expansion of the central European population. The 12 spring and summer birds have appeared on dates ranging from 21st May to 23rd June, whilst the 16 autumn birds have occurred between 25th August and the exceptionally late date of 30th November. Portland is the most favoured site for the species accounting for 19 birds (68% of the total). The mini-influx of five birds during September 2000 is particularly noteworthy.

1967	Portland Bill: female/imm. 25th–27th August
1973	Portland Bill: female/imm. 15th September
1976	Chapman's Pool: female/imm. trapped 19th September
1979	Portland Bill: female/imm. 13th October
1983	Portland Bill: imm. female trapped 30th November
1985	Southwell, Portland: female/imm. 15th September
1989	Durlston CP: 2nd June
	Portland Bill: singing first-summer male 23rd June
1990	Hengistbury: 19th October
1991	Hengistbury: first-summer male 21st May
	Portland Bill: singing male 16th June
1992	Durlston CP: singing male 21st May
	Portland Bill: singing male 10th June
	Abbotsbury: 11th–13th June
1993	Hengistbury: first-summer male 2nd June
1995	Portland Bill: singing male 1st June
1996	Hengistbury: female 29th May
	Portland Bill: singing first-summer male holding territory 14th–17th June, trapped 17th
	Easton, Portland, immature on 6th October.
	Portland Bill: female/imm. 22nd–23rd October
1997	Portland Bill: ad. 'red' male singing 6th June
2000	Southwell, Portland: female/imm. 4th September
	Southwell/Weston, Portland: at least two different fem/imms 11th–13th September
	Priory Corner, Portland: 11th September
	Hengistbury: 29th September
2002	Portland Bill: first-year bird trapped 20th September
	Verne Common, Portland: female/imm. 27th September

The Common Rosefinch is a summer visitor breeding in eastern Europe and eastwards across most of northern Asia to the Pacific, also in parts of central and south-west Asia and Asia Minor. In recent years it has spread westwards in Europe to Scandinavia, parts of central Europe, the Netherlands and eastern France, and has bred in Great Britain. It winters in the Indian sub-continent and parts of south-east Asia.

Bullfinch (Common Bullfinch) *Pyrrhula pyrrhula*

A common resident and uncommon passage migrant

Mansel-Pleydell (1888) considered this species to be a generally distributed resident, whilst Blathwayt (1945) simply referred to it as a numerous resident.

Subsequently its status has remained largely unchanged. The *BTO Atlas* (1968–1972) found evidence of breeding in all 10-km squares (confirmed in 35, probable in one and possible in one), whilst the Tetrad Survey (1987–1994) produced an almost identical result with evidence of breeding in all of the pre-1974 10-km squares (confirmed in 35 and probable in two). The Tetrad Map shows that breeding is generally well distributed throughout the county except for much of the Bournemouth and Poole conurbation, and some areas of open downland, notably the middle portion of Cranborne Chase (ST90 and ST91), to the south and west of Dorchester (SY68) and in west Purbeck (SY78). The relatively limited information available on long-term population trends is contradictory with evidence of an increase at Durlston CP, a decline at Studland NNR and relatively stable situations at the remaining two sites – see Tables 670 to 673.

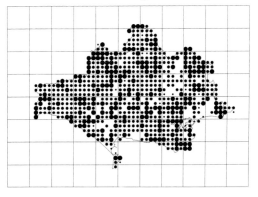

1981	1982	1983	1984	1985	1986	1987	1988	1990	1991	1996	1997	1998	1999
3	4	4	4	5	5	6	6	8	6	8	8	7	8

Table 670. Number of breeding territories at Durlston CP 1981–1999

71	72	73	75	76	77	81	82	83	84	85	86	87	88	89	91	92	93	94	95	96	99
6	8	7	8	8	8	5	3	4	5	4	6	4	4	3	5	5	3	4	5	6	2

Table 671. Number of breeding territories at Studland NNR 1971–1999

73	74	75	76	77	78	81	82	83	84	85	86	87	91	93	97
4	4	4	4	5	5	5	5	5	5	5	5	5	5	4	3

Table 672. Number of breeding territories at Arne NR 1973–1997

1981	1982	1986	1988	1989	1991	1992	1993	1994	1995	1996
4	1	3	1	0	1	1	1	1	0	1

Table 673. Number of breeding territories at Forde Abbey 1981–1996

Some passage occurs at the main coastal watch-points, but it seems likely this mostly involves locally dispersing birds rather than genuine immigrants from afar. Spring passage, which extends from March to May, is very light and sometimes non-existent. Most reports are from Portland Bill where seasonal totals normally vary between 0–12 birds, occasionally more – see Table 674. Although autumn passage, which extends from August to November, is stronger, numbers are still generally small and fluctuate considerably from year to year. At Portland Bill passage is occasionally non-existent with seasonal totals rarely exceeding 15 bird-days, the highest being 90 in 1980 – see Table 674. Peak counts in spring and autumn at this site are normally in single figures, the highest being in 1977 with nine on 29th March and ten on 20th October. At Durlston CP the autumn peak may be solely the result of locally-bred birds in some years, but there is strong evidence of passage in others, most notably during 1987–1992 when pronounced easterly movements occurred during October – see Table 675. In addition, 400 bird-days were recorded at this site during 15th October–14th November 1997 peaking at 48 on 22nd October, the previous highest count being 32 on 30th September 1995. Generally there are relatively few autumn reports from Christchurch Harbour, 13E at Hengistbury on 22nd October 1987 and a peak of ten in autumn 1976 being particularly noteworthy. There was an obvious influx into the county during 22nd–23rd October 1987 when in addition to the high count at Hengistbury on 22nd (13E), there were six at Portland Bill on 22nd, 20W at Durlston CP on 22nd with 36E and W there on 23rd, and 20 at St Aldhelm's Head on 23rd. A movement of 19W was also recorded at West Bexington on 31st October 1976.

	1980	1981	1982	1983	1984	1985	1986	1987	1988	1989
Spring	5	9	12	5	1	0	5	4	18	3
Autumn	c90	39	15	14	6	6	12	29	11	1

	1990	1991	1992	1993	1994	1995	1996	1997	1998	1999
Spring	8	4	4	6	1	22	2	12	23	7
Autumn	0	3	7	7	18	6	0	27	3	0

Table 674. Spring and autumn totals at Portland Bill 1980–1999

	1987	1988	1990	1991	1992
East	–	85	38	60	38
E & W	56	–	–	–	–
Max.	36 on 23rd	20 on 20th	20 on 12th	20 on 13th & 14th	18

Table 675. Autumn movements during October at Durlston CP 1987–1992

Winter flocks of up to 20 birds are frequently recorded, the highest counts being 40–60 at Studland

NNR in 1987, 50 at North Portland in late December 1969, 40 at Holton Heath on 18th November 1984 and 30 at Parkstone in December 1974.

A total of 2,926 birds has been ringed in the county. There has been one foreign recovery involving a bird ringed at St Aldhelm's Head on 5th April 1977 and recovered at Chenehutte, Maine-et-Loire, France on 1st January 1978, a distance of 350km to the south. This is an exceptional record as British birds are normally sedentary, recoveries over 50km being rare. It is interesting to note that two birds flew out to sea at Portland Bill on 26th November 1976.

The Bullfinch breeds throughout much of north and central Europe south to northern Spain, central Italy and the northern Balkans, extending eastwards to Asia Minor and across much of north-central Asia to the Pacific coast and Japan. It is partially migratory over much of its range with birds wintering within and south of the breeding range to the Mediterranean.

Sponsored by Mick and June Shepherd

Hawfinch   *Coccothraustes coccothraustes*

A very rare resident, and scarce passage migrant and winter visitor

The Hawfinch always appears to have been an enigmatic and elusive bird in Dorset. Mansel-Pleydell (1888) commented that this species could only be regarded as an occasional visitor, although it appeared to be resident nearby in the New Forest, and further mentioned two occurrences of breeding, at Poole and Thorncombe, and an influx during the winter of 1872/73. There appears to have been little change in status during the first half of the 20th Century as Blathwayt (1945) described the Hawfinch as "a resident, not common; also a winter visitor" and noted that the latest of a few breeding records was in east Dorset in 1944. In addition, the species occurred at Durlston CP in almost every summer during 1945–1950 with a family party present in 1948.

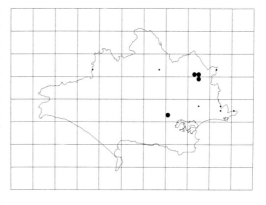

Since 1950 the species has remained a very scarce breeding bird and sporadic visitor with a total absence of reports in some years, even as recently as 1995 – see Fig 63. In 1951 there was a remarkable number of breeding records involving a nest with three young in an orchard near Cranborne during 30th May–8th June with single pairs at two nearby sites in May, and at least three nests elsewhere in east Dorset. Since then, breeding has been confirmed as follows:

1958   Blandford St Mary
1966   Lilliput, Poole: pair 8th September, female and two young 15th September
1968   Child Okeford: family party in a garden for over a week in late August
1969   Near Cranborne
1977   Ferndown: two ads and four juvs feeding in a wild cherry tree 30th July
1983   Marnhull: family group in a garden during August
1989   Wareham Forest: two ads and three juvs on 11th June
1998   Boys Wood near Woodlands: pair carrying nest material 4th May with a single bird on 26th May

In addition to the above, the Tetrad Survey (1987–1994) confirmed breeding in three adjacent tetrads SU01F (Wimborne St Giles Park), SU01K (Edmondsham) and SU00P (Woodlands).

There are occasional spring and summer records which, considering the elusive nature of the species, may also indicate local breeding. These include a pair at Woodlands on 8th June 1963, one, perhaps two heard singing at Cranborne in May 1965 with two pairs near there on 21st May 1966, and one between Damerham and Cranborne on 5th May 1973. Combined with the reports of confirmed breeding, this suggests that a small resident population may exist, albeit largely undetected, in the Cranborne/Woodlands area. Other spring and summer records from the Blandford area, Witchampton, More Crichel and Farnham

Woods confirms that breeding in the county is most likely to occur in the woodlands of Cranborne Chase. Of the remaining breeding season records, five at Abbotsbury on 28th July 1972 is intriguing and perhaps refers to a family party.

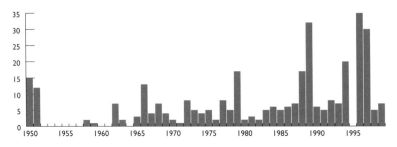

Fig 63. Annual totals 1950–1999

There was no evidence of any regular wintering sites until the 1990s when birds visited Cattistock Churchyard for varying periods in four winters, making it the most reliable site for Hawfinches in the county – see Table 676. The high count of 23 at this site in December 1996 is exceptional and formed part of a notable county-wide influx during the 1996/97 winter, which also included flocks at Sherborne Lake from 16th November to 6th March (maximum of ten on 16th December), and Lydlinch from 9th February to 31st March (maximum of ten on 14th February). There was also a notable influx during the autumn and winter of 1988/89 mainly involving reports of 1–2 birds at widely scattered sites, but 15 were present at Chedington Woods on 18th March. The only other noteworthy counts in winter involve six at Bradford Abbas during January–March 1950, six at Clifton Wood on 17th March 1979 and five at Alweston on 31st December 1994.

	1990/91	1992/93	1993/94	1996/97
Dates	25 Nov–16 Dec	21 Nov–5 Dec	13 Nov–Jan	30 Nov–8 Mar
Max count	1	2	4	23 in Dec

Table 676. Winter records from Cattistock Churchyard 1990–1997

Although most coastal records, particularly those from Portland Bill, Durlston CP and Christchurch Harbour, occur at times of passage, there are occasional sightings in mid-winter, the most notable being one at Portland Bill from 11th–19th February 1986 and up to three at Durlston CP during 24th January–8th February 1987. Although migrants have been recorded from early March to mid-June and from early August to late November, the peak months for passage birds are April and October. Seasonal totals are very small and mainly involve 1–2 birds, the highest day-counts being eight at Durlston CP on 15th October 1994 and five at Southwell, Portland on 30th November 1984 – see Tables 677 and 678. There are also coastal and near-coastal records from West Bexington (five), Weymouth (two), Radipole NR (three), Radipole School (two), Winspit (three), and singles from Studland, Canford Cliffs and Chewton Glen.

	1980	1981	1982	1983	1984	1985	1986	1987	1988	1989
Portland	0	0	0	0	0	1	4	1	0	0
Durlston CP	0	0	0	0	0	0	0	1	0	3
Christchurch Hbr	0	0	0	0	0	0	0	0	0	0

	1990	1991	1992	1993	1994	1995	1996	1997	1998	1999
Portland	0	1	0	0	2	0	0	1	1	1
Durlston CP	1	0	0	0	0	0	0	0	0	0
Christchurch Hbr	0	0	1	0	0	0	0	0	0	0

Table 677. Spring totals at the main coastal watch-points 1980–1999

	1980	1981	1982	1983	1984	1985	1986	1987	1988	1989
Portland	0	0	0	0	5	2	0	0	3	0
Durlston CP	0	0	0	0	0	1	0	1	2	2
Christchurch Hbr	0	0	0	0	0	0	0	0	2	0

	1990	1991	1992	1993	1994	1995	1996	1997	1998	1999
Portland	1	0	0	0	0	0	1	0	0	0
Durlston CP	1	0	0	0	9	0	0	0	0	2
Christchurch Hbr	0	3	2	0	0	0	0	0	2	0

Table 678. Autumn totals at the main coastal watch-points 1980–1999

Only two birds have been ringed in the county.

The Hawfinch breeds widely in north-west Africa and throughout Europe north to Great Britain and southern Scandinavia, extending eastwards across central Asia to the Pacific coast and northern Japan, also a small isolated population in south-central Asia. It is a summer visitor to eastern Europe and central Asia. It winters within much of the European breeding range extending south to the Mediterranean, Asia Minor and parts of the Middle East. The Asiatic populations winter in Japan, eastern Asia and parts of central Asia.

Postscript 2000–2002

In 2000 there were eight records involving 12 birds including three reports during the summer and one sighting from Cattistock Churchyard in late December. In 2001 there were four records involving six birds. In 2002 there were four records involving six birds including two at Cattistock Churchyard throughout February.

Northern Parula   *Parula americana*

Accidental: three records

1968   Southwell, Portland: 9th October
1985   Hengistbury: first-winter female 30th September–12th October, trapped 9th
1988   Portland Bill and Suckthumb Quarry: first-winter male 30th September–7th October, trapped 30th

The Northern Parula is a summer visitor breeding in eastern North America from southern Canada to the Gulf Coast. It winters in southern Florida, the West Indies and Central America. A vagrant to the British Isles with 16 records up to 2000.

Northern Waterthrush   *Seiurus noveboracensis*

Accidental: one record

1996   Portland Bill: 14th–17th October

This first-winter bird was trapped at Portland Bird Observatory on 14th October and remained in and around the Observatory garden until its last day when it was attacked by a Sparrowhawk. A short account can be found in *Birding World*, Vol. 9, Number 10, November 1996 and the Dorset Bird Report for 1996.

The Northern Waterthrush is a summer visitor breeding in northern North America and winters in southern Florida, the West Indies, Central America and northern South America. A vagrant to the British Isles with seven records up to 2000.

Savannah Sparrow   *Passerculus sandwichensis*

Accidental: one record

1982   Portland Bill: 11th–16th April

Great Britain's first Savanna Sparrow was initially found at the Bill on 11th April before moving to the East Cliffs later the same day, where it remained until 16th. The bird was trapped on 12th and subspecifically identified as *A. s. princeps*, colloquially known as the Ipswich Sparrow. A full account can be found in *British Birds*, Vol. 78, Number 12, December 1985, the Dorset Bird Report for 1982 and the Portland Bird Observatory Report for 1982.

The Savannah Sparrow is mainly a summer visitor breeding throughout much of Canada and the northern USA. It winters mainly in the southern USA, Central America and the West Indies. The race *A. s. princeps* breeds on Sable Island off Nova Scotia and winters from Nova Scotia south to southern Georgia. A vagrant to Great Britain with only two records up to 2000.

Dark-eyed Junco   *Junco hyemalis*

Accidental: three records

All three of these birds were found in gardens.

    1983   Christchurch: male 20th May
    1989   Weston, Portland: first-winter male 3rd December–8th April 1990
    1993   Dorchester: male 7th–19th November, trapped 8th

The various races of Dark-eyed Junco breed over much of North America south to northern Mexico and winter in the southern part of the breeding range, the southern USA and northern Mexico. A vagrant to Great Britain with 24 records up to 2002.

Lapland Bunting (Lapland Longspur)   *Calcarius lapponicus*

An uncommon passage migrant, mainly in autumn, and rare winter visitor

There is an old record of one seen near Wareham on 30th January 1912, which was regarded as being doubtful by Blathwayt (1945). Perhaps the first genuine reports for Dorset involve one near Charmouth Beach on 2nd October 1952 and a party of three at Radipole NR during very cold weather on 21st February 1955.

In 1956 there was a remarkable autumn influx at Portland Bill with up to eight birds on 27 dates (75 bird-days) during 22nd September–21st December. Since 1959 the species has been recorded every autumn except for the four consecutive years 1969–1972. Seasonal totals were generally small and only exceeded single figures in four years prior to 1983, but numbers have increased and seasonal totals have exceeded single figures in every subsequent autumn except 1994 – see Fig 64. The earliest record is from 4th to 7th September 1997 at Portland Bill with most passage occurring from mid-September to mid-November and peaking during the second half of October – see Table 679. There is a trickle of reports from mid-November through into December, some of which may refer to wintering birds rather than late migrants.

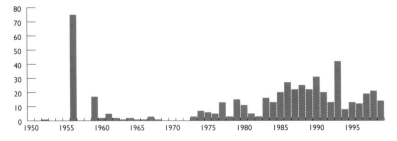

Fig 64. Autumn totals 1952–1999

Sep 1–15	Sep 16–30	Oct 1–15	Oct 16–31	Nov 1–15	Nov 16–30	Dec 1–15	Dec 16–31
2%	22%	19%	35%	15%	5%	2%	0

Table 679. Proportion (%) of autumn migrants half-monthly 1952–1999

482

The main site for autumn migrants is Portland Bill, which accounts for 57% of the total, Portland as a whole accounting for 66% – see Table 680. Christchurch Harbour has also attracted a good total of 113 birds (22% of the seasonal total), but much smaller numbers have been recorded at Durlston CP where 41 of the 42 birds have occurred during 1987–1999. Elsewhere on Purbeck, there were up to five at St Aldhelm's Head during 2nd–7th November 1995 with singles at Ballard Down on 22nd September 1996, and Dancing Ledge on 28th September 1974 and 26th October 1979. Away from the main coastal watch-points, Studland NNR is the most favoured site with about nine, possibly as many as 13 birds during 1962–1993. Otherwise the only autumn sightings from other coastal localities involve one near Charmouth on 2nd October 1952, one at Burton Mere on 8th October 1975, one at Lodmoor NR on 10th November 1975 with two there next day, and a male at Highcliffe on 6th November 1984 – seen earlier at Hengistbury. The only inland record concerns one at Ridgeway Hill on 23rd October 1993.

	Autumn		Winter	
Portland Bill	296	57%	24	63%
elsewhere on Portland	47	9%	2	5%
Durlston CP	42	8%	0	0
Studland NNR	9	2%	2	5%
Christchurch Harbour	113	22%	6	16%
elsewhere	13	3%	4	11%

Table 680. Distribution of autumn and winter birds 1952–1999

Autumn reports typically involve 1–2 birds, occasionally up to five, the highest counts being 12 at Blacknor, Portland on 29th October 1959, and up to eight at Portland Bill on three days from 22nd September 1956 with eight there during 27th October–4th November 1979.

The species is a very scarce visitor during the winter. There were only six records involving eight birds during 1950–1978, but a subsequent increase resulted in near-annual sightings during 1979–1991 with seasonal totals normally ranging from 1–3 birds – see Fig 65. Since then, there has been only one winter report in 1995. Apart from a peak during the second half of December, records are fairly evenly distributed during the remaining half-month periods to the end of February. There are relatively few occurrences of overwintering and long-staying birds, all from Portland Bill, the most notable being two from December 1979 to 29th February 1980. Like the autumn, Portland Bill is the main site for winter birds and accounts for 63% of the seasonal total, Portland as a whole accounting for 68%, followed by Christchurch Harbour with 16% – see Table 680. The remaining winter sightings are three at Radipole NR on 21st February 1955, and singles at Studland Bay on 7th February 1963, Shell Bay on 20th December 1968 and Lodmoor NR on 24th December 1979. All reports involve 1–3 birds, except for a remarkable flock of eight at Portland Bill on 26th December 1982.

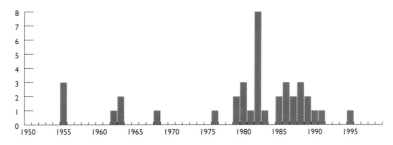

Fig 65. Winter totals 1955–1999

Spring migrants are very rarely recorded as follows:

1981 Portland Bill: male 29th April, female 2nd May and another male 30th–31st May – a remarkable series of records
1982 Hengistbury: 21st March
1984 Portland Bill: 2nd May

1985 Portland Bill: 13th March
1987 Studland NNR: 8th March
       Portland Bill: two 28th April
1990 Hengistbury: 23rd March
1995 Portland Bill: male 12th May

There is also an exceptional summer sighting of one at Central Portland on 15th June 1990.
Only three birds have been ringed in the county.

The Lapland Bunting is a summer visitor breeding across the Holarctic including the fjells of central Scandinavia. In Eurasia, it winters chiefly from the Ukraine eastwards across central Asia to the Pacific coast, but also quite commonly along the North Sea coast from Belgium to Denmark and in smaller numbers on the east coast of Great Britain and north coast of France.

Postscript 2000–2002

In 2000 there were 13 records involving 16 birds during 21st September–19th November, and in 2002 there were nine records involving ten birds during 28th September–5th November. There were no reports in 2001, making this the first year without reports in Dorset since 1972!

Snow Bunting   *Plectrophenax nivalis*

An uncommon passage migrant, mainly in autumn, and rare winter visitor

Mansel-Pleydell (1888) considered this species to be an accidental visitor in winter and listed only four records involving singles at Houghton in 1844, Kimmeridge in February 1868 and Poxwell on an unspecified date, and five near Weymouth on 28th December 1869. It would appear that the Snow Bunting became much commoner during the first half of the 20th Century as Blathwayt (1945) described it as "a winter visitor", which "has occurred on many occasions from the end of October to March, chiefly near the coast and sometimes in small parties".

The species was very scarce during the early 1950s, but since 1955 there has been an increase in occurrences with records in every year except 1965, 1966 and 1972. Annual totals are highly variable, ranging from 1–26 birds – see Fig 66. Since 1950 the Snow Bunting has occurred mainly as an uncommon migrant in the autumn, which accounts for 69% of the total. The earliest reports are 15th September 1996 at Radipole NR and from Hengistbury on 17th September 1980 and 17th September 1992. It is curious that of the 15 birds recorded during September, 11 are from Christchurch Harbour. Passage extends through to early December and peaks between mid-October and mid-November, the months of October and November accounting for 65% of the total – see Table 681.

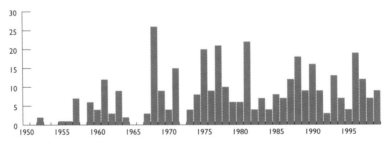

Fig 66. Annual totals 1952–1999 (excluding overwintering birds)

Jan 1–15	Jan 16–31	Feb 1–15	Feb 16–28	Mar 1–15	Mar 16–31	Apr 1–15	Apr 16–30
5%	2%	3%	3%	2%	1%	1%	1%

Sep 1–15	Sep 16–30	Oct 1–15	Oct 16–31	Nov 1–15	Nov 16–30	Dec 1–15	Dec 16–31
<1%	4%	13%	19%	21%	11%	3%	10%

Table 681. Proportion (%) of birds half-monthly 1952–1999

A secondary peak of records during the second half of December is perhaps indicative of an onward movement of birds from traditional wintering sites on the North Sea coasts of England and the Low Countries. Most winter sightings involve short-staying individuals with relatively few instances of overwintering as follows:

1957/58   Studland Bay: up to four 3rd October–25th January
1961/62   Shell/Studland Bays: up to three 17th December–3rd February
1968/69   Shell/Studland Bays: up to four 28th December–16th March
1970/71   Shell/Studland Bays: up to three 31st December–14th March
1973/74   Shell/Studland Bays: up to four 25th November–14th March
1975/76   Ferrybridge/Chesil Beach: up to 12 from 16th October–5th April
           Studland Bay: 2–3 from 10th November -14th December
1981/82   Studland Bay: up to 12 from 28th December–28th February
1991/92   Shell/Studland Bays: up to four 8th November–19th February
           Ferrybridge: one 28th December–1st March

The frequency of wintering during 1968–1976 is noteworthy and the dominance of the sandy beaches/dunes of Studland NNR as the favoured haunt is clear. It is perhaps not surprising that this species should choose to overwinter at sites that most closely resemble their winter habitat along the coasts of the North Sea.

Spring passage is light with the relatively few sightings extending from early March to late April, the latest being 25th April 1984 at Hengistbury and 27th and 29th April 1977 at Ferrybridge.

The Portland Bill/Portland/Ferrybridge area, Christchurch Harbour and Studland NNR are the main sites for the Snow Bunting in Dorset and together account for 79% of the total – see Table 682. Otherwise there is a scattering of records from other coastal and near-coastal sites from Chideock in the west to Bournemouth in the east. The only inland records in recent years involve one at Wynford Eagle on 5th October 1949, one near Bulbarrow on 26th October 1961, and more exceptionally one in a garden at Cerne Abbas during cold weather in February 1969.

	Total	
Chideock to West Bexington	24	6%
Portland Bill	99	26%
elsewhere on Portland	11	3%
The Fleet/Chesil excl. Ferrybridge	6	2%
Ferrybridge	28	7%
Weymouth area incl. Radipole & Lodmoor NRs	8	2%
Purbeck	27	7%
Poole Harbour excl. Studland NNR	11	3%
Studland NNR	64	17%
Poole to Bournemouth	2	1%
Christchurch Harbour	96	25%
inland	2	1%

Table 682. Distribution of birds 1952–1999

Virtually all records involve five or fewer birds, the only exceptions being the overwintering flocks of 12 at Ferrybridge/Chesil Beach during 1975/76 and Studland Bay in 1981/82.

Rather surprisingly no birds have been ringed in the county.

The Snow Bunting is mainly a summer visitor breeding across the Holarctic including the fjells of central Scandinavia with a tiny population in the highlands of Scotland. The main wintering areas in Eurasia extend from northern and eastern Great Britain, the Low Countries and southern Scandinavia eastward across central eastern Europe and central Asia to the Pacific coast.

Postscript 2000–2002

In 2000 there were eight records of single birds, in 2001 there were five records relating perhaps to only three birds, and in 2002 there were five records of singles birds. Most birds (13) occurred during October–December with three during January–March.

Pine Bunting   *Emberiza leucocephalos*

Accidental: one record

   1975   Southwell, Portland: 15th April

A short account of this male bird, seen along Reap Lane, Southwell, can be found in *British Birds*, Vol. 71, Number 7, July 1978.

   The Pine Bunting is a summer visitor breeding from the Urals eastwards across northern Asia to the Pacific coast. It winters in parts of south-west and eastern Asia including the north-west Indian sub-continent, also in very small numbers in Israel. A vagrant to Great Britain with 37 records up to 2002.

Yellowhammer   *Emberiza citrinella*

A common resident and passage migrant

Mansel-Pleydell (1888) described this species as "a well-known resident", whilst Blathwayt (1945) simply referred to it as a common resident.

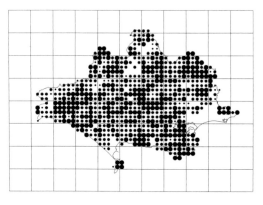

   There has been little change in status subsequently until the recent decline. The *BTO Atlas* (1968–1972) found evidence of breeding in all but one (97%) 10-km squares (confirmed in 35 and probable in one), whilst the Tetrad Survey (1987–1994) produced an almost identical result with evidence of breeding in all but one (97%) of the pre-1974 10-km squares (confirmed in 34 and probable in two). The Tetrad Map shows that the Yellowhammer is a widespread breeding species throughout much of the county, but it is absent from heavily built-up areas such as the Bournemouth and Poole conurbation and Weymouth, as well as the damp lowlands of the Blackmore Vale and parts of the extreme west.

   There is evidence to suggest a modest decline in breeding numbers during the early 1970s followed by a recovery in the early 1980s. Since then, the relatively limited information available on long-term trends shows a more substantial decline in the breeding population, which has accelerated during the 1990s – see Tables 683 to 685. It is particularly alarming that the species no longer breeds at Arne NR where 31 pairs were present in 1980, and that only one pair was reported from Fontmell Down in 1998. Changes in agricultural practices, particularly autumn ploughing and sowing of stubble, are undoubtedly implicated in this decline.

80	81	82	83	84	85	86	87	88	90	91	92	95	96	97	98	99
21	17	22	24	21	23	22	18	17	15	19	19	14	13	10	8	6

Table 683. Number of breeding territories at Durlston CP 1980–1999

68	74	75	76	77	78	79	80	81	82	83	84	85	86	87	91	92	93	94	95	96	97
20	15	12	15	15	20	20	31	25	20	15	15	15	12	12	5	9	5	2	2	0	0

Table 684. Number of breeding territories at Arne NR 1968–1997

1981	1982	1983	1984	1985	1986	1988	1989	1991	1992	1993	1994	1998
16	14	20	13	15	24	28	19	12	15	14	11	1

Table 685. Number of breeding territories at Fontmell Down 1981–1998

   Although there is some evidence of passage at the main coastal watch-points, it is difficult to distinguish between local dispersal, which undoubtedly accounts for a substantial number of records, and possible immigrants resulting from the partial movement of birds from Scandinavia and central Europe towards the south-west. Although the seasonal totals for spring and autumn at Portland Bill fluctuate considerably, there is evidence of a decline in recent years, thus mirroring the situation regarding the breeding population – see Table 686. Peak counts at this site are usually in single figures, the highest in recent years being 20 on 29th October 1983, also 23 on 27th October 1962. Along the Purbeck coast numbers are generally higher, notably at Durlston CP where visual passage was sometimes evident during the 1980s both in spring (mainly April) and autumn (mainly October) – see Tables 687 and 688. In addition to these movements, there was a major influx of 215 birds at Durlston CP on 4th November 1983, whilst notable spring counts at this site include 60 on 12th April 1981 and 60E on 13th April 1986. Elsewhere on Purbeck, 90 at St Aldhelm's Head on

15th October 1987 and 70 at Winspit during August–September 1990 are noteworthy. At Christchurch Harbour, seasonal totals are very small and, since 1980 at least, have rarely exceeded single figures.

	1980	1981	1982	1983	1984	1985	1986	1987	1988	1989
Spring	28	18	6	42	21	13	23	9	19	3
Autumn	161	68	43	193	23	27	31	45	81	60

	1990	1991	1992	1993	1994	1995	1996	1997	1998	1999
Spring	51	25	14	14	6	9	19	11	7	10
Autumn	48	16	13	44	10	39	26	8	10	4

Table 686. Spring and autumn totals at Portland Bill 1980–1999

1981	1982	1983	1985	1986
100S:60W	35W	104E	102E	60E

Table 687. Spring movements at Durlston CP 1981–1986

1983	1984	1985	1987	1988
200E&W	150W:40SE	200W	30W	140E

Table 688. Autumn movements at Durlston CP 1983–1988

Winter flocks are regularly recorded with peak counts typically ranging up to 50 but rarely exceeding 100 birds, the highest being 350 at Chilfrome on 24th January 1981, 200 at Acton in 1967, 200 at Hilton on 27th November 1993, 150 at Portesham on 27th January 1975 and 150 at Puddletown on 23rd December 1993.

A total of 1,755 birds has been ringed in the county.

The Yellowhammer breeds throughout much of northern and central Europe south to northern Spain, central Italy and the northern Balkans, extending eastwards across north-central Asia to about 100°E. It is a summer visitor in the far north and winters mainly within the breeding range extending south to the Mediterranean, Asia Minor, the Middle East, and parts of south-west and central Asia.

Postscript 2000–2002
At Puddletown, counts of 340 during the second winter period of 2002, and 250 birds during the first winter periods of 2000 and 2002 are high by recent standards.

Cirl Bunting   *Emberiza cirlus*

A rare passage migrant and winter visitor – formerly bred

The Cirl Bunting was well-known in the 19th Century, Mansel-Pleydell (1888) describing it as "resident, and not uncommon in Dorsetshire in the neighbourhood of the coast". Blathwayt (1945) considered it to be a locally common resident that showed a decided preference for coastal regions and the chalk, but hinted at some decline by commenting that some former haunts had been deserted.

In 1951 some 42 pairs were reported with half located in the river valleys of the northern chalk between Crichel, Wimborne St Giles and Cranborne, plus outliers near Fordingbridge, Pimperne, Bryanston, Wimborne and probably Iwerne Minster. Most of the remaining population occurred in the coastal strip between Charmouth and Weymouth with four pairs near West Bay, three pairs at Charmouth and neighbouring villages, and two pairs behind Weymouth and East Fleet. Elsewhere there were two pairs at Durlston CP, probably two pairs near Sherborne and a pair at Lytchett Minster. A decline in numbers was evident by 1959 and continued throughout the 1960s. By the time of the *BTO Atlas* (1968–1972), the once favoured Cranborne area was already deserted, the remnant population largely surviving in small isolated pockets along the western coastal strip between Burton Bradstock and West Bexington, in the north-west around Sherborne and Yeovil, and in the extreme south-east of Purbeck at Swanage/Durlston CP. Although the *BTO Atlas* (1968–1972) found evidence of breeding in 14 (38%) 10-km squares, this was only confirmed in two (SY58 and ST51) and probable in five (SY48, ST61, SY77, SY97 and SZ07), whilst many of the records were for 1968 only. Breeding was last proven in 1971 at West Bexington where two pairs reared 12 young. There were a few breeding season records during 1972–1974, the most notable being a singing male at Durlston CP during March–April 1972, a pair at West Bay during 15th–28th July 1972 and singing males (presumably the same bird) at Wyke Regis Churchyard during 22nd March–1st April 1973 and from the end of March–11th May 1974.

Subsequently the species has been recorded in every year except 1982, 1985, 1988 and 1995–1999 inclusive, the latter sequence of absences being of particular concern with regard to possible recolonisation from the increasing population in nearby Devon. The only evidence of possible breeding attempts involves three (a male and two females) at Compton Valence in March 1976 with one there on 16th May 1986, a male at Askerswell on 20th and 25th April 1984 and one at Oakley near Wimborne on 30th March 1987. Most birds (80%) have occurred on passage along the coast, the most favoured site by far being Portland Bill where the dominance of spring sightings is striking – see Table 689. It seems dispersal from breeding sites in Devon is the most likely origin of these birds. Although passage birds have been reported from March to May and August to November, March–April (91%) and October–November (63%) are the peak periods. Winter records are very rare and limited to a male at East Fleet on 3rd January 1977, two pairs at Southwell, Portland on 10th January 1977 and one at Sherborne Park on 31st January 1987.

	Spring		Autumn		Total	
Portland Bill	22	67%	7	44%	29	59%
elsewhere on Portland	4	12%	1	6%	5	10%
Durlston CP	2	6%	1	6%	3	6%
Christchurch Harbour	3	9%	6	38%	9	18%
elsewhere	2	6%	1	6%	3	6%

Table 689. Distribution of migrants 1975–1999

A total of six birds has been ringed in the county.

The Cirl Bunting breeds in north-west Africa, western Europe as far north as south-west England, southern Europe and Asia Minor. It has declined over much of Great Britain and it is now restricted to the south coast of Devon.

Postscript 2000–2002

The sequence of 'blank' years continues with no reports, the last being in 1994.

Sponsored by Paul St. Pierre

Ortolan Bunting   *Emberiza hortulana*

An uncommon passage migrant, mainly in autumn

Blathwayt (1945) referred to a record of one obtained near Weymouth long ago and now in the Dorchester Museum.

The first report in recent years concerns five at Portland Bill on 9th September 1956 with up to three present until 24th September. Subsequently the species has been recorded every autumn except 1962 and 1968 with seasonal totals ranging from 1–20 birds – see Fig 67. Although records extend from 13th August 1997 at Durlston CP to 22nd October 1989 at Portland Bill, the first half of September is the peak time for autumn migrants and accounts for 41% of the total, the month as a whole accounting for 70% – see Table 690.

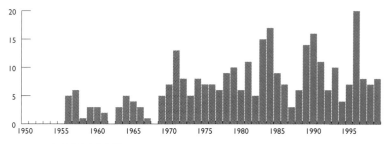

Fig 67. Autumn totals 1956–1999

Apr 1–15	Apr 16–30	May 1–15	May 16–31	Jun 1–15	Jun 16–30	Aug 1–15	Aug 16–31	Sep 1–15	Sep 16–30	Oct 1–15	Oct 16–31
1	6	9	7	1	0	2	35	91	66	19	10

Table 690. Half-monthly totals 1956–1999

Portland is by far the most favoured site for Ortolan Buntings in autumn with c.240 birds (77% of the total) – see Table 691. It should be noted, however, that due to the mobility of birds wandering between the Bill and other nearby parts of the island, particularly the fields around Southwell and Weston, it is impossible to accurately assess numbers in some years. Consequently this figure is likely to be an underestimate and the autumn total for Portland could be as high as c.340 birds.

The species was not recorded at Durlston CP and Christchurch Harbour until 1982, but 27 and 26 birds respectively have subsequently occurred at these sites in autumn. Elsewhere on Purbeck, there are reports of singles at Winspit on 5th September 1972, 13th September 1975, 17th October 1976, 20th September 1990 and 19th September 1995, and St Aldhelm's Head on 25th September 1985 and 10th September 1995. Otherwise the only autumn sightings from other coastal sites involve two at Langton Herring on 16th September 1971 with one there on 1st September 1989, one at Lodmoor NR on 6th September 1983 and one in the Weymouth area on 15th October 1999. In addition, there are two inland records with a remarkable flock of five on the footpath from Corfe Mullen to Upton on 20th October 1971 and one at Sutton Bingham on 17th September 1983.

	Spring		Autumn		Total	
Portland	17	71%	240	77%	257	77%
Durlston CP	0	0	27	9%	27	8%
Christchurch Harbour	7	29%	26	8%	33	10%
elsewhere	0	0	18	6%	18	5%

Table 691. Distribution of migrants 1956–1999

Although most autumn reports involve 1–2 birds, counts of up to five are not infrequent, but exceeded only twice with six at Portland Bill on 26th September 1957 and eight together at Southwell, Portland on 6th September 1978.

Spring migrants are infrequent with the first reported at Portland Bill on 5th May 1960. After a gap of 18 years a further 23 birds occurred between 1978 and 1999 including annual records during 1985–1991 involving a total of 14 birds. Although there are reports extending from 13th April 1989 at Easton, Portland to 2nd June 1980 at Portland Bill, May is the peak month and accounts for 67% of the total – see Table 690. Of the 24 spring records, 17 are from Portland and seven from Christchurch Harbour – see Table 691.

A total of six birds has been ringed in the county.

The Ortolan Bunting is a summer visitor breeding very locally in parts of central Europe, but more widely in southern and eastern Europe from northern Iberia and Sweden eastwards to Asia Minor, extreme south-west Asia and central Asia to about 100°E. It winters in the northern tropics of Africa.

Postscript 2000–2002

In 2000 and 2001, all records were from Portland with singles on 10th, 13th and 23rd September 2000, and 24th September 2001. In 2002, Portland was again the main site with seven singles during 16th August–5th September, whilst singles were also reported from Hengistbury on 28th August, Durlston CP on 28th–29th August, and St Aldhelm's Head on 29th and 31st August.

Rustic Bunting   *Emberiza rustica*

Accidental: five records

All but one of the five records are from Portland.

    1976   Portland Bill: 29th October
    1987   Easton and Weston, Portland: first-winter male 20th–22nd October
    1990   Southwell, Portland: male 7th April
    1993   Stanpit Marsh, Christchurch Harbour: male 20th March
    1998   Southwell, Portland: first-winter (probably female) 18th–19th October

The Rustic Bunting is a summer visitor breeding from Scandinavia eastwards across Siberia to the Pacific coast. It winters mainly in eastern Asia. A vagrant to Great Britain with 444 records up to 2002.

Little Bunting   *Emberiza pusilla*

A very rare passage migrant and winter visitor: 15 records

Since the first at Christchurch Harbour in 1976, there have been 14 further records of single birds. The four spring birds have occurred during 21st April–1st May, but the ten autumn birds have been recorded over a more extended period from 3rd October to 25th November. There is one winter record for December. The five birds trapped with Reed Buntings inland at Lewell in the autumns of 1993 and 1994 are particularly interesting and indicate that more birds may overwinter than reports suggest.

    1976   Wick Hams, Christchurch Harbour: trapped 1st May
    1981   Portland Bill: female 21st–22nd April, trapped 21st
    1984   Easton, Portland: 14th October
    1988   Weston, Portland: 3rd October
    1989   Portland Bill: first-winter trapped 4th October
    1990   North Portland: different singles at Verne Common and Tout Quarry 25th April
    1993   Lewell: single first-winters trapped 7th October, 9th and 25th November
    1994   Lewell: singles trapped 4th and 17th November
    1995   Stanpit Marsh, Christchurch Harbour: 30th December
    2001   Portland Bill: 16th October
            The Grove, Portland: 20th–21st October

The Little Bunting a summer visitor breeding from Lapland eastwards across Siberia to the Pacific coast. It winters in south-east Asia. A vagrant to the British Isles with 649 records up to 1993.

Yellow-breasted Bunting   *Emberiza aureola*

Accidental: two records

Both records are from Portland Bill.

> 1977   Portland Bill: female/imm. 20th–22nd September
> 1993   Portland Bill: female/imm. 8th–10th September

The Yellow-breasted Bunting is a summer visitor breeding from Finland eastwards across much of northern Asia to the Pacific coast. It winters in south-east Asia. A vagrant to Great Britain with 218 records up to 2002.

Reed Bunting   *Emberiza schoeniclus*

A common resident, winter visitor and passage migrant

Both Mansel-Pleydell (1888) and Blathwayt (1945) considered this species to be a common and numerous resident in suitable localities.

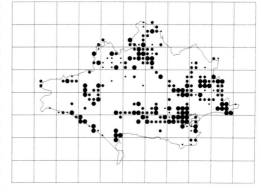

Although there has been little subsequent change in status, there is some evidence of a decline in more recent years. The *BTO Atlas* (1968–1972) revealed evidence of breeding in 31 (84%) 10-km squares (confirmed in 27 and probable in four), whilst the Tetrad Survey (1987–1994) produced a similar result with evidence of breeding in 33 (89%) of the pre-1974 10-km squares (confirmed in 25, probable in six and possible in two). The most notable absence in both surveys was in ST91. The Tetrad Map reflects the Reed Bunting's habitat preferences for wetland and riverine vegetation including damp heathland, bogs and *Phragmites* reedbeds, with breeding concentrated on the damper heaths of the Poole Basin, along river valleys and in the vicinity of coastal marshes.

Selected data on long-term breeding numbers show a variety of trends – see Tables 692 to 696. Populations at Radipole NR, Lodmoor NR and the River Stour between Corfe Mullen and Sturminster Marshall were at a low level during the late 1970s and early 1980s, but increased markedly from the mid-1980s. This increase also occurred to a lesser extent at Arne NR. During the 1990s numbers have declined, most dramatically at Radipole NR where the population has 'crashed' possibly due to the drying of the reedbed. The exception to this overall decline is the River Allen where numbers have been relatively stable throughout the 1990s.

76	77	78	79	80	81	82	83	84	85	86	87	88	89	90	97
28	23	28	20	26	14	12	16	16	25	22	20	18	nc	16	1–3

Table 692. Number of breeding territories at Radipole NR 1976–1997

69	70	71	73	74	75	78	82	83	84	85	86	87	88	89	97
11	14	17	8	9	7	6	6	17	15	27	21	19	18	17	12

Table 693. Number of breeding territories at Lodmoor NR 1969–1997

68	73	74	75	76	79	80	81	83	84	85	86	87	93
15	15	15	15	15	15	20	25	20	20	15	15	12	10

Table 694. Number of breeding territories at Arne NR 1968–1993

78	79	80	81	82	83	84	85	86	87	88	89	90	91	92	93	94	95	96	97	98
6	5	3	5	4	8	4	6	8	8	16	15	13	20	18	12	9	9	8	11	10

Table 695. Number of breeding territories along River Stour between Corfe Mullen and Sturminster Marshall 1978–1998

1989	1990	1991	1992	1993	1994	1995	1996	1997	1998	1999
18	33	24	28	27	32	31	36	36	31	27

Table 696. Number of breeding territories along River Allen 1989–1999

Spring passage at the main coastal watch-points of Portland Bill and Durlston CP is very light and virtually non-existent in some years with seasonal totals rarely exceeding 12 birds – see Table 697. Although migrants are recorded from March through to May, most occur between mid-March and mid-April.

	1980	1981	1982	1983	1984	1985	1986	1987	1988	1989
Portland Bill	28	12	7	21	6	1	1	4	3	1
Durlston CP	nc	6	6	34	7	2	3	4	3	1

	1990	1991	1992	1993	1994	1995	1996	1997	1998	1999
Portland Bill	3	11	1	10	2	0	4	7	1	11
Durlston CP	1	2	0	9	2	2	nc	9	10	1

Table 697. Spring totals (bds) at Portland Bill and Durlston CP 1980–1999

Migration is stronger at Portland Bill and Durlston CP in autumn, but seasonal totals fluctuate considerably from year to year – see Table 698. Passage can extend from August through to early December, but most occurs in October with the peak often during the second half of the month. Peak counts are generally rather modest, ranging in recent years from 5–15 and rarely exceeding 20 birds, the highest being 25 at Portland Bill on 21st October 1981. There is some evidence to suggest that autumn migrants were more numerous at Portland Bill in earlier years, e.g. 140 bird-days during 27th September–5th December 1959, 30 on 26th October 1968 which formed part of an island-wide influx involving an additional 60 birds at two other sites, 46 on 23rd October 1971 including 28W, and 205 bird-days in October 1979. By comparison to the dry coastal watch-points, autumn migration is much heavier at Christchurch Harbour – see Table 698. This reflects the wetland character of the site, but the prominence of visual passage is particularly notable considering how infrequent such movements are reported from Portland Bill and Durlston CP – see Table 699. Not surprisingly peak counts at Christchurch Harbour are considerably higher than at the two other main coastal watch-points, the best being 165E on 12th October 1985, 142 on 23rd September 1985, 136 on 22nd September 1993, 130E on 10th October 1991, 120 on 28th September 1980 and 120E on 28th September 1992. There is also some evidence to suggest that a substantial portion of autumn passage may go largely undetected at other wetland sites. For example, large numbers have been ringed well inland at Lewell including 443 during late October–early November 1990 and 621 in 1993, also 118 were ringed at Keysworth during 1st August–18th September 1992.

	1980	1981	1982	1983	1984	1985	1986	1987	1988	1989
Portland Bill	120	120	138	126	34	85	47	75	110	61
Durlston CP	11	115	73	72	19	14	42	28	49	60
Christchurch Hbr	120	113	181	213	132	363	95	228	208	nc

	1990	1991	1992	1993	1994	1995	1996	1997	1998	1999
Portland Bill	66	57	81	72	46	66	75	102	80	93
Durlston CP	19	20	94	28	25	8	nc	77	22	nc
Christchurch Hbr	233	198	958	418	55	163	463	nc	nc	nc

Table 698. Autumn totals (bds) at the main coastal watch-points 1980–1999

	1981	1982	1983	1984	1985	1986	1987
Total	113E	–	54E, 30W	–	221E; 28S	–	115W; 63E
Max	58E	62E	54E	20W	165E	95E	90W

	1988	1990	1991	1992	1993	1994	1995
Total	–	135E	198E	–	418SorE	55E	131S, 32E
Max	38E	–	130E	120E	136	32E	100S

Table 699. Autumn movements at Christchurch Harbour 1981–1995

Winter flocks are regularly reported, often at sites which are relatively dry. Peak counts typically range up to 50, but rarely exceed 100 birds, the highest being 300 at Studland NNR on 16th January 1987, 200 at Talbot Heath on 10th January 1982, 150 at Lodden Lakes on 21st November 1981 and 130 at Upton Heath on 20th February 1983 with 120 there on 24th October 1982. No winter flocks in excess of 50 have occurred during the 1990s. Cold weather movements are occasionally reported at the main coastal watch-points, e.g. 65 bird-days at Portland Bill during 10th–24th January 1982 with a peak of 20 on 10th.

Since the first reports during the late 1960s, visits of birds to feed in gardens have become a regular feature of the winter. Generally numbers are very small, typically 1–5 birds, so counts of up to 20 from a Verwood garden in 1997 and 1998 are exceptional.

A total of 8,360 birds has been ringed in the county. There have been no foreign recoveries, but there have been two foreign controls from Sweden, one each from Norway and the Netherlands and also two controls from the Channel Islands.

The Reed Bunting breeds widely across much of northern and central Europe, and northern and central Asia as far east as Japan, also more locally in southern Europe, north-west Africa and Asia Minor. It is a summer visitor throughout much of northern and eastern Europe and all but the southernmost part of its Asiatic range. It winters mainly in western, central and southern Europe, north-west Africa, Asia Minor, the Middle East and parts of south-west, central and eastern Asia.

Postscript 2000–2002
At Cranborne Common, 100+ during the second winter period of 2000 is a high count by recent standards.

Sponsored by Tony Taylor

Black-headed Bunting   *Emberiza melanocephala*

A very rare passage migrant: nine records

All records refer to males, seven in spring and early summer between 5th May and 23rd June, one in mid-summer (July) and one in early autumn (August).

- 1970   Weston, Portland: 24th May
- 1974   Southwell, Portland: 4th–6th August
- 1975   Portland Bill: 26th May
- 1977   Verne Common, Portland: 26th–27th May
- 1978   Portland Bill: 5th–9th May, trapped 5th
- 1997   Weston, Portland: first-summer male 3rd June
-        Durlston CP: 23rd June
- 1999   Verne Common Road, Portland: 1st June
- 2000   Portland Bill: 16th July

The Black-headed Bunting is a summer visitor breeding in south-eastern Europe, Asia Minor, the Middle East and extreme south-west Asia. It winters in the north-west of the Indian sub-continent. A vagrant to Great Britain with 166 records up to 2002.

Corn Bunting

Miliaria calandra

A locally common resident

Mansel-Pleydell (1888) described this species as "a common resident, found chiefly in the open parts of the county". Blathwayt (1945) considered it to be a resident and to some extent a passage migrant, which bred numerously, especially in coastal districts.

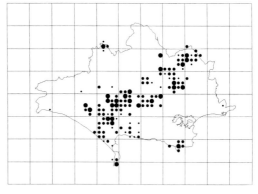

The fortunes of the Corn Bunting in Dorset follow the national pattern. After a decline during the early part of the 20th Century, the revival in agriculture during the Second World War resulted in a reversal of this trend, with an expansion in population that reached a peak in the early 1970s. Reports from the 1950s suggest that despite being absent from much of the west and north of the county, some westwards expansion was evident along the coast towards Burton Bradstock. A survey in 1966 revealed 90 singing males, but only the south-east was well covered. The *BTO Atlas* (1968–1972) represents the peak for the Corn Bunting in Dorset with evidence of breeding in 32 (86%) 10-km squares (confirmed in 19, probable in 12 and possible in one). The species was widely distributed throughout much of the county including the Poole Basin and the Blackmore Vale. The main strongholds were in open country in the east and along the coast, whilst it was noted that the central chalklands had been increasingly colonised during the 1960s. Corn Buntings were absent mainly from the extreme west (ST30, ST40, ST50 and SY39). The next survey in 1978–1980 with good coverage (except in the three squares west of Blandford) produced an estimated total of 170 singing males.

Since the mid-1970s, however, there has been a slow but steady decline, which accelerated suddenly during the 1980s and early 1990s. As a result, the Tetrad Survey (1987–1994) revealed evidence of breeding in only 21 (57%) of the pre-1974 10-km squares (confirmed in 12, probable in six and possible in three). Much of this decline had occurred in the Poole Basin, the Blackmore Vale and along parts of the coastal fringes from Hengistbury in the east to Burton Bradstock in the west. At Portland Bill a relatively stable population of 20-25 singing males during 1978–1982 collapsed to nine in 1983 and 1–3 during 1984–1988 followed by apparent extinction with isolated breeding attempts in 1994 and 1998. In the east, breeding ceased at Hengistbury and in the Wallisdown area of Bournemouth in the mid-1970s. The reasons for this decline are not entirely clear. The collapse of the Portland Bill population is thought to be associated with the more intensive methods of cutting silage, whilst its disappearance from the south-east of the county is due to urban development.

The Tetrad Map shows a breeding distribution virtually restricted to the chalk downlands, but extending from south-west of Dorchester across the south Dorset lowlands to the fringes of the Fleet. In addition, there were isolated populations associated with the limestone areas of Portland, Purbeck in the vicinity of St Aldhelm's Head, and the North Dorset Limestone Ridges to the north of Sherborne (ST61 and ST62).

Since the Tetrad Survey (1987–1994), there is some evidence to suggest that the decline in the breeding population has either halted or the rate of decline diminished. The presence of birds in 18 (49%) of the pre-1974 10-km squares in 1998 is encouraging. Furthermore, breeding reports in 1999, including 3–4 singing males at Portland, but not seemingly in the Bill area, suggest a further small increase in the population.

Despite the fluctuations in the breeding population over the past 50 years, it is surprising that there has been little change in the size of autumn and winter flocks during the same period. Peak counts usually range from 20–50 and rarely exceed 100 birds, the highest counts being 150 at Herrison in late winter 1989, 130 at Wool on 22nd January 1989, 120 nearby at Winfrith on 19th January 1989 and 117 at Holcombe Bottom on 29th February 1992.

The limited passage sometimes recorded from the main coastal watch-points in spring (March–May) and autumn (September–November) refers to local dispersal. Since 1990, seasonal totals at Portland Bill and Durlston CP have been in single figures.

A total of 1,443 birds has been ringed in the county.

The Corn Bunting breeds in north-west Africa and throughout much of Europe north to Great Britain and Denmark, extending eastwards to Asia Minor, parts of the Middle East, and south-west and south-central Asia. Some populations are migratory with birds wintering mainly within, but a little to the south of the breeding range, most notably along the Arabian Gulf.

Postscript 2000–2002

There is continuing evidence to suggest a slight improvement in the Corn Bunting's breeding status in the county, which is also supported by a high winter count of 100+ at Maiden Castle during December 2001.

Bobolink   *Dolichonyx oryzivorus*

Accidental: two records

1992   Southwell, Portland: first-winter 14th–15th September; same near Portland Bird Observatory
            18th September
2002   Wick Fields, Christchurch Harbour: first-winter 1st–23rd November

The Bobolink is a summer visitor, breeding in southern Canada and the northern USA and wintering in South America. A vagrant to Great Britain with 24 records up to 2002.

POTENTIAL ADDITIONS TO
THE DORSET LIST

Chinese Yellow Bittern   *Ixobrychus sinensis*

Accidental: one record of uncertain status

A first-winter *Ixobrychus* bittern was found dying, "having flown into a concrete post", at Radipole NR on 23rd November 1962. It was initially thought to be a Little Bittern *Ixobrychus minutus*, but was considered atypical in certain minor respects and was therefore sent to the British Museum where it was identified as a Chinese Yellow Bittern *Ixobrychus sinensis*. At the time, the bird was presumed to be an escape and the record was generally disregarded until recently. There is no good reason to doubt the original identification, so the main question is whether the Chinese Yellow Bittern was kept in captivity in western Europe in the early 1960s. The recent occurrence of a Chinese Pond Heron *Ardeola bacchus* in Hungary in August 2000, which, is the second record for the Western Palearctic, the first being in Norway in autumn 1973, has renewed interest in the true status of Radipole's Chinese Yellow Bittern.

Catharacta skua sp.

Accidental: one record

As a result of winter storms a confiding *Catharacta* skua was present on the beach at West Bexington from 27th January to 4th February 1996. Although at the time the bird was generally assumed to be an 'odd looking' immature Great Skua *Catharacta skua* in winter plumage, further consideration including examination of photographic evidence suggested that it could be a South Polar Skua *Catharaca maccormicki* – see *Birding World* Vol 13, Number 8, September 2000. Interest in the identification of the West Bexington skua was renewed with the subsequent discovery and identification, based on DNA analysis, of 'wrecked' immature Brown Skuas *Catharacta antarctica* on St Agnes, Isles of Scilly in October 2001 and at Aberavon, Glamorgan in February 2002 – see *Birding World* Vol 15, Number 9, October 2002. It should be mentioned that these records are still under consideration by the appropriate authorities. Whether or not the identity of the West Bexington skua can be decided with certainty solely on photographic evidence remains to be seen.

CATEGORY D SPECIES

Baikal Teal
Anas formosa

Two records

1969 Brownsea: male caught, ringed and released 1st January
1998 Abbotsbury: male with plastic and metal rings 22nd November–11th January 1999

The Abbotsbury bird was obviously an escape, the status of the Brownsea bird remains uncertain.

The Baikal Teal breeds in north and north-east Siberia and winters in Japan, Korea and eastern and south-eastern China.

Marbled Duck
Marmaronetta angustirostris

Two records

1988 Wareham: two 2nd October
1999 Warmwell GPs: pair 30th August–4th September

The Warmwell record has been accepted by BBRC into category D. The fact that these birds arrived at the same time as an influx of Marbled Duck into northern Spain, frequented a typical habitat of small reed-fringed lakes, and their wary nature, all indicate a possible wild origin. Although currently placed in category D, this record represents the best credentials yet for the addition of this species into category A.

The Marbled Duck breeds in isolated pockets in north-west Africa, Spain, and eastwards from the eastern Mediterranean through the Middle East to west-central Asia. It is migratory and dispersive after the breeding season.

White Pelican (Great White Pelican)
Pelecanus onocrotalus

Three records

1951 Lodmoor NR: 7th to 21st April, perhaps 7–10 days earlier and possibly until 24th April;
      presumed same in Poole Harbour area 14th and 18th July and at Wool 15th July
1975 Portland Bill: 5th September
1996 Stanpit Marsh, Christchurch Harbour: 21st–22nd September

The Portland Bill record has been accepted by BBRC into category D.

The White Pelican is a summer visitor breeding in isolated colonies in south-eastern Europe, Turkey and west-central Asia. Most of the European population winters in Egypt. There are other populations scattered throughout sub-Saharan Africa, in the north-west of the Indian sub-continent and south-east Asia.

Greater Flamingo
Phoenicopterus ruber

Six records

1916   Weymouth: shot on 26th August
1932   Abbotsbury: two in November
1953   Poole Harbour: 23rd March–1st April
1968   The Fleet: 27th December–6th April 1969
1975   Portland Bill: two flying past 21st July
1986–89 The Fleet: one present throughout the period; presumed same at Lodmoor NR 6th May 1988

The 1968 record has been accepted by BBRC into category D.

The Greater Flamingo breeds, often erratically, in isolated colonies in France (Camargue), southern Spain, north-west Africa, Egypt, west and south-west Asia including the north-west of the Indian sub-continent, in sub-Saharan Africa and the Caribbean area. It is widely migratory and dispersive throughout the Mediterranean Basin, Arabia, south-west Asia including the Indian sub-continent, sub-Saharan Africa and the Caribbean area.

Saker (Saker Falcon)   *Falco cherrug*

Four records

1996   Poole Harbour: ad. female 17th February
2000   Portland: a large falcon, considered to be this species, seen at several sites 15th March–10th April
2001   Abbotsbury: 17th December
2002   Brownsea: 26th May

The Saker is a summer visitor breeding from the Czech Republic and Hungary eastwards across Europe, Asia Minor, parts of the Middle East and much of central Asia. It winters mainly to the south of its breeding range in south-east Europe, Asia Minor, the Middle East, south-central Asia and East Africa.

Red-headed Bunting   *Emberiza bruniceps*

Possibly a very rare passage migrant

The occurrence of this species as a genuine vagrant to the British Isles is controversial. There is strong evidence to suggest that many, if not all, of the records from the 1950s through to at least the 1970s were escapes from captivity. At the time, large numbers were imported into the British Isles and Low Countries. With a reduction in the importation of cage birds from the Indian sub-continent in recent years, the Red-headed Bunting has become much less numerous in captivity. Consequently, it seems increasingly likely that some of the more recent reports may involve 'wild birds'.

The pattern of occurrence in Dorset closely follows the national trend. The species was first recorded in the county at Portland Bill on 11th October 1955. Subsequently, there were frequent sightings during 1960–1981 – see Table 700. Despite this, it seems likely that the Red-headed Bunting was under-reported during this period. All records during 1960–1980 were from Portland Bill, the 1981 sighting involving a male at Parkstone on 29th September. Although records extend from 3rd May 1978 to 11th October 1955, the peak months are July and September – see Table 701.

1960	1961	1962	1963	1964	1965	1966	1967	1968	1969	1970
1	0	0	?	?	1	1	1	0	0	0

1971	1972	1973	1974	1975	1976	1977	1978	1979	1980	1981
0	0	2	1	1	1	1	1	0	1	1

Table 700. Annual totals 1960–1981

May	Jun	Jul	Aug	Sep	Oct
1	0	4	1	6	1

Table 701. Monthly totals 1955–1981

Apparently there were no reports during 1982–1990. Subsequently, the species has occurred in five years during the 1990s as follows:

1991   Durlston CP: male 26th August
1992   Portland Bill: male 29th July
1994   Easton, Portland: male 5th–6th July
         Langton Herring: male 18th July–13th August, possibly same as above
1997   Portland: male 27th July
1998   Durlston CP: male 15th–16th May

The Red-headed Bunting breeds from the northern end of the Caspian Sea east through Kazakhstan into Mongolia and north-west China, and south into Iran, Afghanistan and Pakistan. It winters in the Indian sub-continent.

SELECTED CATEGORY E SPECIES

Snow Goose   *Anser caerulescens*

Scarce feral resident

The status of this species in Dorset is uncertain, but most records are presumed to refer to feral birds or escapes. The species was apparently first reported in 1972 with one at Nether Cerne from 20th to 22nd April. Subsequently a very small feral population became established in the Poole Harbour area between 1977 and at least 1990 with breeding attempted on Brownsea in 1977 (one young hatched), 1980 (eggs predated), 1981 (eggs predated) and 1983 (nest deserted) – see Table 702.

1977	1978	1979	1980	1981	1982	1983	1984	1985	1986	1987	1988	1989	1990
5	7	nc	5	3	1	1	1	3	3	1	4	2	1

Table 702. Maxima in Poole Harbour 1977–1990

Sightings elsewhere in the county are mainly from coastal sites, notably Christchurch Harbour and the Fleet, with a few records from the river valleys and the north of the county. These may well refer to wanderers from Poole Harbour and perhaps the small feral population based in north-east Hampshire, which reached a maximum of 37 birds in 1992. The most interesting reports are given below:

1980   The Fleet: ten 7th to 10th April
1981   Lodmoor NR: one arrived during cold weather on 25th December and remained until 10th
          January 1982 wandering to Radipole NR on 25th December and 6th January and
          Abbotsbury on 31st December
1983   Durlston CP: one flying west with a flock of Gannets on 18th September

The Snow Goose breeds from north-east Siberia eastwards across Arctic North America to north-west Greenland and winters in the USA and Mexico. In the British Isles genuinely wild birds are considered to occur amongst flocks of Pink-footed Geese (mainly in northern England and Scotland) and Greenland White-fronted Geese (Wexford Slobs and Islay). Otherwise there is a small British feral population.

IMPORTANT BIRD RECORDS FROM PRE-1974 SOUTH-WEST HAMPSHIRE
(now Dorset)
including Christchurch Harbour

INTRODUCTION

This section is a summary of the more significant records from this area prior to 1974.

The 19th Century records are largely based on *Birds of Hampshire and the Isle of Wight* (Kelsall & Munn 1905) and Tony Wise's excellent publication *Birds of Christchurch in the Nineteenth Century* (CHOG 1988). Unfortunately many of the records, particularly those in the Hart and Malmesbury Collections, do not refer to specific sites within the Christchurch area. Although it is likely that most specimens were obtained from areas that are now within Dorset, there is a possibility that some came from areas that remain within Hampshire. Only records that were definitely obtained from sites in present-day Hampshire are excluded.

The main sources of records for the 20th Century prior to 1974 are *Birds of Hampshire and the Isle of Wight* (Cohen 1963), *A Revised List of Hampshire and Isle of Wight Birds* (Cohen & Taverner 1972), the Hampshire Bird Reports up to 1974 and the annual reports of the Christchurch Harbour Ornithological Group from 1956 to 1974.

THE RECORDS

Ruddy Shelduck   *Tadorna ferruginea*

There is a 19th Century record for August 1892, presumably of wild origin.

Black Grouse   *Tetrao tetrix*

The species apparently occurred on the Malmesbury Estate near Hurn until 1902 with a total of 81 shot during the first 40 years of the 19th Century.

Great Shearwater   *Puffinus gravis*

There are two 19th Century records for 1878 and 1894.

Little Bittern   *Ixobrychus minutus*

There are four 19th Century records including singles obtained at Firgrove Beat, Hurn on 26th April 1862 and on the River Stour at Hurn on 9th June 1893, and one subsequently:

    1963   Boscombe: male picked up on the beach 21st April. The bird refused to eat and died a few days later.

Night Heron (Black-crowned Night Heron)   *Nycticorax nycticorax*

There are four 19th Century records including one shot on the River Stour at Christchurch on 6th November 1891, and one subsequently:

    1962   Christchurch: imm. from early January to 28th January

Squacco Heron   *Ardeola ralloides*

There are two 19th Century records involving a male in the Hart Collection at Christchurch procured on 8th June 1832, and one in Lord Malmesbury's collection at Heron Court, which was killed on the River Stour at Blackwater Ferry in June 1893.

Little Egret   *Egretta garzetta*

There is one 19th Century record of a bird shot at Christchurch in July 1882, and one subsequently:

    1956   Hengistbury: 8th May

Purple Heron
Ardea purpurea

There is one record:

> 1970   Hengistbury: adult flying west 13th September

White Stork
Ciconia ciconia

There are two 19th Century records including two in Poole Harbour in April 1884, which were subsequently shot at Christchurch.

Glossy Ibis
Plegadis falcinellus

There are three 19th Century records involving five birds including an immature pair killed in a meadow near Christchurch in September 1859, and two subsequently:

> 1929   Christchurch: one shot 26th October
> 1972   Stanpit Marsh, Christchurch Harbour: 10th August

White-tailed Eagle
Haliaeetus albicilla

There are four 19th Century records involving one shot on the Moors River on 21st February 1824, one shot at Hengistbury on 4th December 1871 with one roosting there for most of the summer of 1885, and one killed at Quomp Copse on 9th January 1893.

Red-footed Falcon
Falco vespertinus

There are two 19th Century records involving a male at Parley in 1854, and a female at Tuckton on 16th May 1882.

Spotted Crake
Porzana porzana

There are several 19th Century records including breeding.

Little Crake
Porzana parva

There are three 19th Century records including singles on 22nd October 1866 and 18th May 1885, and one subsequently:

> 1970   Wick Hams, Christchurch Harbour: female 21st–27th March

Baillon's Crake
Porzana pusilla

Five adults were obtained between 1863 and 1894, whilst there is a fairly convincing, but seemingly un–substantiated breeding record for July 1882.

Crane (Common Crane)
Grus grus

There is one 19th Century record from Iford in 1852, and one subsequently:

> 1963   Hengistbury: 26SE on 3rd November

Black-winged Stilt
Himantopus himantopus

There is a 19th Century record of a male in July 1873.

Collared Pratincole
Glareola pratincola

There is one record:

> 1957   Stanpit Marsh, Christchurch Harbour: 14th September

Killdeer
Charadrius vociferus

The first British specimen was shot in a potato field near Knapp Mill in April 1859.

Dotterel (Eurasian Dotterel)   *Charadrius morinellus*
There are three 19th Century records including five obtained from a 'trip' of these birds at the Portfields in May 1854, and two subsequently:

    1960   Hengistbury: 31st August and 2nd September
    1972   Christchurch Harbour: 27th–28th May

Pectoral Sandpiper   *Calidris melanotos*
There are two records:

    1966   Stanpit Marsh, Christchurch Harbour: 9th October
    1968   Stanpit Marsh, Christchurch Harbour: 7th September

Great Snipe   *Gallinago media*
Nine specimens were obtained between 1849 and 1883.

Short-billed or Long-billed Dowitcher   *Limnodromus griseus/scolopaceus*
There are four records:

    1872   Christchurch Harbour: one shot September
    1902   Stanpit Marsh, Christchurch Harbour: juv. female shot 7th October
    1968   Stanpit Marsh, Christchurch Harbour: two 23rd–27th September
    1973   Stanpit Marsh, Christchurch Harbour: 2nd–3rd December

Long-tailed Skua   *Stercorarius longicaudus*
There are two 19th Century records for 1889 and 1891, and one subsequently:

    1970   Hengistbury: 17th June

Sabine's Gull   *Larus sabini*
One resting on the fluke of an old anchor in Christchurch Harbour on 26th September 1896. There have been two subsequent records:

    1921   Christchurch Harbour: 31st August
    1970   Hengistbury: imm. 19th September

Gull-billed Tern   *Sterna nilotica*
An adult obtained near Christchurch on 14th May 1872, and one subsequently:

    1959   Stanpit Marsh, Christchurch Harbour: 2nd September

Caspian Tern   *Sterna caspia*
One shot at Highcliffe in early autumn 1852, and two subsequently:

    1958   Mudeford: 7th September
    1968   Stanpit Marsh, Christchurch Harbour: 20th July

Whiskered Tern   *Chlidonias hybrida*
There is a single 19th Century record in June 1875, and one subsequently:

    1967   Stanpit Marsh, Christchurch Harbour: 13th–16th August

White-winged Black Tern (White-winged Tern)   *Chlidonias leucopterus*
There are two 19th Century records on 2nd–3rd May 1883 and 18th May 1886, and one subsequently:

    1967   Hengistbury: imm. on 2nd–3rd November

Black Guillemot   *Cepphus grylle*
Five specimens were obtained during the 19th Century including one in breeding plumage shot in April 1877.

Pallas's Sandgrouse
Syrrhaptes paradoxus

Six specimens were obtained during the famous irruption year of 1888.

Yellow-billed Cuckoo
Coccyzus americanus

There is one record:

    1973   Chewton Glen, Highcliffe: 20th October, found dead two days later

    There is an old record of one shot near Avon Castle on 30th October 1901. Avon Castle now lies just within Dorset close to the present Hampshire boundary, but which side of the boundary this individual was shot is unknown!

Scops Owl (Eurasian Scops Owl)
Otus scops

There is a single 19th Century record.

Bee-eater (European Bee-eater)
Merops apiaster

There are two 19th Century records including a male on 21st May 1888.

Roller (European Roller)
Coracias garrulus

There is a single 19th Century record.

Hoopoe
Upupa epops

There are 19th Century records of successful breeding in 1886, 1893, 1897 and 1898.

Shore Lark (Horned Lark)
Eremophila alpestris

There is a single 19th Century record involving a male and female on 21st October 1875.

Red-rumped Swallow
Hirundo daurica

There is one record:

    1973   Hengistbury: 12th September

Tawny Pipit
Anthus campestris

One shot at Stanpit Marsh, Christchurch Harbour in August 1879.

Citrine Wagtail
Motacilla citreola

There is one record:

    1966   Stanpit Marsh, Christchurch Harbour: two first-winter 15th October

Alpine Accentor
Prunella collaris

One shot close to Constable's House during 1885.

Bluethroat
Luscinia svecica

There were seven records from Christchurch Harbour during 1958–1971 on dates ranging from 4th September to 14th October. These include a first-winter female trapped on 7th September 1958 and controlled in Spain on 9th November of the same year, representing the first foreign recovery of a British ringed bird, and a first-winter male of the White-spotted race *L. s. cyanecula* trapped on 19th September 1959.

White's Thrush
Zoothera dauma

The first British specimen, a female, was shot near Heron Court on 24th January 1828.

Aquatic Warbler
Acrocephalus paludicola

There is a 19th Century record involving a bird shot in September 1876. More recently, a minimum of 18 birds were recorded in autumn from Christchurch Harbour during 1956–1973 including three trapped August–September 1972 and two in August 1973. Most birds were trapped.

Great Reed Warbler *Acrocephalus arundinaceus*

There is one record:

    1900   Christchurch: one shot 10th May

Icterine Warbler *Hippolais icterina*

There is one record:

    1966   Hengistbury: 10th September

Melodious Warbler *Hippolais polyglotta*

There is one record:

    1973   Hengistbury: 12th September

Crested Tit *Parus cristatus*

One of the continental race *P. c. mitratus* was shot from a clump of fir trees near Stanpit Marsh, Christchurch Harbour during 1846.

Golden Oriole (European Golden Oriole) *Oriolus oriolus*

There are breeding records during the 19th Century.

Lesser Grey Shrike *Lanius minor*

The first British specimen was shot at Heron Court in September 1842.

Woodchat Shrike *Lanius senator*

There are two 19th Century records involving a female on 21st June 1875 and a male on 29th May 1880, and two subsequently:

    1968   Hengistbury: ad. 19th May
    1970   Hengistbury: imm. trapped 14th October

Nutcracker (Spotted Nutcracker) *Nucifraga caryocatactes*

A male at St Catherine's Hill on 6th November 1868.

Chough (Red-billed Chough) *Pyrrhocorax pyrrhocorax*

Three shot in Christchurch Harbour on 3rd January 1871.

Rose-coloured Starling (Rosy Starling) *Sturnus roseus*

There are three 19th Century records including single males in 1841 and on 8th July 1862.

Serin (European Serin) *Serinus serinus*

There are three records:

    1966   Hengistbury: two 15th October
    1969   Wick Hams, Christchurch Harbour: male 27th October and 5th November
    1970   Stanpit Marsh, Christchurch Harbour: male 13th December

BIRD HIGHLIGHTS OF 2003

The main bird highlights of 2003 are given below. It should be noted that this list is not comprehensive, as the County Recorder had not received all reports at the time of going to press (March 2004). Unless indicated otherwise, these records have not yet been assessed by the British Birds Rarities Committee or the Dorset Rare Birds Panel.

Bean Goose   *Anser fabalis*
A flock of 6 of the Tundra race *A. f. rossicus* at Abbotsbury from 16th to at least 27th February.

Black Brant   *Branta bernicla nigricans*
Singles in the Poole Harbour area from 10th February to 14th March and on the Fleet from 19th October to 2nd November (5th and 6th county records).

Green-winged Teal   *Anas carolinensis*
A male at Coward's Marsh, Christchurch on 16th March and a first-winter male at Sutton Bingham from 12th to 24th November.

Ring-necked Duck   *Aythya collaris*
A female (of unknown origin, possibly pinioned) on the River Stour at Throop from 24th March to 7th April and at nearby Wick, Christchurch from 24th to 27th December. A female at Abbotsbury from 24th April to 7th May.

Ferruginous Duck   *Aythya nyroca*
The regularly returning male remained at Morden Park Lake until at least 26th January with presumably the same bird at Little Sea on 4th and 5th January. This bird was first recorded back in 1994. A first-winter female at Abbotsbury from 1st to 11th December visiting Radipole NR on 7th.

Lesser Scaup   *Aythya affinis*
The long-staying male remained at Little Sea from 2002 to 31st March and returned for its third winter from 15th October into 2004.

Surf Scoter   *Melanitta perspicillata*
An immature flew past Portland Bill on 16th January (10th county record and the fourth bird in five years).

Sooty Shearwater   *Puffinus griseus*
Unseasonal singles at Portland Bill on 2nd, 9th and 20th February.

Cattle Egret   *Bubulcus ibis*
One roosted at Abbotsbury on 23rd March (9th county record).

Great White Egret (Great Egret)   *Ardea alba*
Several records this year. The first flew over Christchurch Harbour on 24th January. On the Fleet, one was present at Abbotsbury or Rodden Hive from 26th to 29th June with it or another at Abbotsbury on 4th August. A colour-ringed bird appeared at Sturminster Marshall GP on 16th August with presumably the same bird nearby at Wimborne on 25th August after a brief visit to Hampshire, and either it or another colour-ringed bird again present intermittently at Sturminster Marshall GP from 4th to 27th October. Finally, one was at Abbotsbury on 20th October. It is difficult to assess how many birds were involved in these sightings, but assuming that only the Sturminster Marshall GP/Wimborne bird was colour-ringed, then at least three possibly five different birds occurred during the year (8th–12th county records).

White Stork   *Ciconia ciconia*
Singles at Coward's Marsh, Christchurch on 17th and 18th March, flying over Dorchester on 29th March and flying over Hengistbury on 9th May.

Black Kite   *Milvus migrans*
Singles at Portland Bill on 8th April and 30th August, a moulting adult in the Weymouth/Portland area from 6th to 10th August and two at St Aldhelm's Head on 12th August. The August sightings represent the first autumn records for the county.

Montagu's Harrier   *Circus pygargus*
Birds held territory for the second year running in the traditional area and successfully reared young.

Rough-legged Buzzard   *Buteo lagopus*
One near Blandford on 12th May.

Red-footed Falcon   *Falco vespertinus*
A first-summer female flew west at Abbotsbury on 29th May with presumably the same at West Bexington later the same day.

Long-tailed Skua   *Stercorarius longicaudus*
An adult at Chesil Cove on 18th May, and singles at Portland Bill on 8th and 13th September.

Sabine's Gull   *Larus sabini*
An unseasonal bird at Portland Bill on 29th May with a single there on 14th November.

Caspian Gull   *Larus cachinnans cachinnans*
A first-winter bird at Corfe Mullen Tip on 19th February. Although this is the first record to be accepted for Dorset, there are several other outstanding claims.

Caspian Tern   *Sterna caspia*
At Portland Bill, two flying west on 7th September and one flying east on the late date of 15th November.

Alpine Swift   *Apus melba*
There was an exceptional report of one at Sandbanks on 5th March, which is by far the earliest county record. Otherwise singles at Lodmoor NR on 28th April, Abbotsbury on 3rd May and Lodmoor NR again on 4th June.

Bee-eater (European Bee-eater)   *Merops apiaster*
Singles at Portland Bill/Southwell on 2nd June and Weston, Portland on 7th June.

Red-rumped Swallow   *Hirundo daurica*
One at Radipole NR on 25th April and subsequently at Lodmoor NR from 25th to 27th April.

Richard's Pipit   *Anthus novaeseelandiae*
Singles at Stanpit Marsh, Christchurch Harbour on 14th October, Portland Bill on 22nd October, and Southwell, Portland on 24th October.

Tawny Pipit   *Anthus campestris*
Singles at Durlston CP on 30th August, Portland Bill on 6th September and West Bay near Bridport on 7th September.

Red-throated Pipit   *Anthus cervinus*
Singles at Weston, Portland on 24th September and Portland Bill on 20th October.

Waxwing (Bohemian Waxwing)   *Bombycilla garrulus*
One, possibly two, at Sandford on 26th January with one found dead nearby at Wareham on 2nd February.

Siberian Stonechat   *Saxicola torquata maura*
One at Weston, Portland on 13th October.

Aquatic Warbler   *Acrocephalus paludicola*
One at Lodmoor NR on 22nd September.

Eastern Olivaceous Warbler   *Hippolais pallida*
One trapped at Portland Bill on 31st August (2nd record for Portland Bird Observatory and the county).

Subalpine Warbler   *Sylvia cantillans*
A first-summer female trapped at Portland Bill on 15th June.

Greenish Warbler   *Phylloscopus trochiloides*
A singing male at Verne Common, Portland on 7th June (10th county record).

Pallas's Warbler (Pallas's Leaf Warbler)   *Phylloscopus proregulus*
At least 11 birds were reported during 27th October–21st November including c. eight on Portland, and singles at Lodmoor NR on 27th October, Winspit on 28th October and Lulworth Cove on 6th November.

Yellow-browed Warbler   *Phylloscopus inornatus*
Astonishingly, singles at Lytchett Bay from 5th December into 2004 and at Radipole NR from 8th to 19th December are the first records of wintering in the county.

Hume's Warbler (Hume's Leaf Warbler)   *Phylloscopus humei*
One at Pennsylvania Castle, Portland on 21st and 22nd November (5th county record).

Radde's Warbler   *Phylloscopus schwarzi*
Singles at Portland Bill on 13th October (trapped) and Wick Fields, Christchurch Harbour on 21st October (10th and 11th county records). The latter is the first sighting from the CHOG recording area.

Dusky Warbler   *Phylloscopus fuscatus*
Singles at Portland Bill on 9th November (trapped) and nearby at Reap Lane, Southwell on 10th November.

Penduline Tit (Eurasian Penduline Tit)   *Remiz pendulinus*
One at Abbotsbury on 24th October, and two at Lodmoor NR on 26th October with one there the next day and presumably the same two again on 15th and 17th December (7th and 8th county records).

Woodchat Shrike   *Lanius senator*
Singles at Langton Herring on 26th May (first-summer male), Lodmoor NR on 31st May (male), Worbarrow Bay on 1st June (female) and Verne Common, Portland on 4th June. A juvenile at Talbot Heath, Bournemouth on 14th September.

Chough (Red-billed Chough)   *Pyrrhocorax pyrrhocorax*
A long-staying individual remained at St Aldhelm's Head from 27th January to 31st March with two reported there on 30th March. For many Dorset birdwatchers, this was the undoubted highlight of the year. Despite the recent series of sightings from Portland Bill in spring 2001, this was still a most unexpected occurrence.

Rose-coloured Starling (Rosy Starling)   *Sturnus roseus*
An adult at Blacknor, Portland on 5th June. Single juveniles at various sites at Portland from 31st August to at least 7th September, Abbotsbury on 18th and 19th September and Wyke Regis, Weymouth on 2nd October (possibly involving the same bird).

Common Rosefinch   *Carpodacus erythrinus*
An exceptional year for this species in Dorset. During the summer there was a first-summer male singing at Verne Common, Portland on 21st June and a female/first-summer male at West Bay near Bridport on 6th July. Portland produced further singles in the autumn at Fortuneswell on 2nd August and 3rd October, Reap Lane, Southwell on 20th September, and the Bill on 1st (trapped), 6th (trapped) and 13th October.

Cirl Bunting   *Emberiza cirlus*
Singles at Portland Bill on 3rd October and Hengistbury on 8th October are the first county records since 1994!

Yellow-breasted Bunting   *Emberiza aureola*
A female/immature at Portland Bill on 3rd September (3rd record for Portland Bill and the county).

GAZETTEER

Abbotsbury Beach	SY 5584–5684	Bindon Abbey	SY 8586
Abbotsbury Hill	SY 5685	Bingham's Melcombe	ST 772021
Abbotsbury Swannery	SY 5783–5784	Binnegar or Binegar Hall	SY 884872
Abbotsbury Village	SY 5785	Bishop's Caundle	ST 6913
Ackling Dyke	SU 0115–0116	Black Down	SY 6087–6187
Acton	SY 9878	Black Hill	SY 8394
AEE Winfrith	see Winfrith	Blackers Hole (Purbeck cliffs)	SZ 007768
Alderholt	SU 1112–1212	Blacknor (Portland)	SY 677714
All Hallows CBs	SU 025126	Blackwater Ferry	SZ 130960
Allen, River/Valley	SZ 0199–SU 0113	Blagdon/Hill	SU 0517
Almer	SY 9198	Blandford	ST 890070
Alton Pancras	ST 6902	Blandford Camp	ST 920080
Alum Chine	SZ 0790	Blandford St Mary	ST 8805
Alweston	ST 6614	Bloxworth	SY 8894
Anvil Point (Purbeck cliffs)	SZ 028768	Bloxworth Heath	SY 8892
Arish Mell (Purbeck cliffs)	SY 855803	Blue Lagoon (Poole Harbour)	SZ 035900
Arne Bay (Poole Harbour)	SY 980890	Bockhampton	see Lower Bockhampton
Arne Farm	SY 973882	Boscombe	SZ 1191
Arne Heath	SY 9688	Boscombe Hospital	SZ 1192
Arne NR	SY 970880	Boscombe Overcliff	SZ 1191
Arne Spit (Poole Harbour)	SY 982888	Boscombe Pier	SZ 112910
Ashley Heath	SU 1104	Bottlebush Down	SU 0115–0215
Asker, River	SY 4692–5492	Bourne Valley	SZ 0693
Askerswell	SY 5292	Bournemouth/Town Centre	SZ 0891
Avon Beach	SZ 1892–1992	Bournemouth East Cliff	SZ 0990
Avon Castle	SU 1303	Bournemouth Pier	SZ 089905
Avon Causeway	SZ 1497	Boveridge	SU 0614–0615
Avon Forest Park	SU 1203	Bovington Camp	SY 830890
Avon, River/Valley	SZ 1692–SU 1307	Bovington/Training Area	SY 8390
Avon Village	SZ 1498	Bowerswain	SU 008099
Avonbourne (Bournemouth)	SZ 123932	Bowleaze Cove	SY 7081
Axe, River	ST 3202–4904	Boys Hill	ST 6710
Badbury Rings	ST 9602–9603	Boys Wood	SU 0509
Bagber	ST 7513	Brackett's Copse	ST 5107
Baiter (Poole)	SZ 0290	Bradford Abbas	ST 5814
Balaclava Bay (Portland)	SY 698742	Bradford Peverell	SY 6592–6593
Ballard Down	SZ 0381–0481	Brand's Bay (Poole Harbour)	SZ 0185–0285
Bardolf Manor (Puddletown)	SY 7695	Branksome	SZ 0592
Barleycrates Lane (Portland)	SY 685710	Branksome Chine	SZ 0689
Barnsfield Heath	SU 1000–1200	Branksome Station	SZ 058920
Batcombe	SY 6104	Brenscombe Hill	SY 9881–9981
Batcome Down	SY 6204	Briantspuddle	SY 8193
Bat's Head (Purbeck cliffs)	SY 795803	Bride, River/Valley	SY 4789–SY 5888
Beacon Heath Pond	SY 973946	Bridehead Lake	SY 588888
Beaminster	ST 4701–4801	Bridging Camp (the Fleet)	SY 6577
Beaulieu Wood	ST 7006	Bridport	SY 4692–4693
Bellows Cross	SU 065137	Brit Estuary	SY 4690
Bere Farm Pond	SY 942934	Brit, River	SY 4690–ST 5001
Bere Heath	SY 8692	Broadmayne	SY 7286
Bere Regis	SY 8494–8495	Broadstone	SZ 0095
Bere Regis CBs	SY 8494 & SY 8593	Broadstone GC	SZ 0096
Bere Stream	SY 8591–ST 8001	Broadwey	SY 6683
Berry Hill (Bournemouth)	SZ 1096	Brockington Farm	SU 019107
Bestwall (Wareham)	SY 929873	Brownsea or Branksea (Island)	SZ 020880
Bexington	see West Bexington	Brownsea Lagoon	SZ 029880
Bincleaves (Weymouth)	SY 6877	Bryanston/Park	ST 8706–8707
Bincombe Hill	SY 6884	Bryanston Weir	ST 878066

Buckland Newton	ST 6805–6905	Chideock	SY 4292
Buckland Ripers	SY 6482	Child Okeford	ST 8312
Bucknowle	SY 9481	Chilfrome	SY 5898
Budden's GP/Farm Lakes	SY 8789	Chiswell (Portland)	SY 6873
Budworth School (Weymouth)	SY 653791	Chiswell Lane (Portland)	SY 6873
Bulbarrow	ST 7705	Christchurch	SZ 1592
Burton (Christchurch)	SZ 1694–1695	Christchurch Beach	see Avon Beach
Burton Bradstock	SY 4889–4989	Christchurch Harbour	SU 1791
Burton Cliff	SY 4889	Christchurch Watermeadows	SZ 158938
Burton Mere	SY 508879	Church Knowle	SY 9381–9481
Butterstreet Cove (the Fleet)	SY 6379	Church Ope Cove (Portland)	SY 698710
Came Down	SY 6886	Clapgate (Wimborne)	SU 0102
Came/Park	SY 7088	Clay Pigeon Hill	ST 6003
Came Wood	SY 6985	Clayesmoor/Lake/School	ST 8614
Camp Down	ST 8808	Cleavel Field	SZ 0086
Canford	SZ 0398	Cleavel Point (Poole Harbour)	SZ 004860
Canford Bridge	SZ 017992	Clenston Wood	ST 8202
Canford Cliffs	SZ 0589	Clifton Wood	ST 5712
Canford Heath	SZ 030960	Cloud's Hill (the Fleet)	SY 592825
Canford Heath Tip	SZ 027966	Clouds Hill (Bovington)	SY 8290
Canford Park	SZ 0398	Cobb (Lyme Regis)	SY 339915
Canford School	SZ 033989	Cogden Beach	SY 5087
Carey	SY 9088	Colehill	SU 030010
Castletown (Portland)	SY 6974	Compton Valence	SY 5993
Catsley Farm (Corscombe)	ST 525039	Coombe	SY 9787
Cattistock/Churchyard	SY 5999	Coombe Bottom	SY 9678
Cerne	see Cerne Abbas	Corfe	see Corfe Castle
Cerne Abbas	ST 6601	Corfe Castle	SY 960820
Cerne, River/Valley	SY 6792–ST 6504	Corfe Mullen	SY 990970
Chafey's Lake (Radipole NR)	SY 6680	Corfe Mullen Tip	SY 980950
Chalbury	SU 0106	Corscombe	ST 5105
Chalbury Common	SU 0206	Coward's Marsh	SZ 1595
Chamberlayne's Farm	SY 845924	Cowgrove (Wimborne)	ST 9800
Chamberlayne's Heath	SY 8391–8491	Cranborne	SU 0513
Champernhay-es Marsh	SY 3596–3597	Cranborne CBs	SU 064131
Chapman's Pool	SY 955771	Cranborne Common	SU 1011
Char, River	SY 3693–ST 4201	Crane, River/Valley	SU 1006–0215
Chard Junction GP or Chard GP	ST 3304	Creech Heath	SY 9283–9284
Chardstock (Devon)	ST 310044	Creech Pond	SY 915830
Charlborough Park	SY 930980	Creekmoor	SY 9993
Charleston	SY 6579	Creekmoor Ponds	SY 997939
Charlton Down	ST 8700	Crichel	see More Crichel
Charlton Marshall	ST 9003	Crichel Lake/Park	ST 9907–9908
Charminster	SY 6792–6892	Cripplestyle	SU 0912
Charminster Watermeadows	SY 6891	Crossways	SY 7688–7788
Charmouth	SY 3693	Dancing Ledge (Purbeck cliffs)	SY 997769
Charmouth Beach	SY 365930	Deans Court (Wimborne)	SZ 010998
Chase Woods	ST 970190	Deadmoor Common	ST 7510–7511
Chedington	ST 4805	Devil's Brook	SY 7794–ST 7604
Chedington Woods	ST 4906–4907	Dewlish	SY 7798
Cheselbourne	SY 7699	Didlington	SU 006077
Chesil, the Chesil Beach/Bank	SY 4988–6873	Divelish, River	ST 7715–7606
Chesil Cove	SY 6873	Doghouse Hill (Seatown)	SY 430915
Chetnole	ST 6007–6008	Doles Hill Plantation	SY 7398
Chetterwood or Chetter Wood	ST 972083	Dorchester	SY 690900
Chettle Down	ST 9414	Dorchester Hospital	SY 685905
Chewton Common	SZ 213942	Druce	SY 7495
Chewton Glen	SZ 218933	Duddle Farm	SY 731908
Chickerell	SY 6480	Duddle Heath	SY 7391
Chickerell Rifle Range	SY 6478	Dudmoor/Farm	SZ 150960

Dudsbury	SZ 0797–0798	Gillingham Clay Pits	see Lodden Lakes
Duncliffe Wood	ST 8221–8222	Glanville's Wootton	ST 6708–6808
Durdle Door (Purbeck cliffs)	SY 806804	Goathorn	
Durlston Bay	SZ 0377–0378	or Goatham/Wood (Poole Harbour)	SZ 010855
Durlston Castle	SZ 034773	Godlingston Heath	SZ 020825
Durlston CP	SZ 030775	Golden Cap	SY 4092
Durweston	ST 8508	Grange Arch (Purbeck)	SY 9181
East Bexington	SY 5485	Grange Heath	SY 9083
East Burton	SY 8386–8387	Green Hill Down	ST 792039
East Chaldon	SY 7983	Green Island (Poole Harbour)	SZ 0086
East Cliffs (Portland)	SY 6868–6869	Greenland Farm (Studland)	SZ 018847
East Farm (Hammoon)	ST 818143	Grimstone	SY 6394
East Fleet	SY 6379–6380	Grove, the (Portland)	SY 6972–7072
East Holme	SY 8985–8986	Grove Point (Portland)	SY 707723
East Knighton	SY 8185	Gussage	see Gussage All Saints
East Lulworth	SY 860820	Gussage All Saints	SU 0010
East Parley	SZ 0998	Gussage Hill	ST 991140
East Parley Common	SZ 0999	Gussage St Michael	ST 9811
East Stoke	SY 8786	Ham Common (Poole)	SY 9790
East Weare (Portland)	SY 7072–7073	Hambledon Hill	ST 8412
Easton (Portland)	SY 6971	Hammoon	ST 8114
Edmondsham	SU 0611	Hampreston	SZ 0598
Eggardon	SY 5394–5494	Hampshire Avon	see Avon, River/Valley
Egmont Bight (Purbeck cliffs)	SY 9477	Hamworthy	SY 990910
Empool CBs	SY 749873	Hamworthy Beach (Poole Harbour)	SY 9990
Encombe House/Lake	SY 9478	Handfast Point (Ballard Down)	SZ 0582
Ensbury (Bournemouth)	SZ 0896	Handley or Sixpenny Handley	ST 9917
Everley	ST 8711 & ST 8812	Harbin Park	ST 9012–9013
Eyebridge (Wimborne)	ST 995001	Hartland Moor	SY 9485–9585
Eype	SY 4492	Hatch Pond (Poole)	SZ 014939
Eype's Mouth	SY 448910	Hawkchurch (Devon)	ST 3400
Fairmile (Blandford/Stickland)	ST 848050	Hazelbury Bryan	ST 7408
Farnham Woods	ST 937160	Henbury/GP	SY 9697
Ferndown	SU 0700	Hengistbury Head	SZ 170908
Ferrybridge	SY 6675–6676	Herbury Gore (the Fleet)	SY 6180
Fiddleford	ST 8013	Herringston Manor	SY 689881
Fiddleford Mill	ST 801136	Herrison	SY 6794
Firgrove Beat	SU 1000	Highcliffe	SZ 2093
Fitzworth/East/North (Poole Harbour)	SY 9986	Hilton	ST 781030
Flag Head Chine	SZ 0588	Hinton Parva	ST 9904
Fleet, the	SY 5683–6675	Hinton St Mary	ST 7816
Fleet Coastguard Cottages	SY 607816	Hod Hill	ST 8510
Folke	ST 660135	Holcombe Bottom	SY 6995
Fontmell Brook	ST 8214–8716	Holdenhurst Road	SZ 1092
Fontmell Down/NR	ST 880180	Holes Bay (Poole Harbour)	SZ 000920
Fontmell Magna	ST 8616–8617	Holnest	ST 6509
Forde Abbey	ST 3505–3605	Holt	SU 0203
Fordington	SY 6690	Holt Forest	SU 0305–0405
Forston	SY 6695	Holt Heath NNR	SU 060040
Fortuneswell (Portland)	SY 6873	Holton Bay/Shore (Poole Harbour)	SY 9590–9690
Frampton Court	SY 6294	Holton Heath	SY 9591
French's Farm (Lytchett Bay)	SY 968931	Holton Heath Island (Poole Harbour)	SY 970917
Friar Waddon	SY 6485	Holwell	SU 0712
Frome, River/Valley	SY 9487–ST 5704	Holwell CBs	SU 072127
Frome Vauchurch	SY 601971	Hooke	ST 5300
Furzey Island (Poole Harbour)	SZ 011871	Hooke Park	SY 5298–5299
Gad Cliff or Gadcliff (Purbeck cliffs)	SY 8779–8879	Hooke, River	SY 5997–ST 5100
Garston Wood	SU 0018–0019	Horton	SU 0207–0307
Gigger's Island (Poole Harbour)	SY 949880	Horton Inn	SU 017086
Gillingham	ST 8026	Houghton/Stubbs	see Winterborne Houghton

Hurn	SZ 1297	Loscombe	SY 5097
Hurn Airport	SZ 110980	Lower Avon/Valley	see Avon, River/Valley
Hurn Common	SZ 1198–1199	Lower Bockhampton	SY 7290
Hurn or Heron Court	SZ 1295	Lower Common	SU 0906
Hurst	SY 7990	Lower Frome Valley	SY 9487–7190
Hyde	SY 8690	Lower Kingcombe	SY 5599
Hyde Hall Lake/Hyde Lakes	SY 869899	Lower Row	SU 0404
Hyde Heath	SY 8791–8891	Luckford Lake	SY 8683
Ibberton	ST 7807	Lulworth	SY 8381
Ibberton Hill	ST 7907	Lulworth Cove	SY 8279
Iford (Christchurch)	SZ 1393	Lulworth Lake	SY 861838
Islington	SY 7591	Lulworth Ranges	SY 8480–8481
Islington Wood	SY 7592–7692	Lydden, River	ST 7616–7303
Iwerne Minster	ST 8614	Lydlinch	ST 7413
Iwerne Steepleton or Stepleton	ST 8611	Lydlinch Common	ST 7313
Jubilee Wood	ST 9504	Lyme Regis	SY 9234
Keysworth (Poole Harbour)	SY 9389–9489	Lytchett Bay (Poole Harbour)	SY 973919
Keysworth Point/Spit (Poole Harbour)	SY 949892	Lytchett Matravers	SY 9495
Kimmeridge	SY 9179	Lytchett Minster	SY 961930
Kimmeridge Bay	SY 905790	Magna Road, Poole	SZ 0397–0497
Kingcombe	see Lower Kingcombe	Maiden Castle	SY 6688–6788
King's Mill (Marnhull)	ST 767172	Maiden Newton	SY 5997–6097
King's Park (Bournemouth)	SZ 1192	Malmesbury Estate	see Hurn Court
King's Stag	ST 7210	Mangerton Stream	SY 4894–5495
Kinson (Bournemouth)	SZ 0696–0796	Manston	ST 8115
Kingston Down	SY 9579–9679	Manswood	ST 9708
Kingston Matravers	SY 9579	Mapperton	SY 5099 &SY 9098
Kingston North Common	SU 1402	Marnhull	ST 780190
Knapp Mill (Christchurch)	SZ 155937	Marnhull Ham	ST 7519
Knighton	SZ 0497	Martin Down (Hampshire)	ST 0419
Knighton Heath Wood	SY 7488	Martinstown	SY 6488
Knoll Beach (Studland)	SZ 0383	Matchams	SU 1201–1301
Knowlton	SU 0210	Melbury Osmond	ST 5707
Lake Gate floods (Corfe Mullen)	SY 992991	Melbury Sampford	ST 5705–5706
Lambert's Castle	SY 370988	Melcombe Regis	SY 680800
Langton/Long (Blandford)	ST 8905	Melcombe Regis Cemetery	SY 672794
Langton Herring	SY 6182	Merley	SZ 022982
Langton Matravers	SZ 000789	Merley Park	SZ 0098–0198
Lawson Clump (Wareham Forest)	SY 922910	Middlebere (Poole Harbour)	SY 9786
Lenthay, River (Sherborne)	see Yeo, River/Valley	Middlebere Farm	SY 968863
Lewell	SY 738899	Middlebere Lake (Poole Harbour)	SY 975866
Lilliput (Poole)	SZ 0489	Middlebere Point (Poole Harbour)	SY 983872
Lim, River	SY 3492–3196	Middlemarsh Grange Woods	ST 6606
Littlebredy or Little Bridy	SY 588890	Milborne St Andrew	SY 8097
Little Canford	SZ 0499	Milborne Wood	SY 7897
Little Minterne Hill	ST 6604	Milton/Abbas	ST 8001–8002
Little Sea (Studland NNR)	SZ 030848	Milton Abbas/Abbey Lake	ST 802015
Littledown Reserve	ST 9910	Milton on Stour	ST 7928–8028
Littlemoor (Weymouth)	SY 6882–6883	Milton Woods	ST 8102
Littlesea (the Fleet)	SY 6478	Minterne Magna	ST 6504
Littlesea Holiday Park	SY 653783	Modbury FF	SY 521900
Lodden Lakes	ST 811257	Moigne Coombe	SY 7787
Lodmoor CP	SY 683810	Monkton Up Wimborne	SU 0113
Lodmoor NR	SY 6881–6981	Moonfleet/Manor (the Fleet)	SY 617806
Lodmoor Tip	SY 6891	Moors River	SZ 1395–SU 1006
Long Bredy	SY 5690	Moors Valley CP	SU 1005–1006
Long Island (Poole Harbour)	SY 988880	Morcombelake	SY 4094
Longburton	ST 6412	Morden	SY 9194
Longham	SZ 0698	Morden Bog/Heath/NNR	SY 910910
Longham Bridge	SZ 064973	Morden Decoy Pond	SY 913919

Morden Park	SY 9092–9093	Poole Power Station	SZ 0090
Morden Park Lake	SY 907928	Poole Quay	SZ 010903
More Crichel	ST 9908	Poole SF	SZ 007937
Moreton	SY 8089	Poole Yacht Club	SZ 0389
Moreton Heath	SY 7888	Portesham	SY 6085
Moreton Plantation	SY 8190–8191	Portland	SY 690720
Motcombe	ST 8424–8425	Portland Bill	SY 6768
Mudeford	SZ 1891–1892	Portland Bird Observatory	SY 681690
Muscliff (Bournemouth)	SZ 0995	Portland Castle	SY 684744
Nether Cerne	SY 670983	Portland Dockyard	SY 6974
Netherbury	SY 4699–4799	Portland Harbour	SY 685760
New Barn Farm (Abbotsbury)	SY 597833	Portland Harbour Breakwaters	SY 6877–6974
Newton Bay (Poole Harbour)	SZ 0085	Portland Heights	SY 688729
Newton Heath	SZ 0084	Potterne Farm (Verwood)	SU 095075
Newton's Cove	SY 6878	Povington/Heath	SY 880834
Norden	SY 9483	Povington Clay Pits	SY 886837
North Chideock	SY 4293–4294	Powerstock	SY 5196
North Haven (Poole Harbour)	SZ 0387	Powerstock Common	SY 540970
North Winterborne Valley	ST 9400–8204	Poxwell	SY 7484
Northmoor (Wareham)	SY 9188	Poyntington Ridge	ST 6520
Nothe, the	SY 6878	Preston	SY 700830
Nottington	SY 6682	Preston Beach	SY 6981
Notton	SY 6095	Prior's Down	ST 7418
Nyland	ST 7521	Puddletown	SY 7594
Oak Hill	SY 8893	Puddletown Forest	SY 737927
Oakers Wood	SY 8091	Puncknowle	SY 5388
Oakley (Wimborne)	SZ 0298	Quomp Copse	SZ 130963
Okeford Common	ST 7811	Radipole NR	SY 6779–6780
Okeford Fitzpaine	ST 8010–8011	Radipole Park	SY 6780
Old Harry Rocks	SZ 055825	Radipole School	SY 667816
Organford	SY 9392	Radipole Village	SY 6681–6781
Osmington	SY 7282–7283	Rampisham	ST 5602
Osmington Bay	SY 7281–7381	Rampisham Hill	ST 550013
Osmington Mills	SY 7381	Rampisham Stream	ST 5800– 5203
Overcombe	SY 6981–6982	Ramsdown Plantation	SZ 1396
Ower (Poole Harbour)	SY 9986	Reap Lane (Portland)	SY 6870
Owermoigne	SY 7685	Redcliff Point	SY 713816
Parley	SZ 090980	Redhorn Bay (Poole Harbour)	SZ 0285
Parley Common	see East Parley Common	Redlands (Weymouth)	SY 6682
Parkstone	SZ 0391	Rempstone	SY 9882
Parkstone Bay (Poole Harbour)	SZ 0290	Rempstone Forest/Heath	SY 9884
Parkstone GC	SZ 0489–0490	Ridge	SY 9386
Patchins Point (Poole Harbour)	SY 988891	Ridge Moors	SY 950870
Penn's Weare (Portland)	SY 700713	Ridgeway, the/Ridgeway Hill	SY 6785–6786
Pennsylvania Castle (Portland)	SY 696711	Ringstead	SY 750814
Pentridge	SU 0317	Ringstead Bay	SY 7581–7681
Perryfields (Portland)	SY 694711	Ringwood Forest	SU 110080
Peveril Down	SZ 037785	Rockley Point (Poole Harbour)	SY 973910
Peveril Point	SZ 040786	Rodden	SY 6184
Piddle, River	SY 9488–ST 6902	Rodden Hive (the Fleet)	SY 604822
Piddlehinton	SY 7197	Rooksmoor Common	ST 7311
Piddletrenthide	SY 7099	Rope Lake Head (Purbeck cliffs)	SY 927775
Pilot's Point (Poole Harbour)	SZ 042860	Round Island (Poole Harbour)	SY 988875
Pimperne	ST 9009	Row	see Lower Row
Pimperne Down	ST 8910	Russell Quay (Poole Harbour)	SY 972896
Pirates Cove (the Fleet)	SY 658769	Ryme Intrinseca	ST 5810
Poole/Town Centre	SZ 0190	Sandbanks	SZ 0387–0487
Poole Grammar School	SZ 015950	Sandbanks Bay (Poole Harbour)	SZ 0488
Poole Harbour Entrance	SZ 0386	Sandford	SY 9289–9389
Poole Park/Lake	SZ 0290–0291	Sandsfoot Castle	SY 675773

Seacombe Bottom/Valley	SY 9876	Swanage Pier	SZ 036788
Seatown	SY 420917	Swineham	SY 936879
Serpentine Rd (Poole)	SZ 0191	Swineham GPs	SY 9387–9388
Shaftesbury	ST 862230	Swineham Point (Poole Harbour)	SY 9487
Shapwick	ST 8301–8401	Sydling Brook	SY 6394–ST 6201
Shell Bay	SU 039863	Sydling St Nicholas	SY 6399
Sherborne	ST 638167	Tadnoll	SY 7986
Sherborne Abbey	ST 637165	Talbot Heath (Bournemouth)	SZ 070930
Sherborne Lake	ST 6416–6516	Tan-Hill Wood	ST 815130
Sherborne Park/Estate	ST 660165	Tarrant Crawford	ST 9203
Sherborne STW	ST 632154	Tarrant Gunville	ST 9212
Sherford Bridge (Wareham Forest)	SY 919927	Tarrant Hinton	ST 9310–9311
Shillingstone	ST 8210–8211	Tarrant Keyneston	ST 9204–9304
Shipstal Point (Poole Harbour)	SY 983884	Tarrant Monkton	ST 9408
Shipton	SY 4991	Tarrant Rawston	ST 9306
Shore Road (Poole)	SZ 0488	Tarrant, River/Valley	ST 9103–ST 9212
Shroton Lines	ST 8413	Tarrant Rushton	ST 9305
Sixpenny Handley	ST 9917	Thorncombe Beacon	SY 4391
Sopley	SZ 1596–1597	Thorncombe Wood	SY 7292
Sopley Wood	SZ 1596	Throop (Bournemouth)	SZ 1195
South Haven (Poole Harbour)	SZ 0386	Tidmoor (the Fleet)	SY 6478
South Lake (Poole Harbour)	SY 9588–9589	Tincleton	SY 7691–7791
Southbourne	SZ 1391–1491	Tincleton CBs	SY 766917
Southdown Avenue (Preston)	SY 690817	Tollard Royal	ST 9417
Southwell/Business Park (Portland)	SY 6870	Toller	see Toller Porcorum
Spetisbury	ST 9102	Toller Down	ST 5102–5202
St Aldhelm's Head	SY 962752	Toller Porcorum	SY 562980
St Catherine's Hill	SZ 147951	Tolpuddle or Tolpiddle	SY 7994
Stalbridge	ST 7317	Top Fields (Portland Bill)	SY 684696
Stanbridge Mill	SU 015090	Tout Quarry (Portland)	SY 686726
Stanpit Marsh	SZ 168920	Town Common	SZ 140960
Stanpit Tip	SZ 167925	Trigon	SY 8888
Stanpit Village	SZ 1792	Tuckton (Christchurch)	SZ 1492
Steeple	SY 911811	Turnerspuddle	SY 8393
Stickland	see Winterborne Stickland	Turnerspuddle Heath	SY 8291
Stinsford	SY 7191	Turnworth	ST 8207
Stoborough	SY 9286	Two Mile Copse (Weymouth)	SY 675822
Stoborough Heath	SY 9285	Tyneham/Valley	SY 8780–8880
Stoford	ST 5613	Uddens	SU 0402
Stokeford Heath	SY 8688–8788	Uddens Heath	SU 0501
Stonebarrow Hill	SY 3893	Ulwell (Swanage)	SZ 0280
Stour Provost	ST 7921	Up Cerne	ST 6502
Stour, River/Valley	SZ 1692–ST 7731	Up Cerne Lake	ST 659027
Stour Row	ST 8221	Upton	SY 980930
Stourpaine	ST 8609	Upton CP	SY 9992
Stratton	SY 6593	Upton Heath	SY 9894–9895
Stubhampton Bottom	ST 900158	Upton House	SY 993930
Studland	SZ 0382	Upwey	SY 6684–6685
Studland Bay	SZ 040840	Verne, or Verne Common (Portland)	SY 695740
Studland NNR/Heath	SZ 025840	Verne Cliffs	SY 693739
Studland Village	SZ 0382	Verne Common Road	SY 6873
Sturminster Marshall	ST 950000	Verwood	SU 0808–0908
Sturminster Marshall GP	SY 955994	Waddock Cross	SY 799910
Sturminster Newton	ST 7813–7814	Waddock Cross CBs	SY 797908
Suckthumb Quarry (Portland)	SY 687708	Wakeham (Portland)	SY 6971
Sugar Hill (Wareham Forest)	SY 8892	Wallisdown (Bournemouth)	SZ 060940
Sutton Bingham Reservoir	ST 549110	Wareham	SY 9287
Sutton Waldron	ST 8615–8616	Wareham Channel (Poole Harbour)	SY 980900
Swanage	SZ 0278–0378	Wareham Forest	SY 900920
Swanage Bay	SZ 037797	Wareham Heath	SY 9087

Wareham River	SY 9487–9287	Winterborne Came	SY 7088
Wareham STW	SY 935888	Winterborne Herringston	SY 689881
Wareham Watermeadows	SY 930870	Winterborne Houghton	ST 820045
Warmwell	SY 7585	Winterborne Kingston	SY 8697
Warmwell GP/Quarry/Tip	SY 7587–7588	Winterborne Monkton	SY 6787
Warmwell Heath	SY 7586	Winterborne Stickland	ST 8304
Warre Wood	SY 5983	Winterborne Zelston	SY 8997
Water Lake Bottom	SU 0314	Winterbourne Abbas	SY 6190
Waterston or Waterson Ridge	SY 7194	Winterbourne Steepleton	SY 6289
Week Common	SZ 1399	Winterbourne Steepleton Pond	SY 622903
Week Farm	SU 135001	Witchampton	ST 9806
West Bay	SY 4690	Witchampton paper mills	ST 999069
West Bexington	SY 5386	Wood Bar Looe (Poole Harbour)	SY 970906
West Cliffs (Portland)	SY 6769–6770	Woodbridge	ST 7112 & ST 8417
West Compton	SY 5694	Woodbury Hill	SY 8594
West Down	SY 8497	Woodlands	SU 050090
West Fleet	SY 5882–5982	Woodsford	SY 7690
West Hants Water Company	SZ 155937	Wool	SY 8486
West Holme	SY 8885	Woolgarston	SY 9881
West Knighton/GP	SY 7488	Woolland	ST 777070
West Milton	SY 5096	Woolsbarrow	SY 893926
West Morden	SY 9095	Wootton Fitzpaine	SY 3795
West Moors	SU 0802–0803	Worbarrow	SY 8779
West Parley	SZ 0898	Worbarrow Bay(Purbeck cliffs)	SY 8679–8680
West Stafford	SY 7289	Worbarrow Tout(Purbeck cliffs)	SY 870796
West Weare (Portland)	SY 6872	Worgret	SY 907870
Weston (Portland)	SY 6871	Worgret Farm	SY 907869
Wey, River	SY 6780–6685	Worth Matravers	SY 9777
Weymouth	SY 6779	Wriggle Valley	ST 5913–6104
Weymouth Backwater	see Radipole NR	Wyke Down	SU 0015
Weymouth Bay	SY 690800	Wyke Regis (Weymouth)	SY 6676–6677
Weymouth Beach	SY 6879	Wynford Eagle	SY 584959
Weymouth Cemetery see Melcombe Regis Cemetery		Wytch	SY 9785
Weymouth Harbour	SY 6778–6878	Wytch Channel (Poole Harbour)	SY 985875
Whatcombe	ST 8301	Wytch Farm	SY 978855
Whatcombe Down	ST 8501	Wytch Lake (Poole Harbour)	SY 980861
Whatcombe Woods	ST 8202	Yates Corner (Portland)	SY 685729
Whitchurch Canonicorum	SY 3995	Yeo, River/Valley	ST 5719–6918
Whitcombe	SY 7188	Yetminster	ST 5910
White Horse Hill	SY 7184–7284		

White Nothe or	
Whitenore or Whitenose	SY 772806
White Sheet	SU 047036
White Sheet Plantation	SU 0403–0503
Wick	SZ 1591
Wick Fields (Xchurch Hbr)	SZ 1691
Wick Hams (Xchurch Hbr)	SZ 167912
Wick Lane (Christchurch)	SZ 1591–1592
Wigbeth Ponds (Horton)	SU 0406
Wimborne	SU 010000
Wimborne Meadows	SY 9999–SZ 0199
Wimborne St Giles or St Giles	SU 0212–0312
Wimborne St Giles Park	SU 0311
Winfrith	SY 815870
Winfrith Heath	SY 8086–8186
Winfrith Newburgh	SY 8084
Winkton	SZ 1696
Winkton Weir	SZ 160956
Winspit/Valley	SY 9776
Winterborne Anderson	SY 8897

The following large land and sea areas of Dorset are shown on the county map.

Land Areas	Sea Areas
Blackmore Vale	Lyme Bay
Central Chalk	Poole Bay
Cranborne Chase	
Marshwood Vale	
Northern Chalk	
Portland	
Central Portland	
North Portland	
Poole Basin	
Purbeck	
Purbeck Ridge	
Southern Chalk	

BIBLIOGRAPHY

British Birds Rarities Committee (BBRC). Annual report. Rare Birds in Great Britain (1958 onwards). *British Birds* 53–96.

Blathwayt, F. L. 1945. A Revised List of the Birds of Dorset. *Proceedings of the DNH&AS* 67: 95–126.

Boys, J. V. 1972. *Check List of the Birds of Dorset.* DNH&AS.

Bull, A. J. 1952. The wildfowl and waders of Poole harbour. *Proceedings of the DNH&AS* 74: 149–170.

Christchurch Harbour Ornithological Group (CHOG). Annual report. *The Birds of Christchurch Harbour* (1956 onwards).

Clark, J. M. and Eyre, J. A. (Eds). 1993. *Birds of Hampshire.* Hampshire Ornithological Society.

Cohen, E. 1963. *Birds of Hampshire and the Isle of Wight.* Oliver & Boyd, Edinburgh & London.

Cohen, E. and Taverner, J. 1972. *A Revised List of Hampshire and Isle of Wight Birds.* Oxford Illustrated Press.

Collins, D. R. Poole Harbour RSPB Ornithological Survey, First Stage Winter/Spring 1984/85.

Cramp, S., Bourne, W. R. P. and Saunders, D. 1974. *The Seabirds of Britain and Ireland.* Readers Union. (Operation Seafarer Survey 1969–1970).

Cramp, S. *et al.* (Eds.) 1977–1994. *Handbook of the birds of Europe, the Middle East and North Africa (The Birds of the Western Palearctic)*; vols I to IX, Oxford University Press, Oxford.

Dorset Bird Club (DBC) and Dorset Natural History & Archaeological Society (DNH&AS). Annual reports on Dorset birds up to the year 1976 were incorporated in the *Proceedings of the DNH&AS.* The annual Dorset Bird Reports for the years 1977 to 1985 were still published by the DNH&AS, but separately as a Supplement to the *Proceedings.* The annual Dorset Bird Reports for the years 1986 to date have been published by the DBC.

Green, G. and Cade, M. 1997. *Where to Watch Birds in Dorset, Hampshire & the Isle of Wight* (2nd edition). Christopher Helm (Publishers) Ltd, a subsidiary of A & C Black, London.

Halliday, J. and Campbell Dr. L. H. 1979. *A Survey of the Birds of the Rivers Avon and Stour.* RSPB and Wessex Water Authority.

Haysom, T. S. 1992. The Status of Some Purbeck Sea Birds 2. *Proceedings of the DNH&AS* 114: 215–220.

Hollom, P. A. D. 1960. *The Popular Handbook of Rarer British Birds.* H. F. & G. Witherby Ltd, London.

Kelsall, J. E. and Munn, P. W. 1905. *The Birds of Hampshire and the Isle of Wight.* H. F. & G. Witherby Ltd, London.

Kenward, R. E., Walls, S. S., Hodder, K. H., Pahkala, M., Freeman, S. N. and Simpson, V. R. 2000. The prevalence of non-breeders in raptor populations: evidence from rings, radio-tags and transect surveys. *Oikos* 91: 271–279.

Lloyd, C. Tasker, M. L. and Partridge, K. 1991. *The status of seabirds in Britain and Ireland.* T. & A. D. Poyser, Berkhamsted. (NCC/Seabird Group Survey 1985–1987).

Mansel-Pleydell, J. C. 1888. *The Birds of Dorsetshire.* Ballantyne, Hanson & Co, Edinburgh & London.

Pickess, B. P. and Day, John Under-Hill (2002). *The Important Birds of Poole Harbour.* The Poole Harbour Study Group, Wareham, Dorset.

Portland Bird Observatory and Field Centre (PBO). Annual report (1955 onwards).

Prendergast, Col E. D. V. and Boys, J . V. 1983. *The Birds of Dorset.* David & Charles, Newton Abbot, London & North Pomfret (Vt).

Pulteney, R. 1799. A catalogue of birds observed in Dorsetshire. *Hutchins, J. The History and Antiquities of the County of Dorset.* (1796–1813, 2nd revised edition).

Sharrock, J. T. R. and E. M. 1976. *Rare Birds in Britain and Ireland.* T. & A. D. Poyser, Berkhamsted.

Shepherd, M. R. 1966. *The Birds of Radipole Lake, Weymouth 1945–1965.*

Shuttleworth, B. M. 1984. *A Gazetteer of Dorset Place-Names.* Dorset Environmental Records Centre.

Vinicombe, K. and Cottridge, D.M. 1996. *Rare Birds in Britain and Ireland A Photographic Record.* Harper Collins Publishers, London.

Wise, A. J. 1988. *Birds of Christchurch in the Nineteenth Century.* CHOG.

INDEX